495

D1093345

ANOMALIES
and CURIOSITIES *of*
MEDICINE

Being
an encyclopedic collection of rare and extraordinary
cases, and of the most striking instances of abnormality in all
branches of medicine and surgery, derived from an exhaustive
research of medical literature from its origin to the present day,
abstracted, classified, annotated, and indexed

by GEORGE M. GOULD, A.M., M.D.

and WALTER L. PYLE, A.M., M.D.

WITH 296 ILLUSTRATIONS IN THE TEXT
AND 12 HALF-TONE PLATES

BELL PUBLISHING COMPANY · NEW YORK

517NO471O

Original copyright 1896 by W. B. Saunders

Published March MCMLVI by The Julian Press, Inc.

This edition published by Bell Publishing Company
a division of Crown Publishers, Inc.
by arrangement with The Julian Press, Inc.

a   b   c   d   e   f   g   h

Manufactured in the United States of America

PREFATORY AND INTRODUCTORY.

SINCE the time when man's mind first busied itself with subjects beyond his own self-preservation and the satisfaction of his bodily appetites, the anomalous and curious have been of exceptional and persistent fascination to him ; and especially is this true of the construction and functions of the human body. Possibly, indeed, it was the anomalous that was largely instrumental in arousing in the savage the attention, thought, and investigation that were finally to develop into the body of organized truth which we now call Science. As by the aid of collected experience and careful inference we to-day endeavor to pass our vision into the dim twilight whence has emerged our civilization, we find abundant hint and even evidence of this truth. To the highest type of philosophic minds it is the usual and the ordinary that demand investigation and explanation. But even to such, no less than to the most naive-minded, the strange and exceptional is of absorbing interest, and it is often through the extraordinary that the philosopher gets the most searching glimpses into the heart of the mystery of the ordinary. Truly it has been said, facts are stranger than fiction. In monstrosities and dermoid cysts, for example, we seem to catch forbidden sight of the secret work-room of Nature, and drag out into the light the evidences of her clumsiness, and proofs of her lapses of skill,—evidences and proofs, moreover, that tell us much of the methods and means used by the vital artisan of Life,—the loom, and even the silent weaver at work upon the mysterious garment of corporeality.

" *La première chose qui s'offre à l'Homme quand il se regarde, c'est son corps,*" says Pascal, and looking at the matter more closely we find that it was the strange and mysterious things of his body that occupied man's earliest as well as much of his later attention. In the beginning, the organs and functions of generation, the mysteries of sex, not the routine of digestion or of locomotion, stimulated his curiosity, and in them he recognized, as it were, an unseen hand reaching down into the world of matter and the workings of bodily organization, and reining them to impersonal service and far-off ends. All ethnologists and students of primitive religion well know the role that has been played in primitive society by the genetic instincts. Among the older naturalists, such as Pliny and Aristotle, and even in the older historians, whose scope included natural as well as civil and political history, the atypic and bizarre, and especially the aberrations of form or function of the generative organs,

1

caught the eye most quickly. Judging from the records of early writers, when Medicine began to struggle toward self-consciousness, it was again the same order of facts that was singled out by the attention. The very names applied by the early anatomists to many structures so widely separated from the organs of generation as were those of the brain, give testimony of the state of mind that led to and dominated the practice of dissection.

In the literature of the past centuries the predominance of the interest in the curious is exemplified in the almost ludicrously monotonous iteration of titles, in which the conspicuous words are curiosa, rara, monstruosa, memorabilia, prodigiosa, selecta, exotica, miraculi, lusibus naturæ, occultis naturæ, etc., etc. Even when medical science became more strict, it was largely the curious and rare that were thought worthy of chronicling, and not the establishment or illustration of the common, or of general principles. With all his sovereign sound sense, Ambrose Paré has loaded his book with references to impossibly strange, and even mythologic cases.

In our day the taste seems to be insatiable, and hardly any medical journal is without its rare or " unique " case, or one noteworthy chiefly by reason of its anomalous features. A curious case is invariably reported, and the insertion of such a report is generally productive of correspondence and discussion with the object of finding a parallel for it.

In view of all this it seems itself a curious fact that there has never been any systematic gathering of medical curiosities. It would have been most natural that numerous encyclopedias should spring into existence in response to such a persistently dominant interest. The forelying volume appears to be the first thorough attempt to classify and epitomize the literature of this nature. It has been our purpose to briefly summarize and to arrange in order the records of the most curious, bizarre, and abnormal cases that are found in medical literature of all ages and all languages—a *thaumatographia medica*. It will be readily seen that such a collection must have a function far beyond the satisfaction of mere curiosity, even if that be stigmatized with the word "idle." If, as we believe, reference may here be found to all such cases in the literature of Medicine (including Anatomy, Physiology, Surgery, Obstetrics, etc.) as show the most extreme and exceptional departures from the ordinary, it follows that the future clinician and investigator must have use for a handbook that decides whether his own strange case has already been paralleled or excelled. He will thus be aided in determining the truth of his statements and the accuracy of his diagnoses. Moreover, to know extremes gives directly some knowledge of means, and by implication and inference it frequently does more. Remarkable injuries illustrate to what extent tissues and organs may be damaged without resultant death, and thus the surgeon is encouraged to proceed to his operation with greater confidence and more definite knowledge as to the issue. If a mad cow may blindly play the part of a successful obstetrician with her horns, certainly a skilled surgeon may hazard entering the womb with his knife. If large portions of an organ,—the lung, a kidney, parts of the liver, or the brain itself,—may be lost by accident, and the patient still live, the physician is taught the lesson of *nil desperandum*, and that if possible to arrest disease of these organs before their total destruction, the prognosis and treatment thereby acquire new and more hopeful phases.

Directly or indirectly many similar examples have also clear medicolegal bearings or suggestions ; in fact, it must be acknowledged that much of the importance of medical jurisprudence lies in a thorough comprehension of the anomalous and rare cases in Medicine. Expert medical testimony has its chief value in showing the possibilities of the occurrence of alleged extreme cases, and extraordinary deviations from the natural. Every expert witness should be able to maintain his argument by a full citation of parallels to any remarkable theory or hypothesis advanced by his clients ; and it is only by an exhaustive knowledge of extremes and anomalies that an authority on medical jurisprudence can hope to substantiate his testimony beyond question. In every poisoning case he is closely questioned as to the largest dose of the drug in question that has been taken with impunity, and the smallest dose that has killed, and he is expected to have the cases of reported idiosyncrasies and tolerance at his immediate command. A widow with a child of ten months' gestation may be saved the loss of reputation by mention of the authentic cases in which pregnancy has exceeded nine months' duration ; the proof of the viability of a seven months' child may alter the disposition of an estate ; the proof of death by a blow on the epigastrium without external marks of violence may convict a murderer ; and so it is with many other cases of a medicolegal nature.

It is noteworthy that in old-time medical literature—sadly and unjustly neglected in our rage for the new—should so often be found parallels of our most wonderful and peculiar modern cases. We wish, also, to enter a mild protest against the modern egotism that would set aside with a sneer as myth and fancy the testimonies and reports of philosophers and physicians, only because they lived hundreds of years ago. We are keenly appreciative of the power exercised by the myth-making faculty in the past, but as applied to early physicians, we suggest that the suspicion may easily be too active. When Paré, for example, pictures a monster, we may distrust his art, his artist, or his engraver, and make all due allowance for his primitive knowledge of teratology, coupled with the exaggerations and inventions of the wonder-lover; but when he describes in his own writing what he or his *confrères* have seen on the battle-field or in the dissecting room, we think, within moderate limits, we owe him credence. For the rest, we doubt not that the modern reporter is, to be mild, quite as much of a myth-maker as his elder brother, especially if we find modern instances that are essentially like the older cases reported in reputable journals or books, and by men presumably honest. In our collection we have endeavored, so far as possible, to cite similar cases from the older and from the more recent literature.

This connection suggests the question of credibility in general. It need hardly be said that the lay-journalist and newspaper reporter have usually been ignored by us, simply because experience and investigation have many times proved that a scientific fact, by presentation in most lay-journals, becomes in some mysterious manner, *ipso facto*, a scientific caricature (or worse !), and if it is so with facts, what must be the effect upon reports based upon no fact whatsoever? It is manifestly impossible for us to guarantee the credibility of chronicles given. If we have been reasonably certain of unreliability, we may not even have mentioned the marvelous statement. Obviously, we could do no more with apparently credible cases, reported by reputable medical men, than to cite author and source and leave the matter there, where our responsibility must end.

But where our proper responsibility seemed likely never to end was in carrying out the enormous labor requisite for a reasonable certainty that we had omitted no searching that might lead to undiscovered facts, ancient or modern. Choice in selection is always, of course, an affair *de gustibus*, and especially when, like the present, there is considerable embarrassment of riches, coupled with the purpose of compressing our results in one handy volume. In brief, it may be said that several years of exhaustive research have been spent by us in the great medical libraries of the United States and Europe in collecting the material herewith presented. If, despite of this, omissions and errors are to be found, we shall be grateful to have them pointed out. It must be remembered that limits of space have forbidden satisfactory discussion of the cases, and the prime object of the whole work has been to carefully collect and group the anomalies and curiosities, and allow the reader to form his own conclusions and make his own deductions.

As the entire labor in the preparation of the forelying volume, from the inception of the idea to the completion of the index, has been exclusively the personal work of the authors, it is with full confidence of the authenticity of the reports quoted that the material is presented.

Complete references are given to those facts that are comparatively unknown or unique, or that are worthy of particular interest or further investigation. To prevent unnecessary loading of the book with foot-notes, in those instances in which there are a number of cases of the same nature, and a description has not been thought necessary, mere citation being sufficient, references are but briefly given or omitted altogether. For the same reason a bibliographic index has been added at the end of the text. This contains the most important sources of information used, and each journal or book therein has its own number, which is used in its stead all through the book (thus, 476 signifies The Lancet, London; 597, the New York Medical Journal; etc.). These bibliographic numbers begin at 100.

Notwithstanding that every effort has been made to conveniently and satisfactorily group the thousands of cases contained in the book (a labor of no small proportions in itself), a complete general index is a practical necessity for the full success of what is essentially a reference-volume, and consequently one has been added, in which may be found not only the subjects under consideration and numerous cross-references, but also the names of the authors of the most important reports. A table of contents follows this preface.

We assume the responsibility for innovations in orthography, certain abbreviations, and the occasional substitution of figures for large numerals, fractions, and decimals, made necessary by limited space, and in some cases to more lucidly show tables and statistics. From the variety of the reports, uniformity of nomenclature and numeration is almost impossible.

As we contemplate constantly increasing our data, we shall be glad to receive information of any unpublished anomalous or curious cases, either of the past or in the future.

For many courtesies most generously extended in aiding our research-work we wish, among others, to acknowledge our especial gratitude and indebtedness to the officers and assistants of the Surgeon-General's Library at Washington, D. C., the Library of the Royal College of Surgeons of London, the Library of the British Museum, the Library of the British Medical Association, the Bibliothèque de Faculté de Médecine de Paris, the Bibliothèque Nationale, and the Library of the College of Physicians of Philadelphia.

GEORGE M. GOULD.
WALTER L. PYLE.

PHILADELPHIA, *October, 1896.*

TABLE OF CONTENTS.

CHAPTER I.

CHAPTER II.

CHAPTER III.

CHAPTER IV.

CHAPTER V.

CHAPTER VI.

CHAPTER VII.

CHAPTER VIII.

CHAPTER IX.

CHAPTER X.

Injuries to the eye, 527—Exophthalmos, 527—Avulsion of the eye, 527—Rupture of the eyeball, 528—Serious sequels of orbital injuries, 528—Gunshot injuries of the orbit, 529—Foreign bodies in the orbit, 531—Foreign bodies in the eyeball, 532—Dislocation of the lens, 533—Injury to the eyeball by birds,

CHAPTER XI.

CHAPTER XII.

CHAPTER XIII.

CHAPTER XIV.

CHAPTER XV.

CHAPTER XVI.

CHAPTER XVII.

CHAPTER XVIII.

ANOMALIES AND
CURIOSITIES OF MEDICINE.

CHAPTER I.

GENETIC ANOMALIES.

Menstruation has always been of interest, not only to the student of medicine, but to the lay-observer as well. In olden times there were many opinions concerning its causation, all of which, until the era of physiologic investigation, were of superstitious derivation. Believing menstruation to be the natural means of exit of the feminine bodily impurities, the ancients always thought a menstruating woman was to be shunned ; her very presence was deleterious to the whole animal economy, as, for instance, among the older writers we find that Pliny [a] remarks : " On the approach of a woman in this state, must will become sour, seeds which are touched by her become sterile, grass withers away, garden plants are parched up, and the fruit will fall from the tree beneath which she sits." He also says that the menstruating women in Cappadocia were perambulated about the fields to preserve the vegetation from worms and caterpillars. According to Flemming,[b] menstrual blood was believed to be so powerful that the mere touch of a menstruating woman would render vines and all kinds of fruit-trees sterile. Among the indigenous Australians, menstrual superstition was so intense that one of the native blacks, who discovered his wife lying on his blanket during her menstrual period, killed her, and died of terror himself in a fortnight. Hence, Australian women during this season are forbidden to touch anything that men use.[c] Aristotle said that the very look of a menstruating woman would take the polish out of a mirror, and the next person looking in it would be bewitched. Frommann [d] mentions a man who said he saw a tree in Goa which withered because a catamenial napkin was hung on it. Bourke remarks that the dread felt by the American Indians in this respect corresponds with the particulars recited by Pliny. Squaws at the time of menstrual purgation are obliged to seclude themselves, and in most instances to occupy isolated lodges, and in all tribes are forbidden to

a 636, L. xxviii., cap. 23.   b de Remediis, 16 and 17.
c Frazer, "The Golden Bough."   d "Tractatus de Fascinatione," Nuremberg, 1675.

prepare food for anyone save themselves. It was believed that, were a menstruating woman to step astride a rifle, a bow, or a lance, the weapon would have no utility. Medicine men are in the habit of making a " protective " clause whenever they concoct a " medicine," which is to the effect that the " medicine " will be effective provided that no woman in this condition is allowed to approach the tent of the official in charge.

Empiricism had doubtless taught the ancient husbands the dangers of sexual intercourse during this period, and the after-results of many such connections were looked upon as manifestations of the contagiousness of the evil excretions issuing at this period. Hence at one time menstruation was held in much awe and abhorrence.

On the other hand, in some of the eastern countries menstruation was regarded as sacred, and the first menstrual discharge was considered so valuable that premenstrual marriages were inaugurated in order that the first ovum might not be wasted, but fertilized, because it was supposed to be the purest and best for the purpose. Such customs are extant at the present day in some parts of India, despite the efforts of the British Government to suppress them, and descriptions of child-marriages and their evil results have often been given by missionaries.

As the advances of physiology enlightened the mind as to the true nature of the menstrual period, and the age of superstition gradually disappeared, the intense interest in menstruation vanished, and now, rather than being held in fear and awe, the physicians of to-day constantly see the results of copulation during this period. The uncontrollable desire of the husband and the mercenary aims of the prostitute furnish examples of modern disregard.

The anomalies of menstruation must naturally have attracted much attention, and we find medical literature of all times replete with examples. While some are simply examples of **vicarious** or **compensatory** menstruation, and were so explained even by the older writers, there are many that are physiologic curiosities of considerable interest. Lhéritier [485] furnishes the oft-quoted history of the case of a young girl who suffered from suppression of menses, which, instead of flowing through the natural channels, issued periodically from vesicles on the leg for a period of six months, when the seat of the discharge changed to an eruption on the left arm, and continued in this location for one year ; then the discharge shifted to a sore on the thumb, and at the end of another six months again changed, the next location being on the upper eyelid ; here it continued for a period of two years. Brierre de Boismont and Meisner describe a case apparently identical with the foregoing, though not quoting the source.

Haller, [400] in a collection of physiologic curiosities covering a period of a century and a half, cites 18 instances of **menstruation from the skin.** Parrot has also mentioned several cases of this nature. Chambers [a] speaks

a 476, 1861, i., 207.

of bloody sweat occurring periodically in a woman of twenty-seven ; the intervals, however, were occasionally but a week or a fortnight, and the exudation was not confined to any one locality. Van Swieten [755] quotes the history of a case of suppression of the menstrual function in which there were convulsive contractions of the body, followed by paralysis of the right arm. Later on, the patient received a blow on the left eye causing amaurosis ; swelling of this organ followed, and one month later blood issued from it, and subsequently blood oozed from the skin of the nose, and ran in jets from the skin of the fingers and from the nails.

D'Andradé [a] cites an account of a healthy Parsee lady, eighteen years of age, who menstruated regularly from thirteen to fifteen and a half years ; the catamenia then became irregular and she suffered occasional hemorrhages from the gums and nose, together with attacks of hematemesis. The menstruation returned, but she never became pregnant, and, later, blood issued from the healthy skin of the left breast and right forearm, recurring every month or two, and finally additional dermal hemorrhage developed on the forehead. Microscopic examination of the exuded blood showed usual constituents present. There are two somewhat similar cases spoken of in French literature.[b] The first was that of a young lady, who, after ten years' suppression of the menstrual discharge, exhibited the flow from a vesicular eruption on the finger. The other case was quite peculiar, the woman being a prostitute, who menstruated from time to time through spots, the size of a five-franc piece, developing on the breasts, buttocks, back, axilla, and epigastrium. Barham [c] records a case similar to the foregoing, in which the menstruation assumed the character of periodic purpura. Duchesne [d] mentions an instance of complete amenorrhea, in which the ordinary flow was replaced by periodic sweats.

Parrot speaks of a woman who, when seven months old, suffered from strumous ulcers, which left cicatrices on the right hand, from whence, at the age of six years, issued a sanguineous discharge with associate convulsions. One day, while in violent grief, she shed bloody tears. She menstruated at the age of eleven, and was temporarily improved in her condition ; but after any strong emotion the hemorrhages returned. The subsidence of the bleeding followed her first pregnancy, but subsequently on one occasion, when the menses were a few days in arrears, she exhibited a blood-like exudation from the forehead, eyelids, and scalp. As in the case under D'Andradé's observation, the exudation was found by microscopic examination to consist of the true constituents of blood. An additional element of complication in this case was the occurrence of occasional attacks of hematemesis.

Menstruation from the Breasts.—Being in close sympathy with the generative function, we would naturally expect to find the female mammæ

---

[a] 772, 1862.

[c] 656, 1847.

[b] 162, 1829, 212, 236.

[d] Monit. d' hôp., 1856, iv., 661.

involved in cases of anomalous menstruation, and the truth of this supposition is substantiated in the abundance of such cases on record. Schenck [a]
reports instances of menstruation from the nipple; and Richter, de Fonte-
chia, Laurentius,[b] Marcellus Donatus,[c] Amatus Lusitanus,[d] and Bierling
are some of the older writers who have observed this anomaly. Paré [e] says
the wife of Pierre de Féure, an iron merchant, living at Chasteaudun,
menstruated such quantities from the breasts each month that several ser-
viettes were necessary to receive the discharge. Cazenave [f] details the history of a case in which the mammary menstruation was associated with a
similar exudation from the face, and Wolff [g] saw an example associated with
hemorrhage from the fauces. In the Lancet (1840–1841) is an instance of
monthly discharge from beneath the left mamma. Finley [h] also writes of an
example of mammary hemorrhage simulating menstruation. Barnes saw a
case in St. George's Hospital, London, 1876, in which the young girl menstruated vicariously from the nipple and stomach. In a London discussion
there was mentioned [i] the case of a healthy woman of fifty who never was
pregnant, and whose menstruation had ceased two years previously, but who
for twelve months had menstruated regularly from the nipples, the hemorrhage being so profuse as to require constant change of napkins. The
mammæ were large and painful, and the accompanying symptoms were those
of ordinary menstruation. Boulger [j] mentions an instance of periodic menstrual discharge from beneath the left mamma. Jacobson [k] speaks of habitual
menstruation by both breasts. Rouxeau [l] describes amenorrhea in a girl of
seventeen, who menstruated from the breast; and Teufard [m] reports a case
in which there was reestablishment of menstruation by the mammæ at the age
of fifty-six. Baker [n] details in full the description of a case of vicarious menstruation from an ulcer on the right mamma of a woman of twenty (Pl. 1).
At the time he was called to see her she was suffering with what was called
"green-sickness." The girl had never menstruated regularly or freely.
The right mamma was quite well developed, flaccid, the nipple prominent,
and the superficial veins larger and more tortuous than usual. The patient
stated that the right mamma had always been larger than the left. The
areola was large and well marked, and ¼ inch from its outer edge, immediately under the nipple, there was an ulcer with slightly elevated edges
measuring about 1¼ inches across the base, and having an opening in its center
¼ inch in diameter, covered with a thin scab. By removing the scab and
making pressure at the base of the ulcer, drops of thick, mucopurulent

a 718, L. ii., obs. 228 ; L. iv., obs. 266.   b 480, L. vii., 278.
c 306, L. iv., c. 26.   d 119, cent. ii., cur. 21.
e 618, 983.   f 462, T. x., 23.
g Obs. med.-chir., L. i., n. 20.   h 256, 1825.
i 476, 1882, i., 786.   j 476, 1840–41, i., 493.
k 454, 1828, xxxi., 83–85.   l Gaz. méd. de Nantes, 1883–4, ii., 39.
m 789, 1872, xiv., 845.   n Southern Jour. of Med. and Pharm., Charleston, March, 1847.

PLATE I.

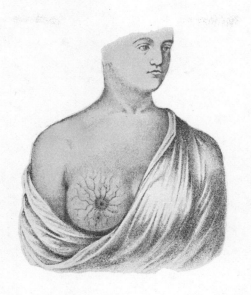

Menstruation from the breast (Baker).

matter were made to exude. This discharge, however, was not offensive to the smell. On March 17, 1846, the breast became much enlarged and congested, as portrayed in Plate 1 (Fig. 1). The ulcer was much inflamed and painful, the veins corded and deep colored, and there was a free discharge of sanguineous yellowish matter. When the girl's general health improved and menstruation became more natural, the vicarious discharge diminished in proportion, and the ulcer healed shortly afterward. Every month this breast had enlarged, the ulcer became inflamed and discharged vicariously, continuing in this manner for a few days, with all the accompanying menstrual symptoms, and then dried up gradually. It was stated that the ulcer was the result of the girl's stooping over some bushes to take an egg from a hen's nest, when the point of a palmetto stuck in her breast and broke off. The ulcer subsequently formed, and ultimately discharged a piece of palmetto. This happened just at the time of the beginning of the menstrual epoch. The accompanying figures, Plate 1 (Figs. 1, 2), show the breast in the ordinary state and at the time of the anomalous discharge.

Hancock [a] relates an instance of menstruation from the left breast in a large, otherwise healthy, Englishwoman of thirty-one, who one and a half years after the birth of the youngest child (now ten years old) commenced to have a discharge of fluid from the left breast three days before the time of the regular period. As the fluid escaped from the nipple it became changed in character, passing from a whitish to a bloody and to a yellowish color respectively, and suddenly terminating at the beginning of the real flow from the uterus, to reappear again at the breast at the close of the flow, and then lasting two or three days longer. Some pain of a lancinating type occurred in the breast at this time. The patient first discovered her peculiar condition by a stain of blood upon the night-gown on awakening in the morning, and this she traced to the breast. From an examination it appeared that a neglected lacerated cervix during the birth of the last child had given rise to endometritis, and for a year the patient had suffered from severe menorrhagia, for which she was subsequently treated. At this time the menses became scanty, and then supervened the discharge of bloody fluid from the left breast, as heretofore mentioned. The right breast remained always entirely passive. A remarkable feature of the case was that some escape of fluid occurred from the left breast during coitus. As a possible means of throwing light on this subject it may be added that the patient was unusually vigorous, and during the nursing of her two children she had more than the ordinary amount of milk (galactorrhea), which poured from the breast constantly. Since this time the breasts had been quite normal, except for the tendency manifested in the left one under the conditions given.

Cases of menstruation through the eyes are frequently mentioned by the older writers. Bellini,[b] Hellwig,[414] and Dodonæus all speak of menstrua-

---

[a] 533, 1895, May 11th.   [b] Zodiacus, etc., 1680.

tion from the eye.   Jonston [447] quotes an example of ocular menstruation in a young Saxon girl, and Bartholinus [190] an instance associated with bloody discharge of the foot.   Guepin [a] has an example in a case of a girl of eighteen, who commenced to menstruate when three years old.   The menstruation was tolerably regular, occurring every thirty-two or thirty-three days, and lasting from one to six days.   At the cessation of the menstrual flow, she generally had a supplementary epistaxis, and on one occasion, when this was omitted, she suffered a sudden effusion into the anterior chamber of the eye. The discharge had only lasted two hours on this occasion.   He also relates an example of hemorrhage into the vitreous humor in a case of amenorrhea. Conjunctival hemorrhage has been noticed as a manifestation of vicarious menstruation by several American observers.   Liebreich found examples of retinal hemorrhage in suppressed menstruation, and Sir James Paget [b] says that he has seen a young girl at Moorfields who had a small effusion of blood into the anterior chamber of the eye at the menstrual period, which became absorbed during the intervals of menstruation.   Blair [c] relates the history of a case of vicarious menstruation attended with conjunctivitis and opacity of the cornea.   Law [d] speaks of a plethoric woman of thirty who bled freely from the eyes, though menstruating regularly.

Relative to **menstruation from the ear**, Spindler,[e] Paullini,[f] and Alibert [g] furnish examples.   In Paullini's case the discharge is spoken of as very foul, which makes it quite possible that this was a case of middle-ear disease associated with some menstrual disturbance, and not one of true vicarious menstruation.   Alibert's case was consequent upon suppression of the menses.   Law [h] cites an instance in a woman of twenty-three, in whom the menstrual discharge was suspended several months.   She experienced fulness of the head and bleeding (largely from the ears), which subsequently occurred periodically, being preceded by much throbbing ; but the patient finally made a good recovery.   Barnes,[i] Stepanoff,[j] and Field [k] adduce examples of this anomaly.   Jouilleton [l] relates an instance of menstruation from the right ear for five years, following a miscarriage.

Hemorrhage from the mouth of a vicarious nature has been frequently observed associated with menstrual disorders.   The Ephemerides,[104] Meibomius,[561] and Rhodius mention instances.   The case of Meibomius was that of an infant, and the case mentioned by Rhodius was associated with hemorrhages from the lungs, umbilicus, thigh, and tooth-cavity.   Allport [m] reports the history of a case in which there was recession of the gingival margins and alveolar processes, the consequence of amenorrhea.   Caso [n] has an in-

a 145, vol. xlvi.   b 476, 1882, i., 786.
c Oglethorpe Med. and Surg. Jour., Savannah, 1858-9, i., 11.
d 224. 1869.   e 748, n. 63.   f 620, cent. iv., obs. 56.
g Jour. de Méd. et Chir. de Toulouse, 1845-6.   h 313, 1867.
i 317, 1826-7.   j 557, 1885, xxiv., 588-595.   k 536, xxiii., 115.
l 461, 1813, 330.   m 450, 1885, iv., 147.   n 538, 1878.

stance of menstruation from the gums, and there is on record the description of a woman, aged thirty-two, who had bleeding from the throat preceding menstruation ; later the menstruation ceased to be regular, and four years previously, after an unfortunate and violent connection, the menses ceased, and the woman soon developed hemorrhoids and hemoptysis. Henry [a] speaks of a woman who menstruated from the mouth ; at the necropsy 207 stones were found in the gall-bladder. Krishaber speaks of a case of lingual menstruation at the epoch of menstruation.

Descriptions of **menstruation from the extremities** are quite numerous. Pechlin [b] offers an example from the foot ; Boerhaave from the skin of the hand ; Ephemerides [104] from the knee ; Albertus from the foot ; Zacutus Lusitanus [c] from the left thumb ; Bartholinus [d] a curious instance from the hand ; and the Ephemerides [e] another during pregnancy from the ankle.

Post [f] speaks of a very peculiar case of edema of the arm alternating with the menstrual discharge. Sennert writes of menstruation from the groin associated with hemorrhage from the umbilicus and gums. Moses [g] offers an example of hemorrhage from the umbilicus, doubtless vicarious. Verduc details the history of two cases from the top of the head, and Kerckring [h] cites three similar instances, one of which was associated with hemorrhage from the hand.

A peculiar mode is **vicarious menstrual hemorrhage through old ulcers, wounds, or cicatrices,** and many examples are on record, a few of which will be described. Calder [i] gives an excellent account of menstruation at an ankle-ulcer, and Brincken [j] says he has seen periodical bleeding from the cicatrix of a leprous ulcer. In the Lancet [k] is an account of a case in the Vienna Hospital of simulated stigmata ; the scar opened each month and a menstrual flow proceeded therefrom ; but by placing a plaster-of-Paris bandage about the wound, sealing it so that tampering with the wound could be easily detected, healing soon ensued, and the imposture was thus exposed. Such would likely be the result of the investigation of most cases of " bleeding wounds " which are exhibited to the ignorant and superstitious for religious purposes.

Hogg [l] publishes a report describing a young lady who injured her leg with the broken steel of her crinoline. The wound healed nicely, but always burst out afresh the day preceding the regular period. Forster [m] speaks of a menstrual ulcer of the face, and Moses [n] two of the head. White, quoted by Barnes, cites an instance of vicarious hemorrhage from five deep fissures

[a] 663, 1757, 384.
[d] 190, cent. i., hist. 13.
[g] 124, 1859.
[j] Christiania, 1834.
[m] 490, 1851, xlvii.

[b] 622, L. i.
[e] 104, dec. i., ann. i., obs. 96.
[h] 473, obs. 60, 85.
[k] 476, 1879, i., 593.

[c] 831, L. ix., obs. 13.
[f] 595, 1841, iv., 215.
[i] 527, 1735, iii., 380.
[l] 476, 1885, ii., 515.
[n] 124, 1859.

of the lips in a girl of fourteen; the hemorrhage was periodical and could not be checked. At the advent of each menstrual period the lips became much congested, and the recently-healed menstrual scars burst open anew.

Knaggs [a] relates an interesting account of a sequel to an operation for ovarian disease. Following the operation, there was a regular, painless menstruation every month, at which time the lower part of the wound re-opened, and blood issued forth during the three days of the catamenia. McGraw [b] illustrates vicarious menstruation by an example, the discharge issuing from an ovariotomy-scar, and Hooper [c] cites an instance in which the vicarious function was performed by a sloughing ulcer. Buchanan [d] and Simpson [e] describe "amenorrheal ulcers." Dupuytren [f] speaks of denudation of the skin from a burn, with the subsequent development of vicarious catamenia from the seat of the injury.

There are cases on record in which the **menstruation** occurs **by the rectum or the urinary tract.** Barbee [g] illustrates this by a case in which cholera morbus occurred monthly in lieu of the regular menstrual discharge. Barrett [h] speaks of a case of vicarious menstruation by the rectum. Astbury [318] says he has seen a case of menstruation by the hemorrhoidal vessels, and instances of relief from plethora by vicarious menstruation in this manner are quite common. Rosenbladt [691] cites an instance of menstruation by the bladder, and Salmuth [i] speaks of a pregnant woman who had her monthly flow by the urinary tract. Ford [j] illustrates this anomaly by the case of a woman of thirty-two, who began normal menstruation at fourteen; for quite a period she had vicarious menstruation from the urinary tract, which ceased after the birth of her last child. The coexistence of a floating kidney in this case may have been responsible for this hemorrhage, and in reading reports of so-called menstruation due consideration must be given to the existence of any other than menstrual derangement before we can accept the cases as true vicarious hemorrhage. Tarnier cites an instance of a girl without a uterus, in whom menstruation proceeded from the vagina. Zacutus Lusitanus [k] relates the history of a case of uterine occlusion, with the flow from the lips of the cervix. There is mentioned an instance of menstruation from the labia.

The occurrence of **menstruation after removal of the uterus or ovaries** is frequently reported. Storer,[l] Clay,[m] Tait,[n] and the British and Foreign Medico-Chirurgical Review [o] report cases in which menstruation took place with neither uterus nor ovary. Doubtless many authentic instances like the preceding could be found to-day. Menstruation after

a 310, 1873.   b 125, 1884, 912–914.   c 547, 1882–3.   d 381, 1879.
e Month. Jour. Med. Sci., Lond., 1855, xx., 347.   f 363, 1828, i., 85.
g 511, 1840.   h 809, 1875.   i 706, cent. iii., obs. 36.
j 125, vol. xxii., 154.   k 831, L. ix., obs. 4.   l 476, 1866, ii., 471.
m 476, 1880, i., 15.   n 548, 1884, i., 662.   o 22, 1873, i., 296.

hysterectomy and ovariotomy has been attributed to the incomplete removal of the organs in question, yet upon postmortem examination of some cases no vestige of the functional organs in question has been found.

Hematemesis is a means of anomalous menstruation, and several instances are recorded. Marcellus Donatus [a] and Benivenius [197] exemplify this with cases. Instances of vicarious and compensatory epistaxis and hemoptysis are so common that any examples would be superfluous. There is recorded [b] an inexplicable case of menstruation from the region of the sternum, and among the curious anomalies of menstruation must be mentioned that reported by Parvin [c] seen in a woman, who, at the menstrual epoch, suffered hemoptysis and oozing of blood from the lips and tongue. Occasionally there was a substitution of a great swelling of the tongue, rendering mastication and articulation very difficult for four or five days. Parvin gives portraits showing the venous congestion and discoloration of the lips.

Instances of **migratory menstruation,** the flow moving periodically from the ordinary passage to the breasts and mammæ, are found in the older writers.[d] Salmuth speaks of a woman [e] on whose hands appeared spots immediately before the establishment of the menses. Cases of semimonthly menstruation [104] and many similar anomalies of periodicity are spoken of.

The Ephemerides contains [f] an instance of the simulation of **menstruation after death,** and Testa [g] speaks of menstruation lasting through a long sleep. Instances of **black menstruation** are to be found, described in full, in the Ephemerides, by Paullini [h] and by Schurig,[i] and in some of the later works ; it is possible that an excess of iron, administered for some menstrual disorder, may cause such an alteration in the color of the menstrual fluid.

Suppression of menstruation is brought about in many peculiar ways, and sometimes by the slightest of causes, some authentic instances being so strange as to seem mythical. Through the Ephemerides [104] we constantly read of such causes as contact with a corpse, the sight of a serpent or mouse, the sight of monsters, etc. Lightning stroke and curious neuroses have been reported as causes. Many of the older books on obstetric subjects are full of such instances, and modern illustrations are constantly reported.

Menstruation in Man.—Periodic discharges of blood in man, constituting what is called " male menstruation," have been frequently noticed and are particularly interesting when the discharge is from the penis or urethra, furnishing a striking analogy to the female function of menstruation. The older authors quoted several such instances, and Mehliss says that in the ancient days certain writers remarked that catamenial lustration from the penis was inflicted on the Jews as a divine punishment. Bartholinus [j]

[a] 306, L. iv., 19.   [b] 108, dec. i., vol. iv., 69.   [c] 764, 1877.

[d] 282, 1733, 359 ; and 105, vol. iii., app., 168.   [e] 706, cent. iii., obs. 18.

[f] 104, dec. iii., ann. iv., obs. 18.   [g] 758, 215.   [h] 620, cent. ii., obs. 8.

[i] 724, 217.   [j] 190, cent. v., hist. 33.

mentions a case in a youth; the Ephemerides several instances; Zacutus Lusitanus, Salmuth,[a] Hagedorn, Fabricius Hildanus, Vesalius,[b] Mead,[c] and Acta Eruditorum[d] all mention instances. Forel[e] saw menstruation in a man. Gloninger[f] tells of a man of thirty-six, who, since the age of seventeen years and five months, had had lunar manifestations of menstruation. Each attack was accompanied by pains in the back and hypogastric region, febrile disturbance, and a sanguineous discharge from the urethra, which resembled in color, consistency, etc., the menstrual flux. King[g] relates that while attending a course of medical lectures at the University of Louisiana he formed the acquaintance of a young student who possessed the normal male generative organs, but in whom the simulated function of menstruation was periodically performed. The cause was inexplicable, and the unfortunate victim was the subject of deep chagrin, and was afflicted with melancholia. He had menstruated for three years in this manner : a fluid exuded from the sebaceous glands of the deep fossa behind the corona glandis ; this fluid was of the same appearance as the menstrual flux. The quantity was from one to two ounces, and the discharge lasted from three to six days. At this time the student was twenty-two years of age, of a lymphatic temperament, not particularly lustful, and was never the victim of any venereal disease. The author gives no account of the after-life of this man, his whereabouts being, unfortunately, unknown or omitted.

Vicarious Menstruation in the Male.—This simulation of menstruation by the male assumes a vicarious nature as well as in the female. Van Swieten,[h] quoting from Benivenius, relates a case of a man who once a month sweated great quantities of blood from his right flank. Pinel mentions a case of a captain in the army (M. Regis), who was wounded by a bullet in the body and who afterward had a monthly discharge from the urethra. Pinel calls attention particularly to the analogy in this case by mentioning that if the captain were exposed to fatigue, privation, cold, etc., he exhibited the ordinary symptoms of amenorrhea or suppression. Fournier[i] speaks of a man over thirty years old, who had been the subject of a menstrual evacuation since puberty, or shortly after his first sexual intercourse. He would experience· pains of the premenstrual type, about twenty-four hours before the appearance of the flow, which subsided when the menstruation began. He was of an intensely voluptuous nature, and constantly gave himself up to sexual excesses. The flow was abundant on the first day, diminished on the second, and ceased on the third. Halliburton,[j] Jouilleton, and Rayman also record male menstruation.

Cases of **menstruation during pregnancy and lactation** are not rare.

a 706, cent. iii., obs. 47.   b 803, L. v., cap. 15.   c 515, 369.
d 106, ann. 1688, 228.   e 239, 1869.   f 129, 1819.
g 251, 1867.   h 755, vol. xiii., sect. 1286.
i 302, iv., 192.   j Weekly Med. Rev., Chicago, 1884, xii., 392.

It is not uncommon to find pregnancy, lactation, and menstruation coexisting. No careful obstetrician will deny pregnancy solely on the regular ,occurrence of the menstrual periods, any more than he would make the diagnosis of pregnancy from the fact of the suppression of menses. Blake [a] reports an instance of catamenia and mammary secretion during pregnancy. Denaux de Breyne mentions a similar case. The child was born by a face-presentation. De Saint-Moulin [b] cites an instance of the persistence of menstruation during pregnancy in a woman of twenty-four, who had never been regular; the child was born at term. Gelly speaks of a case in which menstruation continued until the third month of pregnancy, when abortion occurred. Post,[c] in describing the birth of a two-pound child, mentions that menstruation had persisted during the mother's pregnancy. Rousset [d] reports a peculiar case in which menstruation appeared during the last four months of pregnancy.

There are some cases on record of **child-bearing after the menopause,** as, for instance, that of Pearson,[e] of a woman who had given birth to nine children up to September, 1836 ; after this the menses appeared only slightly until July, 1838, when they ceased entirely. A year and a half after this she was delivered of her tenth child. Other cases, somewhat similar, will be found under the discussion of late conception.

Precocious menstruation is seen from birth to nine or ten years. Of course, menstruation before the third or fourth year is extremely rare, most of the cases reported before this age being merely accidental sanguineous discharges from the genitals, not regularly periodical, and not true catamenia. However, there are many authentic cases of infantile menstruation on record, which were generally associated with precocious development in other parts as well. Billard says that the source of infantile menstruation is the lining membrane of the uterus ; but Camerer explains it as due to ligature of the umbilical cord before the circulation in the pulmonary vessels is thoroughly established. In the consideration of this subject, we must bear in mind the influence of climate and locality on the time of the appearance of menstruation. In the southern countries, girls arrive at maturity at an earlier age than their sisters of the north. Medical reports from India show early puberty of the females of that country. Campbell remarks that girls attain the age of puberty at twelve in Siam, while, on the contrary, some observers report the fact that menstruation does not appear in the Esquimaux women until the age of twenty-three, and then is very scanty, and is only present in the summer months.

Cases of menstruation commencing within a few days after birth and exhibiting periodical recurrence are spoken of by Penada,[f] Neues Han-

a 218, 1856–7, lv., 508.

c 286, 1885–6, i., 543.

e 476, 1836.

b Jour. d'accouch., Liége, 1888, ix., 205.

d Jour. de méd. de Bordeaux, 1856.

f Saggio d'osservazioni, iii.

noverisches Magazin,[a] Drummond,[b] Buxtorf,[c] Arnold,[d] The Lancet,[e] and the British Medical Journal.[f]

Cecil[g] relates an instance of menstruation on the sixth day, continuing for five days, in which six or eight drams of blood were lost. Peeples[h] cites an instance in Texas in an infant at the age of five days, which was associated with a remarkable development of the genital organs and breasts. Van Swieten offers an example at the first month; the British Medical Journal[i] at the second month; Conarmond at the third month. Ysabel, a young slave girl belonging to Don Carlos Pedro of Havana,[j] began to menstruate soon after birth, and at the first year was regular in this function. At birth her mammæ were well developed and her axillæ were slightly covered with hair. At the age of thirty-two months she was three feet ten inches tall, and her genitals and mammæ resembled those of a girl of thirteen. Her voice was grave and sonorous; her moral inclinations were not known. Deever[358] records an instance of a child two years and seven months old who, with the exception of three months only, had menstruated regularly since the fourth month. Harle[k] speaks of a child, the youngest of three girls, who had a bloody discharge at the age of five months which lasted three days and recurred every month until the child was weaned at the tenth month. At the eleventh month it returned and continued periodically until death, occasioned by diarrhea at the fourteenth month. The necropsy showed a uterus $1\frac{5}{8}$ inches long, the lips of which were congested; the left ovary was twice the size of the right, but displayed nothing strikingly abnormal. Baillot and the British Medical Journal[l] cite instances of menstruation at the fourth month. A case is on record[m] of an infant who menstruated at the age of six months, and whose menses returned on the twenty-eighth day exactly. Clark, Wall, and the Lancet[n] give descriptions of cases at the ninth month. Naegele has seen a case at the eighteenth month, and Schmidt and Colly[o] in the second year. Another case[p] is that of a child, nineteen months old, whose breasts and external genitals were fully developed, although the child had shown no sexual desire, and did not exceed other children of the same age in intellectual development. This prodigy was symmetrically formed and of pleasant appearance. Warner[q] speaks of Sophie Gantz, of Jewish parentage, born in Cincinnati, July 27, 1865, whose menses began at the twenty-third month and had continued regularly up to the time of reporting. At the age of three years and six months she was 38 inches tall, 38 pounds in weight, and her girth at the hip was $33\frac{1}{2}$ inches. The pelvis was broad and well shaped, and measured $10\frac{1}{2}$

a 586, xvii., 1519.   b 224, 1879, ii., 47.   c 107, vol. vii., 107.
d 494, 1876, ii., 42.   e 476, 1871, i., 366.   f 224, 1879, i., 841.
g 494, 1885.   h 597, March, 1895.   i 224, 1881, ii., 682.
j 599, 1829.   k 224, 1880, i., 848.   l 224, 1883, ii., 1141.   m 224, 1879, i., 801.
n 476, 1827.   o 548, 1864, 382.   p 516, 1828.   q 459, 1869.

inches from the anterior surface of the spinous process of one ilium to that of the other, being a little more than the standard pelvis of Churchill, and, in consequence of this pelvic development, her legs were bowed. The mammæ and labia had all the appearance of established puberty, and the pubes and axillæ were covered with hair. She was lady-like and maidenly in her demeanor, without unnatural constraint or effrontery. A case some-what similar, though the patient had the appearance of a little old woman,[a] was a child of three whose breasts were as well developed as in a girl of twenty, and whose sexual organs resembled those of a girl at puberty. She had menstruated regularly since the age of two years. Woodruff[b] describes a child who began to menstruate at two years of age and continued regularly thereafter. At the age of six years she was still menstruating, and exhibited beginning signs of puberty. She was 118 cm. tall, her breasts were devel-oped, and she had hair on the mons veneris. Van der Veer[c] mentions an infant who began menstruating at the early age of four months and had continued regularly for over two years. She had the features and develop-ment of a child ten or twelve years old. The external labia and the vulva in all its parts were well formed, and the mons veneris was covered with a full growth of hair. Sir Astley Cooper, Mandelshof, the Ephemerides, Rause, Geoffroy-Saint-Hilaire, and several others[d] report instances of menstruation occurring at three years of age. Le Beau[e] describes an infant-prodigy who was born with the mammæ well formed and as much hair on the mons veneris as a girl of thirteen or fourteen. She menstruated at three and continued to do so regularly, the flow lasting four days and being copious. At the age of four years and five months she was $42\frac{1}{2}$ inches tall; her features were regular, the complexion rosy, the hair chestnut, the eyes blue-gray, her mammæ the size of a large orange, and indications that she would be able to bear children at the age of eight. Prideaux cites a case at five, and Gaugirau Casals, a doctor of Agde,[f] has seen a girl of six years who suffered abdominal colic, hemorrhage from the nose, migraine, and neu-ralgia, all periodically, which, with the association of pruritus of the genitals and engorged mammæ, led him to suspect amenorrhea. He ordered baths, and shortly the menstruation appeared and became regular thereafter. Brierre de Boismont records cases of catamenia at five, seven, and eight years; and Skene[g] mentions a girl who menstruated at ten years and five months. She was in the lowest grade of society, living with a drunken father in a tenement house, and was of wretched physical constitution, quite ignorant, and of low moral character, as evinced by her specific vaginitis. Occurring from nine years to the ordinary time of puberty, many cases are recorded.

a 476, Jan. 29, 1848, 137.   b 538, March 7, 1896.   c 125, 1883.
d 458, Jan., 1811, 115 ; 468, 1809, ix., 96 ; and 109, iv., 44.   e 124, 1832, xi., 42.
f 302, iv., 203.   g 738, 49.

Instances of **protracted menstruation** are, as a rule, reliable, the individuals themselves being cognizant of the nature of true menstruation, and themselves furnishing the requisite information as to the nature and periodicity of the discharge in question. Such cases range even past the century-mark. Many elaborate statistics on this subject have been gathered by men of ability. Dr. Meyer of Berlin quotes the following :—

28 at 50 years of age,		3 at 57 years of age,	
18 " 51 " " "		3 " 58 " " "	
18 " 52 " " "		1 " 59 " " "	
11 " 53 " " "		4 " 60 " " "	
13 " 54 " " "		4 " 62 " " "	
5 " 55 " " "		3 " 63 " " "	
4 " 56 " " "			

These statistics were from examination of 6000 cases of menstruating women. The last seven were found to be in women in the highest class of society.

Mehliss has made the following collection of statistics of a somewhat similar nature :—

	Late Dentition. Male.	Female.	Late Lactation.	Late Menstruation.
Between 40 and 50	0	4	0	0
" 50 " 60	1	4	2	1
" 60 " 70	3	2	1	0
" 70 " 80	3	2	0	7
" 80 " 90	6	2	0	0
" 90 " 100	1	1	0	1
Above 100	6	1	0	1
	20	16	3	10

These statistics seem to have been made with the idea of illustrating the marvelous rather than to give the usual prolongation of these functions. It hardly seems possible that ordinary investigation would show no cases of menstruation between sixty and seventy, and seven cases between seventy and eighty ; however, in searching literature for such a collection, we must bear in mind that the more extraordinary the instance, the more likely it is that it would be spoken of, as the natural tendency of medical men is to overlook the important ordinary and report the nonimportant extraordinary.

Dewees mentions an example of menstruation at sixty-five, and others at fifty-four and fifty-five years. Motte speaks of a case at sixty-one ; Ryan and others, at fifty-five, sixty, and sixty-five ; Parry, from sixty-six to seventy-seven ; Desormeux, from sixty to seventy-five ; Semple, at seventy and eighty-seven ; Higgins,[a] at seventy-six ; Whitehead,[b] at seventy-seven ; Bernstein, at seventy-eight ; Beyrat,[c] at eighty-seven ; Haller, at one hundred ; and highest of all is Blancardi's case, in which menstruation was present at one hundred and six years. In the London Medical and Surgical Journal,1831, are reported cases at eighty and ninety-five years. In Good's System of Nosol-

a 476, 1883, i., 485.   b 548, 1866, i., 407.   c 147, ann. xiii.

ogy [383] there are instances occurring at seventy-one, eighty, and ninety years. There was a woman in Italy whose menstrual function continued from twenty-four to ninety years.[a] Emmet [b] cites an instance of menstruation at seventy, and Brierre de Boismont one of a woman who menstruated regularly from her twenty-fourth year to the time of her death at ninety-two.

Strasberger of Beeskow describes a woman who ceased menstruating at forty-two, who remained in good health up to eighty, suffering slight attacks of rheumatism only, and at this late age was seized with abdominal pains, followed by menstruation, which continued for three years; the woman died the next year. This late menstruation had all the sensible characters of the early one. Kennard [c] mentions a negress, aged ninety-one, who menstruated at fourteen, ceased at forty-nine, and at eighty-two commenced again, and was regular for four years, but had had no return since. On the return of her menstruation, believing that her procreative powers were returning, she married a vigorous negro of thirty-five and experienced little difficulty in satisfying his desires. Du Peyrou de Cheyssiole and Bonhoure [d] speak of an aged peasant woman, past ninety-one years of age, who menstruated regularly.

Petersen [e] describes a woman of seventy-nine, who on March 26th was seized with uterine pains lasting a few days and terminating with hemorrhagic discharge. On April 23d she was seized again, and a discharge commenced on the 25th, continuing four days. Up to the time of the report, one year after, this menstruation had been regular. There is an instance on record of a female who menstruated every three months during the period from her fiftieth to her seventy-fourth year, the discharge, however, being very slight. Thomas [f] cites an instance of a woman of sixty-nine who had had no menstruation since her forty-ninth year, but who commenced again the year he saw her. Her mother and sister were similarly affected at the age of sixty, in the first case attributable to grief over the death of a son, in the second ascribed to fright. It seemed to be a peculiar family idiosyncrasy. Velasquez of Tarentum [g] says that the Abbess of Monvicaro at the very advanced age of one hundred had a recurrence of catamenia after a severe illness, and subsequently a new set of teeth and a new growth of hair.

Late Establishment of Menstruation.—In some cases menstruation never appears until late in life, presenting the same phenomena as normal menstruation. Perfect [h] relates the history of a woman who had been married many years, and whose menstruation did not appear until her forty-seventh year. She was a widow at the time, and had never been pregnant. Up to the time of her death, which was occasioned by a convulsive colic, in her fifty-seventh year, she had the usual prodromes of menstruation followed by the usual discharge. Rodsewitch [i] speaks of a widow of a peasant who

a 124, vol. vii., o. s., 514.   b 125, 1886, 152.   c 519, 1871.
d 280, 1787, xiv., 32.   e 207, Feb., 1840.   f 546, 1852, 148.
g 222, 1840 (translation).   h 564, vol. iii., 593.   i 811, 1879.

menstruated for the first time at the age of thirty-six. Her first coitus took place at the age of fifteen, before any signs of menstruation had appeared, and from this time all through her married life she was either pregnant or suckling. Her husband died when thirty-six years old, and ever since the catamenial flow had shown itself with great regularity. She had borne twins in her second, fourth, and eighth confinement, and altogether had 16 children. Holdefrund in 1836 mentions a case in which menstruation did not commence until the seventieth year, and Hoyer [a] mentions one delayed to the seventy-sixth year. Marx of Krakau [b] speaks of a woman, aged forty-eight, who had never menstruated ; until forty-two years old she had felt no symptoms, but at this time pain began, and at forty-eight regular menstruation ensued. At the time of report, four years after, she was free from pain and amenorrhea, and her flow was regular, though scant. She had been married since she was twenty-eight years of age. A somewhat similar case is mentioned by Gregory [c] of a mother of 7 children who had never had her menstrual flow. There are two instances of delayed menstruation quoted : [d] the first, a woman of thirty, well formed, healthy, of good social position, and with all the signs of puberty except menstruation, which had never appeared ; the second, a married woman of forty-two, who throughout a healthy connubial life had never menstruated. An instance is known to the authors of a woman of forty who has never menstruated, though she is of exceptional vigor and development. She has been married many years without pregnancy.

The medical literature relative to **precocious impregnation** is full of marvelous instances. Individually, many of the cases would be beyond credibility, but when instance after instance is reported by reliable authorities we must accept the possibility of their occurrence, even if we doubt the statements of some of the authorities. No less a medical celebrity than the illustrious Sir Astley Cooper remarks that on one occasion he saw a girl in Scotland, seven years old, whose pelvis was so fully developed that he was sure she could easily give birth to a child ; and Warner's case of the Jewish girl three and a half years old, with a pelvis of normal width, more than substantiates this supposition. Similar examples of precocious pelvic and sexual development are on record in abundance, and nearly every medical man of experience has seen cases of infantile masturbation.

The ordinary period of female maturity is astonishingly late when compared with the lower animals of the same size, particularly when viewed with cases of animal precocity on record. Berthold [e] speaks of a kid fourteen days old which was impregnated by an adult goat, and at the usual period of gestation bore a kid, which was mature but weak, to which it gave milk in abundance, and both the mother and kid grew up strong. Compared with the above, child-bearing by women of eight is not extraordinary.

[a] 108, 1712.   [b] 657, 1889, 9.   [c] 124, 1853.   [d] 302, iv., 193.   [e] 202, 32.

The earliest case of conception that has come to the authors' notice is a quotation in one of the last century books from von Mandelslo[a] of impregnation at six ; but a careful search in the British Museum failed to confirm this statement, and, for the present, we must accept the statement as hearsay and without authority available for reference-purposes.

Molitor[b] gives an instance of precocious pregnancy in a child of eight. It was probably the same case spoken of by Lefebvre[c] and reported to the Belgium Academy : A girl, born in Luxemborg, well developed sexually, having hair on the pubis at birth, who menstruated at four, and at the age of eight was impregnated by a cousin of thirty-seven, who was sentenced to five years' imprisonment for seduction. The pregnancy terminated by the expulsion of a mole containing a well-characterized human embryo. Schmidt's case in 1779[d] was in a child who had menstruated at two, and bore a dead fetus when she was but eight years and ten months old. She had all the appearance and development of a girl of seventeen. Kussmaul gives an example of conception at eight. Dodd[e] speaks of a child who menstruated early and continued up to the time of impregnation. She was a hard worker and did all her mother's washing. Her labor pains did not continue over six hours, from first to the last. The child was a large one, weighing 7 pounds, and afterward died in convulsions. The infant's left foot had but 3 toes. The young mother at the time of delivery was only nine years and eight months old, and consequently must have been impregnated before the age of nine. Meyer gives an astonishing instance of birth in a Swiss girl at nine. Carn describes a case of a child who menstruated at two, became pregnant at eight, and lived to an advanced age. Ruttel reports conception in a girl of nine, and as far north as St. Petersburg a girl has become a mother before nine years. The *Journal de Sçavans*, 1684,[470] contains the report of the case of a boy, who survived, being born to a mother of nine years.

Beck has reported an instance of delivery in a girl a little over ten years of age. There are instances of fecundity at nine years recorded by Ephemerides, Wolffius,[f] Savonarola,[g] and others.[h] Gleaves[i] reports from Wytheville, Va., the history of what he calls the case of the youngest mother in Virginia —Annie H.—who was born in Bland County, July 15, 1885, and, on September 10, 1895, was delivered of a well-formed child weighing 5 pounds. The girl had not the development of a woman, although she had menstruated regularly since her fifth year. The labor was short and uneventful, and, two hours afterward, the child-mother wanted to arise and dress and would have done so had she been permitted. There were no developments of the mammæ nor secretion of milk. The baby was nourished through its short

a 505.
d 753, vol. ii.
g 714, cap. 21, n. 6.
b 171, 1878-9.
e 476, 1881, i., 601.
h 458, T. xxxvii., 542.
c 362, March 8, 1878.
f Lect. Memorabilis, T. i., 620.
i 538, Nov. 16, 1895.

existence (as it only lived a week) by its grandmother, who had a child only a few months old. The parents of this child were prosperous, intelligent, and worthy people, and there was no doubt of the child's age. " Annie is now well and plays about with the other children as if nothing had happened." Harris refers to a Kentucky woman, a mother at ten years, one in Massachusetts a mother at ten years, eight months, and seventeen days, and one in Philadelphia at eleven years and three months. The first case was one of infantile precocity, the other belonging to a much later period, the menstrual function having been established but a few months prior to conception. All these girls had well-developed pelves, large mammæ, and the general marks of womanhood, and bore living children. It has been remarked of 3 very markedly precocious cases of pregnancy that one was the daughter of very humble parents, one born in an almshouse, and the other raised by her mother in a house of prostitution. The only significance of this statement is the greater amount of vice and opportunity for precocious sexual intercourse to which they were exposed ; doubtless similar cases under more favorable conditions would never be recognized as such.

The instance in the *Journal de Sçavans* is reiterated in 1775,[a] which is but such a repetition as is found all through medical literature—" new friends with old faces," as it were. Haller observed a case of impregnation in a girl of nine, who had menstruated several years, and others who had become pregnant at nine, ten, and twelve years respectively. Rowlett,[b] whose case is mentioned by Harris, saw a child who had menstruated the first year and regularly thereafter, and gave birth to a child weighing $7\frac{3}{4}$ pounds when she was only ten years and thirteen days old. At the time of delivery she measured 4 feet 7 inches in height and weighed 100 pounds. Curtis,[c] who is also quoted by Harris, relates the history of Elizabeth Drayton, who became pregnant before she was ten, and was delivered of a full-grown, living male child weighing 8 pounds. She had menstruated once or twice before conception, was fairly healthy during gestation, and had a rather lingering but natural labor. To complete the story, the father of this child was a boy of fifteen. One of the faculty of Montpellier[d] has reported an instance at New Orleans of a young girl of eleven, who became impregnated by a youth who was not yet sixteen. Maygrier[e] says that he knew a girl of twelve, living in the Faubourg Saint-Germain, who was confined.

Harris[f] relates the particulars of the case of a white girl who began to menstruate at eleven years and four months, and who gave birth to an oversized male child on January 21, 1872, when she was twelve years and nine months old. She had an abundance of milk and nursed the child ; the labor was of about eighteen hours' duration, and laceration was avoided. He also speaks of a mulatto girl, born in 1848, who began to menstruate at eleven

a 280, 1775.   b 783, vol. vii.   c 218, Feb. 19, 1863.

d 302, xxxii., 394.   e Ibid.   f 125, 1874.

years and nine months, and gave birth to a female child before she reached thirteen, and bore a second child when fourteen years and seven months old. The child's father was a white boy of seventeen.

The following are some Indian statistics : [a] 1 pregnancy at ten, 6 at eleven, 2 at eighteen, 1 at nineteen.[b] Chevers [266] speaks of a mother at ten and others at eleven and twelve ; and Green, at Dacca, performed craniotomy upon the fetus of a girl of twelve. Wilson [c] gives an account of a girl thirteen years old, who gave birth to a full-grown female child after three hours' labor. She made a speedy convalescence, but the child died four weeks afterward from bad nursing. The lad who acknowledged paternity was nineteen years old. King [d] reports a well-verified case of confinement in a girl of eleven. Both the mother and child did well.

Robertson of Manchester describes a girl, working in a cotton factory, who was a mother at twelve ; de La Motte [474] mentions pregnancy before twelve ; Kilpatrick [e] in a negress, at eleven years and six months ; Fox,[f] at twelve ; Hall,[g] at twelve ; Kinney,[h] at twelve years, ten months, and sixteen days ; Herrick,[i] at thirteen years and nine months ; Murillo,[j] at thirteen years ; Philippart,[k] at fourteen years ; Stallcup, at eleven years and nine months ; Stoakley,[l] at thirteen years ; Walker,[m] at the age of twelve years and eight months ; another case,[n] at twelve years and six months ; and Williams,[o] at eleven.

[a] An editorial article in the Indian Medical Gazette of Sept., 1890, says :—

"The appearance of menstruation is held by the great majority of natives of India to be evidence and proof of marriageability, but among the Hindu community it is considered disgraceful that a girl should remain unmarried until this function is established. The consequence is that girls are married at the age of nine or ten years, but it is understood or professed that the consummation of the marriage is delayed until after the first menstrual period. There is, however, too much reason to believe that the earlier ceremony is very frequently, perhaps commonly, taken to warrant resort to sexual intercourse before the menstrual flux has occurred : it may be accepted as true that premenstrual copulation is largely practised under the cover of marriage in this country.

"From this practice it results that girls become mothers at the earliest possible period of their lives. A native medical witness testified that in about 20 per cent. of marriages children were born by wives of from twelve to thirteen years of age. Cases of death caused by the first act of sexual intercourse are by no means rare. They are naturally concealed, but ever and anon they come to light. Dr. Chevers mentioned some 14 cases of this sort in the last edition of his 'Handbook of Medical Jurisprudence for India,' and Dr. Harvey found 5 in the medicolegal returns submitted by the Civil Surgeons of the Bengal Presidency during the years 1870–71–72.

"Reform must come from conviction and effort, as in every other case, but meantime the strong arm of the law should be put forth for the protection of female children from the degradation and hurt entailed by premature sexual intercourse. This can easily be done by raising the age of punishable intercourse, which is now fixed at the absurd limit of ten years. Menstruation very seldom appears in native girls before the completed age of twelve years, and if the 'age of consent' were raised to that limit, it would not interfere with the prejudices and customs which insist on marriage before menstruation."

[b] 434, Feb., 1845.   [c] 318, 1861–2.   [d] 476, 1868, ii., 618.   [e] 545, 1873.
[f] 286, 1889.   [g] 729, 1859.   [h] 538, 1885.   [i] 593, 1873.   [j] 668, 1875.
[k] 143, 1875.   [l] 526, 1855, xi., 203.   [m] 218, 1846–7.   [n] 822, 1876.   [o] 131, 1874.

In 1816 some girls were admitted to the Paris Maternité as young as thirteen, and during the Revolution several at eleven, and even younger. Smith [a] speaks of a legal case in which a girl, eleven years old, being safely delivered of a living child, charged her uncle with rape. Allen [b] speaks of a girl who became pregnant at twelve years and nine months, and was delivered of a healthy, 9-pound boy before the physician's arrival; the placenta came away afterward, and the mother made a speedy recovery. She was thought to have had "dropsy of the abdomen," as the parents had lost a girl of about the same age who was tapped for ascites. The father of the child was a boy only fourteen years of age.

Marvelous to relate, there are on record several cases of **twins** being **born to a child mother.** Kay reports a case of twins in a girl of thirteen; Montgomery, at fourteen; and Meigs reports the case of a young girl, of Spanish blood, at Maracaibo, who gave birth to a child before she was twelve and to twins before reaching fourteen years.

In the older works, the following authors have reported cases of **pregnancy before the appearance of menstruation:** Ballonius, Vogel, Morgagni, the anatomist of the kidney, Schenck, Bartholinus, Bierling, Zacchias, Charleton, Mauriceau, Ephemerides, and Fabricius Hildanus.

In some cases this precocity seems to be hereditary, being transmitted from mother to daughter, bringing about an almost incredible state of affairs, in which a **girl** is a **grandmother** about the ordinary age of maternity. Kay says that he had reported to him, on "pretty good" authority, an instance of a Damascus Jewess who became a grandmother at twenty-one years. In France [c] they record a young grandmother of twenty-eight. Ketchum [d] speaks of a negress, aged thirteen, who gave birth to a well-developed child which began to menstruate at ten years and nine months and at thirteen became pregnant; hence the negress was a grandmother at twenty-five years and nine months. She had a second child before she was sixteen, who began to menstruate at seven years and six months, thus proving the inheritance of this precocity, and leaving us at sea to figure what degree of grandmother she may be if she lives to an advanced age. Another interesting case of this nature is that of Mrs. C.,[e] born 1854, married in 1867, and who had a daughter ten months after. This daughter married in 1882, and in March, 1883, gave birth to a 9-pound boy. The youthful grandmother, not twenty-nine, was present at the birth. This case was remarkable, as the children were both legitimate.

Fecundity in the old seems to have attracted fully as much attention among the older observers as precocity. Pliny [636] speaks of Cornelia, of the family of Serpios, who bore a son at sixty, who was named Volusius Saturnius; and Marsa, a physician of Venice, was deceived in a pregnancy

a 490, 1848.   b 224, 1885, ii., 913.   c 365, 1867, No. 291.
d 770, 1849.   e 494, June 9, 1883.

in a woman of sixty, his diagnosis being " dropsy." Tarenta records the history of the case of a woman who menstruated and bore children when past the age of sixty. Among the older reports are those of Blanchard [a] of a woman who bore a child at sixty years; Fielitz,[160] one at sixty; Ephemerides, one at sixty-two; Rush,[b] one at sixty; Bernstein,[201] one at sixty years; Schoepfer, at seventy years; and, almost beyond belief, Debes[c] cites an instance as taking place at the very advanced age of one hundred and three. Wallace[d] speaks of a woman in the Isle of Orkney bearing children when past the age of sixty. We would naturally expect to find the age of child-bearing prolonged in the northern countries where the age of maturity is later. Capuron cites an example of child-birth in a woman of sixty; Haller, cases at fifty-eight, sixty-three, and seventy; Dewees, at sixty-one; and Thibaut de Chauvalon, in a woman of Martinique aged ninety years. There was a woman delivered in Germany, in 1723, at the age of fifty-five; one at fifty-one in Kentucky; [e] and one in Russia at fifty.[f] Depasse [g] speaks of a woman of fifty-nine years and five months old who was delivered of a healthy male child, which she suckled, weaning it on her sixtieth birthday. She had been a widow for twenty years, and had ceased to menstruate nearly ten years before. In St. Peter's Church, in East Oxford, is a monument bearing an inscription recording the death in child-birth of a woman sixty-two years old. Cachot [h] relates the case of a woman of fifty-three, who was delivered of a living child by means of the forceps, and a year after bore a second child without instrumental interference. She had no milk in her breasts at the time and no signs of secretion. This aged mother had been married at fifty-two, five years after the cessation of her menstruation, and her husband was a young man, only twenty-four years old.

Kennedy [i] reports a delivery at sixty-two years, and the Cincinnati Enquirer, January, 1863, says: " Dr. W. McCarthy was in attendance on a lady of sixty-nine years, on Thursday night last, who gave birth to a fine boy. The father of the child is seventy-four years old, and the mother and child are doing well." Quite recently there died in Great Britain a Mrs. Henry of Gortree at the age of one hundred and twelve, leaving a daughter of nine years.

Mayham [j] saw a woman seventy-three years old who recovered after delivery of a child. A most peculiar case is that of a widow, seventy years old, a native of Garches.[k] She had been in the habit of indulging freely in wine, and, during the last six months, to decided excess. After an unusually prolonged libation she found herself unable to walk home; she sat down by the roadside waiting until she could proceed, and was so found by a young man who knew her and who proposed helping her home. By the time her

a 213, cent. iv., n. 71.   b 696, ii.   c 290, 248.   d 629, vol. xxii., 543.
e 133, 1872, vi., 138.   f 811, 1881, vi.   g 364, Oct. 1, 1891.
h 616, 1883–4, xxvi., 394.   i 769, 1881.   j 542, Jan., 1891.   k 789, Dec. 3, 1881.

house was reached night was well advanced, and she invited him to stop over night ; finding her more than affable, he stopped at her house over four nights, and the result of his visits was an ensuing pregnancy for Madame.

Multiple births in the aged have been reported from authentic sources. The Lancet [a] quotes a rather fabulous account of a lady over sixty-two years of age who gave birth to triplets, making her total number of children 13. Montgomery, Colomb, and Knehel, each, have recorded the birth of twins in women beyond the usual age of the menopause, and there is a case [b] recorded of a woman of fifty-two who was delivered of twins.

Impregnation without completion of the copulative act by reason of some malformation, such as occlusion of the vagina or uterus, fibrous and unruptured hymen, etc., has been a subject of discussion in the works of medical jurisprudence of all ages ; and cases of conception without entrance of the penis are found in abundance throughout medical literature, and may have an important medicolegal bearing. There is little doubt of the possibility of spermatozoa deposited on the genitalia making progress to the seat of fertilization, as their power of motility and tenacity of life have been well demonstrated. Percy [c] reports an instance in which semen was found issuing from the os uteri eight and one-half days after the last intercourse ; and a microscopic examination of this semen revealed the presence of living as well as dead spermatozoa. We have occasional instances of impregnation by rectal coitus, the semen finding its way into an occluded vaginal canal by a fistulous communication.

Guillemeau,[d] the surgeon of the French king, tells of a girl of eighteen, who was brought before the French officials in Paris, in 1607, on the citation of her husband of her inability to allow him completion of the marital function. He alleged that he had made several unsuccessful attempts to enter her, and in doing so had caused paraphimosis. On examination by the surgeons she was found to have a dense membrane, of a fibrous nature, entirely occluding the vagina, which they incised. Immediately afterward the woman exhibited morning sickness and the usual signs of pregnancy, and was delivered in four months of a full-term child, the results of an impregnation occasioned by one of the unsuccessful attempts at entrance. Such instances are numerous in the older literature, and a mere citation of a few is considered sufficient here. Zacchias,[e] Amand, Fabricius Hildanus, Graaf, the discoverer of the follicles that bear his name, Borellus, Blegny, Blanchard,[f] Diemerbroeck,[g] Duddell, Mauriceau, à Reyes, Riolan,[h] Harvey, the discoverer of the circulation of the blood,[i] Wolfius, Walther, Rongier,[j] Ruysch, Forestus, Ephemerides,[k] and Schurig all mention cases of conception with intact

a 476, 1867, i., 727.   b 538, 1889.   c 130, March 9, 1861.
d 389, L. ii., chap. 8, fol. 108.   e 830, n. 42.   f 213, cent. iii.
g 303, L. i., c. 23.   h 686, L. ii., c. 37.   i 405, L. ii., c. 11.
j 462, T. xlix., 358.   k 104, Dec. 1, ann. iii., obs. 273.

hymen, and in which there was no entrance of the penis.   Tolberg [762] has an example of hymen integrum after the birth of a fetus five months old, and there is recorded [a] a case of tubal pregnancy in which the hymen was intact.

Gilbert [b] gives an account of a case of pregnancy in an unmarried woman, who successfully resisted an attempt at criminal connection and yet became impregnated and gave birth to a perfectly formed female child.   The hymen was not ruptured, and the impregnation could not have preceded the birth more than thirty-six weeks.   Unfortunately, this poor woman was infected with gonorrhea after the attempted assault.   Simmons of St. Louis [c] gives a curious peculiarity of conception, in which there was complete closure of the vagina, subsequent conception, and delivery at term.   He made the patient's acquaintance from her application to him in regard to a malcondition of her sexual apparatus, causing much domestic infelicity.

Lawson [d] speaks of a woman of thirty-five, who had been married ten months, and whose husband could never effect an entrance ; yet she became pregnant and had a normal labor, despite the fact that, in addition to a tough and unruptured hymen, she had an occluding vaginal cyst.   Hickinbotham of Birmingham [e] reports the history of two cases of labor at term in females whose hymens were immensely thickened.   H. Grey Edwards has seen a case of imperforate hymen which had to be torn through in labor ; yet one single act of copulation, even with this obstacle to entrance, sufficed to impregnate.   Champion speaks of a woman who became pregnant although her hymen was intact.   She had been in the habit of having coitus by the urethra, and all through her pregnancy continued this practice.

Houghton [f] speaks of a girl of twenty-five into whose vagina it was impossible to pass the tip of the first finger on account of the dense cicatricial membrane in the orifice, but who gave birth, with comparative ease, to a child at full term, the only interference necessary being a few slight incisions to permit the passage of the head.   Tweedie [g] saw an Irish girl of twenty-three, with an imperforate os uteri, who had menstruated only scantily since fourteen and not since her marriage.   She became pregnant and went to term, and required some operative interference.   He incised at the point of usual location of the os, and one of his incisions was followed by the flow of liquor amnii, and the head fell upon the artificial opening, the diameter of which proved to be one and a half or two inches ; the birth then progressed promptly, the child being born alive.

Guerard [h] notes an instance in which the opening barely admitted a hair ; yet the patient reached the third month of pregnancy, at which time she induced abortion in a manner that could not be ascertained.   Roe gives a

a Collect. Acad. de Méd., Paris, 1756, xii., 151.   b 218, 1872, 298.

c 703, 1847, 62–69.   d 224, 1885, i., 1202.   e 224, 1881, i., 1001.

f 313, 1862.   g 490, vol. xx., 202.   h 261, 1895, No. 15.

case of conception in an imperforate uterus,[a] and Duncan[b] relates the history of a case of pregnancy in an unruptured hymen, characterized by an extraordinary ascent of the uterus. Among many, the following modern observers have also reported instances of pregnancy with hymen integrum : Braun,[c] 3 cases ; Francis,[d] Horton,[e] Oakman,[f] Brill,[g] 2 cases ; Burgess,[h] Haig,[i] Hay,[j] and Smith.[k]

Instances in which the presence of an unruptured hymen has complicated or retarded actual labor are quite common, and until the membrane is ruptured by external means the labor is often effectually obstructed. Among others reporting cases of this nature are Beale,[l] Carey,[m] Davis, Emond,[n] Fetherston, Leisenring,[o] Mackinlay,[p] Martinelli, Palmer,[q] Rousseau, Ware, and Yale.[r]

There are many cases of stricture or complete occlusion of the vagina, congenital or acquired from cicatricial contraction, obstructing delivery, and in some the impregnation seems more marvelous than cases in which the obstruction is only a thin membranous hymen. Often the obstruction is so dense as to require a large bistoury to divide it, and even that is not always sufficient, and the Cesarean operation only can terminate the obstructed delivery ; we cannot surmise how conception could have been possible. Staples[s] records a case of pregnancy and parturition with congenital stricture of the vagina. Maisonneuve[t] mentions the successful practice of a Cesarean operation in a case of congenital occlusion of the vagina forming a complete obstruction to delivery. Verdile[u] records an instance of imperforate vagina in which the rectovaginal wall was divided and the delivery effected through the rectum and anus. Lombard[v] mentions an observation of complete occlusion of the vagina in a woman, the mother of 4 living children and pregnant for the fifth time. Thus, almost incredible to relate, it is possible for a woman to become a mother of a living child and yet preserve all the vaginal evidences of virginity. Cole[w] describes a woman of twenty-four who was delivered without the rupture of the hymen, and Meek[x] remarks on a similar case. We can readily see that, in a case like that of Verdile, in which rectal delivery is effected, the hymen could be left intact and the product of conception be born alive.

A natural sequence to the subject of impregnation without entrance is that of **artificial impregnation.** From being a matter of wonder and

[a] 476, 1851, i., 564.

[b] 769, 1875, iii., 91–93.

[c] Wien. Med. Wochen., 1876, xxvi.. 289–316.

[d] 435, 1871, vi., 253.

[e] 545, 1869, xxi., 314.   [f] 476, 1851, i., 569.

[g] 812, 1882.

[h] 476, 1876, ii., 237.   [i] 180, 1870.   [j] 547, 1873.

[k] 592, 1858–9.

[l] 476, 1859, ii., 98.   [m] 525, 1855, i., 97.

[n] 363, 1862, xxxv., 214.

[o] 547, 1870–1, i., 395.   [p] 476, 1840–1, i., 847.

[q] 778, iv., 211.

[r] 218, 1859-60, lxi., 295.   [s] Northwest Med. and Surg. Jour., St. Paul, 1870–71, i., 183.

[t] 363, 1849, i., 451.   [u] Morgagni, Napoli, 1875, xvii., 747.

[v] 368, 1831.

[w] Western Lancet, San Francisco, 1873–4, ii., 705.

[x] 176, 1874–5, xii., 457.

hearsay, it has been demonstrated as a practical and useful method in those cases in which, by reason of some unfortunate anatomic malformation on either the male or the female side, the marriage is unfruitful. There are many cases constantly occurring in which the birth of an heir is a most desirable thing in a person's life. The historic instance of Queen Mary of England, whose anxiety and efforts to bear a child were the subject of public comment and prayers, is but an example of a fact that is occurring every day, and doubtless some of these cases could be righted by the pursuance of some of the methods suggested.

There have been rumors from the beginning of the century of women being impregnated in a bath, from contact with cloths containing semen, etc., and some authorities in medical jurisprudence have accepted the possibility of such an occurrence. It is not in the province of this work to speculate on what may be, but to give authoritative facts, from which the reader may draw his own deductions. Fertilization of plants has been thought to have been known in the oldest times, and there are some who believe that the library at Alexandria must have contained some information relative to it. The first authentic account that we have of artificial impregnation is that of Schwammerdam, who in 1680 attempted it without success by the fecundation of the eggs of fish. Roesel, his scholar, made an attempt in 1690, but also failed; and to Jacobi, in 1700, belongs the honor of success. In 1780, Abbe Spallanzani, following up the success of Jacobi, artificially impregnated a bitch, who brought forth in sixty-two days 3 puppies, all resembling the male. The illustrious John Hunter advised a man afflicted with hypospadias to impregnate his wife by vaginal injections of semen in water with an ordinary syringe, and, in spite of the simplicity of this method, the attempt was followed by a successful issue. Since this time, Nicholas of Nancy and Lesueur have practised the simple vaginal method; while Gigon, d'Angoulême (14 cases), Girault (10 cases), Marion Sims, Thomas, Salmon, Pajot, Gallard, Courty, Roubaud, Dehaut, and others have used the more modern uterine method with success.

A dog-breeder,[a] by syringing the uterus of a bitch, has succeeded in impregnating her. Those who are desirous of full information on this subject, as regards the modus operandi, etc., are referred to Girault;[b] this author reports in full several examples. One case was that of a woman, aged twenty-five, afflicted with blenorrhea, who, chagrined at not having issue, made repeated forcible injections of semen in water for two months, and finally succeeded in impregnating herself, and was delivered of a living child. Another case was that of a female, aged twenty-three, who had an extra long vaginal canal, probably accounting for the absence of pregnancy. She made injections of semen, and was finally delivered of a child. He also reports the case of a distinguished musician who, by reason of hypospadias, had never

[a] 806, 1884.   [b] 100, 1868, 409.

impregnated his wife, and had resorted to injections of semen with a favorable result. This latter case seems hardly warranted when we consider that men afflicted with hypospadias and epispadias have become fathers. Percy [a] gives the instance of a gentleman whom he had known for some time, whose urethra terminated a little below the frenum, as in other persons, but whose glans bulged quite prominently beyond it, rendering urination in the forward direction impossible. Despite the fact that this man could not perform the ejaculatory function, he was the father of three children, two of them inheriting his penile formation.

The fundamental condition of fecundity being the union of a spermatozoid and an ovum, the object of artificial impregnation is to further this union by introducing semen directly to the fundus of the uterus. The operation is quite simple and as follows : The husband, having been found perfectly healthy, is directed to cohabit with his wife, using a condom. The semen ejaculated is sucked up by an intrauterine syringe (Fig. 1) which has been properly disinfected and kept warm. The os uteri is now exposed and wiped off with some cotton which has been dipped in an antiseptic fluid ; the nozzle of the syringe is introduced to the fundus of the uterus, and some drops of the fluid slowly expressed into the uterus. The woman is then kept in bed on her back. This operation is best

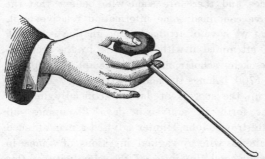

Fig. 1.—Apparatus for artificial impregnation.

carried out immediately before or immediately after the menstrual epoch, and if not successful at the first attempt should be repeated for several months. At the present day artificial impregnation in pisciculture is extensively used with great success.[b]

[a] 130, 1861.

[b] The following extraordinary incident of accidental impregnation, quoted from the American Medical Weekly [1] by the Lancet,[2] is given in brief, not because it bears any semblance of possibility, but as a curious example from the realms of imagination in medicine.

L. G. Capers of Vicksburg, Miss., relates an incident during the late Civil War, as follows : A matron and her two daughters, aged fifteen and seventeen years, filled with the enthusiasm of patriotism, stood ready to minister to the wounds of their countrymen in their fine residence near the scene of the battle of R———, May 12, 1863, between a portion of Grant's army and some Confederates. During the fray a gallant and noble young friend of the narrator staggered and fell to the earth ; at the same time a piercing cry was heard in the house near by. Examination of the wounded soldier showed that a bullet had passed through the scrotum and carried away the left testicle. The same bullet had apparently penetrated the left side of the abdomen of the elder young lady, midway between the umbilicus and the anterior superior spinous process of the ilium, and had become lost in the abdomen. This

Interesting as are all the anomalies of conception, none are more so than those of **unconscious impregnation ;** and some well-authenticated cases can be mentioned. Instances of violation in sleep, with subsequent pregnancy as a result, have been reported in the last century by Valentini,[793] Genselius,[a] and Schurig. Reports by modern authorities seem to be quite scarce, though there are several cases on record of rape during anesthesia, followed by impregnation. Capuron [b] relates a curious instance of a woman who was raped during lethargy, and who subsequently became pregnant, though her condition was not ascertained until the fourth month, the peculiar abdominal sensation exciting suspicion of the true nature of the case, which had previously been thought impossible.

There is a record of a case [c] of a young girl of great moral purity who became pregnant without the slightest knowledge of the source ; although, it might be remarked, such cases must be taken *" cum grano salis."* Cases of conception without the slightest sexual desire or pleasure, either from fright, as in rape, or naturally deficient constitution, have been recorded ; as well as conception during intoxication and in a hypnotic trance, which latter has recently assumed a much mooted legal aspect. As far back as 1680,[215] Duverney speaks of conception without the slightest sense of desire or pleasure on the part of the female.

Conception with Deficient Organs.—Having spoken of conception with some obstructive interference, conception with some natural or acquired deficiency of the functional, organic, or genital apparatus must be considered. It is a well-known fact that women exhibiting rudimentary development of the uterus or vagina are still liable to become pregnant, and many such cases have been recorded ; but the most peculiar cases are those in which pregnancy has appeared after removal of some of the sexual apparatus.

Pregnancy going to term with a successful delivery frequently follows the performance of ovariotomy with astonishing rapidity. Olier [d] cites an

daughter suffered an attack of peritonitis, but recovered in two months under the treatment administered.

Marvelous to relate, just two hundred and seventy-eight days after the reception of the minie-ball, she was delivered of a fine boy, weighing 8 pounds, to the surprise of herself and the mortification of her parents and friends. The hymen was intact, and the young mother strenuously insisted on her virginity and innocence. About three weeks after this remarkable birth Dr. Capers was called to see the infant, and the grandmother insisted that there was something wrong with the child's genitals. Examination showed a rough, swollen, and sensitive scrotum, containing some hard substance. He operated, and extracted a smashed and battered minie-ball. The doctor, after some meditation, theorized in this manner : He concluded that this was the same ball that had carried away the testicle of his young friend, that had penetrated the ovary of the young lady, and, with some spermatozoa upon it, had impregnated her. With this conviction he approached the young man and told him the circumstances ; the soldier appeared skeptical at first, but consented to visit the young mother ; a friendship ensued which soon ripened into a happy marriage, and the pair had three children, none resembling, in the same degree as the first, the heroic *pater familias.*

a 104, 1715.   b 254, 86.   c 525, 1855.   d 363, xlv., 1140.

instance of ovariotomy with a pregnancy of twins three months afterward, and accouchement at term of two well-developed boys. Polaillon [a] speaks of a pregnancy consecutive to ovariotomy, the accouchement being normal at term. Crouch [b] reports a case of successful parturition in a patient who had previously undergone ovariotomy by a large incision. Parsons [c] mentions a case of twin pregnancy two years after ovariotomy attended with abnormal development of one of the children. Cutter [d] speaks of a case in which a woman bore a child one year after the performance of ovariotomy, and Pippingsköld [e] of two cases of pregnancy after ovariotomy in which the stump as well as the remaining ovary were cauterized. Brown [f] relates a similar instance with successful delivery. Bixby,[g] Harding,[h] Walker (1878–9), and Mears [i] all report cases, and others are not at all rare. In the cases following shortly after operation, it has been suggested that they may be explained by the long retention of the ova in the uterus, deposited there prior to operation. In the presence of such facts one can but wonder if artificial fecundation of an ovum derived from another woman may ever be brought about in the uterus of a sterile woman !

Conception Soon After a Preceding Pregnancy.—Conception some-times follows birth (or abortion) with astonishing rapidity, and some women seem for a period of their lives either always pregnant or with infants at their breasts. This prolificity is often alluded to, and is not confined to the lower classes, as often stated, but is common even among the nobility. Illustrative of this, we have examples in some of the reigning families in Europe to-day. A peculiar instance is given by Sparkman [j] in which a woman conceived just forty hours after abortion. Rice [k] mentions the case of a woman who was confined with her first child, a boy, on July 31, 1870, and was again delivered of another child on June 4, 1871. She had become pregnant twenty-eight days after delivery. He also mentions another case of a Mrs. C., who, at the age of twenty-three, gave birth to a child on September 13, 1880, and bore a second child on July 2, 1881. She must have become pregnant twenty-one days after the delivery of her first child.

Superfetation has been known for many centuries ; the Romans had laws prescribing the laws of succession in such cases, and many medical writers have mentioned it. Hippocrates and Aristotle wrote of it, the former at some length. Pliny speaks of a slave who bore two infants, one resembling the master, the other a man with whom she had intercourse, and cites the case as one of super-fetation. Schenck [l] relates instances, and Zacchias, Velchius, and Sinibaldus mention cases. Paré seemed to be well conversant with the possibility as well as the actuality of superfetation ; and Harvey [m] reports that a certain

a 168, 1879, vi., 243.   b 550, xxxv., 71.   c 476, 1866, i., 284.   d 538, 1867–8.
e 321, 1880.   f 548, 1854, ix., 566.   g 476, 1881.
h 476, 1880, i., 93.   i 547, 1879.   j 264, 1876.   k 122, 1881, 206.
l L. iv., De Superfetation, 617.   m 404, fol. 479.

maid, gotten with child by her master, in order to hide her knavery came to London in September, where she lay in by stealth, and being recovered, returned home. In December of the same year she was unexpectedly delivered of another child, a product of superfetation, which proclaimed the crime that she had so cunningly concealed before.

Marcellus Donatus, Goret, Schacher,[717] and Mauriceau[a] mention superfetation. In the Académie des Sciences, at Paris, in 1702, there was mentioned the case of a woman who was delivered of a boy ; in the placenta was discovered a sort of bladder which was found to contain a female fetus of the age of from four to five months ; and in 1729, before the same society, there was an instance in which two fetuses were born a day apart, one aged forty days and the other at full term. From the description, it does not seem possible that either of these were blighted twin pregnancies. Ruysch[b] gives an account of a surgeon's wife at Amsterdam, in 1686, who was delivered of a strong child which survived, and, six hours after, of a small embryo, the funis of which was full of hydatids and the placenta as large and thick as one of three months. Ruysch accompanies his description with an illustrative figure. At Lyons, in 1782, Benoite Franquet was unexpectedly delivered of a child seven months old ; three weeks later she experienced symptoms indicative of the existence of another fetus, and after five months and sixteen days she was delivered of a remarkably strong and healthy child.

Baudeloque[c] speaks of a case of superfetation observed by Desgranges in Lyons in 1780. After the birth of the first infant the lochia failed to flow, no milk appeared in the breasts, and the belly remained large. In about three weeks after the accouchement she had connection with her husband, and in a few days felt fetal movements. A second child was born at term, sixty-eight days after the first ; and in 1782 both children were living. A woman of Arles[d] was delivered on November 11, 1796, of a child at term ; she had connection with her husband four days after ; the lochia stopped, and the milk did not flow after this intercourse. About one and a half months after this she felt quickening again, and naturally supposed that she had become impregnated by the first intercourse after confinement ; but five months after the first accouchement she was delivered of another child at term, the result of a superfetation. Milk in abundance made its appearance, and she was amply able to nourish both children from the breasts. Lachausse[e] speaks of a woman of thirty who bore one child on April 30, 1748, and another on September 16th in the same year. Her breasts were full enough to nourish both of the children. It might be remarked in comment on this case that, according to a French authority, the woman died in 1755, and on dissection was found to have had a double uterus.

[a] 513, app. i., 65.   [b] 698, Tome i., obs. 14.   [c] Traité de l'Art des Accouchemens, ii.
[d] 302, iv., 181.   [e] De superfetation vera in utero simplici, Argentor., 1755.

A peculiar instance of superfetation was reported by Langmore[a] in which there was an abortion of a fetus between the third and fourth months, apparently dead some time, and thirteen hours later a second fetus; an ovum of about four weeks and of perfect formation was found adherent near the fundus. Tyler Smith[b] mentions a lady pregnant for the first time who miscarried at five months and some time afterward discharged a small clot containing a perfectly fresh and healthy ovum of about four weeks' formation. There was no sign of a double uterus, and the patient menstruated regularly during pregnancy, being unwell three weeks before the abortion. Harley and Tanner[c] speak of a woman of thirty-eight who never had borne twins, and who aborted a fetus of four months' gestation; serious hemorrhage accompanied the removal of the placenta, and on placing the hand in the uterine cavity an embryo of five or six weeks was found inclosed in a sac and floating in clear liquor amnii. The patient was the mother of nine children, the youngest of which was three years old.

Young[d] speaks of a woman who three months previously had aborted a three months' fetus, but a tumor still remained in the abdomen, the auscultation of which gave evidence of a fetal heart-beat. Vaginal examination revealed a dilatation of the os uteri of at least one inch and a fetal head pressing out; subsequently a living fetus of about six months of age was delivered. Severe hemorrhage complicated the case, but was controlled, and convalescence speedily ensued. Huse[e] cites an instance of a mother bearing a boy on November 4, 1834, and a girl on August 3, 1835. At birth the boy looked premature, about seven months old, which being the case, the girl must have been either a superfetation or a seven months' child also. Van Bibber of Baltimore says he met a young lady who was born five months after her sister, and who was still living.

The most curious and convincing examples of superfetation are those in which **children of different colors,** either twins or near the same age, are born to the same woman,—similar to that exemplified in the case of the mare who was covered first by a stallion and a quarter of an hour later by an ass, and gave birth at one parturition to a horse and a mule.[f] Parsons[g] speaks of a case at Charleston, S. C., in 1714, of a white woman who gave birth to twins, one a mulatto and the other white. She confessed that after her husband left her a negro servant came to her and forced her to comply with his wishes by threatening her life. Smellie mentions the case of a black woman who had twins, one child black and the other almost white. She confessed having had intercourse with a white overseer immediately after her husband left her bed. Dewees[h] reports a similar case. Newlin of Nashville[i] speaks of a negress who bore twins, one distinctly black with the

a 778, iv., 135.   b 476, April 12, 1856.   c 778, Lond., 1863, iv., 165–169.
d 124, 1868.   e 218, 1856, liv. 294.   f Acad. de Méd., Aug., 1825.
g 629, Oct., 1745.   h 301, 1805, T. clxxiv.   i Quoted in 300, Sept., 1887.

typical African features, while the other was a pretty mulatto exhibiting the distinct characters of the Caucasian race. Both the parents were perfect types of the black African negro. The mother, on being questioned, frankly acknowledged that shortly after being with her husband she had lain a night with a white man. In this case each child had its own distinct cord and placenta.

Archer[a] gives facts illustrating and observations showing: "that a white woman, by intercourse with a white man and negro, may conceive twins, one of which shall be white and the other a mulatto; and that, vice versa, a black woman, by intercourse with a negro and a white man, may conceive twins, one of which shall be a negro and the other a mulatto." Wight[b] narrates that he was called to see a woman, the wife of an East Indian laborer on the Isle of Trinidad, who had been delivered of a fetus 6 inches long, about four months old, and having a cord of about 18 inches in length. He removed the placenta, and in about half an hour the woman was delivered of a full-term white female child. The first child was dark, like the mother and father, and the mother denied any possibility of its being a white man's child; but this was only natural on her part, as East Indian husbands are so intensely jealous that they would even kill an unfaithful wife. Both the mother and the mysterious white baby are doing well. Bouillon[c] speaks of a negress in Guadeloupe who bore twins, one a negro and the other a mulatto. She had sexual congress with both a negro and a white man.

Delmas,[d] a surgeon of Rouen, tells of a woman of thirty-six who was delivered in the hospital of his city on February 26, 1806, of two children, one black and the other a mulatto. She had been pregnant eight months, and had had intercourse with a negro twice about her fourth month of pregnancy, though living with the white man who first impregnated her. Two placentæ were expelled some time after the twins, and showed a membranous junction. The children died shortly after birth.

Pregnancy often takes place in a unicorn or bicorn uterus, leading to similar anomalous conditions. Galle, Hoffman, Massen, and Sanger give interesting accounts of this occurrence, and Ross[e] relates an instance of triple pregnancy in a double uterus. Cleveland[f] describes a discharge of an anomalous deciduous membrane during pregnancy which was probably from the unimpregnated half of a double uterus.

a 541, 1809–10.   b 124, July 6, 1895, 14.   c Bull. de la Société de Méd., 1821.
d 302, iv., 181.   e Médicin, Paris, 1879, v., No. 43.   f 778, 1884, xxvi., 117.

CHAPTER II.

PRENATAL ANOMALIES.

Extrauterine Pregnancy.—In the consideration of prenatal anomalies, the first to be discussed will be those of extrauterine pregnancy. This abnormalism has been known almost as long as there has been any real knowledge of obstetrics. In the writings of Albucasis,[115] during the eleventh century, extrauterine pregnancy is discussed, and later the works of N. Polinus and Cordæus, about the sixteenth century, speak of it; in the case of Cordæus the fetus was converted into a lithopedion and carried in the abdomen twenty-eight years. Horstius in the sixteenth century relates the history of a woman who conceived for the third time in March, 1547, and in 1563 the remains of the fetus were still in the abdomen.

Israel Spach, in an extensive gynecologic work published in 1557, figures a lithopedion drawn in situ in the case of a woman with her belly laid open. He dedicated to this calcified fetus, which he regarded as a reversion, the following curious epigram, in allusion to the classical myth that after the flood the world was repopulated by the two survivors, Deucalion and Pyrrha, who walked over the earth and cast stones behind them, which, on striking the ground, became people. Roughly translated from the Latin, this epigram read as follows : " Deucalion cast stones behind him and thus fashioned our tender race from the hard marble. How comes it that nowadays, by a reversal of things, the tender body of a little babe has limbs nearer akin to stone ? " [a] Many of the older writers mention this form of fetation as a curiosity, but offer no explanation as to its cause. Mauriceau [513] and de Graaf [384] discuss in full extrauterine pregnancy, and Salmuth, Hannæus, and Bartholinus describe it. From the beginning of the eighteenth century this subject always demanded the attention and interest of medical observers. In more modern times, Campbell and Geoffroy-Saint-Hilaire, who named it " Grossesse Pathologique," have carefully defined and classified the forms, and to-day every text-book on obstetrics gives a scientific discussion and classification of the different forms of extrauterine pregnancy.

The site of the conception is generally the wall of the uterus, the Fallopian tube, or the ovary, although there are instances of pregnancy in the vagina, as for example when there is scirrhus of the uterus ; [b] and again, cases

a 844, 274.   b 462, T. li. 55.

supposed to be only extrauterine have been instances simply of double uterus, with single or concurrent pregnancy. Ross [a] speaks of a woman of thirty-three who had been married fourteen years, had borne six children, and who on July 16, 1870, miscarried with twins of about five months' development. After a week she declared that she was still pregnant with another child, but as the physician had placed his hand in the uterine cavity after the abortion, he knew the fetus must be elsewhere or that no pregnancy existed. We can readily see how this condition might lead to a diagnosis of extrauterine pregnancy, but as the patient insisted on a thorough examination, the doctor found by the stethoscope the presence of a beating fetal heart, and by vaginal examination a double uterus. On introducing a sound into the new aperture he discovered that it opened into another cavity ; but as the woman was pregnant in this, he proceeded no further. On October 31st she was delivered of a female child of full growth. She had menstruated from this bipartite uterus three times during the period between the miscarriage of the twins and the birth of the child. Both the mother and child did well.

In most cases there is rupture of the fetal sac into the abdominal cavity or the uterus, and the fetus is ejected into this location, from thence to be removed or carried therein many years ; but there are instances in which the conception has been found in situ, as depicted in Figure 2. A sturdy woman [b] of thirty was executed on January 16, 1735, for the murder of her child. It was ascertained that she had passed her catamenia about the first of the month, and thereafter had sexual intercourse with one of her fellow-prisoners. On dissection both Fallopian tubes were found distended, and the left ovary, which bore signs of conception, was twice as large as the right. Campbell [248] quotes another such case in a woman of thirty-eight who for twenty years had practised her vocation as a Cyprian, and who unexpectedly conceived. At the third month of pregnancy a hard extrauterine tumor was found, which was gradually increasing in size and extending to the left side of the hypogastrium, the associate symptoms of pregnancy, sense of pressure, pain, tormina, and dysuria, being unusually severe. There was subsequently an attack of inflammatory fever, followed by tumefaction of the abdomen, convulsions, and death on the ninth day. The fetus had been contained in the peritoneal coat of the ovary until the fourth month, when one of the feet passed through the cyst and caused the fatal result. Signs of acute peritonitis were seen postmortem, the abdominal cavity was full of blood, and the ovary much lacerated.

The **termination of extrauterine pregnancy** varies ; in some cases the fetus is extracted by operation after rupture ; in others the fetus has been delivered alive by abdominal section ; it may be partially absorbed, or carried many years in the abdomen ; or it may ulcerate through the confining walls, enter the bowels or bladder, and the remnants of the fetal body be discharged.

[a] 476, 1871, ii., 189. [b] 527, vol. v., 277.

The curious cases mentioned by older writers, and called **abortion by the mouth,** etc., are doubtless, in many instances, remnants of extra-uterine pregnancies or dermoid cysts.   Maroldus [507] speaks in full of such cases; Bartholinus, Salmuth,[a] and à Reyes [b] speak of women vomiting remnants of fetuses.   In Germany,[c] in the seventeenth century, there lived a woman who on three different occasions is said to have vomited a fetus.   The last miscarriage in this manner was of eight months' growth and was accom-

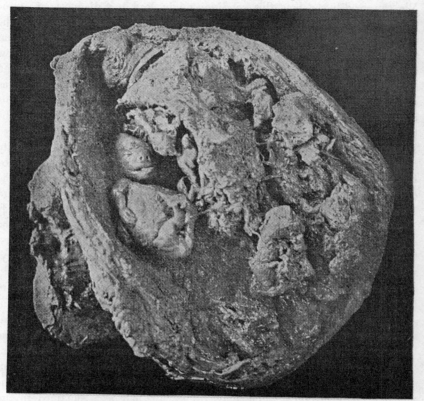

Fig. 2 – Pregnant Fallopian tube laid open, showing the fetus killed by hemorrhage into its membranes, but without the escape of the fetus from the tube (Tuttle and Cragin).

panied by its placenta.   The older observers thought this woman must have had two orifices to her womb, one of which had some connection with the stomach, as they had records of the dissection of a female in whom was found a conformation similar to this.

Discharge of the fetal bones or even the whole of an extrauterine fetus **by the rectum** is not uncommon.   There are two early cases mentioned [d] in

[a] 706, cent. iii., No. 94.   [b] Campus Elys. Jucund., Quæst. 41, 90.
[c] 302, iv., 180.   [d] 629, 1748, 1015.

which the bones of a fetus were discharged at stool, causing intense pain. Armstrong[a] describes an anomalous case of pregnancy in a syphilitic patient who discharged fetal bones by the rectum. Bubendorf[b] reports the spontaneous elimination of a fetal skeleton by the rectum after five years of retention, with recovery of the patient. Butcher[c] speaks of delivery through the rectum at the fourth month, with recovery. Depaul mentions a similar expulsion after a pregnancy of about two months and a half. Jackson[d] reports the dissection of an extrauterine sac which communicated freely with the large intestine. Peck[e] has an example of spontaneous delivery of an extrauterine fetus by the rectum, with recovery of the mother. Skippon,[f] in the early part of the last century, reports the discharge of the bones of a fetus through an " imposthume " in the groin. Other cases of anal discharge of the product of extrauterine conception are recorded by Winthrop, Woodbury, Tuttle, Atkinson, Browne, Weinlechner, Gibson, Littre, Magruder, Gilland, and many others. De Brun du Bois-Noir[g] speaks of the expulsion of extrauterine remains by the anus after seven years, and Heyerdahl[h] after thirteen years. Benham[i] mentions the discharge of a fetus by the rectum ; there was a stricture of the rectum associated with syphilitic patches, necessitating the performance of colotomy.

Bartholinus [190] and Rosseus [692] speak of **fetal bones** being **discharged from the urinary passages.** Ebersbach, in the Ephemerides of 1717, describes a necropsy in which a human fetus was found contained in the bladder. In 1878 White[j] reported an instance of the discharge of fetal remains through the bladder.

Discharge of the Fetus through the Abdominal Walls.—Margaret Parry of Berkshire[k] in 1668 voided the bones of a fetus through the flesh above the os pubis, and in 1684 she was alive and well, having had healthy children afterward. Brodie[l] reports the history of a case in a negress who voided a fetus from an abscess at the navel about the seventeenth month of conception. Modern instances of the discharge of the extrauterine fetus from the walls of the abdomen are frequently reported. Algora[m] speaks of an abdominal pregnancy in which there was spontaneous perforation of the anterior abdominal parietes, followed by death. Bouzal[n] cites an extraordinary case of ectopic gestation in which there was natural expulsion of the fetus through abdominal walls, with subsequent intestinal strangulation. An artificial anus was established and the mother recovered. Brodie, Dunglison, Erich, Rodbard, Fox, and Wilson are among others reporting the expulsion of remnants of ectopic pregnancies through the abdominal parietes. Campbell quotes the case of a Polish woman, aged thirty-five,[o] the mother of nine

a 490, 1835, xvi., 51.   b 140, 1886, xxvi., 269.   c Am. Med. Jour., St. Louis, 1886.
d 218, 1865.   e 218, 1870, lxxxiii., 22.   f 629, 1731.   g 242, 1883.   h 603, 1847.
i 224, 1876.   j 764 (1878), 1879, iii., 101.   k 629, 1700, 219.   l Ibid.
m Clinica, Zaragoza, 1878, ii., 221.   n 497, 1884, 513.   o 504, vol. xix., No. 2.

children, most of whom were stillborn, who conceived for the tenth time, the gestation being normal up to the lying-in period. She had pains followed by extraordinary effusion and some blood into the vagina. After various protracted complaints the abdominal tumor became painful and inflamed in the umbilical region. A breach in the walls soon formed, giving exit to purulent matter and all the bones of a fetus. During this process the patient received no medical treatment, and frequently no assistance in dressing the opening. She recovered, but had an artificial anus all her life. Sarah McKinna[a] was married at sixteen and menstruated for the first time a month thereafter. Ten months after marriage she showed signs of pregnancy and was delivered at full term of a living child ; the second child was born ten months after the first, and the second month after the second birth she again showed signs of pregnancy. At the close of nine months these symptoms, with the exception of the suppression of menses, subsided, and in this state she continued for six years. During the first four years she felt discomfort in the region of the umbilicus. About the seventh year she suffered tumefaction of the abdomen and thought she had conceived again. The abscess burst and an elbow of the fetus protruded from the wound. A butcher enlarged the wound and, fixing his finger under the jaw of the fetus, extracted the head. On looking into the abdomen he perceived a black object, whereupon he introduced his hand and extracted piecemeal an entire fetal skeleton and some decomposed animal-matter. The abdomen was bound up, and in six weeks the woman was enabled to superintend her domestic affairs ; excepting a ventral hernia she had no bad after-results. Kimura,[b] quoted by Whitney, speaks of a case of extrauterine pregnancy in a Japanese woman of forty-one similar to the foregoing, in which an arm protruded through the abdominal wall above the umbilicus and the remains of a fetus were removed through the aperture. The accompanying illustration (Fig. 3) shows the appearance of the arm in situ before extraction of the fetus and the location of the wound.

Bodinier[c] and Lusk [d] report instances of the delivery of an extrauterine fetus by the vagina ; and Mathieson [e] relates the history of the delivery of a living ectopic child by the vagina, with recovery of the mother. Gordon [f] speaks of a curious case in a negress, six months pregnant, in which an extrauterine fetus passed down from the posterior culdesac and occluded the uterus. It was removed through the vagina, and two days later labor-pains set in, and in two hours she was delivered of a uterine child. The placenta was left behind and drainage established through the vagina, and the woman made complete recovery.

Combined Intrauterine and Extrauterine Gestation.—Many well-authenticated cases of combined pregnancy, in which one of the products of

a 629, viii., 517. b 791, 1893. c 616, v., 79.
d 125, xix., 242. e 224, 1884, i., 99. f 817, October, 1848.

conception was intrauterine and the other of extrauterine gestation, have been recorded. Clark and Ramsbotham[a] report instances of double conception, one fetus being born alive in the ordinary manner and the other located extrauterine. Chasser[b] speaks of a case in which there was concurrent pregnancy in both the uterus and the Fallopian tube. Smith[c] cites an instance of a woman of twenty-three who became pregnant in August, 1870. In the following December she passed fetal bones from the rectum, and a month later gave birth to an intrauterine fetus of six months' growth. McGee[d] mentions the case of a woman of twenty-eight who became pregnant in July, 1872, and on October 20th and 21st passed several fetal bones by the rectum, and about four months later expelled some from the uterus. From this time she rapidly recovered her strength and health. Devergie[e] quotes an instance of a woman of thirty who had several children, but who died sud-

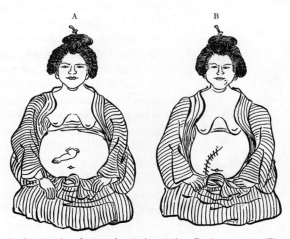

Fig. 3.—A, protrusion of an arm in ectopic gestation; B, after operation (Kimura).

denly, and being pregnant was opened. In the right iliac fossa was found a male child weighing 5 pounds and 5 ounces, 8½ inches long, and of about five months' growth. The uterus also contained a male fetus of about three months' gestation. Figure 4 shows combined intrauterine and extrauterine gestation. Hodgen[f] speaks of a woman of twenty-seven, who was regular until November, 1872; early in January, 1873, she had an attack of pain with peritonitis, shortly after which what was apparently an extrauterine pregnancy gradually diminished. On August 17, 1873, after a labor of eight hours, she gave birth to a healthy fetus. The hand in the uterus detected a tumor to the left, which was reduced to about one-fourth the former size. In April, 1874, the woman still suffered pain and tenderness

a 548, 1856, 591. b 463, Aout., 1812, 415. c 481, February, 1873.
d 681, March, 1875. e Médecine Légale, i., 508. f 703, August, 1874.

in the tumor. Hodgen believed this to have been originally a tubal pregnancy, which burst, causing much hemorrhage and the death of the fetus, together with a limited peritonitis. Beach [a] has seen a twin compound pregnancy in which after connection there was a miscarriage in six weeks, and four years after delivery of an extrauterine fetus through the abdominal walls. Cooke cites an example of intrauterine and extrauterine pregnancy progressing simultaneously to full period of gestation, with resultant death. Rosset [b] reports the case of a woman of twenty-seven, who menstruated last in November, 1878, and on August 5, 1879, was delivered of a well-developed dead female child weighing seven pounds. The uterine contractions were feeble, and the attached placenta was removed only with difficulty; there was considerable hemorrhage. The hemorrhage continued to occur at intervals of two weeks, and an extrauterine tumor remained. Two weeks later septicemia supervened and life was despaired of. On the 15th of October a portion of a fetus of five months' growth in an advanced stage of decomposition protruded from the vulva. After the escape of this putrid mass her health returned, and in four months she was again robust and healthy. Whinery [c] speaks of a young woman who at the time of her second child-birth observed a tumor in the abdomen on her right side and felt motion in it. In about a month she was seized with severe pain which continued a week and then ceased. Health soon improved,

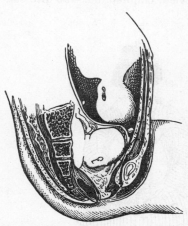

Fig. 4.—Combined intrauterine and extrauterine gestation (Brit. Med. Jour., May 12, 1894).

and the woman afterward gave birth to a third child; subsequently she noticed that the tumor had enlarged since the first birth, and she had a recurrence of pain and a slight hemorrhage every three weeks, and distinctly felt motion in the tumor. This continued for eighteen months, when, after a most violent attack of pain, all movement ceased, and, as she expressed it, she knew the moment the child died. The tumor lost its natural consistence and felt flabby and dead. An incision was made through the linea alba, and the knife came in contact with a hard, gritty substance, three or four lines thick. The escape of several quarts of dark brown fluid followed the incision, and the operation had to be discontinued on account of the ensuing syncope. About six weeks afterward a bone presented at the orifice, which the woman extracted, and this was soon followed by a mass of bones, hair, and putrid matter. The discharge was small, and gradually grew less in quantity and offensiveness, soon ceasing altogether, and the wound closed. By December health was good and the menses had returned.

Ahlfeld, Ambrosioni, Galabin, Packard, Thiernesse, Maxson, de Belamizaran, Dibot, and Chabert are among others recording the phenomenon of coexisting extrauterine and intrauterine pregnancy. Argles[a] mentions simultaneous extrauterine fetation and superfetation.

Sanger[b] mentions a **triple ectopic gestation,** in which there was twin pregnancy in the wall of the uterus and a third ovum at the fimbriated end of the right tube. Careful examination showed this to be a case of intramural twin pregnancy at the point of entrance of the tube and the uterus, while at the abdominal end of the same tube there was another ovum,—the whole being an example of triple unilateral ectopic gestation.

The instances of **delivery of an extrauterine fetus, with viability of the child,** from the abdomen of the mother would attract attention from their rarity alone, but when coupled with associations of additional interest they surely deserve a place in a work of this nature. Osiander[615] speaks of an abdominal fetus being taken out alive, and there is a similar case on record in the early part of this century.[c] The London Medical and Physical Journal, in one of its early numbers, contained an account of an abdominal fetus penetrating the walls of the bladder and being extracted from the walls of the hypogastrium ; but Sennertus gives a case which far eclipses this, both mother and fetus surviving. He says that in this case the woman, while pregnant, received a blow on the lower part of her body, in consequence of which a small tumor appeared shortly after the accident. It so happened in this case that the peritoneum was extremely dilatable, and the uterus, with the child inside, made its way into the peritoneal sac. In his presence an incision was made and the fetus taken out alive. Jessop[d] gives an example of extrauterine gestation in a woman of twenty-six, who had previously had normal delivery. In this case an incision was made and a fetus of about eight months' growth was found lying loose in the abdominal cavity in the midst of the intestines. Both the mother and child were saved. This is a very rare result. Campbell, in his celebrated monograph, in a total of 51 operations had only seen recorded the accounts of two children saved, and one of these was too marvelous to believe. Lawson Tait reports a case in which he saved the child, but lost the mother on the fourth day. Parvin describes a case in which death occurred on the third day. Browne[e] quotes Parry as saying that there is one twin pregnancy in 23 extrauterine conceptions. He gives 24 cases of twin conception, one of which was uterine, the other extrauterine, and says that of 7 in the third month, with no operation, the mother died in 5. Of 6 cases of from four and a half to seven months' duration, 2 lived, and in 1 case at the fifth month there was an

a 476, 1871, ii., 394. b 261, 1893. c 559, 1809, 414.
d 778, xviii., 261; and 610, December, 1876. e 764, 1882, vi., 444–462.

intrauterine fetus delivered which lived. Of 11 such cases at nine months, 6 mothers lived and 6 intrauterine fetuses lived. In 6 of these cases no operation was performed. In one case the mother died, but both the uterine and the extrauterine conceptions lived. In another the mother and intra-uterine fetus died, and the extrauterine fetus lived. Wilson [a] gives an instance of a woman delivered of a healthy female child at eight months which lived. The after-birth came away without assistance, but the woman still pre-sented every appearance of having another child within her, although ex-amination by the vagina revealed none. Wilson called Chatard in consulta-tion, and from the fetal heart-sounds and other symptoms they decided that there was another pregnancy wholly extrauterine. They allowed the case to go twenty-three days, until pains similar to those of labor occurred, and then decided on celiotomy. The operation was almost bloodless, and a living child weighing eight pounds was extracted. Unfortunately, the mother succumbed after ninety hours, and in a month the intrauterine child died from inanition, but the child of extrauterine gestation thrived. Sales [b] gives the case of a negress of twenty-two, who said that she had been "tricked by a negro," and had a large snake in the abdomen, and could dis-tinctly feel its movements. She stoutly denied any intercourse. It was decided to open the abdominal cyst; the incision was followed by a gush of blood and a placenta came into view, which was extracted with a living child. To the astonishment of the operators the uterus was distended, and it was decided to open it, when another living child was seen and extracted. The cyst and the uterus were cleansed of all clots and the wound closed. The mother died of septicemia, but the children both lived and were doing well six weeks after the operation. A curious case was seen in 1814 [c] of a woman who at her fifth gestation suffered abdominal uneasiness at the third month, and this became intolerable at the ninth month. The head of the fetus could be felt through the abdomen; an incision was made through the parietes; a fully developed female child was delivered, but, unfortunately, the mother died of septic infection.

The British Medical Journal quotes: " Pinard (Bull. de l'Acad. de Méd., August 6, 1895) records the following, which he describes as an ideal case. The patient was aged thirty-six, had had no illness, and had been regular from the age of fourteen till July, 1894. During August of that year she had nausea and vomiting; on the 22d and 23d she lost a fluid, which was just pink. The symptoms continued during September, on the 22d and 23d of which month there was a similar loss. In October she was kept in bed for two days by abdominal pain, which reappeared in November, and was then associated with pain in micturition and defecation. From that time till February 26, 1895, when she came under Pinard's care, she was attended by several doctors, each of whom adopted a different

a 125, 1880, xiii., 821–836.   b 593, October, 1870.   c 460, xv., 51.

diagnosis and treatment. One of them, thinking she had a fibroid, made her take in all about an ounce of savin powder, which did not, however, produce any ill effect. When admitted she looked ill and pinched. The left thigh and leg were painful and edematous. The abdomen looked like that of the sixth month of pregnancy. The abdominal wall was tense, smooth, and without lineæ albicantes. Palpation revealed a cystic immobile tumor, extending 2 inches above the umbilicus and apparently fixed by deep adhesions. The fetal parts could only be made out with difficulty by deep palpation, but the heart-sounds were easily heard to the right of and below the umbilicus. By the right side of this tumor one could feel a small one, the size of a Tangerine orange, which hardened and softened under examination. When contracted the groove between it and the large tumor became evident. Vaginal examination showed that the cervix, which was slightly deflected forward and to the right and softened, as in uterine gestation, was continuous with the smaller. Cephalic ballottement was obtained in the large tumor. No sound was passed into the uterus for fear of setting up reflex action ; the diagnosis of extrauterine gestation at about six and a half months with a living child was established without requiring to be clinched by proving the uterus empty. The patient was kept absolutely at rest in bed and the edema of the left leg cured by position. On April 30th the fundus of the tumor was 35 cm. above the symphysis and the uterus 11½ cm. ; the cervix was soft as that of a primipara at term. Operation, May 2d : Uterus found empty, cavity 14½ cm. long. Median incision in abdominal wall ; cyst walls exposed ; seen to be very slight and filled with enormous vessels, some greater than the little finger. On seizing the wall one of these vessels burst, and the hemorrhage was only rendered greater on attempting to secure it, so great was the friability of the walls. The cyst was therefore rapidly opened and the child extracted by the foot. Hemorrhage was restrained first by pressure of the hands, then by pressure-forceps and ligatures. The walls of the cyst were sewn to the margins of the abdominal wound, the edge of the placenta being included in the suture. A wound was thus formed 10 cm. in diameter, with the placenta for its base ; it was filled with iodoform and salicylic gauze. The operation lasted an hour, and the child, a boy weighing 5½ pounds, after a brief period of respiratory difficulties, was perfectly vigorous. There was at first a slight facial asymmetry and a depression on the left upper jaw caused by the point of the left shoulder, against which it had been pressed in the cyst ; these soon disappeared, and on the nineteenth day the boy weighed 12 pounds. The maternal wound was not dressed till May 13th, when it was washed with biniodid, 1 : 4000. The placenta came away piecemeal between May 25th and June 2d. The wound healed up, and the patient got up on the forty-third day, having suckled her infant from the first day after its birth."

	Date of operation.	Name of operator.	Age.	Number of pregnancies preceding.	Period of gestation.	Result to child.	Details of operation.	References.
1	Aug. 14, 1875.	Mr. T. R. Jessup, Leeds, England.	26	1	33d to 34th week.	Living, but died at eleven months from croup.	Placenta not removed; no sac, fetus free in abdominal cavity among intestines.	Tait on Diseases of Women and Abdominal Surgery, vol. i. p. 495.
2	July 9, 1881.	Dr. A. Martin, Berlin.	39	2	7 months.	Alive, cord pulsating, but did not breathe; had a large encephalocele.	Placenta removed after ligation at three points.	Berlin. klin. Woch., December 26, 1881; Harris, "Extrauterine Pregnancy," Am. Jour. Med. Sci., September, 1888.
3	June 6, 1885.	John Williams, London.	30	1	35th week.	Died in a few minutes.	Placenta not removed, sac drained.	Brit. Med Jour., December 3, 1887; Harris, ibid.
4	Nov. 4, 1885.	J. Lazarewitch, Kharkof, Russia.	27	1	9 months.	Lived 26 days.	Placenta and cyst drawn out, pressed up in the abdominal wound, ligated, and large portion removed.	Vrach, St. Petersburg,1886; Harris, ibid.
5	May 29, 1887.	Hector Treub, Leyden.	34	1	2 to 3 weeks before end of term.	Living, weight over 4 pounds. A year later a strong, healthy boy.	After incision of the sac, which bled freely, placenta was perforated with hand, and after extracting child bleeding was controlled by compressing each half of placenta by the hand of operator and assistant until removed: portion of sac extirpated, the rest, intimately adherent to intestines, sewed to abdominal wound and packed with Mikulicz dressing. Supposed to have been an ovarian pregnancy or a pregnancy in a tuboovarian cyst.	Zeitschrift für Geburtsh. und Gynäk., Band xv. S. 384, 1888.
6	Oct. 29, 1887.	Aug. Breisky, Vienna.	39	....	End of 8th month.	Alive and well, weight 5 pounds, but died 3 weeks later from phlebitis of umbilical vein.	Tubal intraligamentous pregnancy. After removing child from the sac, the latter was drawn out, ligated at its juncture with the uterus, and removed, containing placenta and membranes, and cavity drained. Mother recovered perfectly in three weeks.	Wiener med. Wochenschrift, 1887, Nos. 48, 49, and 56; and Eastman, in Am. Jour. Obstet., vol. xxi., 1888.
7	July 10, 1888.	Joseph Eastman, Indianapolis.	39	1	7 months.	Living, weight 4 pounds. Died at eight and a half months from pneumonia.	Intraligamentous tubal pregnancy. Clamped uterine end of tube and broad ligament, and enucleated fetal sac containing placenta intact, and quilted the pedicle with cobbler's stitch, using iron-dyed silk.	Am. Jour. Obstet., 1888, p. 929.
8	Nov. 1, 1888.	R. Olshausen, Berlin.	30	1	9 months.	Living, weight 5 pounds. When a year old, weight 14 pounds.	Fetus free in abdominal cavity, also largest part of placenta, between loops of intestines: the latter adherent to right broad ligament with only about one-third of its periphery. This last portion was easily surrounded, and proved so thin that two mass ligatures of silk were sufficient to securely tie off the placenta with attached portion of broad ligament. Only shreds of fetal membranes were attached to placenta.	Deutsche med. Wochenschrift, 1890, p. 171.
9	Feb. 11, 1889.	Carl Braun von Fernwald, Vienna.	..	2	End of term.	Living, weight over 6 pounds. Died seventy-two hours after birth from lobular pneumonia due to inspiration of amniotic fluid.	Child free in abdominal cavity; placenta adherent to posterior surface of uterus and right broad ligament, extends deep into Douglas's culdesac, and firmly attached to descending colon. After ligating right broad ligament in number of places placenta can be detached in a number of places without much hemorrhage. Removal of sac necessitated elastic ligature around uterus to check bleeding, and supravaginal hysterectomy.	Archiv f. Gynäk., Heft ii., 1890.

	Date	Operator			Term	Result	Remarks	Reference
10	Feb. 27, 1889.	R. Olshausen, Berlin.	32	4	9 months.	Alive, but very much deformed. Died one and half hours after birth.	Sac and placenta left undisturbed and drained with iodoform-gauze packing. Spontaneous expulsion of placenta on thirty-fourth day. Interesting is the daily copious discharge of fluid from the vagina during the eighth month, which was undoubtedly amniotic fluid draining away through tube. No amniotic fluid present during operation.	Deutsche med. Woch., 1890, p. 171.
11	Feb. 4, 1890.	G. Rein, Kiew, Russia	35		37th week.	Living, weight 6 pounds; slight asymmetry of head. Two years after operation was hearty and well.	Intraligamentous tubal pregnancy. Sac, placenta, and fetal membrane removed entire by enucleation from the peritoneum, in the same manner as practised in removal of intraligamentous ovarian cyst.	Centralblatt f. Gynäk., No. 50, 1892.
12	1891.	John W. Taylor, Birmingham, Eng.			9 months.	Living.	Fetus free in abdominal cavity; placenta left behind and drainage-tube introduced, and umbilical cord drawn out of the lower angle of the wound. Patient recovered after very protracted convalescence, complicated by sepsis, thrombosis of left iliac, the inferior cava, the right iliac, and right renal veins.	Obstet. Trans. of London for 1891, p. 1151; and Lusk, in New York Jour. of Gynecol. and Obstet., July, 1893.
13	Jan. 10, 1891.	Prof. Schauta, Vienna.			7 months.	Living.	After tying ovarian artery at the peritoneal fold, which constituted the residue of the infundibulopelvic ligament, he incised the peritoneal covering in a circular line corresponding nearly to the largest circumference of the sac. The enucleation of the latter was readily accomplished without rupture of sac-walls. Considerable hemorrhage resulted from detachment of the ovum from the uterus, which was temporarily controlled by pressure and later by sutures. The peritoneal borders of the cavity were then sutured to the parietal peritoneum, and the cavity itself was drained by a Mikulicz tampon.	Beiträge f. Casuistik Prognose und Therapie der Extrauterine Schwangerschaft, Prag, 1891; Lusk, in New York Jour. of Gynecol. and Obstet., July, 1893.
14	Oct. 23, 1892.	Dr. Mordecai Price, Philadelphia.				Living.	Placenta attached to uterine attachment of left tube and the entire pelvic viscera of the left side from the spine, and extending up to the kidney posteriorly and covering the descending colon. It was slightly wounded in the abdominal incision and the cause of considerable hemorrhage; this was controlled by clamping-forceps, which were allowed to remain until first dressing. The child was enveloped only by amniotic sac, to which were attached the transverse colon and also small intestines to a slight extent. Placenta left and sac packed with iodoform-gauze. Last portion of placenta removed on thirty-fifth day.	Transactions of the State Medical Society of Pennsylvania, 1893, p. 152.
15	Aug. 19, 1893.	Wm. T. Lusk, New York.	33	1	6 months.	Lived twenty-four hours.	Pregnancy started in right tube, and subsequently developed to a great extent between the folds of broad ligaments. Tied ovarian and uterine arteries of right side, and then enucleated entire sac with placenta.	Lusk, "Technique of Primary Celiotomy in Advanced Ectopic Gestation," in N. Y. Jour. of Gynecol. and Obstet., July, 1893.
16	1894.	Hector Treub, Leyden			3 weeks before term.	Lived several weeks.	Fetus free in abdominal cavity. Supravaginal amputation of uterus; removal of placenta and sac. (Private communication from R. P. Harris.)	Bulletin Mém. Soc. Obstét. et Gynécol. de Paris, 1894.
17	April 4, 1894.	X. O. Werder, Pittsburgh.		1	2 weeks before term.	Lived four days.	Child enveloped in amniotic sac and also partly by folds of broad ligaments. Placenta removed after clamping and subsequently tying ovarian and uterine arteries of left side. Part of sac incised, but portion had to be left on account of firm intestinal adhesion. Edges of sac and stump of left broad ligament drawn together by sutures and attached to parietal peritoneum, and drained by Mikulicz gauze packing.	Med. Rec., Nov. 24, 1894.

Quite recently Werder[a] has investigated the question of the **ultimate fate of ectopic children delivered alive.** He has been able to obtain the record of 40 cases. Of these, 18 died within a week after birth; 5 within a month; 1 died at six months of bronchopneumonia; 1 at seven months of diarrhea; 2 at eleven months, 1 from croup; 1 at eighteen months from cholera infantum—making a total of 26 deaths and leaving 14 children to be accounted for. Of these, 5 were reported as living and well after operation, with no subsequent report; 1 was strong and healthy after three weeks, but there has been no report since; 1 was well at six months, then was lost sight of; 1 was well at the last report; 2 live and are well at one year; 2 are living and well at two years; 1 (Beisone's case) is well at seven years; and 1 (Tait's case) is well at fourteen and one-half years. The list given on pages 60 and 61 has been quoted by Hirst and Dorland.[b] It contains data relative to 17 cases in which abdominal section has been successfully performed for advanced ectopic gestation with living children.

Long Retention of Extrauterine Pregnancy.—The time of the retention of an extrauterine gestation is sometimes remarkable, and it is no uncommon occurrence for several pregnancies to successfully ensue during such retention. The Ephemerides contains examples of extrauterine pregnancy remaining in the abdomen forty-six years;[c] Hannæus[d] mentioned an instance remaining ten years, the mother being pregnant in the meantime; Primperosius speaks of a similar instance; de Blegny,[e] one of twenty-five years in the abdomen; Birch, a case of eighteen years in the abdomen, the woman bearing in the meantime; Bayle,[f] one of twenty-six years, and the Ephemerides, another. In a woman of forty-six,[g] the labor pains intervened without expulsion of the fetus. Impregnation ensued twice afterward, each followed by the birth of a living child. The woman lived to be ninety-four, and was persuaded that the fetus was still in the abdomen, and directed a postmortem examination to be made after her decease, which was done, and a large cyst containing an ossified fetus was discovered in the left side of the cavity. In 1716[h] a woman of Joigny when thirty years old, having been married four years, became pregnant, and three months later felt movements and found milk in her breasts. At the ninth month she had labor-pains, but the fetus failed to present; the pains ceased, but recurred in a month, still with a negative result. She fell into a most sickly condition and remained so for eighteen months, when the pains returned again, but soon ceased. Menstruation ceased and the milk in her breasts remained for thirty years. She died at sixty-one of peripneumonia, and on postmortem examination a tumor was found occupying part of the hypogastric and umbilical regions. It weighed eight pounds and consisted of a male

a 538, Nov. 24, 1894.   b 843, 372.   c 104, cent. x., obs. 48.
d Prod. Act., Havn., 107.   e 215, Ann. I., obs. 9, Jan.: obs. 8, Feb.
f 629, London, xii.   g 418, 1721, 422.   h 302, iv., 233.

fetus of full term with six teeth; it had no odor and its sac contained no liquid. The bones seemed better developed than ordinarily; the skin was thick, callous, and yellowish. The chorion, amnion, and placenta were ossified and the cord dried up. Walther [a] mentions the case of an infant which remained almost petrified in the belly of its mother for twenty-three years. No trace of the placenta, cord, or enveloping membrane could be found.

Cordier [b] publishes a paper on ectopic gestation, with particular reference to tubal pregnancy, and mentions that when there is rupture between the broad ligaments hemorrhage is greatly limited by the resistance of the surrounding structures, death rarely resulting from the primary rupture in this location. Cordier gives an instance in which he successfully removed a full-grown child, the result of an ectopic gestation which had ruptured intraligamentally and had been retained nearly two years.

Lospichlerus [c] gives an account of a mother carrying twins, extrauterine, for six years. Mounsey of Riga, physician to the army of the Czarina, sent to the Royal Society in 1748 the bones of a fetus that had been extracted from one of the fallopian tubes after a lodgment of thirteen years. Starkey Middleton [d] read the report of a case of a child which had been taken out of the abdomen, having lain there nearly sixteen years, during which time the mother had borne four children. It was argued at this time that boys were conceived on the right side and girls on the left, and in commenting on this Middleton remarks that in this case the woman had three boys and one girl after the right fallopian tube had lost its function. Chester [e] cites the instance of a fetus being retained fifty-two years, the mother not dying until her eightieth year. Margaret Mathew [f] carried a child weighing eight pounds in her abdomen for twenty-six years, and which after death was extracted. Aubrey [g] speaks of a woman aged seventy years unconsciously carrying an extrauterine fetus for many years, which was only discovered postmortem. She had ceased to menstruate at forty and had borne a child at twenty-seven. Watkins [h] speaks of a fetus being retained forty-three years; James, others for twenty-five, thirty, forty-six, and fifty years; Murfee,[i] fifty-five years; Cunningham,[j] forty years; Johnson,[k] forty-four years; Josephi,[l] fifteen years (in the urinary bladder); Craddock,[m] twenty-two years, and da Costa Simões,[n] twenty-six years.

Long Retention of Uterine Pregnancy.—Cases of long retained intra-uterine pregnancies are on record and deserve as much consideration as those that were extrauterine. Albosius speaks of a mother carrying a child in an ossified condition in the uterus for twenty-eight years.[o] Cheselden speaks

---

a Mem. de Berlin, 1774. b Annals of Gynæcol. and Pædiatry, Aug., 1893.
c Opera, 1737, iii., 89. d 629, 1748, 1018. e 550, vol. v., 104. f 629, 1700, 217.
g 162, March, 1842. h 778, viii., 106. i 774, 1886. j 810, 1855.
k Med. Times and Gaz., London, 1872. l 535, 1805. m 526, 1846.
n 278, 1886. o Observatio Lithopædii Senonensis, 1682.

of a case in which a child was carried many years in the uterus, being converted into a clay-like substance, but preserving form and outline. Caldwell [a] mentions the case of a woman who carried an ossified fetus in her uterus for sixty years. Camerer [b] describes the retention of a fetus in the uterus for forty-six years; Stengel, [c] one for ten years, and Storer and Buzzell, for twenty-two months. Hannæus, in 1686, issued a paper on such a case under the title, "Mater, Infantis Mortui Vivum Sepulchrum," which may be found in French translation. [d]

Buchner [e] speaks of a fetus being retained in the uterus for six years, and Horstius [423] relates a similar case. Schmidt's Jahrbücher [f] contain the report of a woman of forty-nine, who had borne two children. While threshing corn she felt violent pain like that of labor, and after an illness suffered a constant fetid discharge from the vagina for eleven years, fetal bones being discharged with occasional pain. This poor creature worked along for eleven years, at the end of which time she was forced to bed, and died of symptoms of purulent peritonitis. At the necropsy the uterus was found adherent to the anterior wall of the abdomen and containing remnants of a putrid fetus with its numerous bones. There is an instance recorded [g] of the death of a fetus occurring near term, its retention and subsequent discharge being through a spontaneous opening in the abdominal wall one or two months after.

Meigs [h] cites the case of a woman who dated her pregnancy from March, 1848, and which proceeded normally for nine months, but no labor supervened at this time and the menses reappeared. In March, 1849, she passed a few fetal bones by the rectum, and in May, 1855, she died. At the necropsy the uterus was found to contain the remains of a fully developed fetus, minus the portions discharged through a fistulous connection between the uterine cavity and the rectum. In this case there had been retention of a fully developed fetus for nine years. Cox [i] describes the case of a woman who was pregnant seven months, and who was seized with convulsions; the supposed labor-pains passed off, and after death the fetus was found in the womb, having lain there for five years. She had an early return of the menses, and these recurred regularly for four years. Dewees [419] quotes two cases, in one of which the child was carried twenty months in the uterus; in the other, the mother was still living two years and five months after fecundation. Another case [j] was in a woman of sixty, who had conceived at twenty-six, and whose fetus was found, partly ossified, in the uterus after death.

There are many narratives of the **long continuation of fetal movements,** and during recent years, in the Southern States, there was quite a

a 318, 1806, ii., 22-24.   b 280, 1774, v., 338.   c Eyr, Christiania, 1827, ii., 134.
d 280, 1755, iii., 695.   e Miscellan., 1728, 822.   f 720, Nov. 9, 1848.
g 124, v., 530.   h 124, xxv., 541.   i 271, 1867, ii., 385.   j 318, ii., 22.

prevalence of this kind of imposters. Many instances of the exhibition of fetal movements in the bellies of old negro women have been noticed by the lay journals, but investigation proves them to have been nothing more than an exceptional control over the abdominal muscles, with the ability to simulate at will the supposed fetal jerks. One old woman went so far as to show the fetus dancing to the music of a banjo with rhythmical movements. Such imposters flourished best in the regions given to " voodooism." We can readily believe how easy the deception might be when we recall the exact simulation of the fetal movements in instances of pseudocyesis.

The extraordinary diversity of reports concerning the **duration of pregnancy** has made this a much mooted question. Many opinions relative to the longest and shortest period of pregnancy, associated with viability of the issue, have been expressed by authors on medical jurisprudence. There is perhaps no information more unsatisfactory or uncertain. Mistakes are so easily made in the date of the occurrence of pregnancy, or in the date of conception, that in the remarkable cases we can hardly accept the propositions as worthy evidence unless associated with other and more convincing facts, such as the appearance and stage of development of the fetus, or circumstances making conception impossible before or after the time mentioned, etc. It will be our endeavor to cite the more seemingly reliable instances of the anomalies of the time or duration of pregnancy reported in reputable periodicals or books.

Short Pregnancies.—Hasenet[a] speaks of the possibility of a living birth at four months ; Capuron relates the instance of Fortunio Liceti, who was said to have been born at the end of four and a half months and lived to complete his twenty-fourth year. In the case of the Marechal de Richelieu, the Parliament of Paris decreed that an infant of five months possessed that capability of living the ordinary period of existence, *i. e.*, the " viabilité," which the law of France requires for the establishment of inheritance. In his seventh book Pliny gives examples of men who were born out of time. Jonston[b] gives instances of births at five, six, seven, and eight months. Bonnar[c] quotes 5 living births before the one hundred and fiftieth day ; 1 of one hundred and twenty-five days ; 1 of one hundred and twenty days ; 1 of one hundred and thirty-three days, surviving to twenty-one months ; and 1 of one hundred and thirty-five days' pregnancy surviving to eighty years. Maisonneuve[462] describes a case in which abortion took place at four and a half months ; he found the fetus in its membranes two hours after delivery, and, on laying the membranes open, saw that it was living. He applied warmth, and partly succeeded in restoring it ; for a few minutes respiratory movements were performed regularly, but it died in six hours. Taylor[757] quotes Carter concerning the case of a fetus of five months which cried directly after it was born, and in the half hour it lived it tried frequently to breathe. He also quotes Davies,

a Jena, 1705.   b 447, 465.   c 393, 133–4.

mentioning an instance of a fetus of five months, which lived twelve hours, weighing 2 pounds, and measuring 12 inches, and which cried vigorously. The pupillary membrane was entire, the testes had not descended, and the head was well covered with hair. Usher[a] speaks of a woman who in 1876 was delivered of 2 male children on the one hundred and thirty-ninth day ; both lived for an hour; the first weighed 10 ounces 6 drams and measured 9¾ inches ; the other 10 ounces 7 drams, with the same length as the first. Routh[b] speaks of a Mrs. F——, aged thirty-eight, who had borne 9 children and had had 3 miscarriages, the last conception terminating as such. Her husband was away, and returned October 9, 1869. She did not again see her husband until the 3d or 4th of January. The date of quickening was not observed, and the child was born June 8, 1870. During gestation she was much frightened by a rat. The child was weak, the testes undescended, and it lived but eighteen days, dying of symptoms of atrophy. The parents were poor, of excellent character, and although, according to the evidence, this pregnancy lasted but twenty-two weeks and two days, there was absolutely no reason to suspect infidelity.

Ruttel speaks of a child of five months who lived twenty-four hours ; and he saw male twins born at the sixth month weighing 3 pounds each who were alive and healthy a year after. Barker[c] cites the case of a female child born on the one hundred and fifty-eighth day that weighed 1 pound and was 11 inches long. It had rudimentary nails, very little hair on the head, its eyelids were closed, and the skin much shriveled ; it did not suckle properly, and did not walk until nineteen months old. Three and a half years after, the child was healthy and thriving, but weighed only 29½ pounds. At the time of birth it was wrapped up in a box and placed before the fire. Brouzet speaks of living births of from five to six months' pregnancy, and Kopp[d] speaks of a six months' child which lived four days. The Ephemerides contains accounts of living premature births.

Newinton describes a pregnancy of five months terminating with the birth of twins, one of whom lived twenty minutes and the other fifteen. The first was 11½ inches long, and weighed 1 pound 3½ ounces, and the other was 11 inches long, and weighed 1 pound. There is a recent instance of premature birth[e] following a pregnancy of between five and a half and six months, the infant weighing 955 grams. One month after birth, through the good offices of the wet-nurse and M. Villemin, who attended the child and who invented a " couveuse " for the occasion, it measured 38 cm. long.

Moore[f] is accredited with the trustworthy report of the case of a woman who bore a child at the end of the fifth month weighing 1½ pounds and measuring 9 inches. It was first nourished by dropping liquid food into its mouth ; and at the age of fifteen months it was healthy and weighed 18

a 180, 1886, 366.   b 778, xiii., 132.   c 546, 1850, ii., 249, and 392.   d 444, iii., 129.
e 674, 1895, Jan., p. 22.   f 545, 1180 ; and quoted by 548, 1880, ii., 8.

pounds. Eikam[a] saw a case of abortion at the fifth month in which the fetus was 6 inches in length and weighed about 8 ounces. The head was sufficiently developed and the cranial bones considerably advanced in ossification. He tied the cord and placed the fetus in warm water. It drew up its feet and arms and turned its head from one side to the other, opening its mouth and trying to breathe. It continued in this wise for an hour, the action of the heart being visible ten minutes after the movements ceased. From its imperfectly developed genitals it was supposed to have been a female. Professor J. Müller, to whom it was shown, said that it was not more than four months old, and this coincided with the mother's calculation.

Villemin[b] before the Société Obstetricale et Gynécologique reported the case of a two-year-old child, born in the sixth month of pregnancy. That the child had not had six months of intrauterine life he could vouch, the statement being borne out by the last menstrual period of the mother, the date of the first fetal movements, the child's weight, which was $30\frac{1}{2}$ ounces, and its appearance. Budin had had this infant under observation from the beginning and corroborated Villemin's statements. He had examined infants of six or seven months that had cried and lived a few days, and had found the alveolar cavities filled with epithelial cells, the lung sinking when placed in a vessel of water. Charpentier reported a case of premature birth in his practice, the child being not more than six and a half months and weighing $33\frac{1}{3}$ ounces. So sure was he that it would not live that he placed it in a basin while he attended to the mother. After this had been done, the child being still alive, he wrapped it in cotton and was surprised next day to find it alive. It was then placed in a small, well-heated room and fed with a spoon on human milk ; on the twelfth day it could take the breast, since which time it thrived and grew.

There is a case on record[c] of a child viable at six months and twenty days. The mother had a miscarriage at the beginning of 1877, after which menstruation became regular, appearing last from July 3 to 9, 1877. On January 28, 1878, she gave birth to a male infant, which was wrapped in wadding and kept at an artificial temperature. Being unable to suckle, it was fed first on diluted cow's milk. It was so small at birth that the father passed his ring over the foot almost to the knee. On the thirteenth day it weighed 1250 grams, and at the end of a week it was taking the breast. In December, 1879, it had 16 teeth, weighed 10 kilograms, walked with agility, could pronounce some words, and was especially intelligent. Capuron [254] relates an instance of a child born after a pregnancy of six and a half months and in excellent health at two years, and another living at ten years of the same age at birth. Tait[d] speaks of a living female child, born on the one hundred and seventy-ninth day, with no nails on its fingers or toes, no hair, the extremities imperfectly developed, and the skin florid and thin. It

a 558,.B. v., H. 2.   b 791, March, 1895.   c 168, Dec., 1879.   d 476, April 23, 1842.

was too feeble to grasp its mother's nipple, and was fed for three weeks by milk from the breast through a quill. At forty days it weighed 3 pounds and measured 13 inches. Before the expiration of three months it died of measles. Dodd [a] describes a case in which the catamenia were on the 24th of June, 1838, and continued a week ; the woman bore twins on January 11, 1839, one of which survived, the other dying a few minutes after birth. She was never irregular, prompt to the hour, and this fact, coupled with the diminutive size of the children, seemed to verify the duration of the pregnancy. In 1825, Baber of Buxur, India, spoke of a child born at six and a half months, who at the age of fifty days weighed 1 pound and 13 ounces and was 14 inches long. The longest circumference of the head was 10 inches and the shortest 9.1 inches. The child suckled freely and readily. In Spaeth's clinic [b] there was a viable infant at six and a half months weighing 900 grams. Spaeth says that he has known a child of six months to surpass in eventual development its brothers born at full term.

In some cases there seems to be a peculiarity in women which manifests itself by regular premature births. La Motte, van Swieten, and Fordere mention females who always brought forth their conceptions at the seventh month.

The incubator seems destined to be the future means of preserving these premature births. Several successful cases have been noticed, and by means of an incubator Tarnier succeeded in raising infants which at the age of six months were above the average. A full description of the incubator may be found. [c] The modified Auvard incubator is easily made ; the accompanying illustrations (Figs. 5, 6, and 7) explain its mechanism. Several improved incubators have been described in recent years, but the Auvard appears to be the most satisfactory.

The question of **retardation of labor,** like that of premature birth, is open to much discussion, and authorities differ as to the limit of protraction with viability. Aulus Gellius [d] says that, after a long conversation with the physicians and wise men, the Emperor Adrian decided in a case before him, that of a woman of chaste manners and irreproachable character, the child born eleven months after her husband's death was legitimate. Under the Roman law the Decemviri established that a woman may bear a viable child at the tenth month of pregnancy. Paulus Zacchias,[830] physician to Pope Innocent X., declared that birth may be retarded to the tenth month, and sometimes to a longer period. A case was decided in the Supreme Court of Friesland, a province in the northern part of the Netherlands, October, 1634, in which a child born three hundred and thirty-three days after the death of the husband was pronounced legitimate. The Parliament of Paris was gallant enough to come to the rescue of a widow and save her

a 656, 1841.   b 118, May 16, 1882.   c 536, 1883, i., 39.
d L. iii., chap. 16.

reputation by declaring that a child born after a fourteen months' gestation was legitimate. Bartholinus speaks of an unmarried woman of Leipzig who was delivered after a pregnancy of sixteen months. The civil code of France provides that three hundred days shall constitute the longest period

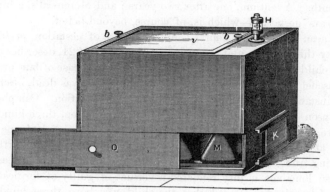

Fig. 5.—Modified Auvard incubator; *v*, glass plate of the movable lid, *b*; *H*, ventilating tube containing small rotary fan; *K*, ventilating slide; *M*, hot-water cans; *O*, slide closing hot-air chamber.

of the legitimacy of an infant; the Scottish law, three hundred days; and the Prussian law, three hundred and one days.

There are numerous cases recorded by the older writers. Amman [128] has one of twelve months' duration; Enguin,[a] one of twelve months';

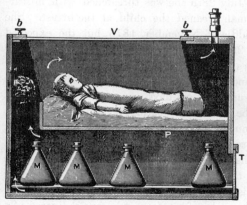

Fig. 6.—Interior view of a modified Auvard incubator.

Fig. 7.—Hot-water can for modified Auvard incubator.

Buchner,[b] a case of twelve months'; Benedictus,[196] one of fourteen months'; de Blegny,[c] one of nineteen months'; Marteau,[d] Osiander, and others of forty-two and forty-four weeks'; and Stark's Archives,[e] one of forty-five

a 462, T. lxi., 163.   b Miscel., 1727, 170.   c 215, Ann. i., 23.
d 462, T. xxv.   e 162, L. ii., 3 st. n. 2.

weeks', living, and also another case of forty-four weeks'. An incredible case is recorded[a] of an infant which lived after a three years' gestation. Instances of twelve months' duration are also recorded.[401, 172 b] Jonston[447] quotes Paschal in relating an instance of birth after pregnancy of twenty-three months; Aventium, one after two years; and Mercurialis, a birth after a four years' gestation—which is, of course, beyond belief.

Thormeau writes from Tours, 1580, of a case of gestation prolonged to the twenty-third month, and Santorini, at Venice, in 1721, describes a similar case, the child reaching adult life. Elvert[c] records a case of late pregnancy, and Henschel[495] one of forty-six weeks, but the fetus was dead. Schneider[d] cites an instance of three hundred and eight days' duration. Campbell says[e] that Simpson had cases of three hundred and nineteen, three hundred and thirty-two, and three hundred and thirty-six days'; Meigs had one of four hundred and twenty. James Reid, in a table of 500 mature births, gives 14 as being from three hundred and two to three hundred and fifteen days'.

Not so long ago a jury rendered a verdict of guilty of fornication and bastardy when it was alleged that the child was born three hundred and seventeen days after intercourse. Taylor relates a case of pregnancy in which the wife of a laborer went to America three hundred and twenty-two days before the birth. Jaffe[f] describes an instance of the prolongation of pregnancy for three hundred and sixty-five days, in which the developments and measurements corresponded to the length of protraction. Bryan[g] speaks of a woman of twenty-five who became pregnant on February 10, 1876, and on June 17th felt motion. On July 28th she was threatened with miscarriage, and by his advice the woman weaned the child at the breast. She expected to be confined the middle of November, 1876, but the expected event did not occur until April 26, 1877, nine months after the quickening and four hundred and forty days from the time of conception. The boy was active and weighed nine pounds. The author cites Meigs' case, and also one of Atlee's, at three hundred and fifty-six days.

Talcott,[h] Superintendent of the State Homeopathic Asylum for the Insane, explained the pregnancy of an inmate who had been confined for four years in this institution as one of protracted labor. He said that many such cases have been reported, and that something less than two years before he had charge of a case in which the child was born. He made the report to the New York Senate Commission on Asylums for the Insane as one of three years' protraction. Tidd[i] speaks of a woman who was delivered of a male child at term, and again in ten months delivered of a well-developed male child weighing 7¼ pounds; he relates the history of another case, in Clifton, W. Va., of a woman expecting confinement on June 1st going over

a 418, 1753, 206. b 462, T. xxvii., 48. c 137, B. iii., 257.
d Annalen der Heilk., 1811, Oct., 87. e 512, 188, viii., 145, 149. f 261, 1890.
g 703, 1877, n. s. xiv., 345. h 224, 1883, ii., 665. i 299, xi., 798.

to September 15th, the fetus being in the uterus over twelve months, and nine months after quickening was felt.

Two extraordinary cases are mentioned,[a] one in a woman of thirty-five, who expected to be confined April 24, 1883. In May she had a few labor-pains that passed away, and during the next six months she remained about as large as usual, and was several times thought to be in the early stages of labor. In September the os dilated until the first and second fingers could be passed directly to the head. This condition lasted about a month, but passed away. At times during the last nine months of pregnancy she was almost unable to endure the movements of the child. Finally, on the morning of November 6th, after a pregnancy of four hundred and seventy-six days, she was delivered of a male child weighing 13 pounds. Both the mother and child did well despite the use of chloroform and forceps. The other case was one lasting sixteen months and twenty days.

In a rather loose argument, Carey reckons a case of three hundred and fifty days. Menzie[b] gives an instance in a woman aged twenty-eight, the mother of one child, in whom a gestation was prolonged to the seventeenth month. The pregnancy was complicated by carcinoma of the uterus. Ballard[c] describes the case of a girl of sixteen years and six months, whose pregnancy, the result of a single intercourse, lasted three hundred and sixty days. Her labor was short and easy for a primipara, and the child was of the average size. Mackenzie[d] cites the instance of a woman aged thirty-two, a primipara, who had been married ten years and who always had been regular in menstruation. The menses ceased on April 28, 1888, and she felt the child for the first time in September. She had false pains in January, 1889, and labor did not begin until March 8th, lasting sixty-six hours. If all these statements are correct, the probable duration of this pregnancy was eleven months and ten days.

Lundie[e] relates an example of protracted gestation of eleven months, in which an anencephalous fetus was born; and Martin of Birmingham describes a similar case of ten and a half months' duration. Raux-Tripier[f] has seen protraction to the thirteenth month. Enguin[g] reports an observation of an accouchement of twins after a pregnancy that had been prolonged for eleven months. Resnikoff[h] mentions a pregnancy of eleven months' duration in an anemic secundipara. The case had been under his observation from the beginning of pregnancy; the patient would not submit to artificial termination at term, which he advised. After a painful labor of twenty-four hours a macerated and decomposed child was born, together with a closely-adherent placenta. Tarnier[i] reports an instance of partus serotinus in which the product of conception was carried in the uterus forty

[a] 790, Dec. 27, 1884.   [b] 381, 1853-4.   [c] 224, 1884, i., 56.
[d] 536, 1889, ii., 522.   [e] 759, April, 1895.   [f] 233, 1847.
[g] 460, 1784, 163.   [h] 261, No. 24, 1894.   [i] Jour. des Sages-Femmes, May 1, 1894.

days after term. The fetus was macerated but not putrid, and the placenta had undergone fatty degeneration. At a recent meeting of the Chicago Gynecological Society, Dr. F. A. Stahl reported the case of a German-Bohemian woman in which the fifth pregnancy terminated three hundred and two days after the last menstruation. Twenty days before there had occurred pains similar to those of labor, but they gradually ceased. The sacral promontory was exaggerated, and the anteroposterior pelvic diameter of the inlet in consequence diminished. The fetus was large and occupied the first position. Version was with difficulty effected and the passage of the after-coming head through the superior strait required expression and traction, during which the child died. The mother suffered a deep laceration of the perineum involving an inch of the wall of the rectum.

Among others reporting instances of protracted pregnancy are Collins,[a] eleven months ; Desbrest,[b] eighteen months ; Henderson,[c] fifteen months ; Jefferies,[d] three hundred and fifty-eight days, and De la Vergne[e] gives the history of a woman who carried an infant in her womb for twenty-nine months ; this case may possibly belong under the head of fetus long retained in the uterus.

Unconscious Pregnancy.—There are numerous instances of women who have had experience in pregnancy unconsciously going almost to the moment of delivery, yet experiencing none of the usual accompanying symptoms of this condition. Crowell[f] speaks of a woman of good social position who had been married seven years, and who had made extensive preparations for a long journey, when she was seized with a " bilious colic," and, to her dismay and surprise, a child was born before the arrival of the doctor summoned on account of her sudden colic and her inability to retain her water. A peculiar feature of this case was the fact that mental disturbance set in immediately afterward, and the mother became morbid and had to be removed to an asylum, but recovered in a few months. Tanner[g] saw a woman of forty-two who had been suffering with abdominal pains. She had been married three years and had never been pregnant. Her catamenia were very scant, but this was attributed to her change of life. She had conceived, had gone to the full term of gestation, and was in labor ten hours without any suspicion of pregnancy. She was successfully delivered of a girl, which occasioned much rejoicing in the household.

Tasker of Kendall's Mills, Me., reports the case of a young married woman calling him for bilious colic. He found the stomach slightly distended and questioned her about the possibility of pregnancy. Both she and her husband informed him that such could not be the case, as her courses had been regular and her waist not enlarged, as she had worn a certain corset all the time. There were no signs of quickening, no change in the breasts, and,

a 318, 1826, xxv., 245.   b 458, 1769.   c 125, 1879, xii., 393.
d Trans. M. Soc. Penna., Phila., 1879.   e 458, 1761.   f 218, 1878.   g 778, 1864.

in fact, none of the usual signs of pregnancy present. He gave her an opiate, and to her surprise, in about six hours she was the mother of a boy weighing five pounds. Both the mother and child made a good recovery. Duke [a] cites the instance of a woman who supposed that she was not pregnant up to the night of her miscarriage. She had menstruated and was suckling a child sixteen months old. During the night she was attacked with pains resembling those of labor and a fetus slipped into the vagina without any hemorrhage ; the placenta came away directly afterward. In this peculiar case the woman was menstruating regularly, suckling a child, and at the same time was unconsciously pregnant.

Isham [b] speaks of a case of unconscious pregnancy in which extremely small twins were delivered at the eighth month. Fox [c] cites an instance of a woman who had borne eight children, and yet unconscious of pregnancy. Merriman [d] speaks of a woman forty years of age who had not borne a child for nine years, but who suddenly gave birth to a stout, healthy boy without being cognizant of pregnancy. Dayral [e] tells of a woman who carried a child all through pregnancy, unconscious of her condition, and who was greatly surprised at its birth. Among the French observers speaking of pregnancy remaining unrecognized by the mother until the period of accouchement, Lozes and Rhades record peculiar cases ; and Mouronval [g] relates an instance in which a woman who had borne three children completely ignored the presence of pregnancy until the pains of labor were felt. Fleishman [h] and Münzenthaler also record examples of unconscious pregnancy.

Pseudocyesis.—On the other hand, instances of pregnancy with imaginary symptoms and preparations for birth are sometimes noticed, and many cases are on record. In fact, nearly every text-book on obstetrics gives some space to the subject of pseudocyesis. Suppression of the menses, enlargement of the abdomen, engorgement of the breasts, together with the symptoms produced by the imagination, such as nausea, spasmodic contraction of the abdomen, etc., are for the most part the origin of the cases of pseudocyesis. Of course, many of the cases are not examples of true pseudocyesis, with its interesting phenomena, but instances of malingering for mercenary or other purposes, and some are calculated to deceive the most expert obstetricians by their tricks. Weir Mitchell [i] delineates an interesting case of pseudocyesis as follows : " A woman, young, or else, it may be, at or past the climacteric, eagerly desires a child or is horribly afraid of becoming pregnant. The menses become slight in amount, irregular, and at last cease or not. Meanwhile the abdomen and breasts enlarge, owing to a rapid taking on of fat, and this is far less visible elsewhere. There comes with this excess of fat the most profound conviction of the fact of pregnancy. By

a 312, 1846.   b 124, 1874.   c 649, 1888.   d 218, 1828.   e 146, 1865.
f 146, 1865.   g 454, 1825, xxiii., 281.   h 834, 1839.   i 533, 1895, 393.

and by the child is felt, the physician takes it for granted, and this goes on until the great diagnostician, Time, corrects the delusion. Then the fat disappears with remarkable speed, and the reign of this singular simulation is at an end." In the same article, Dr. Mitchell cites the two following cases under his personal observation : " I was consulted by a lady in regard to a woman of thirty years of age, a nurse in whom she was interested. This person had been married some three years to a very old man possessed of a considerable estate. He died, leaving his wife her legal share and the rest to distant cousins, unless the wife had a child. For two months before he died the woman, who was very anemic, ceased to menstruate. She became sure that she was pregnant, and thereupon took on flesh at a rate and in a way which seemed to justify her belief. Her breasts and abdomen were the chief seats of this overgrowth. The menses did not return, her pallor increased ; the child was felt, and every preparation made for delivery. At the eighth month a physician made an examination and assured her of the absence of pregnancy. A second medical opinion confirmed the first, and the tenth month found her of immense size and still positive as to her condition. At the twelfth month her menstrual flow returned, and she became sure it was the early sign of labor. When it passed over she became convinced of her error, and at once dropped weight at the rate of half a pound a day despite every effort to limit the rate of this remarkable loss. At the end of two months she had parted with fifty pounds and was, on the whole, less anemic. At this stage I was consulted by letter, as the woman had become exceedingly hysteric. This briefly stated case, which occurred many years ago, is a fair illustration of my thesis.

" Another instance I saw when in general practice. A lady who had several children and suffered much in her pregnancies passed five years without becoming impregnated. Then she missed a period, and had, as usual, vomiting. She made some wild efforts to end her supposed pregnancy, and failing, acquiesced in her fate. The menses returned at the ninth month and were presumed to mean labor. Meanwhile she vomited, up to the eighth month, and ate little. Nevertheless, she took on fat so as to make the abdomen and breasts immense and to excite unusual attention. No physician examined her until the supposed labor began, when, of course, the truth came out. She was pleased not to have another child, and in her case, as in all the others known to me, the fat lessened as soon as the mind was satisfied as to the non-existence of pregnancy. As I now recall the facts, this woman was not more than two months in getting rid of the excess of adipose tissue. Dr. Hirst tells me he has met with cases of women taking on fat with cessation of the menses, and in which there was also a steady belief in the existence of pregnancy. He has not so followed up these cases as to know if in them the fat fell away with speed when once the patient was assured that no child existed within her."

PLATE 2.

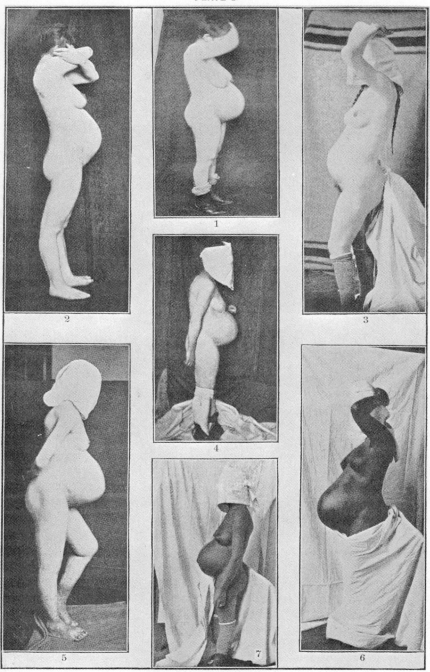

Conditions simulating pregnancy (pseudocyesis) (Hirst): 1. Pendulous belly of rachitis. 2. Normal distention in a primipara at term. 3. Normal distention, seventh month. 4. Pendulous belly of rachitis (Cesarean section). 5. Twins. 6. Pendulous belly of rachitis; fat and tympany. 7. Hydramnios.

Hirst,[a] in an article on the difficulties in the diagnosis of pregnancy, gives several excellent photographs showing the close resemblance between several pathologic conditions and the normal distention of the abdomen in pregnancy (Plate 2). A woman[b] who had several children fell sick with a chest-affection, followed by an edema. For fifteen months she was confined to her bed, and had never had connection with her husband during that time. Her menses ceased; her mammæ became engorged and discharged a serous lactescent fluid; her belly enlarged, and both she and her physician felt fetal movements in her abdomen. As in her previous pregnancies, she suffered nausea. Naturally, a suspicion as to her virtue came into her husband's mind, but when he considered that she had never left her bed for fifteen months he thought the pregnancy impossible. Still the wife insisted that she was pregnant and was confirmed in the belief by a midwife. The belly continued to increase, and about eleven months after the cessation of the menses she had the pains of labor. Three doctors and an accoucheur were present, and when they claimed that the fetal head presented the husband gave up in despair; but the supposed fetus was born shortly after, and proved to be only a mass of hydatids, with not the sign of a true pregnancy. Girard of Lyons[c] speaks of a female who had been pregnant several times, but again experienced the signs of pregnancy. Her mammæ were engorged with a lactescent fluid, and she felt belly-movements like those of a child; but during all this time she had regular menstruation. Her abdomen progressively increased in size, and between the tenth and eleventh months she suffered what she thought to be labor-pains. These false pains ceased upon taking a bath, and with the disappearance of the other signs was dissipated the fallacious idea of pregnancy.

There is mentioned[d] an instance of medicolegal interest of a young girl who showed all the signs of pregnancy and confessed to her parents that she had had commerce with a man. The parents immediately prosecuted the seducer by strenuous legal methods, but when her ninth month came, and after the use of six baths, all the signs of pregnancy vanished. Harvey cites several instances of pseudocyesis, and says we must not rashly determine of the the inordinate birth before the seventh or after the eleventh month. In 1646 a woman, after having laughed heartily at the jests of an ill-bred, covetous clown, was seized with various movements and motions in her belly like those of a child, and these continued for over a month, when the courses appeared again and the movements ceased. The woman was certain that she was pregnant.

The most noteworthy historic case of pseudocyesis is that of Queen Mary of England, or " Bloody Mary," as she was called. To insure the succession of a Catholic heir, she was most desirous of having a son by her consort, Philip, and she constantly prayed and wished for pregnancy. Finally her

a 792, May, 1895. b 302, iv., 235. c Ibid. d Ibid.

menses stopped ; the breasts began to enlarge and became discolored around the nipples. She had morning-sickness of a violent nature and her abdomen enlarged. On consultation with the ladies of her court, her opinion of pregnancy was strongly confirmed. Her favorite amusement then was to make baby-clothes and count on her fingers the months of pregnancy. When the end of the ninth month approached, the people were awakened one night by the joyous peals of the bells of London announcing the new heir. An ambassador had been sent to tell the Pope that Mary could feel the new life within her, and the people rushed to St. Paul's Cathedral to listen to the venerable Archbishop of Canterbury describe the baby-prince and give thanks for his deliverance. The spurious labor pains passed away, and after being assured that no real pregnancy existed in her case, Mary went into violent hysterics, and Philip, disgusted with the whole affair, deserted her ; then commenced the persecution of the Protestants, which blighted the reign.

Putnam [a] cites the case of a healthy brunet, aged forty, the mother of three children. She had abrupt vertical abdominal movements, so strong as to cause her to plunge and sway from side to side. Her breasts were enlarged, the areolæ dark, and the uterus contained an elastic tumor, heavy and rolling under the hand. Her abdomen progressively enlarged to the regular size of matured gestation ; but the extrauterine pregnancy, which was supposed to have existed, was not seen at the autopsy, nothing more than an enlarged liver being found. The movement was due to spasmodic movements of the abdominal muscles, the causes being unknown. Madden [b] gives the history of a primipara of twenty-eight, married one year, to whom he was called. On entering the room he was greeted by the midwife, who said she expected the child about 8 P. M. The woman was lying in the usual obstetric position, on the left side, groaning, crying loudly, and pulling hard at a strap fastened to the bed-post. She had a partial cessation of menses, and had complained of tumultuous movements of the child and overflow of milk from the breasts. Examination showed the cervix low down, the os small and circular, and no signs of pregnancy in the uterus. The abdomen was distended with tympanites and the rectum much dilated with accumulated feces. Dr. Madden left her, telling her that she was not pregnant, and when she reappeared at his office in a few days, he reassured her of the nonexistence of pregnancy ; she became very indignant, triumphantly squeezed lactescent fluid from her breasts, and, insisting that she could feel fetal movements, left to seek a more sympathetic accoucheur. Underhill,[c] in the words of Hamilton, describes a woman as " having acquired the most accurate description of the breeding symptoms, and with wonderful facility imagined that she had felt every one of them." He found the woman on a bed complaining of great labor-pains, biting a handkerchief, and pulling on a cloth

a 218, 1870.   b 310, 1872, liii., 255.   c 318, 1873–4, xix., ii., 844.

attached to her bed. The finger on the abdomen or vulva elicited symptoms of great sensitiveness. He told her she was not pregnant, and the next day she was sitting up, though the discharge continued, but the simulated throes of labor, which she had so graphically pictured, had ceased.

Haultain[a] gives three examples of pseudocyesis, the first with no apparent cause, the second due to carcinoma of the uterus, while in the third there was a small fibroid in the anterior wall of the uterus. Some cases are of purely nervous origin, associated with a purely muscular distention of the abdomen. Clay reported a case due to ascites. Cases of pseudocyesis in women convicted of murder are not uncommon, though most of them are imposters hoping for an extra lease of life.

Croon[b] speaks of a child seven years old on whom he performed ovariotomy for a round-celled sarcoma. She had been well up to May, but since then she had several times been raped by a boy, in consequence of which she had constant uterine hemorrhage. Shortly after the first coitus her abdomen began to enlarge, the breasts to develop, and the areolæ to darken. In seven months the abdomen presented the signs of pregnancy, but the cervix was soft and patulous ; the sound entered three inches and was followed by some hemorrhage. The child was well developed, the mons was covered with hair, and all the associate symptoms tended to increase the deception.

Sympathetic Male Nausea of Pregnancy.—Associated with pregnancy there are often present morning-nausea and vomiting as prominent and reliable symptoms. Vomiting is often so excessive as to be provocative of most serious issue and even warranting the induction of abortion. This fact is well known and has been thoroughly discussed, but with it is associated an interesting point, the occasional association of the same symptoms sympathetically in the husband. The belief has long been a superstition in parts of Great Britain, descending to America, and even exists at the present day. Sir Francis Bacon has written on this subject, the substance of his argument being that certain loving husbands so sympathize with their pregnant wives that they suffer morning-sickness in their own person. No less an authority than S. Weir Mitchell called attention to the interesting subject of sympathetic vomiting in the husband in his lectures on nervous maladies some years ago. He also quotes the following case associated with pseudocyesis :—

" A woman had given birth to two female children. Some years passed, and her desire for a boy was ungratified. Then she missed her flow once, and had thrice after this, as always took place with her when pregnant, a very small but regular loss. At the second month morning-vomiting came on as usual with her. Meanwhile she became very fat, and as the growth was largely, in fact excessively, abdominal, she became easily sure of her condition. She was not my patient, but her husband consulted me as to his own

a 124, April, 1891.   b 318, Feb., 1893.

morning-sickness, which came on with the first occurrence of this sign in his wife, as had been the case twice before in her former pregnancies. I advised him to leave home, and this proved effectual. I learned later that the woman continued to gain flesh and be sick every morning until the seventh month. Then menstruation returned, an examination was made, and when sure that there was no possibility of her being pregnant she began to lose flesh, and within a few months regained her usual size."

Hamill[a] reports an instance of morning-sickness in a husband two weeks after the appearance of menstruation in the wife for the last time. He had daily attacks, and it was not until the failure of the next menses that the woman had any other sign of pregnancy than her husband's nausea. His nausea continued for two months, and was the same as that which he had suffered during his wife's former pregnancies, although not until both he and his wife became aware of the existence of pregnancy. The Lancet[b] describes a case in which the husband's nausea and vomiting, as well as that of the wife, began and ended simultaneously. Judkins[c] cites an instance of a man who was sick in the morning while his wife was carrying a child. This occurred during every pregnancy, and the man related that his own father was similarly affected while his mother was in the early months of pregnancy with him, showing an hereditary predisposition.

The **perverted appetites** and peculiar longings **of pregnant women** furnish curious matter for discussion. From the earliest times there are many such records. Borellus cites an instance, and there are many others, of pregnant women eating excrement with apparent relish. Tulpius, Sennert, Langius, van Swieten, à Castro, and several others report depraved appetites. Several writers have seen avidity for human flesh in such females. Fournier[d] knew a woman with an appetite for the blood of her husband. She gently cut him while he lay asleep by her side and sucked blood from the wounds—a modern "Succubus." Paré[e] mentions the perverted appetites of pregnant women, and says that they have been known to eat plaster, ashes, dirt, charcoal, flour, salt, spices, to drink pure vinegar, and to indulge in all forms of debauchery. Plot[637] gives the case of a woman who would gnaw and eat all the linen off her bed. Hufeland's Journal[452] records the history of a case of a woman of thirty-two, who had been married ten years, who acquired a strong taste for charcoal, and was ravenous for it. It seemed to cheer her and to cure a supposed dyspepsia. She devoured enormous quantities, preferring hard-wood charcoal. Bruyesinus[228] speaks of a woman who had a most perverted appetite for her own milk, and constantly drained her breasts; Krafft-Ebing cites a similar case. Another case[280] is that of a pregnant woman who had a desire for hot and pungent articles of food, and who in a short time devoured a pound of pepper. Scheidemantel cites a

a 780, 1888 ; and 596, 1888, lvii., 635.   b 476, 1878, 66.   c 272, 1892.

d 302, xiv., 624.   e 618, 992.

case in which the perverted appetite, originating in pregnancy, became permanent, but this is not the experience of most observers. The pregnant wife of a farmer in Hassfort-on-the-Main ate the excrement of her husband.[a]

Many instances could be quoted, some in which extreme cases of polydipsia and bulimia developed; these can be readily attributed to the increased call for liquids and food. Other cases of diverse new emotions can be recalled, such as lasciviousness, dirty habits, perverted thoughts, and, on the other hand, extreme piety, chastity, and purity of the mind. Some of the best-natured women are when pregnant extremely cross and irritable, and many perversions of disposition are commonly noticed in pregnancy. There is often a longing for a particular kind of food or dish for which no noticeable desire had been displayed before.

Maternal Impressions.—Another curious fact associated with pregnancy is the apparent influence of the emotions of the mother on the child in utero. Every one knows of the popular explanation of many birth-marks, their supposed resemblance to some animal or object seen by the mother during pregnancy, etc. The truth of maternal impressions, however, seems to be more firmly established by facts of a substantial nature. There is a natural desire to explain any abnormality or anomaly of the child as due to some incident during the period of the mother's pregnancy, and the truth is often distorted and the imagination heavily drawn upon to furnish the satisfactory explanation. It is the customary speech of the dime-museum lecturer to attribute the existence of some "freak" to an episode in the mother's pregnancy. The poor "Elephant-man" firmly believed his peculiarity was due to the fact that his mother while carrying him in utero was knocked down at the circus by an elephant. In some countries the exhibition of monstrosities is forbidden because of the supposed danger of maternal impression. The celebrated "Siamese Twins" for this reason were forbidden to exhibit themselves for quite a period in France.

We shall cite only a few of the most interesting cases from medical literature. Hippocrates saved the honor of a princess, accused of adultery with a negro because she bore a black child, by citing it as a case of maternal impression, the husband of the princess having placed in her room a painting of a negro, to the view of which she was subjected during the whole of her pregnancy. Then, again, in the treatise "De Superfœtatione" there occurs the following distinct statement: "If a pregnant woman has a longing to eat earth or coals, and eats of them, the infant which is born carries on its head the mark of these things." This statement, however, occurs in a work which is not mentioned by any of the ancient authorities, and is rejected by practically all the modern ones; according to Ballantyne, there is, therefore, no absolute proof that Hippocrates was a believer in one of the most popular and long-persisting beliefs concerning fetal deformities.

[a] Ephem. Physico-Medicorum, Leipzig, 1694, 212.

In the explanation of heredity, Hippocrates [a] states " that the body of the male as well as that of the female furnishes the semen.   That which is weak (unhealthy) is derived from weak (unhealthy) parts, that which is strong (healthy) from strong (healthy) parts, and the fetus will correspond to the quality of the semen.   If the semen of one part come in greater quantity from the male than from the female, this part will resemble more closely the father ; if, however, it comes more from the female, the part will rather resemble the mother.   If it be true that the semen comes from both parents, then it is impossible for the whole body to resemble either the mother or the father, or neither the one nor the other in anything, but necessarily the child will resemble both the one and the other in something.   The child will most resemble the one who contributes most to the formation of the parts."   Such was the Hippocratic theory of generation and heredity, and it was ingeniously used to explain the hereditary nature of certain diseases and malformations.   For instance, in speaking of the sacred disease (epilepsy), Hippocrates says : " Its origin is hereditary, like that of other diseases ; for if a phlegmatic person be born of a phlegmatic, and a bilious of a bilious, and a phthisical of a phthisical, and one having spleen disease of another having disease of the spleen, what is to hinder it from happening that where the father and mother were subject to this disease certain of their offspring should be so affected also ?   As the semen comes from all parts of the body, healthy particles will come from healthy parts, and unhealthy from unhealthy parts."

According to Paré,[618] Damascene saw a girl with long hair like a bear, whose mother had constantly before her a picture of the hairy St. John. Paré also appends an illustration showing the supposed resemblance to a bear. Jonston [447] quotes a case of Heliodorus ; it was an Ethiopian, who by the effect of the imagination produced a white child.   Paré [618] describes this case more fully : " Heliodorus says that Persina, Queen of Ethiopia, being impregnated by Hydustes, also an Ethiopian, bore a daughter with a white skin, and the anomaly was ascribed to the admiration that a picture of Andromeda excited in Persina throughout the whole of the pregnancy."   Van Helmont [413] cites the case of a tailor's wife at Mechlin, who during a conflict outside her house, on seeing a soldier lose his hand at her door, gave birth to a daughter with one hand, the other hand being a bleeding stump ; he also speaks of the case of the wife of a merchant at Antwerp, who after seeing a soldier's arm shot off at the siege of Ostend gave birth to a daughter with one arm.   Plot [637] speaks of a child bearing the figure of a mouse ; when pregnant, the mother had been much frightened by one of these animals. Gassendus [356] describes a fetus with the traces of a wound in the same location as one received by the mother.   The Lancet [b] speaks of several cases— one of a child with a face resembling a dog whose mother had been bitten ; one

a 759, Oct., 1895.   b 476, 1863, ii., 27.

of a child with one eye blue and the other black, whose mother during confinement had seen a person so marked; of an infant with fins as upper and lower extremities, the mother having seen such a monster; and another, a child born with its feet covered with scalds and burns, whose mother had been badly frightened by fireworks and a descending rocket. There is [a] the history of a woman who while pregnant at seven months with her fifth child was bitten on the right calf by a dog. Ten weeks after, she bore a child with three marks corresponding in size and appearance to those caused by the dog's teeth on her leg. Kerr [b] reports the case of a woman in her seventh month whose daughter fell on a cooking stove, shocking the mother, who suspected fatal burns. The woman was delivered two months later of an infant blistered about the mouth and extremities in a manner similar to the burns of her sister. This infant died on the third day, but another was born fourteen months later with the same blisters. Inflammation set in and nearly all the fingers and toes sloughed off. In a subsequent confinement, long after the mental agitation, a healthy unmarked infant was born.

Hunt [c] describes a case which has since become almost classic of a woman fatally burned, when pregnant eight months, by her clothes catching fire at the kitchen grate. The day after the burns labor began and was terminated by the birth of a well-formed dead female child, apparently blistered and burned in extent and in places corresponding almost exactly to the locations of the mother's injuries. The mother died on the fourth day.

Webb [d] reports the history of a negress who during a convulsion while pregnant fell into a fire, burning the whole front of the abdomen, the front and inside of the thighs to the knees, the external genitals, and the left arm. Artificial delivery was deemed necessary, and a dead child, seemingly burned much like its mother, except less intensely, was delivered. There was also one large blister near the inner canthus of the eye and some large blisters about the neck and throat which the mother did not show. There was no history of syphilis nor of any eruptive fever in the mother, who died on the tenth day with tetanus.

Graham [e] describes a woman of thirty-five, the mother of seven children, who while pregnant was feeding some rabbits, when one of the animals jumped at her with its eyes "glaring" upon her, causing a sudden fright. Her child was born hydrocephalic. Its mouth and face were small and rabbit-shaped. Instead of a nose, it had a fleshy growth $\frac{3}{4}$ inch long by $\frac{1}{4}$ inch broad, directed upward at an angle of $45°$. The space between this and the mouth was occupied by a body resembling an adult eye. Within this were two small, imperfect eyes which moved freely while life lasted (ten minutes). The child's integument was covered with dark, downy, short hair. The woman recovered and afterward bore two normal children.

a 611, No. 19, May 7, 1842. b 124, July, 1857. c 124, 1881, lxxxi., 186.
d 783, x., 419. e 224, 1868, i., 51.

Parvin mentions an instance of the influence of maternal impression in the causation of a large, vivid, red mark or splotch on the face : "When the mother was in Ireland she was badly frightened by a fire in which some cattle were burned. Again, during the early months of her pregnancy she was frightened by seeing another woman suddenly light the fire with kerosene, and at that time became firmly impressed with the idea that her child would be marked." Parvin [a] also pictures the "turtle-man," an individual with deformed extremities, who might be classed as an ectromelus, perhaps as a phocomelus, or seal-like monster. According to the story, when the mother was a few weeks pregnant her husband, a coarse, rough fisherman, fond of rude jokes, put a large live turtle in the cupboard. In the twilight the wife went to the cupboard and the huge turtle fell out, greatly startling her by its hideous appearance as it fell suddenly to the floor and began to move vigorously.

Fig. 8.—The "turtle-man."

Copeland [b] mentions a curious case in which a woman was attacked by a rattlesnake when in her sixth month of pregnancy, and gave birth to a child whose arm exhibited the shape and action of a snake, and involuntarily went through snake-like movements. The face and mouth also markedly resembled the head of a snake. The teeth were situated like a serpent's fangs. The mere mention of a snake filled the child (a man of twenty-nine) with great horror and rage, "particularly in the snake season." Beale [c] gives the history of a case of a child born with its left eye blackened as by a blow, whose mother was struck in a corresponding portion of the face eight hours before confinement. There is on record [d] an account of a young man of twenty-one suffering from congenital deformities attributed to the fact that his mother was frightened by a guinea-pig having been thrust into her face during pregnancy. He also had congenital deformity of the right auricle. At the autopsy, all the skin, tissues, muscles, and bones were found involved. Owen [e] speaks of a woman who was greatly excited ten months previously by a prurient curiosity to see what appearance the genitals of her brother presented after he had submitted to amputation of the penis on account of carcinoma. The whole penis had been removed. The woman stated that from the time she had thus satisfied herself, her mind was unceasingly engaged in reflecting and sympathizing on the forlorn condition of her brother. While in this mental state she gave birth to a son whose penis was entirely absent, but who was otherwise well and likely to live. The other portions of the genitals were perfect and well developed. The appearance of

a Internat. Med. Mag., Phila., June, 1892. b 218, 1839, 98.
c 476, 1863, ii., 27.   d 536, 1883, i., 381.   e 476, 1863, 25.

the nephew and the uncle was identical. A most peculiar case [a] is stated by Clerc as occurring in the experience of Küss of Strasburg. A woman had a negro paramour in America with whom she had had sexual intercourse several times. She was put in a convent on the Continent, where she stayed two years. On leaving the convent she married a white man, and nine months after she gave birth to a dark-skinned child. The supposition was that during her abode in the convent and the nine months subsequently she had the image of her black paramour constantly before her. Loin [b] speaks of a woman who was greatly impressed by the actions of a clown at a circus, and who brought into the world a child that resembled the fantastic features of the clown in a most striking manner.

Mackay [c] describes five cases in which fright produced distinct marks on the fetus. There is a case mentioned [d] in which a pregnant woman was informed that an intimate friend had been thrown from his horse ; the immediate cause of death was fracture of the skull, produced by the corner of a dray against which the rider was thrown. The mother was profoundly impressed by the circumstance, which was minutely described to her by an eye-witness. Her child at birth presented a red and sensitive area upon the scalp corresponding in location with the fatal injury in the rider. The child is now an adult woman, and this area upon the scalp remains red and sensitive to pressure, and is almost devoid of hair. Mastin of Mobile, Alabama, reports a curious instance of maternal impression. During the sixth month of the pregnancy of the mother her husband was shot, the ball passing out through the left breast. The woman was naturally much shocked, and remarked to Dr. Mastin : "Doctor, my baby will be ruined, for when I saw the wound I put my hands over my face, and got it covered with blood, and I know my baby will have a bloody face." The child came to term without a bloody face. It had, however, a well-defined spot on the left breast just below the site of exit of the ball from its father's chest. The spot was about the size of a silver half-dollar, and had elevated edges of a bright red color, and was quite visible at the distance of one hundred feet. The authors have had personal communication with Dr. Mastin in regard to this case, which he considers the most positive evidence of a case of maternal impression that he has ever met.

Paternal Impressions.—Strange as are the foregoing cases, those of paternal impression eclipse them. Several are on record, but none are of sufficient authenticity to warrant much discussion on the subject. Those below are given to illustrate the method of report. Stahl, quoted by Steinan, 1843, speaks of the case of a child, the father being a soldier who lost an eye in the war. The child was born with one of its eyes dried up in the orbit, in this respect presenting an appearance like that of the father. Schneider [e]

a 239, July 7, 1873.   b 615, 1879–80. xxxi.

c 476, 1891, ii., 1388.   d 844, 213.   e 778, xxviii., 167.

says a man whose wife was expecting confinement dreamt that his oldest son stood beside his bedside with his genitals much mutilated and bleeding. He awoke in a great state of agitation, and a few days later the wife was delivered of a child with exstrophy of the bladder.   Hoare [a] recites the curious story of a man who vowed that if his next child was a daughter he would never speak to it.   The child proved to be a son, and during the whole of the father's life nothing could induce the son to speak to his father, nor, in fact, to any other male person, but after the father's death he talked fluently to both men and women.   Clark [b] reports the birth of a child whose father had a stiff knee-joint, and the child's knee was stiff and bent in exactly the same position as that of its father.

Telegony.—The influence of the paternal seed on the physical and mental constitution of the child is well known.   To designate this condition, *Telegony* is the word that was coined by Weismann in his " Das Keim-plasma," and he defines it as " Infection of the Germ," and, at another time, as " Those doubtful instances in which the offspring is said to resemble, not the father, but an early mate of the mother,"—or, in other words, the alleged influence of a previous sire on the progeny produced by a subsequent one from the same mother.   In a systematic discussion of telegony before the Royal Medical Society, Edinburgh, on March 1, 1895,[c] Brunton Blaikie, as a means of making the definition of telegony plainer by practical example, prefaced his remarks by citing the classic example which first drew the attention of the modern scientific world to this phenomenon.   The facts of this case were communicated in a letter from the Earl of Morton to the President of the Royal Society in 1821, and were as follows : In the year 1815 Lord Morton put a male quagga to a young chestnut mare of $\frac{7}{8}$ Arabian blood, which had never before been bred from.   The result was a female hybrid which resembled both parents.   He now sold the mare to Sir Gore Ousley, who two years after she bore the hybrid put her to a black Arabian horse.   During the two following years she had two foals which Lord Morton thus describes : " They have the character of the Arabian breed as decidedly as can be expected when $\frac{15}{16}$ of the blood are Arabian, and they are fine specimens of the breed ; but both in their color and in the hair of their manes they have a striking resemblance to the quagga.   Their color is bay, marked more or less like the quagga in a darker tint.   Both are distinguished by the dark line along the ridge of the back, the dark stripes across the forehand, and the dark bars across the back part of the legs."   The President of the Royal Society saw the foals and verified Lord Morton's statement.

" Herbert Spencer, in the Contemporary Review for May, 1893, gives several cases communicated to him by his friend Mr. Fookes, whom Spencer says is often appointed judge of animals at agricultural shows.   After giving

a 476, 1831-2, i., 441.   b 548, xv., 258.   c 759, July, 1895.

various examples he goes on to say : ' A friend of mine near this had a valuable Dachshund bitch, which most unfortunately had a litter by a stray sheep-dog. The next year the owner sent her on a visit to a pure Dachshund dog, but the produce took quite as much of the first father as the second, and the next year he sent her to another Dachshund, with the same result. Another case : A friend of mine in Devizes had a litter of puppies, unsought for, by a setter from a favorite pointer bitch, and after this she never bred any true pointers, no matter what the paternity was.'

" Lord Polwarth, whose very fine breed of Border Leicesters is famed throughout Britain, and whose knowledge on the subject of breeding is great, says that ' In sheep we always consider that if a ewe breeds to a Shrop ram, she is never safe to breed pure Leicesters from, as dun or colored legs are apt to come even when the sire is a pure Leicester. This has been proved in various instances, but is not invariable.' "

Hon. Henry Scott says : " Dog-breeders know this theory well ; and if a pure-bred bitch happens to breed to a dog of another breed, she is of little use for breeding pure-bred puppies afterward. Animals which produce large litters and go a short time pregnant show this throwing back to previous sires far more distinctly than others—I fancy dogs and pigs most of all, and probably horses least. The influence of previous sires may be carried into the second generation or further, as I have a cat now which appears to be half Persian (long hair). His dam has very long hair and every appearance of being a half Persian, whereas neither have really any Persian blood, as far as I know, but the grand-dam (a very smooth-haired cat) had several litters by a half-Persian tom-cat, and all her produce since have showed the influence retained. The Persian tom-cat died many years ago, and was the only one in the district, so, although I cannot be absolutely positive, still I think this case is really as stated."

Breeders of Bedlington terriers wish to breed dogs with as powerful jaws as possible. In order to accomplish this they put the Bedlington terrier bitch first to a bull-terrier dog, and get a mongrel litter which they destroy. They now put the bitch to a Bedlington terrier dog and get a litter of puppies which are practically pure, but have much stronger jaws than they would otherwise have had, and also show much of the gameness of the bull-terrier, thus proving that physiologic as well as anatomic characters may be transmitted in this way.

After citing the foregoing examples, Blaikie directs his attention to man, and makes the following interesting remarks :—

" We might expect from the foregoing account of telegony amongst animals that whenever a black woman had a child to a white man, and then married a black man, her subsequent children would not be entirely black. Dr. Robert Balfour of Surinam in 1851 wrote to Harvey that he was continually noticing amongst the colored population of Surinam ' that if a negress had a child or children by a white, and afterward fruitful intercourse with a negro, the latter offspring had generally a lighter color than the parents.' But, as far as I know, this is the only instance of this observation on record. Herbert Spencer has shown that when a pure-bred animal breeds with an animal of a mixed breed, the offspring resembles much more closely the parent of pure blood, and this may explain why the circumstance recorded by Balfour has been so seldom noted. For a negro, who is of very pure blood, will naturally have a stronger influence on the subsequent progeny than an Anglo-Saxon, who comes of a mixed stock. If this be the correct explanation, we should expect that when a white woman married first a black man, and then a white, the children by the white husband would be dark colored. Unfortunately for the proof of telegony, it is very rare that a white woman *does* marry a black man, and then have a white as second husband ; nevertheless, we have a fair number of recorded instances of dark-colored children being born in the above way of white parents.

"Dr. Harvey mentions a case in which 'a young woman, residing in Edinburgh, and born of white (Scottish) parents, but whose mother, some time previous to her marriage, had a natural (mulatto) child by a negro man-servant in Edinburgh, exhibits distinct traces of the negro. Dr. Simpson —afterward Sir James Simpson—whose patient the young woman at one time was, has had no recent opportunities of satisfying himself as to the precise extent to which the negro character prevails in her features ; but he recollects being struck with the resemblance, and noticed particularly that the hair had the qualities characteristic of the negro.' Herbert Spencer got a letter from a 'distinguished correspondent' in the United States, who said that children by white parents had been '*repeatedly*' observed to show traces of black blood when the women had had previous connection with (*i. e.*, a child by) a negro. Dr. Youmans of New York interviewed several medical professors, who said the above was 'generally accepted as a fact.' Prof. Austin Flint, in 'A Text-book of Human Physiology,' mentioned this fact, and when asked about it said : 'He had never heard the statement questioned.'

"But it is not only in relation to color that we find telegony to have been noticed in the human subject. Dr. Middleton Michel gives a most interesting case in the American Journal of the Medical Sciences for 1868 : 'A black woman, mother of several negro children, none of whom were deformed in any particular, had illicit intercourse with a white man, by whom she became pregnant. During gestation she manifested great uneasiness of mind, lest the birth of a mulatto offspring should disclose her conduct. . . . It so happened that her negro husband possessed a sixth digit on each hand, but there was no peculiarity of any kind in the white man, yet when the mulatto child was born it actually presented the deformity of a supernumerary finger.' Taruffi, the celebrated Italian teratologist, in speaking of the subject, says : 'Our knowledge of this strange fact is by no means recent, for Fienus, in 1608, said that most of the children born in adultery have a greater resemblance to the legal than to the real father'—an observation that was confirmed by the philosopher Vanini and by the naturalist Ambrosini. From these observations comes the proverb : 'Filium ex adultera excusare matrem a culpa.' Osiander has noted telegony in relation to moral qualities of children by a second marriage. Harvey said that it has long been known that the children by a second husband resemble the first husband in features, mind, and disposition. He then gave a case in which this resemblance was very well marked. Orton, Burdach (Traité de Physiologie), and Dr. William Sedgwick have all remarked on this physical resemblance ; and Dr. Metcalfe, in a dissertation delivered before this society in 1855, observed that in the cases of widows remarrying the children of the second marriage frequently resemble the first husband.

"An observation probably having some bearing on this subject was made by Count de Stuzeleci (Harvey, *loc. cit.*). He noticed that when an aboriginal female had had a child by a European, she lost the power of conception by a male of her own race, but could produce children by a white man. He believed this to be the case with many aboriginal races ; but it has been disproved, or at all events proved to be by no means a universal law, in every case except that of the aborigines of Australia and New Zealand. Dr. William Sedgwick thought it probable that the unfruitfulness of prostitutes might in some degree be due to the same cause as that of the Australian aborigines who have had children by white men.

" It would seem as though the Israelites had had some knowledge of telegony, for in Deuteronomy we find that when a man died leaving no issue, his wife was commanded to marry her husband's brother, in order that he might ' raise up seed to his brother.' "

We must omit the thorough inquiry into this subject that is offered by Mr. Blaikie. The explanations put forward have always been on one of three main lines :—

(1) The imagination-theory, or, to quote Harvey : " Due to mental causes so operating either on the mind of the female and so acting on her reproductive powers, or on the mind of the male parent, and so influencing the qualities of his semen, as to modify the nutrition and development of the offspring."

(2) Due to a local influence on the reproductive organs of the mother.

(3) Due to a general influence through the fetus on the mother.

Antenatal Pathology.—We have next to deal with the diseases, accidents, and operations that affect the pregnant uterus and its contents ; these are rich in anomalies and facts of curious interest, and have been recognized from the earliest times. In the various works usually grouped together under the general designation of " Hippocratic " are to be found the earliest opinions upon the subject of antenatal pathology which the medical literature of Greece has handed down to modern times.   That there were medical writers before the time of Hippocrates cannot be doubted, and that the works ascribed to the " Father of Medicine" were immediately followed by those of other physicians, is likewise not to be questioned; but whilst nearly all the writings prior to and after Hippocrates have been long lost to the world, most of those that were written by the Coan physician and his followers have been almost miraculously preserved.   As Littré puts it, " Les écrits hippocratiques demeurent isolés au milieu des débris de l'antique littérature médicale."—(Ballantyne.)

The first to be considered is **the transmission of contagious disease to the fetus in utero.**   The first disease to attract attention was **small-pox.**   Devilliers, Blot, and Depaul all speak of congenital small-pox, the child born dead and showing evidences of the typical small-pox pustulation, with a history of the mother having been infected during pregnancy. Watson[a] reports two cases in which a child in utero had small-pox.   In the first case the mother was infected in pregnancy; the other was nursing a patient when seven months pregnant; she did not take the disease, although she had been infected many months before.   Mauriceau[513] delivered a woman of a healthy child at full term after she had recovered from a severe attack of this disease during the fifth month of gestation.   Mauriceau supposed the child to be immune after the delivery.   Vidal reported to the French Academy of Medicine, May, 1871, the case of a woman who gave birth to a living child of about six and one-half months' maturation, which died some hours after birth covered with the pustules of seven or eight days' eruption. The pustules on the fetus were well umbilicated and typical, and could have been nothing but those of small-pox; besides, this disease was raging in the neighborhood at the time.   The mother had never been infected before, and never was subsequently.   Both parents were robust and neither of them had ever had syphilis.   About the time of conception, the early part of December, 1870, the father had suffered from the semiconfluent type, but the mother, who had been vaccinated when a girl, had never been stricken either during or after her husband's sickness.   Quirke[b] relates a peculiar instance of a child born at midnight, whose mother was covered with the eruption eight hours after delivery.   The child was healthy and showed no signs of the contagion, and was vaccinated at once.   Although it remained with its mother all through the sickness, it continued well, with the exception of the ninth day, when a slight fever due to its vaccination appeared. The mother made a good recovery, and the author remarks that had the child been born a short time later, it would most likely have been infected.

Ayer[c] reports an instance of congenital variola in twins.   Chantreuil[d]

a 629, 1743-50, 1043.   b 224, 1886, i., 201.
c 218, 1851, xliv., 397.   d 363, 1870, xliii., 173.

speaks of a woman pregnant with twins who aborted at five and a half months. One of the fetuses showed distinct signs of congenital variola, although the mother and other fetus were free from any symptoms of the disease. In 1853 Charcot reported the birth of a premature fetus presenting numerous variolous pustules together with ulcerations of the derm and mucous membranes and stomach, although the mother had convalesced of the disease some time before. Mitchell[a] describes a case of small-pox occurring three days after birth, the mother not having had the disease since childhood. Shertzer[b] relates an instance of confluent small-pox in the eighth month of pregnancy. The child was born with the disease, and both mother and babe recovered. Among many others offering evidence of variola in utero are Degner, Derham, John Hunter, Blot, Bulkley, Welch, Wright, Digk, Forbes, Marinus, and Bouteiller.

Varicella, Measles, Pneumonia, and even **Malaria** are reported as having been transmitted to the child in utero. Hubbard[c] attended a woman on March 17, 1878, in her seventh accouchement. The child showed the rash of varicella twenty-four hours after birth, and passed through the regular course of chicken-pox of ten days' duration. The mother had no signs of the disease, but the children all about her were infected. Ordinarily the period of incubation is from three to four days, with a premonitory fever of from twenty-four to seventy-two hours' duration, when the rash appears; this case must therefore have been infected in utero. Lomer[d] of Hamburg tells of the case of a woman, twenty-two years, unmarried, pregnant, who had measles in the eighth month, and who gave birth to an infant with measles. The mother was attacked with pneumonia on the fifth day of her puerperium, but recovered; the child died in four weeks of intestinal catarrh. Gautier[e] found measles transmitted from the mother to the fetus in 6 out of 11 cases, there being 2 maternal deaths in the 11 cases.

Netter[f] has observed the case of transmission of pneumonia from a mother to a fetus, and has seen two cases in which the blood from the uterine vessels of patients with pneumonia contained the pneumococcus. Wallick[g] collected a number of cases of pneumonia occurring during pregnancy, showing a fetal mortality of 80 per cent.

Felkin[h] relates two instances of fetal malaria in which the infection was probably transmitted by the male parent. In one case the father near term suffered severely from malaria; the mother had never had a chill. The violent fetal movements induced labor, and the spleen was so large as to retard it. After birth the child had seven malarial paroxysms but recovered, the splenic tumor disappearing.

The modes of infection of the fetus by **syphilis,** and the infection of the mother, have been well discussed, and need no mention here.

a 124, 1830, vii., 555.   b 547, iv., 756.   c 224, 1878, i., 822.   d 261, 1889.
e 140, 1879, 321.   f 300, No. 22, 1889.   g 140, 1889, 439.   h 318, June, 1889.

There has been much discussion on **the effects on the fetus in utero of medicine administered to the pregnant mother,** and the opinions as to the reliability of this medication are so varied that we are in doubt as to a satisfactory conclusion. The effects of drugs administered and eliminated by the mammary glands and transmitted to the child at the breast are well known, and have been witnessed by nearly every physician, and, as in cases of strong metallic purges, etc., need no other than the actual test. However, scientific experiments as to the efficacy of fetal therapeutics have been made from time to time with varying results.

Gusserow of Strasbourg tested for iodin, chloroform, and salicylic acid in the blood and secretions of the fetus after maternal administration just before death. In 14 cases in which iodin had been administered, he examined the fetal urine of 11 cases; in 5, iodin was present, and in the others, absent. He made some similar experiments on the lower animals. Benicke reports having given salicylic acid just before birth in 25 cases, and in each case finding it in the urine of the child shortly after birth.

At a discussion held in New York some years ago as to the real effect on the fetus of giving narcotics to the mother, Dr. Gaillard Thomas was almost alone in advocating that the effect was quite visible. Fordyce Barker was strongly on the negative side. Henning and Ahlfeld, two German observers, vouch for the opinion of Thomas, and Thornburn states that he has witnessed the effect of nux vomica and strychnin on the fetus shortly after birth. Over fifty years ago, in a memoir on "Placental Phthisis," Sir James Y. Simpson advanced a new idea in the recommendation of potassium chlorate during the latter stages of pregnancy. The efficacy of this suggestion is known, and whether, as Simpson said, it acts by supplying extra oxygen to the blood, or whether the salt itself is conveyed to the fetus, has never been definitely settled.

McClintock,[a] who has been a close observer on this subject, reports some interesting cases. In his first case he tried a mixture of iron perchlorid and potassium chlorate three times a day on a woman who had borne three dead children, with a most successful result. His second case failed, but in a third he was successful by the same medication with a woman who had before borne a dead child. In a fourth case of unsuccessful pregnancy for three consecutive births he was successful. His fifth case was extraordinary : It was that of a woman in her tenth pregnancy, who, with one exception, had always borne a dead child at the seventh or eighth month. The one exception lived a few hours only. Under this treatment he was successful in carrying the woman safely past her time for miscarriage, and had every indication for a normal birth at the time of report. Thornburn believes that the administration of a tonic like strychnin is of benefit to a fetus which, by its feeble heart-beats and movements, is thought to be un-

a 224, 1877, ii., 513.

healthy. Porak[a] has recently investigated the passage of substances foreign to the organism through the placenta, and offers an excellent paper on this subject, which is quoted in brief in a contemporary number of Teratologia.[759]

In this important paper, Porak, after giving some historical notes, describes a long series of experiments performed on the guinea-pig in order to investigate the passage of arsenic, copper, lead, mercury, phosphorus, alizarin, atropin, and eserin through the placenta. The placenta shows a real affinity for some toxic substances ; in it accumulate copper and mercury, but not lead, and it is therefore through it that the poison reaches the fetus ; in addition to its pulmonary, intestinal, and renal functions, it fixes glycogen and acts as an accumulator of poisons, and so resembles in its action the liver ; therefore the organs of the fetus possess only a potential activity. The storing up of poisons in the placenta is not so general as the accumulation of them in the liver of the mother. It may be asked if the placenta does not form a barrier to the passage of poisons into the circulation of the fetus ; this would seem to be demonstrated by mercury, which was always found in the placenta and never in the fetal organs. In poisoning by lead and copper the accumulation of the poison in the fetal tissues is greater than in the maternal, perhaps from differences in assimilation and disassimilation or from greater diffusion. Whilst it is not an impermeable barrier to the passage of poisons, the placenta offers a varying degree of obstruction : it allows copper and lead to pass easily, arsenic with greater difficulty. The accumulation of toxic substances in the fetus does not follow the same law as in the adult. They diffuse more widely in the fetus. In the adult the liver is the chief accumulatory organ. Arsenic, which in the mother elects to accumulate in the liver, is in the fetus stored up in the skin ; copper accumulates in the fetal liver, central nervous system, and sometimes in the skin ; lead, which is found specially in the maternal liver, but also in the skin, has been observed in the skin, liver, nervous centers, and elsewhere in the fetus. The frequent presence of poisons in the fetal skin demonstrates its physiologic importance. It has probably not a very marked influence on its health. On the contrary, accumulation in the placenta and nerve centers explains the pathogenesis of abortion and the birth of dead fetuses (" mortinatalité "). Copper and lead did not cause abortion, but mercury did so in two out of six cases. Arsenic is a powerful abortive agent in the guinea-pig, probably on account of placental hemorrhages. An important deduction is that whilst the placenta is frequently and seriously affected in syphilis, it is also the special seat for the accumulation of mercury. May this not explain its therapeutic action in this disease ? The marked accumulation of lead in the central nervous system of the fetus explains the frequency and serious character of saturnine encephalopathic lesions. The presence of arsenic in the

[a] Archives de Méd. expérimentale et d'Anatomie path., March, 1894, p. 192.

fetal skin alone gives an explanation of the therapeutic results of the administration of this substance in skin diseases.

Intrauterine amputations are of interest to the medical man, particularly those cases in which the accident has happened in early pregnancy and the child is born with a very satisfactory and clean stump. Montgomery,[a] in an excellent paper, advances the theory, which is very plausible, that intrauterine amputations are caused by contraction of bands or membranes of organized lymph encircling the limb and producing amputation by the same process of disjunctive atrophy that the surgeons induce by ligature. Weinlechner[b] speaks of a case in which a man devoid of all four extremities was exhibited before the Vienna Medical Society. The amputations were congenital, and on the right side there was a very small stump of the upper arm remaining, admitting the attachment of an artificial apparatus. He was twenty-seven years old, and able to write, to thread a needle, pour water out of a bottle, etc. Cook[c] speaks of a female child born of Indian parents, the fourth birth of a mother twenty-six years old. The child weighed 5½ pounds ; the circumference of the head was 14 inches and that of the trunk 13 inches. The upper extremities consisted of perfect shoulder joints, but only ¼ of each humerus was present. Both sides showed evidences of amputation, the cicatrix on the right side being 1 inch long and on the left ¼ inch long. The right lower limb was merely a fleshy corpuscle ¾ inch wide and ¼ inch long ; to the posterior edge was attached a body resembling the little toe of a newly-born infant. On the left side the limb was represented by a fleshy corpuscle 1 inch long and ¼ inch in circumference, resembling the great toe of an infant. There was no history of shock or

Fig. 9.—Intrauterine amputation (Cook).

injury to the mother. The child presented by the breech, and by the absence of limbs caused much difficulty in diagnosis. The three stages of labor were one and one-half hours, forty-five minutes, and five minutes, respectively. The accompanying illustration (Fig. 9) shows the appearance of the limbs at the time of report.

Figure 10 represents a negro boy, the victim of intrauterine amputation, who learned to utilize his toes for many purposes. The illustration shows his mode of holding his pen.

There is an instance reported[d] in which a child at full term was born with an amputated arm, and at the age of seventeen the stump was scarcely if at all smaller than the other. Blake[e] speaks of a case of congenital

a 309, 1832.   b 118, Jan. 22, 1878.   c 224, 1890, i., 1360.
d 222, Oct., 1837.   e 218, Dec. 20, 1894.

amputation of both the upper extremities. Gillilam [a] mentions a case that shows the deleterious influence of even the weight of a fetal limb resting on a cord or band. His case was that of a fetus, the product of a miscarriage of traumatic origin ; the soft tissues were almost cut through and the bone denuded by the limb resting on one of the two umbilical cords, not encircling it, but in a sling. The cord was deeply imbedded in the tissues.

The coilings of the cord are not limited to compression about the extremities alone, but may even decapitate the head by being firmly wrapped several times about the neck. According to Ballantyne, [759] there is in the treatise De Octimestri Partu, by Hippocrates, a reference to coiling of the umbilical cord round the neck of the fetus. This coiling was, indeed, regarded as one of the dangers of the eighth month, and even the mode of its production is described. It is said that if the cord be extended along one side of the uterus, and the fetus lie more to the other side, then when the *culbute* is performed the funis must necessarily form a loop round the neck or chest of the infant. If it remain in this position, it is further stated, the mother will suffer later and the fetus will either perish or be born with difficulty. If the Hippocratic writers knew that this coiling is sometimes quite innocuous, they did not in any place state the fact.

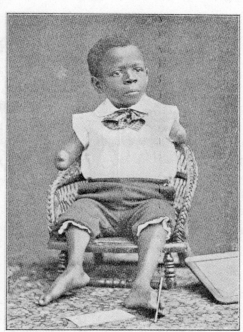

Fig. 10.—Intrauterine amputation.

The accompanying illustrations (Fig. 11) show the different ways in which the funis may be coiled, the coils sometimes being as many as 8.

Bizzen [b] mentions an instance in which from strangulation the head of a fetus was in a state of putrefaction, the funis being twice tightly bound around the neck. Cleveland,[c] Cuthbert,[d] and Germain [e] report analogous instances. Matthyssens [f] observed the twisting of the funis about the arm and neck of a fetus the body of which was markedly wasted. There was complete absence of amniotic fluid during labor. Blumenthal [g] presented to the New York Pathological Society an ovum within which the fetus was under-

a 274, 1872, iii., 230.   b 124, 1852, xxxiii., 565.   c 778, xiii., 1.   d 610, 1874–5.
e 362, ix., 567.   f Ann. Soc. de méd. d'Anvers, 1842, 372.   g 538, 1871, vi., 278.

going intrauterine decapitation. Buchanan [a] describes a case illustrative of the etiology of spontaneous amputation of limbs in utero. Nebinger [b] reports a case of abortion, showing commencing amputation of the left thigh from being encircled by the funis. The death of the fetus was probably due to compression of the cord. Owen [c] mentions an instance in which the left arm and hand of a fetus were found in a state of putrescence from strangulation, the funis being tightly bound around at the upper part. Simpson [d] published an article on spontaneous amputation of the forearm and rudimentary regeneration of the hand in the fetus. Among other contributors to this

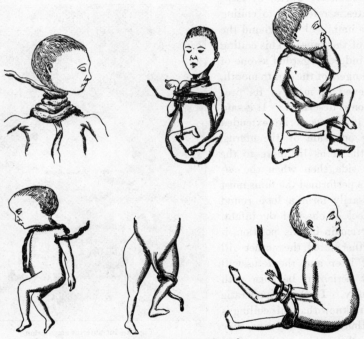

Fig. 11.—Coiling of the cord.

subject are Avery, Boncour, Brown, Ware, Wrangell, Young, Nettekoven, Martin, Macan, Leopold, Hecker, Günther, and Friedinger.

Wygodzky [e] finds that the greatest number of coils of the umbilical cord ever found to encircle a fetus are 7 (Baudelocque), 8 (Credé), and 9 (Müller and Gray). His own case was observed this year in Wilna. The patient was a primipara aged twenty. The last period was seen on May 10, 1894. On February 19th the fetal movements suddenly ceased. On the 20th pains set in about two weeks before term. At noon turbid

a 774, 1839, x., 41.   b 124, 1867, liv., 129.   c 656, 1851, 573.
d Month. Jour. Med. Sc., Edin., 1848.   e 261; and quoted 545, Feb. 29, 1896.

liquor amnii escaped. At 2 P. M., on examination, Wygodzky defined a dead fetus in left occipito-anterior presentation, very high in the inlet. The os was nearly completely dilated, the pains strong. By 4 P. M. the head was hardly engaged in the pelvic cavity. At 7 P. M. it neared the outlet at the height of each pain, but retracted immediately afterward. After 10 P. M. the pains grew weak. At midnight Wygodzky delivered the dead child by expression. Not till then was the cause of delay clear. The funis was very tense and coiled 7 times round the neck and once round the left shoulder; there was also a distinct knot. It measured over 65 inches in length. The fetus was a male, slightly macerated. It weighed over 5 pounds, and was easily delivered entire after division and unwinding of the funis. No marks remained on the neck. The placenta followed ten minutes later and, so far as naked-eye experience indicated, seemed healthy.

Intrauterine fractures are occasionally seen, but are generally the results of traumatism or of some extraordinary muscular efforts on the part of the mother. A blow on the abdomen or a fall may cause them. The most interesting cases are those in which the fractures are multiple and the causes unknown. Spontaneous fetal fractures have been discussed thoroughly, and the reader is referred to any responsible text-book for the theories of causation. Atkinson,[a] De Luna,[b] and Keller report intrauterine fractures of the clavicle. Filippi[c] contributes an extensive paper on the medicolegal aspect of a case of intrauterine fracture of the os cranium. Braun of Vienna reports a case of intrauterine fracture of the humerus and femur. Rodrigue[d] describes a case of fracture and dislocation of the humerus of a fetus in utero. Gaultier[e] reports an instance of fracture of both femora intrauterine. Stanley, Vanderveer, and Young cite instances of intrauterine fracture of the thigh; in the case of Stanley the fracture occurred during the last week of gestation, and there was rapid union of the fragments during lactation. Danyau, Proudfoot, and Smith[f] mention intrauterine fracture of the tibia; in Proudfoot's case there was congenital talipes talus.

Dolbeau[g] describes an instance in which **multiple fractures** were found in a fetus, some of which were evidently postpartum, while others were assuredly antepartum. Hirschfeld[h] describes a fetus showing congenital multiple fractures. Gross[387] speaks of a wonderful case of Chaupier in which no less than 113 fractures were discovered in a child at birth. It survived twenty-four hours, and at the postmortem examination it was found that some were already solid, some uniting, whilst others were recent. It often happens that the intrauterine fracture is well united at birth. There seems to be a peculiar predisposition of the bones to fracture in the cases in which the fractures are multiple and the cause is not apparent.

a 545, 1859–60, iii., 532. b 124, 1873, lxvi., 282. c Imparziale, Firenze, 1879, xix.
d 124, 1854, xxvii., 272. e 458, 1819, 81. f 779, xviii., 215.
g 242, xxxviii., 126. h 363, xxx., 291.

The results to the fetus of injuries to the pregnant mother are most diversified. In some instances the marvelous escape of any serious consequences of one or both is almost incredible, while in others the slightest injury is fatal. Guillemont [a] cites the instance of a woman who was killed by a stroke of lightning, but whose fetus was saved; while Fabricius Hildanus [b] describes a case in which there was perforation of the head, fracture of the skull, and a wound of the groin, due to sudden starting and agony of terror of the mother. Here there was not the slightest history of any external violence.

It is a well-known fact that injuries to the pregnant mother show visible effects on the person of the fetus. The older writers kept a careful record of the anomalous and extraordinary injuries of this character and of their effects. Brendelius tells us of hemorrhage from the mouth and nose of the fetus occasioned by the fall of the mother; Buchner [c] mentions a case of fracture of the cranium from fright of the mother; Reuther describes a contusion of the os sacrum and abdomen in the mother from a fall, with fracture of the arm and leg of the fetus from the same cause; Sachse [d] speaks of a fractured tibia in a fetus, caused by a fall of the mother; Slevogt [e] relates an instance of rupture of the abdomen of a fetus by a fall of the mother; the Ephemerides contains accounts of injuries to the fetus of this nature, and among others mentions a stake as having been thrust into a fetus in utero; Verduc [f] offers several examples, one a dislocation of the fetal foot from a maternal fall; Plocquet [456] gives an instance of fractured femur; Walther [g] describes a case of dislocation of the vertebræ from a fall; and there is also a case [h] of a fractured fetal vertebra from a maternal fall. There is recorded [i] a fetal scalp injury, together with clotted blood in the hair, after a fall of the mother. Autenrieth describes a wound of the pregnant uterus, which had no fatal issue, and there is also another similar case on record. [j]

The modern records are much more interesting and wonderful on this subject than the older ones. Richardson [650] speaks of a woman falling down a few weeks before her delivery. Her pelvis was roomy and the birth was easy; but the infant was found to have extensive wounds on the back, reaching from the 3d dorsal vertebra across the scapula, along the back of the humerus, to within a short distance of the elbow. Part of these wounds were cicatrized and part still granulating, which shows that the process of reparation is as active in utero as elsewhere.

Injuries about the genitalia would naturally be expected to exercise some active influence on the uterine contents; but there are many instances reported in which the escape of injury is marvelous. Gibb [k] speaks of a woman, about eight months pregnant, who fell across a chair, lacerating her

a Lyons, 1590.   b 334, cent. v., obs. 3.   c Miscel. 1728, 1026.   d 452, L. xi.
e 282, ann. x., 172.   f 799, T. i., 197.   g 815, obs. 50.   h 524, v., 326.
i 462, T. xxi.   j 106, 1712, 454.   k 476, 1858, i.

genitals and causing an escape of liquor amnii. There was regeneration of this fluid and delivery beyond term. The labor was tedious and took place two and a half months after the accident. The mother and the female child did well. Purcell [a] reports death in a pregnant woman from contused wound of the vulva. Morland [b] relates an instance of a woman in the fifth month of her second pregnancy, who fell on the roof of a woodshed by slipping from one of the steps by which she ascended to the roof, in the act of hanging out some clothes to dry. She suffered a wound on the internal surface of the left nympha $1\frac{1}{2}$ inch long and $\frac{1}{2}$ inch deep. She had lost about three quarts of blood, and had applied ashes to the vagina to stop the bleeding. She made a recovery by the twelfth day, and the fetal sounds were plainly audible. Cullingworth [c] speaks of a woman who, during a quarrel with her husband, was pushed away and fell between two chairs, knocking one of them over, and causing a trivial wound one inch long in the vagina, close to the entrance. She screamed, there was a gush of blood, and she soon died. The uterus contained a fetus three or four months old, with the membranes intact, the maternal death being due to the varicosity of the pregnant pudenda, the slight injury being sufficient to produce fatal hemorrhage. Carhart [d] describes the case of a pregnant woman, who, while in the stooping position, milking a cow, was impaled through the vagina by another cow. The child was born seven days later, with its skull crushed by the cow's horn. The horn had entered the vagina, carrying the clothing with it.

There are some marvelous cases of recovery and noninterference with pregnancy after **injuries from horns of cattle.** Corey [e] speaks of a woman of thirty-five, three months pregnant, weighing 135 pounds, who was horned by a cow through the abdominal parietes near the hypogastric region; she was lifted into the air, carried, and tossed on the ground by the infuriated animal. There was a wound consisting of a ragged rent from above the os pubis, extending obliquely to the left and upward, through which protruded the great omentum, the descending and transverse colon, most of the small intestines, as well as the pyloric extremity of the stomach. The great omentum was mangled and comminuted, and bore two lacerations of two inches each. The intestines and stomach were not injured, but there was considerable extravasation of blood into the abdominal cavity. The intestines were cleansed and an unsuccessful attempt was made to replace them. The intestines remained outside of the body for two hours, and the great omentum was carefully spread out over the chest to prevent interference with the efforts to return the intestines. The patient remained conscious and calm throughout; finally deep anesthesia was produced by ether and chloroform, three and a half hours after the accident, and in twenty minutes the intestines were all replaced in the abdominal cavity. The edges were pared, sutured, and the wound dressed. The woman was placed in bed, on the

[a] 313, 1870.   [b] 218, 1858–9.   [c] 521, 1885.   [d] 760, 1884.   [e] 133, 1878.

right side, and morphin was administered. The sutures were removed on the ninth day, and the wound had healed except at the point of penetration. The woman was discharged twenty days after, and, incredible to relate, was delivered of a well-developed, full-term child just two hundred and two days from the time of the accident. Both the mother and child did well.

Luce [a] speaks of a pregnant woman who was horned in the lower part of the abdomen by a cow, and had a subsequent protrusion of the intestines through the wound. After some minor complications, the wound healed fourteen weeks after the accident, and the woman was confined in natural labor of a healthy, vigorous child. In this case no blood was found on the cow's horn, and the clothing was not torn, so that the wound must have been made by the side of the horn striking the greatly distended abdomen.

Richard,[b] quoted also by Tiffany,[837] speaks of a woman, twenty-two, who fell in a dark cellar with some empty bottles in her hand, suffering a wound in the abdomen 2 inches above the navel on the left side 8 cm. long. Through this wound a mass of intestines, the size of a man's head, protruded. Both the mother and the child made a good convalescence. Harris [c] cites the instance of a woman of thirty, a multipara, six months pregnant, who was gored by a cow; her intestines and omentum protruded through the rip and the uterus was bruised. There was rapid recovery and delivery at term. Wetmore of Illinois saw a woman who in the summer of 1860, when about six months pregnant, was gored by a cow, and the large intestine and the omentum protruded through the wound. Three hours after the injury she was found swathed in rags wet with a compound solution of whiskey and camphor, with a decoction of tobacco. The intestines were cold to the touch and dirty, but were washed and replaced. The abdomen was sewed up with a darning needle and black linen thread; the woman recovered and bore a healthy child at the full maturity of her gestation.[d] Crowdace [e] speaks of a female pauper, six months pregnant, who was attacked by a buffalo, and suffered a wound about $1\frac{1}{2}$ inch long and $\frac{1}{2}$ inch wide just above the umbilicus. Through this small opening 19 inches of intestine protruded. The woman recovered, and the fetal heart-beats could be readily auscultated.

Major accidents in pregnant women are often followed by the happiest results. There seems to be no limit to what the pregnant uterus can successfully endure. Tiffany,[837] who has collected some statistics on this subject, as well as on operations successfully performed during pregnancy, which will be considered later, quotes[f] the account of a woman of twenty-seven, eight months pregnant, who was almost buried under a clay wall. She received terrible wounds about the head, 32 sutures being used in this location

a 545, 1859. b 236, 1878. c 125, xx.
d Harris, 125, xx. e 500, 1863, vii., 409. f 644, 1881, vi., 203.

alone. Subsequently she was confined, easily bore a perfectly normal female child, and both did well. Sibois [a] describes the case of a woman weighing 190 pounds, who fell on her head from the top of a wall from 10 to 12 feet high. For several hours she exhibited symptoms of fracture of the base of the skull, and the case was so diagnosed ; fourteen hours after the accident she was perfectly conscious and suffered terrible pain about the head, neck, and shoulders. Two days later an ovum of about twenty days was expelled, and seven months after she was delivered of a healthy boy weighing 10½ pounds. She had therefore lost after the accident one-half of a double conception.

Verrier [b] has collected the results of traumatism during pregnancy, and summarizes 61 cases. Prowzowsky [c] cites the instance of a patient in the eighth month of her first pregnancy who was wounded by many pieces of lead pipe fired from a gun but a few feet distant. Neither the patient nor the child suffered materially from the accident, and gestation proceeded ; the child died on the fourth day after birth without apparent cause. Milner [d] records an instance of remarkable tolerance of injury in a pregnant woman. During her six months of pregnancy the patient was accidentally shot through the abdominal cavity and lower part of the thorax. The missile penetrated the central tendon of the diaphragm and lodged in the lung. The injury was limited by localized pneumonia and peritonitis, and the wound was drained through the lung by free expectoration. Recovery ensued, the patient giving birth to a healthy child sixteen weeks later. Belin [e] mentions a stab-wound in a pregnant woman from which a considerable portion of the epiploon protruded. Sloughing ensued, but the patient made a good recovery, gestation not being interrupted. Fancon [f] describes the case of a woman who had an injury to the knee requiring drainage. She was attacked by erysipelas, which spread over the whole body with the exception of the head and neck ; yet her pregnancy was uninterrupted and recovery ensued. Fancon also speaks of a girl of nineteen, frightened by her lover, who threatened to stab her, who jumped from a second-story window. For three days after the fall she had a slight bloody flow from the vulva. Although she was six months pregnant there was no interruption of the normal course of gestation.

Bancroft [g] speaks of a woman who, being mistaken for a burglar, was shot by her husband with a 44-caliber bullet. The missile entered the second and third ribs an inch from the sternum, passed through the right lung, and escaped at the inferior angle of the scapula, about three inches below the spine ; after leaving her body it went through a pine door. She suffered much hemorrhage and shock, but made a fair recovery at the end of four weeks, though pregnant with her first child at the seventh month. At full

a 788, 1887, July 1, 345.   b Rev. Méd.-chir. d. Mal. d. Femmes, Paris, 1888, x., 529.
c 812, 1879, iv., 1113.   d 533, lxi., 243.   e 236, 1878.   f Quoted 844, 251.   g 545, 1876.

term she was delivered by foot-presentation of a healthy boy. The mother at the time of report was healthy and free from cough, and was nursing her babe, which was strong and bright.

All the cases do not have as happy an issue as most of the foregoing ones, though in some the results are not so bad as might be expected. A German female, thirty-six, while in the sixth month of pregnancy, fell and struck her abdomen on a tub. She was delivered of a normal living child, with the exception that the helix of the left ear was pushed anteriorly, and had, in its middle, a deep incision, which also traversed the antihelix and the tragus, and continued over the cheek toward the nose, where it terminated. The external auditory meatus was obliterated. Gurlt speaks of a woman, seven months pregnant, who fell from the top of a ladder, subsequently losing some blood and water from the vagina. She had also persistent pains in the belly, but there was no deterioration of general health. At her confinement, which was normal, a strong boy was born, wanting the arm below the middle, at which point a white bone protruded. The wound healed and the separated arm came away after birth. Wainwright [a] relates the instance of a woman of forty, who when six months pregnant was run over by railway cars. After a double amputation of the legs she miscarried and made a good recovery. Neugebauer [b] reported the history of a case of a woman who, while near her term of pregnancy, committed suicide by jumping from a window. She ruptured her uterus, and a dead child with a fracture of the parietal bone was found in the abdominal cavity. Staples [c] speaks of a Swede of twenty-eight, of Minnesota, who was accidentally shot by a young man riding by her side in a wagon. The ball entered the abdomen two inches above the crest of the right ilium, a little to the rear of the anterior superior spinous process, and took a downward and forward course. A little shock was felt but no serious symptoms followed. In forty hours there was delivery of a dead child with a bullet in its abdomen. Labor was normal and the internal recovery complete. Von Chelius, [265] quoting the younger Naegele, gives a remarkable instance of a young peasant of thirty-five, the mother of four children, pregnant with the fifth child, who was struck on the belly violently by a blow from a wagon pole. She was thrown down, and felt a tearing pain which caused her to faint. It was found that the womb had been ruptured and the child killed, for in several days it was delivered in a putrid mass, partly through the natural passage and partly through an abscess opening in the abdominal wall. The woman made a good recovery. A **curious accident of pregnancy** [d] is that of a woman of thirty-eight, advanced eight months in her ninth pregnancy, who after eating a hearty meal was seized by a violent pain in the region of the stomach and soon afterward with convulsions, supposed to have been puerperal. She died in a few hours, and at the autopsy it was found that labor

a 647, 1877, 59.   b 782 ; and 261, 1890, 88.   c 538, 1876.   d 218, Oct. 1, 1868.

had not begun, but that the pregnancy had caused a laceration of the spleen, from which had escaped four or five pints of blood. Edge[a] speaks of a case of chorea in pregnancy in a woman of twenty-seven, not interrupting pregnancy or retarding safe delivery. This had continued for four pregnancies, but in the fourth abortion took place.

Buzzard[b] had a case of nervous tremor in a woman, following a fall at her fourth month of pregnancy, who at term gave birth to a male child that was idiotic. Beatty[c] relates a curious accident to a fetus in utero. The woman was in her first confinement and was delivered of a small but healthy and strong boy. There was a small puncture in the abdominal parietes, through which the whole of the intestines protruded and were constricted. The opening was so small that he had to enlarge it with a bistoury to replace the bowel, which was dark and congested ; he sutured the wound with silver wire, but the child subsequently died.

Tiffany[837] of Baltimore has collected excellent **statistics of operations during pregnancy ;** and Mann of Buffalo[d] has done the same work, limiting himself to operations **on the pelvic organs,** where interference is supposed to have been particularly contraindicated in pregnancy. Mann, after giving his individual cases, makes the following summary and conclusions :—

(1) Pregnancy is not a general bar to operations, as has been supposed.

(2) Union of the denuded surfaces is the rule, and the cicatricial tissue, formed during the earlier months of pregnancy, is strong enough to resist the shock of labor at term.

(3) Operations on the vulva are of little danger to mother or child.

(4) Operations on the vagina are liable to cause severe hemorrhage, but otherwise are not dangerous.

(5) Venereal vegetations or warts are best treated by removal.

(6) Applications of silver nitrate or astringents may be safely made to the vagina. For such application, phenol or iodin should not be used, pure or in strong solution.

(7) Operations on the bladder or urethra are not dangerous or liable to be followed by abortion.

(8) Operations for vesicovaginal fistulæ should not be done, as they are dangerous, and are liable to be followed by much hemorrhage and abortion.

(9) Plastic operations may be done in the earlier months of pregnancy with fair prospects of a safe and successful issue.

(10) Small polypi may be treated by torsion or astringents. If cut, there is likely to be a subsequent abortion.

(11) Large polypi removed toward the close of pregnancy will cause hemorrhage.

(12) Carcinoma of the cervix should be removed at once.

A few of the **examples** on record **of operations during pregnancy** of

a 244. 1889, i., 516.   b 476, 1868, ii., 479.   c 224, 1879, i., 701.   d 764, 1882.

special interest, will be given below. Polaillon [a] speaks of a double **ovariotomy** on a woman pregnant at three months, with the subsequent birth of a living child at term. Gordon [b] reports five successful ovariotomies during pregnancy, in Lebedeff's clinic. Of these cases, 1 aborted on the fifth day, 2 on the fifteenth, and the other 2 continued uninterrupted. He collected 204 cases with a mortality of only 3 per cent.; 22 per cent. aborted, and 69.4 per cent. were delivered at full term. Kreutzman [c] reports two cases in which ovarian tumors were successfully removed from pregnant subjects without the interruption of gestation. One of these women, a secundipara, had gone two weeks over time, and had a large ovarian cyst, the pedicle of which had become twisted, the fluid in the cyst being sanguineous. May [d] describes an ovariotomy performed during pregnancy at Tottenham Hospital. The woman, aged twenty-two, was pale, diminutive in size, and showed an enormous abdomen (Fig. 12), which measured 50 inches in circumference at the umbilicus and 27 inches from the ensiform cartilage to the pubes. At the operation, 36 pints of brown fluid were drawn off. Delivery took place twelve hours after the operation, the mother recovering, but the child was lost. Galabin [e] had a case of ovariotomy performed on a woman in the sixth month of pregnancy without interruption of pregnancy; Potter [f] had a case of double ovariotomy with safe delivery at term; and Storry [g] had a similar case. Jacobson [h] cites a case of vaginal lithotomy in a patient six and a half months pregnant, with normal delivery at full term. Tiffany quotes Keelan's [i] description of a woman of thirty-five, in the eighth month of pregnancy, from whom he removed a stone weighing $12\frac{1}{2}$ ounces and measuring 2 by $2\frac{1}{2}$ inches, with subsequent recovery and continuation of pregnancy. Rydygier [j] mentions a case of obstruction of the intestine during the sixth month of gestation, showing symptoms of strangulation for seven days, in which he performed abdominal section. Recovery of the woman without abortion ensued. The Revue de Chirurgie, 1887, contains an account of a woman who suffered internal strangulation, on whom celiotomy was performed; she recovered in twenty-five days, and did not miscarry, which shows that severe injury to the intestine with operative interference does not necessarily interrupt pregnancy. Gilmore, [k] without inducing abortion, extirpated the kidney of a negress, aged

Fig. 12.—Ovariotomy during pregnancy. (May, British Med. Jour., Dec. 2, 1893.)

a 653, 1892.　　　　b 261, 1894.　　　　c Occidental Med. Times, Aug., 1892.
d 224, Dec. 2, 1893.　　e 224, 1880.　　　　f 125, 1888.　　　g 476, 1882.
h 476, 1889, i., 628.　　i 224, Oct. 15, 1887.　　j 844, 250.　　　k 125, May, 1871.

thirty-three, for severe and constant pain. Tiffany [a] removed the kidney of a woman of twenty-seven, five months pregnant, without interruption of this or subsequent pregnancies. The child was living. He says that Fancon cites instances of operation without abortion.

Lovort [b] describes an enucleation of the eye in the second month of pregnancy. Pilcher [c] cites the instance of a woman of fifty-eight, eight months in her fourth pregnancy, whose breast and axilla he removed without interruption of pregnancy. Robson,[d] Polaillon, and Coen report similar instances.

Rein speaks of the removal of an enormous echinococcus cyst of the omentum without interruption of pregnancy. Robson [e] reports a multilocular cyst of the ovary with extensive adhesions of the uterus, removed at the tenth week of pregnancy and ovariotomy performed without any interruption of the ordinary course of labor. Russell [f] cites the instance of a woman who was successfully tapped at the sixth month of pregnancy.

McLean [g] speaks of a successful amputation during pregnancy ; Napper, [778] one of the arm ; Nicod, one of the arm ; Russell,[h] an amputation through the shoulder joint for an injury during pregnancy, with delivery and recovery ; and Vesey [i] speaks of amputation for compound fracture of the arm, labor following ten hours afterward with recovery. Keen [j] reports the successful performance of a hip-joint amputation for malignant disease of the femur during pregnancy. The patient, who was five months advanced in gestation, recovered without aborting.

Robson reports a case of strangulated hernia in the third month of pregnancy with stercoraceous vomiting. He performed herniotomy in the femoral region, and there was a safe delivery at full term. In the second month of pregnancy he also rotated an ovarian tumor causing acute symptoms, and afterward performed ovariotomy without interfering with pregnancy. Mann quotes Mundé in speaking of an instance of removal of elephantiasis of the vulva without interrupting pregnancy, and says that there are many cases of the removal of venereal warts without any interference with gestation. Campbell of Georgia operated inadvertently at the second and third month in two cases of vesicovaginal fistula in pregnant women. The first case showed no interruption of pregnancy, but in the second case the woman nearly died and the fistula remained unhealed. Engelmann operated on a large rectovaginal fistula in the sixth month of pregnancy without any interruption of pregnancy, which is far from the general result. Cazin and Rey both produced abortion by forcible dilatation of the anus for fissure, but Gayet used both the fingers and a speculum in a case at five months and the woman went to term. By cystotomy Reamy removed a double hair-pin

a 533, April 16, 1887.   b 238, 1887.   c 648, 1879.   d 224, 1889.
e 224, 1879.   f 535, 127, n. s. ii., 430–433.   g 582, 1852.
h 476, 1872, ii., 632.   i 224, 1878.   j 533, March 26, 1892.

from a woman pregnant six and a half months, without interruption, and according to Mann again, McClintock extracted stones from the bladder by the urethra in the fourth month of pregnancy, and Phillips did the same in the seventh month. Hendenberg and Packard [a] report the removal of a tumor weighing $8\frac{3}{4}$ pounds from a pregnant uterus without interrupting gestation.

The following extract from the University Medical Magazine of Philadelphia illustrates the **after-effects of abdominal hysteropaxy on subsequent pregnancies :—**

" Fraipont (*Annales de la Société Médico-Chirurgicale de Liège*, 1894) reports four cases where pregnancy and labor were practically normal, though the uterus of each patient had been fixed to the abdominal walls. In two of the cases the hysteropexy had been performed over five years before the pregnancy occurred, and, although the bands of adhesion between the fundus and the parietes must have become very tough after so long a period, no special difficulty was encountered. In two of the cases the forceps was used, but not on account of uterine inertia ; the fetal head was voluminous, and in one of the two cases internal rotation was delayed. The placenta was always expelled easily, and no serious postpartum hemorrhage occurred. Fraipont observed the progress of pregnancy in several of these cases. The uterus does not increase specially in its posterior part, but quite uniformly, so that, as might be expected, the fundus gradually detaches itself from the abdominal wall. Even if the adhesions were not broken down they would of necessity be so stretched as to be useless for their original purpose after delivery. Bands of adhesion could not share in the process of involution. As, however, the uterus undergoes perfect involution, it is restored to its original condition before the onset of the disease which rendered hysteropexy necessary."

The coexistence of an extensive tumor of the uterus with pregnancy does not necessarily mean that the product of conception will be blighted. Brochin [b] speaks of a case in which pregnancy was complicated with fibroma of the uterus, the accouchement being natural at term. Byrne [c] mentions a case of pregnancy complicated with a large uterine fibroid. Delivery was effected at full term, and although there was considerable hemorrhage the mother recovered. Ingleby [d] describes a case of fibrous tumor of the uterus terminating fatally, but not until three weeks after delivery. Lusk [e] mentions a case of pregnancy with fibrocystic tumor of the uterus occluding the cervix. At the appearance of symptoms of eclampsia version was performed and delivery effected, followed by postpartum hemorrhage. The mother died from peritonitis and collapse, but the stillborn child was resuscitated. Roberts [f] reports a case of pregnancy associated with a large fibrocellular polypus

a 590, 1890, xxv., 306.   b 363, xlviii., 1178.   c 310, 1877, 170.
d 318, li., 75.   e 125, 1876, ix., 94.   f 476, 1867, i., 333.

of the uterus. A living child was delivered at the seventh month, écrasement was performed, and the mother recovered.

Von Quast [a] speaks of a fibromyoma removed five days after labor. Gervis [b] reports the removal of a large polypus of the uterus on the fifth day after confinement. Davis [c] describes the spontaneous expulsion of a large polypus two days after the delivery of a fine, healthy, male child. Deason [d] mentions a case of anomalous tumor of the uterus during pregnancy which was expelled after the birth of the child; and Daly also [e] speaks of a tumor expelled from the uterus after delivery. Cathell [f] speaks of a case of pregnancy complicated with both uterine fibroids and measles. Other

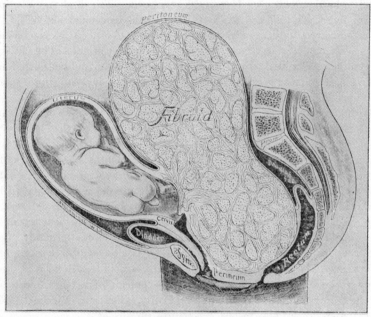

Fig. 13.—Large fibroid blocking the pelvis (Spiegelberg).

cases of a similar nature to the foregoing are too numerous to mention. Figure 13, taken from Spiegelberg, shows a large fibroid blocking the pelvis of a pregnant woman.

There are several peculiar accidents and anomalies not previously mentioned which deserve a place here, viz., those of the membranes surrounding the fetus. Brown [g] speaks of **protrusion of the membranes from the vulva several weeks before confinement.** Davies [h] relates an instance in which there was a copious watery discharge during pregnancy not followed

a Kansas City Med. Index, 1888.   b 778, xi., 4.   c 124, 1843, vi., 519.
d 593, 1859, xvi., 663.   e 778, 1887, xxviii., 170.   f 775, 1886, 157.
g 616, 1872, xv., 246.   h 537, 1834.

by labor. There is a case mentioned [a] in which an accident and an inopportune dose of ergot at the fifth month of pregnancy were followed by rupture of the amniotic sac, and subsequently a constant flow of watery fluid continued for the remaining three months of pregnancy. The fetus died at the time, and was born in an advanced state of putrefaction, by version, three months after the accident. The mother died five months after of carcinoma of the uterus. Montgomery [b] reports the instance of a woman who menstruated last on May 22, 1850, and quickened on September 26th, and continued well until the 11th of November. At this time, as she was retiring, she became conscious that there was a watery discharge from the vagina, which proved to be liquor amnii. Her health was good. The discharge continued, her size increased, and the motions of the child continued active. On the 18th of January a full-sized eight months' child was born. It had an incessant, wailing, low cry, always of evil augury in new-born infants. The child died shortly after. The daily discharge was about 5 ounces, and had lasted sixty-eight days, making 21 pints in all. The same accident of rupture of the membranes long before labor happened to the patient's mother.

Bardt [c] speaks of labor twenty-three days after the flow of the waters; and Cobleigh [d] one of seventeen days; Bradley [e] relates the history of a case of rupture of the membranes six weeks before delivery. Rains [f] cites an instance in which gestation continued three months after rupture of the membranes, the labor-pains lasting thirty-six hours. Griffiths [523] speaks of rupture of the amniotic sac at about the sixth month of pregnancy with no untoward interruption of the completion of gestation and with delivery of a living child. There is another observation [g] of an accouchement terminating successfully twenty-three days after the loss of the amniotic fluid. Campbell [h] mentions delivery of a living child twelve days after rupture of the membranes. Chesney [i] relates the history of a double collection of waters. Wood [j] reports a case in which there was expulsion of a bag of waters before the rupture of the membranes. Bailly, Chestnut, Bjering, Cowger, Duncan, and others also record premature rupture of the membranes without interruption of pregnancy.

Harris [k] gives an instance of the membranes being expelled from the uterus a few days before delivery at the full term. Chatard, Jr., [l] mentions extrusion of the fetal membranes at the seventh month of pregnancy while the patient was taking a long afternoon walk, their subsequent retraction, and normal labor at term. Thurston [m] tells of a case in which Nature had apparently effected the separation of the placenta without alarming hemorrhage, the case being one of placenta prævia, terminating favorably by natural pro-

a 366, 1844–45, v., 163.   b 308, 1857.   c 463, xiii., 33.   d 545, 1877, xxxvii.
e 224, 1871, ii., 612.   f 131, 1875, iii., 253.   g 461, 1807, xiii., 33.   h 218, lxxxvii., 196.
i 481, 1868–69, ii., 346.   j Month. Jour. Med. Sci., Lond. and Edinb., ix., 853.
k 778, vii., 47.   l 125, 1886.   m 224, 1884.

cesses. Playfair[a] speaks of the detachment of the uterine decidua without the interruption of pregnancy.

Guerrant[b] gives a unique example of normal birth at full term in which the placenta was found in the vagina, but not a vestige of the membranes was noticed. The patient had experienced nothing unusual until within three months of expected confinement, since which time there had been a daily loss of water from the uterus. She recovered and was doing her work. There was no possibility that this was a case of retained secundines.

Anomalies of the Umbilical Cord.—Absence of the membranes has its counterpart in the deficiency of the umbilical cord, so frequently noticed in old reports. The Ephemerides, Osiander, Stark's Archives,[160] Thiebault, van der Wiel, Chatton, and Schurig[726] all speak of it, and it has been noticed since. Danthez[c] speaks of the development of a fetus in spite of the absence of an umbilical cord. Stute[d] reports an observation of total absence of the umbilical cord, with placental insertion near the cervix of the uterus.

There is mentioned[e] a bifid funis. The Ephemerides[f] and van der Wiel speak of a duplex funis. Nolde[g] reports a cord 38 inches long; and Werner[h] cites the instance of a funis 51 inches long. There are modern instances in which the funis has been bifid or duplex, and there is also a case reported in which there were two cords in a twin pregnancy, each of them measuring five feet in length. The Lancet[i] gives the account of a most peculiar pregnancy consisting of a placenta alone, the fetus wanting. What this "placenta" was will always be a matter of conjecture.

Occasionally death of the fetus is caused by the formation of knots in the cord, shutting off the fetal circulation; Géry, Grieve, Mastin, Passot, Piogey, Woets, and others report instances of this nature. Newman[j] reports a curious case of twins, in which the cord of one child was encircled by a knot on the cord of the other. Among others, Latimer[k] and Motte[l] report instances of the accidental tying of the bowel with the funis, causing an artificial anus.

The diverse **causes of abortion** are too numerous to attempt giving them all, but some are so curious and anomalous that they deserve mention. Epidemics of abortion are spoken of by Fickius, Fischer, and the Ephemerides. Exposure to cold is spoken of as a cause,[m] and the same is alluded to by the Ephemerides;[n] while another case is given as due to exposure while nude.[o] There are several cases among the older writers in which odors are said to have produced abortion, but as analogues are not to be found in modern literature, unless the odor is very poisonous or pungent, we can give them but little credence. The Ephemerides gives the

a 610, 1879–80.   b 609, 1879–80, ii., 480.   c 368, 1842.   d 363, xxix., 498.
e Solingen,[742]   f 104, dec. i., ann. i., obs. 39.   g 160, vii., 197.   h 160, vii., 523.
i 476, 1842–43.   j 318, 1858, iv., 8–10.   k 545, xlvi., 242.   l 242, liv., 494.
m 108, dec. i., ann. ii., 121.   n 104, dec. ii., ann. i., obs. 116.   o 664, T. iv.

odor of urine as provocative of abortion ; Sulzberger,[a] Meyer,[567] and Albertus [113] all mention odors ; and Vesti gives as a plausible cause [b] the odor of carbonic vapor. The Ephemerides [c] mentions singultus as a cause of abortion. Mauriceau,[513] Pelargus, and Valentini [793] mention coughing. Hippocrates mentions [d] the case of a woman who induced abortion by calling excessively loud to some one. Fabricius Hildanus [334] speaks of abortion following a kick in the region of the coccyx. Gullmannus [e] speaks of an abortion which he attributes to the woman's constant neglect to answer the calls of nature, the rectum being at all times in a state of irritation from her negligence. Hawley [f] mentions abortion at the fourth or fifth month due to the absorption of spirits of turpentine. Solingen [742] speaks of abortion produced by sneezing. Osiander [135] cites an instance in which a woman suddenly arose, and in doing so jolted herself so severely that she produced abortion. Hippocrates speaks of extreme hunger as a cause of abortion. Treuner [g] speaks of great anger and wrath in a woman disturbing her to the extent of producing abortion.

The causes that are observed every day, such as tight lacing, excessive venery, fright, and emotions, are too well known to be discussed here.

There has been reported a recent case of abortion following a viper-bite, and analogues may be found in the writings of Severinus and Oedman, who mention viper-bites as the cause ; but there are so many associate conditions accompanying a snake-bite, such as fright, treatment, etc., any one of which could be a cause in itself, that this is by no means a reliable explanation. Information from India on this subject would be quite valuable.

The Ephemerides speak of bloodless abortion, and there have been modern instances in which the hemorrhage has been hardly noticeable.

Abortion in a twin pregnancy does not necessarily mean the abortion or death of both the products of conception. Chapman [h] speaks of the case of the expulsion of a blighted fetus at the seventh month, the living child remaining to the full term, and being safely delivered, the placenta following. Crisp [i] says of a case of labor that the head of the child was obstructed by a round body, the nature of which he was for some time unable to determine. He managed to push the obstructing body up and delivered a living, full-term child ; this was soon followed by a blighted fetus, which was 11 inches long, weighed 12 ounces, with a placenta attached weighing $6\frac{1}{2}$ ounces. It is quite common for a blighted fetus to be retained and expelled at term with a living child, its twin.

Bacon [j] speaks of twin pregnancy, with the death of one fetus at the fourth month and the other delivered at term. Beall [k] reports the conception of twins,

a Diss. de abortu, c. 6.   b Diss. de abortu, 21.   c 476, dec. ii., ann. 2, obs. 62.
d 416, opp. iv., 600.   e 105, 1730, ii., 374.   f 231, 1858–59, xiv , 469.
g 160, B. iv., 527.   h 550, ix., 194.   i 779, xviii., 272.
j Clinique, Chicago, vii., 403.   k 703, xviii., 122.

with one fetus expelled and the other retained; Beauchamp cites a similar instance. Bothwell [a] describes a twin labor at term, in which one child was living and the other dead at the fifth month and macerated. Belt [b] reports an analogous case. Jameson [c] gives the history of an extraordinary case of twins in which one (dead) child was retained in the womb for forty-nine weeks, the other having been born alive at the expiration of nine months. Hamilton [d] describes a case of twins in which one fetus died from the effects of an injury between the fourth and fifth months and the second arrived at full period. Moore [e] cites an instance in which one of the fetuses perished about the third month, but was not expelled until the seventh, and the other was carried to full term. Wilson [f] speaks of a secondary or blighted fetus of the third month with fatty degeneration of the membranes retained and expelled with its living twin at the eighth month of uterogestation.

There was a case at Riga in 1839 of a robust girl who conceived in February, and in consequence her menses ceased. In June she aborted, but, to her dismay, soon afterward the symptoms of advanced pregnancy appeared, and in November a full-grown child, doubtless the result of the same impregnation as the fetus, was expelled at the fourth month. In 1860 Schuh reported an instance before the Vienna Faculty of Medicine in which a fetus was discharged at the third month of pregnancy and the other twin retained until full term. The abortion was attended with much metrorrhagia, and ten weeks afterward the movements of the other child could be plainly felt and pregnancy continued its course uninterrupted. Bates [g] mentions a twin pregnancy in which an abortion took place at the second month and was followed by a natural birth at full term. Hawkins [h] gives a case of miscarriage, followed by a natural birth at full term; and Newnham [i] cites a similar instance in which there was a miscarriage at the seventh month and a birth at full term.

Worms in the Uterus.—Haines [j] speaks of a most curious case—that of a woman who had had a miscarriage three days previous; she suffered intense pain and a fetid discharge. A number of maggots were seen in the vagina, and the next day a mass about the size of an orange came away from the uterus, riddled with holes, and which contained a number of dead maggots, killed by the carbolic acid injection given soon after the miscarriage. The fact seems inexplicable, but after their expulsion the symptoms immediately ameliorated. This case recalls a somewhat similar one given by the older writers, in which a fetus was eaten by a worm.[k] Analogous are those cases spoken of by Bidel [l] of lumbricoides found in the uterus; by Hole,[m] in which maggots were found in the vagina and uterus; and Simpson,[n] in which the

a 224, 1889, ii., 717.   b 124, 1855, xxix.   c 310, 1842–43, xxii., 15.

d 312, 1843.   e 519, 1870, iv., 208.   f Month. Jour. Med., Lond., 1855.

g 771, 1874.   h 772, 1881.   i 776, 1823.

j 476, 1889, i., 16.   k 104, dec. iii., ann. 7 and 8, obs. 32.

l 235, 1856, li., 549.   m 543, 1889–90.   n 600, 1878–79, 129.

abortion was caused by worms in the womb—if the associate symptoms were trustworthy.

We can find fabulous parallels to all of these in some of the older writings. Paré [a] mentions Lycosthenes' account of a woman in Cracovia in 1494 who bore a dead child which had attached to its back a live serpent, which had gnawed it to death. He gives an illustration (Fig. 14) showing the serpent in situ. He also quotes the case of a woman who conceived by a mariner, and who, after nine months, was delivered by a midwife of a shapeless mass, followed by an animal with a long neck, blazing eyes, and clawed feet. Ballantyne [b] says that in the writings of Hippocrates there is in the work on "Diseases" ($Περὶ νούσων$), which is not usually regarded as genuine, a some-

Fig. 14.—Serpent in a fetus (after Paré).

what curious statement with regard to worms in the fetus. It is affirmed that flat worms develop in the unborn infant, and the reason given is that the feces are expelled so soon after birth that there would not be sufficient time during extrauterine life for the formation of creatures of such a size. The same remark applies to round worms. The proof of these statements is to be found in the fact that many infants expel both these varieties of parasites with the first stool. It is difficult to know what to make of these opinions ; for, with the exception of certain cases in some of the seventeenth and eighteenth century writers, there are no records in medicine of the occurrence of vermes in the infant at birth. It is possible that other things, such as dried pieces of mucus, may have been erroneously regarded as worms.

a 618, 733.   b 759, Oct., 1895.

CHAPTER III.

OBSTETRIC ANOMALIES.

General Considerations.—In discussing obstetric anomalies we shall first consider those strange instances in which stages of parturition are unconscious and for some curious reason the pains of labor absent. Some women are anatomically constituted in a manner favorable to child-birth, and pass through the experience in a comparatively easy manner; but to the great majority the throes of labor are anticipated with extreme dread, particularly by the victims of the present fashion of tight lacing.

It seems strange that a physiologic process like parturition should be attended by so much pain and difficulty. Savages in their primitive and natural state seem to have difficulty in many cases, and even animals are not free from it. We read of the ancient wild Irish women breaking the pubic bones of their female children shortly after birth, and by some means preventing union subsequently, in order that these might have less trouble in child-birth—as it were, a modified and early form of symphysiotomy. In consequence of this custom the females of this race, to quote an old English authority, had a " waddling, lamish gesture in their going." These old writers said that for the same reason the women in some parts of Italy broke the coccyxes of their female children. This report is very likely not veracious, because this bone spontaneously repairs itself so quickly and easily. Rodet and Engelmann,[325] in their most extensive and interesting papers on the modes of accouchement among the primitive peoples, substantiate the fear, pain, and difficulty with which labor is attended, even in the lowest grades of society.

In view of the usual occurrence of pain and difficulty with labor, it seems natural that exceptions to the general rule should in all ages have attracted the attention of medical men, and that literature should be replete with such instances. Pechlin[622] and Maas[a] record instances of **painless births.** The Ephemerides records a birth as having occurred during asphyxia, and also one during an epileptic attack. Storck also speaks of birth during unconsciousness in an epileptic attack; and Haen[395] and others[b] describe cases occurring during the coma attending apoplectic attacks. King[c] reports the histories of two married women, fond mothers and anticipating the event, who gave birth to children, apparently unconsciously. In

[a] 601, 315.   [b] 708, 1719, ii., 610.   [c] 546, 1847, xvi., 234.

the first case, the appearance of the woman verified the assertion ; in the second, a transient suspension of the menstrual influence accounted for it. After some months epilepsy developed in this case.　Crawford [a] speaks of a Mrs. D., who gave birth to twins in her first confinement at full term, and who two years after aborted at three months.　In December, 1868, a year after the abortion, she was delivered of a healthy, living fetus of about five or six months' growth in the following manner : While at stool, she discovered something of a shining, bluish appearance protruding through the external labia, but she also found that when she lay down the tumor disappeared. This tumor proved to be the child, which had been expelled from the uterus four days before, with the waters and membranes intact, but which had not been recognized ; it had passed through the os without pain or symptoms, and had remained alive in the vagina over four days, from whence it was delivered, presenting by the foot.

The state of **intoxication** seems by record of several cases to render birth painless and unconscious, as well as serving as a means of anesthesia in the preanesthetic days.

The feasibility of practising **hypnotism in child-birth** has been discussed, and Fanton [b] reports 12 cases of parturition under the hypnotic influence.　He says that none of the subjects suffered any pain or were aware of the birth, and offers the suggestion that to facilitate the state of hypnosis it should be commenced before strong uterine contractions have occurred.

Instances of parturition or **delivery during sleep, lethargies, trances,** and similar conditions are by no means uncommon.　Heister [c] speaks of birth during a convulsive somnolence, and Osiander [d] of a case during sleep.　Montgomery relates the case of a lady, the mother of several children, who on one occasion was unconsciously delivered in sleep.　Case [e] relates the instance of a French woman residing in the town of Hopedale, who, though near confinement, attributed her symptoms to over-fatigue on the previous day.　When summoned, the doctor found that she had severe lumbar pains, and that the os was dilated to the size of a half-dollar.　At ten o'clock he suggested that everyone retire, and directed that if anything of import occurred he should be called.　About 4 A. M. the husband of the girl, in great fright, summoned the physician, saying :　" Monsieur le Médecin, il y a quelque chose entre les jambes de ma femme," and, to Dr. Case's surprise, he found the head of a child wholly expelled during a profound sleep of the mother.　In twenty minutes the secundines followed.　The patient, who was only twenty years old, said that she had dreamt that something was the matter with her, and awoke with a fright, at which instant, most probably, the head was expelled. She was afterward confined with the usual labor-pains.

Palfrey [f] speaks of a woman, pregnant at term, who fell into a sleep about

a 579, 1868–69, n. s., iv., 305–8.　　　　b 168, 1890.　　　　c 402, xii., 103.
d 135, ii., 74.　　　　　　　　　　　　　e 124, Jan., 1868.　　　f 476, 1864, i., 36.

eleven o'clock, and dreamed that she was in great pain and in labor, and that sometime after a fine child was crawling over the bed. After sleeping for about four hours she awoke and noticed a discharge from the vagina. Her husband started for a light, but before he obtained it a child was born by a head-presentation. In a few minutes the labor-pains returned and the feet of a second child presented, and the child was expelled in three pains, followed in ten minutes by the placenta. Here is an authentic case in which labor progressed to the second stage during sleep.

Weill [a] describes the case of a woman of twenty-three who gave birth to a robust boy on the 16th of June, 1877, and suckled him eleven months. This birth lasted one hour. She became pregnant again and was delivered under the following circumstances : She had been walking on the evening of September 5th and returned home about eleven o'clock to sleep. About 3 A. M. she awoke, feeling the necessity of passing urine. She arose and seated herself for the purpose. She at once uttered a cry and called her husband, telling him that a child was born and entreating him to send for a physician. Weill saw the woman in about ten minutes and she was in the same position, so he ordered her to be carried to bed. On examining the urinal he found a female child weighing 10 pounds. He tied the cord and cared for the child. The woman exhibited little hemorrhage and made a complete recovery. She had apparently slept soundly through the uterine contractions until the final strong pain, which awoke her, and which she imagined was a call for urination.

Samelson [b] says that in 1844 he was sent for in Zabelsdorf, some 30 miles from Berlin, to attend Hannah Rhode in a case of labor. She had passed easily through eight parturitions. At about ten o'clock in the morning, after a partially unconscious night, there was a sudden gush of blood and water from the vagina ; she screamed and lapsed into an unconscious condition. At 10.35 the face presented, soon followed by the body, after which came a great flow of blood, welling out in several waves. The child was a male, middle-sized, and was some little time in making himself heard. Only by degrees did the woman's consciousness return. She felt weary and inclined to sleep, but soon after she awoke and was much surprised to know what had happened. She had seven or eight pains in all. Schultze [c] speaks of a woman who, arriving at the period for delivery, went into an extraordinary state of somnolence, and in this condition on the third day bore a living male child.

Berthier in 1859 observed a case of melancholia with delirium which continued through pregnancy. The woman was apparently unconscious of her condition and was delivered without pain. Cripps [d] mentions a case in which there was absence of pain in parturition. Depaul [e] mentions a woman who fell in a public street and was delivered of a living child during a

a Quoted, 224, 1881, ii., 871. b 224, 1865, ii., Nov.
c 476, 1845, i.   d 476, 1841–42, ii., 367.   e J. d. sages-femmes, Par., 1882, 9.

syncope which lasted four hours. Epley [a] reports painless labor in a patient with paraplegia. Fahnestock [b] speaks of the case of a woman who was delivered of a son while in a state of artificial somnambulism, without pain to herself or injury to the child. Among others mentioning painless or unconscious labor are Behrens (during profound sleep), Eger, Tempel, Panis, Agnoia, Blanckmeister, Whitehill, Gillette, Mattei, Murray, Lemoine, and Möglichkeit.

Rapid Parturition Without Usual Symptoms.—Births unattended by symptoms that are the usual precursors of labor often lead to speedy deliveries in awkward places. According to Willoughby,[824] in Darby, February 9, 1667, a poor fool, Mary Baker, while wandering in an open, windy, and cold place, was delivered by the sole assistance of Nature, Eve's midwife, and freed of her afterbirth. The poor idiot had leaned against a wall, and dropped the child on the cold boards, where it lay for more than a quarter of an hour with its funis separated from the placenta. She was only discovered by the cries of the infant. In "Carpenter's Physiology"[c] is described a remarkable case of instinct in an idiotic girl in Paris, who had been seduced by some miscreant; the girl had gnawed the funis in two, in the same manner as is practised by the lower animals. From her mental imbecility it can hardly be imagined that she had any idea of the object of this separation, and it must have been instinct that impelled her to do it. Sermon[733] says the wife of Thomas James was delivered of a lusty child while in a wood by herself. She put the child in an apron with some oak leaves, marched stoutly to her husband's uncle's house a half mile distant, and after two hours' rest went on her journey one mile farther to her own house; despite all her exertions she returned the next day to thank her uncle for the two hours' accommodation. There is related [d] the history of a case of a woman who was delivered of a child on a mountain during a hurricane, who took off her gown and wrapped the child up in it, together with the afterbirth, and walked two miles to her cottage, the funis being unruptured.

Harvey relates a case, which he learned from the President of Munster, Ireland, of a woman with child who followed her husband, a soldier in the army, in daily march. They were forced to a halt by reason of a river, and the woman, feeling the pains of labor approaching, retired to a thicket, and there alone brought forth twins. She carried them to the river, washed them herself, did them up in a cloth, tied them to her back, and that very day marched, barefooted, 12 miles with the soldiers, and was none the worse for her experience. The next day the Deputy of Ireland and the President of Munster, affected by the story, to repeat the words of Harvey, " did both vouchsafe to be godfathers of the infants."

Willoughby [824] relates the account of a woman who, having a cramp while in bed with her sister, went to an outhouse, as if to stool, and was there delivered of a child. She quickly returned to bed, her going and her return

a 597, xxxvii., 233.   b 218, xxxv., 194.   c 1st edition, 219.   d 279, 1857.

not being noticed by her sleeping sister. She buried the child, " and afterward confessed her wickedness, and was executed in the Stafford Gaol, March 31, 1670." A similar instance is related by the same author of a servant in Darby in 1647. Nobody suspected her, and when delivered she was lying in the same room with her mistress. She arose without awakening anyone, and took the recently delivered child to a remote place, and hid it at the bottom of a feather tub, covering it with feathers; she returned without any suspicion on the part of her mistress. It so happened that it was the habit of the Darby soldiers to peep in at night where they saw a light, to ascertain if everything was all right, and they thus discovered her secret doings, which led to her trial at the next sessions at Darby.

Wagner[a] relates the history of a case of great medicolegal interest. An unmarried servant, who was pregnant, persisted in denying it, and took every pains to conceal it. She slept in a room with two other maids, and, on examination, she stated that on the night in question she got up toward morning, thinking to relieve her bowels. For this purpose she secured a wooden tub in the room, and as she was sitting down the child passed rapidly into the empty vessel. It was only then that she became aware of the nature of her pains. She did not examine the child closely, but was certain it neither moved nor cried. The funis was no doubt torn, and she made an attempt to tie it. Regarding the event as a miscarriage, she took up the tub with its contents and carried it to a sand pit about 30 paces distant, and threw the child in a hole in the sand that she found already made. She covered it up with sand and packed it firmly so that the dogs could not get it. She returned to her bedroom, first calling up the man-servant at the stable. She awakened her fellow-servants, and feeling tired sat down on a stool. Seeing the blood on the floor, they asked her if she had made way with the child. She said : " Do you take me for an old sow ? " But, having their suspicions aroused, they traced the blood spots to the sand pit. Fetching a spade, they dug up the child, which was about one foot below the surface. On the access of air, following the removal of the sand and turf, the child began to cry, and was immediately taken up and carried to its mother, who washed it and laid it on her bed and soon gave it the breast. The child was healthy with the exception of a club-foot, and must have been under ground at least fifteen minutes and no air could have reached it. It seems likely that the child was born asphyxiated and was buried in this state, and only began to assume independent vitality when for the second time exposed to the air. This curious case was verified to English correspondents by Dr. Wagner, and is of unquestionable authority ; it became the subject of a thorough criminal investigation in Germany.

During the funeral procession of Marshal MacMahon in Paris an enormous crowd was assembled to see the cortege pass, and in this crowd was a

a 554, Jan. 17, 1838.

woman almost at the time of delivery ; the jostling which she received in her endeavors to obtain a place of vantage was sufficient to excite contraction, and, in an upright position, she gave birth to a fetus, which fell at her feet. The crowd pushed back and made way for the ambulance officials, and mother and child were carried off, the mother apparently experiencing little embarrassment. Quoted by Taylor,[757] Anderson speaks of a woman accused of child murder, who walked a distance of 28 miles on a single day with her two-days-old child on her back.

There is also a case of a female servant [a] named Jane May, who was frequently charged by her mistress with pregnancy but persistently denied it. On October 26th she was sent to market with some poultry. Returning home, she asked the boy who drove her to stop and allow her to get out. She went into a recess in a hedge. In five minutes she was seen to leave the hedge and follow the cart, walking home, a distance of a mile and a half. The following day she went to work as usual, and would not have been found out had not a boy, hearing feeble cries from the recess of the hedge, summoned a passer-by, but too late to save the child. At her trial she said she did not see her babe breathe nor cry, and she thought by the sudden birth that it must have been a still-born child.

Shortt [b] says that one day, while crossing the esplanade at Villaire, between seven and eight o'clock in the morning, he perceived three Hindoo women with large baskets of cakes of " bratties " on their heads, coming from a village about four miles distant. Suddenly one of the women stood still for a minute, stooped, and to his surprise dropped a fully developed male child to the ground. One of her companions ran into the town, about 100 yards distant, for a knife to divide the cord. A few of the female passers-by formed a screen about the mother with their clothes, and the cord was divided. The after-birth came away, and the woman was removed to the town. It was afterward discovered that she was the mother of two children, was twenty-eight years old, had not the slightest sign of approaching labor, and was not aware of parturition until she actually felt the child between her thighs.

Smith of Madras, in 1862, says he was hastily summoned to see an English lady who had borne a child without the slightest warning. He found the child, which had been born ten minutes, lying close to the mother's body, with the funis uncut. The native female maid, at the lady's orders, had left the child untouched, lifting the bed-clothes to give it air. The lady said that she arose at 5.30 feeling well, and during the forenoon had walked down a long flight of steps across a walk to a small summer-house within the enclosure of her grounds. Feeling a little tired, she had lain down on her bed, and soon experienced a slight discomfort, and was under the impression that something solid and warm was lying in contact with her person. She directed the servant to look below the bed-clothes, and then a female child was discovered.

[a] 548, 1867, i., 500.   [b] 778, 1863.

Her other labors had extended over six hours, and were preceded by all the signs distinctive of childbirth, which fact attaches additional interest to the case. The ultimate fate of the child is not mentioned. Smith quotes Wilson, who said he was called to see a woman who was delivered without pain while walking about the house. He found the child on the floor with its umbilical cord torn across.

Langston [a] mentions the case of a woman, twenty-three, who, between 4 and 5 A. M., felt griping pains in the abdomen. Knowing her condition, she suspected labor, and determined to go to a friend's house where she could be confined in safety. She had a distance of about 600 yards to go, and when she was about half way she was delivered in an upright position of a child, which fell on the pavement and ruptured its funis in the fall. Shortly after, the placenta was expelled, and she proceeded on her journey, carrying the child in her arms. At 5.50 the physician saw the woman in bed, looking well and free from pain, but complaining of being cold. The child, which was her first, was healthy, well nourished, and normal, with the exception of a slight ecchymosis of the parietal bone on the left side. The funis was lacerated transversely four inches from the umbilicus. Both mother and child progressed favorably. Doubtless the intense cold had so contracted the blood-vessels as to prevent fatal hemorrhage to mother and child. This case has a legal bearing in the supposition that the child had been killed in the fall.

There is reported [b] the case of a woman in Wales, who, while walking with her husband, was suddenly seized with pains, and would have been delivered by the wayside but for the timely help of Madame Patti, the celebrated diva, who was driving by, and who took the woman in her carriage to her palatial residence close by. It was to be christened in a few days with an appropriate name in remembrance of the occasion. Coleman [c] met an instance in a married woman, who without the slightest warning was delivered of a child while standing near a window in her bedroom. The child fell to the floor and ruptured the cord about one inch from the umbilicus, but with speedy attention the happiest results were attained. Twitchell [d] has an example in the case of a young woman of seventeen, who was suddenly delivered of a child while ironing some clothes. The cord in this case was also ruptured, but the child sustained no injury. Taylor [757] quotes the description of a child who died from an injury to the head caused by dropping from the mother at an unexpected time, while she was in the erect position; he also speaks of a parallel case on record.

Unusual Places of Birth.—Besides those mentioned, the other awkward positions in which a child may be born are so numerous and diversified that mention of only a few can be made here. Colton [e] tells of a painless labor in an Irish girl of twenty-three, who felt a desire to urinate, and while seated on

a 476, 1864, i., 637. b 548, 1887, ii., 157. c 476, 1864, ii., 377.
d 476, 1864, 476. e 520, 1879, i., 68.

the chamber dropped a child. She never felt a labor-pain, and twelve days afterward rode 20 miles over a rough road to go to her baby's funeral. Leonhard [a] describes the case of a mother of thirty-seven, who had borne six children alive, who was pregnant for the tenth time, and who had miscalculated her pregnancy. During pregnancy she had an attack of small-pox and suffered all through pregnancy with constipation. She had taken a laxative, and when returning to bed from stool was surprised to find herself attached to the stool by a band. The child in the vessel began to cry and was separated from the woman, who returned to bed and suddenly died one-half hour later. The mother was entirely unconscious of the delivery. Westphal [b] mentions a delivery in a water-closet.

Brown [c] speaks of a woman of twenty-six who had a call of nature while in bed, and while sitting up she gave birth to a fine, full-grown child, which, falling on the floor, ruptured the funis. She took her child, lay down with it for some time, and feeling easier, hailed a cab, drove to a hospital with the child in her arms, and wanted to walk upstairs. She was put to bed and delivered of the placenta, there being but little hemorrhage from the cord; both she and her child made speedy recoveries. Thebault [d] reports an instance of delivery in the erect position, with rupture of the funis at the placenta. There was recently a rumor, probably a newspaper fabrication, that a woman while at stool in a railway car gave birth to a child which was found alive on the track afterward.

There is a curious instance on record in which a child was born in a hip-bath and narrowly escaped drowning.[e] The mother was a European woman aged forty, who had borne two children, the last nine years before. She was supposed to have dropsy of the abdomen, and among other treatments was the use of a speculum and caustic applications for inflammation of the womb. The escape of watery fluid for two days was considered evidence of the rupture of an ovarian cyst. At the end of two days, severe pains set in, and a warm hip-bath and an opiate were ordered. While in the bath she bore a fully-matured, living, male child, to the great surprise of herself and her friends. The child might have been drowned had not assistance been close at hand.

Birth by the Rectum.—In some cases in which there is some obstacle to the delivery of a child by the natural passages, the efforts of nature to expel the product of conception lead to an anomalous exit. There are some details of births by the rectum mentioned in the last century by Reta and others. Payne [f] cites the instance of a woman of thirty-three, in labor thirty-six hours, in whom there was a congenital absence of the vaginal orifice. The finger, gliding along the perineum, arrived at a distended anus, just inside of which was felt a fetal head. He anesthetized the patient and delivered the

a 554, No. 24, 1837.   b 807, xxi., 329.   c 224, April 3, 1863.
d 809, 1875, ii., 230.   e 548, 1862, ii., 396.   f 491, 1886, 542.

child with forceps, and without perineal rupture. There was little hemorrhage, and the placenta was removed with slight difficulty. Five months later, Payne found an unaltered condition of the perineum and vicinity ; there was absence òf the vaginal orifice, and, on introducing the finger along the anterior wall of the rectum, a fistula was found, communicating with the vagina ; above this point the arrangement and the situation of the parts were normal. The woman had given birth to three still-born children, and always menstruated easily. Coitus always seemed satisfactory, and no suspicion existed in the patient's mind, and had never been suggested to her, of her abnormality.

Harrison[a] saw a fetus delivered by the anus after rupture of the uterus ; the membranes came away by the same route. In this case the neck of the uterus was cartilaginous and firmly adherent to the adjacent parts. In seven days after the accouchement the woman had completely regained her health. Vallisneri[796] reports the instance of a woman who possessed two uteruses, one communicating with the vagina, the other with the rectum. She had permitted rectal copulation and had become impregnated in this manner. Louis, the celebrated French surgeon, created a furore by a pamphlet entitled "De partium externarum generationi inservientium in mulieribus naturali vitiosa et morbosa dispositione, etc.," for which he was punished by the Sorbonne, but absolved by the Pope. He described a young lady who had no vaginal opening, but who regularly menstruated by the rectum. She allowed her lover to have connection with her in the only possible way, by the rectum, which, however, sufficed for impregnation, and at term she bore by the rectum a well-formed child. Hunter[b] speaks of a case of pregnancy in a woman with a double vagina, who was delivered at the seventh month by the rectum. Mekeln[c] and Andrews[d] give instances of parturition through the anus. Morisani[e] describes a case of extrauterine pregnancy with tubal rupture and discharge into the culdesac, in which there was delivery by the rectum. After an attack of severe abdominal pain, followed by hemorrhage, the woman experienced an urgent desire to empty the rectum. The fetal movements ceased, and a recurrence of these symptoms led the patient to go to stool, at which she passed blood and a seromucoid fluid. She attempted manually to remove the offending substances from the rectum, and in consequence grasped the leg of a fetus. She was removed to a hospital, where a fetus nine inches long was removed from the rectum. The rectal opening gradually cicatrized, the sac became obliterated, and the woman left the hospital well.

Birth Through Perineal Perforation.—Occasionally there is perineal perforation during labor, with birth of the child through the opening. Brown[f] mentions a case of rupture of the perineum with birth of a child between the vaginal opening and the anus. Cassidy[g] reports a case of child-birth through the perineum. A successful operation was performed fifteen days after the

a Reportorio Med.-Chirurg. di Torino, 1825.   b Trans. N. Y. Obs. Soc., 1879, i., 348.
c 372, 1833, 184.   d 526, 1839.   e 838, 1889.   f 476, 1860, i., 496.   g 545, ix., 192.

accident. Dupuytren[a] speaks of the passage of an infant through a central opening of the perineum. Capuron, Gravis, and Lebrun all report accouchement through a perineal perforation, without alteration in the sphincter ani or the fourchet. In his " Diseases of Women " Simpson speaks of a fistula left by the passage of an infant through the perineum. Wilson, Toloshinoff, Stolz, Argles, Demarquay, Harley, Hernu, Martyn, Lamb, Morère, Pollock, and others record the birth of children through perineal perforations.

Birth Through the Abdominal Wall.—Hollerius[421] gives a very peculiar instance in which the abdominal walls gave way from the pressure exerted by the fetus, and the uterus ruptured, allowing the child to be extracted by the hand from the umbilicus ; the mother made a speedy recovery. In such cases delivery is usually by means of operative interference (which will be spoken of later), but rarely, as here, spontaneously. Farquharson[b] and Ill[c] both mention rupture of the abdominal parietes during labor.

There have been cases reported in which the recto-vaginal septum has been ruptured, as well as the perineum and the sphincter ani, giving all the appearance of a birth by the anus.

There is an account[d] of a female who had a tumor projecting between the vagina and rectum, which was incised through the intestine, and proved to be a dead child. Saviard[713] reported what he considered a rather unique case, in which the uterus was ruptured by external violence, the fetus being thrown forward into the abdomen and afterward extracted from an umbilical abscess.

Birth of the Fetus Enclosed in the Membranes.—Harvey[404] says that an infant can rest in its membranes several hours after birth without loss of life. Schurig[726] eventrated a pregnant bitch and her puppies lived in their membranes half an hour. Wrisberg cites three observations of infants born closed in their membranes ; one lived seven minutes ; the other two nine minutes ; all breathed when the membranes were cut and air admitted. Willoughby[824] recorded the history of a case which attracted much comment at the time. It was the birth of twins enclosed in their secundines. The sac was opened and, together with the afterbirth, was laid over some hot coals ; there was, however, a happy issue, the children recovering and living. Since Willoughby's time several cases of similar interest have been noticed, one in a woman[e] of forty, who had been married sixteen years, and who had had several pregnancies in her early married life and a recent abortion. Her last pregnancy lasted about twenty-eight or twenty-nine weeks, and terminated, after a short labor, by the expulsion of the ovum entire. The membranes had not been ruptured, and still enclosed the fetus and the liquor amnii. On breaking them, the fetus was seen floating on the waters, alive, and, though very diminutive, was perfectly formed. It continued to live, and a day afterward took the breast and began to cry feebly. At six weeks it weighed 2 pounds 2 ounces, and at ten months, 12 pounds, but was still very weak and ill-nour-

a 368, 1832, iii., 684.   b 524, 1789.   c 600, 1878-9, xli., 43.   d 470, 1722.   e 492, 1828.

ished. Evans [a] has an instance of a fetus expelled enveloped in its membranes entire and unruptured. The membranes were opaque and preternaturally thickened, and were opened with a pair of scissors; strenuous efforts were made to save the child, but to no purpose. The mother, after a short convalescence, made a good recovery. Forman [b] reports an instance of unruptured membranes at birth, the delivery following a single pain, in a woman of twenty-two, pregnant for a second time. Woodson [c] speaks of a case of twins, one of which was born enveloped in its secundines.

Van Bibber [d] was called in great haste to see a patient in labor. He reached the house in about fifteen minutes, and was told by the midwife, a woman of experience, that she had summoned him because of the expulsion from the womb of something the like of which she had never seen before. She thought it must have been some variety of false conception, and had wrapped it up in some flannel. It proved to be a fetus enclosed in its sac, with the placenta, all having been expelled together and intact. He told the nurse to rupture the membranes, and the child, which had been in the unruptured sac for over twenty minutes, began to cry. The infant lived for over a month, but eventually died of bronchitis.

Cowger [e] reports labor at the end of the seventh month without rupture of the fetal sac. Macknus [f] and Rootes [g] speak of expulsion of the entire ovum at the full period of gestation. Roe mentions a case of parturition with unruptured membrane. Slusser [h] describes the delivery of a full-grown fetus without rupture of the membrane.

"Dry Births."—The reverse of the foregoing are those cases in which, by reason of the deficiency of the waters, the birth is dry. Numerous causes can be stated for such occurrences, and the reader is referred elsewhere for them, the subject being an old one. The Ephemerides speaks of it, and Rudolph [695] discusses its occurrence exhaustively and tells of the difficulties of such a labor. Burrall [i] mentions a case of labor without apparent liquor amnii, delivery being effected by the forceps. Strong [j] records an unusual obstetric case in which there was prolongation of the pregnancy, with a large child, and entire absence of liquor amnii. The case was also complicated with interstitial and subserous fibroids and a contracted pelvis, combined with a posterior position of the occiput and nonrotation of the head. Lente [k] mentions a case of labor without liquor amnii; and Townsend [l] records delivery without any sanguineous discharge. Cosentino [m] mentions a case of the absence of liquor amnii associated with a fetal monstrosity.

Delivery After Death of the Mother.—Curious indeed are those

a 252, 1852-3, i., 146.   b 538, 1896, Feb. 1, 160.   c 124, 1860, 569.
d 510, 1879, iv., 303.   e 538, xxv., 84.   f 476, 1846, i., 186.
g 476, 1845, ii., 474.   h West. Lancet, Cincin., xii., 501.   i 124, cxl., 446.
j 218, cx., 30.   k 124, clxi., 125.   l 124, 1854, 342.
m Arch. di Ostet. e Ginec., p. 41, Feb.-March, 1894.

anomalous cases in which the delivery is effected spontaneously after the death of the mother, or when, by manipulation, the child is saved after the maternal decease. Wegelin [a] gives the account of a birth in which version was performed after death and the child successfully delivered. Bartholinus, Wolff, Schenck, Horstius, Hagendorn, Fabricius Hildanus, Valerius, Rolfinck, Cornarius, Boener, and other older writers cite cases of this kind. Pinard [b] gives a most wonderful case. The patient was a woman of thirty-eight who had experienced five previous normal labors. On October 27th she fancied she had labor pains and went to the Lariboisière Maternité, where, after a careful examination, three fetal poles were elicited, and she was told, to her surprise, of the probability of triplets. At 6 P. M., November 13th, the pains of labor commenced. Three hours later she was having great dyspnea with each pain. This soon assumed a fatal aspect and the midwife attempted to resuscitate the patient by artificial respiration, but failed in her efforts, and then she turned her attention to the fetuses, and, one by one, she extracted them in the short space of five minutes ; the last one was born twelve minutes after the mother's death. They all lived (the first two being females), and they weighed from $4\frac{1}{4}$ to $6\frac{1}{2}$ pounds.

Considerable attention has been directed to the advisability of accelerated and forced labor in the dying, in order that the child may be saved. Belluzzi has presented several papers on this subject. Csurgay of Budapest mentions saving the child by forced labor in the death agonies of the mother. Devilliers [c] considers this question from both the obstetric and medicolegal points of view. Hyneaux mentions forcible accouchement practised on both the dead and the dying. Rogowicz advocates artificial delivery by the natural channel in place of Cesarian section in cases of pending or recent death, and Thévenot [d] discussed this question at length at the International Medico-Legal Congress in 1878. Duer [e] presented the question of postmortem delivery in this country.

Kelly [f] reports the history of a woman of forty who died in her eighth pregnancy, and who was delivered of a female child by version and artificial means. Artificial respiration was successfully practised on the child, although fifteen minutes had elapsed from the death of the mother to its extraction. Driver [g] relates the history of a woman of thirty-five, who died in the eighth month of gestation, and who was delivered postmortem by the vagina, manual means only being used. The operator was about to perform Cesarean section when he heard the noise of the membranes rupturing. Thornton [h] reports the extraction of a living child by version after the death of the mother. Aveling [i] has compiled extensive statistics on all varieties of postmortem deliveries, collecting 44 cases of spontaneous expulsion of the fetus after death of the mother.

[a] 160, B. i., 4 St., n. 7.   [b] 140, Jan., 1889.   [c] 789, 1862, 581.
[d] 140, 1878.   [e] 125, xii., 1 and 374.   [f] 125, viii., 558.
[g] 579, 1860, 494.   [h] 272, 1858.   [i] 778, 1873, xiv., 240.

Aveling states that in 1820 the Council of Cologne sanctioned the placing of a gag in the mouth of a dead pregnant woman, thereby hoping to prevent suffocation of the infant, and there are numerous such laws on record, although most of them pertain to the performance of Cesarean section immediately after death.

Reiss records the death of a woman who was hastily buried while her husband was away, and on his return he ordered exhumation of her body, and on opening the coffin a child's cry was heard. The infant had evidently been born postmortem. It lived long afterward under the name of " Fils de la terre." Willoughby[824] mentions the curious instance in which rumbling was heard from the coffin of a woman during her hasty burial. One of her neighbors returned to the grave, applied her ear to the ground, and was sure she heard a sighing noise. A soldier with her affirmed her tale, and together they went to a clergyman and a justice, begging that the grave be opened. When the coffin was opened it was found that a child had been born, which had descended to her knees. In Derbyshire, to this day, may be seen on the parish register : " April ye 20, 1650, was buried Emme, the wife of Thomas Toplace, who was found delivered of a child after she had lain two hours in the grave."

Johannes Matthaeus relates the case of a buried woman, and that some time afterward a noise was heard in the tomb. The coffin was immediately opened, and a living female child rolled to the feet of the corpse. Hagendorn mentions the birth of a living child some hours after the death of the mother. Dethardingius mentions a healthy child born one-half hour after the mother's death. In the Gentleman's Magazine [a] there is a record of an instance, in 1759, in which a midwife, after the death of a woman whom she had failed to deliver, imagined that she saw a movement under the shroud, and found a child between its mother's legs. It died soon after. Valerius Maximus says that while the body of the mother of Gorgia Epirotas was being carried to the grave, a loud noise was heard to come from the coffin, and on examination a live child was found between the thighs,—whence arose the proverb : " Gorgiam prius ad funus elatum, quam natum fuisse."

Other cases of postmortem delivery are less successful, the delivery being delayed too late for the child to be viable. The first of Aveling's cases was that of a pregnant woman who was hanged by a Spanish Inquisitor in 1551. While still hanging, four hours later, two children were said to have dropped from her womb. The second case was of a woman of Madrid, who after death was shut in a sepulcher. Some months after, when the tomb was opened, a dead infant was found by the side of the corpse. Rolfinkius tells of a woman who died during parturition, and her body being placed in a cellar, five days later a dead boy and girl were found on the bier. Bartholinus is accredited with the following : Three midwives failing to deliver a woman,

[a] xxix., 390.

she died, and forty-eight hours after death her abdomen swelled to such an extent as to burst her grave-clothes, and a male child, dead, was seen issuing from the vagina. Bonet[216] tells of a woman, who died in Brussels in 1633, who, undelivered, expired in convulsions on Thursday. On Friday abdominal movements in the corpse were seen, and on Sunday a dead child was found hanging between the thighs. According to Aveling, Herman of Berne reports the instance of a young lady whose body was far advanced in putrefaction, from which was expelled an unbroken ovum containing twins. Even the placenta showed signs of decomposition. Naumann relates the birth of a child on the second day after the death of the mother. Richter of Weissenfels, in 1861, reported the case of a woman who died in convulsions, and sixty hours after death an eight months' fetus came away. Stapedius writes to a friend of a fetus being found dead between the thighs of a woman who expired suddenly of an acute disease. Schenk mentions that of a woman, dying at 5 p. m., a child having two front teeth was born at 3 a. m. Veslingius tells of a woman dying of epilepsy on June 6, 1630, from whose body, two days later, issued a child. Wolfius relates the case of a woman dying in labor in 1677. Abdominal movements being seen six hours after death, Cesarean section was suggested, but its performance was delayed, and eighteen hours after a child was spontaneously born. Hoyer of Mulhausen tells of a child with its mouth open and tongue protruding, which was born while the mother was on the way to the grave. Bedford of Sydney, according to Aveling, relates the story of a case in which malpractice was suspected on a woman of thirty-seven, who died while pregnant with her seventh child. The body was exhumed, and a transverse rupture of the womb six inches long above the cervix was found, and the body of a dead male child lay between the thighs. In 1862, Lanigan tells of a woman who was laid out for funeral obsequies, and on removal of the covers for burial a child was found in bed with her. Swayne is credited with the description of the death of a woman whom a midwife failed to deliver. Desiring an inquest, the coroner had the body exhumed, when, on opening the coffin, a well-developed male infant was found parallel to and lying on the lower limbs, the cord and placenta being entirely unattached from the mother.

Some time after her decease Harvey found between the thighs of a dead woman a dead infant which had been expelled postmortem. Mayer[a] relates the history of a case of a woman of forty-five who felt the movement of her child for the fourth time in the middle of November. In the following March she had hemoptysis, and serious symptoms of inflammation in the right lung following, led to her apparent death on the 31st of the month. For two days previous to her death she had failed to perceive the fetal movements. She was kept on her back in a room, covered up and undisturbed, for thirty-six hours, the members of the family occasionally visiting her to sprinkle holy

a 801, 1854.

water on her face. There was no remembrance of cadaveric distortion of the features or any odor. When the undertakers were drawing the shroud on they noticed a half-round, bright-red, smooth-looking body between the genitals which they mistook for a prolapsed uterus. Early on April 2d, a few hours before interment, the men thought to examine the swelling they had seen the day before. A second look showed it to be a dead female child, now lying between the thighs and connected with the mother by the umbilical cord. The interment was stopped, and Mayer was called to examine the body, but with negative results, though the signs of death were not plainly visible for a woman dead fifty-eight hours. By its development the body of the fetus confirmed the mother's account of a pregnancy of twenty-one weeks. Mayer satisfies himself at least that the mother was in a trance at the time of delivery and died soon afterward.

Moritz [a] gives the instance of a woman dying in pregnancy, undelivered, who happened to be disinterred several days after burial. The body was in an advanced state of decomposition, and a fetus was found in the coffin. It was supposed that the pressure of gas in the mother's body had forced the fetus from the uterus. Ostmann [b] speaks of a woman married five months, who was suddenly seized with rigors, headache, and vomiting. For a week she continued to do her daily work, and in addition was ill-treated by her husband. She died suddenly without having any abdominal pain or any symptoms indicative of abortion. The body was examined twenty-four hours after death and was seen to be dark, discolored, and the abdomen distended. There was no sanguineous discharge from the genitals, but at the time of raising the body to place it in the coffin, a fetus, with the umbilical cord, escaped from the vagina. There seemed to have been a rapid putrefaction in this case, generating enough pressure of gas to expel the fetus as well as the uterus from the body. This at least is the view taken by Hoffman and others in the solution of these strange cases.

Antepartum Crying of the Child.—There are on record fabulous cases of children crying in the uterus during pregnancy, and all sorts of unbelievable stories have been constructed from these reported occurrences. Quite possible, however, and worthy of belief are the cases in which the child has been heard to cry during the progress of parturition—that is, during delivery. Jonston [c] speaks of infants crying in the womb, and attempts a scientific explanation of the fact. He also quotes the following lines in reference to this subject :—

> " Mirandum fœtus materna clausus in alvo
> Dicitur insuetos ore dedisse sonos.
> Causa subest ; doluit se angusta sede teneri,
> Et cupiit magnæ cernere moliis opus.
> Aut quia quærendi studio vis fessa parentum
> Aucupii aptas innuit esse manus."

a Quoted by 124, cvi., 117.   b 807, Band 28, 228.   c 447, 464.

The Ephemerides [a] gives examples of the child hiccoughing in the uterus. Cases of crying before delivery, some in the vagina, some just before the complete expulsion of the head from the os uteri, are very numerous in the older writers ; and it is quite possible that on auscultation of the pregnant abdomen fetal sounds may have been exaggerated into cries. Bartholinus,[b] Borellus, [c] Boyle, Buchner, Paullini, Mezger, Riolanus, Lentillus, Marcellus Donatus, [d] and Wolff [e] all speak of children crying before delivery ; and Mazinus [f] relates the instance of a puppy whose feeble cries could be heard before expulsion from the bitch. Osiander fully discusses the subject of infants crying during parturition.

McLean [g] describes a case in which he positively states that a child cried lustily in utero during application of the forceps. He compared the sound as though from a voice in the cellar. This child was in the uterus, not in the vagina, and continued the crying during the whole of the five minutes occupied by delivery.

Cesarean Section.—Although the legendary history of Cesarean section is quite copious, it is very seldom that we find authentic records in the writings of the older medical observers. The works of Hippocrates, Aretæus, Galen, Celsus, and Aetius contain nothing relative to records of successful Cesarean sections. However, Pliny says that Scipio Africanus was the first and Manlius the second of the Romans who owed their lives to the operation of Cesarean section ; in his seventh book he says that Julius Cæsar was born in this way, the fact giving origin to his name. Others deny this and say that his name came from the thick head of hair which he possessed. It is a frequent subject in old Roman sculpture, and there are many delineations of the birth of Bacchus by Cesarean section from the corpse of Semele. Greek mythology tells us of the birth of Bacchus in the following manner : After Zeus burnt the house of Semele, daughter of Cadmus, he sent Hermes in great haste with directions to take from the burnt body of the mother the fruit of seven months. This child, as we know, was Bacchus. Æsculapius, according to the legend of the Romans, had been excised from the belly of his dead mother, Corinis, who was already on the funeral pile, by his benefactor, Apollo ; and from this legend all products of Cesarean sections were regarded as sacred to Apollo, and were thought to have been endowed with sagacity and bravery.

Old records tell us that one of the kings of Navarre was delivered in this way, and we also have records of the birth of the celebrated Doge, Andreas Doria, by this method. Jane Seymour was supposed to have been delivered of Edward VI. by Cesarean section, the father, after the consultation of the physicians was announced to him, replying : "Save the child by all means, for I shall be able to get mothers enough." Robert II. of Scotland was sup-

---

[a] 104, dec. ii., ann. v., obs. 194, and obs. 15.   [b] 190, cent. i., hist. 18.

[c] Cent. iii., obs. 72.   [d] 306, L. vi., cap. ii., 620.

[e] Lect. memor., T. ii., 647, 666, 983.   [f] 514, T. iii., 8.   [g] 125, xxii., 166.

posed to have been delivered in this way after the death of his mother, Margery Bruce, who was killed by being thrown from a horse. Shakespere's immortal citation of Macduff, "who was from his mother's womb untimely ripped," must have been such a case, possibly crudely done, perchance by cattle-horn. Pope Gregory XIV. was said to have been taken from his mother's belly after her death. The Philosophical Transactions,[629] in the last century, contain accounts of Cesarean section performed by an ignorant butcher and also by a midwife; and there are many records of the celebrated case performed by Jacob Nüfer, a cattle gelder, at the beginning of the sixteenth century.

By the advent of antisepsis and the improvements of Porro and others, Cesarean section has come to be a quite frequent event, and a record of the successful cases would hardly be considered a matter of extraordinary interest, and would be out of the province of this work, but a citation of anomalous cases will be given. Baldwin[a] reports a case of Cesarean section on a typical rachitic dwarf of twenty-four, who weighed 100 pounds and was only $47\frac{1}{2}$ inches tall. It was the ninth American case, according to the calculation of Harris, only the third successful one, and the first successful one in Ohio. The woman had a uniformly contracted pelvis whose anteroposterior diameter was about $1\frac{1}{4}$ inches. The hygienic surroundings for the operation were not of the best, as the woman lived in a cellar. Tait's method of performing the operation was determined upon and successfully performed. Convalescence was prompt, and in three weeks the case was dismissed. The child was a female of $7\frac{1}{2}$ pounds which inherited the deformities of its mother. It thrived for nine and a half months, when it died of angina Ludovici. Figure 15 represents the mother and child.

Harris[124] gives an account of an operation upon a rachitic dwarf who was impregnated by a large man, a baby weighing 14 pounds and measuring 20 inches being delivered by the knife. St. Braun[b] gives the account of a Porro-Cesarean operation in the case of a rachitic dwarf 3 feet 10 inches tall, in which both the mother and child recovered. Mundé[c] speaks of twins being delivered by Cesarean section. Franklin[d] gives the instance of a woman delivered at full term of a living child by this means, in whom was also found a dead fetus. It lay behind the stump of the amputated cervix, in the culdesac of Douglas. The patient died of hemorrhage.

Croston[e] reports a case of Cesarean section on a primipara of twenty-four at full term, with the delivery of a double female monster weighing $12\frac{1}{2}$ pounds. This monster consisted of two females of about the same size, united from the sternal notch to the navel, having one cord and one placenta. It was stillborn. The diagnosis was made before operation by vaginal examination. In a communication to Croston, Harris remarked that this was the first suc-

a 533, Aug. 9, 1890, 138.   b 657, 1888 ; quoted by 124, 1890.
c 218, 1876, ci., 747.   d 224, 1894.   e 218, Dec. 21, 1893.

cessful Cesarean section for double monstrous conception in America, and added that in 1881 Collins and Leidy performed the same operation without success.

Instances of **repeated Cesarean section** were quite numerous, and the pride of the operators noteworthy, before the uterus was removed at the first operation, as is now generally done. Bacque [a] reports two sections in the same woman, and Bertrandi speaks of a case in which the operation was successfully executed many times in the same woman. Rosenberg [b] reports three cases repeated successfully by Leopold of Dresden. Skutsch reports a case in

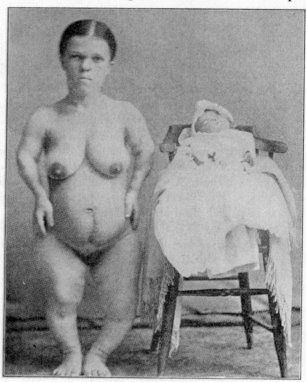

Fig. 15.—Cesarean operation on a dwarf (Baldwin).

which it was twice performed on a woman with a rachitic pelvis, and who the second time was pregnant with twins ; the children and mother recovered. Zweifel [c] cites an instance in which two Cesarean sections were performed on a patient, both of the children delivered being in vigorous health. Stolz [d] relates a similar case. Beck [e] gives an account of a Cesarean operation twice on the same woman ; in the first the child perished, but in the second it survived. Merinar [f] cites an instance of a woman thrice opened. Parravini [g] gives a

a 463, xi., 572.   b 125, 1891.   c 261, 1889, No. 13.   d 368, 1885, iii., 182
e 593, 1849-50, vi., 355.   f 264, 1856, xi., 172.   g 360, 1860, 273.

similar instance. Charlton [a] gives an account of the performance carried out successfully four times in the same woman; Chisholm [b] mentions a case in which it was twice performed. Michaelis of Kiel [c] gives an instance in which he performed the same operation on a woman four times, with successful issues to both mother and children, despite the presence of peritonitis the last time. He had operated in 1826, 1830, 1832, and 1836. Coe [d] and Gueniot [e] both mention cases in which Cesarean section had been twice performed with successful terminations as regards both mothers and children. Rosenberg [f] tabulates a number of similar cases from medical literature.

Cases of **Cesarean section by the patient herself** are most curious, but may be readily believed if there is any truth in the reports of the operation being done in savage tribes. Felkin [g] gives an account of a successful case performed in his presence, with preservation of the lives of both mother and child, by a native African in Kahura, Uganda Country (Fig. 16). The

Fig. 16.—Cesarean operation in Uganda.

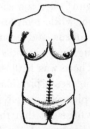

Fig. 17.—Suture of abdominal walls after Cesarean section in Africa.

Fig. 18.—Knife used in performing Cesarean section in Africa.

young girl was operated on in the crudest manner, the hemorrhage being checked by a hot iron. The sutures were made by means of seven thin, hot iron spikes, resembling acupressure-needles, closing the peritoneum and skin (Fig. 17). The wound healed in eleven days, and the mother made a complete recovery. Thomas Cowley [h] describes the case of a negro woman who, being unable to bear the pains of labor any longer, took a sharp knife and made a deep incision in her belly—deep enough to wound the buttocks of her child, and extracted the child, placenta and all. A negro horse-doctor was called, who sewed the wound up in a manner similar to the way dead bodies are closed at the present time.

a 318, 1837, xlvii., 417.   b 318, 1808, iv., 178.   c 628, Heft vii., viii., 1836.
d New York Polyclinic, Aug. 15, 1894.   e 789, July 5, 1894.
f 125, xxiv., No. 10, 1891.   g 318, April, 1884.   h Lond. Med. Jour., 1785, vi., 366.

Barker [a] gives the instance of a woman who, on being abused by her husband after a previous tedious labor, resolved to free herself of the child, and slyly made an incision five inches long on the left side of the abdomen with a weaver's knife. When Barker arrived the patient was literally drenched with blood and to all appearance dead. He extracted a dead child from the abdomen and bandaged the mother, who lived only forty hours. In his discourses on Tropical Diseases Moseley speaks of a young negress in Jamaica who opened her uterus and extracted therefrom a child which lived six days; the woman recovered. Barker relates another case [b] in Rensselaer County, N. Y., in which the incision was made with the razor, the woman likewise recovering. There is an interesting account [c] of a poor woman at Prischtina, near the Servian frontier, who, suffering greatly from the pains of labor, resolved to open her abdomen and uterus. She summoned a neighbor to sew up the incision after she had extracted the child, and at the time of report, several months later, both the mother and child were doing well.

Madigan [d] cites the case of a woman of thirty-four, in her seventh confinement, who, while temporarily insane, laid open her abdomen with a razor, incised the uterus, and brought out a male child. The abdominal wound was five inches long, and extended from one inch above the umbilicus straight downward. There was little or no bleeding and the uterus was firmly contracted. She did not see a physician for three hours. The child was found dead and, with the placenta, was lying by her side. The neighbors were so frightened by the awful sight that they ran away, or possibly the child might have been saved by ligature of the funis. Not until the arrival of the clergyman was anything done, and death ultimately ensued.

A most wonderful case of endurance of pain and heroism was one occurring in Italy,[e] which attracted much European comment at the time. A young woman, illegitimately pregnant, at full term, on March 28th, at dawn, opened her own abdomen on the left side with a common knife such as is generally used in kitchens. The wound measured five inches, and was directed obliquely outward and downward. She opened the uterus in the same direction, and endeavored to extract the fetus. To expedite the extraction, she drew out an arm and amputated it, and finding the extraction still difficult, she cut off the head and completely emptied the womb, including the placenta. She bound a tight bandage around her body and hid the fetus in a straw mattress. She then dressed herself and attended to her domestic duties. She afterward mounted a cart and went into the city of Viterbo, where she showed her sister a cloth bathed in blood as menstrual proof that she was not pregnant. On returning home, having walked five hours, she was seized with an attack of vomiting and fainted. The parents called Drs. Serpieri and Baliva, who relate the case. Thirteen hours had elapsed from the infliction of the wound,

a 597, 1830–1, i., 381.   b 599, ii., 40.   c Wien. med. Wochenschrift, 1880, No. 13.
d 476, 1884, i., 146.   e 359, May 2, 1886.

through which the bulk of the intestines had been protruding for the past six hours. The abdomen was irrigated, the toilet made, and after the eighteenth day the process of healing was well progressed, and the woman made a recovery after her plucky efforts to hide her shame.

Cases like the foregoing excite no more interest than those on record in which an **abdominal section** has been accidental, as, for instance, **by cattle-horns,** and the fetus born through the wound. Zuboldie [a] speaks of a case in which a fetus was born from the wound made by a bull's horn in the mother's abdomen. Deneux [294] describes a case in which the wound made by the horn was not sufficiently large to permit the child's escape, but it was subsequently brought through the opening. Pigné [b] speaks of a woman of thirty-eight, who in the eighth month of her sixth pregnancy was gored by a bull, the horn effecting a transverse wound 27 inches long, running from one anterior spine to the other. The woman was found cold and insensible and

Fig. 19.—Accouchement by a bull (after an engraving dated 1647).

with an imperceptible pulse. The small intestines were lying between the thighs and covered with coagulated blood. In the process of cleansing, a male child was expelled spontaneously through a rent in the uterus. The woman was treated with the usual precautions and was conscious at midday. In a month she was up. She lived twenty years without any inconvenience except that due to a slight hernia on the left side. The child died at the end of a fortnight.

In a very exhaustive article Harris of Philadelphia [c] has collected nearly all the remaining cases on record, and brief extracts from some of them will be given below. In Zaandam, Holland, 1647, a farmer's wife was tossed by a furious bull. Her abdomen was ripped open, and the child and membranes escaped. The child suffered no injuries except a bruised upper lip and lived nine months. The mother died within forty hours of her injuries. Figure

a 297, ii., n. 43.   b 162, July, 1836.   c 125, 1887, xx., 673.

19, taken from an engraving dated 1647, represents an accouchement by a mad bull, possibly the same case. In Dillenberg, Germany, in 1779, a multipara was gored by an ox at her sixth month of pregnancy ; the horn entered the right epigastric region, three inches from the linea alba, and perforated the uterus. The right arm of the fetus protruded ; the wound was enlarged and the fetus and placenta delivered. Thatcher [a] speaks of a woman who was gored by a cow in King's Park, and both mother and child were safely delivered and survived.

In the Parish of Zecoytia, Spain, in 1785, Marie Gratien was gored by an ox in the superior portion of her epigastrium, making a wound eight inches long which wounded the uterus in the same direction. Dr. Antonio di Zubeldia and Don Martin Monaco were called to take charge of the case. While they were preparing to effect delivery by the vagina, the woman, in an attack of singultus, ruptured the line of laceration and expelled the fetus, dead. On the twenty-first day the patient was doing well. The wound closed at the end of the sixteenth week. The woman subsequently enjoyed excellent health and, although she had a small ventral hernia, bore and nursed two children.

Marsh [b] cites the instance of a woman of forty-two, the mother of eight children, who when eight months pregnant was horned by a cow. Her clothes were not torn, but she felt that the child had slipped out, and she caught it in her dress. She was seen by some neighbors twelve yards from the place of accident, and was assisted to her house. The bowels protruded and the child was separated from the funis. A physician saw the woman three-quarters of an hour afterward and found her pulseless and thoroughly exhausted. There was considerable but not excessive loss of blood, and several feet of intestine protruded through the wound. The womb was partially inverted through the wound, and the placenta was still attached to the inverted portion. The wound in the uterus was Y-shaped. The mother died in one and a half hours from the reception of her injuries, but the child was uninjured.

Scott [c] mentions the instance of a woman thirty-four years old who was gored by an infuriated ox while in the ninth month of her eighth pregnancy. The horn entered at the anterior superior spinous process of the ilium, involving the parietes and the uterus. The child was extruded through the wound about half an hour after the occurrence of the accident. The cord was cut and the child survived and thrived, though the mother soon died. Stalpart [d] tells the almost incredible story of a soldier's wife who went to obtain water from a stream and was cut in two **by a cannonball** while stooping over. A passing soldier observed something to move in the water, which, on investigation, he found to be a living child in its membranes. It was christened by order of one Cordua and lived for some time after.

Postmortem Cesarean Section.—The possibility of delivering a child

[a] 319, July, 1850, 88.　　[b] 538, 1867.　　[c] 518, 1885, iii., 341.　　[d] Dissert. de Foet. Nutrit., 45.

by Cesarean section after the death of the mother has been known for a long time to the students of medicine. In the olden times there were laws making compulsory the opening of the dead bodies of pregnant women shortly after death. Numa Pompilius established the first law, which was called "lex regia," and in later times there were many such ordinances. A full description of these laws is on record.[302] Life was believed possible after a gestation of six months or over, and, as stated, some famous men were supposed to have been born in this manner. François de Civile, who on great occasions signed himself "trois fois enterré et trois fois par le grâce de Dieu, ressucité," saw the light of the world by a happy Cesarean operation on his exhumed mother. Fabricius Hildanus and Bourton report similar instances. Bourton cites among others the case of an infant who was found living twelve hours after the death of his mother. Dufour [a] and Mauriceau [513] are two older French medical writers who discuss this subject. Flajani [344] speaks of a case in which a child was delivered at the death of its mother, and some of the older Italian writers discuss the advisability of the operation in the moribund state before death actually ensues. Heister [411] writes of the delivery of the child after the death of the mother by opening the abdomen and uterus.

Harris [b] relates several interesting examples. In Peru in 1794 a Sambi woman was killed by lightning, and the next day the abdomen was opened by official command and a living child was extracted. The Princess von Swartzenberg, who was burned to death at a ball in Paris in 1810, was said to have had a living child removed from her body the next day. Like all similar instances, this was proved to be false, as her body was burned beyond the possibility of recognition, and, besides, she was only four months pregnant. Harris [b] mentions another case of a young woman who threw herself from the Pont Neuf into the Seine. Her body was recovered, and a surgeon who was present seized a knife from a butcher standing by and extracted a living child in the presence of the curious spectators. Campbell [248] discusses this subject most thoroughly, though he advances no new opinions upon it.

Duer tabulates the successful results of a number of cases of Cesarean section after death as follows :—

Children extracted between 1 and	5 minutes after death of the mother,	21
" " " 10 and 15	" " " " "	13
" " " 15 and 30	" " " " "	2
" " 1 hour	" " " "	2
" " 2 hours	" " " "	2

Garezky of St. Petersburg [c] collected reports of 379 cases of Cesarean section after death with the following results : 308 were extracted dead ; 37 showed signs of life ; 34 were born alive. Of the 34, only 5 lived for any length of time. He concludes that if extracted within five or six minutes after death, they may be born alive ; if from six to ten minutes, they may

[a] 462, T. xix., 263.   [b] 125, 1880, 141.   [c] Quoted by 545, Aug. 23, 1879.

still be born alive, though asphyxiated; if from ten to twenty-six minutes, they will be highly asphyxiated. In a great number of these cases the infant was asphyxiated or dead in one minute. Of course, if the death is sudden, as by apoplexy, accident, or suicide, the child's chances are better. These statistics seem conscientious and reliable, and we are safe in taking them as indicative of the usual result, which discountenances the old reports of death as taking place some time before extraction.

Peuch [a] is credited with statistics showing that in 453 operations 101 children gave signs of life, but only 45 survived.

During the Commune of Paris, Tarnier, one night at the Maternité, was called to an inmate who, while lying in bed near the end of pregnancy, had been killed by a ball which fractured the base of the skull and entered the brain. He removed the child by Cesarean section and it lived for several days. In another case a pregnant woman fell from a window for a distance of more than 30 feet, instant death resulting; thirty minutes at least after the death of the mother an infant was removed, which, after some difficulty, was resuscitated and lived for thirteen years. Tarnier states that delivery may take place three-quarters of an hour or even an hour after the death of the mother, and he also quotes an extraordinary case by Hubert of a successful Cesarean operation two hours after the mother's death; the woman, who was eight months pregnant, was instantly killed while crossing a railroad track. [b]

Hoffman [c] records the case of a successful Cesarean section done ten minutes after death. The patient was a woman of thirty-six, in her eighth month of pregnancy, who was suddenly seized with eclampsia, which terminated fatally in ten hours. Ten minutes after her last respiration the Cesarean section was performed and a living male child delivered. This infant was nourished with the aid of a spoon, but it died in twenty-five hours in consequence of its premature birth and enfeebled vitality.

Green [d] speaks of a woman, nine months pregnant, who was run over by a heavily laden stage-coach in the streets of Southwark. She died in about twenty minutes, and in about twenty minutes more a living child was extracted from her by Cesarean section. There was a similar case in the Hôpital St. Louis, in Paris, in 1829; but in this case the child was born alive five minutes after death. Squire [e] tells of a case in which the mother died of dilatation of the aorta, and in from twenty to thirty minutes the child was saved. In comment on this case Aveling is quoted as saying that he believed it possible to save a child one hour after the death of the mother. No less an authority than Playfair speaks of a case in which a child was born half an hour after the death of the mother. Beckman [f] relates the history of a woman who died suddenly in convulsions. The incision was made about five minutes after death, and a male child about four pounds in weight was

a 844, 644.   b 844, 645.   c 261, 1895, No. 50, 1319.

d 550, xii., 46–51.   e 476, 1877, ii., 89.   f 199, 1869.

extracted.   The child exhibited feeble heart-contractions and was despaired of.
Happily, after numerous and persistent means of resuscitation, applied for
about two and a half hours, regular respirations were established and the
child eventually recovered.   Walter [a] reports a successful instance of removal
of the child after the death of the mother from apoplexy.

Cleveland [b] gives an account of a woman of forty-seven which is of special
interest.   The mother had become impregnated five months after the cessation of menstruation, and a uterine sound had been used in ignorance of
the impregnation at this late period.   The mother died, and one hour later a
living child was extracted by Cesarean section.   There are two other recent
cases recorded of extraction after an hour had expired from the death.   One
is cited by Veronden [c] in which the extraction was two hours after death,
a living child resulting, and the other by Blatner [d] in which one hour had
elapsed after death, when the child was taken out alive.

Cases of **rupture of the uterus during pregnancy** from the pressure
of the contents and delivery of the fetus by some unnatural passage are
found in profusion through medical literature, and seem to have been of
special interest to the older observers.   Benivenius [e] saw a case in which the
uterus ruptured and the intestines protruded from the vulva.   An instance
similar to the one recorded by Benivenius is also found in the last century in
Germany.[742]   Bouillon [f] and Desbois, two French physicians of the last
century, both record examples of the uterus rupturing in the last stages of
pregnancy and the mother recovering.   Schreiber [g] gives an instance of rupture
of the uterus occasioned by the presence of a 13-pound fetus, and there is
recorded [h] the account of a rupture caused by a 20-pound fetus that made its
way into the abdomen.   We find old accounts of cases of rupture of the
uterus with birth by the umbilicus and the recovery of the woman.[i]   Vespré [j]
describes a case in which the uterus was ruptured by the feet of the fetus.

Farquharson [k] has an account of a singular case in midwifery in which the
abdomen ruptured from the pressure of the fetus; and quite recently Geo-
ghegan [l] illustrates the possibilities of uterine pressure in pregnancy by a postmortem examination after a fatal parturition, in which the stomach was found
pushed through the diaphragm and lying under the left clavicle.   Heywood
Smith[m] narrates the particulars of a case of premature labor at seven months
in which rupture of the uterus occurred and, notwithstanding the fact that
the case was complicated by placenta prævia, the patient recovered.

Rupture of the uterus and recovery does not necessarily prevent subsequent
successful pregnancy and delivery by the natural channels.   Whinery [n] relates

a 573, 1855, v., 179.   b 125, 1878, xi., 626–632.   c 780, 1876, iv., 7.
d 125, 1875, viii., 160.   e L. iv., obs. B., 13.
f Histoire de la Soc. Royale de Méd., Paris, 1776, 310.   g 160, iii., 235.
h Samml. Medic. Wahrnehmungen, 1 B., 363.   i 108, dec. i., viii., 90.
j 462, T. xlii., 84.   k 524, 1789.
l 465, 1881, 52.   m 476, 1875, ii., 911.   n 124, Oct., 1866.

an instance of a ruptured uterus in a healthy Irish woman of thirty-seven from whom a dead child was extracted by abdominal section and who was safely delivered of a healthy female child about one year afterward. Analogous to this case is that of Lawrence,[a] who details the instance of a woman who had been delivered five times of dead children ; she had a very narrow pelvis and labor was always induced at the eighth month to assure delivery. In her sixth pregnancy she had miscalculated her time, and, in consequence, her uterus ruptured in an unexpected parturition, but she recovered and had several subsequent pregnancies.

Occasionally there is a **spontaneous rupture of the vagina** during the process of parturition, the uterus remaining intact. Wiltshire reports such a case in a woman who had a most prominent sacrum ; the laceration was transverse and quite extensive, but the woman made a good recovery. Schauta pictures an exostosis on the promontory of the sacrum (Fig. 20). Blenkinsop[b] cites an instance in which the labor was neither protracted nor abnormally severe, yet the rupture of the vagina took place with the escape of the child

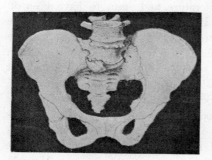

Fig. 20.—Knob-like exostosis on the promontory (Schauta).

into the abdomen of the mother, and was from thence extracted by Cesarean section. A peculiarity of this case was the easy expulsion from the uterus, no instrumental or other manual interference being attempted and the uterus remaining perfectly intact.

In some cases there is extensive **sloughing of the genitals after parturition** with recovery far beyond expectation. Gooch mentions a case in which the whole vagina sloughed, yet to his surprise the patient recovered. Aetius and Benivenius speak of recovery in such cases after loss of the whole uterus. Cazenave of Bordeaux[c] relates a most marvelous case in which a primipara suffered in labor from an impacted head. She was twenty-five, of very diminutive stature, and was in labor a long time. After labor, sloughing of the parts commenced and progressed to such an extent that in one month there were no traces of the labia, nymphæ, vagina, perineum, or anus. There was simply a large opening extending from the meatus urinarius to the coccyx. The rectovaginal septum, the lower portion of the rectum, and the neck of the bladder were obliterated. The woman survived, although she always experienced great difficulty in urination and in entirely emptying the rectum. A similar instance is reported[d] in a woman of thirty who was thirty-six hours in labor. The fundus of the uterus

a 224, 1885, 601.   b 656, No. xi., Dec. 2, 1841.
c 330, No. 84, Feb. 7, 1839.   d 124, Aug., 1838.

descended into the vagina and the whole uterine apparatus was removed. The lower part of the rectum depended between the labia ; in the presence of the physician the nurse drew this out and it separated at the sphincter ani. On examining the parts a single opening was seen, as in the preceding case, from the pubes to the coccyx. Some time afterward the end of the intestine descended several inches and hung loosely on the concave surface of the rectum. A sponge was introduced to support the rectum and prevent access of air. The destruction of the parts was so complete and the opening so large as to bring into view the whole inner surface of the pelvis, in spite of which, after prolonged suppuration, the wound cicatrized from behind forward and health returned, except as regards the inconvenience of feces and urine. Milk-secretion appeared late and lasted two months without influencing the other functions.

There are cases in which, through the ignorance of the midwife or the physician, **prolapsed pelvic organs** are mistaken for afterbirth and **extracted.** There have been instances in which the whole uterus and its appendages, not being recognized, have been dragged out. Walters[a] cites the instance of a woman of twenty-two, who was in her third confinement. The midwife in attendance, finding the afterbirth did not come away, pulled at the funis, which broke at its attachment. She then introduced her hand and tore away what proved to be the whole of the uterus, with the right ovary and fallopian tube, a portion of the round ligament, and the left tube and ovarian ligament attached to it. A large quantity of omentum protruded from the vulva and upper part of the vagina, and an enormous rent was left. Walters saw the woman twenty-one hours afterward, and ligated and severed the protruding omentum. On the twenty-eighth day, after a marvelous recovery, she was able to drive to the Royal Berkshire Hospital, a distance of five miles. At the time of report, two years and six months after the mutilation, she was in perfect health. Walters looked into the statistics of such cases and found 36 accidental removals of the uterus in the puerperium with 14 recoveries. All but three of these were without a doubt attended by previous inversion of the uterus.

A medical man was tried for manslaughter in 1878[b] because he made a similar mistake. He had delivered a woman by means of the forceps, and, after delivery, brought away what he thought a tumor. This " tumor " consisted of the uterus, with the placenta attached to the fundus, the funis, a portion of the lateral ligament, containing one ovary and about three inches of vagina. The uterus was not inverted. A horrible case, with similar results, happened in France, and was reported by Tardieu.[c] A brutal peasant, whose wife was pregnant, dragged out a fetus of seven months, together with the uterus and the whole intestinal canal, from within 50 cm. of the pylorus to within 8 cm. of the ileocecal valve. The woman was seen three-quarters of

a 476, 1884, ii., 779.   b 548, 1878, ii., 728.   c 141, xxxix., 157, 172.

an hour after the intestines had been found in the yard (where the brute had thrown them), still alive and reproaching her murderer. Hoffman [a] cites an instance in which a midwife, in her anxiety to extract the afterbirth, made traction on the cord, brought out the uterus, ovaries, and tubes, and tore the vulva and perineum as far as the anus.

Woodson [b] tells the story of a negress who was four months pregnant, and who, on being seized with severe uterine pains in a bath, succeeded in seizing the fetus and dragging it out, but inverting the uterus in the operation. There is a case recorded [c] of a girl of eighteen, near her labor, who, being driven from her house by her father, took refuge in a neighboring house, and soon felt the pains of child-birth. The accoucheur was summoned, pronounced them false pains, and went away. On his return he found the girl dying, with her uterus completely inverted and hanging between her legs. This unfortunate maiden had been delivered while standing upright, with her elbows on the back of a chair. The child suddenly escaped, bringing with it the uterus, but as the funis ruptured the child fell to the floor. Wagner pictures partial prolapse of the womb in labor (Fig. 21).

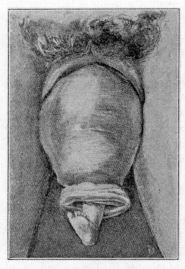

Fig. 21.—Partial prolapse of the womb in labor (Wagner).

It would too much extend this chapter to include the many **accidents incident to labor**, and only a few of especial interest will be given. Cases like rupture of an aneurysm during labor, extensive hemorrhage, the entrance of air into the uterine veins and sinuses, and common lacerations will be omitted, together with complicated births like those of double monsters, etc., but there are several other cases that deserve mention. Eldridge [d] gives an instance of separation of the symphysis pubis during labor,—a natural symphysiotomy. A separation of ¾ inch could be discerned at the symphysis, and in addition the sacroiliac synchondrosis was also quite movable. The woman had not been able to walk in the latter part of her pregnancy. The child weighed 10½ pounds and had a large head in a remarkably advanced stage of ossification, with the fontanelles nearly closed. Delivery was effected, though during the passage of the head the pubes separated to such an extent that Eldridge placed two fingers between them. The mother recovered, and had perfect union and normal locomotion.

[a] 807, 1865.   [b] 124, 1860.
[c] American System of Obstetrics, Hirst.   [d] 269, 1884, xlix., 495.

Sanders[a] reports a case of the separation of the pubic bones in labor. Studley[b] mentions a case of fracture of the pelvis during instrumental delivery. Humphreys[c] cites a most curious instance. The patient, it appears, had a large exostosis on the body of the pubes which, during parturition, was forced through the walls of the uterus and bladder, resulting in death. Kilian reports four cases of death from perforation of the uterus in this manner. Schauta pictures such an exostosis (Fig. 22).

Chandler[d] relates an instance in which there was laceration of the liver during parturition; and Hubbard[e] records a case of rupture of the spleen after labor.

Symphysiotomy is an operation consisting of division of the pubic symphysis in order to facilitate delivery in narrow pelves. This operation has undergone a most remarkable revival during the past two years. It originated in a suggestion by Pineau in his work on surgery in 1598,[f] and in 1665 was first performed by La Courvée upon a dead body in order to save the child, and afterward by Plenk, in 1766,[g] for the same purpose. In 1777 Sigault first proposed the operation on the living, and Ferrara was the one to carry out, practically, the proposition,—although Sigault is generally considered to be the first symphysiotomist, and the procedure is very generally known as the "Sigaultean operation." From Ferrara's time to 1858, when the operation had practically died out, it had been performed 85 times, with a recorded mortality of 33 per cent.

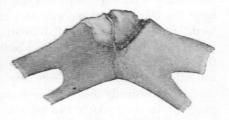

Fig. 22.—Exostosis on the symphysis (Schauta).

In 1866 the Italians, under the leadership of Morisani of Naples, revived the operation, and in twenty years had performed it 70 times with a mortality of 24 per cent. Owing to rigid antiseptic technic, the last 38 of these operations (1886 to 1891) showed a mortality of only $5\frac{1}{3}$ per cent., while the infant-mortality was only $10\frac{2}{3}$ per cent. The modern history of this operation is quite interesting, and is very completely reviewed by Hirst and Dorland.[h]

In November, 1893, Hirst reported 212 operations since 1887, with a maternal mortality of 12.73 per cent. and a fetal mortality of 28 per cent. In his later statistics Morisani gives 55 cases with 2 maternal deaths and 1 infantile death, while Zweifel[i] reports 14 cases from the Leipzig clinic with no maternal death and 2 fetal deaths, 1 from asphyxia and 1 from pneumonia, two days after birth. All the modern statistics are correspondingly encouraging.

a Trans. Amer. Instit. Homeopathy.   b 125, 1879, xii., 269.
c 531, 1857-8, iii., 322–326. d 218, xxxiii., 398. e 597, xxx., 75.
f 533, Jan. 12, 1895. g 843, 401. h 843, 401. i 261, No. 22, 1893.

Irwin reports a case in which the firm **attachment of the fetal head** to the uterine parietes rendered delivery without artificial aid impossible, and it was necessary to perform craniotomy. The right temporal region of the child adhered to the internal surface of the neck of the uterus, being connected by membranes. The woman was forty-four years old, and the child was her fourth.

Delay in the Birth of the Second Twin.—In twin pregnancies there is sometimes a delay of many days in the birth of a second child, even to such an extent as to give suspicion of superfetation. Pignot speaks of one twin two months before the other. De Bosch speaks of a delay of seventeen days; and there were 2 cases on record in France in the last century, [a] one of which was delayed ten days, and the other showed an interval of seven weeks between the delivery of the twins. There is an old case on record [b] in which there was an interval of six weeks between deliveries; Jansen [160] gives an account of three births in ten months; Pinart [c] mentions a case with an interval of ten days; Thilenius, one of thirteen days; and Ephemerides, one of one week. Wildberg[d] describes a case in which one twin was born two months after the other, and there was no secretion of milk until after the second birth. A full description of Wildberg's case is given in another journal [e] in brief, as follows: A woman, eighteen months married, was in labor in the eighth month of pregnancy. She gave birth to a child, which, though not fully matured, lived. There was no milk-secretion in her breasts, and she could distinctly feel the movements of another child; her abdomen increased in size. After two months she had another labor, and a fully developed and strong child was born, much heavier than the first. On the third day after, the breasts became enlarged, and she experienced considerable fever. It was noticeable in this case that a placenta was discharged a quarter of an hour after the first birth. Irvine [f] relates an instance of thirty-two days' delay; and Pfau[g] one of seven days'.

Carson [h] cites the instance of a noblewoman of forty, the mother of four children, who was taken ill about two weeks before confinement was expected, and was easily delivered of a male child, which seemed well formed, with perfect nails, but weakly. After the birth the mother never became healthy or natural in appearance. She was supposed to be dying of dropsy, but after forty-four days the mystery was cleared by the birth of a fine, well-grown, and healthy daughter. Both mother and child did well.

Addison [i] describes the case of a woman who was delivered of a healthy male child, and everything was well until the evening of the fourth day, when intense labor-pains set in, and well-formed twins about the size of a pigeon's egg were born. In this strange case, possibly an example of superfetation,

a 418, 1751, 107; and 418, 1752, 112.   b 160, iv. B., 771.   c 462, T. xl., 448.
d 611, April 5, 1845.   e 136, 1844, 3 Heft.   f 546, Dec. 28, 1844.
g 611, April 20, 1844.   h 224, 1880, i., 242.   i 476, 1886, i., 477.

the patient made a good recovery and the first child lived. A similar case is reported by Lumby [a] in which a woman was delivered on January 18th, by a midwife, of a full-grown and healthy female child. On the third day she came down-stairs and resumed her ordinary duties, which she continued until February 4th (seventeen days after). At this time she was delivered of twins, a boy and a girl, healthy and well-developed. The placenta was of the consistency of jelly and had to be scooped away with the hand. The mother and children did well. This woman was the mother of ten children besides the product of this conception, and at the latter occurrence had entire absence of pains and a very easy parturition.

Pincott [b] had a case with an interval of seven weeks between the births; Vale [c] 1 of two months; Bush [d] 1 of seventeen days; and Burke [e] 1 with an interval of two months. Douglas [f] cites an instance of twins being born four days apart. Bessems of Antwerp, in 1866, mentions a woman with a bicornate uterus who bore two twins at fifty-four days' interval.

a 224, 1878, i., 227.   b 224, 1886.   c 476, 1842.
d 535, 1825, 121.   e 582, 1855, 241.   f 538, xxvii., 196.

CHAPTER IV.

PROLIFICITY.

General Historic Observations.—Prolificity is a much discussed subject, for besides its medical and general interest it is of importance in social as well as in political economy. Superfluous population was a question that came to consciousness early; Aristotle spoke of legislation to prevent the increase of population and the physical and mental deterioration of the race,—he believed in a population fixed as regards numbers,—and later Lycurgus transformed these precepts into a terrible law. Strabonius reports that the inhabitants of Cathea brought their infants at the age of two months before a magistrate for inspection. The strong and promising were preserved and the weak destroyed. The founders of the Roman Empire followed a similar usage. With great indignation Seneca, Ovid, and Juvenal reproved this barbarity of the Romans. With the domination of Christianity this custom gradually diminished, and Constantine stopped it altogether, ordering succor to the people too poor to rear their own children. The old Celts were so jealous of their vigor that they placed their babes on a shield in the river, and regarded those that the waves respected as legitimate and worthy to become members of their clans. In many of the Oriental countries, where the population is often very excessive and poverty great, the girl babies of the lower classes were destroyed. At one time the crocodiles, held sacred in the Nile, were given the surplus infants. By destroying the females the breeding necessarily diminished, and the number of the weaker and dependent classes became less. In other countries persons having children beyond their ability to support were privileged to sell them to citizens, who contracted to raise them on condition that they became their slaves.

General Law, and the Influence of War.—In the increase of the world's population, although circumstances may for the time alter it, a general average of prolificity has, in the long run, been maintained. In the history of every nation artificial circumstances, such as fashion, war, poverty, etc., at some period have temporarily lowered the average of prolificity; but a further search finds another period, under opposite circumstances, which will more than compensate for it. The effect of a long-continued war or wars on generation and prolificity has never been given proper consideration. In such times marriages become much less frequent; the husbands are separated

144

from their wives for long periods ; many women are left widows ; the females become in excess of the males ; the excitement of the times overtops the desire for sexual intercourse, or, if there is the same desire, the unprolific prostitute furnishes the satisfaction ; and such facts as these, coupled with many similar ones, soon produce an astonishing effect upon the comparative birth-rate and death-rate of the country. The resources of a country, so far as concerns population, become less as the period of peace-disturbance is prolonged. Mayo-Smith[a] quotes von Mayr in the following example of the influence of the war of 1870–71 on the birth-rate in Bavaria,—the figures for births are thrown back nine months, so as to show the time of conception : Before the war under normal conception the number of births was about 16,000 per month. During the war it sank to about 2000 per month. Immediately on the cessation of hostilities it arose to its former number, while the actual return of the troops brought an increase of 2000 per month. The maximum was reached in March, 1872, when it was 18,450. The war of 1866 seems to have passed over Germany without any great influence, the birth-rate in 1865 being 39.2 ; in 1866, 39.4 ; in 1867, 38.3 ; in 1868, 38.4. On the other hand, while the birth-rate in 1870 was 40.1, in 1871 it was only 35.9 ; in 1872 it recovered to 41.1, and remained above 41 down to 1878. Von Mayr believes the war had a depressing influence upon the rate apart from the mere absence of the men, as shown in the fact that immediately upon the cessation of hostilities it recovered in Bavaria, although it was several months before the return of the troops.

Mayo-Smith, in remarking on the influence of war on the marriage-rate, says that in 1866 the Prussian rate fell from 18.2 to 15.6, while the Austrian rate fell from 15.5 to 13.0. In the war of 1870–71 the Prussian rate fell from 17.9 in 1869 to 14.9 in 1870 and 15.9 in 1871 ; but in the two years after peace was made it rose to 20.6 and 20.2, the highest rates ever recorded. In France the rate fell from 16.5 to 12.1 and 14.4, and then rose to 19.5 and 17.7, the highest rates ever recorded in France.

Influence of Rural and Urban Life.—Rural districts are always very prolific, and when we hear the wails of writers on " Social Economy," bemoaning the small birth-rates of their large cities, we need have no fear for urban extinction, as emigration from the country by many ambitious sons and daughters, to avail themselves of the superior advantages that the city offers, will not only keep up but to a certain point increase the population, until the reaction of overcrowding, following the self-regulating law of compensation, starts a return emigration.

The effect of climate and race on prolificity, though much spoken of, is not so great a factor as supposed. The inhabitants of Great Britain are surpassed by none in the point of prolificity ; yet their location is quite northern. The Swedes have always been noted for their fecundity. Olaf

[a] Statistics and Sociology, New York, 1895.

Rudbeck [a] says that from 8 to 12 was the usual family number, and some ran as high as 25 or 30. According to Lord Kames, in Iceland before the plague (about 1710) families of from 15 to 20 were quite common. The old settlers in cold North America were always blessed with large families, and Quebec is still noted for its prolificity. There is little difference in this respect among nations, woman being limited about the same everywhere, and the general average of the range of the productive function remaining nearly identical in all nations. Of course, exception must be made as to the extremes of north or south.

Ancient and Modern Prolificity.—Nor is there much difference between ancient and modern times. We read in the writings of Aristotle, Pliny, and Albucasis of the wonderful fertility of the women of Egypt, Arabia, and other warm countries, from 3 to 6 children often being born at once and living to maturity ; but from the wonder and surprise shown in the narration of these facts, they were doubtless exceptions, of which parallels may be found in the present day. The ancient Greek and Roman families were no larger than those of to-day, and were smaller in the zenith of Roman affluence, and continued small until the period of decadence.

Legal Encouragement of Prolificity.—In Quebec Province, Canada, according to a Montreal authority,[b] 100 acres of land are allotted to the father who has a dozen children by legitimate marriage. The same journal states that, stimulated by the premium offered, families of 20 or more are not rare, the results of patriotic efforts. In 1895, 1742 "chefs de famille" made their claim according to the conditions of the law, and one, Paul Bellanger, of the River du Loup, claimed 300 acres as his premium, based on the fact that he was the father of 36 children. Another claimant, Monsieur Thioret de Sainte Geneviève, had been presented by his wife, a woman not yet thirty years old, with 17 children. She had triplets twice in the space of five years and twins thrice in the mean time. It is a matter of conjecture what the effect would be of such a premium in countries with a lowering birth-rate, and a French medical journal, quoting the foregoing, regretfully wishes for some countrymen at home like their brothers in Quebec.

Old Explanations of Prolificity.—The old explanation of the causation of the remarkable exceptions to the rules of prolificity was similar to that advanced by Empedocles, who says that the greater the quantity of semen, the greater the number of children at birth. Paré,[618] later, uses a similar reason to explain the causation of monstrosities, grouping them into two classes, those due to deficiency of semen, such as the acephalous type, and those due to excess, such as the double monsters. Hippocrates, in his work on the " Nature of the Infant," tells us that twins are the result of a single coitus, and we are also informed that each infant has a chorion ; so that both kinds of plural gestation (monochorionic and dichorionic) were known to the ancients. In this treatise it is further stated that the twins may be male or female, or both males or both females ; the male is formed when the semen is thick and strong.

The greatest number of children at a single birth that it is possible for a woman to have has never been definitely determined. Aristotle gives it as his opinion that one woman can bring forth no more than 5 children at a single birth, and discredits reports of multiplicity above this number ; while Pliny, who is not held to be so trustworthy, positively states that there were authentic records of as many as 12 at a birth. Throughout the ages in which superstitious distortion of facts and unquestioning credulity was unchecked, all sorts of incredible accounts of prolificity are found. Martin Cromerus, a Polish historian, quoted by Paré, who has done some good work in statistical research on this subject, says [a] that Margaret, of a noble and ancient family near Cracovia, the wife of Count Virboslaus, brought forth 36 living children on January 20, 1296.

The celebrated case of Countess Margaret, daughter of Florent IV., Earl of Holland, and spouse of Count Hermann of Henneberg, was supposed to have occurred just before this, on Good Friday, 1278. She was at this time forty-two years of age, and at one birth brought forth 365 infants, 182 males, 182 females, and 1 hermaphrodite. They were all baptized in two large brazen dishes by the Bishop of Treras, the males being called John, the females Elizabeth. During the last century the basins were still on exhibition in the village church of Losdun, and most of the visitors to Hague went out to see them, as they were reckoned one of the curiosities of Holland. The affliction was ascribed to the curse of a poor woman who, holding twins in her arms, approached the Countess for aid. She was not only denied alms, but was insulted by being told that her twins were by different fathers, whereupon the poor woman prayed God to send the Countess as many children as there were days in the year. There is room for much speculation as to what this case really was. There is a possibility that it was simply a case of hydatidiform or multiple molar pregnancy, elaborated by an exhaustive imagination and superstitious awe. As late as 1799 there was a woman of a town of Andalusia who was reported to have been delivered of 16 male infants, 7 of which were alive two months later.

Mayo-Smith remarks that the **proportion of multiple births** is not more than 1 per cent. of the total number of parturitions. The latest statistics, by Westergaard, give the following averages to number of cases of 100 births in which there were 2 or more at a birth :—

Sweden, ... 1.45	Germany, ... 1.24	Bavaria, ... 1.38
Denmark, ... 1.34	Holland, ... 1.30	Prussia, ... 1.26
Scotland, ... 1.22	Norway, ... 1.32	Saxony, ... 1.20
Italy, ... 1.21	Austria, ... 1.17	Switzerland, . . 1.16
France, ... 0.99	Belgium, ... 0.97	Spain, ... 0.85

[a] 618, 1014.

In Prussia, from 1826 to 1880, there were 85 cases of quadruplets and 3 cases of 5 at a birth.

The most extensive statistics in regard to multiple births are those of Veit, who reviews 13,000,000 births in Prussia. According to his deductions, twins occur once in 88 births; triplets, once in 7910; and quadruplets, once in 371,126. Recent statistics supplied by the Boards of Health of New York and Philadelphia place the frequency of twin births in these cities at 1 in every 120 births, while in Bohemia twins occur once in about 60 births, a proportion just twice as great.[a] Of 150,000 twin pregnancies studied by Veit, in one-third both children were boys; in slightly less than one-third both were girls; in the remaining third both sexes were represented.

Authentic records of 5 and 6 at a birth are extremely rare and infinitesimal in proportion. The reputed births in excess of 6 must be looked on with suspicion, and, in fact, in the great majority of reports are apochryphal.

The **examples of multiple births** of a single pregnancy will be taken up under their respective numbers, several examples of each being given, together with the authorities. Many twin and triplet brothers have figured prominently in history, and, in fact, they seem especially favored. The instance of the Horatii and the Curatii, and their famous battle, on which hung the fate of Rome and Alba, is familiar to every one, their strength and wisdom being legendary with the Romans.

Twins and triplets, being quite common, will not be considered here, although there are 2 cases of interest of the latter that deserve citation. Sperling[839] reports 2 instances of triplets; in the first there was 1 placenta and chorion, 2 amnions, and the sex was the same; in the second case, in which the sexes were different, there were 3 placentas, 3 chorions, and 3 amnions. What significance this may have is only a matter of conjecture. Petty[b] describes a case of triplets in which one child was born alive, the other 2 having lost their vitality three months before. Mirabeau[c] has recently found that triple births are most common (1 to 6500) in multiparous women between thirty and thirty-four years of age. Heredity seems to be a factor, and duplex uteruses predispose to multiple births. Ross[d] reports an instance of double uterus with triple pregnancy.

Quadruplets are supposed to occur once in about every 400,000 births. There are 72 instances recorded in the Index Catalogue of the Surgeon General's Library, U. S. A., up to the time of compilation, not including the subsequent cases in the Index Medicus. At the Hôtel-Dieu, in Paris, in 108,000 births, covering a period of sixty years, mostly in the last century, there was only one case of quadruplets. The following extract of an account of the birth of quadruplets is given by Dr. De Leon of Ingersoll, Texas :—

" I was called to see Mrs. E. T. Page, January 10, 1890, about 4 o'clock

a 844, 142. b 490, 1845.
c Ueber Drillingsgeburten, München, 1894. d Médecin. Paris, 1879, v., No. 43, 2.

A. M. ; found her in labor and at full time, although she assured me that her ' time ' was six weeks ahead. At 8 o'clock A. M. I delivered her of a girl baby ; I found there were triplets, and so informed her. At 11 A. M. I delivered her of the second girl, after having rectified presentation, which was singular, face, hands, and feet all presented ; I placed in proper position and practised ' version.' This child was ' still-born,' and after considerable effort by artificial respiration it breathed and came around ' all right.' The third girl was born at 11.40 A. M. This was the smallest one of the four. In attempting to take away the placenta, to my astonishment I found the feet of another child. At 1 P. M. this one was born ; the head of this child got firmly impacted at the lower strait, and it was with a great deal of difficulty and much patient effort that it was finally disengaged ; it was blocked by a mass of placenta and cords. The first child had its own placenta ; the second and third had their placenta ; the fourth had also a placenta. They weighed at birth in the aggregate 19½ pounds without cloth- ing ; the first weighed 6 pounds ; the second 5 pounds ; the third 4½ pounds ; the fourth 4 pounds. Mrs. Page is a blònde, about thirty-six years old, and has given birth to 14 children, twins three times before this, one pair by her first husband. She has been married to Page three years, and has had 8 children in that time. I have waited on her each time. Page is an Englishman, small, with dark hair, age about twenty-six, and weighs about 115 pounds. They are in St. Joseph, Mo., now, having contracted with Mr. Uffner of New York to travel and exhibit themselves in Denver, St. Joseph, Omaha, and Nebraska City, then on to Boston, Mass., where they will spend the summer."

There is a report from Canada [a] of the birth of 4 living children at one time. The mother, a woman of thirty-eight, of small stature, weighing 100 pounds, had 4 living children of the ages of twelve, ten, eight, and seven years, respectively. She had aborted at the second month, and at full term was delivered of 2 males, weighing, respectively, 4 pounds 9¼ ounces and 4 pounds 3 ounces ; and of 2 females, weighing 4 pounds 3 ounces and 3 pounds 13¾ ounces, respectively. There was but one placenta, and no more exhaustion or hemorrhage than at a single birth. The father weighed 169 pounds, was forty-one years old, and was 5 feet 5 inches tall, healthy and robust. The Journal of St. Petersburg, a newspaper of the highest standard, stated that at the end of July, 1871, a Jewish woman residing in Courland gave birth to 4 girls, and again, in May, 1872, bore 2 boys and a girl ; the mother and the 7 children, born within a period of ten months, were doing well at the time of the report. In the village of Iwokina, on May 26, 1854, [b] the wife of a peasant bore 4 children at a birth, all surviv- ing. Bousquet [c] speaks of a primiparous mother, aged twenty-four, giving birth to 4 living infants, 3 by the breech and 1 by the vertex, apparently all

a 250, Oct., 1883.   b 476, 1857, ii., 259.   c 140, 1894, ii., 55.

in one bag of membranes. They were nourished by the help of 3 wet-nurses. Bedford [a] speaks of 4 children at a birth, averaging 5 pounds each, and all nursing the mother.

Quintuplets are quite rare, and the Index Catalogue of the Surgeon General's Library, U. S. A., gives only 19 cases, reports of a few of which will be given here, together with others not given in the Catalogue, and from less scientific though reliable sources. In the year 1731 [282] there was one case of quintuplets in Upper Saxony and another near Prague, Bohemia. In both of these cases the children were all christened and had all lived to maturity. Garthshore [b] speaks of a healthy woman, Margaret Waddington, giving birth to 5 girls, 2 of which lived; the 2 that lived weighed at birth 8 pounds 12 ounces and 9 pounds, respectively. He discusses the idea that woman was meant to bear more than one child at a birth, using as his argument the existence of the double nipple and mamma, to which might be added the not infrequent occurrence of polymazia.

In March, 1736, [c] in a dairy cellar in the Strand, London, a poor woman gave birth to 3 boys and 2 girls. In the same journal was reported the birth at Wells, Somersetshire, in 1739, of 4 boys and a girl, all of whom were christened and were healthy. Paré [d] in 1549 gives several instances of 5 children at a birth, and Pliny reports that in the peninsula of Greece there was a woman who gave birth to quintuplets on four different occasions. Petritus, a Greek physician,[e] speaks of the birth of quintuplets at the seventh month. Two males and one female were born dead, being attached to the same placenta; the others were united to a common placenta and lived three days. Chambon [f] mentions an instance of 5 at a birth. Not far from Berne, Switzerland, the wife of John Gelinger, a preacher in the Lordship of Berne, brought forth twins, and within a year after she brought forth quintuplets, 3 sons and 2 daughters.[g] There is a similar instance reported in 1827 [h] of a woman of twenty-seven who, having been delivered of twins two years before, was brought to bed with 5 children, 3 boys and 2 girls. Their length was from $15\frac{1}{2}$ to $16\frac{1}{2}$ inches. Although regularly formed, they did not seem to have reached maturity. The mother was much exhausted, but recovered. The children appeared old-looking, had tremulous voices, and slept continually; during sleep their temperatures seemed very low.

Kennedy [i] showed before the Dublin Pathological Society 5 fetuses with the involucra, the product of an abortion at the third month. At Naples in 1839 Giuseppa Califani gave birth to 5 children; and about the same time Paddock reported the birth in Franklin County, Pa., of quintuplets. The Lancet[j] relates an account of the birth of quintuplets, 2 boys and 3 girls, by the wife of a peasant on March 1, 1854. Moffitt [k] records the

a 538, 1867.   b 629, 1787, 344.   c 374, Oct. 5, 1736.
d 618, L. xxv., chap. iii., 54.   e 302, iv., 183.   f 302, xix., 389.   g 618, 1014.
h 371, T. ii., 1827.   i 476, 1837, 743.   j 476, 1857, ii., 259.   k 545, 1881.

birth at Monticello, Ill., of quintuplets. The woman was thirty-five years of age; examination showed a breech presentation; the second child was born by a foot-presentation, as was the third, but the last was by a head-presentation. The combined weight was something over 19 pounds, and of the 5, 3 were still-born, and the other 2 died soon after birth. The Elgin Courant (Scotland), 1858, speaks of a woman named Elspet Gordon, at Rothes, giving birth to 3 males and 2 females. Although they were six months' births, the boys all lived until the following morning. The girls were still-born. One of the boys had two front teeth when born. Dr. Dawson of Rothes is the obstetrician mentioned in this case.

The following recent instance is given with full details to illustrate the difficulties attending the births of quintuplets. Stoker [a] has reported the case of a healthy woman, thirty-five years old, 5 feet 1 inch high, and of slight build, whom he delivered of 5 fetuses in the seventh month of pregnancy, none of the children surviving. The patient's mother had on two occasions given birth to twins. The woman herself had been married for six years and had borne 4 children at full term, having no difficulty in labor. When she came under observation she computed that she had been pregnant for six months, and had had her attention attracted to the unusually large size of her abdomen. She complained of fixed pain in the left side of the abdomen, on which side she thought she was larger. Pains set in with regularity and the labor lasted eight and three-quarter hours. After the rupture of the membranes the first child presented by the shoulder. Version was readily performed; the child was dead (recently). Examination after the birth of the first child disclosed the existence of more than one remaining fetus. The membranes protruded and became tense with each contraction. The presentation was a transverse one. In this case also there was little difficulty in effecting internal version. The child lived a couple of hours. The third fetus was also enclosed in a separate sac, which had to be ruptured. The child presented by the breech and was delivered naturally, and lived for an hour. In the fourth case the membranes had likewise to be ruptured, and alarming hemorrhage ensued. Version was at once practised, but the chin became locked with that of the remaining fetus. There was some difficulty and considerable delay in freeing the children, though the extent of locking was not at any time formidable. The child was dead (recently). The fifth fetus presented by the head and was delivered naturally. It lived for half an hour. The placenta was delivered about five minutes after the birth of the last child, and consisted of two portions united by a narrow isthmus. One, the smaller, had two cords attached centrally and close together; the other, and larger, had two cords attached in a similar way and one where it was joined to the isthmus. The organ appeared to be perfectly healthy. The cord of the fourth child was so short that it had to be ligated in the vagina. The

a 476, 1895, ii., 1164.

children were all females and of about the same size, making a total weight of 8 pounds. The mother rallied quickly and got on well.

Trustworthy records of **sextuplets** are, of course, extremely scarce. There are few catalogued at Washington, and but two authentic cases are on record in the United States. On December 30, 1831,[368] a woman in Dropin was delivered of 6 daughters, all living, and only a little smaller than usual in size. The mother was not quite twenty years old, but was of strong constitution. The 6 lived long enough to be baptized, but died the evening of their births. There was a case[a] of sextuplets in Italy in 1844. In Maine, June 27, 1847, a woman was delivered of 6 children, 2 surviving and, together with the mother, doing well.[b] In 1885 there was reported the birth of sextuplets in Lorca, Spain, of which only one survived. [c] At Dallas, Texas, in 1888,[d] Mrs. George Hirsh of Navarro County gave birth to 6 children, the mother and the children all doing well. There were 4 boys and 2 girls, and they were all perfect, well formed, but rather small.

Valsalli[e] gives an instance which is quoted by the Medical News[f] without giving the authority. Valsalli's account, which differs slightly from the account in the Medical News, is briefly as follows : While straining at stool on the one hundred and fifteenth day of pregnancy the membranes ruptured and a foot prolapsed, no pain having been felt before the accident. A fetus was delivered by the midwife. Valsalli was summoned and found the woman with an enormously distended abdomen, within which were felt numerous fetal parts ; but no fetal heart-sounds or movements were noticed. The cervix was only slightly dilated, and, as no pains were felt, it was agreed to wait. On the next day the membranes were ruptured and 4 more fetuses were delivered. Traction on the umbilical cord started hemorrhage, to check which the physician placed his hand in the uterine cavity. In this most arduous position he remained four hours until assistance from Lugano came. Then, in the presence of the three visiting physicians, a sixth amniotic sac was delivered with its fetus. The woman had a normal convalescence, and in the following year gave birth to healthy, living twins. The News says the children all moved vigorously at birth ; there were 4 males and 2 females, and for the 6 there was only one placenta. The mother, according to the same authority, was thirty-six years of age, and was in her second pregnancy.

Multiple Births over Six.—When we pass sextuplets the records of multiple births are of the greatest rarity and in modern records there are almost none. There are several cases mentioned by the older writers whose statements are generally worthy of credence, which, however incredible, are of sufficient interest at least to find a place in this chapter. Albucasis affirms that he knew of the birth of **seven** children at one time ; and d'Alechampius reports that Bonaventura, the slave of one Savelli, a gentleman of Siena, gave

---

a 152, 1844, 343.   b 218, 1847.   c 373, 1885.
d 450, Nov. 17, 1888.   e 360, 1888.   f 533, March 23, 1895.

birth to 7 children, 4 of whom were baptized. At the Parish of San Ildefonso, Valladolid, Julianna, wife of Benito Quesada, gave birth to 3 children in one day, and during the following night to 4 more.[a] Sigebert, in his Chronicles, says that the mother of the King of Lombardy had borne 7 children at a birth. Borellus [b] says that in 1650 the lady of the then present Lord Darre gave birth to **eight** perfect children at one parturition and that it was the unusual event of the country.

Mrs. Timothy Bradlee of Trumbull County, Ohio, in 1872 is reported to have given birth to 8 children at one time.[c] They were healthy and living, but quite small. The mother was married six years previously and then weighed 273 pounds. She had given birth to 2 pairs of twins, and, with these 3 boys and 5 girls, she had borne 12 children in six years. She herself was a triplet and her father and her mother were of twin births and one of her grandmothers was the mother of 5 pairs of twins. This case was most celebrated and was much quoted, several British journals extracting it.

Fig. 23.—Pregnancy with 11 fetuses (after Paré).

Watering of Maregnac [d] speaks of the simultaneous birth of 8 children at one time. When several months pregnant the woman was seized with colicky pains and thought them a call of nature. She went into a vineyard to answer it, and there, to her great astonishment, gave birth to 8 fetuses. Watering found them enclosed in a sac, and thought they probably had died from mutual pressure during growth. The mother made a good recovery.

In 1755 Seignette of Dijon [e] reports the simultaneous birth of **nine** children. Franciscus Picus Mirandulæ, quoted by Paré, says that one Dorothea, an Italian, bore 20 children at 2 confinements, the first time bearing 9 and the second time **eleven.** He gives a picture of this marvel of prolificity, in which her belly is represented as hanging down to her knees, and supported by a girdle from the neck (Fig. 23). In the Annals, History, and Guide to Leeds and York, according to Walford,[813] there is mention of Ann Birch, who in 1781 was delivered

a 373, Nov. 22, 1885 ; quoted by 476, 1885, ii., 1125 ; and several other authorities.
b Observ., cent. ii., Paris, 1656.   c 218, Sept. 26, 1872.
d 349, June, 1880   e 280, 1755, i., 300.

of 10 children.   One daughter, the sole survivor of the 10, married a market
gardener named Platt, who was well known in Leeds.   Jonston [447] quotes
Baytraff as saying that he knew of a case in which 9 children were born
simultaneously ; and also says that the Countess of Altdorf gave birth to
twelve at one birth.   Albucasis mentions a case of **fifteen** well-formed
children at a birth.   According to Le Brun,[a] Gilles de Trazegines, who
accompanied Saint Louis to Palestine, and who was made Constable of
France, was one of **thirteen** infants at a simultaneous accouchement.   The
Marquise, his mother, was impregnated by her husband before his departure,
and during his absence had 13 living children.   She was suspected by the
native people and thought to be an adulteress, and some of the children
were supposed to be the result of superfetation.   They condemned them
all to be drowned, but the Marquis appeared upon the scene about this time
and, moved by compassion, acknowledged all 13.   They grew up and thrived,
and took the name of Trazegines, meaning, in the old language, 13 drowned,
although many commentaries say that "*gines*" was supposed to mean in the
twelfth century "*nes*," or, in full, the interpretation would be "13 born."

Cases in which there is a **repetition of multiple births** are quite numerous, and sometimes so often repeated as to produce a family the size of which
is almost incredible.   Aristotle is credited with saying[b] that he knew the
history of a woman who had quintuplets four times.   Pliny's case of quintuplets four times repeated has been mentioned ; and Paré,[618] who may be
believed when he quotes from his own experience, says that the wife of the
last Lord de Maldemeure, who lived in the Parish of Seaux, was a marvel
of prolificity.   Within a year after her marriage she gave birth to twins ;
in the next year to triplets ; in the third year to quadruplets ; in the fourth
year to quintuplets, and in the fifth year bore sextuplets ; in this last labor she
died.   The then present Lord de Maldemeure, he says, was one of the final
sextuplets.   This case attracted great notice at the time, as the family was
quite noble and very well known.   Seaux, their home, was near Chambellay.
Picus Mirandulæ gathered from the ancient Egyptian inscriptions that the
women of Egypt brought forth sometimes 8 children at a birth, and that one
woman bore 30 children in 4 confinements.   He also cites, from the
history of a certain Bishop of Necomus, that a woman named Antonia, in
the Territory of Mutina, Italy, now called Modena, had brought forth 40
sons before she was forty years of age, and that she had had 3 and 4 at
a birth.   At the auction of the San Donato collection of pictures a portrait
of Dianora Frescobaldi, by one of the Bronzinos in the sixteenth century,
sold for about $3000.   At the bottom of this portrait was an inscription
stating that she was the mother of 52 children.   This remarkable woman
never had less than 3 at a birth, and tradition gives her as many as 6.

Merriman[c] quotes a case of a woman, a shopkeeper named Blunet, who

a 302, iv., 183.   b 302, xix., 389.   c 374, Sept., 1783, iii , 753.

had 21 children in 7 successive births. They were all born alive, and 12 still survived and were healthy. As though to settle the question as to whom should be given the credit in this case, the father or the mother, the father experimented upon a female servant, who, notwithstanding her youth and delicateness, gave birth to 3 male children that lived three weeks. According to despatches from Lafayette, Indiana, investigation following the murder, on December 22, 1895, of Hester Curtis, an aged woman of that city, developed the rather remarkable fact that she had been the mother of 25 children, including 7 pairs of twins.

According to a French authority the wife of a medical man at Fuentemajor, in Spain, forty-three years of age,[a] was delivered of triplets 13 times. Puech read a paper before the French Academy in which he reports 1262 twin births in Nîmes from 1790 to 1875, and states that of the whole number in 48 cases the twins were duplicated, and in 2 cases thrice repeated, and in one case 4 times repeated.

Warren[b] gives an instance of a lady, Mrs. M——, thirty-two years of age, married at fourteen, who, after the death of her first child, bore twins, one living a month and the other six weeks. Later she again bore twins, both of whom died. She then miscarried with triplets, and afterward gave birth to 12 living children, as follows: July 24, 1858, 1 child; June 30, 1859, 2 children; March 24, 1860, 2 children; March 1, 1861, 3 children; February 13, 1862, 4 children; making a total of 21 children in eighteen years, with remarkable prolificity in the later pregnancies. She was never confined to her bed more than three days, and the children were all healthy.

A woman in Schlossberg, Germany, gave birth to twins; after a year, to triplets, and again, in another year, to 3 fairly strong boys.[c] In the State Papers, Domestic Series, Charles I., according to Walford,[813] appears an extract from a letter from George Garrard to Viscount Conway, which is as follows: "Sir John Melton, who entertained you at York, hath buried his wife, Curran's daughter. Within twelve months she brought him 4 sons and a daughter, 2 sons last summer, and at this birth 2 more and a daughter, all alive." Swan[d] mentions a woman who gave birth to 6 children in seventeen months in 2 triple pregnancies. The first terminated prematurely, 2 children dying at once, the other in five weeks. The second was uneventful, the 3 children living at the time of the report. Rockwell[e] gives the report of a case of a woman of twenty-eight, herself a twin, who gave birth to twins in January, 1879. They died after a few weeks, and in March, 1880, she again bore twins, one living three and the other nine weeks. On March 12, 1881, she gave birth to triplets. The first child, a male, weighed 7 pounds; the second, a female, $6\frac{1}{4}$ pounds; the

a 365, Oct. 1, 1863.   b 218, 1862, 331.   c 224, 1878, ii., 767.
d 512, March, 1893.   e 612, Columbus, 1881.

third, a male, 5½ pounds. The third child lived twenty days, the other two died of cholera infantum at the sixth month, attributable to the bottle-feeding. Banerjee[a] gives the history of a case of a woman of thirty being delivered of her fourth pair of twins. Her mother was dead, but she had 3 sisters living, of one of which she was a twin, and the other 2 were twins. One of her sisters had 2 twin terms, 1 child surviving; like her own children, all were females. A second sister had a twin term, both males, 1 surviving. The other sister aborted female twins after a fall in the eighth month of pregnancy. The name of the patient was Mussamat Somni, and she was the wife of a respectable Indian carpenter.

There are recorded the most wonderful accounts of prolificity, in which, by repeated multiple births, a woman is said to have borne children almost beyond belief. A Naples correspondent to a Paris Journal[b] gives the following: " About 2 or 3 stations beyond Pompeii, in the City of Nocera, lives Maddalena Granata, aged forty-seven, who was married at twenty-eight, and has given birth to 52 living and dead children, 49 being males. Dr. de Sanctis, of Nocera, states that she has had triplets 15 times."

Peasant Kirilow[c] was presented to the Empress of Russia in 1853, at the age of seventy years. He had been twice married, and his first wife had presented him with 57 children, the fruits of 21 pregnancies. She had quadruplets four times, triplets seven times, and twins thrice. By his second wife he had 15 children, twins six times, and triplets once. This man, accordingly, was the father of 72 children, and, to magnify the wonder, all the children were alive at the time of presentation. Herman, in some Russian statistics, [d] relates the instance of Fedor Vassilet, a peasant of the Moscow Jurisdiction, who in 1872, at the age of seventy-five years, was the **father of 87 children.** He had been twice married ; his first wife bore him 69 children in 27 accouchements, having twins sixteen times, triplets seven times, and quadruplets four times, but never a single birth. His second wife bore him 18 children in 8 accouchements. In 1872, 83 of the 87 children were living. The author says this case is beyond all question, as the Imperial Academy of St. Petersburg, as well as the French Academy, have substantial proof of it. The family are still living in Russia, and are the object of governmental favors. The following fact is interesting from the point of exaggeration, if for nothing else: " The New York Medical Journal is accredited with publishing the following extract from the history of a journey to Saragossa, Barcelona, and Valencia, in the year 1585, by Philip II. of Spain. The book was written by Henrique Cock, who accompanied Philip as his private secretary. On page 248 the following statements are to be found : At the age of eleven years, Margarita Goncalez, whose father was a Biscayian, and whose mother was French, was married to her first husband, who was forty years

a 540, June 1, 1894.   b Quoted by 536, 1886, i., 57.
c 476, 1857, ii., 259.   d 476, 1878, i., 289.

old. By him she had 78 boys and 7 girls. He died thirteen years after the marriage, and, after having remained a widow two years, the woman married again. By her second husband, Thomas Gchoa, she had 66 boys and 7 girls. These children were all born in Valencia, between the fifteenth and thirty-fifth year of the mother's age, and at the time when the account was written she was thirty-five years old and pregnant again. Of the children, 47 by the first husband and 52 by the second were baptized ; the other births were still or premature. There were 33 confinements in all."

Extreme Prolificity by Single Births.—The number of children a woman may bring forth is therefore not to be accurately stated ; there seems to be almost no limit to it, and even when we exclude those cases in which remarkable multiplicity at each birth augments the number, there are still some almost incredible cases on record. The statistics of the St. Pancras Royal Dispensary, 1853, estimated the number of children one woman may bear as from 25 to 69. Eisenmenger relates the history of a case of a woman in the last century bearing 51 children, and there is another case [a] in which a woman bore 44 children, all boys. Atkinson [b] speaks of a lady married at sixteen, dying when she was sixty-four, who had borne 39 children, all at single births, by one husband, whom she survived. The children, 32 daughters and 7 sons, all attained their majority. There was a case of a woman in America [c] who in twenty-six years gave birth to 22 children, all at single births. Thoresby in his " History of Leeds," 1715, mentions three remarkable cases—one the wife of Dr. Phineas Hudson, Chancellor of York, as having died in her thirty-ninth year of her twenty-fourth child ; another of Mrs. Joseph Cooper, as dying of her twenty-sixth child, and, lastly, of Mrs. William Greenhill, of a village in Hertford, England, who gave birth to 39 children during her life. Brand, a writer of great repute, in his " History of Newcastle," quoted by Walford,[813] mentions as a well attested fact the wife of a Scotch weaver who bore 62 children by one husband, all of whom lived to be baptized.

A curious epitaph is to be seen at Conway, Carnarvonshire :—

> " Here lieth the body of Nicholas Hookes, of Conway, gentleman, who was
> one-and-fortieth child of his father, William Hookes, Esq., by Alice, his
> wife, and the father of 27 children. He died 20th of March, 1637."

On November 21, 1768, Mrs. Shury, the wife of a cooper, in Vine Street, Westminster, was delivered of 2 boys, making 26 by the same husband. She had previously been confined with twins during the year.

It would be the task of a mathematician to figure the **possibilities of paternity** in a man of extra long life who had married several prolific women during his prolonged period of virility. A man by the name of Pearsons of Lexton, Nottingham, at the time of the report had been married 4 times. By his first 3 wives he had 39 children and by his last 14, making a

a 559, 1806, 1 B., 127. b 224, 1883, ii., 557. c 218, Sept. 26, 1872.

total of 53.   He was 6 feet tall and lived to his ninety-sixth year.   We have already mentioned the two Russian cases in which the paternity was 72 and 87 children respectively, and in " Notes and Queries," June 21, 1856, there is an account of David Wilson of Madison, Ind., who had died a few years previously at the age of one hundred and seven.   He had been 5 times married and was the father of 47 children, 35 of whom were living at the time of his death.

On a tomb in Ely, Cambridgeshire, there is an inscription saying that Richard Worster, buried there, died on May 11, 1856, the tomb being in memory of his 22 sons and 5 daughters.

Artaxerxes was supposed to have had 106 children ; Conrad, Duke of Moscow, 80 ; and in the polygamous countries the number seems incredible. Herotinus was said [a] to have had 600 ; and Jonston also quotes instances of 225 and even of 650 in the Eastern countries.

Recently there have been published accounts of the alleged experiments of Luigi Erba, an Italian gentleman of Perugia, whose results have been announced.   About forty years of age and being quite wealthy, this bizarre philanthropist visited various quarters of the world, securing women of different races ; having secured a number sufficient for his purposes, he retired with them to Polynesia, where he is accredited with maintaining a unique establishment with his household of females.   In 1896, just seven years after the experiment commenced, the reports say he is the father of 370 children.

The following is a report from Raleigh, N. C., on July 28, 1893, to the New York Evening Post :—

" The fecundity of the negro race has been the subject of much comment and discussion.   A case has come to light in this State that is one of the most remarkable on record.   Moses Williams, a negro farmer, lives in the eastern section of this State.   He is sixty-five years old (as nearly as he can make out), but does not appear to be over fifty.   He has been married twice, and by the two wives has had born to him 45 children.   By the first wife he had 23 children, 20 of whom were girls and 3 were boys.   By the second wife he had 22 children—20 girls and 2 boys.   He also has about 50 grandchildren.   The case is well authenticated."

We also quote the following, accredited to the " Annals of Hygiene : "—

" Were it not part of the records of the Berks County courts, we could hardly credit the history of John Heffner, who was accidentally killed some years ago at the age of sixty-nine.   He was married first in 1840.   In eight years his wife bore him 17 children.   The first and second years of their marriage she gave birth to twins.   For four successive years afterward she gave birth to triplets.   In the seventh year she gave birth to one child and died soon afterward.   Heffner engaged a young woman to look after his large brood of babies, and three months later she became the second Mrs. Heffner.   She

[a] 447, 466.

presented her husband with 2 children in the first two years of her wedded life. Five years later she had added 10 more to the family, having twins 5 times. Then for three years she added but 1 a year. At the time of the death of the second wife 12 of the 32 children had died. The 20 that were left did not appear to be any obstacle to a young widow with one child consenting to become the third wife of the jolly little man, for he was known as one of the happiest and most genial of men, although it kept him toiling like a slave to keep a score of mouths in bread. The third Mrs. Heffner became the mother of 9 children in ten years, and the contentment and happiness of the couple were proverbial. One day, in the fall of 1885, the father of the 41 children was crossing a railroad track and was run down by a locomotive and instantly killed. His widow and 24 of the 42 children are still living."

Many Marriages.—In this connection it seems appropriate to mention a few examples of multimarriages on record, to give an idea of the possibilities of the extent of paternity. St. Jerome mentions a widow who married her twenty-second husband, who in his time had taken to himself 20 loving spouses. A gentleman living in Bordeaux[184] in 1772 had been married 16 times. DeLongueville, a Frenchman, lived to be one hundred and ten years old, and had been joined in matrimony to 10 wives, his last wife bearing him a son in his one hundred and first year.

Possible Descendants.—When we indulge ourselves as to the possible number of living descendants one person may have, we soon get extraordinary figures. The Madrid Estafette[a] states that a gentleman, Señor Lucas Nequeiras Saez, who emigrated to America seventy years previously, recently returned to Spain in his own steamer, and brought with him his whole family, consisting of 197 persons. He had been thrice married, and by his first wife had 11 children at 7 births; by his second wife, 19 at 13 births, and by his third wife, 7 at 6 births. The youngest of the 37 was thirteen years old and the eldest seventy. This latter one had a son aged forty-seven and 16 children besides. He had 34 granddaughters, 45 grandsons, 45 great granddaughters, 39 great grandsons, all living. Señor Saez himself was ninety-three years old and in excellent health.

At Litchfield, Conn., there is said to be the following inscription : [487]—

> "Here lies the body of Mrs. Mary, wife of Dr. John Bull, Esq. She died November 4, 1778, ætat. ninety, having had 13 children, 101 grandchildren, 274 great grandchildren, and 22 great-great grandchildren, a total of 410; surviving, 336."

In Esher Church there is an inscription, scarcely legible, which records the death of the mother of Mrs. Mary Morton on April 18, 1634, and saying that she was the wonder of her sex and age, for she lived to see nearly 400 issued from her loins.

<hr />

[a] 224, 1883, ii., 207.

The following is a communication to "Notes and Queries," March 21, 1891 : "Mrs. Mary Honeywood was daughter and one of the coheiresses of Robert Waters, Esq., of Lenham, in Kent. She was born in 1527 ; married in February, 1543, at sixteen years of age, to her only husband, Robert Honeywood, Esq., of Charing, in Kent. She died in the ninety-third year of her age, in May, 1620. She had 16 children of her own body, 7 sons and 9 daughters, of whom one had no issue, 3 died young—the youngest was slain at Newport battle, June 20, 1600. Her grandchildren, in the second generation, were 114 ; in the third, 228, and in the fourth, 9 ; so that she could almost say the same as the distich doth of one of the Dalburg family of Basil : ' Rise up, daughter, and go to thy daughter, for thy daughter's daughter hath a daughter.'

"In Markshal Church, in Essex, on Mrs. Honeywood's tomb is the following inscription : ' Here lieth the body of Mary Waters, the daughter and co-heir of Robert Waters, of Lenham, in Kent, wife of Robert Honeywood, of Charing, in Kent, her only husband, who had at her decease, lawfully descended from her, 367 children, 16 of her own body, 114 grandchildren, 228 in the third generation, and 9 in the fourth. She lived a most pious life and died at Markshal, in the ninety-third year of her age and the forty-fourth of her widowhood, May 11, 1620.' (From ' Curiosities for the Ingenious,' 1825.)   S. S. R."

Animal prolificity, though not finding a place in this work, presents some wonderful anomalies.[a]

[a] In illustration we may note the following : In the Illustrated London News, May 11, 1895, is a portrait of "Lady Millard," a fine St. Bernard bitch, the property of Mr. Thorp of Northwold, with her litter of 21 puppies, born on February 9, 1895, their sire being a magnificent dog—"Young York." There is quoted an incredible account [1] of a cow, the property of J. N. Sawyer of Ohio, which gave birth to 56 calves, one of which was fully matured and lived, the others being about the size of kittens ; these died, together with the mother. There was a cow in France, in 1871, delivered of 5 calves.

[1] 609, 1879, i., 525.

CHAPTER V.

MAJOR TERATA.

Monstrosities have attracted notice from the earliest time, and many of the ancient philosophers made references to them. In mythology we read of Centaurs, impossible beings who had the body and extremities of a beast ; the Cyclops, possessed of one enormous eye ; or their parallels in Egyptian myths, the men with pectoral eyes,—the creatures " whose heads do beneath their shoulders grow ;" and the Fauns, those sylvan deities whose lower extremities bore resemblance to those of a goat. Monsters possessed of two or more heads or double bodies are found in the legends and fairy tales of every nation. Hippocrates, his precursors, Empedocles and Democritus, and Pliny, Aristotle, and Galen, have all described monsters, although in extravagant and ridiculous language.

Ballantyne remarks that the occasional occurrence of double monsters was a fact known to the Hippocratic school, and is indicated by a passage in *De morbis muliebribus*, in which it is said that labor is gravely interfered with when the infant is dead or apoplectic or double. There is also a reference to monochorionic twins (which are by modern teratologists regarded as monstrosities) in the treatise *De Superfœtatione*, in which it is stated that " a woman, pregnant with twins, gives birth to them both at the same time, just as she has conceived them ; the two infants are in a single chorion."

Ancient Explanations of Monstrosities.—From the time of Galen to the sixteenth century many incredible reports of monsters are seen in medical literature, but without a semblance of scientific truth. There has been little improvement in the mode of explanation of monstrous births until the present century, while in the Middle Ages the superstitions were more ludicrous and observers more ignorant than before the time of Galen. In his able article on the teratologic records of Chaldea, Ballantyne[a] makes the following trite statements : " Credulity and superstition have never been the peculiar possession of the lower types of civilization only, and the special beliefs that have gathered round the occurrence of teratologic phenomena have been common to the cultured Greek and Roman of the past, the ignorant peasant of modern times, and the savage tribes of all ages. Classical writings, the literature of the Middle Ages, and the popular beliefs of the present day all contain views

[a] 759, 1894, 130.

161

concerning teratologic subjects which so closely resemble those of the Chaldean magi as to be indistinguishable from them.   Indeed, such works as those of Obsequens, Lycosthenes, Licetus, and Ambroise Paré only repeat, but with less accuracy of description and with greater freedom of imagination, the beliefs of ancient Babylon.   Even at the present time the most impossible cases of so-called 'maternal impressions' are widely scattered through medical literature; and it is not very long since I received a letter from a distinguished member of the profession asking me whether, in my opinion, I thought it possible for a woman to give birth to a dog.   Of course, I do not at all mean to infer that teratology has not made immense advances within recent times, nor do I suggest that on such subjects the knowledge of the magi can be compared with that of the average medical student of the present; but what I wish to emphasize is that, in the literature of ancient Babylonia, there are indications of an acquaintance with structural defects and malformations of the human body which will compare favorably with even the writings of the sixteenth century of the Christian era."

Fig. 24.—Dog-boy (after Paré).

Many reasons were given for the existence of monsters, and in the Middle Ages these were as faulty as the descriptions themselves.   They were interpreted as divinations, and were cited as forebodings and examples of wrath, or even as glorifications of the Almighty.   The semi-human creatures were invented or imagined, and cited as the results of bestiality and allied forms of sexual perversion prevalent in those times.   We find minute descriptions and portraits of these impossible results of wicked practices in many of the older medical books.   According to Paré[a] there was born in 1493, as the result of illicit intercourse between a woman and a dog, a creature resembling in its upper extremities its mother, while its lower extremities were the exact counterpart of its canine father (Fig. 24).   This particular case was believed by Bateman and others to be a precursor to the murders and wickedness that followed in the time of Pope Alexander I.   Volateranus, Cardani, and many others cite instances of this kind.   Lycosthenes says that in the year 1110, in the bourg of Liège, there was found a creature with the head, visage, hands, and feet of a man, and the rest of the body like that of a pig.   Paré quotes this case and gives an illustration.   Rhodiginus[b] mentions a shepherd of Cybare by the name of Cratain, who had connection with a female goat and

a 618, 1031.   b 679, L. xxv., chap. 32.

impregnated her, so that she brought forth a beast with a head resembling that of the father, but with the lower extremities of a goat. He says that the likeness to the father was so marked that the head-goat of the herd recognized it, and accordingly slew the goatherd who had sinned so unnaturally.

In the year 1547, at Cracovia,[191] a very strange monster was born, which lived three days. It had a head shaped like that of a man; a nose long and hooked like an elephant's trunk; the hands and feet looking like the web-foot of a goose; and a tail with a hook on it. It was supposed to be a male, and was looked upon as a result of sodomy. Rueff[a] says that the procreation of human beings and beasts is brought about —

(1) By the natural appetite;

(2) By the provocation of nature by delight;

(3) By the attractive virtue of the matrix, which in beasts and women is alike.

Plutarch, in his "Lesser Parallels," says that Aristonymus Ephesius, son of Demonstratus, being tired of women, had carnal knowledge with an ass, which in the process of time brought forth a very beautiful child, who became the maid Onoscelin. He also speaks of the origin of the maiden Hippona, or as he calls her, Hippo, as being from the connection of a man with a mare. Aristotle mentions this in his paradoxes, and we know that the patron of horses was Hippona. In Helvetia[191] was reported the existence of a colt (whose mother had been covered by a bull) that was half horse and half bull. One of the kings of France was supposed to have been presented with a colt with the hinder part of a hart, and which could outrun any horse in the kingdom. Its mother had been covered by a hart.

Writing in 1557, Lycosthenes reports the mythical birth of a serpent by a woman. It is quite possible that some known and classified type of monstrosity was indicated here in vague terms. In 1726 Mary Toft, of Godalming, in Surrey, England, achieved considerable notoriety throughout Surrey, and even over all England, by her extensively circulated statements that she bore rabbits. Even at so late a day as this the credulity of the people was so great that many persons believed in her. The woman was closely watched, and being detected in her maneuvers confessed her fraud. To show the extent of discussion this case called forth, there are no less than nine pamphlets and books in the Surgeon-General's library at Washington devoted exclusively to this case of pretended rabbit-breeding. Hamilton in 1848, and Hard[b] in 1884, both report the births in this country of fetal monstrosities with heads which showed marked resemblance to those of dogs. Doubtless many of the older cases of the supposed results of bestiality, if seen to-day, could be readily classified among some of our known forms of monsters. Modern investigation has shown us the sterile results of the connections between man and beast or between beasts of

a "The Expert Midwife," London, 1637.   b 269, xlviii., 246.

different species, and we can only wonder at the simple credulity and the imaginative minds of our ancestors. At one period certain phenomena of nature, such as an eclipse or comet, were thought to exercise their influence on monstrous births. Rueff mentions that in Sicily there happened a great eclipse of the sun, and that women immediately began to bring forth deformed and double-headed children.

Before ending these preliminary remarks, there might be mentioned the marine monsters, such as mermaids, sea-serpents, and the like, which from time to time have been reported; even at the present day there are people who devoutly believe that they have seen horrible and impossible demons in the sea. Paré[a] describes and pictures a monster, at Rome, on November 3, 1520, with the upper portion of a child apparently about five or six years old, and the lower part and ears of a fish-like animal. He also pictures a sea-devil in the same chapter, together with other gruesome examples of the power of imagination.

Fig. 25.—Bird-boy (after Paré).

Early Teratology.—Besides such cases as the foregoing, we find the medieval writers report likely instances of terata, as, for instance, Rhodiginus, [679] who speaks of a monster in Italy with two heads and two bodies; Lycosthenes saw a double monster, both components of which slept at the same time; he also says this creature took its food and drink simultaneously in its two mouths. Even Saint Augustine says that he knew of a child born in the Orient who, from the belly up, was in all parts double.

The first evidences of a step toward classification and definite reasoning in regard to the causation of monstrosities were evinced by Ambroise Paré in the sixteenth century, and though his ideas are crude and some of his phenomena impossible, yet many of his facts and arguments are worthy of consideration. Paré attributed the cause of anomalies of excess to an excessive quantity of semen, and anomalies of default to deficiency of the same fluid. He has collected many instances of double terata from reliable sources, but has interspersed his collection with accounts of some hideous and impossible creatures, such as are illustrated in the accompanying figure (Fig. 25), which shows a creature that was born shortly after a battle of

a 618, 1053.

Louis XII., in 1512 ; it had the wings, crest, and lower extremity of a bird and a human head and trunk ; besides, it was an hermaphrodite, and had an extra eye in the knee. Another illustration represents a monstrous head found in an egg, said to have been sent for examination to King Charles at Metz in 1569. It represented the face and visage of a man, with small living serpents taking the place of beard and hair. So credulous were people at this time that even a man so well informed as Paré believed in the possibility of these last two, or at least represented them as facts. At this time were also reported **double hermaphroditic terata,** seemingly without latter-day analogues. Rhodiginus [a] speaks of a two-headed monster born in Ferrari, Italy, in 1540, well formed, and with two sets of genitals, one male and the

Fig. 26.—Bicephalic and hermaphroditic monster (after Paré).　　Fig. 27.—Double hermaphroditic monster (after Paré).

other female (Fig. 26). Paré [b] gives a picture (Fig. 27) of twins, born near Heidelberg in 1486, which had double bodies joined back to back ; one of the twins had the aspect of a female and the other of a male, though both had two sets of genitals.

Scientific Teratology.—About the first half of the eighteenth century what might be called the positive period of teratology begins. Following the advent of this era come Méry, Duverney, Winslow, Lémery, and Littre. In their works true and concise descriptions are given and violent attacks are made against the ancient beliefs and prejudices. From the beginning of the second half of the last century to the present time may be termed the scientific epoch of teratology. We can almost with a certainty start this era with

[a] 679, L. xxiv., chap. 30.　　[b] 618, 1016.

the names of Haller, Morgagni, Geoffroy-Saint-Hilaire, and Meckel, who adduced the explanations asked for by Harvey and Wolff. From the appearance of the treatise by Geoffroy-Saint-Hilaire, teratology has made enormous strides, and is to-day well on the road to becoming a science. Hand in hand with embryology it has been the subject of much investigation in this century, and to enumerate the workers of the present day who have helped to bring about scientific progress would be a task of many pages. Even in the **artificial production of monsters** much has been done, and a glance at the work of Dareste [a] well repays the trouble. Essays on teratogenesis, with reference to batrachians, have been offered by Lombardini ; and by Lereboullet and Knoch with reference to fishes. Foll and Warynski [b] have reported their success in obtaining visceral inversion, and even this branch of the subject promises to become scientific.

Terata are seen **in the lower animals** and always excite interest. Paré [c] gives the history of a sheep with three heads, born in 1577 ; the

central head was larger than the other two, as shown in the accompanying illustration (Fig. 28). Many of the Museums of Natural History contain evidences of animal terata. At Hallæ is a two-headed mouse ; the Conant Museum in Maine contains the skeleton of an adult sheep with two heads ; there was an account of a two-headed pigeon published in France in 1734 ; [d] Leidy found a two-headed snake in a field near Philadelphia ; Geoffroy-

Fig. 28.—Three-headed sheep (after Paré).

Saint-Hilaire and Conant both found similar creatures, and there is one in the Museum at Harvard ; Wyman saw a living double-headed snake in the Jardin des Plantes in Paris in 1853, and many parallel instances are on record.

Classification.—We shall attempt no scientific discussion of the causation or embryologic derivation of the monster, contenting ourselves with simple history and description, adding any associate facts of interest that may be suggested. For further information, the reader is referred to the authors cited or to any of the standard treatises on teratology.

Many classifications of terata have been offered, and each possesses some advantage. The modern reader is referred to the modification of the grouping of Geoffroy-Saint-Hilaire given by Hirst and Piersol [417], or those of Blanc [212] and Guinard [390]. For convenience, we have adopted the following classification, which will include only those monsters that have *lived after*

---

[a] Recherches sur la production artificielle des monstruosités, etc., Paris, 1894, 8°.
[b] Recueil zoologique suisse, 1883.   [c] 618, 1034.   [d] Mémoires de l'Acad. des Sciences.

birth, and who have attracted general notice or attained some fame in their time, as attested by accounts in contemporary literature.

CLASS 1.—Union of several fetuses.
CLASS 2.—Union of two distinct fetuses by a connecting band.
CLASS 3.—Union of two distinct fetuses by an osseous junction of the cranial bones.
CLASS 4.—Union of two distinct fetuses in which one or more parts are eliminated by the junction.
CLASS 5.—Fusion of two fetuses by a bony union of the ischii.
CLASS 6.—Fusion of two fetuses below the umbilicus into a common lower extremity.
CLASS 7.—Bicephalic monsters.
CLASS 8.—Parasitic monsters.
CLASS 9.—Monsters with a single body and double lower extremities.
CLASS 10.—Diphallic terata.
CLASS 11.—Fetus in fetu, and dermoid cysts.
CLASS 12.—Hermaphrodites.

CLASS I.—**Triple Monsters.**—Haller and Meckel were of the opinion that no cases of triple monsters worthy of credence are on record, and since their time this has been the popular opinion.

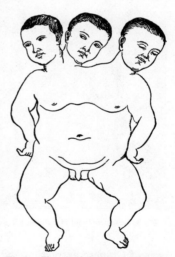

Fig. 29.—Three-headed monster (Galvagni).

Surely none have ever lived. Licetus [486] describes a human monster with two feet and seven heads and as many arms. Bartholinus [a] speaks of a three-headed monster who after birth gave vent to horrible cries and expired. Borellus [841] speaks of a three-headed dog, a veritable Cerberus. Blasius [214] published an essay on triple monsters in 1677. Bordenave [b] is quoted as mentioning a human monster formed of three fetuses, but his description proves clearly that it was only the union of two. Probably the best example of this anomaly that we have was described by Galvagni at Cattania in 1834. This monster had two necks, on one of which was a single head normal in dimensions. On the other neck were two heads, as seen in the accompanying illustration (Fig. 29). Geoffroy-Saint-Hilaire mentions several cases, and Martin de Pedro publishes a description of a case in Madrid in 1879. There are also on record some cases of triple monster by inclusion which will be spoken of later. Instances in the lower animals have been seen, the three-headed sheep of Paré, already spoken of, being one.

CLASS II.—**Double Monsters.**—A curious mode of junction, probably the most interesting, as it admits of longer life in these monstrosities, is that of a simple cartilaginous band extending between two absolutely distinct and

a 190, cent. vi., obs. 49, 278.   b 302, xxxiv., 158.

different individuals. The band is generally in the sternal region. In 1752[374] there was described a remarkable monstrosity which consisted of conjoined twins, a perfect and an imperfect child, connected at their ensiform cartilages by a band 4 inches in circumference. The **Hindoo sisters,** described by Dr. Andrew Berry,[a] lived to be seven years old; they stood face to face, with their chests 6½ inches and their pubes 8½ inches apart. Mitchell[b] describes the full-grown female twins, born at Newport, Ky., called the **Newport twins.** The woman who gave birth to them became impregnated, it is said, immediately after seeing the famous Siamese twins, and the products of this pregnancy took the conformation of those celebrated exhibitionists.

Fig. 30.—Siamese twins at eighteen years of age.

Perhaps the best known of all double monsters were the **Siamese twins.** They were exhibited all over the globe and had the additional benefit and advertisement of a much-mooted discussion as to the advisability of their severance, in which opinions of the leading medical men of all nations were advanced. The literature on these famous brothers is simply stupendous. The amount of material in the Surgeon-General's library at Washington would surprise an investigator. A curious volume in this library is a book containing clippings, advertisements, and divers portraits of the twins. It will be impossible to speak at all fully on this subject, but a short history and running review of their lives will be given: Eng and Chang were born in Siam about May, 1811. Their father was of Chinese extraction and had gone to Siam and there married a woman whose father was also a Chinaman. Hence, for the most part, they were of Chinese blood, which probably accounted for their dark color and Chinese features. Their mother was about thirty-five years old at the time of their birth and had borne 4 female children prior to Chang and Eng. She afterward had twins several times, having eventually 14 children in all. She gave no history of special significance of the pregnancy, although she averred that the head of one and the feet of the other were born at the same time. The twins were both feeble at birth, and Eng continued delicate, while Chang thrived. It was only with difficulty that their lives were saved, as Chowpahyi, the reigning king, had a superstition that such freaks of nature always presaged evil to the country. They were really discovered by Robert Hunter, a British merchant at Bangkok, who in 1824 saw them boating and stripped to the waist. He prevailed on the parents and King Chow-pahyi to allow them to go away for exhibition. They were first taken out of the country by a certain Captain Coffin. The first scientific description of them was given by Professor J. C. Warren, who examined them in Boston, at the Harvard University, in 1829. At that time Eng was 5 feet 2 inches and Chang 5 feet 1½ inches in height. They presented all

Fig. 31.—Siamese twins in old age.

the characteristics of Chinamen and wore long black queues coiled thrice around their heads, as shown by the accompanying illustration (Fig. 30). After an eight-weeks' tour over the Eastern States they went to London, arriving at that port November 20, 1829. Their tour in France was forbidden on the same grounds as the objection to the exhibition of Ritta-Christina, namely, the possibility of causing the production of monsters by maternal impressions in pregnant women. After their European tour they returned to the United States and settled down as farmers in North Carolina, adopting the name of Bunker. When forty-four years of age they married two sisters, English women, twenty-six and twenty-eight years of age, respectively. Domestic infelicity soon compelled them to keep the wives at different houses, and they alternated weeks in visiting each wife. Chang had six children and Eng five, all healthy and strong. In 1869 they made another trip to Europe, ostensibly to consult the most celebrated surgeons of Great Britain and France on the advisability of being separated. It was stated that a feeling of antagonistic hatred after a quarrel prompted them to seek "surgical separation," but the real cause was most likely to replenish their depleted exchequer by renewed exhibition and advertisement.

A most pathetic characteristic of these illustrious brothers was the affection and forbearance they showed for each other until shortly before their death. They bore each other's trials and petty maladies with the greatest sympathy, and in this manner rendered their lives far more agreeable than a casual observer would suppose possible. They both became Christians and members or attendants of the Baptist Church.

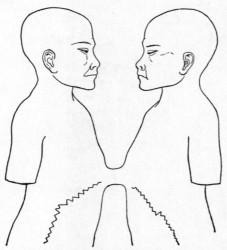

Fig. 32.—Diagram from a cast showing the position of the ligament and of the primary anterior incisions. During life the twins never assumed the face-to-face position in which they are here represented, and which is without doubt that of their fetal life.

Figure 31 is a representation of the Siamese twins in old age. On each side of them is a son. The original photograph is in the Mütter Museum, College of Physicians, Philadelphia.

The feasibility of the operation of separating them was discussed by many of the leading men of America, and Thompson, Fergusson, Syme, Sir J. Y. Simpson, Nélaton, and many others in Europe, with various reports and opinions after examination. These opinions can be seen in full in nearly any large medical library. At this time they had diseased and atheromatous arteries, and Chang, who was quite intemperate, had marked spinal curvature, and shortly afterward became hemiplegic. They were both partially blind in their two anterior eyes, possibly from looking outward and obliquely. The point of junction was about the sterno-xiphoid angle, a cartilaginous band extending from sternum to sternum. In 1869 Simpson measured this band and made the distance on the superior aspect from sternum to sternum $4\frac{1}{2}$ inches, though it is most likely that during the early period of exhibition it was not over 3 inches. The illustration shows very well the position of the joining band (Fig. 32).

The twins died on January 17, 1874, and a committee of surgeons from the College of Physicians of Philadelphia, consisting of Doctors Andrews, Allen, and Pancoast, went to North Carolina to perform an autopsy on the body, and, if possible, to secure it. They made a long and most interesting report on the results of their trip to the College. The arteries, as was anticipated, were found to have undergone calcareous degeneration. There was an hepatic connection through the band, and also some interlacing diaphragmatic fibers therein. There was slight vascular intercommunication of the livers and independence of the two peritoneal cavities and the intestines (Fig. 33). The band itself was chiefly a coalescence of the xyphoid cartilages, surrounded by areolar tissue and skin (Fig. 34).

The "Orissa sisters," or **Radica-Doddica,** shown in Europe in 1893, were similar to the Siamese twins in conformation. They were born in

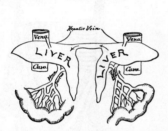

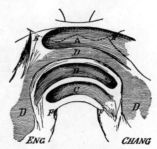

Fig. 33.—Diagrammatic representation of the livers, portraying the relations of the vessels, etc. The arrows show the direction in which an injection passed from Chang to Eng.

Fig. 34.—Diagrammatic representation of the band. *A*, upper or hepatic pouch of Chang; *E, E* (dotted line), union of the ensiform cartilages; *D*, connecting liver band, or the "tract of portal continuity;" *B*, the peritoneal pouch of Eng; *C*, the lower peritoneal pouch of Chang; *F, F*, lower border of the band.

Orissa, India, September, 1889, and were the result of the sixth pregnancy, the other five being normal. They were healthy girls, four years of age, and apparently perfect in every respect, except that, from the ensiform cartilage to the umbilicus, they were united by a band 4 inches long and 2 inches wide (Fig. 35). The children when facing each other could draw their chests three or four inches apart, and the band was so flexible that they could sit on either side of the body. Up to the date mentioned it was not known whether the connecting band contained viscera. A portrait of these twins was shown at the World's Fair in Chicago.

In the village of Arasoor, district of Bhavany, there was reported a monstrosity in the form of two female children, one 34 inches and the other 33¾ inches high, connected by the sternum. They were said to have had small-pox and to have recovered. They seemed to have had individual nervous systems, as when one was pinched the other did not feel it, and while one slept the other was awake. There must have been some vascular connection, as medicine given to one affected both.

Fig. 36 shows a mode of cartilaginous junction by which each component of a double monster may be virtually independent.

Operations on Conjoined Twins.—Swingler [a] speaks of two girls joined at the xiphoid cartilage and the umbilicus, the band of union being 1½ inches thick, and running below the middle of it was the umbilical cord, common to both. They first ligated the cord, which fell off in nine days, and then separated the twins with the bistoury. They each made early recovery and lived.

In the Ephemerides of 1690 König gives a description of two Swiss sisters born in 1689 and united belly to belly, who were separated by means

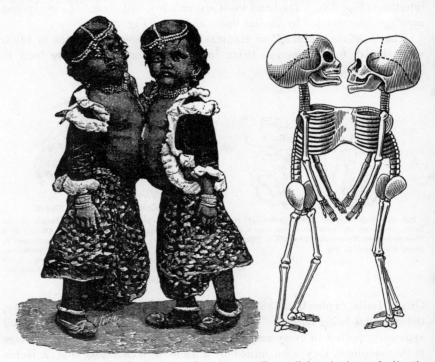

Fig. 35.—Radica-Doddica, the "Orissa Sisters."   Fig. 36.—Skeleton showing a mode of junction of independent double monsters.

of a ligature and the operation afterward completed by an instrument. The constricting band was formed by a coalition of the xiphoid cartilages and the umbilical vessels, surrounded by areolar tissue and covered with skin. Le Beau [b] says that under the Roman reign, A. D. 945, two male children were brought from Armenia to Constantinople for exhibition. They were well formed in every respect and united by their abdomens. After they had been for some time an object of great curiosity, they were removed by governmental order, being considered a presage of evil. They returned, however, at

[a] Quoted 302, vol. xxxiv.   [b] Histoire du Bas-Empire, 1776.

the commencement of the reign of Constantine VII., when one of them took sick and died. The surgeons undertook to preserve the other by separating him from the corpse of his brother, but he died on the third day after the operation.

In 1866 Boehm[a] gives an account of Guzenhausen's case of twins who were united sternum to sternum. An operation for separation was performed without accident, but one of the children, already very feeble, died three days after; the other survived. The last attempt at an operation like this was in 1881, when Biaudet and Buginon attempted to separate conjoined sisters (Marie-Adèle) born in Switzerland on June 26th. Unhappily, they were very feeble and life was despaired of when the operation was performed, on October 29th. Adèle died six hours afterward, and Marie died of peritonitis on the next day.

CLASS III.—Those monsters joined by a fusion of some of the cranial bones are sometimes called **craniopagi.** A very ancient observation of this kind is cited by Geoffroy-Saint-Hilaire. These two girls were born in 1495, and lived to be ten years old. They were normal in every respect, except that they were joined at the forehead, causing them to stand face to face and belly to belly (Fig. 37). When one walked forward, the other was compelled to walk backward; their noses almost touched, and their eyes were directed laterally. At the death of one an attempt to separate the other from the cadaver was made, but it was unsuccessful, the second soon dying; the operation necessitated opening the cranium and parting the meninges.

Fig. 37.—Craniopagus (after Paré).

Bateman [191] said that in 1501 there was living an instance of double female twins, joined at the forehead. This case was said to have been caused in the following manner: Two women, one of whom was pregnant with the twins at the time, were engaged in an earnest conversation, when a third, coming up behind them, knocked their heads together with a sharp blow. Bateman describes the death of one of the twins and its excision from the other, who died subsequently, evidently of septic infection. There is a possibility that this is merely a duplication of the account of the preceding case with a slight anachronism as to the time of death.

At a foundling hospital in St. Petersburg [b] there were born two living girls, in good health, joined by the heads. They were so united that the nose of one, if prolonged, would strike the ear of the other; they had perfectly independent existences, but their vascular systems had evident connection.

[a] 161, 1866, 152.   [b] 573, July, 1855.

Through extra mobility of their necks they could really lie in a straight line, one sleeping on the side and the other on the back. There is a report [a] of two girls joined at their vertices, who survived their birth. With the exception of this junction they were well formed and independent in existence. There was no communication of the cranial cavities, but simply fusion of the cranial bones covered by superficial fascia and skin (Fig. 38). Daubenton has seen a case of union at the occiput,[b] but further details are not quoted.

CLASS IV.—The next class to be considered is that in which the individuals are separate and well formed, except that the point of fusion is a common part, eliminating their individual components in this location. The **pygopagous twins** belong in this section. According to Bateman,[191] twins were born in 1493 at Rome joined back to back, and survived their birth. The same authority speaks of a female child who was born with " 2 bellies,

4 arms, 4 legs, 2 heads, and 2 sets of privates, and was exhibited throughout Italy for gain's sake." **The " Biddenden Maids "** were born in Biddenden, Kent, in 1100.[c] Their names were Mary and Eliza Chulkhurst, and their parents were fairly well-to-do people. They were supposed to have been united at the hips and the shoulders, and lived until 1134. At the death of one it was proposed to separate them, but the remaining sister refused, saying, "As we came together, we will also go together," and, after about six hours of this Mezentian existence, they died. They bequeathed to the church-wardens of the parish and their successors land to the extent of 20 acres, at the present time bringing a rental of about $155.00 annually, with the instructions that the money was to be spent in the distribution of cakes

Fig. 38.—Twins joined at forehead.

(bearing the impression of their images, to be given away on each Easter Sunday to all strangers in Biddenden) and also 270 quartern loaves, with cheese in proportion, to all the poor in said parish. Ballantyne has accompanied his description of these sisters by illustrations, one of which shows the cake (Fig. 39). Heaton [d] gives a very good description of these maids; and a writer in " Notes and Queries " of March 27, 1875, gives the following information relative to the bequest :—

" On Easter Monday, at Biddenden, near Staplehurst, Kent, there is a distribution, according to ancient custom, of ' Biddenden Maids' cakes,' with bread and cheese, the cost of which is defrayed from the proceeds of some

a 212, 259.   b 302, xxxiv.   c 759, Oct., 1895.   d 224, 1869, i., 363.

20 acres of land, now yielding £35 per annum, and known as the 'Bread and Cheese Lands.' About the year 1100 there lived Eliza and Mary Chulkhurst, who were joined together after the manner of the Siamese twins, and who lived for thirty-four years, one dying, and then being followed by her sister within six hours. They left by their will the lands above alluded to, and their memory is perpetuated by imprinting on the cakes their effigies 'in their habit as they lived.' The cakes, which are simple flour and water, are four inches long by two inches wide, and are much sought after as curiosities. These, which are given away, are distributed at the discretion of the church-wardens, and are nearly 300 in number. The bread and cheese amounts to 540 quartern loaves and 470 pounds of cheese. The distribution is made on land belonging to the charity, known as the Old Poorhouse.

Formerly it used to take place in the Church, immediately after the service in the afternoon, but in consequence of the unseemly disturbance which used to ensue the practice was discontinued. The Church used to be filled with a congregation whose conduct was occasionally so reprehensible that sometimes the church-wardens had to use their wands for other purposes than symbols of office. The impressions of the 'maids' on the cakes are of a primitive character, and are made by boxwood dies cut in 1814. They bear the date 1100, when Eliza and Mary Chulkhurst are supposed to have been born, and also their age at death, thirty-four years."

Ballantyne [759] has summed up about all there is to be said on this national monstrosity, and his discussion of the case from its historic as well as teratologic standpoint is so excellent that his conclusions will be quoted :—

Fig. 39.—Biddenden Maids' cake (Ballantyne).

" It may be urged that the date fixed for the birth of the Biddenden Maids is so remote as to throw grave doubt upon the reality of the occurrence. The year 1100 was, it will be remembered, that in which William Rufus was found dead in the New Forest, 'with the arrow either of a hunter or an assassin in his breast.' According to the Anglo-Saxon Chronicle, several 'prodigies' preceded the death of this profligate and extravagant monarch. Thus it is recorded that 'at Pentecost blood was observed gushing from the earth at a certain town of Berkshire, even as many asserted who declared that they had seen it. And after this, on the morning after Lammas Day, King William was shot.' Now, it is just possible that the birth of the Biddenden Maids may have occurred later, but have been antedated by the popular tradition to the year above mentioned. For such a birth would, in the opinion of the times, be regarded undoubtedly as a most evident prodigy or omen of evil. Still, even admitting that the date 1100 must be allowed to stand, its remoteness from the present time is not a convincing argument against a belief in the real occurrence of the phenomenon ; for of the dicephalic Scottish brothers, who lived in 1490, we have credible historic evidence. Further, Lycosthenes, in his "Chronicon Prodigiorum atque Ostentorum" (p. 397), published in 1557, states, upon what authority I know not, that in the year 1112 joined twins resembling the Biddenden phenomenon in all points save in sex were born in England. The passage is as follows : 'In Anglia natus est puer geminus a clune ad superiores partes ita divisus, ut duo haberet capita, duo corpora integra ad renes cum suis brachiis, qui baptizatus triduo supervixit.' It is just possible that in some way or other this case has been confounded with the story of Biddenden ; at any rate, the occurrence of such a statement in Lycosthenes' work is of more than passing interest. Had there been no bequest of land in connection with the case of the Kentish Maids, the whole affair would probably soon have been forgotten.

"There is, however, one real difficulty in accepting the story handed down to us as authentic,—the nature of the teratologic phenomenon itself. All the records agree in stating that the Maids were joined together at the shoulders and hips, and the impression on the cakes and the pictures on the 'broadsides' show this peculiar mode of union, and represent the bodies as quite separate in the space between the above-named points. The Maids are shown with four feet and two arms, the right and left respectively, whilst the other arms (left and right) are fused together at the shoulder according to one illustration, and a little above the elbow according to another. Now, although it is not safe to say that such an anomaly is impossible, I do not know of any case of this peculiar mode of union ; but it may be that, as Prof. A. R. Simpson has suggested, the Maids had four separate arms, and were in the habit of going about with their contiguous arms round each other's necks, and that this gave rise to the notion that these limbs were united. If this be so, then the teratologic difficulty is removed, for the case becomes perfectly comparable with the well-known but rare type of double terata known as the pygopagous twins, which is placed by Taruffi with that of the ischiopagous twins in the group dicephalus lecanopagus. Similar instances, which are well known to students of teratology, are the Hungarian sisters (Helen and Judith), the North Carolina twins (Millie and Christine), and the Bohemian twins (Rosalie and Josepha Blazek). The interspace between the thoraces may, however, have simply been the addition of the first artist who portrayed the Maids (from imagination?); then it may be surmised that they were ectopagous twins.

" Pygopagous twins are fetuses united together in the region of the nates and having each its own pelvis. In the recorded cases the union has been usually between the sacra and coccyges, and has been either osseous or (more rarely) ligamentous. Sometimes the point of junction was the middle line posteriorly, at other times it was rather a posterolateral union; and it is probable that in the Biddenden Maids it was of the latter kind; and it is likely, from the proposal made to separate the sisters after the death of one, that it was ligamentous in nature.

" If it be granted that the Biddenden Maids were pygopagous twins, a study of the histories of other recorded cases of this monstrosity serves to demonstrate many common characters. Thus, of the 8 cases which Taruffi has collected, in 7 the twins were female; and if to these we add the sisters Rosalie and Josepha Blazek and the Maids, we have 10 cases, of which 9 were girls. Again, several of the pygopagous twins, of whom there are scientific records, survived birth and lived for a number of years, and thus resembled the Biddenden terata. Helen and Judith, for instance, were twenty-three years old at death; and the North Carolina twins, although born in 1851, are still alive. There is, therefore, nothing inherently improbable in the statement that the Biddenden Maids lived for thirty-four years. With regard also to the truth of the record that the one Maid survived her sister for six hours, there is confirmatory evidence from scientifically observed instances, for Joly and Peyrat (Bull. de l'Acad. Méd., iii., pp. 51 and 383, 1874) state that in the case seen by them the one infant lived ten hours after the death of the other. It is impossible to make any statement with regard to the internal structure of the Maids or to the characters of their genital organs, for there is absolutely no information forthcoming upon these points. It may simply be said, in conclusion, that the phenomenon of Biddenden is interesting not only on account of the curious bequest which arose out of it, but also because it was an instance of a very rare teratologic type, occurring at a very early period in our national history."

Possibly the most famous example of twins of this type were **Helen and Judith, the Hungarian sisters,** born in 1701 at Szony, in Hungary. They were the objects of great curiosity, and were shown successively in Holland, Germany, Italy, France, England, and Poland. At the age of nine they were placed in a convent, where they died almost simultaneously in their twenty-second year. During their travels all over Europe they were examined by many prominent physiologists, psychologists, and naturalists; Pope and several minor poets have celebrated their existence in verse; Buffon speaks of them in his "Natural History," and all the works on teratology for a century or more have mentioned them. A description of them can be best given by a quaint translation by Fisher of the Latin lines composed by a Hungarian physician and inscribed on a bronze statuette of them : [a] —

> Two sisters wonderful to behold, who have thus grown as one,
> That naught their bodies can divide, no power beneath the sun.
> The town of Szoenii gave them birth, hard by far-famed Komorn,
> Which noble fort may all the arts of Turkish sultans scorn.
> Lucina, woman's gentle friend, did Helen first receive ;
> And Judith, when three hours had passed, her mother's womb did leave.
> One urine passage serves for both ;—one anus, so they tell ;
> The other parts their numbers keep, and serve their owners well.
> Their parents poor did send them forth, the world to travel through,
> That this great wonder of the age should not be hid from view.
> The inner parts concealed do lie hid from our eyes, alas !
> But all the body here you view erect in solid brass.

They were joined back to back in the lumbar region, and had all their parts separate except the anus between the right thigh of Helen and the left of Judith and a single vulva.   Helen was the larger, better looking,

the more active, and the more intelligent. Judith at the age of six became hemiplegic, and afterward was rather delicate and depressed.   They menstruated at sixteen and continued with regularity, although one began before the other.   They had a mutual affection, and did all in their power to alleviate the circumstances of their sad position.   Judith died of cerebral and pulmonary affections, and Helen, who previously enjoyed good health, soon after her sister's first indisposition suddenly sank into a state of collapse, although preserving her mental faculties, and expired almost immediately after her sister.   They had measles and small-pox simultaneously, but were affected in different degree by the maladies. The emotions, inclinations, and appetites were not simultaneous.   Eccardus, in a very inter-

Fig. 40.—The Hungarian sisters.

esting paper, discusses the physical, moral, and religious questions in reference to these wonderful sisters, such as the advisability of separation, the admissibility of matrimony, and, finally, whether on the last day they would rise as joined in life, or separated.

There is an account [b] of two united females, similar in conjunction to the "Hungarian sisters," who were born in Italy in 1700.   They were killed at the age of four months by an attempt of a surgeon to separate them.

a 773, 1866.   b 105, v., 445.

In 1856 there was reported to have been born in Texas twins after the manner of Helen and Judith, united back to back, who lived and attained some age. They were said to have been of different natures and dispositions, and inclined to quarrel very often.

Pancoast [a] gives an extensive report of **Millie-Christine,** who had been extensively exhibited in Europe and the United States. They were born of slave parents in Columbus County, N. C., July 11, 1851 ; the mother, who had borne 8 children before, was a stout negress of thirty-two, with a large pelvis. The presentation was first by the stomach and afterward by the breech. These twins were united at the sacra by a cartilaginous or possibly osseous union. They were exhibited in Paris in 1873, and provoked as much discussion there as in the United States. Physically, Millie was the weaker, but had the stronger will and the dominating spirit. They menstruated regularly from the age of thirteen. One from long habit yielded instinctively to the other's movements, thus preserving the necessary harmony. They ate separately, had distinct thoughts, and carried on distinct conversations at the same time. They experienced hunger and thirst generally simultaneously, and defecated and urinated nearly at the same times. One, in tranquil sleep, would be wakened by a call of nature of the other. Common sensibility was experienced near the location of union. They were intelligent and agreeable and of pleasant appearance, although

Fig. 41.—Millie-Christine (Pancoast).

slightly under size ; they sang duets with pleasant voices and accompanied themselves with a guitar ; they walked, ran, and danced with apparent ease and grace. Christine could bend over and lift Millie up by the bond of union.

A recent example of the pygopagus type was **Rosa-Josepha Blazek,** [b] born in Skerychov, in Bohemia, January 20, 1878. These twins had a broad bony union in the lower part of the lumbar region, the pelvis being obviously completely fused. They had a common urethral and anal aperture, but a double vaginal orifice, with a very apparent septum. The sensation was distinct in each, except where the pelves joined. They were exhibited in Paris

a 631, 1871, i.   b 778, xxii., 265.

in 1891, being then on an exhibition tour around the world.   Rosa was the
stronger, and when she walked or ran forward she drew her sister with her,
who must naturally have reversed her steps.   They had independent thoughts
and separate minds ; one could sleep while the other was awake.   Many of
their appetites were different, one preferring beer, the other wine ; one relished
salad, the other detested it, etc.   Thirst and hunger were not simultaneous.
Baudoin [a] describes their anatomic construction, their mode of life, and their
mannerisms and tastes in a quite recent article.   Fig. 42 is a reproduction
of an early photograph of the twins, and Fig. 43 represents a recent photograph of these " Bohemian twins," as they are now called.

Fig. 42.—Blazek sisters.

The latest record we have of this type of monstrosity is that given by
Tynberg to the County Medical Society of New York, May 27, 1895.   The
mother was present with the remarkable twins in her arms, crying at the top
of their voices.   These two children were born at midnight on April 15th.
Tynberg remarked that he believed them to be distinct and separate children,
and not dependent on a common arterial system ; he also expressed his intention of separating them, but did not believe the operation could be performed
with safety before another year.   Jacobi [b] describes in full Tynberg's instance
of pygopagus.   He says the confinement was easy ; the head of one was born
first, soon followed by the feet and the rest of the twins.   The placenta was

single and the cord consisted of two branches. The twins were united below the third sacral vertebræ in such a manner that they could lie alongside of each other. They were females, and had two vaginæ, two urethræ, four labia minora, and two labia majora, one anus, but a double rectum divided by a septum. They micturated independently but defecated simultaneously. They virtually lived separate lives, as one might be asleep while the other cried, etc.

CLASS V.—While instances of **ischiopagi** are quite numerous, few have attained any age, and, necessarily, little notoriety. Paré[a] speaks of twins

Fig. 43.—Bohemian twins.

united at the pelves, who were born in Paris July 20, 1570. They were baptized, and named **Louis and Louise.** Their parents were well known in the rue des Gravelliers. According to Bateman,[191] and also Rueff, in the year 1552 there were born, not far from Oxford, female twins, who, from the description given, were doubtless of the ischiopagus type. They seldom wept, and one was of a cheerful disposition, while the other was heavy and drowsy, sleeping continually. They only lived a short time, one expiring a day before the other. Licetus[486] speaks of Mrs. John Waterman, a resident of Fishertown, near Salisbury, England, who gave birth to a double female monster on October 26, 1664, which evidently from the description was

[a] 618, 1010.

joined by the ischii. It did not nurse, but took food by both the mouths; all its actions were done in concert; it was possessed of one set of genito-urinary organs; it only lived a short while. Many people in the region flocked to see the wonderful child, whom Licetus called "Monstrum Anglicum." It is said that at the same accouchement the birth of this monster was followed by the birth of a well-formed female child, who survived. Geoffroy-Saint-Hilaire quotes a description of twins who were born in France on October 7, 1838, symmetrically formed and united at their ischii. One was christened **Marie-Louise,** and the other **Hortense-Honorine.** Their avaricious parents took the children to Paris for exhibition, the exposures of which soon sacrificed their lives. In the year 1841 there was born in the island of Ceylon, of native parents, a monstrous child that was soon

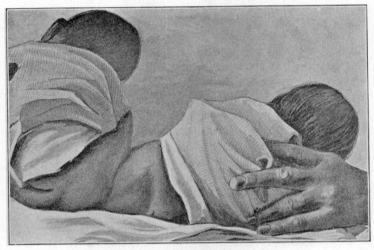

Fig. 44.—Tynberg's case.

brought to Columbo, where it lived only two months.[a] It had two heads and seemed to have duplication in all its parts except the anus and male generative organs. Montgomery[b] speaks of a double child born in County Roscommon, Ireland, on the 24th of July, 1827. It had two heads, two chests with arms complete, two abdominal and pelvic cavities united end to end, and four legs, placed two on either side. It had only one anus, which was situated between the thighs. One of the twins was dark haired and was baptized Mary, while the other was a blonde and was named Catherine. These twins felt and acted independently of each other; they each in succession sucked from the breast or took milk from the spoon, and used their limbs vigorously. One vomited without affecting the other, but the feces were discharged through a common opening.

a 318, vol. lxi., 58.   b 313, vol. xv.

Goodell [a] speaks of **Minna and Minnie Finley,** who were born in Ohio and examined by him. They were fused together in a common longitudinal axis, having one pelvis, two heads, four legs, and four arms. One was weak and puny and the other robust and active ; it is probable that they had but one rectum and one bladder. Goodell accompanies his description by the mention of several analogous cases. Ellis [b] speaks of female twins, born in Millville, Tenn., and exhibited in New York in 1868, who were joined at the pelves in a longitudinal axis. Between the limbs on either side were to be seen well-developed female genitals, and the sisters had been known to urinate from both sides, beginning and ending at the same time.

Huff [c] details a description of the **"Jones twins,"** born on June 24, 1889, in Tipton County, Indiana, whose spinal columns were in apposition at the lower end. The labor, of less than two hours' duration, was completed

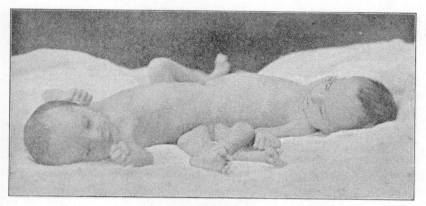

Fig. 45.—The Jones twins.

before the arrival of the physician. Lying on their mother's back, they could both nurse at the same time. Both sets of genitals and ani were on the same side of the line of union, but occupied normal positions with reference to the legs on either side. Their weight at birth was 12 pounds and their length 22 inches. Their mother was a medium-sized brunette of 19, and had one previous child then living at the age of two ; their father was a finely formed man 5 feet 10 inches in height. The twins differed in complexion and color of the eyes and hair. They were publicly exhibited for some time, and died February 19 and 20, 1891, at St. John's Hotel, Buffalo, N. Y. Figure 45 shows their appearance several months after birth.

CLASS VI.—In our sixth class, the first record we have is from the Commentaries of Sigbert, which contains a description of a monstrosity born in the reign of the Emperor Theodosius, who had two heads, two chests with four

a 547, 1870.   b 218, 1871, 218 *et seq.*   c 125, vol. xxii., 923.

arms attached, but a single lower extremity. The emotions, affections, and appetites were different. One head might be crying while the other laughed, or one feeding while the other was sleeping. At times they quarreled and occasionally came to blows. This monster is said to have lived two years, one part dying four days before the other, which evinced symptoms of decay like its inseparable neighbor.

Roger of Wendover[689] says that in Lesser Brittany and Normandy, in 1062, there was seen a female monster, consisting of two women joined about the umbilicus and fused into a single lower extremity. They took their food by two mouths but expelled it at a single orifice. At one time, one of the women laughed, feasted, and talked, while the other wept, fasted, and kept a religious silence. The account relates how one of them died, and the survivor bore her dead sister about for three years before she was overcome by the oppression and stench of the cadaver. Bateman[191] describes the birth of a boy in 1529, who had two heads, four ears, four arms, but only two thighs and two legs. Buchanan[a] speaks at length of the famous **"Scottish Brothers,"** who were the cynosure of the eyes of the Court of James III. of Scotland. This monster consisted of two men, ordinary in appearance in the superior extremities, whose trunks fused into a single lower extremity. The King took diligent care of their education, and they became proficient in music, languages, and other court accomplishments. Between them they would carry on animated conversations, sometimes merging into curious debates, followed by blows. Above the point of union they had no synchronous sensations, while below, sensation was common to both. This monster lived twenty-eight years, surviving the royal patron, who died June, 1488. One of the brothers died some days before the other, and the survivor, after carrying about his dead brother, succumbed to "infection from putrescence." There was reported to have been born[191] in Switzerland a double-headed male monster, who in 1538, at the age of thirty, was possessed of a beard on each face, the two bodies fused at the umbilicus into a single lower extremity. These two twins resembled one another in contour and countenance. They were so joined that at rest they looked upon one another. They had a single wife, with whom they were said to have lived in harmony. In the Gentleman's Magazine about one hundred and fifty years since there was given the portrait and description of a double woman, who was exhibited all over the large cities of Europe. Little can be ascertained anatomically of her construction, with the exception that it was stated that she had two heads, two necks, four arms, two legs, one pelvis, and one set of pelvic organs.

The most celebrated monster of this type was **Ritta-Christina** (Figs. 46 and 47), who was born in Sassari, in Sardinia, March 23, 1829. These twins were the result of the ninth confinement of their mother, a woman of thirty-two. Their superior extremities were double, but they joined in a common trunk

a Rerum Scoticarum Historia, Aberdeen, 1762, L. xiii.

at a point a little below the mammæ. Below this point they had a common trunk and single lower extremities. The right one, christened Ritta, was feeble and of a sad and melancholy countenance ; the left, Christina, was vigorous and of a gay and happy aspect. They suckled at different times, and sensations in the upper extremities were distinct. They expelled urine and feces simultaneously, and had the indications in common. Their parents, who were very poor, brought them to Paris for the purpose of public exhibition, which at first was accomplished clandestinely, but finally interdicted by the public authorities, who feared that it would open a door for psychologic discussion and speculation. This failure of the parents to secure public patronage increased their poverty and hastened the death of the children by unavoidable exposure in a cold room. The nervous system of the twins had little in common except in the line of union, the anus, and the sexual organs,

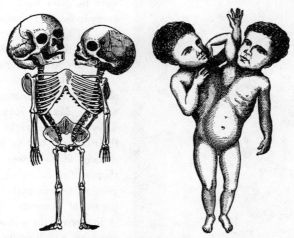

Fig. 46.—Skeleton of Ritta-Christina.   Fig. 47.—Ritta-Christina.

and Christina was in good health all through Ritta's sickness ; when Ritta died, her sister, who was suckling at the mother's breast, suddenly relaxed hold and expired with a sigh. At the postmortem, which was secured with some difficulty on account of the authorities ordering the bodies to be burned, the pericardium was found single, covering both hearts. The digestive organs were double and separate as far as the lower third of the ilium, and the cecum was on the left side and single, in common with the lower bowel. The livers were fused and the uterus was double. The vertebral columns, which were entirely separate above, were joined below by a rudimentary os innominatum. There was a junction between the manubrium of each. Sir Astley Cooper saw a monster in Paris in 1792 which, by his description, must have been very similar to Ritta-Christina.

The **Tocci brothers** were born in 1877 in the province of Turin, Italy. They each had a well-formed head, perfect arms, and a perfect thorax to the sixth rib ; they had a common abdomen, a single anus, two legs, two sacra, two vertebral columns, one penis, but three buttocks, the central one containing a rudimentary anus.   The right boy was christened Giovanni-Batista, and the

Fig. 48.—The Tocci brothers.

left Giacomo. Each individual had power over the corresponding leg on his side, but not over the other one. Walking was therefore impossible. All their sensations and emotions were distinctly individual and independent. At the time of the report, in 1882, they were in good health and showed every indication of attaining adult age. Figure 48 represents these twins as they were exhibited several years ago in Germany.

McCallum[a] saw two female children in Montreal in 1878 named **Marie - Rosa Drouin**. They formed a right angle with their single trunk, which commenced at the lower part of the thorax of each. They had a single genital fissure and the external organs of generation of a female. A little over three inches from the anus was a rudimentary limb with a movable articulation ; it measured five inches in length and tapered to a fine point, being furnished with a distinct nail, and it contracted strongly to irritation. Marie, the left child, was of fair complexion and more strongly developed than Rosa. The sensations of hunger and thirst were not experienced at the same time, and one might be asleep while the other was crying. The pulsations and the respiratory movements were not synchronous. They were the products of the second gestation of a mother aged twenty-six, whose abdomen was of such preternatural size during pregnancy that she was ashamed to appear in public.

[a] 778, vol. xx., 120.

The order of birth was as follows : one head and body, the lower extremity, and the second body and head.

CLASS VII.—There are many instances of **bicephalic monsters** on record. Paré [a] mentions and gives an illustration of a female apparently single in conformation, with the exception of having two heads and two necks. The Ephemerides, Haller, Schenck, and Archenholz cite examples, and there is an old account [b] of a double-headed child, each of whose heads were baptized, one called Martha and the other Mary. One was of a gay and the other a sad visage, and both heads received nourishment; they only lived a couple of days. There is another similar record of a Milanese girl who had two heads, but was in all other respects single, with the exception that after death she was found to have had two stomachs. Besse mentions a Bavarian woman of twenty-six with two heads, one of which was comely and the other extremely ugly; Batemen [191] quotes what is apparently the same case—a woman in Bavaria in 1541 with two heads, one of which was deformed, who begged from door to door, and who by reason of the influence of pregnant women was given her expenses to leave the country.

A more common occurrence of this type is that in which there is fusion of the two heads. Moreau [c] speaks of a monster in Spain which was shown from town to town. Its heads were fused; it had two mouths and two noses; in each face an eye well conformed and placed above the nose; there was a third eye in the middle of the forehead common to both heads; the third eye was of primitive development and had two pupils. Each face was well formed and had its own chin. Buffon mentions a cat, the exact analogue of Moreau's case. Sutton [d] speaks of a photograph sent to Sir James Paget in 1856 by William Budd of Bristol. This portrays a living child with a supernumerary head, which had mouth, nose, eyes, and a brain of its own (Fig. 49). The eyelids were abortive, and as there was no orbital cavity the eyes stood out in the form of naked globes on the forehead. When born, the corneas of both heads were transparent, but then became opaque from exposure. The brain of the supernumerary head was quite visible from without, and was covered by a membrane beginning to slough. On the right side of the head was a rudimentary external ear. The nurse said that when the child sucked some milk regurgitated through the supernumerary mouth. The great physiologic interest in this case lies in the fact that every movement and every act of the natural face was simultaneously repeated by the supernumerary face in a perfectly consensual manner, *i. e.*, when the natural mouth sucked, the second mouth sucked; when the natural face cried, yawned, or sneezed, the second face did likewise; and the eyes of the two heads moved in unison. The fate of the child is not known.

Home [e] speaks of a child born in Bengal with a most peculiar fusion of

a 618, 1006.   b 469, 1665.   c Quoted, 302, xxxiv., 171.
d 275, 1895, 133.   e 629, 1791, 299.

the head. The ordinary head was nearly perfect and of usual volume, but fused with its vertex and reversed was a supernumerary head (Fig. 50). Each head had its own separate vessels and brain, and each an individual sensibility, but if one had milk first the other had an abundance of saliva in its mouth. It narrowly escaped being burned to death at birth, as the midwife, greatly frightened by the monstrous appearance, threw it into the fire to destroy it, from whence it was rescued, although badly burned, the vicious conformation of the accessory head being possibly due to the accident. At the age of four it was bitten by a venomous serpent and, as a result, died. Its skull is in the possession of the Royal College of Surgeons in London.

Fig. 49.—Infant with a supernumerary head   Fig. 50.—Two-headed boy (Home's case).
　　　　(after Sutton).

The following well-known story of Edward Mordake, though taken from lay sources, is of sufficient notoriety and interest to be mentioned here :—

" One of the weirdest as well as most melancholy stories of human deformity is that of Edward Mordake, said to have been heir to one of the noblest peerages in England. He never claimed the title, however, and committed suicide in his twenty-third year. He lived in complete seclusion, refusing the visits even of the members of his own family. He was a young man of fine attainments, a profound scholar, and a musician of rare ability. His figure was remarkable for its grace, and his face—that is to say, his natural face—was that of an Antinous. But upon the back of his head was another face, that of a beautiful girl, ' lovely as a dream, hideous as a devil.' The female face was a mere mask, ' occupying only a small portion of the posterior part of the skull, yet exhibiting every sign of intelligence, of a malignant sort, however.' It would be seen to smile and sneer while Mordake was weeping. The eyes would follow the movements of the spectator, and the lips would 'gibber without ceasing.' No voice was audible, but Mordake avers that he was kept from his rest at night by the hateful whispers of his 'devil twin,' as he called it, 'which never sleeps, but talks to me forever of such things as they only speak of in hell. No imagination can conceive the dreadful temptations it sets before me. For some unforgiven wickedness of my forefathers I am knit to this fiend—for a fiend it surely is. I' beg and beseech you to crush it out of human semblance, even if I die for it.' Such were the words of the hapless Mordake to Manvers and Treadwell, his physicians. In spite of careful watching he managed to procure poison, whereof he died, leaving a letter requesting that the 'demon face' might be destroyed before his burial, ' lest it continues its dreadful whisperings in my grave.' At his own request he was interred in a waste place, without stone or legend to mark his grave."

A most curious case was that of a Fellah woman[a] who was delivered at Alexandria of a bicephalic monster of apparently eight months' pregnancy. This creature, which was born dead, had one head white and the other black, the change of color commencing at the neck of the black head. The bizarre head was of negro conformation and fully developed, and the colored skin was found to be due to the existence of pigment similar to that found in the black race. The husband of the woman had a light brown skin, like an ordinary Fellah man, and it was ascertained that there were some negro laborers in port during the woman's pregnancy ; but no definite information as to her relations with them could be established, and whether this was a case of maternal impression or superfetation can only be a matter of conjecture.

Fantastic monsters, such as acephalon, paracephalon, cyclops, pseudencephalon, and the janiceps (Fig. 51), prosopthoracopagus (Fig. 52), disprosopus (Fig. 53), etc., although full of interest, will not be discussed here, as none are ever viable for any length of time, and the declared intention of this chapter is to include only those beings who have lived.

CLASS VIII.—The next class includes the **parasitic terata,** monsters that consist of one perfect body, complete in every respect, but from the neighborhood of whose umbilicus depends some important portion of a second body. Paré, Benivenius, and Columbus describe adults with acephalous monsters attached to them. Schenck mentions 13 cases, 3 of which were observed by him. Aldrovandus[116] shows 3 illustrations under the name of "monstrum bicorpum monocephalon." Buxtorf[b] speaks of a case in which the nates and lower extremities of one body proceeded out of the abdomen of the other, which was otherwise perfect. Reichel and Anderson[c] mention a living parasitic monster, the inferior trunk of one body proceeding from the pectoral region of the other.

[a] 789, Aug. 5, 1848.   [b] 107, vol. vii., n. xii., 101.   [c] 629, vol. lxxix.

Paré[a] says that there was a man in Paris in 1530, quite forty years of age, who carried about a parasite without a head, which hung pendant from his belly. This individual was exhibited and drew great crowds. Paré

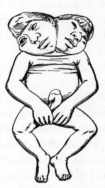

Fig. 51.—Janiceps.   Fig. 52.—Prosopthoracopagus.   Fig. 53.—Disprosopus.

appends an illustration, which is, perhaps, one of the most familiar in all teratology. He also[b] gives a portrait (Fig. 54) of a man who had a parasitic head

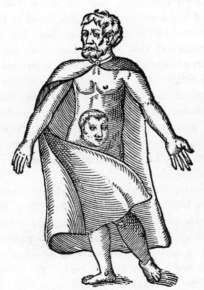

Fig. 54.—Parasitic monster (after Paré).   Fig. 55.—Thoracopagus. Lazarus-Joannes Baptista
                                                                       Colloredo.

proceeding from his epigastrium, and who was born in Germany the same year that peace was made with the Swiss by King Francis. This creature lived

a 618, 1007.   b 618, 1012.

to manhood and both heads were utilized in alimentation. Bartholinus [a] details a history of an individual named **Lazarus-Joannes Baptista Colloredo** (Fig. 55), born in Genoa in 1617, who exhibited himself all over Europe. From his epigastrium hung an imperfectly developed twin that had one thigh, hands, body, arms, and a well-formed head covered with hair, which in the normal position hung lowest. There were signs of independent existence in the parasite, movements of respiration, etc., but its eyes were closed, and, although saliva constantly dribbled from its open mouth, nothing was ever ingested. The genitals were imperfect and the arms ended in badly formed hands. Bartholinus examined this monster at twenty-two, and has given the best report, although while in Scotland in 1642 he was again examined, and accredited with being married and the father of several children who were fully and admirably developed. Moreau quotes a case of an infant similar in conformation to the foregoing monster, who was born in Switzerland in 1764, and whose supernumerary parts were amputated by means of a ligature. Winslow reported before the Académie Royale des Sciences the history of a girl of twelve who died at the Hôtel-Dieu in 1733. She was of ordinary height and of fair conformation, with the exception that hanging from the left flank was the inferior half of another girl of diminutive proportions. The supernumerary body was immovable, and hung so heavily that it was said to be supported by the hands or by a sling. Urine and feces were evacuated at intervals from the parasite, and received into a diaper constantly worn for this purpose. Sensibility in the two was common, an impression applied to the parasite being felt by the girl. Winslow gives an interesting report of the dissection of this monster, and mentions that he had seen an Italian child of eight who had a small head proceeding from under the cartilage of the third left rib. Sensibility was common, pinching the ear of the parasitic head causing the child with the perfect head to cry. Each of the two heads received baptism, one being named John and the other Matthew. A curious question arose in the instance of the girl, as to whether the extreme unction should be administered to the acephalous fetus as well as to the child.

In 1742, during the Ambassadorship of the Marquis de l'Hôpital at Naples, he saw in that city an aged man, well conformed, with the exception that, like the little girl of Winslow, he had the inferior extremities of a male child growing from his epigastric region. Haller and Meckel have also observed cases like this. Bordat described before the Royal Institute of France, August, 1826, a Chinaman, twenty-one years of age, who had an acephalous fetus attached to the surface of his breast (possibly " A-ke ").

Dickinson [b] describes a wonderful child five years old, who, by an extraordinary freak of nature, was an amalgamation of two children. From the body of an otherwise perfectly formed child was a supernumerary head pro-

a 190, hist. lviii.   b 703, 1880.

truding from a broad base attached to the lower lumbar and sacral region. This cephalic mass was covered with hair about four or five inches long, and showed the rudiments of an eye, nose, mouth, and chin. This child was on exhibition when Dickinson saw it. Montaré and Reyes were commissioned by the Academy of Medicine of Havana to examine and report on a monstrous girl of seven months, living in Cuba. The girl was healthy and well developed, and from the middle line of her body between the xiphoid cartilage and the umbilicus, attached by a soft pedicle, was an accessory individual, irregular, of ovoid shape, the smaller end, representing the head, being upward. The parasite measured a little over 1 foot in length, 9 inches about the head, and 7¾ inches around the neck. The cranial bones were distinctly felt, and the top of the head was covered by a circlet of hair. There were two rudimentary eyebrows; the left eye was represented by a minute perforation

Fig. 56.—Louise L.

encircled with hair; the right eye was traced by one end of a mucous groove which ran down to another transverse groove representing the mouth; the right third of this latter groove showed a primitive tongue and a triangular tooth, which appeared at the fifth month. There was a soft, imperforate nose, and the elements of the vertebral column could be distinguished beneath the skin; there were no legs; apparently no vascular sounds; there was separate sensation, as the parasite could be pinched without attracting the perfect infant's notice. The mouth of the parasite constantly dribbled saliva, but showed no indication of receiving aliment.[a]

Louise L., known as **"La dame à quatre jambes,"** was born in 1869, and had attached to her pelvis another rudimentary pelvis and two atrophied legs of a parasite, weighing 8 kilos. The attachment was effected by means of a pedicle 33 cm. in diameter, having a bony basis, and being fixed without a joint. The attachment almost obliterated the vulva and the perineum was displaced far backward. At the insertion of the parasite were two rudimentary mammæ, one larger than the other (Fig. 56). No genitalia were seen on the parasite and it exhibited no active movements, the joints of both limbs being ankylosed. The woman could localize sensations in the parasite except those of the feet. She had been married five years, and bore, in the space of three years, two well-formed daughters.

Quite recently there was exhibited in the museums of the United States an individual bearing the name "**Laloo,**" who was born in Oudh, India, and was the second of four children. At the time of examination he was about nineteen years of age. The upper portion of a parasite was firmly attached

[a] 224, 1886, i., 81.

to the lower right side of the sternum of the individual by a bony pedicle, and lower by a fleshy pedicle, and apparently contained intestines. The anus of the parasite was imperforate ; a well-developed penis was found, but no testicles ; there was a luxuriant growth of hair on the pubes. The penis of the parasite was said to show signs of erection at times, and urine passed through it without the knowledge of the boy. Perspiration and elevation of temperature seemed to occur simultaneously in both. To pander to the morbid curiosity of the curious, the " Dime Museum " managers at one time shrewdly clothed the parasite in female attire, calling the two brother and sister ; but there is no doubt that all the traces of sex were of the male type. An analogous case was that of " **A-Ke**," a Chinaman, who was exhibited in London early in the century, and of whom and his parasite anatomic models are seen in our museums. Figure 58 represents an epignathus, a peculiar type of parasitic monster, in which the parasite is united to the inferior maxillary bone of the autosite.

Fig. 57.—Laloo.

CLASS IX.—Of " Lusus naturæ " none is more curious than that of **duplication of the lower extremities.** Paré [a] says that on January 9, 1529, there was living in Germany a male infant having four legs and four arms. In Paris, at the Académie des Sciences, on September 6, 1830, there was presented by Madame Hen, a midwife, a living male child with four legs, the anus being nearly below the middle of the third buttock ; and the scrotum between the two left thighs, the testicles not yet descended. There was a well-formed and single pelvis, and the supernumerary legs were immovable. Aldrovandus mentions several similar instances, and gives the figure of one born in Rome ; he also describes several quadruped birds. Bardsley [b] speaks of a male child with one head, four arms, four legs, and double generative organs. He gives a portrait of the child when it was a little over a year old. Heschl published in Vienna in 1878 a description of a girl of seventeen, who instead of having a duplication of the superior body, as in "Millie-Christine, the two-headed nightingale," had double parts below the second lumbar vertebra. Her head and upper body resembled a comely, delicate girl of twelve.

Wells [a] describes Mrs. B., aged twenty, still alive and healthy (Fig. 59). The duplication in this case begins just above the waist, the spinal column dividing at the third lumbar vertebra, below this point everything being double. Micturition and defecation occur at different times, but menstruation occurs simultaneously. She was married at nineteen, and became pregnant a year later on the left side, but abortion was induced at the fourth month on account of persistent nausea and the expectation of impossible delivery. Whaley,[b] in speaking of this case, said Mrs. B. utilized her outside legs for walking; he also remarks that when he informed her that she was pregnant on the left side she replied, "I think you are mistaken; if it had been on my right side I would come nearer believing it ;"—and after further questioning he found, from the patient's observation, that her right genitals were almost invariably used for coitus.

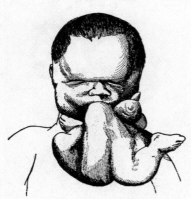

Fig. 58.—Epignathus.

Bechlinger of Para, Brazil,[c] describes a woman of twenty-five, a native of Martinique, whose father was French and mother a quadroon, who had a modified duplication of the lower body. There was a third leg attached to a continuation of the processus coccygeus of the sacrum, and in addition to well-developed mammæ regularly situated, there were two rudimentary ones close together above the pubes. There were two vaginæ and two well-developed vulvæ, both having equally developed sensations. The sexual appetite was markedly developed, and coitus was practised in both vaginæ. A somewhat similar case, possibly the same, is that of **Blanche Dumas,** born in 1860. She had a very broad pelvis, two imperfectly developed legs, and a supernumerary limb attached to the symphysis, without a joint, but with slight passive movement. There was a duplication of bowel, bladder, and genitalia. At the junction of the rudimentary limb with the body, in front, were two rudimentary mammary glands, each containing a nipple (Fig. 60).

Other instances of supernumerary limbs will be found in Chapter VI.

CLASS X.—The instances of **diphallic terata,** by their intense interest to the natural bent of the curious mind, have always elicited much discussion. To many of these cases have been attributed exaggerated function,

a 125, 1888, 1266.   b 224, 1889, i., 96.   c Annals of Gynecology, 1888.

notwithstanding the fact that modern observation almost invariably shows that the virile power diminishes in exact proportion to the extent of duplication. Taylor [757] quotes a description of a monster, exhibited in London, with two distinct penises, but with only one distinct testicle on either side. He could exercise the function of either organ.

Fig. 59.—Dipygus (Wells).

Schenck, Schurig, Bartholinus, Loder, and Ollsner report instances of diphallic terata ; the latter case [a] was in a soldier of Charles VI., twenty-two years old, who applied to the surgeon for a bubonic affection, and who declared that he passed urine from the orifice of the left glans and also said that he was incapable of true coitus. Valentini mentions an instance in a boy of four, in which the two penises were superimposed. Bucchettoni [b] speaks of a man with two penises placed side by side. There was an anonymous case described [c] of a man of ninety-three with a penis which was for more than half its length divided into two distinct members, the right being somewhat larger than the left. From the middle of the penis up to the symphysis only the lower wall of the urethra was split. Jenisch [d] describes a diphallic infant, the offspring of a woman of twenty-five who had been married five years. Her first child was a well-formed female, and the second, the infant in question, cried much during the night, and several times vomited dark-green matter. In lieu of one penis there were two, situated near each other, the right one of natural size and the left larger, but not furnished with a prepuce. Each penis had its own urethra, from which dribbled urine and some meconium. There was a

Fig. 60.—Blanche Dumas.

a Medicorum Siles. Satyræ. Lipsiæ, 1736.   b Anatomia, etc., p. 120, Œniponte, 1740.
c 559, 1808, Band ii., 335.   d Med. Corresp.-Blatt des württemb. ärztl. Ver., Stuttg., 1837.

duplication of each scrotum, but only one testicle in each, and several other minor malformations (Fig. 61).

Goré, reported by Velpeau,[a] has seen an infant of eight and one-half

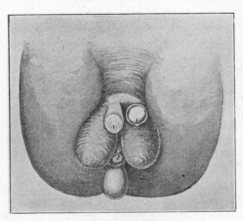

Fig. 61.—Double penis (Jenisch's case).

months with two penises and three lower extremities. The penises were 4 cm. apart and the scrotum divided, containing one testicle in each side. Each penis was provided with a urethra, urine being discharged from both simultaneously. In a similar case, spoken of by Geoffroy-Saint-Hilaire, the two organs were also separate, but urine and semen escaped sometimes from one, sometimes from both.

The most celebrated of all the diphallic terata was **Jean Baptista dos Santos,** who when but six months old was spoken of by Acton. His father and mother were healthy and had two well-formed children. He was easily born after an uneventful pregnancy. He was good-looking, well proportioned, and had two distinct penises, each as large as that of a child of six months. Urination proceeded simultaneously from both penises ; he had also two scrotums. Behind and between the legs there was another limb, or rather two, united throughout their length. It was connected to the pubis by a short stem ½ inch long and as large as the little finger, consisting of separate bones and cartilages.

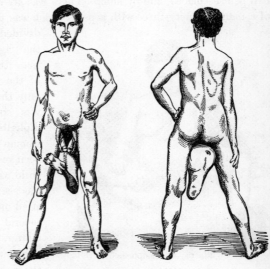

Fig. 62.—Jean Baptista dos Santos.

on the anal aspect, and a joint freely movable. There was a patella in the supernumerary limb This compound limb had no power of motion, but was endowed with sensibility. A journal in London,[a] after quoting Acton's description, said that the child had been exhibited in Paris, and that the surgeons advised operation. Fisher,[b] to whom we are indebted for an exhaustive work in Teratology, received a report from Havana in July, 1865, which detailed a description of Santos at twenty-two years of age, and said that he was possessed of extraordinary animal passion, the sight of a female alone being sufficient to excite him. He was said to use both penises, after finishing with one continuing with the other ; but this account of him does not agree with later descriptions, in which no excessive sexual ability had been noticed. Hart[c] describes the adult Santos in full, and accompanies his article with an illustration. At this time he was said to have developed double genitals, and possibly a double bladder communicating by an imperfect septum. At adulthood the anus was three inches anterior to the os coccygeus. In the sitting or lying posture the supernumerary limb rested on the front of the inner surface of the lower third of his left thigh. He was in the habit of wearing this limb in a sling, or bound firmly to the right thigh, to prevent its unseemly dangling when erect. The perineum proper was absent, the entire space between the anus and the posterior edge of the scrotum being occupied by the pedicle. Santos' mental and physical functions were developed above normal, and he impressed everybody with his accomplishments. Geoffroy-Saint-Hilaire records an instance in which the conformation was similar to that of Santos. There was a third lower extremity consisting of two limbs fused into one with a single foot containing ten distinct digits. He calls the case one of arrested twin development.

Van Buren and Keyes[d] describe a case in a man of forty-two, of good, healthy appearance. The two distinct penises of normal size were apparently well formed and were placed side by side, each attached at its root to the symphysis. Their covering of skin was common as far as the base of the glans ; at this point they seemed distinct and perfect, but the meatus of the left was imperforate. The right meatus was normal, and through it most of the urine passed, though some always dribbled through an opening in the perineum at a point where the root of the scrotum should have been. On lifting the double-barreled penis this opening could be seen and was of sufficient size to admit the finger. On the right side of the aperture was an elongated and rounded prominence similar in outline to a labium majus. This prominence contained a testicle normal in shape and sensibility, but slightly undersized, and surrounded, as was evident from its mobility, by a tunica vaginalis. The left testicle lay on the tendon of the adductor longus in the left groin ; it was not fully developed, but the patient had sexual desires, erections, and emissions. Both penises became erect simultaneously,

a 549, April, 1847, 322.   b 773, 1866.   c 476, 1866, i., 71.
d " Surgical Diseases of the Genito-Urinary Organs," New York, 1874.

the right more vigorously. The left leg was shorter than the right and congenitally smaller ; the mammæ were of normal dimensions.

Sangalli [a] speaks of a man of thirty-five who had a supernumerary penis, furnished with a prepuce and capable of erection. At the apex of the glans opened a canal about 12 cm. long, through which escaped monthly a serous fluid. Smith [b] mentions a man who had two penises and two bladders, on one of which lithotomy was performed. According to Ballantyne, Taruffi, the scholarly observer of terata, mentions a child of forty-two months and height of 80 cm. who had two penises, each furnished with a urethra and well-formed scrotal sacs which were inserted in a fold of the groin. There were two testicles felt in the right scrotum and one in the left. Fecal evacuations escaped through two anal orifices. There is also another case mentioned similar to the foregoing in a man of forty ; but here there was an osseous projection in the middle line behind the bladder. This patient said that erection was simultaneous in both penises, and that he had not married because of his chagrin over his deformity. Cole [c] speaks of a child with two well-developed male organs, one to the left and the other to the right of the median line, and about $\frac{1}{4}$ or $\frac{1}{2}$ inch apart at birth. The urethra bifurcated in the perineal region and sent a branch to each penis, and urine passed from each meatus. The scrotum was divided into three compartments by two raphes, and each compartment contained a testicle. The anus at birth was imperforate, but the child was successfully operated on, and at its sixtieth day weighed 17 pounds.

Lange [d] says that an infant was brought to Karg for relief of anal atresia when fourteen days old. It was found to possess duplicate penises, which communicated each to its distinct half of the bladder as defined by a median fold. The scrotum was divided into three portions by two raphes, and each lateral compartment contained a fully formed testicle. This child died because of its anal malformation, which we notice is a frequent associate of malformations or duplicity of the penis. There is an example in an infant described [e] in which there were two penises, each about $\frac{1}{2}$ inch long, and a divided scrotal sac $2\frac{1}{2}$ inches long. Englisch [f] speaks of a German of forty who possessed a double penis of the bifid type.

Ballantyne and his associates define diphallic terata as individuals provided with two more or less well-formed and more or less separate penises, who may show also other malformations of the adjoining parts and organs (e. g., septate bladder), but who are not possessed of more than two lower limbs. This definition excludes, therefore, the cases in which in addition to a double penis there is a supernumerary lower extremity—such a case, for example, as that of Jean Baptista dos Santos, so frequently described by teratologists. It also excludes the more evident double terata, and, of course, the cases of

a "La scienza a e la prat. dell. anat. patolog." Pavia, 1875, i., 117.   b 775, 1878, 91.
c 579, 1894, 159.   d 720, 1895, 215.   e 759, April, 1895.   f Quoted 759, Oct., 1895.

duplication of the female genital organs (double clitoris, vulva, vagina, and uterus). Although Schurig, Meckel, Himly, Taruffi, and others give bibliographic lists of diphallic terata, even in them erroneous references are common, and there is evidence to show that many cases have been duplicated under different names. Ballantyne and Skirving [a] have consulted all the older original references available and eliminated duplications of reports, and, adhering to their original definition, have collected and described individually 20 cases ; they offer the following conclusions :—

1. Diphallus, or duplication of the penis in an otherwise apparently single individual, is a very rare anomaly, records of only 20 cases having been found in a fairly exhaustive search through teratologic literature. As a distinct and well-authenticated type it has only quite recently been recognized by teratologists.

2. It does not of itself interfere with intrauterine or extrauterine life ; but the associated anomalies (*e. g.*, atresia ani) may be sources of danger. If not noticed at birth, it is not usually discovered till adult life, and even then the discovery is commonly accidental.

3. With regard to the functions of the pelvic viscera, urine may be passed by both penises, by one only, or by neither. In the last instance it finds exit by an aperture in the perineum. There is reason to believe that semen may be passed in the same way; but in most of the recorded cases there has been sterility, if not inability to perform the sexual act.

4. All the degrees of duplication have been met with, from a fissure of the glans penis to the presence of two distinct penises inserted at some distance from each other in the inguinal regions.

5. The two penises are usually somewhat defective as regards prepuce, urethra, etc. ; they may lie side by side, or more rarely may be situated anteroposteriorly ; they may be equal in size, or less commonly one is distinctly larger than the other ; and one or both may be perforate or imperforate.

6. The scrotum may be normal or split; the testicles, commonly two in number, may be normal or atrophic, descended or undescended ; the prostate may be normal or imperfectly developed, as may also the vasa deferentia and vesiculæ seminales.

7. The commonly associated defects are : More or less completely septate bladder, atresia ani, or more rarely double anus, double urethra, increased breadth of the bony pelvis with defect of the symphysis pubis, and possibly duplication of the lower end of the spine, and hernia of some of the abdominal contents into a perineal pouch. Much more rarely, duplication of the heart, lungs, stomach, and kidneys has been noted, and the lower limbs may be shorter than normal.

CLASS XI.—Cases of **fetus in fetu,** those strange instances in which one might almost say that a man may be pregnant with his brother or sister, or in

[a] 759, 1895.

which an infant may carry its twin without the fact being apparent, will next be discussed. The older cases were cited as being only a repetition of the process by which Eve was born of Adam. Figure 63 represents an old engraving showing the birth of Eve. Bartholinus, the Ephemerides, Otto, Paullini, Schurig, and Plot speak of instances of fetus in fetu. Ruysch [a] describes a tumor contained in the abdomen of a man which was composed of hair, molar teeth, and other evidences of a fetus. Huxham reported to the Royal Society in 1748 the history of a child which was born with a tumor near the anus larger than the whole body of the child; this tumor contained rudiments of an embryo. Young [b] speaks of a fetus which lay encysted between the laminæ of the transverse mesocolon, and Highmore published a report of a fetus in a cyst communicating with the duodenum.

Fig. 63.—Birth of Eve (after an old engraving).

Dupuytren gives an example in a boy of thirteen, in whom was found a fetus. Gaetano-Nocito, cited by Philipeaux,[302] has the history of a man of twenty-seven who was taken with a great pain in the right hypochondrium, and from which issued subsequently fetal bones and a mass of macerated embryo. His mother had had several double pregnancies, and from the length of the respective tibiæ one of the fetuses seemed to be of two months' and the other of three months' intrauterine life. The man died five years after the abscess had burst spontaneously. Brodie [c] speaks of a case in which fetal remains were taken from the abdomen of a girl of two and one-half years.

Gaither [d] describes a child of two years and nine months, supposed to be affected with ascites, who died three hours after the physician's arrival. In its abdomen was found a fetus weighing almost two pounds and connected to the child by a cord resembling an umbilical cord. This child was healthy for about nine months, and had a precocious longing for ardent spirits, and drank freely an hour before its death.

Blundell [e] says that he knew " a boy who was literally and without evasion with child, for the fetus was contained in a sac communicating with the abdomen and was connected to the side of the cyst by a short umbilical cord; nor did the fetus make its appearance until the boy was eight or ten years

a 698, Tome ii.   b 550, i., 234.   c 550, 1819.

d 598, 1809, i., 170 *et seq.*   e 476, 1828–1829, 260.

old, when after much enlargement of pregnancy and subsequent flooding the boy died." The fetus, removed after death, on the whole not very imperfectly formed, was of the size of about six or seven months' gestation. Bury [a] cites an account of a child that had a second imperfectly developed fetus in its face and scalp. There was a boy by the name of Bissieu [b] who from the earliest age had a pain in one of his left ribs ; this rib was larger than the rest and seemed to have a tumor under it. He died of phthisis at fourteen, and after death there was found in a pocket lying against the transverse colon and communicating with it all the evidences of a fetus.

At the Hôpital de la Charité in Paris, Velpeau startled an audience of 500 students and many physicians by saying that he expected to find a rudimentary fetus in a scrotal tumor placed in his hands for operation. His diagnosis proved correct, and brought him resounding praise, and all wondered as to his reasons for expecting a fetal tumor. It appears that he had read with care a report by Fatti [c] of an operation on the scrotum of a child which had increased in size as the child grew, and was found to contain the ribs, the vertebral column, the lower extremities as far as the knees, and the two orbits of a fetus ; and also an account [d] of a similar operation performed by Wendt of Breslau on a Silesian boy of seven. The left testicle in this case was so swollen that it hung almost to the knee, and the fetal remains removed weighed seven ounces.

Sulikowski [e] relates an instance of congenital fetation in the umbilicus of a girl of fourteen, who recovered after the removal of the anomaly. Aretæos described to the members of the medical fraternity in Athens [f] the case of a woman of twenty-two, who bore two children after a seven months' pregnancy. One was very rudimentary and only $2\frac{1}{2}$ inches long, and the other had an enormous head resembling a case of hydrocephalus. On opening the head of the second fetus, another, three inches long, was found in the medulla oblongata, and in the cranial cavity with it were two additional fetuses, neither of which was perfectly formed.

Broca [g] speaks of a fetal cyst being passed in the urine of a man of sixty-one ; the cyst contained remnants of hair, bone, and cartilage. Atlee [h] submits quite a remarkable case of congenital ventral gestation, the subject being a girl of six, who recovered after the discharge of the fetal mass from the abdomen. McIntyre [i] speaks of a child of eleven, playing about and feeling well, but whose abdomen progressively increased in size $1\frac{1}{2}$ inches each day. After ten days there was a large fluctuating mass on the right side ; the abdomen was opened and the mass enucleated ; it was found to contain a fetal mass weighing nearly five pounds, and in addition ten pounds of fluid were removed. The child made an early recovery. Rogers [j] mentions a fetus that

a 490, 1834.   b 302, iv., 179.   c 240, 1826.   d 240, 1829.
e 233, 1851–2, 17, 143.   f 536, April 16, 1862.   g 362, No. 26, 1868.
h 768, 1879.   i 616, Feb., 1894.   j 131, 1875.

was found in a man's bladder. Bouchacourt [a] reports the successful extirpation of the remains of a fetus from the rectum of a child of six. Miner [b]
describes a successful excision of a congenital gestation.

Modern literature is full of examples, and nearly every one of the foregoing instances could be paralleled from other sources. Rodriguez [c] is quoted
as reporting that in July, 1891, several newspapers in the city of Mexico
published, under the head of "A Man-mother," a wonderful story, accompanied by wood-cuts, of a young man from whose body a great surgeon had
extracted a "perfectly developed fetus." One of these wood-cuts represented
a tumor at the back of a man opened and containing a crying baby. In
commenting upon this, after reviewing several similar cases of endocymian
monsters that came under his observation in Mexico, Rodriguez tells what
the case which had been so grossly exaggerated by the lay journals really
was : An Indian boy, aged twenty-two, presented a tumor in the sacrococ-
cygeal region measuring 53 cm. in circumference at the base, having a vertical
diameter of 17 cm. and a transverse diameter of 13 cm. It had no pedicle
and was fixed, showing unequal consistency. At birth this tumor was about
the size of a pigeon's egg. A diagnosis of dermoid cyst was made and two
operations were performed on the boy, death following the second. The
skeleton showed interesting conditions ; the rectum and pelvic organs were
natural, and the contents of the cyst verified the diagnosis.

Quite similar to the cases of fetus in fetu are the instances of **dermoid
cysts.** For many years they have been a mystery to physiologists, and their
origin now is little more than hypothetic. At one time the fact of finding such
a formation in the ovary of an unmarried woman was presumptive evidence
that she was unchaste ; but this idea was dissipated as soon as examples were
reported in children, and to-day we have a well-defined difference between
congenital and extrauterine pregnancy. Dermoid cysts of the ovary may
consist only of a wall of connective tissue lined with epidermis and containing distinctly epidermic scales which, however, may be rolled up in firm
masses of a more or less soapy consistency ; this variety is called by Orth
epidermoid cyst ; or, according to Warren, a form of cyst made up of skin
containing small and ill-defined papillæ, but rich in hair follicles and sebaceous glands. Even the erector pili muscle and the sudoriparous gland are
often found. The hair is partly free and rolled up into thick balls or is
still attached to the walls. A large mass of sebaceous material is also found
in these cysts. Thomson reports a case of dermoid cyst of the bladder containing hair, which cyst he removed. It was a pedunculated growth, and it
was undoubtedly vesical and not expelled from some ovarian source through
the urinary passage, as sometimes occurs.

The simpler forms of the ordinary dermoid cysts contain bone and teeth.
The complicated teratoma of this class may contain, in addition to the pre-

a 368, 1850.   b 230, 1874.   c 791, April, 1893.

PLATE 3.

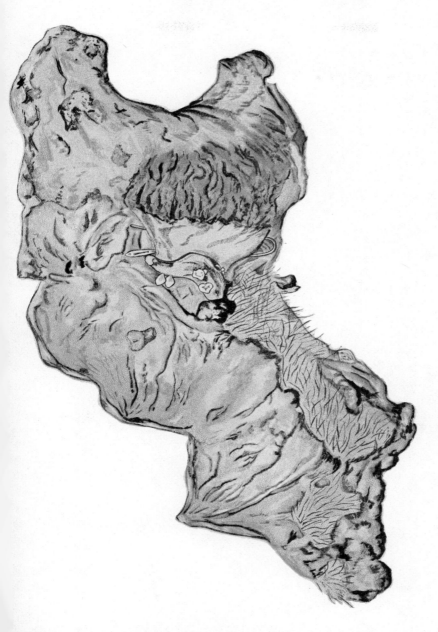

Dermoid cyst laid open, showing maxillary bone containing teeth ; the head of one of the long bones ; skin with hair growing from its surface ; serous membrane (probe passed underneath) ; mucous membrane of stomach directly next to serous membrane (Baldy).

viously mentioned structures, cartilage and glands, mucous and serous membrane, muscle, nerves, and cerebral substance, portions of eyes, fingers with nails, mammæ, etc. Figure 64 represents a cyst containing long red hair that was removed from a blonde woman aged forty-four years who had given birth to six children. Cullingworth reports the history of a woman in whom both ovaries were apparently involved by dermoids, who had given birth to 12 children and had three miscarriages—the last, three months before the removal of the growths. The accompanying illustration (Pl. 3), taken

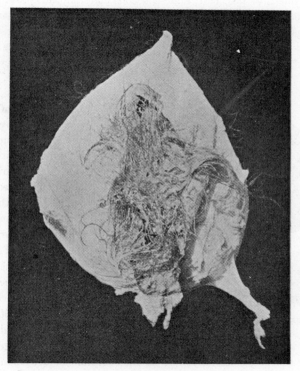

Fig. 64.—Dermoid cyst containing long red hair, removed from a light-haired woman aged forty-four years (Montgomery).

from Baldy,[a] pictures a dermoid cyst of the complicated variety laid open and exposing the contents in situ. Mears of Philadelphia reports a case of ovarian cyst removed from a girl of six and a half by Bradford of Kentucky in 1875. From this age on to adult life many similar cases are recorded. Nearly every medical museum has preserved specimens of dermoid cysts, and almost all physicians are well acquainted with their occurrence. The curious formations and contents and the bizarre shapes are of great variety. Graves[b] mentions a dermoid cyst containing the left side of a human

[a] "An American Text-Book of Gynecology," Philadelphia, 1894.   [b] 533, 1895, 212.

face, an eye, a molar tooth, and various bones. Dermoid cysts are found also in regions of the body quite remote from the ovary. The so-called "orbital wens" are true inclusion of the skin of a congenital origin, as are the nasal dermoids and some of the cysts of the neck.

Weil reported the case of a man of twenty-two years who was born with what was supposed to be a spina bifida in the lower sacral region. According to Senn, the swelling never caused any pain or inconvenience until it inflamed, when it opened spontaneously and suppurated, discharging a large quantity of offensive pus, hair, and sebaceous material, thus proving it to have been a dermoid. The cyst was freely incised, and there were found numerous openings of sweat glands, from which drops of perspiration escaped when the patient was sweating.

Fig. 65.—Large lingual dermoid protruding from the mouth (after Gray).

Dermoid cysts of the thorax are rare. Bramann reported a case in which a dermoid cyst of small size was situated over the sternum at the junction of the manubrium with the gladiolus, and a similar cyst in the anterior median line of the neck near the left cornu of the hyoid bone. Chitten removed a dermoid from the sternum of a female of thirty-nine, the cyst containing 11 ounces of atheromatous material. In the Museum of St. Bartholomew's Hospital in London there is a congenital tumor which was removed from the anterior mediastinum of a woman of twenty-one, and contained portions of skin, fat, sebaceous material, and two pieces of bone similar to the superior maxilla, and in which several teeth were found. Dermoids are found in the palate and pharynx, and open dermoids of the conjunctiva are classified by Sutton with the moles. According to Senn, Barker collected sixteen dermoid tumors of the tongue. Bryk successfully removed a tumor of this nature the size of a fist. Wellington Gray removed an enormous lingual dermoid from the mouth of a negro. It contained 40 ounces of atheromatous material (Fig. 65). Dermoids of the rectum are reported. Duyse [a] reports the history of a case of labor during which a rectal dermoid was expelled. The dermoid contained a cerebral vesicle, a

[a] La Flandre Méd., March 14, 1895.

rudimentary eye, a canine and a molar tooth, and a piece of bone. There is little doubt that many cases of fetus in fetu reported were really dermoids of the scrotum.

Ward [a] reports the successful removal of a dermoid cyst weighing 30 pounds from a woman of thirty-two, the mother of two children aged ten and twelve, respectively. The report is briefly as follows : " The patient has always been in good health until within the last year, during which time she has lost flesh and strength quite rapidly, and when brought to my hospital by her physician, Dr. James of Williamsburg, Kansas, was quite weak, although able to walk about the house. A tumor had been growing for a number of years, but its growth was so gradual that the patient had not considered her condition critical until quite recently. The tumor was diagnosed to be cystoma of the left ovary. Upon opening the sac with the trocar we were confronted by complications entirely unlooked for, and its use had to be abandoned entirely because the thick contents of the cyst would not flow freely, and the presence of sebaceous matter blocked the instrument. As much of the fluid as possible was removed, and the abdominal incision was enlarged to allow of the removal of the large tumor. An ovarian hematoma the size of a large orange was removed from the right side. We washed the intestines quite as one would wash linen, since some of the contents of the cyst had escaped into the abdominal cavity. The abdomen was closed without drainage, and the patient placed in bed without experiencing the least shock. Her recovery was rapid and uneventful. She returned to her home in four weeks after the operation.

" The unusual feature in this case was the nature of the contents of the sac. There was a large quantity of long straight hair growing from the cyst wall and an equal amount of loose hair in short pieces floating through the tumor-contents, a portion of which formed nuclei for what were called ' moth-balls,' of which there were about $1\frac{1}{2}$ gallons. These balls, or marbles, varied from the size of moth-balls, as manufactured and sold by druggists, to that of small walnuts. They seemed to be composed of sebaceous matter, and were evidently formed around the short hairs by the motion of the fluid produced by walking or riding. There was some tissue resembling true skin attached to the inner wall of the sac."

There are several cases of **multiple dermoid cysts** on record, and they may occur all over the body. Jamieson [b] reports a case in which there were 250, and in Maclaren's case there were 132. According to Crocker, Hebra and Rayer also each had a case. In a case of Sangster, reported by Politzer, although most of the dermoids, as usual, were like fibroma-nodules and therefore the color of normal skin, those over the mastoid processes and clavicle were lemon-yellow, and were generally thought to be xanthoma until they were excised, and Politzer found they were typical dermoid cysts with the usual contents of degenerated epithelium and hair.

a Internat. Med. Magaz., Phila., July, 1895.   b 318, Sept., 1873, 223.

Hermaphroditism.—Some writers claim that Adam was the first hermaphrodite and support this by Scriptural evidence.[a]　We find in some of the ancient poets traces of an Egyptian legend in which the goddess of the moon was considered to be both male and female.　From mythology we learn that Hermaphroditus was the son of Hermes, or Mercury, and Venus Aphrodite, and had the powers both of a father and mother.　In speaking of the foregoing Ausonius writes, "Cujus erat facies in quâ paterque materque cognosci possint, nomen traxit ab illis."　Ovid and Virgil both refer to legendary hermaphrodites, and the knowledge of their existence was prevalent in the olden times.　The ancients considered the birth of hermaphrodites bad omens, and the Athenians threw them into the sea, the Romans, into the Tiber.　Livy speaks of an hermaphrodite being put to death in Umbria, and another in Etruria.　Cicero, Aristotle, Strabonius, and Pliny all speak concerning this subject.　Martial [b] and Tertullian noticed this anomaly among the Romans.　Aetius and Paulus Ægineta speak of females in Egypt with prolonged clitorides which made them appear like hermaphrodites.　Throughout the Middle Ages we frequently find accounts, naturally exaggerated, of double-sexed creatures.　Harvey, Bartholinus, Paullini, Schenck, Wolff, Wrisberg, Zacchias, Marcellus Donatus, Haller, Hufeland, de Graff, and many others discuss hermaphroditism.　Many classifications have been given, as, *e. g.*, real and apparent; masculine, feminine, or neuter; horizontal and vertical; unilateral and bilateral, etc.　The anomaly in most cases consists of a malformation of the external genitalia.　A prolonged clitoris, prolapsed ovaries, grossness of figure, and hirsute appearance have been accountable for many supposed instances of hermaphrodites.　On the other hand, a cleft scrotum, an ill-developed penis, perhaps hypospadias or epispadias, rotundity of the mammæ, and feminine contour have also provoked accounts of similar instances.　Some cases have been proved by dissection to have been true hermaphrodites, portions or even entire genitalia of both sexes having been found.

Numerous accounts, many mythical, but always interesting, are given of these curious persons.　They have been accredited with having performed the functions of both father and mother, notwithstanding the statements of some of the best authorities that they are always sterile.　Observation has shown that the sexual appetite diminishes in proportion to the imperfections in the genitalia, and certainly many of these persons are sexually indifferent.

We give descriptions of a few of the most famous or **interesting instances of hermaphroditism.**　Paré [c] speaks of a woman who, besides a vulva, from which she menstruated, had a penis, but without prepuce or signs of erectility.　Haller alludes to several cases in which prolonged clitorides have been the cause of the anomaly.　In commenting on this form of hermaphroditism Albucasius [115] describes a necessary operation for the removal of the clitoris.

---

[a] Genesis, chap. i., verse 27.　　　[b] 509, lib. 1, ep. 91.　　　[c] 618, L. xxv., chap. vi.

Columbus [a] relates the history of an Ethiopian woman who was evidently a spurious female hermaphrodite. The poor wretch entreated him to cut off her penis, an enlarged clitoris, which she said was an intolerable hindrance to her in coitus. De Graff and Riolan describe similar cases. There is an old record of a similar creature, supposing herself to be a male, who took a wife, but previously having had connection with a man, the outcome of which was pregnancy, was shortly after marriage delivered of a daughter. There is an account [b] of a person in Germany who, for the first thirty years of life, was regarded as feminine, and being of loose morals became a mother. At a certain period she began to feel a change in her sexual inclinations ; she married and became the father of a family. This is doubtless a distortion of the facts of the case of **Catherine or Charles Hoffman,** born in 1824, and who was considered a female until the age of forty. At puberty she had the instincts of a woman, and cohabitated with a male lover for twenty years. Her breasts were well formed and she menstruated at nineteen. At the age of forty-six her sexual desires changed, and she attempted coitus as a man, with such evident satisfaction that she married a woman soon afterward. Fitch speaks of a house-servant [c] with masculine features and movements, aged twenty-eight, and 5 feet and 9 inches tall, who was arrested by the police for violating the laws governing prostitution. On examination, well-developed male and female organs of generation were found. The labia majora were normal and flattened on the anterior surface. The labia minora and hymen were absent. The vagina was spacious and the woman had a profuse leukorrhea. She stated that several years previously she gave birth to a normal child. In place of a clitoris she had a penis which, in erection, measured $5\frac{1}{4}$ inches long and $3\frac{5}{8}$ inches in circumference. The glans penis and the urethra were perfectly formed. The scrotum contained two testicles, each about an inch long ; the mons veneris was sparsely covered with straight, black hair. She claimed functional ability with both sets of genitalia, and said she experienced equal sexual gratification with either. Semen issued from the penis, and every three weeks she had scanty menstruation, which lasted but two days.

Beclard [d] showed **Marie-Madeline Lefort,** nineteen years of age, $1\frac{1}{2}$ meters in height. Her mammæ were well developed, her nipples erectile and surrounded by a brown areola, from which issued several hairs. Her feet were small, her pelvis large, and her thighs like those of a woman. Projecting from the vulva was a body looking like a penis 7 cm. long and slightly erectile at times ; it was imperforate and had a mobile prepuce. She had a vulva with two well-shaped labia as shown by the accompanying illustration (Fig. 66). She menstruated slightly and had an opening at the root of the clitoris. The parotid region showed signs of a beard and she had

a De re anatomica, L. xxv.   b 224, 1889, i., 1038.
c 597, Nov. 22, 1890.   d Faculté de Méd. de Paris, 1815.

hair on her upper lip.   On August 20, 1864, a person came into the Hôtel-Dieu, asking treatment for chronic pleurisy.   He said his age was sixty-five, and he pursued the calling of a mountebank, but remarked that in early life he had been taken for a woman.   He had menstruated at eight and had been examined by doctors at sixteen.   The menstruation continued until 1848, and at its cessation he experienced the feelings of a male.   At this time he presented the venerable appearance of a long-bearded old man (Fig. 67).   At the autopsy, about two months later, all the essentials of a female were delineated.   A Fallopian tube, ovaries, uterus, and round ligaments were found, and a drawing in cross-section of the parts was

Fig. 66.—Marie-Madeline Lefort at sixteen years of age.

Fig. 67.—Marie-Madeline Lefort at sixty-five years of age.

made (Fig. 68).   There is no doubt but that this individual was Marie-Madeline Lefort in age.

Worbe [a] speaks of a person who was supposed to be feminine for twenty-two years.   At the age of sixteen she loved a farmer's son, but the union was delayed for some reason, and three years later her grace faded and she became masculine in her looks and tastes.   It was only after lengthy discussion, in which the court took part, that it was definitely settled that this person was a male.

Adelaide Préville, [664] who was married as a female, and as such lived the last ten years of her life in France, was found on dissection at the Hôtel-

a 461, Jan. et Fev., 1816.

Dieu to be a man. A man was spoken of in both France and Germany [a] who passed for many years as a female. He had a cleft scrotum and hypospadias, which caused the deception. Sleeping with another servant for three years, he constantly had sexual congress with her during this period, and finally impregnated her. It was supposed in this case that the posterior wall of the vagina supplied the deficiency of the lower boundary of the urethra, forming a complete channel for the semen to proceed through. Long ago in Scotland [302] a servant was condemned to death by burial alive for impregnating his master's daughter while in the guise and habit of a woman. He had always been considered a woman. We have heard of a recent trustworthy account of a pregnancy and delivery in a girl who had been impregnated by a bed-fellow who on examination proved to be a male pseudohermaphrodite.

Fournier [b] speaks of an individual in Lisbon in 1807 who was in the highest degree of perfection, both male and female. The figure was graceful, the voice feminine, the mammæ well developed, and menstruation was regular. The female genitalia were normal except the labia majora, which were rather diminutive. The thighs and the pelvis were not so wide as those of a woman. There was some beard on the chin, but it was worn close. The male genitalia were of the size and appearance of

Fig. 68.—Mesial section showing the generative organs of Marie-Madeline Lefort. The sound is introduced into the vagina, and from thence into the orifice of the urethra; *U*, the uterus; *O*, the ovary and Fallopian tube.

a male adult and were covered with the usual hair. This person had been twice pregnant and aborted at the third and fifth month. During coitus the penis became erect, etc.

Schrell [c] describes a case in which, independent of the true penis and testicles, which were well formed, there existed a small vulva furnished with labia and nymphæ, communicating with a rudimentary uterus provided with round ligaments and imperfectly developed ovaries. Schrell remarks that in this case we must notice that the female genitalia were imperfectly developed, and adds that perfect hermaphroditism is a physical impossibility without great alterations of the natural connections of the bones and other

[a] 789, Aug. 26, 1856. [b] 302, iv., 164.
[c] Med.-Chir. prakt. Archiv von Bader, etc., i., 1804.

parts of the pelvis.　Cooper [a] describes a woman with an enormous development of the clitoris, an imperforate uterus, and absence of vagina; at first
sight of the parts they appeared to be those of a man.

In 1859 Hugier succeeded in restoring a vagina to a young girl of twenty
who had an hypertrophied clitoris and no signs of a vagina.　The accompanying illustrations show the conformation of the parts before operation
with all the appearance of ill-developed male genitalia, and the appearance
afterward with restitution of the vaginal opening (Fig. 69).

Virchow in 1872, Boddaert in 1875, and Marchand in 1883 report cases
of duplication of the genitalia, and call their cases true hermaphrodites from
an anatomic standpoint.　There is a specimen in St. Bartholomew's Hospital
in London from a man of forty-four, who died of cerebral hemorrhage.　He

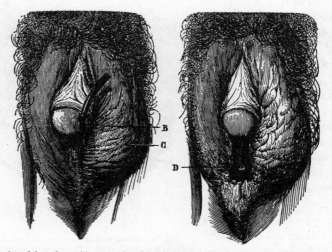

Fig. 69.—Occlusion of the vulva and hypertrophy of the clitoris, before and after operation; B, sound introduced
into a narrow vulvar orifice; C, labium majus containing an ovary; D, urinary meatus.

was well formed and had a beard and a full-sized penis.　He was married,
and it was stated that his wife had two children.[b]　The bladder and the internal organs of generation were those of a man in whom neither testis had
descended into the scrotum, and in whom the uterus masculinus and vagina
were developed to an unusual degree.　The uterus, nearly as large as in the
adult female, lay between the bladder and rectum, and was enclosed between
two layers of peritoneum, to which, on either side of the uterus, were attached
the testes.　There was also shown [619] in London the pelvic organs from a case
of complex or vertical hermaphroditism occurring in a child of nine months
who died from the effects of an operation for the radical cure of a right inguinal hernia.　The external organs were those of a male with undescended

a 392, 1840, 243.　　　　　　　　　　　　　　　　b 779, xliv., 102.

PLATE 4.

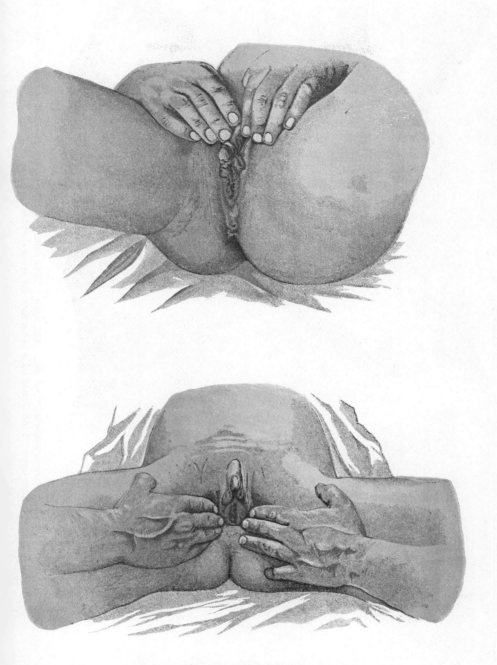

Pseudo-external bilateral hermaphroditism (Krug).

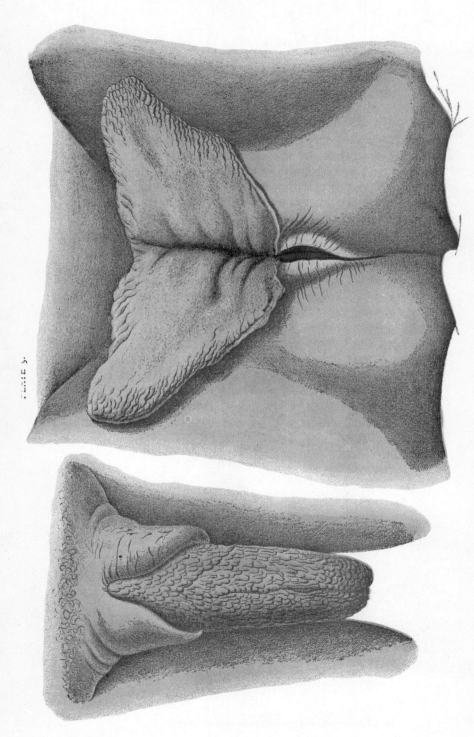

Hottentot apron, natural size (Billroth, "Frauenkrankheiten," vol. iii.). Left figure : Adult woman standing upright, the apron hanging between the thighs.
Right figure : Adult woman lying on her back, the apron spread out to the sides.

testes. The bladder was normal and its neck was surrounded by a prostate gland. Projecting backward were a vagina, uterus, and broad ligaments, round ligaments, and Fallopian tubes, with the testes in the position of the ovaries. There were no seminal vesicles. The child died eleven days after the operation. The family history states that the mother had had 14 children and eight miscarriages. Seven of the children were dead and showed no abnormalities. The fifth and sixth children were boys and had the same sexual arrangement.

Barnes, Chalmers, Sippel, and Litten describe cases of **spurious hermaphroditism** due to elongation of the clitoris. In Litten's case [a] the clitoris was 3½ inches long, and there was hydrocele of the processus vaginalis on both sides, making tumors in the labium on one side and the inguinal canal on the other, which had been diagnosed as testicles and again as ovaries. There was associate cystic ovarian disease. Plate 4 is taken from a case of false external bilateral hermaphroditism. Phillips [b] mentions four cases of spurious hermaphroditism in one family, and recently Pozzi [c] tells of a family of nine individuals in whom this anomaly was observed. The first was alive and had four children ; the second was christened a female but was probably a male ; the third, fourth, and fifth were normal but died young ; the sixth daughter was choreic and feeble-minded, aged twenty-nine, and had one illegitimate child ; the seventh, a boy, was healthy and married ; the eighth was christened a female, but when seventeen was declared by the Faculty to be a male ; the ninth was christened a female, but at eighteen the genitals were found to be those of a male, though the mammæ were well developed.

O'Neill [d] speaks of a case in which the clitoris was five inches long and one inch thick, having a groove in its inferior surface reaching down to an oblique opening in the perineum. The scrotum contained two hard bodies thought to be testicles, and the general appearance was that of hypospadias. Postmortem a complete set of female genitalia was found, although the ovaries were very small. The right round ligament was exceedingly thick and reached down to the bottom of the false scrotum, where it was firmly attached. The hard bodies proved to be on one side an irreducible omental hernia, probably congenital, and on the other a hardened mass having no glandular structure. The patient was an adult. As we have seen, there seems to be a **law of evolution in hermaphroditism** which prevents perfection. If one set of genitalia are extraordinarily developed, the other set are correspondingly atrophied. In the case of extreme development of the clitoris and approximation to the male type we must expect to find imperfectly developed uterus or ovaries. This would answer for one of the causes of sterility in these cases.

There is a type of hermaphroditism in which the sex cannot be definitely

[a] 161, lxxv.   [b] 778, xxviii., 158.   [c] 368, 1885, ii., 109.   [d] 124, 1851, 588.

declared, and sometimes dissection does not definitely indicate the predominating sex. Such cases are classed under the head of **neuter hermaphrodites,** possibly an analogy of the "genus epicœnum" of Quintilian. **Marie Dorothée,** of the age of twenty-three, was examined and declared a girl by Hufeland and Mursina, while Stark, Raschig, and Martens maintained that she was a boy. This formidable array of talent on both sides provoked much discussion in contemporary publications, and the case attracted much notice. Marc saw her in 1803,[a] at which time she carried contradicting certificates as to her sex. He found an imperforate penis, and on the inferior face near the root an opening for the passage of urine. No traces of nymphæ, vagina, testicles, nor beard were seen. The stature was small, the form debilitated, and the voice effeminate. Marc came to the conclusion that it was impossible for any man to determine either one sex or the other. Everard Home dissected a dog with apparent external organs of the female, but discovered that neither sex was sufficiently pronounced to admit of classification. Home also saw at the Royal Marine Hospital at Plymouth, in 1779, a marine who some days after admission was reported to be a girl. On examination Home found him to possess a weak voice, soft skin, voluminous breasts, little beard, and the thighs and legs of a woman. There was fat on the pubis, the penis was short and small and incapable of erection, the testicles of fetal size ; he had no venereal desires whatever, and as regards sex was virtually neuter.

The legal aspect of hermaphroditism has always been much discussed. Many interesting questions arise, and extraordinary complications naturally occur. In Rome a hermaphrodite could be a witness to a testament, the exclusive privilege of a man, and the sex was settled by the predominance. If the male aspect and traits together with the generative organs of man were most pronounced, then the individual could call himself a man. "Hermaphroditus an ad testamentum adhiberi possit qualitas sexus incalescentis ostendit."

There is a peculiar case on record [b] in which the question of legal male inheritance was not settled until the individual had lived as a female for fifty-one years. This person was married when twenty-one, but finding coitus impossible, separated after ten years, and though dressing as a female had coitus with other women. She finally lived with her brother, with whom she eventually came to blows. She prosecuted him for assault, and the brother in return charged her with seducing his wife. Examination ensued, and at this ripe age she was declared to be a male.

The literature on hermaphroditism is so extensive that it is impossible to select a proper representation of the interesting cases in this limited space, and the reader is referred to the modern French works on this subject, in which the material is exhaustive and the discussion thoroughly scientific.

a 302, xxi., 104.   b 359, July 29, 1895.

CHAPTER VI.

MINOR TERATA.

Ancient Ideas Relative to Minor Terata.—The ancients viewed with great interest the minor structural anomalies of man, and held them to be divine signs or warnings in much the same manner as they considered more pronounced monstrosities. In a most interesting and instructive article, Ballantyne[a] quotes Ragozin in saying that the Chaldeo-Babylonians, in addition to their other numerous subdivisions of divination, drew presages and omens for good or evil from the appearance of the liver, bowels, and viscera of animals offered for sacrifice and opened for inspection, and from the natural defects or monstrosities of babies or the young of animals. Ballantyne names this latter subdivision of divination **fetomancy** or **teratoscopy,** and thus renders a special chapter as to omens derived from monstrous births, given by Lenormant :—

" The prognostics which the Chaldeans claimed to draw from monstrous births in man and the animals are worthy of forming a class by themselves, insomuch the more as it is the part of their divinatory science with which, up to the present time, we are best acquainted. The development that their astrology had given to ' généthliaque,' or the art of horoscopes of births, had led them early to attribute great importance to all the teratologic facts which were there produced. They claimed that an experience of 470,000 years of observations, all concordant, fully justified their system, and that in nothing was the influence of the stars marked in a more indubitable manner than in the fatal law which determined the destiny of each individual according to the state of the sky at the moment when he came into the world. Cicero, by the very terms which he uses to refute the Chaldeans, shows that the result of these ideas was to consider all infirmities and monstrosities that new-born infants exhibited as the inevitable and irremediable consequence of the action of these astral positions. This being granted, the observation of similar monstrosities gave, as it were, a reflection of the state of the sky, on which depended all terrestrial things ; consequently, one might read in them the future with as much certainty as in the stars themselves. For this reason the greatest possible importance was attached to the teratologic auguries which occupy so much space in the fragments of the great treatise on terrestrial presages which have up to the present time been published."

The rendering into English of the account of 62 teratologic cases in the human subject with the prophetic meanings attached to them by Chaldean diviners, after the translation of Opport, is given as follows by Ballantyne, some of the words being untranslatable :—

" When a woman gives birth to an infant—

(1) that has the ears of a lion, there will be a powerful king in the country ;

(2) that wants the right ear, the days of the master (king) will be prolonged (reach old age) ;

(3) that wants both ears, there will be mourning in the country, and the country will be lessened (diminished) ;

(4) whose right ear is small, the house of the man (in whose house the birth took place) will be destroyed ;

(5) whose ears are both small, the house of the man will be built of bricks ;

(6) whose right ear is *mudissu tehaat* (monstrous), there will be an androgyne in the house of the new-born ;

(7) whose ears are both *mudissu* (deformed), the country will perish and the enemy rejoice ;

(8) whose right ear is round, there will be an androgyne in the house of the new-born ;

(9) whose right ear has a wound below, and *tur re ut* of the man, the house will be destroyed ;

(10) that has two ears on the right side and none on the left, the gods will bring about a stable reign, the country will flourish, and it will be a land of repose ;

(11) whose ears are both closed, *sa a au ;*

(12) that has a bird's beak, the country will be peaceful ;

(13) that has no mouth, the mistress of the house will die ;

(14) that has no right nostril, the people of the world will be injured ;

(15) whose nostrils are absent, the country will be in affliction, and the house of the man will be ruined ;

(16) whose jaws are absent, the days of the master (king) will be prolonged, but the house (where the infant is born) will be ruined.

When a woman gives birth to an infant—

(17) that has no lower jaw, *mut ta at mat*, the name will not be effaced ;

(20) that has no nose, affliction will seize upon the country, and the master of the house will die ;

(21) that has neither nose nor virile member (penis), the army of the king will be strong, peace will be in the land, the men of the king will be sheltered from evil influences, and Lilit (a female demon) shall not have power over them ;

(22) whose upper lip overrides the lower, the people of the world will rejoice (*or* good augury for the troops) ;

(23) that has no lips, affliction will seize upon the land, and the house of the man will be destroyed ;

(24) whose tongue is *kuri aat*, the man will be spared (?) ;

(25) that has no right hand, the country will be convulsed by an earthquake ;

(26) that has no fingers, the town will have no births, the *bar* shall be lost ;

(27) that has no fingers on the right side, the master (king) will not pardon his adversary (*or* shall be humiliated by his enemies) ;

(28) that has six fingers on the right side, the man will take the *lukunu* of the house ;

(29) that has six very small toes on both feet, he shall not go to the *lukunu ;*

(30) that has six toes on each foot, the people of the world will be injured (calamity to the troops) ;

(31) that has the heart open and that has no skin, the country will suffer from calamities ;
(32) that has no penis, the master of the house will be enriched by the harvest of his field ;
(33) that wants the penis and the umbilicus, there will be ill-will in the house, the woman (wife) will have an overbearing eye (be haughty) ; but the male descent of the palace will be more extended.

When a woman gives birth to an infant—

(34) that has no well-marked sex, calamity and affliction will seize upon the land ; the master of the house shall have no happiness ;
(35) whose anus is closed, the country will suffer from want of nourishment ;
(36) whose right testicle (?) is absent, the country of the master (king) will perish ;
(37) whose right foot is absent, his house will be ruined and there will be abundance in that of the neighbor ;
(38) that has no feet, the canals of the country will be cut (intercepted) and the house ruined ;
(39) that has the right foot in the form of a fish's tail, the booty of the country of the humble will not be *imas sa bir;*
(40) whose hands and feet are like four fishes' tails (fins), the master (king) shall perish (?) and his country shall be consumed ;
(41) whose feet are moved by his great hunger, the house of the *su su* shall be destroyed ;
(42) whose foot hangs to the tendons of the body, there will be great prosperity in the land ;
(43) that has three feet, two in their normal position (attached to the body) and the third between them, there will be great prosperity in the land ;
(44) whose legs are male and female, there will be rebellion ;
(45) that wants the right heel, the country of the master (king) will be destroyed.

When a woman gives birth to an infant—

(46) that has many white hairs on the head, the days of the king will be prolonged ;
(47) that has much *ipga* on the head, the master of the house will die, the house will be destroyed ;
(48) that has much *pinde* on the head, joy shall go to meet the house (that has a head on the head, the good augury shall enter at its aspect into the house) ;
(49) that has the head full of *hali,* there will be ill-will toward him and the master (king) of the town shall die ;
(50) that has the head full of *siksi,* the king will repudiate his masters ;
(51) that has some pieces of flesh (skin) hanging on the head, there shall be ill-will ;
(52) that has some branches (?) (excrescences) of flesh (skin) hanging on the head, there shall be ill-will, the house will perish ;
(53) that has some formed fingers (horns?) on the head, the days of the king will be less and the years lengthened (in the duration of his old age) ;
(54) that has some *kali* on the head, there will be a king of the land ;
(55) that has a —— of a bird on the head, the master of the house shall not prosper ;
(56) that has some teeth already through (cut), the days of the king will arrive at old age, the country will show itself powerful over (against) strange (feeble) lands, but the house where the infant is born will be ruined ;
(57) that has the beard come out, there will be abundant rains ;
(58) that has some *birta* on the head, the country will be strengthened (reinforced) ;
(59) that has on the head the mouth of an old man and that foams (slabbers), there will be great prosperity in the land, the god Bin will give a magnificent harvest (inundate the land with fertility), and abundance shall be in the land ;
(60) that has on one side of the head a thickened ear, the first-born of the men shall live a long time (?) ;

(61) that has on the head two long and thick ears, there will be tranquility and the pacification of litigation (contests) ;
(62) that has the figure in horn (like a horn ?) . . ."

As ancient and as obscure as are these records, Ballantyne has carefully gone over each, and gives the following lucid explanatory comments :—

"What 'ears like a lion' (No. 1) may have been it is difficult to determine ; but doubtless the direction and shape of the auricles were so altered as to give them an animal appearance, and possibly the deformity was that called 'orechio ad ansa' by Lombroso. The absence of one or both ears (Nos. 2 and 3) has been noted in recent times by Virchow (Archiv für path. Anat., xxx., p. 221), Gradenigo (Taruffi's 'Storia della Teratologia,' vi., p. 552), and others. Generally some cartilaginous remnant is found, but on this point the Chaldean record is silent. Variations in the size of the ears (Nos. 4 and 5) are well known at the present time, and have been discussed at length by Binder (Archiv für Psychiatrie und Nervenkrankheiten, xx., 1887) and others. The exact malformation indicated in Nos. 6 and 7 is, of course, not to be determined, although further researches in Assyriology may clear up this point. The 'round ear' (No. 8) is one of Binder's types, and that with a 'wound below' (No. 9) probably refers to a case of fistula auris congenita (Toynbee, 'Diseases of the Ear,' 1860). The instance of an infant born with two ears on the right side (No. 10) was doubtless one of cervical auricle or preauricular appendage, whilst closure of the external auditory meatus (No. 11) is a well-known deformity.

"The next thirteen cases (Nos. 12–24) were instances of anomalies of the mouth and nose. The 'bird's beak' (No. 12) may have been a markedly aquiline nose ; No. 13 was a case of astoma ; and Nos. 14 and 15 were instances of stenosis or atresia of the anterior nares. Fetuses with absence of the maxillæ (Nos. 16 and 17) are in modern terminology called agnathous. Deformities like that existing in Nos. 20 and 21 have been observed in paracephalic and cyclopic fetuses. The coincident absence of nose and penis (No. 21) is interesting, especially when taken in conjunction with the popular belief that the size of the former organ varies with that of the latter. Enlargement of the upper lip (No. 22), called epimacrochelia by Taruffi, and absence of the lips (No. 23), known now under the name of brachychelia, have been not unfrequently noticed in recent times. The next six cases (Nos. 25–30) were instances of malformations of the upper limb : Nos. 25, 26, and 27 were probably instances of the so-called spontaneous or intrauterine amputation ; and Nos. 28, 29, and 30 were examples of the comparatively common deformity known as polydactyly. No. 31 was probably a case of ectopia cordis.

"Then follow five instances of genital abnormalities (Nos. 32–36), consisting of absence of the penis (epispadias ?), absence of penis and umbilicus (epispadias and exomphalos ?), hermaphroditism, imperforate anus, and nondescent of one testicle. The nine following cases (Nos. 37–45) were anomalies of the lower limbs : Nos. 37, 38, and 42 may have been spontaneous amputations ; Nos. 39 and 40 were doubtless instances of webbed toes (syndactyly), and the deformity indicated in No. 45 was presumably talipes equinus. The infant born with three feet (No. 43) was possibly a case of parasitic monstrosity, several of which have been reported in recent teratologic literature ; but what is meant by the statement concerning 'male and female legs' it is not easy to determine.

"Certain of the ten following prodigies (Nos. 46–55) cannot in the present state of our knowledge be identified. The presence of congenital patches of white or gray hair on the scalp, as recorded in No. 46, is not an unknown occurrence at the present time ; but what the Chaldeans meant by *ipga, pinde, hali, siksi,* and *kali* on the head of the new-born infant it is impossible to tell. The guess may be hazarded that cephalhematoma, hydrocephalus, meningocele, nevi, or an excessive amount of vernix caseosa were the conditions indicated, but a wider acquaintance with the meaning of the cuneiform characters is necessary before any certain identification is possible. The 'pieces of skin hanging from the head' (No. 51) may have been fragments of the membranes; but there is nothing in the accompanying prediction to help us to trace the origin of the popular belief in the good luck following the baby born with a caul. If No. 53 was a case of congenital horns on the head, it must be regarded as a unique example, unless, indeed, a form of fetal ichthyosis be indicated.

"The remaining observations (No. 56–62) refer to cases of congenital teeth (No. 56), to deformity of the ears (Nos. 60 and 61), and a horn (No. 62)."

From these early times almost to the present day similar significance has been attached to minor structural anomalies. In the following pages the individual anomalies will be discussed separately and the most interesting examples of each will be cited. It is manifestly evident that the **object of this chapter** is to mention the most striking instances of abnormism and to give accompanying descriptions of associate points of interest, rather than to offer a scientific exposition of teratology, for which the reader is referred elsewhere.

Congenital defect of the epidermis and true skin is a rarity in pathology. Pastorello [a] speaks of a child which lived for two and a half hours whose hands and feet were entirely destitute of epidermis; the true skin of those parts looked like that of a dead and already putrefying child. Hanks [b] cites the history of a case of antepartum desquamation of the skin in a living fetus. Hochstetter [c] describes a full-term, living male fetus with cutaneous defect on both sides of the abdomen a little above the umbilicus. The placenta and membranes were normal, a fact indicating that the defect was not due to amniotic adhesions; the child had a club-foot on the left side. The mother had a fall three weeks before labor.

Abnormal Elasticity of the Skin.—In some instances the skin is affixed so loosely to the underlying tissues and is possessed of so great elasticity that it can be stretched almost to the same extent as India rubber. There have been individuals who could take the skin of the forehead and pull it down over the nose, or raise the skin of the neck over the mouth. They also occasionally have an associate muscular development in the subcutaneous tissues similar to the panniculus adiposus of quadrupeds, giving them preternatural motile power over the skin. The man recently exhibited under the title of the "**Elastic-Skin Man**" was an example of this anomaly. The first of this class of exhibitionists was seen in Buda-Pesth some years since and possessed great elasticity in the skin of his whole body; even his nose could be stretched. Figure 70 represents a photograph of an exhibitionist named Felix Wehrle, who besides having the power to stretch his skin could readily bend his fingers backward and forward. The photograph was taken in January, 1888.

In these congenital cases there is loose attachment of the skin without hypertrophy, to which the term **dermatolysis** is restricted by Crocker. Job van Meekren,[560] the celebrated Dutch physician of the seventeenth century,

[a] 153, July, 1845. [b] 125, 1880, 595. [c] 263, 1894, 542.

states that in 1657 a Spaniard, Georgius Albes, is reported to have been able to draw the skin of the left pectoral region to the left ear, or the skin under the face over the chin to the vertex. The skin over the knee could be extended half a yard, and when it retracted to its normal position it was not in folds. Seiffert examined a case of this nature in a young man of nineteen, and, contrary to Kopp's supposition, found that in some skin from over the left second rib the elastic fibers were quite normal, but there was transformation of the connective tissue of the dermis into an unformed tissue like a

Fig. 70.—An "elastic-skin man."

myxoma, with total disappearance of the connective-tissue bundles. Laxity of the skin after distention is often seen in multipara, both in the breasts and in the abdominal walls, and also from obesity, but in all such cases the skin falls in folds, and does not have a normal appearance like that of the true "elastic-skin man."

Occasionally **abnormal development of the scalp** is noticed. McDowall [a] records an instance in an epileptic idiot of twenty-two. On each side of the median line of the head there were five deep furrows (Fig. 71), more curved and shorter as the distance from the median line increased. In the illustration the hair in the furrows is left longer than that on the rest of the head. The patient was distinctly microcephalic and the right side of the body was markedly wasted. The folds were due to hypertrophy of the muscles and scalp, and the same sort of furrowing is noticed when a dog "pricks his ears." This case may possibly be considered as an example of reversion to inferior types. Cowan [b] records two cases of the foregoing nature in idiots. The first case (Fig. 72) was a paralytic idiot of thirty-nine, whose cranial development was small in proportion to the size of the face and body ; the cranium was oxycephalic ; the scalp was lax and redundant and the hair thin ; there were 13 furrows, five on each side running anteroposteriorly, and three in the occipital region running transversely. The occipitofrontalis muscle had no action on them. The second case was that of an idiot of forty-four of a more degraded type than the previous one. The cranium was round and bullet-shaped and the hair generally thick. The scalp was not so lax as in the other case, but the furrows were more crooked. By tickling the scalp over the back of the neck the two median furrows involuntarily deepened.

Impervious Skin.—There have been individuals who claimed that their skin was impervious to ordinary puncture, and from time to time these individuals have appeared in some of the larger medical clinics of the world for inspection. According to a recent number of the London Graphic, there is in Berlin a Singhalese who baffles all investigations by physicians by the impenetrability of his skin. The bronzed Easterner, a Hercules in shape, claims to have found an elixir which will render the human skin impervious to any metal point or sharpened edge of a knife or dagger, and calls himself the " Man with Iron Skin." He is now exhibiting himself, and his greatest feat is to pass with his entire body through a hoop the inside of which is hardly

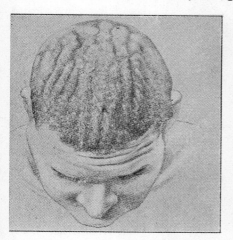

Fig. 71.—Abnormal development of scalp (McDowall).   Fig. 72.—Abnormal development of scalp (Cowan).

big enough to admit his body and is closely set with sharp knife-points, daggers, nails, and similar things. Through this hoop he squeezes his body with absolute impunity. The physicians do not agree as to his immunity, and some of them think that Rhannin, which is his name, is a fakir who has by long practice succeeded in hardening himself against the impressions of metal upon his skin. The professors of the Berlin clinic, however, considered it worth while to lecture about the man's skin, pronouncing it an inexplicable matter. This individual performed at the London Alhambra in the latter part of 1895. Besides climbing with bare feet a ladder whose rungs were sharp-edged swords, and lying on a bed of nail points with four men seated upon him, he curled himself up in a barrel, through whose inner edges nails projected, and was rolled about the stage at a rapid rate. Emerging from thence uninjured, he gracefully bows himself off the stage.

Some individuals claim immunity from burns and show many interesting feats in handling fire. As they are nothing but skilful "fire jugglers" they deserve no mention here. The immunity of the participants in the savage fire ceremonies will be discussed in Chapter IX.

Albinism is characterized by the absolute or relative absence of pigment of the skin, due to an arrest, insufficiency, or retardation of this pigment. Following Trélat and Guinard, we may divide albinism into two classes,—general and partial.

Fig. 73.—An albino family.

As to the etiology of albinism, there is no known cause of the complete form. Heredity plays no part in a number of cases investigated by the authors. D'Aubé, by his observations on white rabbits, believes that the influence of consanguinity is a marked factor in the production of albinism ; there are, however, many instances of heredity in this anomaly on record, and this idea is possibly in harmony with the majority of observers. Geoffroy-Saint-Hilaire has noted that albinism can also be the consequence of a pathologic condition having its origin in adverse surroundings, the circumstances of the parents, such as the want of exercise, nourishment, light, etc.

Lesser knew a family in which six out of seven were albinos, and in some tropical countries, such as Loango, Lower Guinea, it is said to be endemic. It is exceptional for the parents to be affected ; but in a case of Schlegel, quoted by Crocker, the grandfather was an albino, and Marey[a] describes the case of the Cape May albinos, in which the mother and father were "fair emblems of the African race," and of their children three were black and three were white, born in the following order : two consecutive black boys,

a 124, 1839.

two consecutive white girls, one black girl, one white boy. Sym of Edinburgh [a] relates the history of a family of seven children, who were alternately white and black. All but the seventh were living and in good health and mentally without defect. The parents and other relatives were dark. Figure 73 portrays an albino family by the name of Cavalier who exhibited in Minneapolis in 1887.

Examples of the total absence of pigment occur in all races, but particularly is it interesting when seen in negroes who are found absolutely white but preserving all the characteristics of their race, as, for instance, the kinky, woolly hair, flattened nose, thick lips, etc. René Caillé, in his " Voyage à Tombouctou," says that he saw a white infant, the offspring of a negro and negress. Its hair was white, its eyes blue, and its lashes flaxen. Its pupils were of a reddish color, and its physiognomy that of a Mandingo. He says such cases are not at all uncommon ; they are really negro albinos. Thomas Jefferson, in his " History of Virginia," has an excellent description of these negroes, with their tremulous and weak eyes ; he remarks that they freckle easily. Buffon speaks of Ethiops with white twins, and says that albinos are quite common in Africa, being generally of delicate constitution, twinkling eyes, and of a low degree of intelligence ; they are despised and ill-treated by the other negroes. Prichard, quoted by Sedgwick, speaks of a case of atavic transmission of albinism through the male line of the negro race. The grandfather and the grandchild were albinos, the father being black. There is a case [b] of a brother and sister who were albinos, the parents being of ordinary color but the grandfather an albino. Coinde, quoted by Sedgwick, speaks of a man who, by two different wives, had three albino children.

A description of the ordinary type of albino would be as follows : The skin and hair are deprived of pigment ; the eyebrows and eyelashes are of a brilliant white or are yellowish ; the iris and the choroid are nearly or entirely deprived of coloring material, and in looking at the eye we see a roseate zone and the ordinary pink pupil ; from absence of pigment they necessarily keep their eyes three-quarters closed, being photophobic to a high degree. They are amblyopic, and this is due partially to a high degree of ametropia (caused by crushing of the eyeball in the endeavor to shut out light) and from retinal exhaustion and nystagmus. Many authors have claimed that they have little intelligence, but this opinion is not true. Ordinarily the reproductive functions are normal, and if we exclude the results of the union of two albinos we may say that these individuals are fecund.

Partial albinism is seen. The parts most often affected are the genitals, the hair, the face, the top of the trunk, the nipple, the back of the hands and fingers. Folker [c] reports the history of a case of an albino girl having pink eyes and red hair, the rest of the family having pink eyes and white

[a] 476, July 11, 1891. [b] 580, Aug., 1888. [c] 476, 1876, i., 795.

hair. Partial albinism, necessarily congenital, presenting a piebald appearance, must not be confounded with leukoderma, which is rarely seen in the young and which will be described later.

Albinism is found **in the lower animals,** and is exemplified ordinarily by rats, mice, crows, robins, etc. In the Zoologic Garden at Baltimore two years ago was a pair of pure albino opossums. The white elephant is celebrated in the religious history of Oriental nations, and is an object of veneration and worship in Siam. White monkeys and white roosters are also worshiped. In the Natural History Museum in London there are stuffed examples of albinism and melanism in the lower animals.

Melanism is an anomaly, the exact contrary of the preceding. It is characterized by the presence in the tissues and skin of an excessive amount of pigment. True total melanism is unknown in man, in whom is only observed partial melanism, characterized simply by a pronounced coloration of part of the integument.

Some curious instances have been related [a] of an infant with a two-colored face, and of others with one side of the face white and the other black; whether they were cases of partial albinism or partial melanism cannot be ascertained from the descriptions.

Such epidermic anomalies as ichthyosis, scleroderma, and molluscum simplex, sometimes appearing shortly after birth, but generally seen later in life, will be spoken of in the chapter on Anomalous Skin Diseases.

Human horns are anomalous outgrowths from the skin and are far more frequent than ordinarily supposed. Nearly all the older writers cite examples. Aldrovandus, Amatus Lusitanus, Boerhaave, Dupré, Schenck, Riverius, Vallisneri, and many others mention horns on the head. In the ancient times horns were symbolic of wisdom and power. Michael Angelo in his famous sculpture of Moses has given the patriarch a pair of horns. Rhodius [680] observed a Benedictine monk who had a pair of horns and who was addicted to rumination. Fabricius [333] saw a man with horns on his head, whose son ruminated; the son considered that by virtue of his ruminating characteristics his father had transmitted to him the peculiar anomaly of the family. Fabricius Hildanus [334] saw a patient with horns all over the body and another with horns on the forehead. Gastaher [b] speaks of a horn from the left temple; Zacutus Lusitanus [831] saw a horn from the heel; Wroe, [629] one of considerable length from the scapula; Cosnard, one from the bregma; the Ephemerides, from the foot; Borellus, from the face and foot, and Ash, [c] horns all over the body. Home, Cooper, and Treves have collected examples of horns, and there is one 11 inches long and $2\frac{1}{2}$ in circumference in a London museum. Lozes collected reports of 71 cases of horns,—37 in females, 31 in males, and three in infants. Of this number, 15 were on the head, eight on the face, 18 on the lower extremities, eight on the trunk, and three on the glans

a 683, 1696, 254.   b 418, 1776.   c 629, 176.

penis. Wilson [a] collected reports of 90 cases,—44 females, 39 males, the sex not being mentioned in the remainder. Of these 48 were on the head, four on the face, four on the nose, 11 on the thigh, three on the leg and foot, six on the back, five on the glans penis, and nine on the trunk. Lebert's [482] collection numbered 109 cases of cutaneous horns. The greater frequency among females is admitted by all authors. Old age is a predisposing cause. Several patients over seventy have been seen and one of ninety-seven. [b]

Instances of cutaneous horns, when seen and reported by the laity, give rise to most amusing exaggerations and descriptions. The following account [c] is given in New South Wales, obviously embellished with apocryphal details by some facetious journalist : The child, five weeks old, was born with hair two inches long all over the body ; his features were fiendish and his eyes shone like beads beneath his shaggy brows. He had a tail 18 inches long, horns from the skull, a full set of teeth, and claw-like hands ; he snapped like a dog and crawled on all fours, and refused the natural sustenance of a normal child. The mother almost became an imbecile after the birth of the monster. The country people about Bomballa considered this devil-child a punishment for a rebuff that the mother gave to a Jewish peddler selling Crucifixion-pictures. Vexed by his persistence, she said she would sooner have a devil in her house than his picture.

Lamprey [d] has made a minute examination of the much-spoken-of "Horned Men of Africa." He found that this anomaly was caused by a congenital malformation and remarkable development of the infraorbital ridge of the maxillary bone (Fig. 74). He described several cases, and through an interpreter found that they were congenital, followed no history of traumatism, caused little inconvenience, and were unassociated with disturbance of the sense of smell. He also learned that the deformity was quite rare in the Cape Coast region, and received no information tending to prove the conjecture that the tribes in West Africa used artificial means to produce the anomaly, although such custom is prevalent among many aborigines.

Probably the most remarkable case of a horn was that of Paul Rodrigues, a Mexican porter, [e] who, from the upper and lateral part of his head, had a horn 14 inches in circumference and divided into three shafts, which he concealed by constantly wearing a peculiarly shaped red cap. There is in Paris a wax model of a horn, eight or nine inches in length, removed from an old woman by the celebrated Souberbielle. Figure 75 is from a wax model supposed to have been taken from life, showing an enormous grayish-black horn proceeding from the forehead. Warren mentions a case under the care of Dubois, in a woman from whose forehead grew a horn six inches in diameter and six inches in height. It was hard at the summit and had a fetid

[a] 550, vol. xxvii., p. 60.   [b] 418, 1776, i., 311.   [c] Quoted in 759, April, 1894.
[d] 224, 1887, ii., 1273.   [e] New York Medical Repository, 1820.

odor. In 1696 there was an old woman in France who constantly shed long horns from her forehead, one of which was presented to the King. Bartholinus mentions a horn 12 inches long. Voigte cites the case of an old woman who had a horn branching into three portions, coming from her forehead. Sands [a] speaks of a woman who had a horn 6¾ inches long, growing from her head. There is an account [b] of the extirpation of a horn nearly ten inches in length from the forehead of a woman of eighty-two. Bejau [c] describes a woman of forty from whom he excised an excrescence resembling a ram's horn, growing from the left parietal region. It curved forward and nearly reached the corresponding tuberosity. It was eight cm. long, two cm. broad at the base, and 1½ cm. at the apex, and was quite mobile. It began to grow at the age of eleven and had constantly increased. Vidal presented

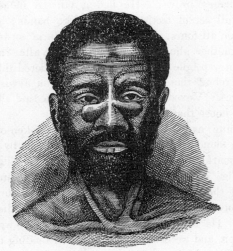

Fig. 74.—" African horned man " (Lamprey).   Fig. 75.—Wax model of a large frontal horn.

before the Académie de Médecine in 1886 a twisted horn from the head of a woman. This excrescence was ten inches long, and at the time of presentation reproduction of it was taking place in the woman. Figure 76 shows a case of ichthyosis cornea pictured in the Lancet, 1850. [d]

There was a woman of seventy-five, living near York, [e] who had a horny growth from the face which she broke off and which began to reproduce, the illustration (Fig. 77) representing the growth during twelve months. Lall [f] mentions a horn from the cheek ; Gregory reports one that measured 7½ inches long that was removed from the temple of a woman in Edinburgh ; Chariere of Barnstaple saw a horn that measured seven inches growing from the nape of a woman's neck ; Kameya Iwa [g] speaks of a dermal horn of the

a 597, 1851.   b 124, 1857.   c 749, 1886, 487.   d 476, 1850, ii., 342.
e 779, xvi., 267.   f 435,1883.   g Tokei Iji Shinshi, 1881.

auricle; Saxton of New York has excised several horns from the tympanic membrane of the ear; Noyes [a] speaks of one from the eyelid; Bigelow [b]

Fig. 76.—Ichthyosis cornea.

Fig. 77.—Facial horn.

mentions one from the chin; Minot [c] speaks of a horn from the lower lip, and Doran [d] of one from the neck.

Gould [e] cites the instance of a horn growing from an epitheliomatous penis. The patient was fifty-two years of age and the victim of congenital phimosis. He was circumcised four years previously, and shortly after the wound healed there appeared a small wart, followed by a horn about the size of a marble. Jewett speaks of a penile horn $3\frac{1}{2}$ inches long and $3\frac{3}{4}$ inches in diameter; Pick mentions one $2\frac{1}{2}$ inches long (Fig. 78). There is an account [f] of a Russian peasant boy who had a horn on his penis from earliest childhood. Johnson [g] mentions a case of a horn from the scrotum, which was of sebaceous origin and was subsequently supplanted by an epithelioma. Ash reported the case of a girl

Fig. 78.—Horn of the penis (after Pick).

named Annie Jackson, living in Waterford, Ireland, who had horny excres-

[a] 538, 1869.   [b] 331, 1867, vol. xix.   [c] 218, 1864.   [d] 779, 1881.
[e] 476, 1887, i., 421.   [f] 224, Aug. 13, 1887.   [g] 476, 1844.

cences from her joints, arms, axillæ, nipples, ears, and forehead. Locke speaks of a boy at the Hôpital de la Charité in Paris, who had horny excrescences four inches long and $1\frac{1}{2}$ inches in circumference growing from his fingers and toes.

Wagstaffe [a] presents a horn which grew from the middle of the leg six inches below the knee in a woman of eighty. It was a flattened spiral of more than two turns, and during forty years' growth had reached the length of 14.3 inches. Its height was 3.8 inches, its skin-attachment 1.5 inches in diameter, and it ended in a blunt extremity of 0.5 inch in diameter. Stephens [b] mentions a dermal horn on the buttocks at the seat of a carcinomatous cicatrix. Harris [c] and Domonceau [d] speak of horns from the leg. Cruveilhier [e] saw a Mexican Indian who had a horn four inches long and eight inches in circumference growing from the left lumbar region. It had been sawed off twice by the patient's son and was finally extirpated by Faget.

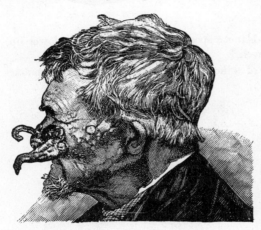

Fig. 79.—Cutaneous horns. Showing beginning epitheliomatous degeneration of the base (after Pancoast).

The length of the pieces was 12 inches. Bellamy [f] saw a horn on the clitoris about the size of a tiger's claw in a woman of seventy. It had its origin from beneath the preputium clitoridis.

Horns are generally solitary, but cases of multiple formation are known. Lewin and Heller record a syphilitic case with eight cutaneous horns on the palms and soles. A female patient of Manzuroff had as many as 185 horns. Pancoast [g] reports the case of a man whose nose, cheeks, forehead, and lips were covered with horny growths, which had apparently undergone epitheliomatous degeneration. The patient was a sea-captain of seventy-eight, and had been exposed to the winds all his life. He had suffered three attacks of erysipelas from prolonged exposure. When he consulted Pancoast the horns had nearly all fallen off and were brought to the physician for inspection; and the photograph (Fig. 79) was taken after the patient had tied the horns in situ on his face.

Anomalies of the Hair.—Congenital alopecia is quite rare, and it is seldom that we see instances of individuals who have been totally destitute of hair from birth. Danz [h] knew of two adult sons of a Jewish family who

a 779, 1870.
b 435, 1872.
c 527, 1842.
d 462, xiv., 145.
e Anat. patholog. du corps humain.
f 779, 1870.
g 631, 1878.
h 160, 1792.

never had hair or teeth. Sedgwick [a] quotes the case of a man of fifty-eight who ever since birth was totally devoid of hair and in whom sensible perspiration and tears were absent. A cousin on his mother's side, born a year before him, had precisely the same peculiarity. Buffon says that the Turks and some other people practised depilatory customs by the aid of ointments and pomades, principally about the genitals. Atkinson [b] exhibited in Philadelphia a man of forty who never had any distinct growth of hair since birth, was edentulous, and destitute of the sense of smell and almost of that of taste. He had no apparent perspiration, and when working actively he was obliged to wet his clothes in order to moderate the heat of his body. He could sleep in wet clothes in a damp cellar without catching cold. There was some hair in the axillæ and on the pubes, but only the slightest down on the scalp, and even that was absent on the skin. His maternal grandmother and uncle were similarly affected ; he was the youngest of 21 children, had never been sick, and though not able to chew food in the ordinary manner, he had never suffered from dyspepsia in any form. He was married and had eight children. Of these, two girls lacked a number of teeth, but had the ordinary quantity of hair. Hill [c] speaks of an aboriginal man in Queensland who was entirely devoid of hair on the head, face, and every part of the body. He had a sister, since dead, who was similarly hairless. Hill mentions the accounts given of another black tribe, about 500 miles west of Brisbane, that contained hairless members. This is very strange, as the Australian aboriginals are a very hairy race of people.

Hutchinson [d] mentions a boy of three and a half in whom there was congenital absence of hair and an atrophic condition of the skin and appendages. His mother was bald from the age of six, after alopecia areata. Schede reports two cases of congenitally bald children of a peasant woman (a boy of thirteen and a girl of six months). They had both been born quite bald, and had remained so. In addition there were neither eyebrows nor eyelashes and nowhere a trace of lanugo. The children were otherwise healthy and well formed. The parents and brothers were healthy and possessed a full growth of hair. Thurman [e] reports a case of a man of fifty-eight, who was almost devoid of hair all his life and possessed only four teeth. His skin was very delicate and there was absence of sensible perspiration and tears. The skin was peculiar in thinness, softness, and absence of pigmentation. The hair on the crown of the head and back was very fine, short, and soft, and not more in quantity than that of an infant of three months. There was a similar peculiarity in his cousin-german. Williams mentions the case of a young lady of fifteen with scarcely any hair on the eyebrows or head and no eyelashes. She was edentulous and had never sensibly perspired. She improved under tonic treatment.

a 222, 1863, i., 453.   b 218, March 29, 1883.   c 224, 1881. i., 177.
d 650, 1885–6, ii., 116.   e 550, xxxi., 71.

Rayer quotes the case of Beauvais, who was a patient in the Hôpital de la Charité in 1827. The skin of this man's cranium was apparently completely naked, although in examining it narrowly it was found to be beset with a quantity of very white and silky hair, similar to the down that covers the scalp of infants ; here and there on the temples there were a few black specks, occasioned by the stumps of several hairs which the patient had shaved off. The eyebrows were merely indicated by a few fine and very short hairs ; the free edges of the eyelids were without cilia, but the bulb of each of these was indicated by a small, whitish point. The beard was so thin and weak that Beauvais clipped it off only every three weeks. A few straggling hairs were observed on the breast and pubic region, as in young people on the approach of puberty. There was scarcely any under the axillæ. It was rather more abundant on the inner parts of the legs. The voice was like that of a full-grown and well-constituted man. Beauvais was of an amorous disposition and had had syphilis twice. His mother and both sisters had good heads of hair, but his father presented the same defects as Beauvais.

Instances are on record of women devoid of hair about the genital region. Riolan says that he examined the body of a female libertine who was totally hairless from the umbilical region down.

Congenital alopecia is seen **in animals.** There is a species of dog, a native of China but now bred in Mexico and in the United States, which is distinguished for its congenital alopecia. The same fact has been observed occasionally in horses, cattle, and dogs. Heusner [a] has seen a pigeon destitute of feathers, and which engendered a female which in her turn transmitted the same characteristic to two of her young.

Sexualism and Hair Growth.—The growth or development of the hair may be accelerated by the state of the organs of generation. This is peculiarly noticeable in the pubic hairs and the beard, and is fully exemplified in the section on precocious development (Chapter VII.); however, Moreau de la Sarthe showed a child to the Medical Faculty of Paris in whom precocious development of the testicles had influenced that of the hair to such a degree that, at the age of six, the chest of this boy was as thickly set with hair as is usually seen in adults. It is well known that eunuchs often lose a great part of their beards, and after removal of the ovaries women are seen to develop an extra quantity of hair. Gerberon [b] tells of an infant with a beard, and Paullini [c] and the Ephemerides mention similar instances.

Bearded women are not at all infrequent. Hippocrates mentions a female who grew a beard shortly after menstruation had ceased. It is a well-recognized fact that after the menopause women become more hirsute, the same being the case after removal of any of the functional generative apparatus. Vicat saw a virgin who had a beard, and Joch [d]

a 390, 153.　　　　　　　　　　　　　　　b 215, ann.,ii.

c 620, cent. iii., obs. 64.　　　　　　　　　　d Dissert., etc., Jenae.

speaks of "fœminis barbati." Leblond [a] says that certain women of Ethiopia and South America have beards and little or no menstruation. He also says that sterility and excessive chastity are causes of female beards, and cites the case of Schott of a young widow who secluded herself in a cloister and soon had a beard.

Barbara Urster, who lived in the 16th century, had a beard to her girdle. The most celebrated "bearded woman" was Rosine-Marguerite Müller, who died in a hospital in Dresden in 1732, with a thick beard and heavy mustache. Julia Pastrana had her face covered with thick hair and had a full beard and mustache. She exhibited defective dentition in both jaws, and the teeth present were arranged in

Fig. 80.—Julia Pastrana.

an irregular fashion. She had pronounced prognathism, which gave her a simian appearance (Fig. 80). Ecker examined in 1876 a woman who died at Fribourg, whose face contained a full beard and a luxuriant mustache.

Fig. 81. Fig. 82.

Bearded insane women (Harris).

Harris [b] reports several cases of bearded women, inmates of the Coton Hill Lunatic Asylum. One of the patients was eighty-three years of age and had

a 302, iii., 9. b 224, June 2, 1894.

been insane forty-four years following a puerperal period. She would not permit the hair on her face to be cut, and the curly white hairs had attained a length of from eight to ten inches on the chin, while on the upper lip the hairs were scarcely an inch. This patient was quite womanly in all her sentiments (Fig. 81). The second case was a woman of thirty-six, insane from emotional melancholia. She had tufts of thick, curly hair on the chin two inches long, light yellowish in color, and a few straggling hairs on the upper lip. The third case (Fig. 82) was that of a woman of sixty-four, who exhibited a strong passion for the male sex. Her menstruation had been regular until the menopause. She plaited her beard, and it was seven or

Fig. 83.—" Bearded woman."

eight inches long on the chin and one inch on the lip. This woman had extremely hairy legs. Another case was that of a woman of sixty-two, who, though bald, developed a beard before the climacteric. Her structural proportions were feminine in character, and it is said that her mother, who was sane, had a beard also. A curious case was that of a woman of twenty-three (Mrs. Viola M.), who from the age of three had a considerable quantity of hair on the side of the cheek which eventually became a full beard. She was quite feminine and was free from excessive hair elsewhere, her nose and forehead being singularly bare. Her voice was very sweet; she was married at seventeen and a half, having two normal children, and nursed each for one month. " The bearded woman" of every circus side-show is an evidence of the curious interest in which these women are held. The accompanying illustration (Fig. 83) is a representation of a " bearded woman" born in Bracken County, Ky. Her beard measured 15 inches in length.

There is a class of anomalies in which there is an **exaggerated development of hair.** We would naturally expect to find the primitive peoples, who are not provided with artificial protection against the wind, supplied with an extra quantity of hair or having a hairy coat like animals; but this is sometimes found among civilized people. This abnormal presence of hair on the human body has been known for many years; the description of Esau in the

Bible is an early instance. Aldrovandus says that in the sixteenth century there came to the Canary Islands a family consisting of a father, son, and two daughters, who were covered all over their bodies by long hair, and their portrait, certainly reproduced from life, resembles the modern instances of "dog men."

In 1883 there was shown in England and France, afterward in America, a girl of seven named "Krao," a native of Indo-China. The whole body of this child was covered with black hair. Her face was of the prognathic type, and this, with her extraordinary prehensile powers of feet and lips, gave her the title of "Darwin's missing link." In 1875 there was exhibited in Paris, under the name of "l'homme-chien" Adrien Jeftichew, a Russian

Fig. 84.—Two examples of extreme hirsuties in a family.

peasant of fifty-five, whose face, head, back, and limbs were covered with a brown hairy coat looking like wool and several centimeters long. The other parts of the body were also covered with hair, but less abundantly. This individual had a son of three, Theodore, who was hairy like himself.

A family living in Burmah (Shive-Maon, whose history is told by Crawford and Yule), consisting of a father, a daughter, and a granddaughter, were nearly covered with hair. Figure 84 represents a somewhat similar family who were exhibited in this country.

Teresa Gambardella, a young girl of twelve, mentioned by Lombroso, was covered all over the body, with the exception of the hands and feet, by thick, bushy hair. This hypertrichosis was exemplified in this country only a few months since by a person who went the rounds of the dime museums under the euphonious name of "Jo-Jo, the dog-face boy." His face was truly that of a skye-terrier (Fig. 85).

Sometimes the hairy anomalies are but instances of **nævus pilosus.** The Indian ourang-outang woman examined at the office of the Lancet was an example of this kind. Hebra, Hildebrandt, Jablokoff, and Klein describe similar cases. Many of the older "wild men" were individuals bearing extensive hairy moles.

Rayer remarks that he has seen a young man of sixteen who exhibited himself to the public under the name of a new species of wild man whose breast and back were covered with light brown hair of considerable length.

Fig. 85.—"Jo-Jo."   Fig. 86.—"Woman with a mane" (nævus pilosus).

The surface upon which it grew was of a brownish hue, different from the color of the surrounding integument. Almost the whole of the right arm was covered in the same manner. On the lower extremity several tufts of hair were observed implanted upon brown spots from seven to eight lines in diameter symmetrically disposed upon both legs. The hair was brown, of the same color as that of the head. Bichat[a] informs us that he saw at Paris an unfortunate man who from his birth was afflicted with a hairy covering of his face like that of a wild boar, and he adds that the stories which were current among the vulgar of individuals with a boar's head, wolf's head, etc., un-

a Anat. Générale, Paris, 1812, T. iv., 827.

doubtedly referred to cases in which the face was covered to a greater or less degree with hair. Villermé saw a child of six at Poitiers in 1808 whose body, except the feet and hands, was covered with a great number of prominent brown spots of different dimensions, beset with hair shorter and not so strong as that of a boar, but bearing a certain resemblance to the bristles of that animal. These spots occupied about one-fifth of the surface of this child's skin. Campaignac in the early part of this century exhibited a case in which there was a large tuft of long black hair growing from the shoulder. Dufour [a] has detailed a case of a young man of twenty whose sacral region contained a tuft of hair as long and black, thick and pliant, as that of the head, and, particularly remarkable in this case, the skin from which it grew was as fine and white as the integument of the rest of the body. There was a woman exhibited recently, under the advertisement of " the lady with a mane," who had growing from the center of her back between the shoulders a veritable mane of long, black hair, which doubtless proceeded from a form of nævus (Fig. 86).

Fig. 87.—Large nævus pilosus resembling "bathing-tights."

Duyse [b] reports a case of extensive hypertrichosis of the back in a girl aged nine years ; her teeth were normal ; there was pigmentation of the back and numerous pigmentary nevi on the face. Below each scapula there were tumors of the nature of fibroma molluscum. In addition to hairy nevi on the other parts of the body there was localized ichthyosis.

Ziemssen figures an interesting case of nævus pilosus resembling " bathing tights " (Fig. 87). There were also present several benign tumors (fibroma molluscum) and numerous smaller nevi over the body. Schulz first observed the patient in 1878. This individual's name was Blake, and he stated that he was born with a large nævus spreading over the upper parts of the thighs and lower parts of the trunk, like bathing-tights, and resembling the pelt of an animal. The same was true of the small hairy parts and the larger and smaller tumors. Subsequently the altered portions of the skin had gradually become somewhat larger. The skin of the large hairy nævus, as well as that of the smaller ones, was stated by Schulz to have been in the main thickened, in part uneven, verrucose, from very light to intensely dark brown in color ; the consistency of the larger mammiform and smaller tumors soft, doughy, and elastic. The case was really one of large congenital nævus pilosus and fibroma molluscum combined.

A Peruvian boy was shown at the Westminster Aquarium with a dark, hairy mole situated in the lower part of the trunk and on the thighs in the position of bathing tights. Nevins Hyde records two similar cases with

[a] 162, T. xxvi., 274.   [b] La Flandre Mèd., Oct. 4, 1894.

dermatolytic growths.[a]   A sister of the Peruvian boy referred to had a still larger growth, extending from the nucha all over the back.   Both she and her brother had hundreds of smaller hairy growths of all sizes scattered irregularly over the face, trunk, and limbs.   According to Crocker, a still more extraordinary case, with extensive dermatolytic growths all over the back and nevi of all sizes elsewhere, is described and engraved in "Lavater's Physiognomy," 1848.   Baker[b] describes an operation in which a large mole occupying half the forehead was removed by the knife.

In some instances the **hair and beard is of an enormous length.**

Fig. 88.—Example of excessive growth of hair.

Erasmus Wilson of London saw a female of thirty-eight, whose hair measured 1.65 meters long.   Leonard of Philadelphia speaks of a man in the interior of this country whose beard trailed on the ground when he stood upright, and measured 2.24 meters long.   Not long ago there appeared the famous so-called "Seven Sutherland Sisters," whose hair touched the ground, and with whom nearly every one is familiar through a hair tonic which they extensively advertised.   In Nature, January 9, 1892, is an account of a Percheron horse whose mane measured 13 feet and whose tail measured almost ten feet, probably the greatest example of excessive mane development on record.   Figure 88 represents Miss Owens, an exhibitionist, whose hair measured eight feet three inches.   In Leslie's Weekly, January 2, 1896, there is a portrait of an old negress named Nancy Garrison whose woolly hair was equally as long.

The Ephemerides[c] contains the account of a woman who had hair from the mons veneris which hung to the knees; it was affected with plica polonica, as was also the other hair of the body.

Rayer saw a Piedmontese of twenty-eight, with an athletic build, who had but little beard or hair on the trunk, but whose scalp was covered with a most extraordinary crop. It was extremely fine and silky, was artificially frizzled, dark brown in color, and formed a mass nearly five feet in circumference.

Certain pathologic conditions may give rise to **accidental growths of hair.** Boyer was accustomed to quote in his lectures the case of a man who, having an inflamed tumor in the thigh, perceived this part becoming covered in a short time with numerous long hairs. Rayer speaks of several instances of this kind. In one the part affected by a blister in a child of two became covered with hair. Another instance was that of a student of medicine, who after bathing in the sea for a length of time, and exposing himself to the hot sun, became affected with coppery patches, from which there sprang a growth of hair. Bricheteau, quoted by the same authority, speaks of a woman of twenty-four, having white skin and hair of deep black, who after a long illness occasioned by an affection analogous to marasmus became covered, especially on the back, breast, and abdomen, with a multitude of small elevations similar to those which appear on exposure to cold. These little elevations became brownish at the end of a few days, and short, fair, silky hair was observed on the summit of each, which grew so rapidly that the whole surface of the body with the exception of the hands and face became velvety. The hair thus evolved was afterward thrown out spontaneously and was not afterward reproduced.

Anomalies of the Color of the Hair.—New-born infants sometimes have tufts of hair on their heads which are perfectly white in color. Schenck speaks of a young man whose beard from its first appearance grew white. Young men from eighteen to twenty occasionally become gray ; and according to Rayer, paroxysms of rage, unexpected and unwelcome news, diseases of the scalp such as favus, wounds of the head, habitual headache, over-indulgence of the sexual appetite, mercurial courses too frequently repeated, too great anxiety, etc., have been known to blanch the hair prematurely.

The well-accepted fact of the **sudden changing of the color** of the hair from violent emotions or other causes has always excited great interest, and many ingenious explanations have been devised to account for it. There is a record in the time of Charles V. of a young man who was committed to prison in 1546 for seducing his girl companion, and while there was in great fear and grief, expecting a death-sentence from the Emperor the next day. When brought before his judge, his face was wan and pale and his hair and beard gray, the change having taken place in the night. His beard was filthy with drivel, and the Emperor, moved by his pitiful condition, pardoned him. There was a clergyman [a] of Nottingham whose daughter at the age of thirteen experienced a change from jet-blackness of the hair to white in a single night, but this was confined to a spot on the back of the head $1\frac{1}{2}$

[a] 564, iii., 515.

inches in length. Her hair soon became striped, and in seven years was totally white. The same article speaks of a girl in Bedfordshire, Maria Seeley, aged eight, whose face was swarthy, and whose hair was long and dark on one side and light and short on the other. One side of her body was also brown, while the other side was light and fair. She was seen by the faculty in London, but no cause could be established.

Voigtel mentions the occurrence of canities almost suddenly. Bichat had a personal acquaintance whose hair became almost entirely gray in consequence of some distressing news that reached him. Cassan [a] records a similar case. According to Rayer, a woman by the name of Pérat, summoned before the Chamber of Peers to give evidence in the trial of the assassin Louvel, was so much affected that her hair became entirely white in a single night. Byron makes mention of this peculiar anomaly in the opening stanzas of the " Prisoner of Chillon : "—

> " My hair is gray, but not with years,
>   Nor grew it white
>   In a single night,
> As men's have grown from sudden fears."

The commentators say that Byron had reference to Ludovico Sforza and others. The fact of the change is asserted of Marie Antoinette, the wife of Louis XVI., though in not quite so short a period, grief and not fear being the cause. Ziemssen cites Landois' case of a compositor of thirty-four who was admitted to a hospital July 9th with symptoms of delirium tremens ; until improvement began to set in (July 13th) he was continually tormented by terrifying pictures of the imagination. In the night preceding the day last mentioned the hair of the head and beard of the patient, formerly blond, became gray. Accurate examination by Landois showed the pigment contents of the hair to be unchanged, and led him to believe that the white color was solely due to the excessive development of air-bubbles in the hair shaft. Popular belief brings the premature and especially the sudden whitening into connection with depressing mental emotions. We might quote the German expression—" Sich graue Haare etwas wachsen lassen " (" To worry one's self gray "). Brown-Séquard observed on several occasions in his own dark beard hairs which had turned white in a night and which he epilated. He closes his brief communication on the subject with the belief that it is quite possible for black hair to turn white in one night or even in a less time, although Hebra and Kaposi discredit sudden canities (Duhring). Raymond and Vulpian [b] observed a lady of neurotic type whose hair during a severe paroxysm of neuralgia following a mental strain changed color in five hours over the entire scalp except on the back and sides ; most of the hair changed from black to red, but some to quite white, and in two days

a 162, Jan., 1827.   b 476, Oct. 14, 1882.

all the red hair became white and a quantity fell off. The patient recovered her general health, but with almost total loss of hair, only a few red, white, and black hairs remaining on the occipital and temporal regions. Crocker cites the case of a Spanish cock which was nearly killed by some pigs. The morning after the adventure the feathers of the head had become completely white, and about half of those on the back of the neck were also changed.

Dewees[a] reports a case of puerperal convulsions in a patient under his care which was attended with sudden canities. From 10 A. M. to 4 P. M. 50 ounces of blood were taken. Between the time of Dr. Dewees' visits, not more than an hour, the hair anterior to the coronal suture turned white. The next day it was less light, and in four or five days was nearly its natural color. He also mentions two cases of sudden blanching from fright.

Fowler[b] mentions the case of a healthy girl of sixteen who found one morning while combing her hair, which was black, that a strip the whole length of the back hair was white, starting from a surface about two inches square around the occipital protuberance. Two weeks later she had patches of ephelis over the whole body.

Prentiss, in Science, October 3, 1890, has collected numerous instances of sudden canities, several of which will be given :—

"In the Canada Journal of Medical Science, 1882, p. 113, is reported a case of sudden canities due to business-worry. The microscope showed a great many air-vesicles both in the medullary substance and between the medullary and cortical substance.

"In the Boston Medical and Surgical Journal, 1851, is reported a case of a man thirty years old, whose hair ' was scared ' white in a day by a grizzly bear. He was sick in a mining camp, was left alone, and fell asleep. On waking he found a grizzly bear standing over him.

"A second case is that of a man of twenty-three years who was gambling in California. He placed his entire savings of $1100 on the turn of a card. He was under tremendous nervous excitement while the cards were being dealt. The next day his hair was perfectly white.

"In the same article is the statement that the jet-black hair of the Pacific Islanders does not turn gray gradually, but when it does turn it is sudden, usually the result of fright or sudden emotions."

D'Alben, quoted by Fournier,[c] describes a young man of twenty-four, an officer in the regiment of Touraine in 1781, who spent the night in carnal dissipation with a mulatto, after which he had violent spasms, rendering flexion of the body impossible. His beard and hair on the right side of the body was found as white as snow, the left side being unchanged. He appeared before the Faculté de Montpelier, and though cured of his nervous symptoms his hair was still white, and no suggestion of relief was offered him.

Louis of Bavaria, who died in 1294, on learning of the innocence of his

a Phila. Med. Museum, iii., 219.　　　b 476, 1853, i., 556.　　　c 302, iv., 176.

wife, whom he had put to death on a suspicion of her infidelity, had a change of color in his hair, which became white almost immediately. Vauvilliers, the celebrated Hellenist, became white-haired almost immediately after a terrible dream, and Brizard, the comedian, experienced the same change after a narrow escape from drowning in the Rhone. The beard and the hair of the Duke of Brunswick whitened in twenty-four hours after hearing that his father had been mortally wounded at the battle of Auerstadt.

De Schweinitz [a] speaks of a well-formed and healthy brunette of eighteen in whom the middle portion of the cilia of the right upper eyelid and a number of the hairs of the lower lid turned white in a week. Both eyes were myopic, but no other cause could be assigned. Another similar case is cited by Hirshberg, [b] and the authors have seen similar cases. Thornton of Margate records the case of a lady in whom the hair of the left eyebrow and eyelashes began to turn white after a fortnight of sudden grief, and within a week all the hair of these regions was quite white and remained so. No other part was affected nor was there any other symptom. After a traumatic ophthalmitis of the left and sympathetic inflammation of the right eye in a boy of nine, Schenck observed that a group of cilia of the right upper lid and nearly all the lashes of the upper lid of the left eye, which had been enucleated, turned silvery-white in a short time. Ludwig has known the eyelashes to become white after small-pox. Communications are also on record of local decolorization of the eyebrows and lashes in neuralgias of isolated branches of the trigeminus, especially of the supraorbital nerve.

Temporary and Partial Canities.—Of special interest are those cases in which whiteness of the hair is only temporary. Thus, Compagne mentions a case in which the black hair of a woman of thirty-six began to fade on the twenty-third day of a malignant fever, and on the sixth day following was perfectly white, but on the seventh day the hairs became darker again, and on the fourteenth day after the change they had become as black as they were originally. Wilson records a case in which the hair lost its color in winter and regained it in summer. Sir John Forbes, according to Crocker, had gray hair for a long time, then suddenly it all turned white, and after remaining so for a year it returned to its original gray.

Grayness of the hair is sometimes only partial. According to Crocker an adult whose hair was generally brown had a tuft of white hair over the temple, and several like cases are on record. Lorry tells us that grayness of one side only is sometimes occasioned by severe headache. Hagedorn has known the beard to be black in one place and white in another. Brandis mentions the hair becoming white on one side of the face while it continued of its former color on the other. Rayer quotes cases of canities of the whole of one side of the body.

Richelot observed white mottling of hair in a girl sick with chlorosis.

a 792, May, 1889.   b 262, 1888.

The whitening extended from the roots to a distance of two inches. The probable cause was a temporary alteration of the pigment-forming function. When the chlorosis was cured the natural color returned. Paullini and Riedlin, as well as the Ephemerides, speak of different colored hair in the same head, and it is not at all rare to see individuals with an anomalously colored patch of hair on the head. The members of the ancient house of Rohan were said to possess a tuft of white hair on the front of their heads.

Michelson of Königsberg describes a curious case in a barrister of twenty-three affected with partial canities. In the family of both parents there was stated to be congenital premature canities, and some white hairs had been observed even in childhood. In the fifteenth year, after a grave attack of scarlet fever, the hair to a great extent fell out. The succeeding growth of hair was stated to have been throughout lighter in tissue and color and fissured at the points. Soon after bunches of white hair appeared on the occiput, and in the succeeding years small patches of decolored hairs were observed also on the anterior and lateral portions of the scalp. In the spring of 1880 the patient exhibited signs of infiltration of the apex of the right lung, and afterward a violent headache came on. At the time of the report the patient presented the appearance shown in Figure 89. The complexion was delicate throughout, the eyelashes and eyelids dark brown, the moustache and whiskers blond, and in the latter were a few groups of white hair. The white patches were chiefly on the left side of the head. The hairs growing on

Fig. 89.—Mottled hair (Michelson).

them were unpigmented, but otherwise normal. The patient stated that his head never sweated. He was stout and exhibited no signs of internal disease, except at the apex of the right lung.

Anomalous Color Changes of the Hair.—The hair is liable to undergo certain changes of color connected with some modification of that part of the bulb secreting its coloring-matter. Alibert, quoted by Rayer, gives us a report of the case of a young lady who, after a severe fever which followed a very difficult labor, lost a fine head of hair during a discharge of viscid fluid, which inundated the head in every part. He tells us, further, that the hair grew again of a deep black color after the recovery of the patient. The same writer tells of the case of James B——, born with brown hair, who, having lost it all during the course of a sickness, had it replaced with a crop of the brightest red. White and gray hair has also, under peculiar circumstances, been replaced by hair of the same color as the individual had in youth. We are even assured by Bruley that in 1798 the white hair of a woman sixty years of age changed to black a few days before her death. The bulbs in this case were found of great size, and appeared gorged with a substance from which the hair derived its color. The white hairs that remained, on the contrary, grew from shriveled bulbs much smaller than those producing the black. This patient died of phthisis.[a]

A very singular case, published early in the century, was that of a woman whose hair, naturally fair, assumed a tawny red color as often as she was affected with a certain fever, and returned to its natural hue as soon as the symptoms abated.[b] Villermé[302] alludes to the case of a young lady, sixteen years of age, who had never suffered except from trifling headaches, and who, in the winter of 1817, perceived that the hair began to fall out from several parts of her head, so that before six months were over she became entirely bald. In the beginning of January, 1819, her head became covered with a kind of black wool over those places that were first denuded, and light brown hair began to develop from the rest of the scalp. Some of this fell out again when it had grown from three to four inches; the rest changed color at different distances from its end and grew of a chestnut color from the roots. The hair, half black, half chestnut, had a very singular appearance.

Alibert and Beigel relate cases of women with blond hair which all came off after a severe fever (typhus in one case), and when it grew again it was quite black. Alibert also saw a young man who lost his brown hair after an illness, and after restoration it became red. According to Crocker, in an idiotic girl of epileptic type (in an asylum at Edinburgh), with alternating phases of stupidity and excitement, the hair in the stupid phase was blond and in the excited condition red. The change of color took place in the course of two or three days, beginning first at the free ends, and remaining of the same tint for seven or eight days. The pale hairs had more air-spaces than the darker ones. There was much structural change in the brain and spinal cord. Smyly of Dublin reported a case of suppurative disease of the temporal bone, in which the hair changed from a mouse-color to a reddish-brown; and Squire records a congenital case in a deaf mute, in whom the hair on the left side was in light patches of true auburn and dark patches of dark brown like a tortoise-shell cap; on the other side the hair was a dark brown. Crocker mentions the changes which have occurred in rare instances after death from dark brown to red.

Chemic colorations of various tints occur. Blue hair is seen in workers in cobalt mines and indigo works; green hair in copper smelters; deep red-brown hair in handlers of crude anilin; and the hair is dyed a purplish-brown whenever chrysarobin applications used on a scalp come in contact with an alkali, as when washed with soap. Among such cases in older

[a] 458, T. iv., 290.   [b] 454, T. v., 59.

literature Blanchard and Marcellus Donatus speak of green hair; Rosse saw two instances of the same, for one of which he could find no cause; the other patient worked in a brass foundry.

Many **curious causes** are given **for alopecia.** Gilibert and Merlet [a] mention sexual excess; Marcellus Donatus [b] gives fear; the Ephemerides speaks of baldness from fright; and Leo Africanus, in his description of Barbary, describes endemic baldness. Neyronis [c] makes the following observation: A man of seventy-three, convalescent from a fever, one morning, about six months after recovery perceived that he had lost all his hair, even his eyelashes, eyebrows, nostril-hairs, etc. Although his health continued good, the hair was never renewed.

The principal **anomalies of the nails** observed are absence, hypertrophy, and displacement of these organs. Some persons are born with finger-nails and toe-nails either very rudimentary or entirely absent; in others they are of great length and thickness. The Chinese nobility allow their finger-nails to grow to a great length and spend much time in the care of these nails. Some savage tribes have long and thick nails resembling the claws of beasts, and use them in the same way as the lower animals. There is a description of a person with finger-nails that resembled the horns of a goat. [d] Neuhof, in his books on Tartary

Fig. 90.—Deformed toe-nails.

and China, says that many Chinamen have two nails on the little toe, and other instances of double nails have been reported.

The nails may be reversed or arise from anomalous positions. Bartholinus [e] speaks of nails from the inner side of the digits; in another case, in which the fingers were wanting, he found the nails implanted on the stumps. Tulpius says he knew of a case in which nails came from the articulations of three digits; and many other curious arrangements of nails are to be found.

Rouhuot sent a description and drawing of some monstrous nails to the Académie des Sciences de Paris (Fig. 90). The largest of these was the left great toe-nail, which, from its extremity to its root, measured $4\frac{3}{4}$ inches; the laminæ of which it consisted were placed one over the other, like the tiles on a roof, only reversed. This nail and several of the others were of unequal thickness and were variously curved, probably on account of the pressure of the shoe or the neighboring digits. Rayer mentions two nails sent to him by Bricheteau, physician of the Hôpital Necker, belonging to an old

a Diss. calvites, Paris, 1662.   b 306, L. i., cap. i., p. 15.

c 463, v., 73.   d 282, Nov., 1734, 173.   e 190, cent. ii., hist. 44.

woman who had lived in the Salpétrière. They were very thick and spirally twisted, like the horns of a ram. Saviard informs us that he saw a patient at the Hôtel Dieu who had a horn like that of a ram, instead of a nail, on each great toe, the extremities of which were turned to the metatarsus and overlapped the whole of the other toes of each foot. The skeleton of Simore, preserved in Paris, is remarkable for the ankylosis of all the articulations and the considerable size of all the nails. The fingers and toes, spread out and ankylosed, ended in nails of great length and nearly of equal thickness. A woman by the name of Melin, living in the last century in Paris, was surnamed " the woman with nails ; " according to the description given by Saillant in 1776 she presented another and not less curious instance of the excessive growth of the nails.

Musaeus [a] gives an account of the nails of a girl of twenty, which grew to such a size that some of those of the fingers were five inches in length. They were composed of several layers, whitish interiorly, reddish-gray on the exterior, and full of black points. These nails fell off at the end of four months and were succeeded by others. There were also horny laminæ on the knees and shoulders and elbows which bore a resemblance to nails, or rather talons. They were sensitive only at the point of insertion into the skin. Various other parts of the body, particularly the backs of the hands, presented these horny productions. One of them was four inches in length. This horny growth appeared after small-pox. Ash, in the Philosophical Transactions, records a somewhat similar case in a girl of twelve.

Anomalies of the Teeth.—Pliny, Colombus, van Swieten, Haller, Marcellus Donatus, Baudelocque, Soemmering, and Gardien all cite instances in which children have come into the world with several teeth already erupted. Haller [400] has collected 19 cases of **children born with teeth.** Polydorus Virgilus describes an infant who was born with six teeth. Some celebrated men are supposed to have been born with teeth ; Louis XIV. was accredited with having two teeth at birth. Bigot, a physician and philosopher of the sixteenth century ; Boyd, the poet ; Valerian, Richard III., as well as some of the ancient Greeks and Romans, were reputed to have had this anomaly. The significance of the natal eruption of teeth is not always that of vigor, as many of the subjects succumb early in life. There were two cases typical of fetal dentition shown before the Académie de Médecine de Paris. One of the subjects had two middle incisors in the lower jaw and the other had one tooth well through. Levison [b] saw a female born with two central incisors in the lower jaw.

Thomas [c] mentions a case of antenatal development of nine teeth. Puech, Mattei, Dumas, Belluzi, and others report the eruption of teeth in the newborn. In Dumas' case the teeth had to be extracted on account of ulceration of the tongue.

a Diss. de unguibus monstrosis, Hafniæ, 1716.   b 476, 1846, ii., 699.   c 125, vii., 501.

Instances of **triple dentition** late in life are quite numerous, many occurring after a hundred years. Mentzelius speaks of a man of one hundred and ten who had nine new teeth. Lord Bacon cites the case of a Countess Desmond, who when over a century old had two new teeth ; Hufeland saw an instance of dentition at one hundred and sixteen ; Nitzsch speaks of one at one hundred, and the Ephemerides contain an account of a triple dentition at one hundred and twenty. There is an account [a] of a country laborer who lost all his teeth by the time he arrived at his sixtieth year of age, but about a half year afterward a new set made their appearance. Bisset [b] mentions an account of an old woman who acquired twelve molar teeth at the age of ninety-eight. Carre [c] notes a case of dental eruption in an individual of eighty-five. Mazzoti speaks of a third dentition, and Ysabeau [d] writes of dentition of a molar at the age of ninety-two. There is a record of a physician of the name of Slave who retained all his second teeth until the age of eighty, when they fell out ; after five years another set appeared, which he retained until his death at one hundred. In the same report [e] there is mentioned an old Scotchman who died at one hundred and ten, whose teeth were renewed at an advanced age after he had lost his second teeth. One of the older journals [282] speaks of dentition at seventy, eighty-four, ninety, and one hundred and fourteen. The Philosophical Transactions of London contain accounts of dentition at seventy-five and eighty-one. Bassett [f] tells of an old woman who had twelve molar teeth at the age of eighty-eight. In France there is recorded dentition at eighty-five [g] and an account of an old man of seventy-three who had six new teeth. [h] Von Helmont relates an instance of triple dentition at the same age. There is recorded in Germany an account of a woman of ninety who had dentition at forty-seven and sixty-seven, each time a new set of teeth appearing ; Hunter and Pétrequin have observed similar cases. Carter [i] describes an example of third dentition. Lison [j] makes a curious observation of a sixth dentition.

Edentulousness.—We have already noticed the association of congenital alopecia with edentulousness, but, strange to say, Magitot has remarked that " l'homme-chien," was the subject of defective dentition. Borellus found atrophy of all the dental follicles in a woman of sixty who never had possessed any teeth. Fanton-Touvet saw a boy of nine who had never had teeth, and Fox a woman who had but four in both jaws ; Tomes cites several similar instances. Hutchinson [k] speaks of a child who was perfectly edentulous as to temporary teeth, but who had the permanent teeth duly and fully erupted. Guilford [l] describes a man of forty-eight, who was edentulous from birth, who also totally lacked the sense of smell, and was almost without the sense

a 534, 1784, iii., 105.   b 524, Lond., 1787, viii., 370.   c 368, 1860, xv., 585.
d 460, xxxv., 316 (1766).   e 302, vol. iv.   f 524, 787.
g 368, 1860.   h 363, Oct. 9, 1875.   i 133, 1876.
j 235, xiii., 190.   k 476, 1883, i., 894.   l 296, 1883.

of taste ; the surface of his body was covered with fine hairs and he had never had visible perspiration. This is probably the same case quoted in the foregoing paragraph in regard to the anomalies of hair. Otto, quoted by Sedgwick, speaks of two brothers who were both totally edentulous. It might be interesting in this connection to note that Oudet found in a fetus at term all the dental follicles in a process of suppuration, leaving no doubt that, if the fetus had been born viable, it would have been edentulous. Giraldès mentions the absence of teeth in an infant of sixteen months. Bronzet describes a child of twelve, with only half its teeth, in whom the alveolar borders receded as in age. Baumes remarks that he had seen a man who never had any teeth.

The anomalies of **excessive dentition** are of several varieties, those of simple supernumerary teeth, double or triple rows, and those in anomalous positions. Ibbetson saw a child with five incisors in the inferior maxillary bone, and Fanton-Touvet describes a young lady who possessed five large incisors of the first dentition in the superior maxilla. Rayer [a] notes a case of dentition of four canines, which first made their appearance after pain for eight days in the jaws and associated with convulsions. In an Ethiopian Soemmering has seen one molar too many on each side and in each jaw. Ploucquet and Tesmer have seen five incisors and Fanchard six. Many persons have the supernumerary teeth parallel with their neighbors, anteriorly or posteriorly. Costa [b] reports a case in which there were five canine teeth in the upper jaw, two placed laterally on either side, and one on the right side behind the other two. The patient was twenty-six years of age, well formed and in good health.

In some cases there is **fusion of the teeth.** Pliny, Bartholinus, and Melanthon pretend to have seen the union of all the teeth, making a continuous mass. In the " Musée de l'École dentaire de Paris " there are several milk-teeth, both of the superior and inferior maxilla, which are fused together. Bloch cites a case in which there were **two rows of teeth** in the superior maxilla. Hellwig [414] has observed **three rows of teeth,** and the Ephemerides contain an account of a similar anomaly.

Extraoral Dentition.—Probably the most curious anomaly of teeth is that in which they are found in other than normal positions. Albinus speaks of teeth in the nose and orbit ; Borellus, in the palate ; Fabricius Hildanus,[334] under the tongue ; Schenck, from the palate ; and there are many similar modern records. Heister in 1743 wrote a dissertation on extraoral teeth. The following is a recent quotation :[c]—

" In the Norsk Magazin für Lægevidenskaben, January, 1895, it is reported that Dr. Dave, at a meeting of the Medical Society in Christiania, showed a tooth removed from the nose of a woman aged fifty-three. The patient had consulted him for ear-trouble, and the tooth was found accidentally during the routine examination. It was easily removed, having

a 302, viii., 411.   b 358, March, 1895.   c 224, 1895, ii., 512.

been situated in a small depression at the junction of the floor and external wall of the nasal cavity, 22 mm. from the external nares. This patient had all her teeth ; they were placed somewhat far from each other. The tooth resembled a milk canine ; the end of the imperfect root was covered with a fold of mucous membrane, with stratified epithelium. The speaker suggested that part of the mucous membrane of the mouth with its tooth-germ had become impacted between the superior and premaxillary bones and thus cut off from the cavity of the mouth. Another speaker criticised this fetal dislocation and believed it to be due to an inversion—a development in the wrong direction—by which the tooth had grown upward into the nose. The same speaker also pointed out that the stratified epithelium of the mucous membrane did not prove a connection with the cavity of the mouth, as it is known that cylindric epithelium-cells after irritative processes are replaced by flat ones."

Delpech saw a young man in 1829 who had an opening in the palatine vault occasioned by the extraction of a tooth. This opening communicated with the nasal fossa by a fracture of the palatine and maxillary bones ; the employment of an obturator was necessary. It is not rare to see teeth, generally canine, make their eruption from the vault of the palate ; and these teeth are not generally supernumerary, but examples of vice and deviation of position. Fanton-Touvet, however, gives an example of a supernumerary tooth implanted in the palatine arch. Branch [a] describes a little negro boy who had two large teeth in the nose ; his dentition was otherwise normal, but a portion of the nose was destroyed by ulceration. Roy [b] describes a Hindoo lad of fourteen who had a tooth in the nose, supposed to have been a tumor. It was of the canine type, and was covered with enamel to the junction with the root, which was deeply imbedded in the side and upper part of the antrum. The boy had a perfect set of permanent teeth and no deformity, swelling, or cystic formation of the jaw. This was clearly a case of extrafollicular development and eruption of the tooth in an anomalous position, the peculiarity being that while in other similar cases the crown of the tooth shows itself at the floor of the nasal cavity from below upward, in this instance the dental follicle was transposed, the eruption being from above downward. Hall [c] cites an instance in which the right upper canine of a girl erupted in the nose. The subject showed marked evidence of hereditary syphilis. Carver [d] describes a child who had a tooth growing from the lower right eyelid. The number of deciduous teeth was perfect ; although this tooth was canine it had a somewhat bulbulous fang.

Of **anomalies of the head** the first to be considered will be the anencephalous monsters who, strange to say, have been known to survive birth. Clericus [e] cites an example of life for five days in a child **without a cere-**

a 548, 1884, i., 425.   b 476, 1883, ii., 772.   c 476, 1883, ii., 862.
d 476, 1887, ii., 763.   e 215, 1781.

brum. Heysham [a] records the birth of a child without a cerebrum and remarks that it was kept alive for six days. There was a child born alive in Italy in 1831 without a brain or a cerebellum—in fact, no cranial cavity—and yet it lived eleven hours.[b] A somewhat similar case is recorded in the last century.[108] In the Philosophical Transactions [c] there is mentioned a child virtually born without a head who lived four days ; and Le Duc records a case of a child born without brain, cerebellum, or medulla oblongata, and who lived half an hour. Brunet [d] describes an anencephalous boy born at term who survived his birth. Saviard [469] delivered an anencephalous child at term which died in thirty-six hours. Lawrence [e] mentions a child with brain and cranium deficient that lived five days. Putnam [f] speaks of a female nosencephalous monster that lived twenty-nine hours. Angell and Elsner in March, 1895,[230] reported a case of anencephaly, or rather pseudencephaly, associated with double divergent strabismus and limbs in a state of constant spastic contraction. The infant lived eight days. Geoffroy-Saint-Hilaire cites an example of anencephaly which lived a quarter of an hour. Fauvel mentioned one that lived two hours, and Sue describes a similar instance in which life persisted for seven hours and distinct motions were noticed. Malacarne saw life in one for twelve hours, and Méry has given a description of a child born without brain that lived almost a full day and took nourishment. In the Hôtel-Dieu in Paris in 1812 Serres saw a monster of this type which lived three days, and was fed on milk and sugared water, as no nurse could be found who was willing to suckle it.

Fraser [g] mentions a brother and sister, aged twenty and thirty, respectively, who from birth had exhibited signs of **defective development of the cerebellum.** They lacked power of coordination and walked with a drunken, staggering gait ; they could not touch the nose with the finger when their eyes were shut, etc. The parents of these unfortunate persons were perfectly healthy, as were the rest of their family. Cruveilhier cites a case of a girl of eleven who had absolutely no cerebellum, with the same symptoms which are characteristic in such cases. There is also recorded the history of a man [h] who was deficient in the corpus callosum ; at the age of sixty-two, though of feeble intelligence, he presented no signs of nervous disorder. Claude Bernard made an autopsy on a woman who had no trace of olfactory lobes, and after a minute inquiry into her life he found that her sense of smell had been good despite her deficiency.

Buhring relates the history of a case somewhat analogous to viability of anencephalous monsters. It was a bicephalous child that lived thirty-two hours after he had ligated one of its heads. [i]

Ward [j] mentions an instance of congenital absence of the corpora callo-

a 524, iii., 250.   b 476, 1832-3, i., 570.   c 629, 1700, 23.   d Progrès de la Méd., 1698.
e 550, 1814.   f Archiv. Scientif. and Prac. M. & S., 1873, 342.
g 381, 1880, 199.   h 212, 158.   i 827, Oct., 1843.   j 490, 1846, ii., 575.

sum. Paget [a] and Henry mention cases in which the corpora callosum, the fornix, and septum lucidum were imperfectly formed. Maunoir [b] reports congenital malformation of the brain, consisting of almost complete absence of the occipital lobe. The patient died at the twenty-eighth month. Combettes [c] reports the case of a girl who died at the age of eleven who had complete absence of the cerebellum in addition to other minor structural defects; this was probably the case mentioned by Cruveilhier.[d]

Diminution in volume of the head is called **microcephaly**. Probably the most remarkable case on record is that mentioned by Lombroso. The

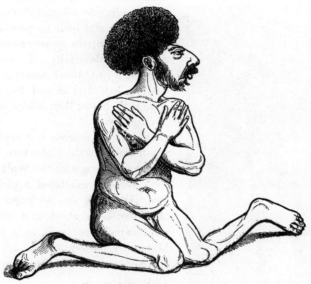

Fig. 91.—Microcephalic "Aztec man."

individual was called "l'homme-oiseau," or the human bird, and his cranial capacity was only 390 c. c. Lombroso speaks of another individual

[a] 550, xxix., 55.   [b] 242, 1876, i., 163.   [c] 242, 1830, v., 148.

[d] The argument that the brain is not the sole organ of the mind is in a measure substantiated by a wonderful case of a decapitated rooster, reported from Michigan.[1] A stroke of the knife had severed the larynx and removed the whole mass of the cerebrum, leaving the inner aspect and base of the skull exposed. The cerebrum was partly removed; the external auditory meatus was preserved. Immediately after the decapitation the rooster was left to its supposed death struggles, but it ran headless to the barn, where it was secured and subsequently fed by pushing corn down its esophagus, and allowing water to trickle into this tube from the spout of an oil-can. The phenomena exhibited by the rooster were quite interesting. It made all the motions of pecking, strutted about, flapped its wings, attempted to crow, but, of course, without making any sound. It exhibited no signs of incoordination, but did not seem to hear. A ludicrous exhibition was the absurd, sidelong *pas seul* made toward the hens.

[1] 632, 1880, ii., 5.

called "l'homme-lapin," or man-rabbit, whose cranium was only slightly larger than that of the other, measuring 490 mm. in circumference. Castelli alludes to endemic microcephaly among some of the peoples of Asia. We also find it in the Caribbean Islands, and from the skulls and portraits of the ancient Aztecs we are led to believe that they were also microcephalic.

Two creatures of celebrity were Maximo and Bartola, who for twenty-five years have been shown in America and in Europe under the name of the "Aztecs" or the "Aztec children" (Fig. 91). They were male and female and very short, with heads resembling closely the bas-reliefs on the

Fig. 92.—Microcephalic boy.

ancient Aztec temples of Mexico. Their facial angle was about 45°, and they had jutting lips and little or no chin. They wore their hair in an enormous bunch to magnify the deformity. These curiosities were born in Central America and were possibly half Indian and Negro. They were little better than idiots in point of intelligence.

Figure 92 represents a microcephalic youth known as the "Mexican wild boy," who was shown with the Wallace circus.

Virchow [a] exhibited a girl of fourteen whose face was no larger than that of a new-born child, and whose head was scarcely as large as a man's fist. Magitot reported a case of a microcephalic woman of thirty who weighed 70 pounds.

Hippocrates and Strabonius both speak of head-binding as a custom inducing **artificial microcephaly,** and some tribes of North American Indians still retain this custom.

As a rule, microcephaly is attended with associate idiocy and arrested development of the rest of the body. Ossification of the fontanelles in a mature infant would necessarily prevent full development of the brain. Osiander and others have noticed this anomaly. There are cases on record in which the fontanelles have remained open until adulthood.

Augmentation of the volume of the head is called **macrocephaly,** and there are a number of curious examples related. Benvenuti describes an individual, otherwise well formed, whose head began to enlarge at

[a] Quoted 538, 1884, 522.

seven. At twenty-seven it measured over 37 inches in circumference and the man's face was 15 inches in height; no other portion of his body increased abnormally; his voice was normal and he was very intelligent. He died of apoplexy at the age of thirty.[a]

Fournier[b] speaks of a cranium in the cabinet of the Natural History Museum of Marseilles of a man by the name of Borghini, who died in 1616. At the time he was described he was fifty years old, four feet in height; his head measured three feet in circumference and one foot in height. There was a proverb in Marseilles, "Apas maï de sen que Borghini," meaning in the local dialect, "Thou hast no more wit than Borghini." This man, whose fame became known all over France, was not able, as he grew older, to maintain the weight of his head, but carried a cushion on each shoulder to prop it up. Fournier also quotes the history of a man who died in the same city in 1807 at the age of sixty-seven. His head was enormous, and he never lay on a bed for thirty years, passing his nights in a chair, generally reading or writing. He only ate once in twenty-four or thirty hours, never warmed himself, and never used warm water. His knowledge was said to have been great and encyclopedic, and he pretended never to have heard the proverb of Borghini. There is related the account of a Moor, who was seen in Tunis early in this century, thirty-one years of age, of middle height, with a head so prodigious in dimensions that crowds flocked after him in the streets. His nose was quite long, and his mouth so large that he could eat a melon as others would an apple. He was an imbecile. William Thomas Andrews was a dwarf seventeen years old, whose head measured in circumference 35 inches; from one external auditory meatus to another, 27¼ inches; from the chin over the cranial summit to the suboccipital protuberance, 37½ inches; the distance from the chin to the pubes was 20 inches; and from the pubes to the soles of the feet, 16; he was a monorchid.[c] James Cardinal, who died in Guy's Hospital in 1825, and who was so celebrated for the size of his head, only measured 32½ inches in head-circumference.

The **largest healthy brains on record,** that is, of men of prominence, are those of Cuvier, weighing 64⅓ ounces;[d] of Daniel Webster, weighing 63¾ ounces (the circumference of whose head was 23¾ inches);[e] of Abercrombie, weighing 63 ounces, and of Spurzheim, weighing 55$\frac{1}{16}$ ounces. Byron and Cromwell had abnormally heavy brains, showing marked evidence of disease.

A curious instance in this connection is that quoted by Pigné,[f] who gives an account of a double brain found in an infant. Keen reports finding a fornix which, instead of being solid from side to side, consisted of two lateral halves with a triangular space between them.

When the augmentation of the volume of the cranium is caused by an abundant quantity of serous fluid the anomaly is known as **hydrocephaly.**

[a] Actes de la société impér. des curieux de la nature, tom. viii.   [b] 302, iv., 142.

[c] 593, 1856, xiii., 778.   [d] 678, Dec., 1883.   [e] 124, 1853, 110.   [f] 242, 1846, xxi., 144.

In this condition there is usually no change in the size of the brain-structure

Fig. 93.—Hydrocephalic child.

itself, but often the cranial bones are rent far asunder. Minot speaks of a hydrocephalic infant whose head measured $27\frac{1}{2}$ inches in circumference; Bright describes one whose head measured 32 inches; and Klein, one 43 inches. Figure 93 represents a child of six whose head circumference was 36 inches. Figure 94 shows a hydrocephalic adult who was exhibited through this country.

There is a record [a] of a curious monster born of healthy half-caste African parents. The deformity was caused by a **deficiency of osseous material of the bones of the head.** There was considerable arrest of develop-

Fig. 94.—Hydrocephaly in an adult.

ment of the parietal, temporal, and superior maxillary bones, in consequence of which a very small amount of the cerebral substance could be protected by

[a] 778, 1868, ix., 31.

the membranous expansion of the cranial centers. The inferior maxilla and the frontal bone were both perfect; the ears were well developed and the tongue strong and active; the nostrils were imperforate and there was no roof to the mouth nor floor to the nares. The eyes were curiously free from eyelashes, eyelids, or brows. The cornea threatened to slough. There was double harelip on the left side; the second and third fingers of both hands were webbed for their whole length; the right foot wanted the distal phalanx of the great toe and the left foot was clubbed and drawn inward. The child swallowed when fed from a spoon, appeared to hear, but exhibited no sense of light. It died shortly after the accompanying sketch (Fig. 95) was made.

Fig. 95.—Monster from deficiency of the bones of the head.

Occasionally a deficiency in the osseous material of the cranium or an abnormal dilatation of the fontanelles gives rise to a hernia of the meninges, which, if accompanied by cerebrospinal fluid in any quantity, causes a large and peculiarly shaped tumor called **meningocele** (Fig. 96). If there is a protrusion of brain-substance itself, a condition known as hernia cerebri results.

Fig. 96.—Meningocele.

Complete absence of the inferior maxilla is much rarer in man than in animals. Nicolas and Prenant have described a curious case of this anomaly in a sheep. Gurlt has named subjects presenting the total or partial absence of the inferior maxilla, agnathes or hemiagnathes. Simple **atrophy** of the inferior maxilla has been seen in man as well as in the lower animals, but is much less frequent than atrophy of the superior maxilla. Langenbeck reports the case of a young man who had the inferior maxilla so atrophied that in infancy it was impossible for him to take milk from the breast. He had also almost complete immobility of the jaws. Boullard[a] reports a deformity of the visage, resulting in a deficiency of the condyles of the lower jaw. Maurice[b] made an observa-

a 242, 1849, xxiv., 281.　　　　b 146, 1861, i., 696.

tion on a vice of conformation of the lower jaw which rendered lactation impossible, probably causing the death of the infant on this account. Tomes gives a description of a lower jaw the development of the left ramus of which had been arrested. Canton [a] mentions arrest of development of the left perpendicular ramus of the lower jaw combined with malformation of the external ear.

Exaggerated prominence of the maxillaries is called **prognathism**; that of the superior maxilla is seen in the North American Indians. Inferior prognathism is observed in man as well as in animals. The bull-dog, for example, displays this, but in this instance the deformity is really superior brachygnathism, the superior maxilla being arrested in development.

Congenital absence of the nose is a very rare anomaly. Maisonneuve has seen an example in an individual in which, in place of the nasal appendix, there was a plane surface perforated by two small openings a little less than one mm. in diameter and three mm. apart.

Fig. 97.—Thomas Wedders.

Exaggeration in volume of the nose is quite frequent. Ballonius [185] speaks of a nose six times larger than ordinary. Viewing the Roman celebrities, we find that Numa, to whom was given the surname Pompilius, had a nose which measured six inches. Plutarch, Lycurgus, and Solon had a similar enlargement, as had all the kings of Italy except Tarquin the Superb.

Early in the last century a man, Thomas Wedders (or Wadhouse), with a nose $7\frac{1}{2}$ inches long, was exhibited throughout Yorkshire. This man expired as he had lived, in a condition of mind best described as the most abject idiocy. The accompanying illustration (Fig. 97) is taken from a reproduction of an old print and is supposed to be a true likeness of this unfortunate individual.

There are curious pathologic formations about the nose which increase its volume so enormously as to interfere with respiration and even with alimentation; but these will be spoken of in another chapter.

There have been some celebrities whose noses were undersized. The Duc de Guise, the Dauphin d'Auvergne, and William of Orange, celebrated in the romances of chivalry, had extremely short noses.

There are a few recorded cases of **congenital division of the nose.** Bartholinus,[b] Borellus, and the Ephemerides speak of duplex noses. Thomas of Tours has observed congenital fissure of the nose. Riker[c] reports the case of an infant of three weeks who possessed a supernumerary nose on the right nasal bone near the inner canthus of the eye. It was pear-shaped, with

a 779, xii., 237.   b 190, cent. i., hist. xxv.   c 176, 1878, 196.

its base down, and was the size of the natural nose of an infant of that age, and air passed through it. Hubbell, Ronaldson,[a] and Luscha speak of **congenital occlusion of the posterior nares.** Smith[b] and Jarvis[c] record cases of **congenital occlusion of the anterior nares.**

Anomalies in size of the mouth are not uncommon. Fournier quotes the history of a man who had a mouth so large that when he opened it all his back teeth could be seen. There is a history of a boy of seventeen[d] who had a preternaturally-sized mouth, the transverse diameter being $6\frac{1}{2}$ inches. The mother claimed that the boy was born with his foot in his mouth and to this fact attributed his deformity. The negro races are noted for their large mouths and thick lips. A negro called " Black Diamond," recently exhibited in Philadelphia, could put both his fists in his mouth.

Morgan[e] reports two cases of **congenital macrostoma** accompanied by

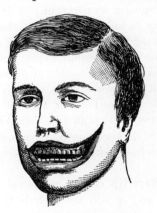

Fig. 98.—Macrostoma by ascending
lateral fissure.

Fig. 99.—Macrostoma by lateral
fissures.

malformation of the auricles and by auricular appendages. Van Duyse[f] mentions congenital macrostoma with preauricular tumors and a dermoid of the eye. Macrostoma is sometimes produced by lateral fissures (Fig. 99). In other cases this malformation is unilateral and the fissure ascends (Fig. 98), in which instance the fissure may be accompanied by a fistula of the duct of Stensen. Sometimes there is associated with these anomalies curious terminations of the salivary ducts, either through the cheek by means of a fistula or on the anterior part of the neck.

Microstoma.—There are a few cases on record in which the mouth has been so small or ill-defined as not to admit of alimentation. Mollière knew an individual of forty whose mouth was the exact size of a ten-centime piece.

Buchnerus[g] records a case of congenital **atresia of the mouth.** Cayley,

a 318, 1880, xxvi., 1035.   b 548, 1863, i., 320.   c 597, xlvi., 536.   d 206, vol. iv., part iii.
e 548, 1881, ii., 613.   f Ann. Soc. de méd. de Gand., 1882, 141.   g 105, 1730, ii., 210.

Smith,[a] Sourrouille,[b] and Stankiewicz of Warsaw discuss atresia of the mouth. Cancrum oris, scarlet fever, burns, scurvy, etc., are occasional causes that have been mentioned, the atresia in these instances taking place at any time of life.

Anomalies of the Lips.—The aboriginal tribes are particularly noted for their large and thick lips, some of which people consider enormous lips signs of adornment. Elephantiasis or other pathologic hypertrophy of the labial tissues can produce revolting deformity, such as is seen in Figure 100, representing an individual who was exhibited several years ago in Philadelphia. We have in English the expression, "pulling a long lip." Its origin is said to date back to a semimythical hero of King Arthur's time, who, "when sad at heart and melancholic," would let one of his lips drop below his waist, while he turned the other up like a cap on his head.

Blot[e] records a case of monstrous congenital **hypertrophy of the** superior

Fig. 100.—Elephantiasis of the face, with hypertrophy of the upper lip.

lip in an infant of eight months. Buck[d] successfully treated by surgical operations a case of congenital hypertrophy of the under lip, and Detmold[e] mentions a similar result in a young lady with hypertrophy of the lip and lower part of the nose. Murray[f] reports an undescribed malformation of the lower lip occurring in one family. Weiss has reported cases of exstrophy of the lips.

Hare-lip may be unilateral or double, and may or may not include the palatine arch. In the worst cases it extends in fissures on both sides to the orbit (Fig. 101). In other cases the minimum degree of this deformity is seen (Fig. 102).

Congenital absence of the tongue does not necessarily make speech, taste, or deglutition impossible. Jussieu cites the case of a girl who was born without a tongue but who spoke very distinctly. Berdot[g] describes a case in which the tongue was deficient, without apparent disturbance of any of the functions. Riolan mentions speech after loss of the tongue from small-pox. Boddington[h] gives an account of Margaret Cutting, who spoke readily and intelligibly, although she had lost her tongue. Saulquin[i] has an observation of a girl without a tongue who spoke, sang, and swallowed normally. Aurran, Bartholinus, Louis, Parsons, Tulpius, and others mention speech without the presence of a tongue.

[a] 476, 1876, i., 13.   [b] 363. lvi., 707.   [c] Bull. Soc. de chir. de Par., 1873, ii., 332.
[d] 773, 1882, 171.   [e] 594, 1844, iii., 38.   [f] 222, 1860, xxvi., 502.
[g] 107, vol. viii., 185.   [h] 629, 1732-44, ix., 126.   [i] 460, 1764, xx., 328.

Philib [a] reports a case in which mutism, almost simulating that of one congenitally deaf, was due to **congenital adhesions of the tongue** to the floor of the buccal cavity. Speech was established after removal of the abnormal adhesion. Routier speaks of **ankylosis of the tongue** of seventeen years' duration.

Jurist [b] records such **abnormal mobility of the tongue** that the patient was able to project the tongue into the nasopharynx. Wherry and Winslow record similar instances.

There have been individuals with **bifid tongues,** after the normal type of serpents and saurians, and others who possessed a **supernumerary tongue.** Rev. Henry Wharton, Chaplain to Archbishop Sancroft, in his journal, written in the seventeenth century, says that he was born with two tongues and

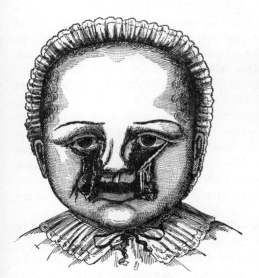

Fig. 101.—Double hare-lip.

Fig. 102.—Slight hare-lip, with fissure of the lower eyelid (Kraske).

passed through life so, one, however, gradually atrophying. In the polyclinic of Schnitzer in Vienna in 1892 Hajek observed in a lad of twelve an accessory tongue 2.4 cm. in length and eight mm. in breadth, forming a tumor at the base of the normal tongue. It was removed by scissors, and on histologic examination proved to be a true tongue with the typical tissues and constituents. Borellus, Ephemerides, Eschenbach, Mortimer,[c] Penada, and Schenck speak of double tongues, and Avicenna and Schenck have seen fissured tongues. Dolaeus [d] records an instance of double tongue in a paper entitled " De puella bilingui," and Beaudry and Brothers [e] speak of cleft

a 454, 1829, xxxiii., 265.

c 629, 486. d 280, 1755, iii., 411.

b 538, xxviii., 539.

e 538, xxxiii., 109.

tongue. Braine [a] records a case in which there was a large hypertrophied fold of membrane coming from each side of the upper lip.

In some cases there is marked **augmentation of the volume of the tongue.** Fournier [b] has seen a juggler with a tongue so long that he could extrude it six inches from his mouth. He also refers to a woman in Berlin with a long tongue, but it was thinner than that of a cat. When she laughed it hung over her teeth like a curtain, and was always extremely cold to the touch. In the same article there is a description of a man with a very long neck who could touch his tongue to his chest without reclining his head. Congenital and acquired hypertrophy of the tongue will be discussed later.

Amatus Lusitanus [c] and Portal [d] refer to the presence of **hair on the tongue,** and later there was an account of a medical student [e] who complained of dyspepsia and a sticky sensation in the mouth. On examination a considerable growth of hair was found on the surface of the tongue. The hairs would be detached in vomiting but would grow again, and when he was last seen they were one inch long. Such are possibly nevoid in formation.

The ordinary **anomalies of the palate** are the fissures, unilateral, bilateral, median, etc. : they are generally associated with hare-lip. The median fissure commencing between the middle incisors is quite rare.

Many curious forms of obturator or **artificial palate** are employed to remedy congenital defects. Sercombe [f] mentions a case in which destruction of the entire palate was successfully relieved by mechanical means. In some instances among the lower classes these obturators are simple pieces of wood, so fashioned as to fit into the palatine cleft, and not infrequently the obturator has been swallowed, causing obstruction of the air-passages or occluding the esophagus.

Abnormalism of the Uvula.—Examples of double uvula are found in the older writers, and Hagendorn speaks of a man who was born without a uvula. The Ephemerides and Salmuth describe uvulæ so defective as to be hardly noticeable. Bolster, Delius, Hodges, Mackenzie of Baltimore, Orr, Riedel, Schufeldt, and Tidyman are among observers reporting bifurcated and double uvula, and they are quite common. Ogle [g] records instances of congenital absence of the uvula.

Anomalies of the Epiglottis.—Morgagni mentions a man without an epiglottis who ate and spoke without difficulty. He thought the arytenoids were so strongly developed that they replaced the functions of the missing organ. Enos of Brooklyn in 1854 reported absence of the epiglottis without interference with deglutition.[h] Manifold [i] speaks of a case of bifurcated epiglottis. Deblois [j] records an instance of congenital **web of the**

a Proc. M. Soc. Lond., 1874–5, ii., 21.   b 302, iv., 149.

c 119, cent. vi., cur. 65.   d 639, iv., 507.   e 611, Aug. 13, 1842.

f 550, xxxix., 91.   g 548, 1865, ii., 414.   h 230, 1864, iv., 353.

i 476, 1851, i., 10.   j 597, xxxix., 660.

vocal bands. Mackenzie [a] removed a congenital papillomatous web which had united the vocal cords until the age of twenty-three, thus establishing the voice. Poore also recorded a case of congenital web in the larynx. Elsberg and Scheff mention occlusion of the rima glottidis by a membrane.

Instances of **duplication of the epiglottis** attended with a species of **double voice** possess great interest. French [b] described a man of thirty, by occupation a singer and contortionist, who became possessed of an extra voice when he was sixteen. In high and falsetto tones he could run the scale from A to F in an upper and lower range. The compass of the low voice was so small that he could not reach the high notes of any song with it, and in singing he only used it to break in on the falsetto and produce a sensation. He was supposed to possess a double epiglottis. [c]

Roe [d] describes a young lady who could whistle at will with the lower part of her throat and without the aid of her lips. Laryngeal examination showed that the fundamental tones were produced by vibrations of the edges of the vocal cords, and the modifications were effected by a minute adjustment of the ventricular bands, which regulated the laryngeal opening above the cord, and pressing firmly down closed the ventricle and acted as a damper, preventing the vibrations of the cords except in their middle third. Morgan in the same journal mentions the case of a boy of nineteen, who seemed to be affected with laryngeal catarrh, and who exhibited distinct diphthongia. He was seen to have two glottic orifices with associate bands. The treatment was directed to the catarrh and consequent paresis of the posterior bands, and he soon lost his evidences of double voice. [e]

Complete **absence of the eyes** is a very rare anomaly. Wordsworth [f] describes a baby of seven weeks, otherwise well formed and healthy, which had congenital absence of both eyes. The parents of this child were in every respect healthy. There are some cases of monstrosities with closed, adherent eyelids and absence of eyes. [g] Holmes [h] reports a case of congenital absence of both eyes, the child otherwise being strong and perfect. The child died of

[a] 224, 1874, i., 317.   [b] Quoted 224, 1880, ii., 311.

[c] 148, vol. ii., 271.   [d] Archives of Laryngology, Jan. 1, 1882.

[e] The following is a description of the laryngeal formation of a singer who has recently acquired considerable notice by her ability to sing notes of the highest tones and to display the greatest compass of voice. It is extracted from a Cleveland, Ohio, newspaper : "She has unusual development of the larynx, which enables her to throw into vibration and with different degrees of rapidity the entire length of the vocal cords or only a part thereof. But of greatest interest is her remarkable control over the muscles which regulate the division and modification of the resonant cavities, the laryngeal, pharyngeal, oral, and nasal, and upon this depends the quality of her voice. The uvula is bifurcated, and the two divisions sometimes act independently. The epiglottis during the production of the highest notes rises upward and backward against the posterior pharyngeal wall in such a way as almost entirely to separate the pharyngeal cavities, at the same time that it gives an unusual conformation to those resonant chambers."

[f] 476, 1881, ii., 875.   [g] 240, 1828.   [h] 268, 1869, xxvi., 163.

cholera infantum. He also reports a case very similar in a female child of American parents. In a girl of eight, of German parents, he reports deficiency of the external walls of each orbit, in addition to great deformity of the side of the head. He also gives an instance of congenital paralysis of the levator palpebræ muscles in a child whose vision was perfect and who was otherwise perfect. Holmes also reports a case of enormous congenital exophthalmos, in which the right eye protruded from the orbit and was no longer covered by the cornea. Kinney[a] has an account of a child born without eyeballs. The delivery was normal, and there was no history of any maternal impression; the child was otherwise healthy and well formed.

Landes[b] reports the case of an infant in which both eyes were absent. There were six fingers on each hand and six toes on each foot. The child lived a few weeks. In some instances of supposed absence of the eyeball the eye is present but diminutive and in the posterior portion of the orbit. There are instances of a **single orbit with no eyes** and also a **single orbit containing two eyes.**[c] Again we may have two orbits with an absence of eyes but the presence of the lacrimal glands, or the eyes may be present or very imperfectly developed. Mackenzie mentions cases in which the orbit was more or less completely wanting and a mass of cellular tissue in each eye.

Cases of **living cyclopia,** or individuals with one eye in the center of the forehead after the manner of the mythical Cyclops, are quite rare. Vallentini in 1884[d] reports a case of a male cyclopic infant which lived for seventy-three hours. There were median fissures of the upper lip, preauricular appendages, oral deformity, and absence of the olfactory proboscis. The fetus was therefore a cyclops arrhynchus, or cyclocephalus. Blok[e] describes a new-born infant which lived for six or seven hours, having but one eye and an extremely small mouth.

The **"Four-eyed Man of Cricklade"** was a celebrated English monstrosity of whom little reliable information is obtainable. He was visited by W. Drury, who is accredited with reporting the following:—

"'So wondrous a thing, such a lusus naturæ, such a scorn and spite of nature I have never seen. It was a dreadful and shocking sight.' This unfortunate had four eyes placed in pairs, 'one eye above the other and all four of a dull brown, encircled with red, the pupils enormously large.' The vision in each organ appeared to be perfect. 'He could shut any particular eye, the other three remaining open, or, indeed, as many as he chose, each several eye seeming to be controlled by his will and acting independently of the remainder. He could also revolve each eye separately in its orbit, looking backward with one and forward with another, upward with one and

a 218, 1854, li., 25.   b 538, Nov. 3, 1894.   c 418, 1751, 49.

d Atti dell' Accad. med.-chir. di Perugia, vi., fasc. 3 & 4, 1894.

e Weekblad van het Nederlandsch Tijdschr. voor Geneeskunde, xxx., 2d part, 414, Sept., 1894; also extracted in 759.

downward with another simultaneously.' He was of a savage, malignant disposition, delighting in ugly tricks, teasing children, torturing helpless animals, uttering profane and blasphemous words, and acting altogether like the monster, mental and physical, that he was. 'He could play the fiddle, though in a silly sort, having his notes on the left side, while closing the right pair of eyes. He also sang, but in a rough, screeching voice not to be listened to without disgust.' "

There is a recent report [a] of a child born in Paris with its eyes in the top of its head. The infant seemed to be doing well and crowds of people have flocked to see it. Recent reports speak of a child born in Portland, Oregon, which had a median rudimentary eye between two normal eyes. Fournier describes an infant born with perfectly formed eyes, but with adherent eyelids and closed ocular aperture. Forlenze has seen the pupils adherent to the conjunctiva, and by dissection has given sight to the subject.

Dubois [b] cites an instance of **supernumerary eyelid.** At the external angle of the eyelid was a fold of conjunctiva which extended 0.5 cm. in front of the conjunctiva, to which it did not adhere, therefore constituting a fourth eyelid. Fano [c] presents a similar case in a child of four months, in whom no other anomaly, either of organs or of vision, was observed. On the right side, in front of the external half of the sclerotic, was observed a semilunar fold with the concavity inward, and which projected much more when the lower lid was depressed. When the eyelid rolled inward the fold rolled with the globe, but never reached so far as the circumference of the cornea and did not interfere with vision.

Total **absence of both irides** has been seen in a man of eighteen. [d] Dixon reports a case of total aniridia with excellent sight in a woman of thirty-seven. [e] In Guy's Hospital there was seen a case of complete congenital absence of the iris.[392] Hentzschel [f] speaks of a man with congenital absence of the iris who had five children, three of whom exhibited the same anomaly while the others were normal. Benson, Burnett, Demaux, Lawson, Morison, Reuling, Samelson, and others also report congenital deficiency of the irides in both eyes.

Jeaffreson [445] describes a female of thirty, living in India, who was affected with complete **ossification of the iris.** It was immovable and quite beautiful when seen through the transparent cornea; the sight was only slightly impaired. No cause was traceable.

Multiple Pupils.—More than one **pupil** in the eye has often been noticed, and as many as six have been seen. They may be congenital or due to some pathologic disturbance after birth. Marcellus Donatus [306] speaks of two pupils in one eye. Beer, Fritsche, and Heuermann are among the older writers who have noticed supernumerary pupils. Higgens in 1885 described

---

a Amer. Med. Review, Dec., 1895.   b 145, vol. xxxiv.   c 145, 1863, 1.
d 476, 1882, i., 265.   e 548, 1858, ii., 35.   f Quoted 476, 1830–1, i., 384.

a boy whose right iris was perforated by four pupils,—one above, one to the inner side, one below, and a fourth to the outer side. The first three were slit-shaped ; the fourth was the largest and had the appearance as of the separation of the iris from its insertion. There were two pupils in the left eye, both to the outer side of the iris, one being slit-like and the other resembling the fourth pupil in the right eye. All six pupils commenced at the periphery, extended inward, and were of different sizes. The fundus could be clearly seen through all of the pupils, and there was no posterior staphyloma nor any choroidal changes. There was a rather high degree of myopia. This peculiarity was evidently congenital, and no traces of a central pupil nor marks of a past iritis could be found. Clinical Sketches [a] contains quite an extensive article on and several illustrations of congenital anomalies of the iris.

Double crystalline lenses are sometimes seen. Fritsch and Valisneri have seen this anomaly and there are modern references to it. Wordsworth [b] presented to the Medical Society of London six members of one family, all of whom had congenital **displacement of the crystalline lens** outward and upward. The family consisted of a woman of fifty, two sons, thirty-five and thirty-seven, and three grandchildren—a girl of ten and boys of five and seven. The irides were tremulous.

Clark [c] reports a case of congenital **dislocation of both crystalline lenses.** The lenses moved freely through the pupil into the anterior chambers. The condition remained unchanged for four years, when glaucoma supervened.

Differences in Color of the Two Eyes.—It is not uncommon to see people with different colored eyes. Anastasius I. had one black eye and the other blue, from whence he derived his name " Dicore," by which this Emperor of the Orient was generally known. Two distinct colors have been seen in an iris. Berry gives a colored illustration of such a case.

The varieties of **strabismus** are so common that they will be passed without mention. Kuhn [d] presents an exhaustive analysis of 73 cases of congenital defects of the movements of the eyes, considered clinically and didactically. Some or all of the muscles may be absent or two or more may be amalgamated, with anomalies of insertion, false, double, or degenerated, etc.

The influence of **heredity in the causation of congenital defects of the eye** is strikingly illustrated by De Beck.[e] In three generations twelve members of one family had either coloboma iridis or irideremia. He performed two operations for the cure of cataract in two brothers. The operations were attended with difficulty in all four eyes and followed by cyclitis. The result was good in one eye of each patient, the eye most recently blind. Posey [f] had a case of coloboma in the macular region in a patient who had a

a 275, April, 1895.   b 476, 1878, i., 86.   c 765, 1894.
d Beit. z. Augenh., Heft xix., 1895. e Trans. 765, 1894. f 792, Nov., 1894.

supernumerary tooth.   He believes the defects were inherited, as the patient's mother also had a supernumerary tooth.

Nunnely[a] reports cases of congenital malformation in three children of one family.   The globes of two of them (a boy and a girl) were smaller than natural, and in the boy in addition were flattened by the action of the recti muscles and were soft; the sclera were very vascular and the corneæ conical, the irides dull, thin, and tremulous; the pupils were not in the axis of vision, but were to the nasal side.   The elder sister had the same congenital condition, but to a lesser degree.   The other boy in the family had a total absence of irides, but he could see fairly well with the left eye.

Anomalies of the Ears.—Bilateral absence of the external ears is quite rare, although there is a species of sheep, native of China, called the " Yung-ti," in which this anomaly is constant.   Bartholinus, Lycosthenes, Paré, Schenck, and Oberteuffer have remarked on deficient external ears.   Guys, the celebrated Marseilles litterateur of the eighteenth century, was born with only one ear.   Chantreuil[b] mentions obliteration of the external auditory canal in the new-born.   Bannofont reports a case of congenital imperforation of the left auditory canal existing near the tympanic membrane with total deafness in that ear.   Lloyd[c] described a fetus showing absence of the external auditory meatus on both sides.   Munro[d] reports a case of congenital absence of the external auditory meatus of the right ear; and Richardson[e] speaks of congenital malformation of the external auditory apparatus of the right side.   There is an instance[f] of absence of the auditory canal with but partial loss of hearing.   Mussey[g] reports several cases of congenitally deficient or absent aural appendages.   One case was that in which there was congenital absence of the external auditory meatus of both ears without much impairment of hearing.   In neither ear of N. W. Goddard, aged twenty-seven, of Vermont, reported in 1834, was there a vestige of an opening or passage in the external ear, and not even an indentation.   The Eustachian tube was closed.   The integuments of the face and scalp were capable of receiving acoustic impressions and of transmitting them to the organs of hearing.   The authors know of a student of a prominent New York University who is congenitally deficient in external ears, yet his hearing is acute.   He hides his deformity by wearing his hair long and combed over his ears.

The knowledge of anomalous auricles is lost in antiquity.   Figure 103 represents the head of an Ægipan in the British Museum showing a supernumerary auricle.   As a rule, **supernumerary auricles** are preauricular appendages.   Warner, in a report of the examination of 50,000 children, quoted by Ballantyne, describes 33 with supernumerary auricles, represented by sessile or pedunculated outgrowths in front of the tragus.   They are more commonly unilateral, always congenital, and can be easily removed, giving rise

a 550, xlv., 43.   b 242, 1867, xlii., 149.   c 779, 1846, i., 139.
d 476, 1869, ii., 41.   e 476, 1882, i., 465.   f 218, xi., 419.   g 124, 1837, xxi., 378.

to no unpleasant symptoms. They have a soft and elastic consistency, and are usually composed of a hyaline or reticular cartilaginous axis covered with connective or adipose tissue and skin bearing fine hairs; sometimes both cartilage and fat are absent. They are often associated with some form of defective audition—harelip, ocular disturbance, club-feet, congenital hernia, etc. These supernumerary members vary from one to five in number and are sometimes hereditary. Reverdin describes a man having a supernumerary nipple on the right side of his chest, of whose five children three had preauricular appendages. Figure 104 represents a girl with a supernumerary auricle in the neck, described in the Lancet, 1888.[a] A little girl under Birkett's care in Guy's Hospital more than answered to Macbeth's requisition, "Had I three ears I'd hear thee!" since she possessed two superfluous ones at the sides of the neck, somewhat lower than the angle of the jaw, which were well developed as to their external contour and made up of fibrocartilage.[b] There is mentioned the case of a boy of six months[c]

Fig. 103.—Ægipan with supernumerary auricle (British Museum).

Fig. 104.—Supernumerary auricle in the neck.

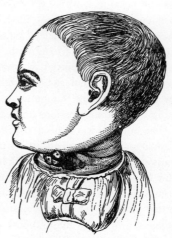

Fig. 105.—Supernumerary auricle.

on the left side of whose neck, over the middle anterior border of the sterno-cleidomastoid muscle, was a nipple-like projection ½ inch in length; a rod of

a 476, 1888, i., 312.   b 548, 1858, 528.   c 476, 1889, ii., 1003.

cartilage was prolonged into it from a thin plate, which was freely movable in the subcutaneous tissue, forming a striking analogue to an auricle (Fig. 105). Moxhay [a] cites the instance of a mother who was frightened by the sight of a boy with hideous contractions in the neck, and who gave birth to a child with two perfect ears and three rudimentary auricles on the right side, and on the left side two rudimentary auricles.

In some people there is an **excessive development of the auricular muscles,** enabling them to move their ears in a manner similar to that of the lower animals. Of the celebrated instances the Abbé de Marolles, says Vigneul-Marville, bears witness in his " Mémoires " that the Regent Crassot could easily move his ears. Saint Augustine mentions this anomaly.

Double tympanitic membrane is spoken of by Loeseke.[489] There is sometimes **natural perforation** of the tympanum in an otherwise perfect ear, which explains how some people can blow tobacco-smoke from the ear. Fournier [b] has seen several Spaniards and Germans who could perform this feat, and knew one man who could smoke a whole cigar without losing any smoke, since he made it leave either by his mouth, his ears, or in both ways. Fournier in the same article mentions that he has seen a woman with ears over four inches long.

Strange to say, there have been reports of cases in which the **ossicles** were deficient without causing any imperfection of hearing. Caldani [c] mentions a case with the incus and malleus deficient, and Scarpa [715] and Torreau [d] quote instances of deficient ossicles. Thomka in 1895 reported a case of supernumerary tympanic ossicle, the nature of which was unknown, although it was neither an inflammatory product nor a remnant of Meckel's cartilage.

Absence of the Limbs.—Those persons born without limbs are either the subjects of intrauterine amputation or of embryonic malformation. Probably the most celebrated of this class was Marc Cazotte, otherwise known as " Pépin," who died in Paris in the last century at the age of sixty-two of a chronic intestinal disorder. He had no arms, legs, or scrotum, but from very jutting shoulders on each side were well-formed hands. His abdomen ended in a flattened buttock with badly-formed feet attached. He was exhibited before the public and was celebrated for his dexterity. He performed nearly all the necessary actions, exhibited skilfulness in all his movements, and was credited with the ability of coitus. He was quite intellectual, being able to write in several languages. His skeleton is preserved in the Musée Dupuytren (Fig. 106). Flachsland [e] speaks of a woman who three times had borne children without arms and legs. Hastings [f] describes a living child born without any traces of arms or legs (Fig. 107). Garlick [g] has seen a child with neither upper nor lower extremities. In place of them were short stumps three or four inches long, closely resembling the ordinary stumps after

a 224, 1870.   b 302, iv., 148.   c 401, vi., 142.   d 379, vi., 321.
e Observat. patholog. Anat., p. 44.   f 776, 1826, ii., 39.   g 656, 1849.

amputation.   The head, chest, body, and male genitals were well formed, and

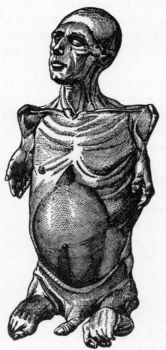

the child survived.   Hutchinson [a] reports the history of a child born without extremities, probably the result of intrauterine amputation.   The flaps were healed at the deltoid insertion and just below the groin.   Paré [b] says he saw in Paris a man without arms, who by means of his head and neck could crack a whip or hold an axe.   He ate by means of his feet, dealt and played cards, and threw dice with the same members, exhibiting such dexterity that finally his companions refused to play with him.   He was proved to be a thief and a murderer and was finally hanged at Gueldres (Fig. 108).   Paré also relates having seen a woman in Paris who sewed, embroidered, and did other things with her feet.   Jansen [470] speaks of a man in Spain, born without arms, who could use his feet as well as most people use their arms.   Schenck and Lotichius give descriptions of armless people.

Fig. 106.—"Pépin" (Musée Dupuytren).

Hulke [c] describes a child of four whose upper limbs were absent, a small dimple only being in their place.   He had free movement of the shoulders in every direction, and could grasp objects between his cheeks and his acromian process ; the prehensile power of the toes was well developed,

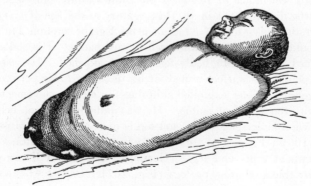

Fig. 107.—Limbless child.

as he could pick up a coin thrown to him.   A monster of the same conforma-

a 779, 1853, 343.   b 618, 1020.   c 550, 1877, 65.

tion was the celebrated painter, Ducornet (Fig. 109), who was born at Lille on the 10th of January, 1806. He was completely deprived of arms, but the rest of the body was well formed with the exception of the feet, of which the second toe was faulty. The deformity of the feet, however, had the happiest result, as the space between the great toe and its neighbor was much larger than ordinary and the toes much more mobile. He became so skilful in his adopted profession that he finally painted a picture eleven feet in height (representing Mary Magdalene at the feet of Christ after the resurrection), which was purchased by the Government and given to the city of Lille. Broca describes James Leedgwood, who was deprived of his arms and had only one leg. He exhibited great dexterity with his single foot, wrote, discharged a pistol, etc.; he was said to have been able to pick up a sewing-needle on a slippery surface with his eyes blindfolded. Capitan described to the Société d'anthropologie de Paris a young man without arms, who was said to play a violin and cornet with his feet.

Fig. 108.—Armless man (after Paré).

He was able to take a kerchief from his pocket and to blow his nose; he could make a cigarette, light it, and put it in his mouth, play cards, drink from a glass, and eat with a fork by the aid of his dexterous toes. There was a creature exhibited some time since in the principal cities of France, who was called the " l'homme tronc." He was totally deprived of all his members. Curran [a] describes a Hindoo, a prostitute of forty, with congenital absence of both upper extremities. A slight fleshy protuberance depended from the cicatrix of the humerus and shoulder-joint of the left side, and until the age of ten there was one on the right side. She performed many tricks with her toes (Fig. 110). Caldani speaks of a monster without arms, Davis [b] mentions one, and Smith [c] describes a boy of four with his upper limbs entirely absent. Breschet has seen a child of nine with only portions of the upper arms and deformity of lower extremities and pelvis. Paré [d] says that

Fig. 109.—Cæsar Ducornet.

a 536, 1887, i., 116.   b 530, 1885, 338.   c 767, 1873, 89.   d 618, 1018.

he saw in Paris in 1573, at the gate of St. Andrew des Arts, a boy of nine, a native of a small village near Guise, who had no legs and whose left foot

was represented by a fleshy body hanging from the trunk; he had but two fingers hanging on his right hand, and had between his legs what resembled a virile penis. Paré attributes this anomaly to a default in the quantity of semen.

The figure and skeleton of Harvey Leach, called " Hervio Nono," is in the museum of the University College in London. The pelvis was comparatively weak, the femurs hardly to be recognized, and the right tibia and foot defective; the left foot was better developed, although far from being in due proportion to the trunk above. He was one of the most remarkable gymnasts of his day, and notwithstanding the distortion of his lower limbs had marvelous power and agility in them. As an arena-horseman, either standing or sitting, he was scarcely excelled. He walked and even ran quite well, and his power of leaping, partly with his feet and partly with his hands, was unusual. His lower limbs were so short that, erect, he touched the floor with

Fig. 110.—Hindoo armless woman (Curran).

his fingers, but he earned his livelihood as much with his lower as with his upper limbs. In his skeleton his left lower limb, between the hip and heel, measured 16 inches, while the right, between the same points, measured nine inches (Fig. 111).[a]

Hare[b] mentions a boy of five and a half whose head and trunk were the same as in any other child of like age. He was $22\frac{1}{2}$ inches high, had no spinal curvature, but was absolutely devoid of lower extremities. The right arm was two inches long and the left $2\frac{1}{4}$. Each contained the head and a small adjoining portion of the humerus. The legs were represented by masses of cellular tissue and fat covered by skin which projected about an inch. He was intelligent, had a good memory, and exhibited considerable activity. He seemed to have had more than usual mobility and power of flexion of the lower lumbar region. When on his back he was unable to rise up, but resting on the lower part of the pelvis he

Fig. 111.—Harvey Leach.

was able to maintain himself erect. He usually picked up objects with his teeth, and could hold a coin in the axilla as he rolled from place to place.

a 476, 1864, ii., 60.   b 779, 1858–9, x., 308.

His rolling was accomplished by a peculiar twisting of the thorax and bending of the pelvis. There was no history of maternal impression during pregnancy; no injury, and no hereditary disposition to anomalous members. Figure 112 represents a boy with congenital deficiency of the lower extremities. who was exhibited a few years ago in Philadelphia. In Figure 113, which represents a similar case in a girl whose photograph is deposited in the Mütter Museum of the College of Physicians, Philadelphia, we see how cleverly the congenital defect may be remedied by mechanical contrivance. With her crutches and artificial legs this girl was said to have moved about easily.

Parvin[a] describes a "turtle-man" as an ectromelian, almost entering the class of phocomelians or seal-like monsters ; the former term signifies abortive or imperfect formation of the members. The hands and feet were normally developed, but the arms, forearms, and legs are much shortened (see page 84).

The "turtle-woman" of Demerara[b] (Fig. 114) was so called because her mother when pregnant was frightened by a turtle, and also from the child's fancied resemblance to a turtle. The femur was six inches long ; the woman had a foot of six bones, four being toes, viz., the first and second phalanges of the first and second toes. She had an acetabulum, capsule, and ligamentum teres, but no tibia or fibula ; she also had a defective right forearm. She was never

Fig. 112.—Congenital deficiency of the lower extremities.

the victim of rachitis or like disease, but died of syphilis in the Colonial Hospital. In her twenty-second year she was delivered of a full-grown child free of deformity.

There was a woman living in Bavaria, under the observation of Buhl, [c] who had congenital absence of both femurs and both fibulas. Almost all the muscles of the thigh existed, and the main attachment to the pelvis was by a large capsular articulation. Charpentier gives the portrait of a woman in whom there was a uniform diminution in the size of the limbs. Debout portrays a young man with almost complete absence of the thigh and leg,

a International Med. Mag., Phila., June, 1892. b 476, 1867, ii., 578. c 368, 1861, No. 48.

 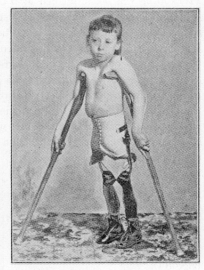

Fig. 113.—Congenital deficiency of the lower extremities with remedial apparatus.

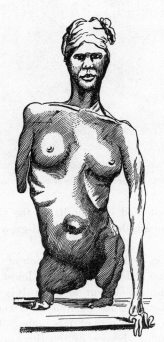 

Fig. 114.—The "turtle-woman."

Fig. 115.—Defective development
of the right leg (Debout).

from whose right hip there depended a foot (Fig. 115). Accrell [a] describes a peasant of twenty-six, born without a hip, thigh, or leg on the right side. The external genital organs were in their usual place, but there was only one testicle in the scrotum. The man was virile. The rectum instead of opening outward and underneath was deflected to the right.

Supernumerary Limbs.—Haller reports several cases of supernumerary extremities. Plancus[b] speaks of an infant with a complete third leg, and Dumeril [c] cites a similar instance. Geoffroy-Saint-Hilaire presented to the Académie des Sciences in 1830 a child with four legs and feet who was in good health. Amman saw a girl with a large thigh attached to her nates. Below the thigh was a single leg made by the fusion of two legs. No patella was found and the knee was anchylosed. One of the feet of the supernu-

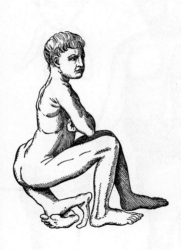

Fig. 116.—Gustav Evrard (after Guérin).

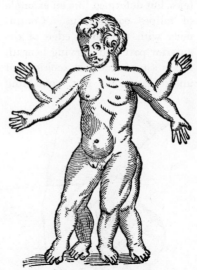

Fig. 117.—Eight-limbed monster (after Paré).

merary limb had six toes, while the other, which was merely an outgrowth, had two toes on it.

According to Jules Guérin, the child named Gustav Evrard was born with a thigh ending in two legs and two imperfect feet depending from the left nates (Fig. 116).

Tucker [d] describes a baby born in the Sloane Maternity in New York, October 1, 1894, who had a third leg hanging from a bony and fleshy union attached to the dorsal spine. The supernumerary leg was well formed and had a left foot attached to it. Larkin and Jones [e] mention the removal of a meningocele and a supernumerary limb from an infant of four months. This

a Med. Chirurg., Anat. Cases, London, 1758, 8°.   b De monstris, etc., Venetiis, 1749.
c Bull. de la soc. philom., iii., 3.   d 125, Jan., 1895.   e 224, 1889, ii., 310.

limb contained three fingers only, one of which did not have a bony skeleton.

Paré [a] says that on the day the Venetians and the Genevois made peace a monster was born in Italy which had four legs of equal proportions, and besides had two supernumerary arms from the elbows of the normal limbs. This creature lived and was baptized (Fig. 117).

Anomalies of the Feet.—Hatte [b] has seen a woman who bore a child that had three feet. Bull [c] gives a description of a female infant with the left foot double or cloven. There was only one heel, but the anterior portion consisted of an anterior and a posterior part. The anterior foot presented a great toe and four smaller ones, but deformed like an example of talipes equinovarus. Continuous with the outer edge of the anterior part and curving beneath it was a posterior part, looking not unlike a second foot, containing

Fig. 118.—Double foot (Bull).

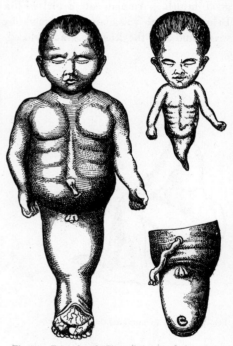

Fig. 119.—Examples of "Sirens," showing fusion of the lower extremities.

six well-formed toes situated directly beneath the other five. The eleven toes were all perfect and none of them were webbed (Fig. 118).

There is a class of monsters called " **Sirens** " on account of their resemblance to the fabulous creatures of mythology of that name. Under the influence of compression exercised in the uterus during the early period of gestation fusion of the inferior extremities is effected. The accompanying illustration shows the appearance of these monsters (Fig. 119), which are thought to resemble the enchantresses celebrated by Homer.

Anomalies of the Hand.—Blumenbach speaks of an officer who, having

[a] 618, 1017.   [b] 462, T. ii., 229.   [c] 218, 1875, xciii., 1293.

lost his right hand, was subsequently presented by his wife with infants of both sexes showing the same deformity. Murray [a] cites the instance of a woman of thirty-eight, well developed, healthy, and the mother of normal children, who had a double hand. The left arm was abnormal, the flexion of the elbow imperfect, and the forearm terminated in a double hand with only rudimentary thumbs. In working as a charwoman she leaned on the back of the flexed carpus. The double hand could grasp firmly, though the maximum power was not so great as that of the right hand. Sensation was equally acute in all three of the hands. The middle and ring fingers of the supernumerary hand were webbed as far as the proximal joints, and the movements of this hand were stiff and imperfect. No single finger of the two hands could be extended while the other seven were flexed (Fig. 120).

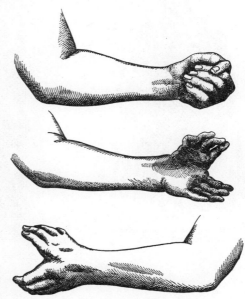

Fig. 120.—Double hand (Murray).

Giraldès saw an infant in 1864 with somewhat the same deformity, but in which the disposition of the muscles and tendons permitted the ordinary movements (Fig. 121).

Absence of Digits.—Maygrier [b] describes a woman of twenty-four who instead of having a hand on each arm had only one finger, and each foot had but two toes. She was delivered of two female children in 1827 and one in 1829, each having exactly the same deformities. Her mother was perfectly formed, but the father had but one toe on his foot and one finger on his left hand.

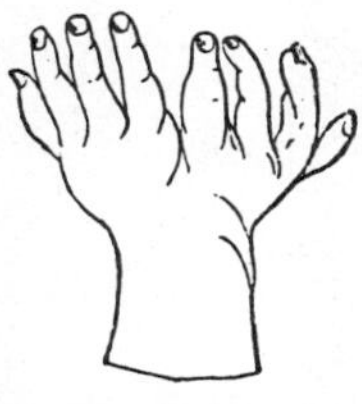

Köhler [c] gives photographs of quite a remarkable case of suppression and deformity of the digits of both the fingers and toes (Fig. 122).

Fig. 121.—Double hand (Giraldès).

Figure 123 shows a man who was recently exhibited in Philadelphia. He had but two fingers on each hand and two toes on each foot, and resembles Köhler's case in the anomalous digital conformation.

Figure 124 represents an exhibitionist with congenital suppression of four digits on each hand.

a 650, 1861–4, iv., 163 ; also 550, xlvi.
b Essai sur les monstres humaines, Diss. Inaug.   c 199, March 6, 1893.

Fig. 122.—Suppression and deformity
of digits (Köhler).

Fig. 123.—Suppression of digits.

Fig. 124.—Suppression of digits.

Tubby[a] has seen a boy of three in whom the first, second, and third toes of each foot were suppressed, the great toe and the little toe being so overgrown that they could be opposed. In this family for four generations 15 individuals out of 22 presented this defect of the lower extremity. The patient's brothers and a sister had exactly the same deformity, which has been called " lobster-claw foot."

Falla of Jedburgh speaks of an infant who was born without forearms or hands ; at the elbow there was a single finger attached by a thin string of tissue. This was the sixth child, and it presented no other deformity. Falla also says that instances of intrauterine digital amputation are occasionally seen.

According to Annandale, **supernumerary digits** may be classified as follows :—

(1) A deficient organ, loosely attached by a narrow pedicle to the hand or foot (or to another digit).

(2) A more or less developed organ, free at its extremity, and articulating with the head or sides of a metacarpal, metatarsal, or phalangeal bone.

(3) A fully developed separate digit.

(4) A digit intimately united along its whole length with another digit, and having either an additional metacarpal or metatarsal bone of its own, or articulating with the head of one which is common to it and another digit.

Superstitions relative to supernumerary fingers have long been prevalent. In the days of the ancient Chaldeans it was for those of royal birth especially that divinations relative to extra digits were cast. Among the ancients we also occasionally see illustrations emblematic of wisdom in an individual with many fingers, or rather double hands, on each arm.

Hutchinson,[b] in his comments on a short-limbed, polydactylous dwarf (Fig. 125) which was dissected by Ruysch, the celebrated Amsterdam anatomist, writes as follows :—

" This quaint figure is copied from Theodore Kerckring's ' Spicilegium Anatomicum,' published in Amsterdam in 1670. The description states that the body was that of an infant found drowned in the river on October 16, 1668. It was dissected by the renowned Ruysch. A detailed description of the skeleton is given. My reason for now reproducing the plate is that it offers an important item of evidence in reference to the development of short-limbed dwarfs. Although we must not place too much reliance on the accuracy of the draughtsman, since he has figured some superfluous lumbar vertebræ, yet there can be no doubt that the limbs are much too short for the trunk and head. This remark especially applies to the lower limbs and pelvis. These are exactly like those of the Norwich dwarf and of the skeleton in the Heidelberg Museum which I described in a recent number of the ' Archives.' The point of extreme interest in the present case

a 476, Feb. 17, 1894.   b 166, April, 1893.

is that this dwarfing of the limbs is associated with polydactylism. Both the hands have seven digits. The right foot has eight and the left nine. The conditions are not exactly symmetrical, since in some instances a metacarpal or metatarsal bone is wanting; or, to put it otherwise, two are welded together. It will be seen that the upper extremities are so short that the tips of the digits will only just touch the iliac crests.

Fig. 125.—Skeleton of a short-limbed, polydactylous dwarf.

"This occurrence of short limbs with polydactylism seems to prove conclusively that the condition may be due to a modification of development of a totally different nature from rickets. It is probable that the infant was not at full term. Among the points which the author has noticed in his description are that the fontanelle was double its usual size; that the orbits were somewhat deformed; that the two halves of the lower jaw were already united; and that the ribs were short and badly formed. He also, of course, draws attention to the shortness of the limbs, the stoutness of the long bones, and the supernumerary digits. I find no statement that the skeleton was deposited in any museum, but it is very possible that it is still in existence in Amsterdam, and if so it is very desirable that it should be more exactly described."

In Figure 126, A represents division of thumb after Guyot-Daubès, B shows a typical case of supernumerary fingers, and C pictures Morand's case of duplication of several toes.

Forster gives a sketch of a hand with nine fingers and a foot with nine toes. Voight records an instance of 13 fingers on each hand and 12 toes on each foot. Saviard saw

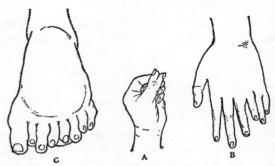

Fig. 126.—Supernumerary fingers and toes.

an infant at the Hôtel-Dieu in Paris in 1687 which had 40 digits, ten on each member. Annandale relates the history of a woman who had six fingers and two thumbs on each hand, and another who had eight toes on one foot.

Meckel tells of a case in which a man had 12 fingers and 12 toes, all well formed, and whose children and grandchildren inherited the deformity. Mason[a] has seen nine toes on the left foot. There is recorded[b] the account of a child who had 12 toes and six fingers on each hand, one fractured. Braid[c] describes talipes varus in a child of a few months who had ten toes. There is also on record[d] a collection of cases of from seven to ten fingers on each hand and from seven to ten toes on each foot. Scherer[e] gives an illustration of a female infant, otherwise normally formed, with seven fingers on each hand, all united and bearing claw-like nails. On each foot there was a double halux and five other digits, some of which were webbed.

The influence of heredity on this anomaly is well demonstrated. Réaumur was one of the first to prove this, as shown by the Kelleia family of Malta, and there have been many corroboratory instances reported; it is shown to last for three, four, and even five generations; intermarriage with normal persons finally eradicates it.

It is particularly in places where consanguineous marriages are prevalent that supernumerary digits persist in a family. The family of Foldi in the tribe of Hyabites living in Arabia are very numerous and confine their marriages to their tribe. They all have 24 digits, and infants born with the normal number are sacrificed as being the offspring of adultery. The inhabitants of the village of Eycaux in France, at the end of the last century, had nearly all supernumerary digits either on the hands or feet. Being isolated in an inaccessible and mountainous region, they had for many years intermarried and thus perpetuated the anomaly. Communication being opened, they emigrated or married strangers and the sexdigitism vanished. Maupertuis recalls the history of a family living in Berlin whose members had 24 digits for many generations. One of them being presented with a normal infant refused to acknowledge it. There is an instance in the Western United States[f] in which supernumerary digits have lasted through five generations. Cameron[g] speaks of two children in the same family who were polydactylic, though not having the same number of supernumerary fingers.

Smith and Norwell[h] report the case of a boy of fifteen both of whose hands showed webbing of the middle and ring fingers and accessory nodules of bone between the metacarpals, and six toes on each foot. The boy's father showed similar malformations, and in five generations 21 out of 28 individuals were thus malformed, ten females and 11 males. The deformity was especially transmitted in the female line.

Instances of **supernumerary thumbs** are cited by Panaroli,[i] Ephemerides, Munconys, as well as in numerous journals since. This anomaly is

a 705, 1879, n. s., ix., 37–42.   b 476, 1832, ii., 673.   c 225, 1848. i., 339.
d 562, 1870.   e Archiv f. Kinderheilk., xvii., 1894, 244.   f 130, No. 16.
g Montreal Med. Jour., Dec., 1894.   h 224, July 7, 1894.   i 617, iii., obs. 48.

not confined to man alone; apes, dogs, and other lower animals possess it. Bucephalus, the celebrated horse of Alexander, and the horse of Cæsar were said to have been cloven-hoofed.

Hypertrophy of the digits is the result of many different processes, and true hypertrophy or gigantism must be differentiated from acromegaly, elephantiasis, leontiasis, and arthritis deformans, for which distinction the reader is referred to an article by Park.[a]   Park also calls attention to the difference between acquired gigantism, particularly of the finger and toes, and another condition of congenital gigantism, in which either after or before birth there is a relatively disproportionate, sometimes enormous, overgrowth of perhaps one finger or two, perhaps of a limited portion of a hand or foot, or possibly of a part of one of the limbs.   The best collection of this kind of specimens is in the College of Surgeons in London.

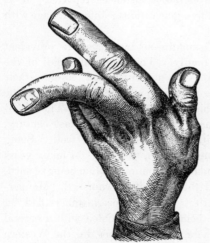

Curling[b] quotes a most peculiar instance of hypertrophy of the fingers in a sickly girl (Fig. 127).   The middle and ring fingers of the right hand were of unusual size, the middle finger measuring $5\frac{1}{2}$ inches in length and four inches in circumference.   On the left hand the thumb and middle fingers were hypertrophied and the index finger was as long as the middle one of the right hand.   The middle finger had a lateral curvature outward, due to a displacement of the extensor tendon.   This affection resembled acromegaly.   Curling cites similar cases, one in a Spanish gentleman, Governor of Luzon, in the Philippine Islands, in 1850, who had an extraordinary middle finger, which he concealed by carrying it in the breast of his coat.

Fig. 127.—Hypertrophied fingers.

Hutchinson[619] exhibited a photograph showing the **absence of the radius** and **thumb,** with shortening of the forearm.   Conditions more or less approaching this had occurred in several members of the same family.   In some they were associated with defects of development in the lower extremities also.

The varieties of **club-foot**—talipes varus, valgus, equinus, equino-varus, etc.—are so well known that they will be passed with mention only of a few persons who have been noted for their activity despite their deformity. Tyrtée, Parini, Byron, and Scott are among the poets who were club-footed;

a Inter. Med. Mag., Phila., July, 1895.   b 550, 1845, xxviii., 623.

some writers say that Shakespeare suffered in a slight degree from this deformity. Agesilas, Gensérie, Robert II., Duke of Normandy, Henry II., Emperor of the West, Otto II., Duke of Brunswick, Charles II., King of Naples, and Tamerlane were victims of deformed feet. Mlle. Vallière, the mistress of Louis XIV., was supposed to have both club-foot and hip-disease. Genu valgum and genu varum are ordinary deformities and quite common in all classes.

Transpositions of the character of the vertebræ are sometimes seen. In man the lumbar vertebræ have sometimes assumed the character of the sacral vertebræ, the sacral vertebræ presenting the aspect of lumbar vertebræ, etc. It is quite common to see the first lumbar vertebra presenting certain characteristics of the dorsal.

Numerical anomalies of the vertebræ are quite common, generally in the lumbar and dorsal regions, being quite rare in the cervical, although there have been instances of six or eight cervical vertebræ. In the lower animals the vertebræ are prolonged into a tail, which, however, is sometimes absent, particularly when hereditary influence exists. It has been noticed in the class of dogs whose tails are habitually amputated to improve their appearance that the tail gradually decreases in length. Some breeders deny this fact.

Human Tails.—The prolongation of the coccyx sometimes takes the shape of a caudal extremity in man. Broca and others claim that the sacrum and the coccyx represent the normal tail of man, but examples are not infrequent in which there has been a fleshy or bony tail appended to the coccygeal region. **Traditions of tailed men** are old and widespread, and tailed races were supposed to reside in almost every country. There was at one time an ancient belief that all Cornishmen had tails, and certain men of Kent were said to have been afflicted with tails in retribution for their insults to Thomas à Becket. Struys, a Dutch traveler in Formosa in the seventeenth century, describes a wild man caught and tied for execution who had a tail more than a foot long, which was covered with red hair like that of a cow.

The Niam Niams of Central Africa are reported to have tails smooth and hairy and from two to ten inches long. Hubsch of Constantinople remarks that both men and women of this tribe have tails. Carpus, or Berengarius Carpensis, as he is called, in one of his Commentaries said that there were some people in Hibernia with long tails, but whether they were fleshy or cartilaginous could not be known, as the people could not be approached. Certain supposed tailed races which have been described by sea-captains and voyagers are really only examples of people who wear artificial appendages about the waists, such as palm-leaves and hair. A certain Wesleyan missionary, George Brown, in 1876 spoke of a formal breeding of a tailed race in Kali, off the coast of New Britain. Tailless children were slain at once, as they would be exposed to public ridicule. The tailed men of Borneo are people afflicted with hereditary malformation analogous to sexdigitism.   A tailed race of princes have ruled Rajoopootana, and are fond of their ancestral mark.[638]   There are fabulous stories told of canoes in the East Indies which have holes in their benches made for the tails of the rowers.   At one time in the East the presence of tails was taken as a sign of brute force.

There was reported from Caracas[a] the discovery of a tribe of Indians in Paraguay who were provided with tails.   The narrative reads somewhat after this manner : One day a number of workmen belonging to Tacura Tuyn while engaged in cutting grass had their mules attacked by some Guayacuyan Indians.   The workmen pursued the Indians but only succeeded in capturing a boy of eight.   He was taken to the house of Señor Francisco Galeochoa, at Posedas, and was there discovered to have a tail ten inches long.   On interrogation the boy stated that he had a brother who had a tail as long as his own, and that all the tribe had tails.

Aetius, Bartholinus, Falk, Harvey, Kölping, Hesse, Paulinus, Strauss, and

Fig. 128.—Caudal appendix observed in a child in the clinic of M. Gosselin.

Wolff give descriptions of tails.   Blanchard [213] says he saw a tail fully a span in length : and there is a description in 1690 of a man by the name of Emanuel König, a son of a doctor of laws,[570] who had a tail half a span long, which grew directly downward from the coccyx and was coiled on the perineum, causing much discomfort.   Jacob[b] describes a pouch of skin resembling a tail which hung from the tip of the coccyx to the length of six inches.   It was removed and was found to be thicker than the thumb, consisted of distinctly jointed portions with synovial capsules.   Gosselin saw at his clinic a caudal appendix in an infant which measured about ten cm. (Fig. 128). Lissner says that in 1872 he assisted in the delivery of a young girl who had a tail consisting of a coccyx prolonged and covered with skin, and in 1884 he saw the same girl, at this time the tail measuring nearly 13 cm.

Virchow received for examination a tail three inches long amputated from a boy of eight weeks.   Ornstein, chief physician of the Greek army, describes a Greek of twenty-six who had a hairless, conical tail, free only at the tip, two inches long and containing three vertebræ.   He also remarks that other instances have been observed in recruits.   Thirk of Broussa in 1820 described the tail of a Kurd of twenty-two which contained four vertebræ. Belinovski[c] gives an account of a hip-joint amputation and extirpation of a fatty caudal extremity, the only one he had ever observed.

Before the Berlin Anthropological Society there were presented two adult male Papuans, in good health and spirits, who had been brought from New

a 476, 1885, ii., 452.   b 311, 1827.   c 270, 1892.

Guinea; their coccygeal bones projected $1\frac{1}{2}$ inches. Oliver Wendell Holmes in the Atlantic Monthly, June, 1890, says that he saw in London a photograph of a boy with a considerable tail. The "Moi Boy" was a lad of twelve, who was found in Cochin China, with a tail a foot long which was simply a mass of flesh. Miller [a] tells of a West Point student who had an elongation of the coccyx, forming a protuberance which bulged very visibly under the skin. Exercise at the riding school always gave him great distress, and the protuberance would often chafe until the skin was broken, the blood trickling into his boots.

Bartels [b] presents a very complete article in which he describes 21 persons born with tails, most of the tails being merely fleshy protuberances. Darwin [289] speaks of a person with a fleshy tail and refers to a French article on human tails. [c]

Science [d] contains a description of a negro child born near Louisville, eight weeks old, with a pedunculated tail $2\frac{1}{2}$ inches long, with a base $1\frac{1}{4}$ inches in circumference. The tail resembled in shape a pig's tail and had grown $\frac{1}{4}$ inch since birth. It showed no signs of cartilage or bone, and had its origin from a point slightly to the left of the median line and about an inch above the end of the spinal column.

Dickinson [e] recently reported the birth of a child with a tail (Fig. 129). It was a well-developed female between $5\frac{1}{2}$ and six pounds in weight. The coccyx was covered with the skin on both the anterior and posterior surfaces. It thus formed a tail of the size of the nail of the little finger, with a length of nearly $\frac{3}{16}$ inch on the inner surface and $\frac{3}{8}$ inch on the rear surface. This little tip could be raised from the body and it slowly sank back.

In addition to the familiar caudal projection of the human fetus, Dickinson mentions a group of other **vestigial remains** of a former state of things. Briefly these are:—

(1) The plica semilunaris as a vestige of the nictitating membrane of certain birds.

(2) The pointed ear, or the turned-down tip of the ears of many men.

(3) The atrophied muscles, such as those that move the ear, that are well developed in certain people, or that shift the scalp, resembling the action of a horse in ridding itself of flies.

(4) The supracondyloid foramen of the humerus.

(5) The vermiform appendix.

(6) The location and direction of the hair on the trunk and limbs.

(7) The dwindling wisdom-teeth.

(8) The feet of the fetus strongly deflected inward, as in the apes, and persisting in the early months of life, together with great mobility and a distinct projection of the great toe at an angle from the side of the foot.

a 545, 1881, 165. b 157, 1880. c 669, 1867-8, p. 625.
d 727, June 6, 1884. e 227, viii., 568, 1894.

(9) The remarkable grasping power of the hand at birth and for a few weeks thereafter, that permits young babies to suspend their whole weight on a cane for a period varying from half a minute to two minutes.

Horrocks [a] ascribes to these anal tags a pathologic importance. He claims that they may be productive of fistula in ano, superficial ulcerations, fecal concretions, fissure in ano, and that they may hypertrophy and set up tenesmus and other troubles. The presence of human tails has given rise to discussion between friends and opponents of the Darwinian theory. By some it is

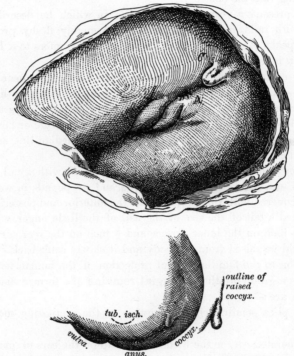

outline of raised coccyx.

tub. isch.

vulva.

coccyx.

anus.

Fig. 129.—Skin-covered coccyx forming a rudimentary tail in a female child at birth: *C*, coccyx; *A*, anus (Dickinson).

considered a reversion to the lower species, while others deny this and claim it to be simply a pathologic appendix.

Anomalies of the Spinal Canal and Contents.—When there is a default in the spinal column, the vice of conformation is called spina bifida. This is of two classes: first, a simple opening in the vertebral canal, and, second, a large cleft sufficient to allow the egress of spinal membranes and substance. Figure 130 represents a large congenital sacral tumor.

Achard [b] speaks of partial **duplication** of the central canal of the spinal cord. De Cecco [c] reports a singular case of duplication of the lumbar seg-

a Quar. Med. Jour., July, 1894.   b 242, 1888, 922.   c Morgagni, Napoli, 1857, i., 307.

ment of the spinal cord.   Wagner speaks of duplication of a portion of the spinal cord.

Foot [a] records a case of **amyelia,** or absence of the spinal cord, in a fetus with hernia cerebri and complete fissure of the spinal column.   Nicoll and Arnold [b] describe an anencephalous fetus with absence of spinal marrow ; and Smith also records the birth of an amyelitic fetus.[c]

In some persons there are exaggerated **curvatures of the spine.**   The first of these curvatures is called kyphosis, in which the curvature is posterior ; second, lordosis, in which the curvature is anterior ; third, scoliosis, in which it is lateral, to the right or left.

Kyphosis is the most common of the deviations in man and is most often found in the dorsal region, although it may be in the lumbar region.   Congenital kyphosis is very rare in man, is generally seen in monsters, and when it does exist is usually accompanied by lordosis

Fig. 130.—Sacral tumor (Mütter Mus., Col. of Phys.).

or spina bifida.   We sometimes observe a condition of anterior curvature of the lumbar and sacral regions, which might be taken for a congenital lordosis, but this is really a deformity produced after birth by the physiologic weight of the body.   Figure 131 represents a case of lordosis caused by paralysis of the spinal muscles.

Analogous to this is what the accoucheurs call spondylolisthesis.   **Scoliosis** may be a cervicodorsal, dorsolumbar, or lumbosacral curve, and the inclination of the vertebral column may be to the right or left (Figs. 132 and 133).   The pathologists divide scoliosis into a myopathic variety, in which the trouble is a physiologic antagonism of the muscles ; or osteopathic, ordinarily associated with rachitis, which latter variety is generally accountable for congenital scoliosis.   In some cases the diameter of the chest is shortened to an almost incredible degree, but may yet be compatible with life.   Glover [d] speaks of an extraordinary deformity of the chest with lateral curvature of the spine, in which the diameter from the pit of the stomach to the spinal integument was only $5\frac{1}{2}$ inches.

Fig. 131.—Lordosis, —paralysis of spinal muscle (Hirst).

Supernumerary ribs are not at all uncommon in man, nearly every medical museum having some examples. Cervical ribs are not rare.   Gordon [e] describes a young man of seventeen

a 536, Dublin, 1865, xi., 435.   b 124, xxii., 253.   c 476, 1848, ii., 400.
d 476, 1857, i., 263.   e 355, Oct. 15, 1894.

in whom there was a pair of supernumerary ribs attached to the cervical vertebræ. Bernhardt [a] mentions an instance in which cervical ribs caused motor and sensory disturbances. Dumerin of Lyons showed an infant of eight days which had an arrested development of the 2d, 3d, 4th, and 5th ribs. Cases of deficient ribs are occasionally met. Wistar in 1818 gives an account of a person in whom one side of the thorax was at rest while the other performed the movements of breathing in the usual manner.

In some cases we see **fissure of the sternum,** caused either by deficient union or absence of one of its constituent parts. In the most exaggerated cases these fissures permit the exit of the heart, and as a general rule ecto-

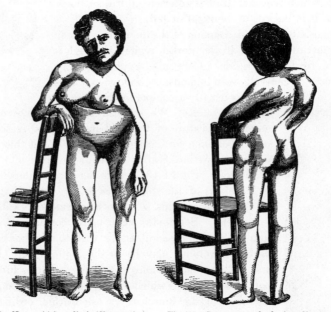

Fig. 132.—Non-rachitic scoliosis (Charpentier).   Fig. 133.—Same woman, back view (Charpentier).

pies of the heart are thus caused. Pavy [b] has given a most remarkable case of sternal fissure in a young man of twenty-five, a native of Hamburg. He exhibited himself in one medical clinic after another all over Europe, and was always viewed with the greatest interest. In the median line, corresponding to the absence of sternum, was a longitudinal groove bounded on either side by a continuous hard ridge which articulated with the costal cartilages. The skin passed naturally over the chest from one side to another, but was raised at one part of the groove by a pulsatile swelling which occupied the position of the right auricle. The clavicle and the two margins of the sternum had no connections whatever, and below the groove was a hard

a 199, 1894.   b 548, 1857, ii., 522.

substance corresponding to the ensiform cartilage, which, however, was very elastic, and allowed the patient, under the influence of the pectoral muscles, when the upper extremity was fixed, to open the groove to nearly the extent of three inches, which was more than twice its natural width. By approximating his arms he made the ends of his clavicles overlap. When he coughed, the right lung suddenly protruded from the chest through the groove and ascended a considerable distance above the clavicle into the neck. Between the clavicles another pulsatile swelling was easily felt but hardly seen, which was doubtless the arch of the aorta, as by putting the fingers on it one could feel a double shock, synchronous with distention and recoil of a vessel or opening and closing of the semilunar valves.

Madden [a] pictures (Figs. 134 and 135) a Swede of forty with congenital

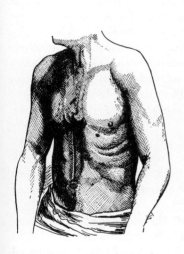

Fig. 134.—Congenital fissure of sternum
(Madden).

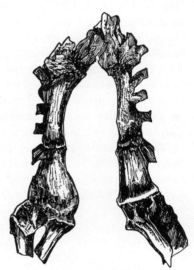

Fig. 135.—Congenital fissure of the sternum.

absence of osseous structure in the middle line of the sternum, leaving a fissure $5\frac{3}{8} \times 1\frac{3}{6} \times 2$ inches, the longest diameter being vertical. Madden also mentions several analogous instances on record. Groux's case was in a person of forty-five, and the fissure had the vertical length of four inches. Hodgen [b] of St. Louis reports a case in which there was exstrophy of the heart through the fissure. Slocum [c] reports the occurrence of a sternal fissure $3 \times 1\frac{1}{2}$ inches in an Irishman of twenty-five. Madden also cites the case of Abbott in an adult negress and a mother. Obermeier mentions several cases.[d] Gibson and Malet [e] describe a presternal fissure uncovering the base of the heart. Ziemssen, Wrany, and Williams also record congenital fissures of the sternum.

a 597, 1885, 406.   b 133, Oct., 1878.   c 768, 1860, iii., 310.
d 161, 1869, xlvi., 209.   e 451, xiv., 1.

Thomson[a] has collected 86 cases of **thoracic defects** and summarizes his paper by saying that the structures deficient are generally the hair in the mammary and axillary regions, the subcutaneous fat over the muscles, nipples, and breasts, the pectorals and adjacent muscles, the costal cartilages and anterior ends of ribs, the hand and forearm; he also adds that there may be a hernia of the lung, not hereditary, but probably due to the pressure of the arm against the chest. De Marque[508] gives a curious instance in which the chin and chest were congenitally fastened together. Muirhead[b] cites an instance in which a firm, broad strip of cartilage resembling sternomastoid extended from below the left ear to the left upper corner of the sternum, being entirely separate from the jaw.

Some preliminary knowledge of embryology is essential to understand the formation of **branchial fissures,** and we refer the reader to any of the standard works on embryology for this information. Dzondi was one of the first to recognize and classify congenital fistulas of the neck. The proper classification is into lateral and median fissures. In a case studied by Février[c] the exploration of a lateral pharyngeal fistula produced by the introduction of the sound violent reflex phenomena, such as pallor of the face and irregular, violent beating of the heart. The rarest of the lateral class is the preauricular fissure, which has been observed by Février, Le Dentu, Marchand, Peyrot, and Routier.

The median congenital fissures of the neck are probably caused by defective union of the branchial arches, although Arndt thinks that he sees in these median fistulas a persistence of the hypobranchial furrow which exists normally in the amphioxus. They are less frequent than the preceding variety.

The most typical form of **malformation of the esophagus** is imperforation or obliteration. Van Cuyck of Brussels in 1824 delivered a child which died on the third day from malnutrition. Postmortem it was found that the inferior extremity of the esophagus to the extent of about two inches was converted into a ligamentous cord. Porro[d] describes a case of congenital obliteration of the esophagus which ended in a cecal pouch about one inch below the inferior portion of the glottidean aperture and from this point to the stomach only measured an inch; there was also tracheal communication. The child was noticed to take to the breast with avidity, but after a little suckling it would cough, become livid, and reject most of the milk through the nose, in this way almost suffocating at each paroxysm; it died on the third day.

In some cases the esophagus is divided, one portion opening into the bronchial or other thoracic organs. Brentano[e] describes an infant dying ten days after birth whose esophagus was divided into two portions, one

a 759, Jan., 1855.   b 224, 1887, 177.
c Société de Chirurgie, 1892.   d 151, 1871.   e 242, 1894.

terminating in a culdesac, the other opening into the bronchi ; the left kidney was also displaced downward. Blasius [214] describes an anomalous case of duplication of the esophagus. Grashuys, and subsequently Vicq d'Azir, saw a dilatation of the esophagus resembling the crop of a bird.

Anomalies of the Lungs.—Carper describes a fetus of thirty-seven weeks in whose thorax he found a very voluminous thymus gland but no lungs. These organs were simply represented by two little oval bodies having no lobes, with the color of the tissue of the liver. The heart had only one cavity but all the other organs were perfectly formed. This case seems to be unique. Tichomiroff [a] records the case of a woman of twenty-four who died of pneumonia in whom the left lung was entirely missing. No traces of a left bronchus existed. The subject was very poorly developed physically. Tichomiroff finds four other cases in literature, in all of which the left lung was absent. Théremin and Tyson record cases of the absence of the left lung.

Supplementary pulmonary lobes are occasionally seen in man and are taken by some authorities to be examples of retrogressive anomalies tending to prove that the derivation of the human race is from the quadrupeds which show analogous pulmonary malformation. Eckley [b] reports an instance of supernumerary lobe of the right lung in close connection with the vena azygos major (Fig.

Fig. 136.—Supernumerary lung: 1, upper lobe of right lung; 2, middle or cuneate lobe; 3, lower lobe; 4, supernumerary lobe; 5, vena azygos major; 6, descending vena cava; 7, phrenic nerve (Eckley).

136). Collins [c] mentions a similar case. Bonnet and Edwards speak of instances of four lobes in the right lung. Testut and Marcondès [d] report a description of a lung with six lobes.

Anomalies of the Diaphragm.—Diemerbroeck is said to have dissected a human subject in whom the diaphragm and mediastinum were apparently missing, but such cases must be very rare, although we frequently find marked deficiency of this organ. Bouchaud [e] reports an instance of absence of the right half of the diaphragm in an infant born at term. Lawrence [f] mentions congenital deficiency of the muscular fibers of the left half of the diaphragm with

a Inter-Monatschr. f. Anat. u. Physiol., 1895.   b Chicago M. Times, June, 1895.
c 310, lviii., 252.   d Gaz. hebd. d. sc. méd. de Bordeaux, 1880, i., 1045.
e 242, xxxviii., 344.   f 476, 1852, ii., 327.

displacement of the stomach. The patient died of double pneumonia. Carruthers, McClintock, Polaillon, and van Geison also record instances of congenital deficiency of part of the diaphragm. Recently Dittel[a] reported unilateral defect in the diaphragm of an infant that died soon after birth. The stomach, small intestines, and part of the large omentum lay in the left pleural cavity ; both the phrenic nerves were normal. Many similar cases of diaphragmatic hernia have been observed. In such cases the opening may be large enough to allow a great part of the visceral constituents to pass into the thorax, sometimes seriously interfering with respiration and circulation by the pressure which ensues. Alderson[b] reports a fatal case of diaphragmatic hernia with symptoms of pneumothorax. The stomach, spleen, omentum, and transverse colon were found lying in the left pleura. Berchon[c] mentions double perforation of the diaphragm with hernia of the epiploön. The most extensive paper on this subject was contributed by Bodwitch,[d] who, besides reporting an instance in the Massachusetts General Hospital, gives a numerical analysis of all the cases of this affection found recorded in the writings of medical authors between the years 1610 and 1846. Hillier[e] speaks of an instance of congenital diaphragmatic hernia in which nearly all the small intestines and two-thirds of the large passed into the right side of the thorax. Macnab[f] reports an instance in which three years after the cure of empyema the whole stomach constituted the hernia. Recently Joly[g] described a congenital hernia of the stomach in a man of thirty-seven, who died from collapse following lymphangitis, persistent vomiting, and diarrhea. At the postmortem there was found a defect in the diaphragm on the left side, permitting herniation of the stomach and first part of the duodenum into the left pleural cavity. There was no history of traumatism to account for strangulation. Longworth[h] cites an instance of **inversion of the diaphragm** in a human subject. Bartholinus[i] mentions **coalition of the diaphragm and liver ;** and similar cases are spoken of by Morgagni and the Ephemerides. Hoffman[420] describes diaphragmatic junction with the lung.

Anomalies of the Stomach.—The Ephemerides contains the account of a dissection in which the stomach was found wanting, and also speaks of two instances of **duplex stomach.** Bartholinus,[190] Heister, Hufeland, Morgagni, Riolan, and Sandifort[j] cite examples of duplex stomach. Bonet speaks of a case of vomiting which was caused by a double stomach. Struthers[k] reports two cases in which there were two cavities to the stomach. Struthers also mentions that Morgagni, Home, Monro, Palmer, Larry, Blasius, Hufeland, and Walther also record instances in which there was contraction in the

a 261, May 19, 1894.   b 476, 1858, ii., 396.   c 363, xxxv.. 447.
d 231, ix.   e 476, 1861, i., 391   f 476, 1878, i., 11.
g 342, Jan., 1894.   h 274, 1877, xii., 279.   i 190, cent. iv., n. 20.
j Observ. anat. path., L. iv., pp. 27, 45.   k Month. J. M. Sc., Lond., 1851, xii., 121.

middle of the stomach, accounting for their instances of duplex stomach. Musser [a] reports an instance of hour-glass contraction of the stomach. Hart [b] dissected the stomach of a woman of thirty which resembled the stomach of a predaceous bird, with patches of tendon on its surface. The right extremity instead of continuously contracting ended in a culdesac one-half as large as the greater end of the stomach. The duodenum proceeded from the depression marking the lesser arch of the organ midway between the cardiac orifice and the right extremity. Crooks [c] speaks of a case in which the stomach of an infant terminated in a culdesac.

Hernia of the stomach is not uncommon, especially in diaphragmatic or umbilical deficiency. There are many cases on record, some terminating fatally from strangulation or exposure to traumatism. Paterson [d] reports a case of congenital hernia of the stomach into the left portion of the thoracic cavity. It was covered with fat and occupied the whole left half of the thoracic cavity. The spleen, pancreas, and transverse colon were also superior to the diaphragm. Death was caused by a well-defined round perforation at the cardiac curvature the size of a sixpence.

Anomalies of the Intestines.—The Ephemerides contains the account of an example of double cecum, and Alexander [e] speaks of a double colon, and there are other cases of duplication of the bowel recorded. There is an instance of coalition of the jejunum with the liver,[104] and Treuner [f] parallels this case. Aubery, Charrier, Poelman, and others speak of congenital division of the intestinal canal. Congenital occlusion is quite frequently reported.

Fig. 137.—Double stomach.

Dilatation of the colon frequently occurs as a transient affection, and by its action in pushing up the diaphragm may so seriously interfere with the action of the heart and lungs as to occasionally cause heart-failure. Fenwick has mentioned an instance of this nature. According to Osler there is a chronic form of dilatation of the colon in which the gut may reach an enormous size. The coats may be hypertrophied without evidence of any special organic change in the mucosa. The most remarkable instance has been reported by Formad. The patient, known as the **"balloon-man,"** aged twenty-three at the time of his death, had had a distended abdomen from infancy. Postmortem the colon was found as large as that of an ox, the circumference ranging from 15 to 30 inches. The weight of the contents was 47 pounds. Cases are not uncommon in children. Osler [g] reports three well-marked cases under his care. Chapman [h] mentions a case in which the liver

a 547, 1883–1884, xiv., 331.   b 311, iv., 326.   c 776, 1826, ii., 38.   d 381, 1854, ii., 26.
e 272, 1880, n. s., iv., 511.   f 160, Band ii., 90.   g 165, 1893.   h 224, 1878, i., 566.

was displaced by dilatation of the sigmoid flexure. Mya[a] reports two cases of congenital dilatation and hypertrophy of the colon (megacolon congenito). Hirschsprung, Genersich, Faralli, Walker, and Griffiths all record similar instances, and in all these cases the clinical features were obstinate constipation and marked meteorismus.

Imperforate Anus.—Cases in which the anus is imperforate or the

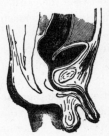

rectum ends in a blind pouch are occasionally seen. In some instances the rectum is entirely absent, the colon being the termination of the intestinal tract. There are cases on record in which the rectum communicated with the anus solely by a fibromuscular cord. Anorectal atresia is the ordinary imperforation of the anus, in which the rectum terminates in the middle of the sacral cavity. The rectum may be deficient from the superior third of the sacrum, and in this position is quite inacces-

Fig. 138.—Anus absent; the rectum ends in the bladder (after Ball).

sible for operation.

A compensatory **coalition of the bowel** with the bladder or urethra is sometimes present, and in these cases the feces are voided by the urinary passages. Huxham[b] mentions the fusion of the rectum and colon with the bladder, and similar instances are reported by Dumas[c] and Baillie. Zacutus Lusitanus[831] describes an infant with an imperforate membrane over its anus who voided feces through the urethra for three months. After puncture of the membrane, the discharge came through the natural passage and the child lived; Morgagni mentions a somewhat similar case in a little girl living in Bologna, and other modern instances have been reported. The rectum may terminate in the vagina (Fig. 139).

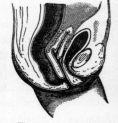

Masters[d] has seen a child who lived nine days in whom the sigmoid flexure of the colon terminated in the fundus of the bladder. Guinard[390] pictures a case in which there was communication between the rectum and the bladder. In Figure 140 *a* represents the rectum; *b* the bladder; *c* the point of communication; *g* shows the cellular tissue of the scrotum.

Fig. 139.—Anus is absent; rectum ends in the vagina (after Ball).

There is a description[e] of a girl of fourteen, otherwise well constituted and healthy, who had **neither external genital organs nor anus.** There was a plain dermal covering over the genital and anal region. She ate regularly, but every three days she experienced pain in the umbilicus and much intestinal irritation, followed by severe vomiting of stercoraceous matter; the pains then ceased and she cleansed her mouth with aromatic washes, remaining well until the following third day. Some of the

a 747, An. 48, 1894, 215.   b 629, n. 422.   c 664, T. iii., n. 55, p. 288.
d 224, 1862, ii., 555.   e 463, viii.

urine was evacuated by the mammæ. The examiners displayed much desire to see her after puberty to note the disposition of the menstrual flow, but no further observation of her case can be found.

Fournier [a] narrates that he was called by three students, who had been trying to deliver a woman for five days. He found a well-constituted woman of twenty-two in horrible agony, who they said had not had a passage of the bowels for eight days, so he prescribed an enema. The student who was directed to give the enema found to his surprise that there was no anus, but by putting his finger in the vagina he could discern the floating end of the rectum, which was full of feces. There was an opening in this suspended rectum about the size of an undistended anus. Lavage was practised by a cannula introduced through the opening, and a great number of cherry stones

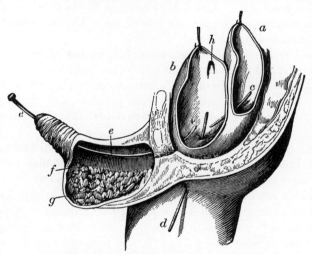

Fig. 140.—Abnormal junction of the rectum and bladder.

agglutinated with feces followed the water, and labor was soon terminated. The woman afterward confessed that she was perfectly aware of her deformity, but was ashamed to disclose it before. There was an analogue of this case found by Mercurialis [b] in a child of a Jew called Teutonicus.

Gerster [c] reports a rare form of imperforate anus, with malposition of the left ureter, obliteration of the ostia of both ureters, with consequent hydronephrosis of a confluent kidney. There was a minute opening into the bladder, which allowed the passage of meconium through the urethra. Burge [d] mentions the case of what he calls "sexless child," in which there was an imperforate anus and no pubic arch; the ureters discharged upon a tumor the size of a teacup extending from the umbilicus to the pubes. A postmortem examination confirmed the diagnosis of sexless child.

[a] 302, iv., 155.   [b] De morb. puer., L. 1.   [c] 597, 1878, xxviii., 516.   [d] 597, 1870, 39.

The Liver.—The Ephemerides, Frankenau,[a] von Horne, Molinetti, Schenck,[b] and others speak of deficient or **absent liver**. Zacutus Lusitanus [c] says that he once found a mass of flesh in place of the liver. Lieutaud [d] is quoted as describing a postmortem examination of an adult who had died of hydropsy, in whom the liver and spleen were entirely missing. The portal vein discharged immediately into the vena cava; this case is probably unique, as no authentic parallel could be found.

Laget [e] reports an instance of **supernumerary lobe in the liver.** Van Buren [f] describes a supernumerary liver. Sometimes there is rotation, real or apparent, caused by transposition of the characteristics of the liver. Handy [g] mentions such a case. Kirmisson [h] reports a singular anomaly of the liver which he calls double displacement by interversion and rotation on the vertical axis. Actual displacements of the liver as well as what is known as wandering liver are not uncommon. The operation for floating liver will be spoken of later.

Hawkins [i] reports a case of congenital **obliteration of the ductus communis choledochus** in a male infant which died at the age of four and a half months. Jaundice appeared on the eighth day and lasted through the short life. The hepatic and cystic ducts were pervious and the hepatic duct obliterated. There were signs of hepatic cirrhosis and in addition an inguinal hernia.

The Gall-Bladder.—Harle [j] mentions the case of a man of fifty, in whom he could find no gall-bladder; Patterson[k] has seen a similar instance in a man of twenty-five. Purser [l] describes a double gall-bladder.

The spleen has been found deficient or wanting by Lebby, Ramsay, and others, but more frequently it is seen doubled. Cabrolius,[245] Morgagni, and others have found two spleens in one subject; Cheselden and Fallopius report three; Fantoni mentions four found in one subject; Guy-Patin has seen five, none as large as the ordinary organ; Hollerius, Kerckringius, and others have remarked on multiple spleens. There is a possibility that in some of the cases of multiple spleens reported the organ is really single but divided into several lobes. Albrecht [m] mentions a case shown at a meeting of the Vienna Medical Society of a very large number of spleens found in the mesogastrium, peritoneum, on the mesentery and transverse mesocolon, in Douglas' pouch, etc. There was a spleen "the size of a walnut" in the usual position, with the splenic artery and vein in their normal position. Every one of these spleens had a capsule, was covered by peritoneum, and exhibited the histologic appearance of splenic tissue. According to the review of this article, Toldt explains the case by assuming that other parts of the celomic epithelium,

a 350. n. 7.	b 718, L. iii.	c 831, L. ii., obs. 3.	d 302, iv., 154.
e 242, 1874, 42.	f N. York M. Times, 1853-1854, iii., 126.		g 526, 1850, vi., 204.
h 242, 1880, 112.	i 476, April 6, 1895.		j 476, 1856, ii., 304.
k 548, 1864, ii., 476.	l 476, 1886, ii., 1079.		m 476, 1895, i., 1346.

besides that of the mesogastrium, are capable of forming splenic tissue. Jameson [a] reports a case of double spleen and kidneys. Bainbrigge [b] mentions a case of supernumerary spleen causing death from the patient being placed in the supine position in consequence of fracture of the thigh. Peevor [c] mentions an instance of second spleen. Béclard and Guy-Patin have seen the spleen congenitally misplaced on the right side and the liver on the left; Borellus and Bartholinus with others have observed misplacement of the spleen.

The Pancreas.—Lieutaud has seen the pancreas missing and speaks of [d] a double pancreatic duct that he found in a man who died from starvation; Bonet [216] speaks of a case similar to this last.

There are several cases of **complete transposition of the viscera** on record. This bizarre anomaly was probably observed first in 1650 by Riolanus, but the most celebrated case was that of Morand in 1660, and Méry described the instance later which was the subject of the following quatrain:—

> "La nature, peu sage et sans doute en débauche,
> Plaça le foie au côté gauche,
> Et de même, vice versa,
> Le cœur à le droite plaça."

Young [e] cites an example in a woman of eighty-five who died at Hammersmith, London. She was found dead in bed, and in a postmortem examination, ordered to discover if possible the cause of death, there was seen complete transposition of the viscera. The heart lay with its base toward the left, its apex toward the right, reaching the lower border of the 4th rib, under the right mamma. The vena cava was on the left side and passed into the pulmonary cavity of the heart, which was also on the left side, the aorta and systemic ventricle being on the right. The left splenic vein was lying on the superior vena cava, the liver under the left ribs, and the spleen on the right side underneath the heart. The esophagus was on the right of the aorta, and the location of the two ends of the stomach was reversed; the sigmoid flexure was on the right side. Davis [f] describes a similar instance in a man.

Herrick [g] mentions transposition of viscera in a man of twenty-five. Barbieux [h] cites a case of transposition of viscera in a man who was wounded in a duel. The liver was to the left and the spleen and heart to the right, etc. Albers, Baron, Béclard, Boyer, Bull, Mackensie, Hutchinson, Hunt, Murray, Dareste, Curran, Duchesne, Musser, Sabatier, Shrady, Vulpian, Wilson, and Wehn are among others reporting instances of transposition and inversion of the viscera.

[a] 435, 1874, ix., 11.   [b] 490, xxxviii., 1052.   [c] 435, 1885, xx., 216.
[d] Hist. Anat. Med., i., 248.   [e] 476, 1861, i., 630.   [f] 476, 1879, i., 789.
[g] 538, July 28, 1894.   [h] Ann. de la méd. physiol., Par., xiii.,518.

Congenital extroversion or eventration is the result of some congenital deficiency in the abdominal wall; instances are not uncommon, and some patients live as long as do cases of umbilical hernia proper. Ramsey[a] speaks of entire want of development of the abdominal parietes. Robertson, Rizzoli, Tait, Hamilton, Brodie, Denis, Dickie, Goyrand, and many others mention extroversion of viscera from parietal defects. The different forms of **hernia** will be considered in another chapter.

There seem to be no authentic cases of complete **absence of the kidney** except in the lowest grades of monstrosities. Becker, Blasius, Rhodius, Baillie, Portal, Sandifort, Meckel, Schenck, and Stoll are among the older writers who have observed the absence of one kidney. In a recent paper Ballowitz has collected 213 cases, from which the following extract has been made by the British Medical Journal :—

"Ballowitz (Virchow's Archiv, August 5, 1895) has collected as far as possible all the recorded cases of congenital absence of one kidney. Excluding cases of fused kidney and of partial atrophy of one kidney, he finds 213 cases of complete absence of one kidney, upon which he bases the following conclusions : Such deficiency occurs almost twice as often in males as in females, a fact, however, which may be partly accounted for by the greater frequency of necropsies on males. As to age, 23 occurred in the fetus or newly born, most having some other congenital deformity, especially imperforate anus ; the rest were about evenly distributed up to seventy years of age, after which only seven cases occurred. Taking all cases together, the deficiency is more common on the left than on the right side ; but while in males the left kidney is far more commonly absent than the right, in females the two sides show the defect equally. The renal vessels were generally absent, as also the ureter, on the abnormal side (the latter in all except 15 cases) ; the suprarenal was missing in 31 cases. The solitary kidney was almost always normal in shape and position, but much enlarged. Microscopically the enlargement would seem to be due rather to hyperplasia than to hypertrophy. The bladder, except for absence of the opening of one ureter, was generally normal. In a large number of cases there were associated deformities of the organs of generation, especially of the female organs, and these were almost invariably on the side of the renal defect ; they affected the conducting portion much more than the glandular portion—that is, uterus, vagina, and Fallopian tubes in the female, and vas deferens or vesiculæ seminales in the male, rather than the ovaries or testicles. Finally, he points out the practical bearing of the subject—for example, the probability of calculus causing sudden suppression of urine in such cases—and also the danger of surgical interference, and suggests the possibility of diagnosing the condition by ascertaining the absence of the opening of one ureter in the bladder by means of the cystoscope, and also the likelihood

[a] Northwest Med. and Surg. Jour., Chicago, 1857, xiv., 450.

of its occurring where any abnormality of the genital organs is found, especially if this be unilateral."

Green[a] reports the case of a female child in which the right kidney and right Fallopian tube and ovary were absent without any rudimentary structures in their place. Guitéras and Riesman[843] have noted the absence of the right kidney, right ureter, and right adrenal in an old woman who had died of chronic nephritis. The left kidney although cirrhotic was very much enlarged.

Tompsett[b] describes a necropsy made on a coolie child of nearly twelve

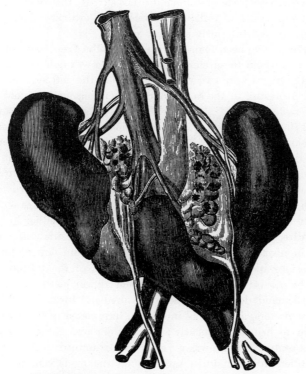

Fig. 141.—Renal symphysis and supernumerary kidney (Rayer).

months, in which it was seen that in the place of a kidney there were two left organs connected at the apices by a prolongation of the cortical substance of each; the child had died of neglected malarial fever. Sandifort[c] speaks of a case of double kidneys and double ureters, and cases of **supernumerary kidney** are not uncommon, generally being segmentation of one of the normal kidneys. Rayer has seen three kidneys united and formed like a horseshoe (Fig. 141). We are quite familiar with the ordinary " **horseshoe kidney**," in which two normal kidneys are connected.

a 224, Feb. 23, 1895.   b 224, 1879, ii., 602.   c 710, fasc. iii.

There are several forms of displacement of the kidneys, the most common being the "**floating kidney**," which is sometimes successfully removed or fixed ; Rayer has made an extensive study of this anomaly.

The kidney may be **displaced** to the pelvis, and Guinard [390] quotes an instance in which the left kidney was situated in the pelvis, to the left of the rectum and back of the bladder. The ureter of the left side was very short. The left renal artery came from the bifurcation of the aorta and the primitive iliacs. The right kidney was situated normally, and received from the aorta two arteries, whose volume did not surpass the two arteries supplying the left suprarenal capsule, which was in its ordinary place. Displacements of the kidney anteriorly are very rare.

The **ureters** have been found multiple ; Griffon [a] reports the history of a male subject in whom the ureter on the left side was double throughout its whole length ; there were two vesical orifices on the left side one above the other ; and Morestin, in the same journal, mentions ureters double on both sides in a female subject. Molinetti [572] speaks of six ureters in one person. Littre in 1705 described a case of coalition of the ureters. Allen [b] describes an elongated kidney with two ureters. Coëyne [c] mentions duplication of the ureters on both sides. Lediberder [d] reports a case in which the ureter had double origin. Tyson [e] cites an instance of four ureters in an infant. Penrose [f] mentions the absence of the upper two-thirds of the left ureter, with a small cystic kidney, and there are parallel cases on record.

The ureters sometimes have anomalous terminations either in the rectum, vagina, or directly in the urethra. This latter disposition is realized normally in a number of animals and causes the incessant flow of urine, resulting in a serious inconvenience. Flajani speaks of the termination of the ureters in the pelvis ; Nebel [g] has seen them appear just beneath the umbilicus ; and Lieutaud describes a man who died at thirty-five, from another cause, whose ureters, as large as intestines, terminated in the urethral canal, causing him to urinate frequently ; the bladder was absent. In the early part of this century [h] there was a young girl examined in New York whose ureters emptied into a reddish carnosity on the mons veneris. The urine dribbled continuously, and if the child cried or made any exertion it came in jets. The genital organs participated but little in the deformity, and with the exception that the umbilicus was low and the anus more anterior than natural, the child was well formed and its health good. Colzi [i] reports a case in which the left ureter opened externally at the left side of the hymen a little below the normal meatus urinarius. There is a case described [j] of a man who evidently suffered from a patent urachus, as the urine passed in jets

a 242, 1894. b 547, 1873–4, iv., 220. c 242, 1874, xliii., 55.
d 242, 1834–5, ix., 187. e 629, Lond., 1731, iii., 146. f 779, xl., 161.
g Comment. Acad. Palat., vol. v., n. xii. h 302, iv., 159.
i 747, May, 1895. j Mém. de l'Acad. de Chir., vol. xxx.

as if controlled by a sphincter from his umbilicus. Littre mentions a patent urachus in a boy of eighteen. Congenital dilatation of the ureters is occasionally seen in the new-born. Shattuck [a] describes a male fetus showing reptilian characters in the sexual ducts. There was ectopia vesicæ and prolapse of the intestine at the umbilicus; the right kidney was elongated; the right vas deferens opened into the ureter. There was persistence in a separate condition of the two Müllerian ducts which opened externally inferiorly, and there were two ducts near the openings which represented anal pouches. Both testicles were in the abdomen. Ord [b] describes a man in whom one of the Müllerian ducts was persistent.

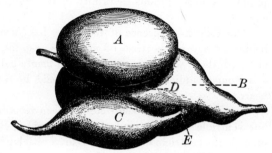

Fig. 142.—Triple bladder (Scibelli).

Anomalies of the Bladder.—Blanchard, Blasius, Haller, Nebel, and Rhodius mention cases in which the bladder has been found absent and we have already mentioned some cases, but the instances in which the bladder has been duplex are much more frequent. Bourienne, Oberteuffer, Ruysch, Bartholinus, Morgagni, and Franck speak of vesical duplication. There is a description [c] of a man who had two bladders, each receiving a ureter. Bussiere [d] describes a triple bladder, and Scibelli of Naples [e] mentions an instance in a subject who died at fifty-seven with symptoms of retention of urine. In the illustration (Fig. 142), B represents the normal bladder, A and C the supplementary bladders, with D and E their respective points of entrance into B. As will be noticed, the ureters terminate in the supplementary bladders. Fantoni [336] and Malgetti cite instances of quintuple bladders.

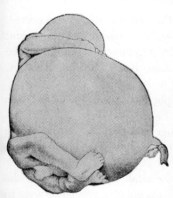

Fig. 143.—Dilatation of the fetal bladder.

The Ephemerides speaks of a case of coalition of the bladder with the os pubis and another case of coalition with the omentum. Prochaska [652] mentions vesical fusion with the uterus, and we have already described union with the rectum and intestine.

Exstrophy of the bladder is not rare, and is often associated with hypo-

a Jour. of Path. and Bacter., July, 1895.   b 491, 1880, 109.
c Jour. de Trevoux, 1702.   d 629, n. 268.   e 222, 1864, ii., 328.

spadias, epispadias, and other malformations of the genitourinary tract. It consists of a deficiency of the abdominal wall in the hypogastric region, in which is seen the denuded bladder. It is remedied by many different and ingenious plastic operations.

In an occasional instance in which there is occlusion at the umbilicus and again at the neck of the bladder this organ becomes so distended as to produce a most curious deformity in the fetus. Figure 143 shows such a case.

The Heart.—Absence of the heart has never been recorded in human beings except in the case of monsters, as, for example, the omphalosites, although there was a case reported and firmly believed by the ancient authors, —a Roman soldier in whom Telasius said he could discover no vestige of a heart.[a]

The absence of one ventricle has been recorded. Schenck [b] has seen the left ventricle deficient, and the Ephemerides, Behr, and Kerckring [c] speak of a single ventricle only in the heart. Riolan [685] mentions a heart in which both ventricles were absent. Jurgens reported in Berlin, February 1, 1882, an autopsy on a child who had lived some days after birth, in which the left ventricle of the heart was found completely absent. Playfair [d] showed the heart of a child which had lived nine months in which one ventricle was absent. In King's College Hospital in London there is a heart of a boy of thirteen in which the cavities consist of a single ventricle and a single auricle.

Duplication of the heart, notwithstanding the number of cases reported, has been admitted with the greatest reserve by Geoffroy-Saint-Hilaire and by a number of authors. Among the celebrated anatomists who describe duplex heart are Littre, Meckel, Collomb, Panum, Behr, Paullini, Rhodius, Winslow, and Zacutus Lusitanus.

The Ephemerides [e] cites an instance of triple heart, and Johnston [f] has seen a triple heart in a goose.

The phenomenon of "blue-disease," or congenital cyanosis, is due to the **patency of the foramen ovale**, which, instead of closing at birth, persists sometimes to adult life.

Perhaps the most unique collection of congenital malformations of the heart from persons who have reached the age of puberty was to be seen in London in 1895.[619] In this collection there was an adult heart in which the foramen ovale remained open until the age of thirty-seven; there were but two pulmonary valves; there was another heart showing a large patent foramen ovale from a man of forty-six; and there was a septum ventriculorum of an adult heart from a woman of sixty-three, who died of carcinoma of the breast, in which the foramen ovale was still open and would admit the fore

a 302, xxxiv., 207.   b 718, L. ii., obs. 184.   c 473, obs. 469.   d 778, vol. xii., 169
e 104, dec. i., an. 9, obs. 108.   f "Med. Bemerk. und Untersuch.," Band ii., 103

finger. This woman had shown no symptoms of the malformation. There were also hearts in which the interventricular septum was deficient, the ductus arteriosus patent, or some valvular malformation present. All these persons had reached puberty.

Displacements of the heart are quite numerous. Deschamps of Laval made an autopsy on an old soldier which justified the expression, "He had a heart in his belly." This organ was found in the left lumbar region; it had, with its vessels, traversed an anomalous opening in the diaphragm. Franck observed in the Hospital of Colmar a woman with the heart in the epigastric region. Ramel[a] and Vetter speak of the heart under the diaphragm.

Inversion of the heart is quite frequent, and we often find reports of cases of this anomaly. Fournier[b] describes a soldier of thirty years, of middle height, well proportioned and healthy, who was killed in a duel by receiving a wound in the abdomen; postmortem, the heart was found in the position of the right lung; the two lungs were joined and occupied the left chest.

The anomalies of the vascular system are so numerous that we shall dismiss them with a slight mention. Malacarne in Torino in 1784 described a double aorta, and Hommelius[c] mentions an analogous case. The following case is quite an interesting anatomic anomaly : A woman since infancy had difficulty in swallowing, which was augmented at the epoch of menstruation and after exercise; bleeding relieved her momentarily, but the difficulty always returned. At last deglutition became impossible and the patient died of malnutrition. A necropsy revealed the presence of the subclavicular artery passing between the tracheal artery and the esophagus, compressing this latter tube and opposing the passage of food.

Anomalies of the Breasts.—The first of the anomalies of the generative apparatus to be discussed, although not distinctly belonging under this head, will be those of the mammæ.

Amazia, or complete absence of the breast, is seldom seen. Pilcher[d] describes an individual who passed for a female, but who was really a male, in whom the breasts were absolutely wanting. Foerster, Froriep, and Ried cite instances associated with thoracic malformation. Greenhow[e] reports a case in which the mammæ were absent, although there were depressed rudimentary nipples and areolæ. There were no ovaries and the uterus was congenitally imperfect.

There was a negress spoken of in 1842 in whom the right breast was missing, and there are cases of but one breast, mentioned by King,[f] Paull,[g] and others.[h] Scanzoni has observed absence of the left mamma with absence of the left ovary.

a 462, tome xlix., p. 423. b 302, iv., 150. c 282, 1737.
d 476, 1878, i., 915. e 550, 1864, 195. f 548, 1858.
g 476, 1862, i., 648. h Thesé de Paris, ann. x., No. 53, p. 15.

Micromazia is not so rare, and is generally seen in females with associate genital troubles. **Excessive development of the mammæ,** generally being a pathologic phenomenon, will be mentioned in another chapter. However, among some of the indigenous negroes the female breasts are naturally very large and pendulous. This is well shown in Figure 144, which represents a woman of the Bushman tribe nursing an infant. The breasts are sufficiently pendulous and loose to be easily thrown over the shoulder.

Polymazia is of much more frequent occurrence than is supposed. Julia, the mother of Alexander Severus, was surnamed "Mammea" because she had supernumerary breasts. Anne Boleyn, the unfortunate wife of Henry VIII. of England, was reputed to have had six toes, six fingers,

Fig. 144.—Bushwoman nursing her infant.

and three breasts. Lynceus says that in his time there existed a Roman woman with four mammæ, very beautiful in contour, arranged in two lines, regularly, one above the other, and all giving milk in abundance. Rubens has pictured a woman with four breasts; the painting may be seen in the Louvre in Paris.

There was a young and wealthy heiress who addressed herself to the ancient faculty at Tübingen, asking, as she displayed four mammæ, whether, should she marry, she would have three or four children at a birth. This was a belief with which some of her elder matron friends had inspired her, and which she held as a hindrance to marriage.

Leichtenstern, who has collected 70 cases of polymazia in females and 22 in males, thinks that accessory breasts or nipples are due to atavism, and that our most remote inferiorly organized ancestors had many breasts, but that by constantly bearing but one child, from being polymastic, females have gradually become bimastic. Some of the older philosophers contended that by the presence of two breasts woman was originally intended to bear two children.

Hirst [a] says: "Supernumerary breasts and nipples are more common than is generally supposed. Bruce found 60 instances in 3956 persons examined (1.56 per cent.). Leichtenstern places the frequency at one in 500. Both observers declare that men present the anomaly about twice as frequently as women. It is impossible to account for the accessory glands on

[a] 792, May, 1896.

the theory of reversion, as they occur with no regularity in situation, but may develop at odd places on the body. The most frequent position is on the pectoral surface below the true mammæ and somewhat nearer the middle line, but an accessory gland has been observed on the left shoulder over the prominence of the deltoid, on the abdominal surface below the costal cartilages, above the umbilicus, in the axilla, in the groin, on the dorsal surface, on the labium majus, and on the outer aspect of the left thigh. Ahlfeld explains the presence of mammæ on odd parts of the body by the theory that portions of the embryonal material entering into the composition of the mammary gland are carried to and implanted upon any portion of the exterior of the body by means of the amnion."

Possibly the greatest number of accessory mammæ reported is that of Neugebauer in 1886, who found ten in one person. Peuch in 1876 collected 77 cases, and since then Hamy, Quinquaud, Whiteford, Engstrom, and Mitchell Bruce have collected cases. Polymazia must have been known in the olden times, and we still have before us the old images of Diana, in which this goddess is portrayed with numerous breasts, indicating her ability to look after the growing child. Figure 145 shows an ancient Oriental statue of Artemisia or Diana now at Naples.

Fig. 145.—Statue of a polymastic Artemisia or Diana.

Bartholinus [a] has observed a Danish woman with three mammæ, two ordinarily formed and a third forming a triangle with the others and resembling the breasts of a fat man. In the village of Phullendorf in Germany early in this century there was an old woman who sought alms from place to place, exhibiting to the curious four symmetrical breasts, arranged parallel. She was extremely ugly, and when on all fours, with her breasts pendulous, she resembled a beast. The authors have seen a man with six distinct nipples, arranged as regularly as those of a bitch or sow. The two lower were quite small. This man's body was covered with heavy, long hair, making him a very conspicuous object when seen naked during bathing. The hair was absent for a space of nearly an inch about the nipples. Borellus speaks of a woman with three mammæ, two as ordinarily, the third to the left side, which gave milk, but not the same quantity as the others. Gardiner[b] describes a mulatto woman who had four mammæ, two of which were near the axillæ, about four inches in circumference, with proportionate sized nipples. She became a mother at fourteen, and gave milk from all her breasts. In his "Dictionnaire Philosophique" Voltaire gives the history of a woman with four well-formed

[a] 190, cent. iv.   [b] 302, iv., 152.

and symmetrically arranged breasts ; she also exhibited an excrescence, covered with a nap-like hair, looking like a cow-tail.　Percy thought the excrescence a prolongation of the coccyx, and said that similar instances were seen in savage men of Borneo.

Percy [a] says that among some prisoners taken in Austria was found a woman of Valachia, near Roumania, exceedingly fatigued, and suffering intensely from the cold.　It was January, and the ground was covered with three feet of snow.　She had been exposed with her two infants, who had been born twenty days, to this freezing temperature, and died on the next day. An examination of her body revealed five mammæ, of which four projected as ordinarily, while the fifth was about the size of that of a girl at puberty.

Fig. 146.—Woman with two axillary mammæ (Charpentier).

They all had an intense dark ring about them ; the fifth was situated about five inches above the umbilicus.　Percy injected the subject and dissected and described the mammary blood-supply.　Hirst [b] mentions a negress of nineteen who had nine mammæ, all told, and as many nipples. The two normal glands were very large.　Two accessory glands and nipples below them were small and did not excrete milk.　All the other glands and nipples gave milk in large quantities.　There were five nipples on the left and four on the right side.　The patient's mother had an accessory mamma on the abdomen that secreted milk during the period of lactation.

Charpentier has observed in his clinic a woman with two supplementary

a 302, iv., 152.　　　　　　　　　　　　　　　　b 792, May, 1896.

axillary mammæ with nipples. They gave milk as the ordinary mammæ (Fig. 146). Robert saw a woman who nourished an infant by a mamma on the thigh. Until the time of pregnancy this mamma was taken for an ordinary nevus, but with pregnancy it began to develop and acquired the size of a citron. Figure 147 is from an old wood-cut showing a child suckling at a supernumerary mamma on its mother's thigh while its brother is at the natural breast. Jenner speaks of a breast on the outer side of the thigh four inches below the great trochanter. Hare[a] describes a woman of thirty-seven who secreted normal milk from her axillæ. Lee[b] mentions a woman of thirty-five with four mammæ and four nipples ; she suckled with the pectoral and not the axillary breasts. McGillicudy describes a pair of rudimentary abdominal mammæ, and there is another similar case recorded.[c] Har-

tung[d] mentions a woman of thirty who while suckling had a mamma on the left labium majus. It was excised, and microscopic examination showed its structure to be that of a rudimentary nipple and mammary gland. Leichtenstern cites a case of a mamma on the left shoulder nearly under the insertion of the deltoid, and Klob[e] speaks of an acromial accessory mamma situated on the shoulder over the greatest prominence of the deltoid. Hall[f] reports the case of a functionally active supernumerary mamma over the costal cartilage of the 8th rib. Jussieu[g] speaks of a woman who had three breasts, one of which was situated on the

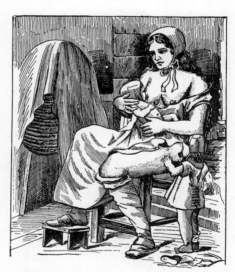

Fig. 147.—Functional supernumerary mamma on the thigh.

groin and with which she occasionally suckled ; her mother had three breasts, but they were all situated on the chest. Saunois[h] details an account of a female who had two supernumerary breasts on the back. Bartholinus (quoted by Meckel) and Manget also mention mammæ on the back, but Geoffroy-Saint-Hilaire questions their existence. Martin[i] gives a very clear illustration of a woman with a supernumerary breast below the natural organ (Fig. 148). Sneddon,[j] who has collected quite a number of cases of polymazia, quotes the case of a woman who had two swellings in each axilla in

a 476, 1860, ii., 405.   b 550, xxi., 266.   c 451, 1878, xiii., 425.

d Inaug. diss., Erlangen, 1872.   e 833, 1858, i., 52.

f Quart. Med. Jour., April, 1894.   g 476, xii., 618.   h Thesé de Paris.

i Archiv. für Klinische Chirurgie, 1893.   j 381, 1879, p. 92.

which gland-structure was made out, but with no external openings, and which had no anatomic connection with the mammary glands proper. Shortly after birth they varied in size and proportion, as the breasts were full or empty, and in five weeks all traces of them were lost. Her only married sister had similar enlargements at her third confinement.

Polymazia sometimes seems to be **hereditary.** Robert saw a daughter whose mother was polymastic, and Woodman [a] saw a mother and eldest daughter who each had three nipples. Lousier [b] mentions a woman wanting a mamma who transmitted this vice of conformation to her daughter. Handyside says he knew two brothers in both of whom breasts were wanting.

Supernumerary nipples alone are also seen, as many as five having been found on the same breast. Neugebauer reports eight supernumerary nipples in one case. Hollerus has seen a woman who had two nipples on the same breast which gave milk with the same regularity and the same abundance as the single nipple. The Ephemerides contains a description of a triple nipple. Barth [c] describes a " mamma erratica " on the face in front of the right ear which enlarged during menstruation.

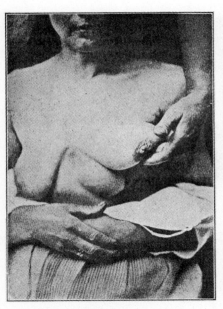

Fig. 148.—Supernumerary breast (Martin).

Cases of **deficiency of the nipples** have been reported by the Ephemerides, Lentilius, Severinus, and Werckardus.

Cases of functional male mammæ will be discussed in Chapter IX.

Complete absence of the hymen is very rare, if we may accept the statements of Devilliers, Tardieu, and Brouardel, as they have never seen an example in the numerous young girls they have examined from a medico-legal point of view.

Duplication or biperforation of the hymen is also a very rare anomaly of this membrane. In this instance the hymen generally presents two lateral orifices, more or less irregular and separated by a membranous band, which gives the appearance of duplicity. Roze reported from Strasburg in 1866 a case of this kind, and Delens [d] has observed two examples of

a 778, ix., 50.　　　　b " Dissert. sur la lactation," Paris, 1802, p. 15.
c 161, 1888, 569.　　　　d " Annales d'hygiène publique et de médecine légale," 1877.

biperforate hymen, which show very well that this disposition of the membrane is due to a vice of conformation. The first was in a girl of eleven, in which the membrane was of the usual size and thickness, but was duplicated on either side. In her sister of nine the hymen was normally conformed. The second case was in a girl under treatment by Cornil in 1876 for vaginitis. Her brother had accused a young man of eighteen of having violated her, and on examination the hymen showed a biperforate conformation ; there were two oval orifices, their greatest diameter being in the vertical plane ; the openings were situated on each side of the median line, about five mm. apart; the dividing band did not appear to be cicatricial, but presented the same roseate coloration as the rest of the hymen. Since this report quite a number of cases have been recorded.

The different varieties of the hymen will be left to the works on obstetrics. As has already been observed, labor is frequently seriously complicated by a persistent and tough hymen.

Deficient vulva may be caused by the persistence of a thick hymen, by congenital occlusion, or by absolute absence in vulvar structure. Bartholinus, Borellus, Ephemerides, Julius, Vallisneri, and Baux are among the older writers who mention this anomaly, but as it is generally associated with congenital occlusion, or complete absence of the vagina, the two will be considered together.

Complete **absence of the vagina** is quite rare. Baux[a] reports a case of a girl of fourteen in whom " there was no trace of fundament or of genital organs." Oberteuffer[b] speaks of a case of absent vagina. Vicq d'Azir[c] is accredited with having seen two females who, not having a vagina, copulated all through life by the urethra, and Fournier sagely remarks that the extra large urethra may have been a special dispensation of nature. Bosquet[d] describes a young girl of twenty with a triple vice of conformation—an obliterated vulva, closure of the vagina, and absence of the uterus. Menstrual hemorrhage took place from the gums. Clarke[e] has studied a similar case which was authenticated by an autopsy.

O'Ferral of Dublin, Gooch, Davies, Boyd, Tyler Smith, Hancock, Coste, Kluyskens, Debrou, Braid, Watson, and others are quoted by Churchill as having mentioned the absence of the vagina. Amussat[f] observed a German girl who did not have a trace of a vagina and who menstruated regularly. Griffith[g] describes a specimen in the Museum of St. Bartholomew's Hospital, London, in which the ovaries lay on the surface of the pelvic peritoneum and there was neither uterus nor vagina ; the pelvis had some of the characteristics of the male type. Matthews Duncan has observed a somewhat similar case, the vagina not measuring more than an inch in length. Ferguson[h] describes a prostitute of eighteen who had never menstruated. The

a 460, 1758, viii., 59.   b 160, Band ii., 627.   c 302, iv., 162.
d 778, xxvii., 123.   e 476, 1872, ii., 225.   f 368, Dec. 12, 1865.
g 778, xxvii., 128.   h Planet, N. Y., 1883, 1.

labia were found well developed, but there was no vagina, uterus, or ovaries. Coitus had been through the urethra, which was considerably distended, though not causing incontinence of urine. Hulke reports a case of congenital atresia of the vagina in a brunette of twenty, menstruation occurring through the urethra. He also mentions the instance of congenital atresia of the vagina with hernia of both ovaries into the left groin in a servant of twenty, and the case of an imperforate vagina in a girl of nineteen with an undeveloped uterus.

Brodhurst[a] reports an instance of absence of the vagina and uterus in a girl of sixteen who at four years of age showed signs of approaching puberty. At this early age the mons was covered with hair, and at ten the clitoris was three inches long and two inches in circumference. The mammæ were well developed. The labia descended laterally and expanded into folds, resembling the scrotum.

Azéma[b] reports an instance of complete absence of the vagina and impermeability and probable absence of the col uterinus. The deficiencies were remedied by operation. Bérard[c] mentions a similar deformity and operation in a girl of eighteen. Gooding[d] cites an instance of absent vagina in a married woman, the uterus discharging the functions. Gosselin[e] reports a case in which a voluminous tumor was formed by the retained menstrual fluid in a woman without a vagina. An artificial vagina was created, but the patient died from extravasation of blood into the peritoneal cavity. Carter, Polaillon, Martin, Curtis, Worthington, Hall, Hicks, Molière, Patry, Dolbeau, Desormeaux, and Gratigny also record instances of absence of the vagina.

There are some cases reported in extramedical literature which might be cited. Bussy Rabutin in his Mémoires in 1639 speaks of an instance. The celebrated Madame Récamier was called by the younger Dumas an involuntary virgin ; and in this connection could be cited the malicious and piquant sonnet :—

Chateaubriand et Madame Récamier.

" Juliette et René s'aimaient d'amour si tendre
Que Dieu, sans les punir, a pu leur pardonner :
Il n'avait pas voulu que l'une pût donner
Ce que l'autre ne pouvait prendre. "

Duplex vagina has been observed by Bartholinus, Malacarne, Asch, Meckel, Osiander, Purcell, and other older writers. In more modern times reports of this anomaly are quite frequent. Hunter[f] reports a case of labor at the seventh month in a woman with a double vagina, and delivery through the rectum. Atthill and Watts speak of double vagina with single uterus.

a 548, 1852, 187.   b 140, 193.   c 363, 1841, iii., 377.
d 476, 1879, i., 430.   e 363, xl., 225.   f 125, xi., 593.

Robb [a] of Johns Hopkins Hospital reports a case of double vagina in a patient of twenty suffering from dyspareunia. The vaginal orifice was contracted ; the urethra was dilated and had evidently been used for coitus. A membrane divided the vagina into two canals, the cervix lying in the right half; the septum was also divided. Both the thumbs of the patient were so short that their tips could scarcely meet those of the little fingers. Double vagina is also reported by Anway, Moulton, Freeman, Frazer, Haynes, Lemaistre, Boardman, Dickson, Dunoyer, and Rossignol. This anomaly is usually associated with bipartite or double uterus. Wilcox [b] mentions a primipara, three months pregnant, with a double vagina and a bicornate uterus, who was safely delivered of several children. Haller and Borellus have seen double vagina, double uterus, and double ovarian supply ; in the latter case there was also a double vulva. Sanger [c] speaks of a supernumerary vagina connecting with the other vagina by a fistulous opening, and remarks that this was not a case of patent Gärtner's duct.

Cullingworth [d] cites two cases in which there were **transverse septa of the vagina.** Stone [e] reports five cases of transverse septa of the vagina. Three of the patients were young women who had never borne children or suffered injury. Pregnancy existed in each case. In the first the septum was about two inches from the introitus, and contained an opening about $\frac{1}{2}$ inch in diameter which admitted the tip of the finger. The membrane was elastic and thin and showed no signs of inflammation. Menstruation had always been regular up to the time of pregnancy. The second was a duplicate of the first, excepting that a few bands extended from the cervix to the membranous septum. In the third the lumen of the vagina, about two inches from the introitus, was distinctly narrowed by a ridge of tissue. There was uterine displacement and some endocervicitis, but no history of injury or operation and no tendency to contraction. The two remaining cases occurred in patients seen by Dr. J. F. Scott. In one the septum was about $1\frac{3}{4}$ inches from the entrance to the vagina and contained an orifice large enough to admit a uterine probe. During labor the septum resisted the advance of the head for several hours, until it was slit in several directions. In the other, menstruation had always been irregular, intermissions being followed by a profuse flow of black and tarry blood, which lasted sometimes for fifteen days and was accompanied by severe pain. The septum was $1\frac{1}{2}$ inches from the vaginal orifice and contained an opening which admitted a uterine sound. It was very dense and tight and fully $\frac{1}{8}$ inch in thickness.

Mordie [f] reported a case of congenital deficiency of the rectovaginal septum which was successfully remedied by operation.

Anomalous Openings of the Vagina.—The vagina occasionally opens abnormally into the rectum, into the bladder, the urethra, or upon the

a 446, April, 1895.   b 647, 1877.   c 261, Sept. 22, 1894.
d 476, 1889, i., 726.   e 218, May 30, 1895. f 476, 1888, ii., 166.

abdominal parietes. Rossi reports from a hospital in Turin the case of a Piedmontese girl in whom there was an enormous tumor corresponding to the opening of the vaginal orifice ; no traces of a vagina could be found. The tumor was incised and proved to be a living infant. The husband of the woman said that he had coitus without difficulty by the rectum, and examination showed that the vagina opened into the rectum, by which means impregnation had been accomplished. Bonnain [a] and Payne [b] have observed analogous cases of this abnormality of the vaginal opening and subsequent accouchement by the anus. Payne's case was of a woman of thirty-five, well formed, who had been in labor thirty-six hours, when the physician examined and looked in vain for a vaginal opening ; the finger, gliding along the perineum, came in contact with the distended anus, in which was recognized the head of the fetus. The woman from prolongation of labor was in a complete state of prostration, which caused uterine inertia. Payne anesthetized the patient, applied the forceps, and extracted the fetus without further accident. The vulva of this woman five months afterward displayed all the characteristics of virginity, the vagina opened into the rectum, and menstruation had always been regular. This woman, as well as her husband, averred that they had no suspicion of the anomaly and that coitus (by the anus) had always been satisfactory.

Opening of the vagina upon the parietes, of which Le Fort has collected a number of cases, has never been observed in connection with a viable fetus.

Absence of the labia majora has been observed, especially by Pozzi, to the exclusion of all other anomalies. It is the rule in exstrophy of the bladder.

Absence of the nymphæ has also been observed, particularly by Auvard and by Perchaux, and is generally associated with imperfect development of the clitoris. Constantinedes [c] reports absence of the external organs of generation, probably also of the uterus and its appendages, in a young lady. Van Haartman, LeFort, Magee, and Ogle cite cases of absence of the external female organs. Riolan [d] in the early part of the seventeenth century reported a case of defective nymphæ ; Neubauer in 1774 offers a contrast to this case in an instance of **triple nymphæ.**

The **nymphæ** are sometimes enormously **enlarged** by hypertrophy, by varicocele, or by elephantiasis, of which latter type Rigal de Gaillac has observed a most curious case. There is also a variety of enlargement of the clitoris which seems to be constant in some races ; it may be a natural hypertrophy, or perhaps produced by artificial manipulation.

The peculiar conditions under which the Chinese women are obliged to live, particularly their mode of sitting, is said to have the effect of causing **unusual development of the mons veneris and the labia majora.** On the other hand, some of the lower African races have been distinguished by

a 789, Sept. 4, 1888.   b 168, 1886, p. 854.   c 250, 1870–1, iii., 77.   d 685, L. ii., c. 35.

the deficiency in development of the labia majora, mons veneris, and genital hair. In this respect they present an approximation to the genitals of the anthropoid apes, among whom the orang-outang alone shows any tendency to formation of the labia majora.

The labial appendages of the **Hottentot female** have been celebrated for many years. Blumenbach and others of the earlier travelers found that the apron-like appearance of the genitals of the Hottentot women was due to abnormal hypertrophy of the labia and nymphæ (Pl. 5). According to John Knott, the French traveler, Le Vaillant, said that the more coquettish among the Hottentot girls are excited by extreme vanity to practise artificial elongation of the nympha and labia. They are said to pull and rub these parts, and even to stretch them by hanging weights to them. Some of them are said to spend several hours a day at this process, which is considered one of the important parts of the toilet of the Hottentot belle, this malformation being an attraction for the male members of the race. Merensky says that in Basutoland the elder women begin to practise labial manipulation on their female children shortly after infancy, and Adams has found this custom to prevail in Dahomey ; he says that the King's seraglio includes 3000 members, the elect of his female subjects, all of whom have labia up to the standard of recognized length. Cameron found an analogous practice among the women of the shores of Lake Tanganyika. The females of this nation manipulated the skin of the lower part of the abdomens of the female children from infancy, and at puberty these women exhibit a cutaneous curtain over the genitals which reaches half-way down the thighs.

A corresponding development of the preputian clitorides, attaining the length of 18 mm. or even more, has been observed among the females of Bechuanaland. The greatest elongation measured by Barrow was five inches, but it is quite probable that it was not possible for him to examine the longest, as the females so gifted generally occupied very high social positions.

Morgagni describes a **supernumerary left nympha,** and Petit is accredited with seeing a case which exhibited neither nymphæ, clitoris, nor urinary meatus. Mauriceau performed nymphotomy on a woman whose nymphæ were so long as to render coitus difficult. Morand [575] quotes a case of congenital malformation of the nymphæ, to which he attributed impotency.

There is sometimes **coalition of the labia and nymphæ,** which may be so firm and extensive as to obliterate the vulva. Debout[a] has reported a case of absence of the vulva in a woman of twenty upon whom he operated, which was the result of the fusion of the labia minora, and this with an enlarged clitoris gave the exteral appearance of an hermaphrodite.

The **absence of the clitoris** coincides with epispadias in the male, and in atrophy of the vulva it is common to find the clitoris rudimentary ; but a more frequent anomaly is hypertrophy of the clitoris.

[a] 235, 1864, 26, tome xlv.

Among the older authorities quoting instances of **enlarged clitorides** are Bartholinus, Schenck, Hellwig, Rhodius, Riolanus, and Zacchias. Albucasis[115] describes an operation for enlarged clitoris, Chabert ligated one, and Riedlin[a] gives an instance of an enlarged clitoris, in which there appeared a tumor synchronous with the menstrual epoch.

We learn from the classics that there were certain females inhabiting the borders of the Ægean Sea who had a sentimental attachment for one another which was called " Lesbian love," and which carried them to the highest degree of frenzy. The immortal effusions of Sappho contain references to this passion. The solution of this peculiar ardor is found in the fact that some of the females had enlarged clitorides, strong voices, robust figures, and imitated men. Their manner was imperative and authoritative to their sex, who worshiped them with perverted devotion. We find in Martial[b] mention of this perverted love, and in the time of the dissolute Greeks and Romans ridiculous jealousies for unfaithfulness between these women prevailed. Aetius said that the Egyptians practised amputation of the clitoris, so that enlargement of this organ must have been a common vice of conformation along the Nile. It was also said that the Egyptian women practised circumcision on their females at the age of seven or eight, the time chosen being when the Nile was in flood. Bertherand[c] cites examples of enlarged clitorides in Arab women ; Bruce testifies to this circumstance in Abyssinia, and Mungo Park has observed it in the Mandingos and the Ibbos.

Sonnini[d] says that the women of Egypt had a natural excrescence, fleshy in consistency, quite thick and pendulous, coming from the skin of the mons veneris. Sonnini says that in a girl of eight he saw one of these caruncles which was $\frac{1}{2}$ inch long, and another on a woman of twenty which was four inches long, and remarks that they seem peculiar only to women of distinct Egyptian origin.

Duhouset[e] says that in circumcision the Egyptian women not only remove a great part of the body of the clitoris with the prepuce, but also adjacent portions of the nymphæ ; Gallieni[f] found a similar operation customary on the upper banks of the Niger.

Otto at Breslau in 1824 reports seeing a negress with a clitoris $4\frac{1}{2}$ inches long and $1\frac{1}{2}$ inches in the transverse diameter ; it projected from the vulva and when supine formed a complete covering for the vaginal orifice. The clitoris may at times become so large as to prevent coitus, and in France has constituted a legitimate cause for divorce. This organ is very sensitive, and it is said that in cases of supposed catalepsy a woman cannot bear titillation of the clitoris without some visible movement.

Columbus cites an example of a clitoris as long as a little finger ; Haller

a 683, 1695, 295.　　b 509, L. i., epigram 91.　　c " Méd. et Hygiène des Arabes," p. 190.
d " Voyage dans la Haute et la Basse-Egypt.," Paris, 1799.　　　　　e 243, xii., 126.
f Bull. de la Soc. de Geog., iv., 1883, 573.

mentions one which measured seven inches, and there is a record [a] of an enlarged clitoris which resembled the neck of a goose and which was 12 inches long. Bainbridge [b] reports a case of enlarged clitoris in a woman of thirty-two who was confined with her first child. This organ was five inches in length and of about the diameter of a quiescent penis. Figure 149 shows a well-marked case of hypertrophy of the clitoris. Rogers [c] describes a woman of twenty-five in a reduced state of health with an enormous clitoris and warts about the anus; there were also manifestations of tuberculosis. On questioning her, it was found that she had formerly masturbated; later she had sexual intercourse several times with a young man, but after his death she commenced self-abuse again, which brought on the present enlargement. The clitoris was ligated and came away without leaving disfigurement.

Cassano and Pedretti of Naples reported an instance of monstrous clitoris in 1860 before the Academy of Medicine.

In some cases **ossification of the clitoris** is observed. Fournier [302] speaks of a public woman in Venice who had an osseous clitoris; it was said that men having connection with her invariably suffered great pain, followed by inflammation of the penis.

There are a few instances recorded of **bifid clitoris,** and Arnaud [d] cites the history of a woman who had a **double clitoris.** Secretain [e] speaks of a clitoris which was in a permanent state of erection.

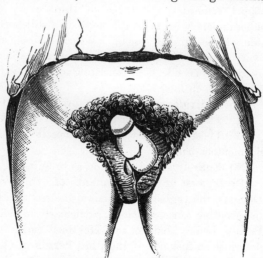

Fig. 149.—Hypertrophy of the clitoris.

Complete absence of the ovaries is seldom seen, but there are instances in which one of the ovaries is missing. Hunter, Vidal, and Chaussier report in full cases of the absence of the ovaries, and Thudicum has collected 21 cases of this nature. Morgagni, Pears, [f] and Cripps have published observations in which both ovaries were said to have been absent. Cripps speaks of a young girl of eighteen who had an infantile uterus and no ovaries; she neither menstruated nor had any signs of puberty. Lauth cites the case of a woman whose ovaries and uterus were rudimentary, and who exhibited none of the principal physiologic characteristics of her sex;

a 302, v., 374.   b 548, 1860, i., 45.   c 778, xii., 84.   d " Mém. de Chirurg.," tome i.
e Soc. d. sc. méd. de Gannat., xxiii., 1868-9, 22.   f 629, 1805, 225.

on the other hand, Ruband describes a woman with only rudimentary ovaries who was very passionate and quite feminine in her aspect.

At one time the existence of genuine **supernumerary ovaries** was vigorously disputed, and the older records contain no instances, but since the researches of Beigel, Puech, Thudicum, Winckler, de Sinéty, and Paladino the presence of multiple ovaries is an incontestable fact. It was originally thought that supernumerary ovaries as well as supernumerary kidneys were simply segmentations of the normal organs and connected to them by portions of the proper substance ; now, however, by the recent reports we are warranted in admitting these anomalous structures as distinct organs. It has even been suggested that it is the persistence of these ovaries that causes the menstruation of which we sometimes hear as taking place after ovariotomy. Sippel[a] records an instance of third ovary ; Mangiagalli[b] has found a supernumerary ovary in the body of a still-born child, situated to the inner side of the normal organ. Winckel discovered a large supernumerary ovary connected to the uterus by its own ovarian ligament. Klebs found two ovaries on one side, both consisting of true ovarian tissue, and connected by a band $\frac{3}{5}$ inch long.

Doran divides supernumerary ovaries into three classes :—

(1) The ovarium succentauriatum of Beigel.

(2) Those cases in which two masses of ovarian tissue are separated by ligamentous bands.

(3) Entirely separate organs, as in Winckel's case.

Prolapsus or displacement of the ovaries into the culdesac of Douglas, the vaginal wall, or into the rectum can be readily ascertained by the resulting sense of nausea, particularly in defecation or in coitus. Mundé, Barnes, Lentz, Madden, and Heywood Smith report instances, and Cloquet describes an instance of **inguinal hernia of the ovary** in which the uterus as well as the Fallopian tube were found in the inguinal canal. Debierre[c] mentions that Puech has gathered 88 instances of inguinal hernia of the ovary and 14 of the crural type, and also adds that Otte[d] cites the only instance in which crural ovarian hernia has been found on both sides. Such a condition with other associate malformations of the genitalia might easily be mistaken for an instance of hermaphroditic testicles.

The Fallopian tubes are rarely absent on either side, although Blasius[214] reports an instance of deficient oviducts. Blot[e] reports a case of atrophy, or rather rudimentary state of one of the ovaries, with absence of the tube on that side, in a woman of forty.

Doran[f] has an instance of multiple Fallopian tubes, and Richard, in 1851, says several varieties are noticed. These tubes are often found fused

a 261, 1889, No. 18.   b 152, 1879, i., 149.
c "Les vices de conformation des organs génitaux," etc. Par.,1892.   d 199, 1857, 345.
e "Compt. rend. Soc. de biol.," iii., 176.   Par., 1857.   f 778, 1887.

or adherent to the ovary or to the uterus ; but Fabricius[333] describes the symphysis of the Fallopian tube with the rectum.

Absence of the uterus is frequently reported. Lieutaud and Richerand [302] are each said to have dissected female subjects in whom neither the uterus nor its annexed organs were found. Many authors are accredited with mentioning instances of defective or deficient uteri, among them Bosquet, [a] Boyer,[b] Walther,[314] Le Fort, Calori, Pozzi, Mundé, and Strauch. Balade [c] has reported a curious absence of the uterus and vagina in a girl of eighteen. Azam, Bastien, Bibb, Bovel, Warren, Ward, and many others report similar instances, and in several cases all the adnexa as well as the uterus and vagina were absent, and even the kidney and bladder malformed.

Phillips [d] speaks of two sisters, both married, with congenital absence of the uterus. In his masterly article on " Heredity," [e] Sedgwick quotes an instance of total absence of the uterus in three out of five daughters of the same family ; two of the three were twice married.

Double uterus is so frequently reported that an enumeration of the cases would occupy several pages. Bicorn, bipartite, duplex, and double uteruses are so called according to the extent of the duplication. The varieties range all the way from slight increase to two distinct uteruses, with separate appendages and two vaginæ. Meckel, Boehmer, and Callisen are among the older writers who have observed double uterus with associate double vagina. Figure 150 represents a transverse section of a bipartite uterus with a double vagina. The so-called uterus didelphus is really a duplex uterus, or a veritable double uterus, each segment having the appearance of a complete unicorn uterus more or less joined to its neighbor (Fig. 151). Vallisneri [f] relates the history of a woman who was poisoned by cantharides who had two uteruses, one opening into the vagina, the other into the rectum. Morand, Bartholinus, Tiedemann, Ollivier, Blundell, and many others relate instances of double uterus in which impregnation had occurred, the fetus being retained until the full term.

Purcell of Dublin [g] says that in the summer of 1773 he opened the body of a woman who died in the ninth month of pregnancy. He found a uterus of ordinary size and form as is usual at this period of gestation, which contained a full-grown fetus, but only one ovary attached to a single Fallopian tube. On the left side he found a second uterus, unimpregnated and of usual size, to which another ovary and tube were attached. Both of these uteruses were distinct and almost entirely separate.

Pregnancy with Double Uterus.—Hollander [h] describes the following anomaly of the uterus which he encountered during the performance of a celiotomy :—

" There were found two uteruses, the posterior one being a normal organ

a 462, iv., 128. b 565, ii., 19. c Jour. de Médicine de Bordeaux, Oct. 4, 1891.
d 224, June 18, 1870. e 549, July, 1863, 457. f " Esperienze d'osservaz.," etc
g 629, lxiv., 474. h 261, 1895, No. 4, p. 375.

Fig. 150.—Bipartite uterus with double vagina.

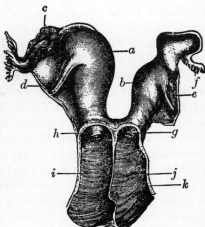

Fig. 151.—Didelphic uterus and divided vagina: *a*, right segment; *b*, left segment; *c, d*, right ovary and round ligament; *f, e*, left ovary and round ligament; *g, j*, left cervix and vagina; *k*, vaginal septum; *h, i*, right cervix and vagina.

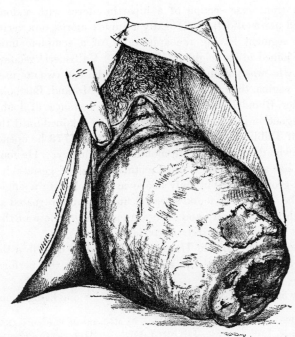

Fig. 152.—Complete prolapse of the uterus, with eversion of vagina (Keen and White).

with its adnexa; connected with this uterus was another one, anterior to it. The two uteruses had a common cervix; the anterior of the two organs had no adnexa, though there were lateral peritoneal ligaments; it had become pregnant." Hollander explains the anomaly by stating that probably the Müllerian ducts or one of them had grown excessively, leading to a folding off of a portion which developed into the anterior uterus.

Other cases of double uterus with pregnancy are mentioned on page 49.

When there is simultaneous pregnancy in each portion of a double uterus a complication of circumstances arises. Debierre quotes an instance of a woman who bore one child on July 16, 1870, and another on October 31st of the same year, and both at full term. She had only had three menstrual periods between the confinements. The question as to whether a case like this would be one of superfetation in a normal uterus, or whether the uterus was double, would immediately arise. There would also be the possibility that one of the children was of protracted gestation or that the other was of premature birth. Article 312 of the Civil Code of France accords a minimum of one hundred and eighty and a maximum of three hundred days for the gestation of a viable child. (See *Protracted Gestation.*)

Voight [a] is accredited with having seen a **triple uterus,** and there are several older parallels on record. Thilow mentions a uterus which was divided into three small portions.

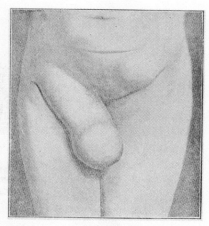

Fig. 153.—Inguinal hernia containing a gravid womb (Winckel).

Of the different **anomalous positions of the uterus,** most of which are acquired, the only one that will be mentioned is that of complete prolapse of the uterus (Fig. 152). In this instance the organ may hang entirely out of the body and even forbid locomotion.

Of 19 cases of **hernia of the uterus** quoted by Debierre 13 have been observed in the inguinal region (Fig. 153), five on the right and seven on the left side. In the case of Roux in 1891 the hernia existed on both sides. The uterus has been found twice only in crural hernia and three times in umbilical hernia. There is one case recorded, according to Debierre, in which the uterus was one of the constituents of an obturator hernia. Sometimes its appendages are found with it. Döring, Lédesma, Rektorzick, and Scazoni have found the uterus in the sac of an inguinal hernia; Léotaud, Murray, and Hagner in an umbilical hernia. The accompanying illustration (Fig. 154) represents hernia of the gravid womb through the linea alba.

a 503, iii., 175.

Absence of the penis is an extremely rare anomaly, although it has been noted by Schenck,[a] Borellus, Bouteiller, Nélaton, and others. Fortunatus Fidelis [b] and Révolat describe a newly born child with absence of external genitals, with spina bifida and umbilical hernia. Nélaton [c] describes a child of two entirely without a penis, but both testicles were found in the scrotum; the boy urinated by the rectum. Ashby and Wright [d] mention complete absence of the penis, the urethra opening at the margin of the anus outside the external sphincter; the scrotum and testicles were well developed. Murphy [e] gives the description of a well-formed infant apparently without a penis; the child passed urine through an opening in the lower part of the abdomen just above the ordinary location of the penis; the scrotum was present. Incisions were made into a small swelling just below the urinary

Fig. 154.—Hernia of the gravid womb through the linea alba.

opening in the abdomen which brought into view the penis, the glans being normal but the body very small. The treatment consisted of pressing out the glans daily until the wound healed; the penis receded spontaneously. It is stated that the organ would doubtless be equal to any requirements demanded of it. Demarquay quotes a somewhat similar case in an infant, but it had no urinary opening until after operation.

Among the older writers speaking of deficient or absent penis are Bartholinus,[190] Bauhinus, Cattierus, the Ephemerides, Frank, Panaroli,[617] van der Wiel, and others. Renauldin [f] describes a man with a small penis and enormous mammæ. Goschler,[g] quoted by Jacobson, speaks of a well-developed man of twenty-two, with abundant hair on his chin and suprapubi-

a 718, lib. iv., chap. 9.　　　b De relationibus medicorum, no. 357.　　　c 363, 1854
d "Dis. of Children," p. 53.　　e 224, 1885, ii., 62.　　f 565, tome i., p. 294.　　g 808, 1857

region and the scrotum apparently perfect, with median raphe; a careful search failed to show any trace of a penis; on the anterior wall of the rectum four lines above the anus was an orifice which gave vent to urine; the right testicle and cord were normal, but there was an acute orchitis in the left. Starting from just in front of the anal orifice was a fold of skin $1\frac{1}{2}$ inches long and $\frac{3}{4}$ inch high continuous with the raphe, which seemed to be formed of erectile tissue and which swelled under excitement, the enlargement lasting several minutes with usually an emission from the rectum. It was possible to pass a sound through the opening in the rectum to the bladder through a urethra $1\frac{1}{2}$ inches wide; the patient had control of the bladder and urinated from every three to five hours.

Many instances of **rudimentary development of the penis** have been recorded, most of them complicated with cryptorchism or other abnormality of the sexual organs. In other instances the organ is present, but the infantile type is present all through life; sometimes the subjects are weak in intellect and in a condition similar to cretinism. Kaufmann quotes a case in a weakly boy of twelve whose penis was but $\frac{3}{4}$ inch long, about as thick as a goose-quill, and feeling as limp as a mere tube of skin; the corpora cavernosa were not entirely absent, but ran only from the ischium to the junction of the fixed portion of the penis, suddenly terminating at this point. Nothing indicative of a prostate could be found. The testicles were at the entrance of the inguinal canal and the glans was only slightly developed.

Binet[a] speaks of a man of fifty-three whose external genitalia were of the size of those of a boy of nine. The penis was of about the size of the little finger, and contained on each side testicles not larger than a pea. There was no hair on the pubes or the face, giving the man the aspect of an old woman. The prostate was almost exterminated and the seminal vesicles were very primitive in conformation. Wilson was consulted by a gentleman of twenty-six as to his ability to perform the marital function. In size his penis and testicles hardly exceeded those of a boy of eight. He had never felt desire for sexual intercourse until he became acquainted with his intended wife, since when he had erections and nocturnal emissions. The patient married and became the father of a family; those parts which at twenty-six were so much smaller than usual had increased at twenty-eight to normal adult size. There are three cases on record in the older literature of penises extremely primitive in development. They are quoted by the Ephemerides, Plater,[635] Schenck,[b] and Zacchias. The result in these cases was impotency.

In the Army and Medical Museum at Washington are two injected specimens of the male organ divested of skin. From the meatus to the pubis they measure $6\frac{1}{2}$ and $5\frac{1}{2}$ inches; from the extremity to the termination of either crus $9\frac{3}{4}$ and $8\frac{3}{4}$ inches, and the circumferences are $4\frac{3}{4}$ and $4\frac{1}{4}$ inches. Between these two we can strike an average of the size of the normal penis.

a 242, 1883.   b 718, lib. iv., obs. 12.

In some instances the penis is so large as to forbid coitus and even inconvenience its possessor, measuring as much as ten or even more inches in length.
Extraordinary cases of large penis are reported by Albinus [114] (who mentions
it as a cause for sterility), Bartholinus,[189] Fabricius Hildanus, Paullini, Peyer,
Plater, Schurig, [a] Sinibaldus,[737] and Zacchias.   Several cases of enormous
penises in the new-born have been observed by Wolff [b] and others. [c]

The **pénis palmé,** or *suture de la verge* of the French, is the name given
to those examples of single cutaneous envelope for both the testicles and
penis ; the penis is adherent to the scrotum by its inferior face ; the glans only
is free and erection is impossible.   Chrétien cites an instance in a man of
twenty-five, and Schrumpf of Wesserling [d] describes an example of this rare
anomaly.   The penis and testes were inclosed in a common sac, a slight projection not over ¼ inch long being seen from the upper part of this curious
scrotum.   When the child was a year old a plastic operation was performed
on this anomalous member with a very satisfactory result.   Petit describes
an instance in which the penis was slightly fused with the scrotum.

There are many varieties of **torsion of the penis.**   The glans itself may
be inclined laterally, the curvature may be total, or there may be a veritable
rotation, bringing the inferior face above and the superior face below.   Gay [e]
describes a child with epispadias whose penis had undergone such torsion on
its axis that its inferior surface looked upward to the left, and the child
passed urine toward the left shoulder.   Follin [f] mentions a similar instance
in a boy of twelve with complete epispadias, and Verneuil and Guerlin
also record cases, both complicated with associate maldevelopment.   Caddy [g]
mentions a youth of eighteen who had congenital torsion of the penis without hypospadias or epispadias.   There was a complete half-turn to the left, so
that the slit-like urinary meatus was reversed and the frenum was above.
Among the older writers who describe incurvation or torsion of the penis
are Arantius,[h] the Ephemerides, Haenel,[401] Petit, [i] Schurig, Tulpius,[j] and
Zacchias.[830]

Zacutus Lusitanus [k] speaks of torsion of the penis from freezing.   Paullini [l] mentions a case the result of masturbation, and Hunter [m] speaks of
torsion of the penis associated with arthritis.

Ossification of the Penis.—MacClellan [n] speaks of a man of fifty-two
whose penis was curved and distorted in such a manner that urine could not
be passed without pain and coitus was impossible.   A bony mass was discovered in the septum between the corpora cavernosa ; this was dissected out
with much hemorrhage and the upward curvature was removed, but there

a "Spermatologia," p. 109.   b "Lect. Memorab.," tome i., p. 34.
c "Mémoires concernant les Arts," 1672, 27.   d 369, 1882.   e 779, xvi., 189.
f 789, 1862.   g 476, Sept. 15, 1894.   h 718, L. iv., no. 14.
i 625, Supplement.   j 842, L. iii., no. 39.   k 831, L. iii., obs. 118.
l 620, cent. iv., obs. 92.   m "References on Venereal Diseases," etc.
n Nouveau Journal des Sciences Médicales, March, 1878.

resulted a slight inclination in the opposite direction. The formation of bone and cartilage in the penis is quite rare. Velpeau, Kauffmann, Lenhoseck, and Duploy are quoted by Jacobson as having seen this anomaly. There is an excellent preparation in Vienna figured by Demarquay, but no description is given. The Ephemerides and Paullini [a] describe osseous penises.

The complete **absence of the frenum and prepuce** has been observed in animals but is very rare in man. The incomplete or irregular development is more frequent, but most common is excessive development of the prepuce, constituting phimosis, when there is abnormal adherence with the glans. Instances of phimosis, being quite common, will be passed without special mention. Deficient or absent prepuce has been observed by Blasius,[214] Marcellus Donatus,[306] and Gilibert. Partial deficiency is described by Petit, Severinus, and others.

There may be imperforation or congenital occlusion of some portion of **the urethra,** causing enormous accumulation of urine in the bladder, but fortunately there is generally in such cases some anomalous opening of the urethra giving vent to the excretions. Tulpius [b] mentions a case of deficient urethra. In the Ephemerides there is an account of a man who had a constant flow of semen from an abnormal opening in the abdomen. La Peyronia [c] describes a case of impotence due to ejaculation of the spermatic ducts into the bladder instead of into the urethra, but remarks that there was a cicatrix of a wound of the neighboring parts. There are a number of instances in which the urethra has terminated in the rectum. Congenital dilatation of the urethral canal is very rare, and generally accompanied by other malformation.

Duplication of the urethra or the existence of two permeable canals is not accepted by all the authors, some of whom contend that one of the canals either terminates in a culdesac or is not separate in itself. Verneuil has published an article clearly exposing a number of cases, showing that it is possible for the urethra to have two or more canals which are distinct and have separate functions. Fabricius Hildanus [d] speaks of a double aperture to the urethra; Marcellus Donatus [e] describes duplicity of the urethra, one of the apertures being in the testicle; and there is another case on record [f] in which there was a urethral aperture in the groin. A case of double urethra in a man of twenty-five living in Styria [g] who was under treatment for gonorrhea is described, the supernumerary urethra opening above the natural one and receiving a sound to the depth of 17 cm. There was purulent gonorrhea in both urethræ. Vesalius [h] has an account of a double urethral aperture, one of which was supposed to give spermatic fluid and the other urine. Borellus, Testa, and Cruveilhier have reported similar instances. Instances of **double penis** have been discussed under the head of diphallic terata, page 194.

[a] 620, cent. i, obs. 72.   [b] 842, L. xliv., cap. 36.   [c] 563, i., 427.
[d] 334, cent. i., obs. 76.   [e] 306, L. vi., c. ii., 619.   [f] 524, vol. ii., 440.
[g] 536, 1887, vol. ii.   [h] 804, L. v., c. 18.

Hypospadias and epispadias (Fig. 155) are names given to malformations of the urethra in which the wall of the canal is deficient either above or below.   These anomalies are particularly interesting, as they are nearly always found in male hermaphrodites, the fissure giving the appearance of a vulva, as the scrotum is sometimes included, and even the perineum may be fissured in continuity with the other parts, thus exaggerating the deception. There seems to be an element of heredity in this malformation, and this allegation is exemplified by Sedgwick, who quotes a case from Heuremann in which a family of females had for generations given birth to males with hypospadias.   Belloc [a] mentions a man whose urethra terminated at the base of the frenum who had four sons with the same deformity.   Picardat [b] men-

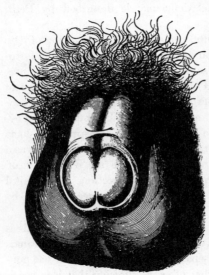

Fig. 155.—Complete epispadias.

tions a father and son, both of whom had double urethral orifices, one above the other, from one of which issued urine and from the other semen— a fact that shows the possibility of inheritance of this malformation. Patients in whom the urethra opens at the root of the penis, the meatus being imperforate, are not necessarily impotent ; as, for instance, Fournier [c] knew of a man whose urethra opened posteriorly who was the father of four children.   Fournier supposed that the semen ejaculated vigorously and followed the fissure on the back of the penis to the uterus, the membrane of the vagina supplanting the deficient wall of the urethra.   The penis was short, but about as thick as ordinary.

Gray [d] mentions a curious case in a man afflicted with hypospadias who, suffering with delusions, was confined in the insane asylum at Utica.   When he determined to get married, fully appreciating his physical defect, he resolved to imitate nature, and being of a very ingenious turn of mind, he busied himself with the construction of an **artificial penis**.   While so engaged he had seized every opportunity to study the conformation of this organ, and finally prepared a body formed of cotton, six inches in length, and shaped like a penis, minus a prepuce.   He sheathed it in pig's gut and gave it a slight vermilion hue.   To the touch it felt elastic, and its shape was maintained by a piece of gutta-percha tubing, around which the cotton was firmly wound.   It was fastened to the waist-band by means of straps, a central and an upper one being so arranged that the penis could be thrown into

a 302, xxiv.   b Thesé de Paris, 1858, No. 91.   c 302, iv., 162.   d 773, 1870 an erect position and so maintained. He had constructed a flesh-colored covering which completely concealed the straps. With this artificial member he was enabled to deceive his wife for fifteen months, and was only discovered when she undressed him while he was in a state of intoxication. To further the deception he had told his wife immediately after their marriage that it was quite indecent for a husband to undress in the presence of his wife, and therefore she had always retired first and turned out the light. Partly from fear that his virile power would be questioned and partly from ignorance, the duration of actual coitus would approach an hour. When the discovery was made, his wife hid the instrument with which he had perpetrated a most successful fraud upon her, and the patient subsequently attempted coitus by contact with unsuccessful results, although both parties had incomplete orgasms. Shortly afterward evidences of mental derangement appeared and the man became the subject of exalted delusions. His wife, at the time of report, had filed application for divorce. Haslam [a] reports a case in which loss of the penis was compensated for by the use of an ivory succedaneum. Parallel instances of this kind have been recorded by Ammann [b] and Jonston.[c]

Entire **absence of the male sexual apparatus** is extremely rare, but Blondin and Velpeau have reported cases.

Complete absence of the testicles, or anorchism, is a comparatively rare anomaly, and it is very difficult to distinguish between anorchism and arrest of development, or simple atrophy, which is much more common. Fisher of Boston [d] describes the case of a man of forty-five, who died of pneumonia. From the age of puberty to twenty-five, and even to the day of death, his voice had never changed and his manners were decidedly effeminate. He always sang soprano in concert with females. After the age of twenty-five, however, his voice became more grave and he could not accompany females with such ease. He had no beard, had never shaved, and had never exhibited amorous propensities or desire for female society. When about twenty-one he became associated with a gay company of men and was addicted to the cup, but would never visit houses of ill-fame. On dissection no trace of testicles could be found; the scrotum was soft and flabby. The cerebellum was the exact size of that of a female child.

Individuals with one testicle are called **monorchids,** and may be divided into three varieties :—

(1) A solitary testicle divided in the middle by a deep fissure, the two lobes being each provided with a spermatic cord on the same side as the lobe.

(2) Testicles of the same origin, but with coalescence more general.

(3) A single testicle and two cords.

Gruber of St. Petersburg [e] held a postmortem on a man in January,

[a] 476, 1828, ii., 182.   [b] "Irenicum Numæ," p. 133.   [c] 445, p 406.
[d] 124, Feb., 1839.   [e] 553, Heft i., 1868.

1867, in whom the right half of the scrotum, the right testicle, epididymis, and the scrotal and inguinal parts of the right vas deferens were absent. Gruber examined the literature for thirty years up to the time of his report, and found 30 recorded postmortem examinations in which there was absence of the testicle, and in eight of these both testicles were missing. As a rule, natural eunuchs have feeble bodies, are mentally dull, and live only a short time. The penis is ordinarily defective and there is sometimes another associate malformation. They are not always disinclined toward the opposite sex.

Polyorchids are persons who have more than two testicles. For a long time the abnormality was not believed to exist, and some of the observers denied the proof by postmortem examination of any of the cases so diagnosed, but there is at present no doubt of the fact,—three, four, and five testicles having been found at autopsies. Russell, one of the older writers on the testicle, mentions a monk who was a triorchid, and was so salacious that his indomitable passion prevented him from keeping his vows of chastity. The amorous propensities and generative faculties of polyorchids have always been supposed greater than ordinary. Russell reports another case of a man with a similar peculiarity, who was prescribed a concubine as a reasonable allowance to a man thus endowed.

Morgagni and Meckel say that they never discovered a third testicle in dissections of reputed triorchids, and though Haller [a] has collected records of a great number of triorchids, he has never been able to verify the presence of the third testicle on dissection. Some authors, including Haller, have demonstrated heredity in examples of polyorchism. There is an old instance [b] in which two testicles, one above the other, were found on the right side and one on the left. Macann [c] describes a recruit of twenty, whose scrotum seemed to be much larger on the right than on the left side, although it was not pendulous. On dissection a right and left testicle were found in their normal positions, but situated on the right side between the groin and the normal testicle was a supernumerary organ, not in contact, and having a separate and short cord. Prankard [d] also describes a man with three testicles. Three cases of triorchidism were found in recruits in the British Army.[e] Lane [f] reports a supernumerary testis found in the right half of the scrotum of a boy of fifteen. In a necropsy held on a man killed in battle, Hohlberg [g] discovered three fully developed testicles, two on the right side placed one above the other. The London Medical Record of 1884 quotes Jdanoff of St. Petersburg in mentioning a soldier of twenty-one who had a supernumerary testicle erroneously diagnosed as inguinal hernia. Quoted by the same reference, Bulatoff mentions a soldier who had a third testicle, which diagnosis was confirmed by several of his confrères. They recommended dismissal of the man from the service, as the third testicle, usually resting in some portion of the inguinal canal, caused extra exposure to traumatic influence.

a 400, L. xxvii., 412.   b 504, xviii., 362.   c 656, 1842.   d 654, 1842.
e 476, 1865, ii., 501.   f 224, Dec. 1, 1894.   g 812, 1882, 38, 642.

Venette[a] gives an instance of four testicles, and Scharff, in the Ephemerides, mentions five; Blasius[214] mentions more than three testicles, and, without citing proof, Buffon admits the possibility of such occurrence and adds that such men are generally more vigorous.

Russell[b] mentions four, five, and even six testicles in one individual; all were not verified on dissection. He cites an instance of six testicles, four of which were of usual size and two smaller than ordinary.

Baillie, the Ephemerides, and Schurig mention **fusion of the testicles,** or synorchidism, somewhat after the manner of the normal disposition of the batrachians and also the kangaroos, in the former of which the fusion is abdominal and in the latter scrotal. Kerckring[c] has a description of an individual in whom the scrotum was absent.

In those cases in which the testicles are still in the abdominal cavity the individuals are termed **cryptorchids.** Johnson[d] has collected the results of postmortem examinations of 89 supposed cryptorchids. In eight of this number no testicles were found postmortem, the number found in the abdomen was uncertain, but in 18 instances both testicles were found in the inguinal canal, and in eight only one was found in the inguinal canal, the other not appearing. The number in which the semen was examined microscopically was 16, and in three spermatozoa were found in the semen; one case was dubious, spermatozoa being found two weeks afterward on a boy's shirt. The number having children was ten. In one case a monorchid generated a cryptorchid child. Some of the cryptorchids were effeminate, although others were manly with good evidences of a beard. The morbid, hypochondriac, the voluptuous, and the imbecile all found a place in Johnson's statistics; and although there are evidences of the possession of the generative function, still, we are compelled to say that the chances are against fecundity of human cryptorchids. In this connection might be quoted the curious case mentioned by Geoffroy-Saint-Hilaire, of a soldier who was hung for rape. It was alleged that no traces of testicles were found externally or internally, yet semen containing spermatozoa was found in the seminal vesicles. Spermatozoa have been found days and weeks after castration, and the individuals during this period were capable of impregnation, but in these cases the reservoirs were not empty, although the spring had ceased to flow. Beigel, in Virchow's Archives, mentions a cryptorchid of twenty-two who had nocturnal emissions containing spermatozoa and who indulged in sexual congress. Partridge[e] describes a man of twenty-four who, notwithstanding his condition, gave evidences of virile seminal flow.

In some cases there is **anomalous position of the testicle.** Hough[f] mentions an instance in which, from the great pain and sudden appearance, a small tumor lying against the right pubic bone was supposed to be a strangu-

a 215, an. ii., 38.   b " Obs. on Testicles," Edinburgh, 1833.   c 473, obs. xii.
d 775, 1884.   e 476, 1860, i., 66.   f 545, 1884.

lated hernia. There were two well-developed testicles in the scrotum, and the hernia proved to be a third. McElmail [a] describes a soldier of twenty-nine, who two or three months before examination felt a pricking and slight burning pain near the internal aperture of the internal inguinal canal, succeeded by a swelling until the tumor passed into the scrotum. It was found in the upper part of the scrotum above the original testicle, but not in contact, and was about half the size of the normal testicle; its cord and epididymis could be distinctly felt and caused the same sensation as pressure on the other testicle did.

Marshall [b] mentions a boy of sixteen in whom the right half of the scrotum was empty, although the left was of normal size and contained a testicle. On close examination another testicle was found in the perineum; the boy said that while running he fell down, four years before, and on getting up suffered great pain in the groin and this pain recurred after exertion. This testicle was removed successfully to the scrotum. Horsley collected 20 instances of operators who made a similar attempt, Annandale being the first one; his success was likely due to antisepsis, as previously the testicles had always sloughed. There is a record of a dog remarkable for its salacity who had two testicles in the scrotum and one in the abdomen; some of the older authors often indulged in playful humor on this subject.

Brown [c] describes a child with a swelling in the perineum both painful and elastic to the touch. The child cried if pressure was applied to the tumor and there was every evidence that the tumor was a testicle. Hutcheson, quoted by Russell,[d] has given a curious case in an English seaman who, as was the custom at that time, was impressed into service by H. M. S. Druid in 1807 from a trading ship off the coast of Africa. The man said he had been examined by dozens of ship-surgeons, but was invariably rejected on account of rupture in both groins. The scrotum was found to be an empty bag, and close examination showed that the testicles occupied the seats of the supposed rupture. As soon as the discovery was made the man became unnerved and agitated, and on re-examining the parts the testicles were found in the scrotum. When he found that there was no chance for escape he acknowledged that he was an impostor and gave an exhibition in which, with incredible facility, he pulled both testes up from the bottom of the scrotum to the external abdominal ring. At the word of command he could pull up one testicle, then another, and let them drop simultaneously; he performed other like feats so rapidly that the movements could not be distinguished.

In this connection Russell speaks of a man whose testicle was elevated every time the east wind blew, which caused him a sense of languor and re-

a 523, 1856, ix., 91.   b 548, 1883.
c 436, 1891, ii., 546.   d "Obs. on Testicles." Edinb., 1833.

laxation ; the same author describes a man whose testicles ascended into the inguinal canal every time he was in the company of women.

Inversion of the testicle is of several varieties and quite rare ; it has been recognized by Sir Astley Cooper, Boyer, Maisonneuve, Royet, and other writers.

The anomalies of the vas deferens and **seminal vesicles** are of little interest and will be passed with mention of the case of Weber,[a] who found the seminal vesicles double ; a similar conformation has been seen in hermaphrodites.

[a] 559, May, 1811, 88.

CHAPTER VII.

ANOMALIES OF STATURE, SIZE, AND DEVELOPMENT.

Giants.—The fables of mythology contain accounts of horrible monsters, terrible in ferocity, whose mission was the destruction of the life of the individuals unfortunate enough to come into their domains. The ogres known as the Cyclops, and the fierce anthropophages, called Lestrygons, of Sicily, who were neighbors of the Cyclops, are pictured in detail in the "Odyssey" of Homer. Nearly all the nations of the earth have their fairy tales or superstitions of monstrous beings inhabiting some forest, mountain, or cave; and pages have been written in the heroic poems of all languages describing battles between these monsters and men with superhuman courage, in which the giant finally succumbs.

The word giant is derived indirectly from the old English word "geant," which in its turn came from the French of the conquering Normans. It is of Greek derivation, "γίγας"—or the Latin, "gigas." The Hebrew parallel is "nophel," or plural, "nephilim."

Ancient Giants.—We are told in the Bible[a] that the bedstead of Og, King of Basham, was 9 cubits long, which in English measure is 16½ feet. Goliath of Gath, who was slain by David, stood 6 cubits and a span tall—about 11 feet. The body of Orestes, according to the Greeks, was 11½ feet long. The mythical Titans, 45 in number, were a race of Giants who warred against the Gods, and their descendants were the Gigantes. The height attributed to these creatures was fabulous, and they were supposed to heap up mountains to scale the sky and to help them to wage their battles. Hercules, a man of incredible strength, but who is said to have been not over 7 feet high, was dispatched against the Gigantes.

Pliny describes Gabbaras, who was brought to Rome by Claudius Cæsar from Arabia and was between 9 and 10 feet in height, and adds that the remains of Posio and Secundilla, found in the reign of Augustus Cæsar in the Sallustian Gardens, of which they were supposed to be the guardians, measured 10 feet 3 inches each. In common with Augustine, Pliny believed that the stature of man has degenerated, but from the remains of the ancients so far discovered it would appear that the modern stature is about the same as

a Deuteronomy iii., 11.

324

the ancient. The beautiful alabaster sarcophagus discovered near Thebes in 1817 and now in Sir John Soane's Museum in Lincoln's Inn Fields in London measures 9 feet 4 inches long. This unique example, the finest extant, is well worth inspection by visitors in London.

Herodotus says the shoes of Perseus measured an equivalent of about 3 feet, English standard. Josephus tells of Eleazar, a Jew, among the hostages sent by the King of Persia to Rome, who was nearly 11 feet high. Saxo, the grammarian, mentions a giant 13½ feet high and says he had 12 companions who were double his height. Ferragus, the monster supposed to have been slain by Roland, the nephew of Charlemagne, was said to have been nearly 11 feet high. It was said that there was a giant living in the twelfth century under the rule of King Eugene II. of Scotland who was 11½ feet high.

There are fabulous stories told of the Emperor Maximilian. Some accounts say that he was between 8½ and 9 feet high, and used his wife's bracelet for a finger-ring, and that he ate 40 pounds of flesh a day and drank six gallons of wine. He was also accredited with being a great runner, and in his earlier days was said to have conquered single-handed eight soldiers. The Emperors Charlemagne and Jovianus were also accredited with great height and strength.

In the olden times there were extraordinary stories of the giants who lived in Patagonia. Some say that Magellan gave the name to this country because its inhabitants measured 5 cubits. The naturalist Turner says that on the river Plata near the Brazilian coast he saw naked savages 12 feet high; and in his description of America, Thévenot confirms this by saying that on the coast of Africa he saw on a boat the skeleton of an American giant who had died in 1559, and who was 11 feet 5 inches in height. He claims to have measured the bones himself. He says that the bones of the leg measured 3 feet 4 inches, and the skull was 3 feet and 1 inch, just about the size of the skull of Borghini, who, however, was only of ordinary height. In his account of a voyage to the Straits of Magellan, Jacob Lemaire says that on December 17, 1615, he found at Port Desire several graves covered with stones, and beneath the stones were skeletons of men which measured between 10 and 11 feet. The ancient idea of the Spaniards was that the men of Patagonia were so tall that the Spanish soldiers could pass under their arms held out straight; yet we know that the Patagonians exhibit no exaggeration of height—in fact, some of the inhabitants about Terra del Fuego are rather diminutive. This superstition of the voyagers was not limited to America; there were accounts of men in the neighborhood of the Peak of Teneriffe who had 80 teeth in their head and bodies 15 feet in height.

Discoveries of " Giants' Bones."—Riolan,[685] the celebrated anatomist, says that there was to be seen at one time in the suburbs of Saint Germain the tomb of the giant Isoret, who was reputed to be 20 feet tall; and that in

1509, in digging ditches at Rouen, near the Dominicans, they found a stone tomb containing a monstrous skeleton, the skull of which would hold a bushel of corn ; the shin-bone measured about 4 feet, which, taken as a guide, would make his height over 17 feet. On the tomb was a copper plate which said that the tomb contained the remains of "the noble and puissant lord, the Chevalier Riçon de Vallemont." Plater,[635] the famous physician, declares that he saw at Lucerne the true human bones of a subject that must have been at least 19 feet high.

Valence in Dauphiné boasted of possessing the bones of the giant Bucart, the tyrant of the Vivarias, who was slain by his vassal, Count de Cabillon. The Dominicans had the shin-bone and part of the knee-articulation, which, substantiated by the frescoes and inscriptions in their possession, showed him to be 22½ feet high. They claimed to have an os frontis in the medical school of Leyden measuring $9.1 \times 12.2 \times .5$ inches, which they deduce must have belonged to a man 11 or 12 feet high.

It is said that while digging in France in 1613 there was disinterred the body of a giant bearing the title "Theutobochus Rex," and that the skeleton measured 25 feet long, 10 feet across the shoulders, and 5 feet from breast to back. The shin-bone was about 4 feet long, and the teeth as large as those of oxen. This is likely another version of the finding of the remains of Bucart.

Near Mezarino in Sicily in 1516 there was found the skeleton of a giant whose height was at least 30 feet ; his head was the size of a hogshead, and each tooth weighed 5 ounces ; and in 1548 and in 1550 there were others found of the height of 30 feet. The Athenians found near their city skeletons measuring 34 and 36 feet in height. In Bohemia in 758 it is recorded that there was found a human skeleton 26 feet tall, and the leg-bones are still kept in a medieval castle in that country. In September, 1691, there was the skull of a giant found in Macedonia which held 210 pounds of corn.

General Opinions.—All the accounts of giants originating in the finding of monstrous bones must of course be discredited, as the remains were likely those of some animal. Comparative anatomy has only lately obtained a hold in the public mind, and in the Middle Ages little was known of it. The pretended giants' remains have been those of mastodons, elephants, and other animals. From Suetonius we learn that Augustus Cæsar pleased himself by adorning his palaces with so-called giants' bones of incredible size, preferring these to pictures or images. From their enormous size we must believe they were mastodon bones, as no contemporary animals show such measurements. Bartholinus [a] describes a large tooth for many years exhibited as the canine of a giant which proved to be nothing but a tooth of a spermaceti whale (Cetus dentatus), quite a common fish. Hand [b] described an alleged giant's skeleton shown in London early in the eighteenth century,

a 190, cent. i., hist. 98.   b 629, No. 168.

and which was composed of the bones of the fore-fin of a small whale or of a porpoise.

The celebrated Sir Hans Sloane, who treated this subject very learnedly, arrived at the conclusion that while in most instances the bones found were those of mastodons, elephants, whales, etc., in some instances accounts were given by connoisseurs who could not readily be deceived. However, modern scientists will be loath to believe that any men ever existed who measured over 9 feet; in fact, such cases with authentic references are extremely rare. Quetelet considers that the tallest man whose stature is authentically recorded was the " Scottish Giant " of Frederick the Great's regiment of giants. This person was not quite 8 feet 3 inches tall. Buffon, ordinarily a reliable authority, comes to a loose conclusion that there is no doubt that men have lived who were 10, 12, and even 15 feet tall ; but modern statisticians cannot accept this deduction from the references offered.

From the original estimation of the height of Adam (Henrion once calculated that Adam's height was 123 feet and that of Eve 118) we gradually come to 10 feet, which seemed to be about the favorite height for giants in the Middle Ages. Approaching this century, we still have stories of men from 9 to 10 feet high, but no authentic cases. It was only in the latter part of the last century that we began to have absolutely authentic heights of giants, and to-day the men showing through the country as measuring 8 feet generally exaggerate their height several inches, and exact measurement would show that but few men commonly called giants are over $7\frac{1}{2}$ feet or weigh over 350 pounds. Dana[a] says that the number of giants figuring as public characters since 1700 is not more than 100, and of these about 20 were advertised to be over 8 feet. If we confine ourselves to those accurately and scientifically measured the list is surprisingly small. Topinard measured the tallest man in the Austrian army and found that he was 8 feet $4\frac{1}{2}$ inches. The giant Winckelmeyer measured 8 feet 6 inches in height. Ranke measured Marianne Wehde, who was born in Germany in the present century, and found that she measured 8 feet $4\frac{1}{4}$ inches when only sixteen and a half years old.

In giants, as a rule, the great stature is due to excessive growth of the lower extremities, the size of the head and that of the trunk being nearly the same as those of a man or boy of the same age. On the other hand, in a natural dwarf the proportions are fairly uniform, the head, however, being always larger in proportion to the body, just as we find in infants. Indeed, the proportions of " General Tom Thumb " were those of an ordinary infant of from thirteen to fifteen months old.

Figure 156 shows a portrait of two well-known exhibitionists of about the same age, and illustrates the possible extremes of anomalies in stature.

Recently, the **association of acromegaly with gigantism** has been

[a] 723, Feb., 1895.

noticed, and in these instances there seems to be an acquired uniform enlargement of all the bones of the body. Brissaud and Meige[a] describe the case of a male of forty-seven who presented nothing unusual before the age of sixteen, when he began to grow larger, until, having reached his majority, he measured 7 feet 2 inches in height and weighed about 340 pounds. He remained well and very strong until the age of thirty-seven, when he overlifted, and following this he developed an extreme deformity of the spine and trunk, the latter " telescoping into itself " until the nipples were on a level with the anterior superior spines of the ilium. For two years he suffered with debility, fatigue, bronchitis, night-sweats, headache, and great thirst. Mentally he was dull ; the bones of the face and extremities showed the hypertrophies characteristic of acromegaly, the soft parts not being involved. The circumference of the trunk at the nipples was 62 inches, and over the most prominent portion of the kyphosis and pigeon-breast, 74 inches. The authors agree with Dana and others that there is an intimate relation between acromegaly and gigantism, but they go further and compare both to the growth of the body. They call attention to the strik-

Fig. 156.—Giantess and dwarf of the same age.

ing resemblance to acromegaly of the disproportionate growth of the boy at adolescence, which corresponds so well to Marie's terse description of this disease : " The disease manifests itself by preference in the bones of the extremities and in the extremities of the bones," and conclude with this rather striking and aphoristic proposition : " Acromegaly is gigantism of the adult ; gigantism is acromegaly of adolescence."

The many theories of the cause of gigantism will not be discussed here, the reader being referred to volumes exclusively devoted to this subject.

Celebrated Giants.—Mention of some of the most famous giants will be made, together with any associate points of interest.

a Jour. de Méd. et de Chir. prat., Jan. 25, 1895.

Becanus, physician to Charles V., says that he saw a youth 9 feet high and a man and a woman almost 10 feet. Ainsworth says that in 1553 the Tower of London was guarded by three brothers claiming direct descent from Henry VIII., and surnamed Og, Gog, and Magog, all of whom were over 8 feet in height. In his "Chronicles of Holland" in 1557 Hadrianus Barlandus said that in the time of John, Earl of Holland, the giant Nicholas was so large that men could stand under his arms, and his shoe held 3 ordinary feet. Among the yeoman of the guard of John Frederick, Duke of Hanover, there was one Christopher Munster, 8½ feet high, who died in 1676 in his forty-fifth year. The giant porter of the Duke of Würtemberg was 7½ feet high. "Big Sam," the porter at Carleton Palace, when George IV. was Prince of Wales, was 8 feet high. The porter of Queen Elizabeth, of whom there is a picture in Hampton Court, painted by Zucchero, was 7½ feet high ; and Walter Parson, porter to James I., was about the same height. William Evans, who served Charles I., was nearly 8 feet ; he carried a dwarf in his pocket.

In the seventeenth century, in order to gratify the Empress of Austria, Guy-Patin made a congress of all the giants and dwarfs in the Germanic Empire. A peculiarity of this congress was that the giants complained to the authorities that the dwarfs teased them in such a manner as to make their lives miserable.

Plater speaks of a girl in Basle, Switzerland, five years old, whose body was as large as that of a full-grown woman and who weighed when a year old as much as a bushel of wheat. He also mentions a man living in 1613, 9 feet high, whose hand was 1 foot 6 inches long. Peter van den Broecke speaks of a Congo negro in 1640 who was 8 feet high. Daniel, the porter of Cromwell, was 7 feet 6 inches high ; he became a lunatic.

Frazier speaks of Chilian giants 9 feet tall. There is a chronicle which says one of the Kings of Norway was 8 feet high. Merula says that in 1538 he saw in France a Flemish man over 9 feet. Keysler mentions seeing Hans Brau in Tyrol in 1550, and says that he was nearly 12 feet high.

Jonston [447] mentions a lad in Holland who was 8 feet tall. Pasumot [a] mentions a giant of 8 feet.

Edmund Mallone was said to have measured 7 feet 7 inches. Wierski, a Polander, presented to Maximilian II., was 8 feet high. At the age of thirty-two there died in 1798 a clerk of the Bank of England who was said to have been nearly 7½ feet high. The Daily Advertiser for February 23, 1745, says that there was a young colossus exhibited opposite the Mansion House in London who was 7 feet high, although but fifteen years old. In the same paper on January 31, 1753, is an account of MacGrath, whose skeleton is still preserved in Dublin. In the reign of George I., during the time of the Bartholomew Fair at Smithfield, there was exhibited an Englishman seventeen years old who was 8 feet tall.

[a] " Voyages physiques dans les Pyrénées."

Nicephorus tells of Antonius of Syria, in the reign of Theodosius, who died at the age of twenty-five with a height of 7 feet 7 inches. Artacæcas, in great favor with Xerxes, was the tallest Persian and measured 7 feet. John Middleton, born in 1752 at Hale, Lancashire, humorously called the "Child of Hale," and whose portrait is in Brasenose College, Oxford, measured 9 feet 3 inches tall. In his "History of Ripton," in Devonshire, 1854, Bigsby gives an account of a discovery in 1687 of a skeleton 9 feet long. In 1712 in a village in Holland there died a fisherman named Gerrit Bastiaansen who was 8 feet high and weighed 500

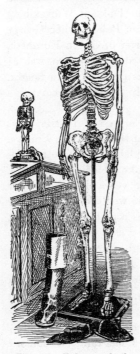

pounds. During Queen Anne's reign there was shown in London and other parts of England a most peculiar anomaly—a German giantess without hands or feet who threaded a needle, cut gloves, etc. About 1821 there was issued an engraving of Miss Angelina Melius, nineteen years of age and 7 feet high, attended by her page, Señor Don Santiago de los Santos, from the Island of Manilla, thirty-five years old and 2 feet 2 inches high. "The Annual Register" records the death of Peter Tuchan at Posen on June 18, 1825, of dropsy of the chest. He was twenty-nine years old and 8 feet 7 inches in height; he began to grow at the age of seven. This monster had no beard; his voice was soft; he was a moderate eater. There was a giant exhibited in St. Petersburg, June, 1829, 8 feet 8 inches in height, who was very thin and emaciated.

Dr. Adam Clarke, who died in 1832, measured a man 8 feet 6 inches tall. Frank Buckland, in his "Curiosities of Natural History," says that Brice, the French giant, was 7 feet 7 inches. Early in

Fig. 157.—Skeleton of the "Irish Giant" in the Royal College of Surgeons, London.

1837 there was exhibited at Parma a young man formerly in the service of the King of the Netherlands who was 8 feet 10 inches high and weighed 401 pounds. Robert Hale, the "Norfolk Giant," who died in Yarmouth in 1843 at the age of forty-three, was 7 feet 6 inches high and weighed 452 pounds. The skeleton of Cornelius McGrath, now preserved in the Trinity College Museum, Dublin, is a striking example of gigantism. At sixteen years he measured 7 feet 10 inches.

O'Brien or Byrne, **the Irish giant**, was supposed to be 8 feet 4 inches in height at the time of his death in 1783 at the age of twenty-two. The story of his connection with the illustrious John Hunter is quite interesting. Hunter had vowed that he would have the skeleton of O'Brien, and O'Brien was equally averse to being boiled in the distinguished scientist's kettle. The giant was tormented all his life by the constant assertions of Hunter and by his persistence in locating him. Finally, when, following the usual early decline of his class of anomalies, O'Brien came to his death-bed, he bribed some fishermen to take his body after his death to the middle of the Irish Channel and sink it with leaden weights. Hunter, it is alleged, was informed of this and overbribed the prospective undertakers and thus secured the body. It has been estimated that it cost Hunter nearly 500 pounds sterling to gain possession of the skeleton of the "Irish Giant." The kettle in which the body was boiled, together with some interesting literature relative to the circumstances, are preserved in the Museum of the Royal College of Surgeons in London, and were exhibited at the meeting of the British Medical Association in 1895 with other Hunterian relics. The skeleton, which is now one of the features of the Museum, is reported to measure 92¾ inches in height, and is mounted alongside that of Caroline Crachami, the Sicilian dwarf, who was exhibited as an Italian princess in London in 1824. She did not grow after birth and died at the age of nine (Fig. 157).

Fig. 158.—Ben Hicks.

Patrick Cotter, the successor of O'Brien, and who for awhile exhibited under this name, claiming that he was a lineal descendant of the famous Irish King, Brian Boru, who he declared was 9 feet in height, was born in 1761, and died in 1806 at the age of forty-five. His shoe was 17 inches long, and he was 8 feet 4 inches tall at his death.

In the Museum of Madame Tussaud in London there is a wax figure of Loushkin, said to be the tallest man of his time. It measures 8 feet 5 inches, and is dressed in the military uniform of a drum-major of the Imperial Preobrajensky Regiment of Guards. To magnify his height there is a figure of the celebrated dwarf, "General Tom Thumb," in the palm of his hand. Figure 158 represents a well-known American giant, Ben Hicks, who was called "the Denver Steeple."

Buffon refers to a Swedish giantess who he affirms was 8 feet 6 inches tall. Chang, the "Chinese Giant," whose smiling face is familiar to nearly all the modern world, was said to be 8 feet tall. In 1865, at the age of nineteen, he measured 7 feet 8 inches. At Hawick, Scotland, in 1870, there was an Irishman 7 feet 8 inches in height, 52 inches around the chest, and who weighed 22 stone. Figure 159 shows an American giantess known as " Leah, the Giantess." At the age of nineteen she was 7 feet 2 inches tall and weighed 165 pounds.

On June 17, 1871, there were married at Saint-Martins-in-the-Field in London Captain Martin Van Buren Bates of Kentucky and Miss Anna

Fig. 159.—" Leah, the Giantess."

Swann of Nova Scotia, two celebrated exhibitionists, both of whom were over 7 feet. Captain Bates, familiarly known as the " Kentucky Giant," years ago was a familiar figure in many Northern cities, where he exhibited himself in company with his wife, the combined height of the two being greater than that of any couple known to history. Captain Bates was born in Whitesburg, Letcher County, Ky., on November 9, 1845. He enlisted in the Southern army in 1861, and though only sixteen years old was admitted to the service because of his size. At the close of the war Captain Bates had attained his great height of 7 feet 2½ inches. His body was well proportioned and his weight increased until it reached 450 pounds. He traveled as a curiosity from 1866 to 1880, being connected with various amusement organizations. He visited nearly all the large cities and towns in the United States, Canada, Great Britain, France, Spain, Germany, Switzerland, Austria, and Russia. While in England in 1871 the Captain met Miss Anna H. Swann, known as the " Nova Scotia Giantess," who was two years the junior of her giant lover. Miss Swann was justly proud of her height, 7 feet 5½ inches. The two were married soon afterward. Their combined height of 14 feet 8 inches marked them as the tallest married couple known to mankind.

Captain Bates' parents were of medium size. His father, a native of Virginia, was 5 feet 10 inches high and weighed 160 pounds. His mother was 5 feet 3 inches tall and weighed 125 pounds. The height of the father of Mrs. Anna Swann Bates was 6 feet and her mother was 5 feet and 2 inches high, weighing but 100 pounds.

A recent newspaper dispatch says: "Captain M. V. Bates, whose remarkable height at one time attracted the attention of the world, has recently retired from his conspicuous position and lives in comparative obscurity on his farm in Guilford, Medina County, O., half a mile east of Seville."

In 1845 there was shown in Paris Joachim Eleiceigui, the Spanish giant, who weighed 195 kilograms (429 pounds) and whose hands were 42 cm. (16½ inches) long and of great beauty. In 1882 at the Alhambra in London there was a giantess by the name of Miss Marian, called the "Queen of the Amazons," aged eighteen years, who measured 2.45 meters (96½ inches). William Campbell, a Scotchman, died at Newcastle in May, 1878. He was so large that the window of the room in which the deceased lay and the brick-work to the level of the floor had to be taken out, in order that the coffin might be lowered with block and tackle three stories to the ground. On January 27, 1887, a Greek, although a Turkish subject, recently died of phthisis in Simferopol. He was 7 feet 8 inches in height and slept on three beds laid close together.

Giants of History.—A number of persons of great height, particularly sovereigns and warriors, are well-known characters of history, viz., William of Scotland, Edward III., Godefroy of Bouillon, Philip the Long, Fairfax, Moncey, Mortier, Kléber; there are others celebrated in modern times. Rochester, the favorite of Charles II.; Pothier, the jurist; Bank, the English naturalist; Gall, Billat-Savarin, Benjamin Constant, the painter David, Bellart, the geographer Delamarche, and Care, the founder of the Gentleman's Magazine, were all men of extraordinary stature.

Dwarfs.—The word "dwarf" is of Saxon origin (dwerg, dweorg) and corresponds to the "pumilio" or "nanus" of the Romans. The Greeks believed in the **pygmy people** of Thrace and Pliny speaks of the Spithamiens. In the "Iliad" Homer writes of the pygmies and Juvenal also describes them; but the fantasies of these poets have given these creatures such diminutive stature that they have deprived the traditions of credence. Herodotus relates that in the deserts of Lybia there were people of extreme shortness of stature. The Bible [a] mentions that no dwarf can officiate at the altar. Aristotle and Philostratus speak of pygmy people descended from Pygmæus, son of Dorus. In the seventeenth century van Helmont supposed that there were pygmies in the Canary Islands, and Abyssinia, Brazil, and Japan in the older times were repeatedly said to contain pygmy races. Relics

[a] Lev. xxi., 20.

of what must have been a pygmy race have been found in the Hebrides, and in this country in Kentucky and Tennessee.

Dr. Schweinfurth, the distinguished African traveler, confirms the statements of Homer, Herodotus, and Aristotle that there was a race of pygmies near the source of the Nile. Schweinfurth says that they live south of the country occupied by the Niam-Niam, and that their stature varies from 4 feet to 4 feet 10 inches. These people are called the Akkas, and wonderful tales are told of their agility and cunning, characteristics that seem to compensate for their small stature.

In 1860 Paul DuChaillu speaks of the existence of an African people called the Obongos, inhabiting the country of the Ashangos, a little to the south of the equator, who were about 1.4 meters in height. There have been people found in the Esquimaux region of very diminutive stature. Battel discovered another pygmy people near the Obongo who are called the Dongos. Kolle describes the Kenkobs, who are but 3 to 4 feet high, and another tribe called the Reebas, who vary from 3 to 5 feet in height. The Portuguese speak of a race of dwarfs whom they call the Bakka-bakka, and of the Yogas, who inhabit territory as far as the Loango. Nubia has a tribe of dwarfs called the Sukus, but little is known of them. Throughout India there are stories of dwarf tribes descended from the monkey-God, or Hoonuman of the mythologic poems.

In the works of Humboldt and Burgoa there is allusion to the tradition of a race of pygmies in the unexplored region of Chiapas near the Isthmus of Tehuantepec in Central America. There is an expedition of anthropologists now on the way to discover this people. Professor Starr of Chicago on his return from this region reported many colonies of undersized people, but did not discover any pygmy tribes answering to the older legendary descriptions. Figure 160 represents two dwarf Cottas measuring 3 feet 6 inches in height.

The African pygmies who were sent to the King of Italy and shown in Rome resembled the pygmy travelers of Akka that Schweinfurth saw at the court of King Munza at Monbuttu. These two pygmies at Rome were found in Central Africa and were respectively about ten and fifteen years old. They spoke a dialect of their own and different from any known African tongue ; they were partly understood by an Egyptian sergeant, a native of Soudan, who accompanied them as the sole survivor of the escort with which their donor, Miani, penetrated Monbuttu. Miani, like Livingstone, lost his life in African travel. These dwarfs had grown rapidly in recent years and at the time of report measured 1.15 and 1.02 meters. In 1874 they were under the care of the Royal Geographical Society of Italy. They were intelligent in their manner, but resented being lionized too much, and were prone to scratch ladies who attempted to kiss them.[a]

[a] 476, 1874, i., 896.

The " Aztec Children " in 1851, at the ages of seven and six years, another pair of alleged indigenous pygmies, measured 33¾ and 29½ inches in height and weighed 20¾ and 17 pounds respectively.   The circumference of their heads did not equal that of an ordinary infant at birth.

It is known that at one time the ancients **artificially produced dwarfs**

Fig. 160.—Dwarf Cottas.

by giving them an insufficient alimentation when very young.   They soon became rachitic from their deprivation of lime-salts and a great number perished, but those who survived were very highly prized by the Roman Emperors for their grotesque appearance.   There were various recipes for dwarfing children.   One of the most efficient in the olden times was said to have been anointing the backbone with the grease of bats, moles, dormice, and such animals ; it was also said that puppies were dwarfed by frequently washing the feet and backbone, as the consequent drying and hardening of the parts were alleged to hinder their extension. To-day the growth of boys intended to be jockeys is kept down by excessive sweating.

Ancient Popularity of Dwarfs.—At one time a dwarf was a necessary appendage of every noble family. The Roman Emperors all had their dwarfs. Julia, the niece of Augustus, had a couple of dwarfs, Conopas and Andromeda, each of whom was 2 feet 4 inches in height. It was the fashion at one time to have dwarfs noted for their wit and wisdom. Philos of Cos, tutor of Ptolemy Philadelphus, was a dwarf, as were Carachus, the friend of Saladin ; Alypius of Alexandria, who was only 2 feet high ; Lucinus Calvus, who was only 3 feet high, and Æsop, the famous Greek fabulist. Later in the Middle Ages and even to the last century dwarfs were seen at every Court. Lady Montagu describes the dwarfs at the Viennese Court as " devils bedaubed with diamonds." They had succeeded the Court Jester and exercised some parts of this ancient office. At this time the English ladies kept monkeys for their amusement. The Court dwarfs were allowed unlimited freedom of speech, and in order to get at truths other men were afraid to utter one of the Kings of Denmark made one of his dwarfs Prime Minister.

Charles IX. in 1572 had nine dwarfs, of which four had been given to him by King Sigismund-Augustus of Poland and three by Maximilian II. of Germany. Catherine de Médicis had three couples of dwarfs at one time, and in 1579 she had still five pygmies, named Merlin, Mandricart, Pelavine, Rodomont, and Majoski. Probably the last dwarf in the Court of France was Balthazar Simon, who died in 1662.

Sometimes many dwarfs were present at great and noble gatherings. In Rome in 1566 the Cardinal Vitelli gave a sumptuous banquet at which the table-attendants were 34 dwarfs. Peter the Great of Russia had a passion for dwarfs, and in 1710 gave a great celebration in honor of the marriage of his favorite, Valakoff, with the dwarf of the Princess Prescovie Theodorovna. There were 72 dwarfs of both sexes present to form the bridal party. Subsequently, on account of dangerous and difficult labor, such marriages were forbidden in Russia.

In England and in Spain the nobles had the portraits of their dwarfs painted by the celebrated artists of the day. Velasquez has represented Don Antonio el Inglès, a dwarf of fine appearance, with a large dog, probably to bring out the dwarf's inferior height. This artist also painted a great number of other dwarfs at the Court of Spain, and in one of his paintings he portrays the Infanta Marguerite accompanied by her male and female dwarfs. Reproductions of these portraits have been given by Garnier.[a] In the pic-

a " Les Nains et les Géants." Paris, 1884.

tures of Raphael, Paul Veronese, and Dominiquin, and in the "Triumph of Cæsar" by Mantegna, representations of dwarfs are found, as well as in other earlier pictures representing Court events. At the present time only Russia and Turkey seem to have popular sympathy for dwarfs, and this in a limited degree.

Intellectual Dwarfs.—It must be remarked, however, that many of the dwarfs before the public have been men of extraordinary intelligence, possibly augmented by comparison. In a postmortem discussed at a meeting of the Natural History Society at Bonn in 1868 it was demonstrated by Schaufhausen that in a dwarf subject the brain weighed $\frac{1}{19}$ of the body, in contradistinction to the average proportion of adults, from 1 to 30 to 1 to 44. The subject was a dwarf of sixty-one who died in Coblentz, and was said to have grown after his thirtieth year. His height was 2 feet 10 inches and his weight 45 pounds. The circumference of the head was 520 mm. and the brain weighed 1183.33 gm. and was well convoluted. This case was one of simple arrest of development, affecting all the organs of the body; he was not virile. He was a child of large parents; had two brothers and a sister of ordinary size and two brothers dwarfs, one 5 inches higher and the other his size.

Several personages famous in history have been dwarfs. Attila, the historian Procopius, Gregory of Tours, Pépin le Bref, Charles III., King of Naples, and Albert the Grand were dwarfs. About the middle of the seventeenth century the French episcopacy possessed among its members a dwarf renowned for his intelligence. This diminutive man, called Godeau, made such a success in literature that by the grace of Richelieu he was named the Archbishop of Grasse. He died in 1672. The Dutch painter Doos, the English painter Gibson (who was about 3 feet in height and the father of nine infants by a wife of about the same height), Prince Eugene, and the Spanish Admiral Gravina were dwarfs. Fleury and Garry, the actors; Hay, a member of Parliament from Sussex in the last century; Hussein-Pasha, celebrated for his reforms under Selim III.; the Danish antiquarian and voyager, Arendt, and Baron Denon were men far below the average size. Varro says that there were two gentlemen of Rome who from their decorations must have belonged to an Equestrian Order, and who were but 2 Roman cubits (about 3 feet) high. Pliny also speaks of them as preserved in their coffins.

It may be remarked that perhaps certain **women are predisposed to give birth to dwarfs.** Borwilaski had a brother and a sister who were dwarfs. In the middle of the seventeenth century a woman brought forth four dwarfs, and in the eighteenth century a dwarf named Hopkins had a sister as small as he was. Thérèse Souvray, the dwarf fiancée of Bébé, had a dwarf sister 41 inches high. Virey has examined a German dwarf of eight who was only 18 inches tall, *i. e.*, about the length of a newly-born infant. The parents were of ordinary size, but had another child who was also a dwarf.

There are **two species of dwarfs,** the first coming into the world under normal conditions, but who in their infancy become afflicted with a sudden arrest of development provoked by some malady; the second are born very small, develop little, and are really dwarfs from their birth; as a rule they are well conformed, robust, and intelligent. These two species can be distinguished by an important characteristic. The rachitic dwarfs of the first class are incapable of perpetuating their species, while those of the second category have proved more than once their virility. A certain number of dwarfs have married with women of normal height and have had several children, though this is not, it is true, an indisputable proof of their generative faculties; but we have instances in which dwarfs have married dwarfs and had a family sometimes quite numerous. Robert Skinner (25 inches) and Judith (26 inches), his wife, had 14 infants, well formed, robust, and of normal height.

Celebrated Dwarfs.—Instances of some of the most celebrated dwarfs will be cited with a short descriptive mention of points of interest in their lives:—

Vladislas Cubitas, who was King of Poland in 1305, was a dwarf, and was noted for his intelligence, courage, and as a good soldier. **Geoffrey Hudson,** the most celebrated English dwarf, was born at Oakham in England in 1619. At the age of eight, when not much over a foot high, he was presented to Henriette Marie, wife of Charles I., in a pie; he afterward became her favorite. Until he was thirty he was said to be not more than 18 inches high, when he suddenly increased to about 45 inches. In his youth he fought several duels, one with a turkey cock, which is celebrated in the verse of Davenant. He became a popular and graceful courtier, and proved his bravery and allegiance to his sovereign by assuming command of a royalist company and doing good service therein. Both in moral and physical capacities he showed his superiority. At one time he was sent to France to secure a midwife for the Queen, who was a Frenchwoman. He afterward challenged a gentleman by the name of Croft to fight a duel, and would accept only deadly weapons; he shot his adversary in the chest; the quarrel grew out of his resentment of ridicule of his diminutive size. He was accused of participation in the Papist Plot and imprisoned by his political enemies in the Gate House at Westminster, where he died in 1682 at the advanced age of sixty-three. In Scott's "Peveril of the Peak" Hudson figures prominently. This author seemed fond of dwarfs.

About the same epoch Charles I. had a page in his court named Richard Gibson, who was remarkable for his diminutive size and his ability as a miniature painter. This little artist espoused another of his class, Anne Shepherd, a dwarf of Queen Henriette Marie, about his size (45 inches). Mistress Gibson bore nine children, five of whom arrived at adult age and were of ordinary proportions. She died at the age of eighty; her husband afterward became the drawing master of Princesses Mary and Anne, daughters of James II.; he died July 23, 1690, aged seventy-five years.

In 1730 there was born of poor fisher parents at Jelst a child named Wybrand Lokes. He became a very skilful jeweler, and though he was of diminutive stature he married a woman of medium height, by whom he had several children. He was one of the smallest men ever exhibited, measuring but 25½ inches in height. To support his family better, he abandoned his trade and with great success exhibited himself throughout Holland and England. After having amassed a great fortune he returned to his country, where he died in 1800, aged seventy. He was very intelligent, and proved his power of paternity, especially by one son, who at twenty-three was 5 feet 3 inches tall, and robust.

Another celebrated dwarf was Nicolas Ferry, otherwise known as **Bébé**. He was born at Plaine in the Vosges in 1741; he was but 22 cm. (8½ inches) long, weighed 14 ounces at birth, and was carried on a plate to the church for baptism. At five Bébé was presented to King Stanislas of Poland. At fifteen he measured 29 inches. He was of good constitution, but was almost an idiot; for example, he did not recognize his mother after fifteen days' separation. He was quite lax in his morals, and exhibited no evidences of good nature except his lively attachment for his royal master, who was himself a detestable character. He died at twenty-two in a very decrepit condition, and his skeleton is preserved in the Museum of Natural History in Paris. Shortly before his death Bébé became engaged to a female dwarf named Thérèse Souvray, who at one time was exhibited in Paris at the Théâtre Conti, together with an older sister. Thérèse lived to be seventy-three, and both she and her sister measured only 30 inches in height. She died in 1819.

Aldrovandus [116] gives a picture of a famous dwarf of the Duc de Créqui who was only 30 inches tall, though perfectly formed; he also speaks of some dwarfs who were not over 2 feet high.

There was a Polish gentleman named Joseph Borwilaski, born in 1739, who was famed all over Europe. He became quite a scholar, speaking French and German fairly well. In 1860, at the age of twenty-two, and 28 inches in height, he married a woman of ordinary stature, who bore him two infants well conformed. He was exhibited in many countries, and finally settled at Durham, England, where he died in 1837 at the almost incredible age of ninety-eight, and is buried by the side of the Falstaffian Stephen Kemble. Mary Jones of Shropshire, a dwarf 32 inches tall and much deformed, died in 1773 at the age of one hundred. These two instances are striking examples of **great age in dwarfs** and are therefore of much interest. Borwilaski's parents were tall in stature and three of his brothers were small; three of the other children measured 5 feet 6 inches. Diderot has written a history of this family.

Richeborg,[324] a dwarf only 23 inches in height, died in Paris in 1858 aged ninety years. In childhood he had been a servant in the House of Orleans and afterward became their pensioner. During the Revolution he passed in and out of Paris as an infant in a nurse's arms, thus carrying dispatches memorized which might have proved dangerous to carry in any other manner.

At St. Philip's, Birmingham, there is the following inscription on a tomb : "In memory of Mannetta Stocker, who quitted this life on the 4th day of May, 1819, at the age of thirty-nine years, the smallest woman in the

Fig. 161.—Female dwarf with her nusband and child.

kingdom, and one of the most accomplished." She was born in Krauma, in the north of Austria, under normal conditions. Her growth stopped at the age of four, when she was 33 inches tall. She was shown in many villages and cities over Europe and Great Britain ; she was very gay, played well on the piano, and had divers other accomplishments.

In 1742 there was shown in London a dwarf by the name of Robert Skinner, .63 meters in height, and his wife, Judith, who was a little larger. Their exhibition was a great success and they amassed a small fortune ; during twenty-three years they had 14 robust and well-formed children. Judith died in 1763, and Robert grieved so much after her that he himself expired two years later.

Figure 161 shows a female dwarf with her husband and child, all of whom were exhibited some years since in the Eastern United States. The likeness of the child to the mother is already noticeable.

Buffon speaks of dwarfs 24, 21, and 18 inches high, and mentions one individual, aged thirty-seven, only 16 inches tall, whom he considers the smallest person on record. Virey in 1818 speaks of an English child of eight or nine who was but 18 inches tall. It had the intelligence of a child of three or four ; its dentition was delayed until it was two years old and it did not walk until four. The parents of this child were of ordinary stature.

At the "Cosmorama" in Regent Street in 1848[a] there was a Dutch boy of ten exhibited. He was said to be the son of an apothecary and at the time of his birth weighed nine pounds. He continued to grow for six months and at the expiration of that time weighed 12 pounds; since then, however, he had only increased four pounds. The arrest of development seemed to be connected with hydrocephalus; although the head was no larger than that of a child of two, the anterior fontanelle was widely open, indicating that there was pressure within. He was strong and muscular; grave and sedate in his manner; cheerful and affectionate; his manners were polite and engaging; he was expert in many kinds of handicraft; he possessed an ardent desire for knowledge and aptitude for education.

Rawdon[b] described a boy of five and a half, at the Liverpool Infirmary for Children, who weighed 10½ pounds and whose height was 28 or 29 inches. He uttered no articulate sound, but evidently possessed the sense of hearing. His eyes were large and well formed, but he was apparently blind. He suckled, cut his teeth normally, but had tonic contractions of the spine and was an apparent idiot.

Hardie[c] mentions a girl of sixteen and a half whose height was 40 inches and weight 35¼ pounds, includ-

Fig. 162.—Dwarf, height 34 inches, weight 309 pounds.

ing her clothes. During intrauterine life her mother had good health and both her parents had always been healthy. She seemed to stop growing at her fourth year. Her intellect was on a par with the rest of her body. Sometimes she would talk and again she would preserve rigid silence for a long time. She had a shuffling walk with a tendency to move on her toes. Her temporary teeth were shed in the usual manner and had been replaced by canines and right first molar and incisors on the right side. There was no

a 476, 1848, ii., 490.   b 224, 1879, i., 386.   c 224, 1887, i., 730.

indication of puberty except a slight development of the hips. She was almost totally imbecile, but could tell her letters and spell short words. The circumference of the head was 19 inches, and Ross pointed out that the tendon-reflexes were well marked, as well as the ankle-clonus; he diagnosed the case as one of parencephalus. Figure 162 represents a most curious case of a dwarf named Carrie Akers, who, though only 34 inches tall, weighed 309 pounds.

In recent years several dwarfs have commanded the popular attention, but none so much as **" General Tom Thumb,"** the celebrated dwarf of Barnum's Circus. Charles Stratton, surnamed "Tom Thumb," was born at Bridgeport, Conn., on January 11, 1832; he was above the normal weight of the new-born. He ceased growing at about five months, when his height was less than 21 inches. Barnum, hearing of this phenomenon in his city, engaged him, and he was shown all over the world under his assumed name. He was presented to Queen Victoria in 1844, and in the following year he was received by the Royal Family in France. His success was wonderful, and even the most conservative journals described and commented on him. He gave concerts, in which he sang in a nasal voice; but his "drawing feat" was embracing the women who visited him. It is said that in England alone he kissed a million females; he prided himself on his success in this function, although his features were anything but inviting. After he had received numerous presents and had amassed a large fortune he returned to America in 1864, bringing with him three other dwarfs, the "Sisters Warren" and "Commodore Nutt." He married one of the Warrens, and by her had one child, Minnie, who died some months after birth of cerebral congestion. In 1883 Tom Thumb and his wife, Lavinia, were still living, but after that they dropped from public view and have since died.

In 1895 the wife of a dwarf named Morris gave birth to twins at Blaenavon, North Wales. Morris is only 35 inches in height and his wife is even smaller. They were married at Bartholmey Church and have since been traveling through England under the name of "General and Mrs. Small," being the smallest married couple in the world. At the latest reports the mother and her twins were doing well.

The Rossow Brothers have been recently exhibited to the public. These brothers, Franz and Carl, are twenty and eighteen years respectively. Franz is the eldest of 16 children and is said to weigh 24 pounds and measure 21 inches in height; Carl is said to weigh less than his brother but is 29 inches tall. They give a clever gymnastic exhibition and are apparently intelligent. They advertise that they were examined and still remain under the surveillance of the Faculty of Göttingen.

Next to the success of "Tom Thumb" probably no like attraction has been so celebrated as the "Lilliputians," whose antics and wit so many Americans have in late years enjoyed. They were a troupe of singers and comedians composed entirely of dwarfs; they exhibited much talent in all their performances, which were given for several years and quite recently in all the large cities of the United States. They showed themselves to be worthy rivals for honors in the class of entertainments known as burlesques. As near as could be ascertained, partly from the fact that they all spoke German fluently and originally gave their performance entirely in German, they were collected from the German and Austrian Empires.

The "Princess Topaze" was born near Paris in 1879. According to a recent report she is perfectly formed and is intelligent and vivacious. She is 23½ inches tall and weighs 14 pounds. Her parents were of normal stature.

Not long since the papers recorded the death of Lucia Zarete, a Mexican girl, whose exact proportions were never definitely known; but there is no doubt that she was the smallest midget ever exhibited in this country. Her exhibitor made a fortune with her and her salary was among the highest paid to modern "freaks."

Miss H. Moritz, an American dwarf (Fig. 163), at the age of twenty weighed 36 pounds and was only 22 inches tall.

Precocious development is characterized by a hasty growth of the subject, who at an early period of life attains the dimensions of an adult. In some of these instances the anomaly is associated with precocious puberty, and after acquiring the adult growth at an early age there is an apparent cessation of the devel-

Fig. 163.—Dwarf, 22 inches tall.

opment. In adult life the individual shows no distinguishing characters.

The first to be considered will be those cases, sometimes called **"man-boys,"** characterized by early puberty and extraordinary development in infancy. Histories of remarkable children have been transmitted from the time of Vespasian. We read in the "Natural History" of Pliny that in Salamis, Euthimedes had a son who grew to 3 Roman cubits (4½ feet) in three years; he was said to have little wit, a dull mind, and a slow and heavy gait; his voice was manly, and he died at three of general debility. Phlegon[a] says that Craterus, the brother of King Antigonus, was an infant, a young man, a mature man, an old man, and married and begot children all in the space of seven years. It is said that King Louis II. of Hungary was born so long before his time that he had no skin; in his second year he

a "De Mirab.," cap. 32.

was crowned, in his tenth year he succeeded, in his fourteenth year he had a complete beard, in his fifteenth he was married, in his eighteenth he had gray hair, and in his twentieth he died. Rhodiginus [a] speaks of a boy who when he was ten years impregnated a female. In 1741 there was a boy born at Willingham, near Cambridge,[b] who had the external marks of puberty at twelve months, and at the time of his death at five years he had the appearance of an old man. He was called "prodigium Willinghamense." The Ephemerides and some of the older journals record instances of penile erection immediately after birth.

It was said that Philip Howarth, who was born at Quebec Mews, Portman Square, London, February 21, 1806, lost his infantile rotundity of form and feature after the completion of his first year and became pale and extremely ugly, appearing like a growing boy. His penis and testes increased in size, his voice altered, and hair grew on the pubes. At the age of three he was 3 feet $4\frac{1}{2}$ inches tall and weighed $51\frac{1}{4}$ pounds. The length of his penis when erect was $4\frac{1}{2}$ inches and the circumference 4 inches ; his thigh-measure was $13\frac{1}{2}$ inches, his waist-measure 24 inches, and his biceps 7 inches. He was reported to be clever, very strong, and muscular. An old chronicle says that in Wisnang Parish, village of Tellurge, near Tygure, in Lordship Kiburge, there was born on the 26th of May, 1548, a boy called Henry Walker, who at five years was of the height of a boy of fourteen and possessed the genitals of a man. He carried burdens, did men's work, and in every way assisted his parents, who were of usual size.

There is a case cited by the older authors [c] of a child born in the Jura region who at the age of four gave proof of his virility, at seven had a beard and the height of a man. The same journal also speaks of a boy of six, 1.62 meters tall, who was perfectly proportioned and had extraordinary strength. His beard and general appearance, together with the marks of puberty, gave him the appearance of a man of thirty.

In 1806 Dupuytren presented to the Medical Society in Paris a child $3\frac{1}{2}$ feet high, weighing 57 pounds, who had attained puberty.

There are on record six modern cases of early puberty in boys,[666] one of whom died at five with the signs of premature senility ; at one year he had shown signs of enlargement of the sexual organs. There was another who at three was 3 feet $6\frac{3}{4}$ inches high, weighed 50 pounds, and had seminal discharges. One of the cases was a child who at birth resembled an ordinary infant of five months. From four to fifteen months his penis enlarged, until at the age of three it measured when erect 3 inches. At this age he was 3 feet 7 inches high and weighed 64 pounds. The last case mentioned was an infant who experienced a change of voice at twelve months and showed hair on the pubes. At three years he was 3 feet $4\frac{1}{2}$ inches tall and weighed $51\frac{1}{4}$ pounds. Smith, in Brewster's Journal, 1829, records the

[a] 679, L. viii., cap. 8. [b] 629, 1745. [c] " Recueil de l'Académie des Sciences," 1668.

case of a boy who at the age of four was well developed ; at the age of six he was 4 feet 2 inches tall and weighed 74 pounds ; his lower extremities were extremely short proportionally and his genitals were as well developed as those of an adult. He had a short, dark moustache but no hair on his chin, although his pubic hair was thick, black, and curly. Ruelle [a] describes a child of three and a quarter years who was as strong and muscular as one at eight. He had full-sized male organs and long black hair on the pubes. Under excitement he discharged semen four or five times a day ; he had a deep male voice, and dark, short hair on the cheek and upper lip.

Stone [b] gives an account of a boy of four who looked like a child of ten and exhibited the sexual organs of a man with a luxuriant growth of hair on the pubes. This child was said to have been of great beauty and a miniature model of an athlete. His height was 4 feet $\frac{1}{4}$ inch and weight 70 pounds ; the penis when semiflaccid was $4\frac{1}{4}$ inches long ; he was intelligent and lively, and his back was covered with the acne of puberty. A peculiar fact as regards this case was the statement of the father that he himself had had sexual indulgence at eight. Stone parallels this case by several others that he has collected from medical literature. Breschet in 1821 reported the case of a boy born October 20, 1817, who at three years and one month was 3 feet $6\frac{3}{4}$ inches tall ; his penis when flaccid measured 4 inches and when erect $5\frac{1}{4}$ inches, but the testicles were not developed in proportion. Lopez [c] describes a mulatto boy of three years ten and a half months whose height was 4 feet $\frac{1}{2}$ inch and weight 82 pounds ; he measured about the chest $27\frac{1}{2}$ inches and about the waist 27 inches ; his penis at rest was 4 inches long and had a circumference of $3\frac{1}{2}$ inches, although the testes were not descended. He had evidences of a beard and his axillæ were very hairy ; it is said he could with ease lift a man weighing 140 pounds. His body was covered with acne simplex and had a strong spermatic odor, but it was not known whether he had any venereal appetite.

Johnson [d] mentions a boy of seven with severe gonorrhea complicated with buboes which he had contracted from a servant girl with whom he slept. At the Hôpital des Enfans Malades children at the breast have been observed to masturbate. Fournier and others assert having seen infantile masturbators, and cite a case of a girl of four who was habitually addicted to masturbation from her infancy but was not detected until her fourth year ; she died shortly afterward in a frightful state of marasmus. Vogel alludes to a girl of three in whom repeated attacks of epilepsy occurred after six months' onanism. Van Bambeke mentions three children from ten to twenty months old, two of them females, who masturbated.

Bidwell describes a boy of five years and two months who during the year previous had erections and seminal emissions. His voice had changed and he had a downy moustache on his upper lip and hair on the pubes ; his

a 233, Feb. 28, 1843.   b 124, 1852.   c 124, 1843.   d 476, 1860, i., Feb.

height was 4 feet 3½ inches and his weight was 82½ pounds. His penis and testicles were as well developed as those of a boy of seventeen or eighteen, but from his facial aspect one would take him to be thirteen. He avoided the company of women and would not let his sisters nurse him when he was sick.

Pryor[a] speaks of a boy of three and a half who masturbated and who at five and a half had a penis of adult size, hair on the pubes, and was known to have had seminal emissions. Woods[b] describes a boy of six years and seven months who had the appearance of a youth of eighteen. He was 4 feet 9 inches tall and was quite muscular. He first exhibited signs of precocious growth at the beginning of his second year and when three years old he had hair on the pubes. There is an instance[c] in which a boy of thirteen had intercourse with a young woman at least a dozen times and succeeded in impregnating her. The same journal mentions an instance in which a boy of fourteen succeeded in impregnating a girl of the same age. Chevers[266] speaks of a young boy in India who was sentenced to one year's imprisonment for raping a girl of three.

Douglass[d] describes a boy of four years and three months who was 3 feet 10½ inches tall and weighed 54 pounds ; his features were large and coarse, and his penis and testes were of the size of those of an adult. He was unusually dull, mentally, quite obstinate, and self-willed. It is said that he masturbated on all opportunities and had vigorous erections, although no spermatozoa were found in the semen issued. He showed no fondness for the opposite sex. The history of this rapid growth says that he was not unlike other children until the third year, when after wading in a small stream several hours he was taken with a violent chill, after which his voice began to change and his sexual organs to develop.

Blanc[212] quotes the case described by Cozanet in 1875 of Louis Beran, who was born on September 29, 1869, at Saint-Gervais, of normal size. At the age of six months his dimensions and weight increased in an extraordinary fashion. At the age of six years he was 1.28 meters high (4 feet 2⅜ inches) and weighed 80 pounds. His puberty was completely manifested in every way ; he eschewed the society of children and helped his parents in their labors. Campbell[e] showed a lad of fourteen who had been under his observation for ten years. When fifteen months old this prodigy had hair on his pubes and his external genitals were abnormally large, and at the age of two years they were fully developed and had not materially changed in the following years. At times he manifested great sexual excitement. Between four and seven years he had seminal discharges, but it was not determined whether the semen contained spermatozoa. He had the muscular development of a man of twenty-five. He had shaved several years. The boy's education was defective from his failure to attend school.

a 778, xxii., 521.   b 476, 1882, ii., 377.   c 224, 1887, i., 918.
d 597, 1889.   e 536, No. 2591, 551.

The accompanying illustration (Fig. 164) represents a boy of five years and three months of age whose height at this time was 4 feet and his physical development far beyond that usual at this age, his external genitals resembling those of a man of twenty. His upper lip was covered by a mustache, and the hirsute growth elsewhere was similarly precocious.

The inscription on the tombstone of James Weir in the Parish of Carluke, Scotland, says that when only thirteen months old he measured 3 feet 4 inches in height and weighed 5 stone. He was pronounced by the faculty of Edinburgh and Glasgow to be the most extraordinary child of his age. Linnæus saw a boy at the Amsterdam Fair who at the age of three weighed 98 pounds. In Paris, about 1822, there was shown an infant Hercules of seven who was more remarkable for obesity than general development. He was 3 feet 4 inches high, 4 feet 5 inches in circumference, and weighed 220 pounds. He had prominent eyebrows, black eyes, and his complexion resembled that of a fat cook in the heat. Borellus [841] details a description of a giant child. There is quoted from Boston [a] the report of a boy of fifteen months weighing 92 pounds who died at Coney Island. He was said to have been of phenomenal size from infancy and was exhibited in several museums during his life.

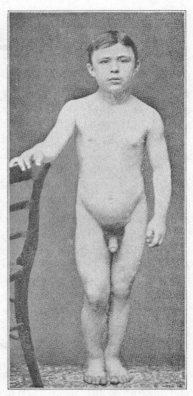

Fig. 164.—Precocious development in a boy of five years and three months.

Desbois of Paris mentions an extraordinary instance of **rapid growth** in a boy of eleven who grew 6 inches in fifteen days.

Large and Small New-born Infants.—There are many accounts of new-born infants who were characterized by their diminutive size. On page 66 we have mentioned Usher's instance of twins born at the one hundred and thirty-ninth day weighing each less than 11 ounces; Barker's case of a female child at the one hundred and fifty-eighth day weighing 1 pound; Newinton's case of twins at the fifth month, one weighing 1 pound and the other 1 pound 3½ ounces; and on page 67 is an account of Eikam's five-months' child, weighing 8 ounces. Of full-term children Sir Everard

[a] 224, Aug. 31, 1895.

Home, in his Croonian Oration in 1824,[a] speaks of one borne by a woman who was traveling with the baggage of the Duke of Wellington's army. At her fourth month of pregnancy this woman was attacked and bitten by a monkey, but she went to term, and a living child was delivered which weighed but a pound and was between 7 and 8 inches long. It was brought to England and died at the age of nine, when 22 inches high. Baker[b] mentions a child fifty days' old that weighed 1 pound 13 ounces and was 14 inches long. Mursick[c] describes a living child who at birth weighed but $1\frac{3}{4}$ pounds. In June, 1896, a baby weighing $1\frac{1}{4}$ pounds was born at the Samaritan Hospital, Philadelphia.

Scott[d] has recorded the birth of a child weighing $2\frac{1}{2}$ pounds, and another $3\frac{1}{4}$ pounds. In the Chicago Inter-Ocean there is a letter dated June 20, 1874, which says that Mrs. J. B. McCrum of Kalamazoo, Michigan, gave birth to a boy and girl that could be held in the palm of the hand of the nurse. Their aggregate weight was 3 pounds 4 ounces, one weighing 1 pound 8 ounces, the other 1 pound 12 ounces. They were less than 8 inches long and perfectly formed; they were not only alive but extremely vivacious.

There is an account[e] of female twins born in 1858 before term. One weighed $22\frac{1}{2}$ ounces, and over its arm, forearm, and hand one could easily pass a wedding-ring. The other weighed 24 ounces. They both lived to adult life; the larger married and was the mother of two children, which she bore easily. The other did not marry, and although not a dwarf, was under-sized; she had her catamenia every third week. Post[f] describes a 2-pound child.

On the other hand, there have been **infants characterized by their enormous size at birth.** Among the older writers, Cranz[g] describes an infant which at birth weighed 23 pounds; Fern[h] mentions a fetus of 18 pounds; and Mittehauser[398] speaks of a new-born child weighing 24 pounds. Von Siebold in his "Lucina"[495] has recorded a fetus which weighed $22\frac{1}{2}$ pounds. It is worthy of comment that so great is the rarity of these instances that in 3600 cases, in the Rotunda Hospital, Dublin, only one child reached 11 pounds.

There was a child born in Sussex in 1869[i] which weighed $13\frac{1}{2}$ pounds and measured $26\frac{1}{2}$ inches. Warren[j] delivered a woman in Derbyshire of male twins, one weighing 17 pounds 8 ounces and the other 18 pounds. The placenta weighed 4 pounds, and there was an ordinary pailful of liquor amnii. Both the twins were muscular and well formed; the parents were of ordinary stature, and at last reports the mother was rapidly convalescing. Burgess[k] mentions an 18-pound new-born child; and Meadows[l] has seen

a 629, 1825.   b Trans. Med. and Physical Soc. of Calcutta, 1825, i., 364.
c 124, 1874.   d 224, 1885, ii.   e 224, 1886, i., 54.   f 286, 1885–86, i., 543.
g "Comments de rupto in partu dolor," etc.   h 800, L. ii., no. 12.
i 548, 1869, i., 618.   j 476, 1884, ii., 1029.   k 616, 1875.   l 548, 1860.

a similar instance. Eddowes [a] speaks of the birth of a child at Crewe, a male, which weighed 20 pounds 2 ounces and was 23 inches long. It was $14\frac{1}{2}$ inches about the chest, symmetrically developed, and likely to live. The mother, who was a schoolmistress of thirty-three, had borne two previous children, both of large size. In this instance the gestation had not been prolonged, the delivery was spontaneous, and there was no laceration of the parts.

Chubb [b] says that on Christmas Day, 1852, there was a child delivered weighing 21 pounds. The labor was not severe and the other children of the family were exceptionally large. Dickinson [c] describes a woman, a terti-para, who had a most difficult labor and bore an extremely large child. She had been thirty-six hours in parturition, and by evisceration and craniotomy was delivered of a child weighing 16 pounds. Her first child weighed 9 pounds, her second 20, and her third, the one described, cost her her life soon after delivery.

There is a history of a Swedish woman in Boston [d] who was delivered by the forceps of her first child, which weighed $19\frac{3}{4}$ pounds and which was $25\frac{3}{4}$ inches long. The circumference of the head was $16\frac{3}{4}$ inches, of the neck $9\frac{1}{4}$, and of the thigh $10\frac{3}{4}$ inches.

Rice [e] speaks of a child weighing $20\frac{1}{4}$ pounds at birth. Johnston [f] de-scribes a male infant who was born on November 26, 1848, weighing 20 pounds, and Smith [g] another of the same weight. Baldwin [h] quotes the case of a woman who after having three miscarriages at last had a child that weighed 23 pounds. In the delivery there was extensive laceration of the anterior wall of the vagina; the cervix and perineum, together with an inch of the rectum, were completely destroyed.

Beach [i] describes a birth of a young giant weighing $23\frac{3}{4}$ pounds. Its mother was Mrs. Bates, formerly Anna Swann, the giantess who married Captain Bates. Labor was rather slow, but she was successfully delivered of a healthy child weighing $23\frac{3}{4}$ pounds and 30 inches long. The secun-dines weighed ten pounds and there were nine quarts of amniotic fluid.

There is a recent record [j] of a Cesarian section performed on a woman of forty in her twelfth pregnancy and one month beyond term. The fetus, which was almost exsanguinated by amputation, weighed $22\frac{1}{2}$ pounds. Bumm [k] speaks of the birth of a premature male infant weighing 4320 gm. ($9\frac{1}{2}$ pounds) and measuring 54 cm. long. Artificial labor had been induced at the thirty-fifth week in the hope of delivering a living child, the three preceding infants having all been still-born on account of their large size. Although the mother's pelvis was wide, the disposition to bear huge infants was so great as to render the woman virtually barren.

a 476, 1884, ii., 911.   b 224, 1879, i., 143.   c 227, 1894, 225.   d 381, 1879, i., 255.
e 218, 1876.   f 124, 1881.   g 545, 1878, 512.   h 227, 1894, 228.
i 538, March 22, 1879.   j Repertoire d'Obstet. et de Gynéc., May 25, 1891.
k Cor.-Bl. f. schweiz. Aerzte, p. 117, Feb. 15, 1895.

Congenital asymmetry and hemihypertrophy of the body are most peculiar anomalies and must not be confounded with acromegaly or myxedema, in both of which there is similar lack of symmetric development. There seems to be no satisfactory clue to the causation of these abnormalisms. Most frequently the left side is the least developed, and there is a decided difference in the size of the extremities.

Finlayson [a] reports a case of a child affected with congenital unilateral hypertrophy associated with patches of cutaneous congestion. Logan [b] men-

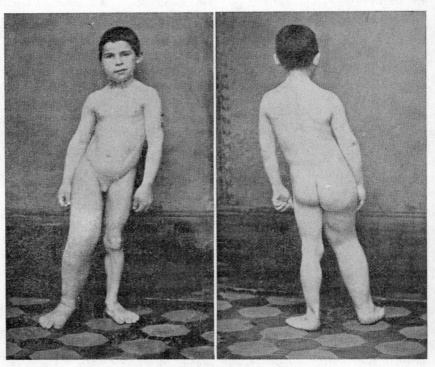

Fig. 165.—Case of hemihypertrophy (Adams).

tions hypertrophy in the right half of the body in a child of four, first noticed shortly after birth; Langlet [c] also speaks of a case of congenital hypertrophy of the right side. Broca [d] and Trélat [e] were among the first observers to discuss this anomaly.

Tilanus of Munich in 1893 reported a case of hemihypertrophy in a girl of ten. The whole right half of the body was much smaller and better developed than the left, resulting in a limping gait. The electric reaction

a 381, 1884, xxi., 327.   b N. Orl. J. M., 1868, xxi., 733.
c Union méd. et scient. du nord-est, Reims, 1882, vi., 276.
d 368, 1859, xiv., 445.   e 162, 1869, i., 536, 676.

and the reflexes showed no abnormality. The asymmetry was first observed when the child was three. Mobius and Demme report similar cases.

Adams [a] reports an unusual case of hemihypertrophy in a boy of ten. There was nothing noteworthy in the family history, and the patient had suffered from none of the diseases of childhood. Deformity was noticeable at birth, but not to such a degree relatively as at a later period. The increased growth affected the entire right half of the body, including the face, but was most noticeable in the leg, thigh, and buttock. Numerous telangiec-

Fig. 166.—Unilateral hypertrophy (Milne).

Fig. 167.—The Tompkins child, age thirteen months.

tatic spots were scattered irregularly over the body, but most thickly on the right side, especially on the outer surface of the leg. The accompanying illustration (Fig. 165) represents the child's appearance at the time of report.

Jacobson [b] reports the history of a female child of three years with nearly universal giant growth (Riesenwuchs). At first this case was erroneously diagnosed as acromegaly. The hypertrophy affected the face, the genitals, the left side of the trunk, and all the limbs.

Milne [c] records a case of hemihypertrophy in a female child of one year

[a] 165, Dec., 1894.   [b] 161, 1895, cxxxix., 104.   [c] Quarterly Med. Jour., April, 1895.

(Fig. 166). The only deviation from uniform excess of size of the right side was shown in the forefinger and thumb, which were of the same size as on the other hand; and the left side showed no overgrowth in any of its members except a little enlargement of the second toe. While hypertrophy of one side is the usual description of such cases, the author suggests that there may be a condition of defect upon the other side, and he is inclined to think that in this case the limb, hand, and foot of the left side seemed rather below the average of the child's age. In this case, as in others previously reported, there were numerous telangiectatic spots of congestion scattered irregularly over the body. Milne[a] also reported later to the Sheffield Medico-Chirurgical Society an instance of unilateral hypertrophy in a female child of nineteen months. The right side was involved and the anomaly was believed to be due to a deficiency of growth of the left side as well as over-development of the right. There were six teeth on the right side and one on the left.

Fig. 168.—Baby Chambers.

Obesity.—The abnormality of the adipose system, causing in consequence an augmentation of the natural volume of the subject, should be described with other anomalies of size and stature. Obesity may be partial, as seen in the mammæ or in the abdomen of both women and men, or may be general; and it is of general obesity that we shall chiefly deal. Lipomata, being distinctly pathologic formations, will be left for another chapter.

The cases of **obesity in infancy and childhood** are of considerable interest, and we sometimes see cases that have been termed examples of "congenital corpulency." Figure 167 represents a baby of thirteen months that weighed 75 pounds. Figure 168 shows another example of infantile obesity, known as "Baby Chambers." Elliotson[322] describes a female infant not a year old which weighed 60 pounds. There is an instance on record of a girl of four who weighed 256 pounds.[b] Tulpius[c] mentions a girl of five who weighed 150 pounds and had the strength of a man. He says that the acquisition of fat did not commence until some time after birth. Ebstein reports an instance given to him by Fisher of Moscow of a child in Pomerania who at the age of six weighed 137 pounds and was 46 inches tall; her girth was 46 inches and the circumference of her head was 24 inches. She was the offspring of ordinary-sized parents, and lived in narrow and sometimes needy circumstances. The child was intelligent and had an animated expression of countenance.

Bartholinus mentions a girl of eleven who weighed over 200 pounds. There is an instance recorded of a young girl in Russia who weighed nearly 200 pounds when but twelve. Wulf, quoted by Ebstein, describes a child which died at birth weighing 295 ounces. It was well proportioned and looked like a child three months old, except that it had an enormous development of fatty tissue. The parents were not excessively large, and the mother stated that she had had children before of the same proportions. Grisolles[a] mentions a child who was so fat at twelve months that there was constant danger of suffocation; but, marvelous to relate, it lost all its obesity when two and a half, and later was remarkable for its slender figure. Figure 169 shows a girl born in Carbon County, Pa., who weighed 201 pounds when nine years old. McNaughton[b] describes Susanna Tripp, who at six years of age weighed 203 pounds and was 3 feet 6 inches tall and measured 4 feet 2 inches around the waist. Her younger sister, Deborah, weighed 119 pounds; neither of the two weighed over 7 pounds at birth and both began to grow at the fourth month. On October, 1788, there died at an inn in the city of York the surprising "Worcestershire Girl" at the age of five. She had an exceedingly beautiful face and was quite active. She was 4 feet in height and larger around the breast and waist; her thigh measured 18 inches and she weighed nearly 200 pounds. In February, 1814, Mr. S. Pauton was married to the only daughter of Thomas Allanty of Yorkshire; although she was but thirteen she was 13 stone weight (182 pounds). At seven years she had weighed 7 stone (98 pounds). Williams[787] mentions several instances of fat children. The first was a German girl who at birth weighed 13 pounds; at six months, 42 pounds; at four years, 150 pounds; and at twenty years, 450 pounds. Isaac Butterfield, born near Leeds in 1781, weighed 100 pounds in 1782 and was 3 feet 13 inches tall. There was a child named Everitt, exhibited in London in 1780, who at eleven months was 3 feet 9 inches tall and measured around the loins over 3 feet. William Abernethy[c] at the age of thirteen weighed 22 stone (308 pounds) and measured 57 inches around the waist. He was 5 feet 6 inches tall. There was a girl of ten[d] who was 1.45 meters (4 feet 9 inches) high and weighed 175 pounds. Her manners were infantile and her intellectual development

---

[a] "Vorlesungen über specielle Pathologie und Therapie, Deutsche Ausgabe," Leipzig, 1848, ii., 265.

[b] 599, 1829.　　　　　　　　[c] 548, 1862, i., 363.　　　　　　　　[d] 677, 1869, No. 2.

was much retarded. She spoke with difficulty in a deep voice ; she had a most voracious appetite.

At a meeting of the Physical Society of Vienna on December 4, 1894, [a] there was shown a girl of five and a half who weighed 250 pounds. She was just shedding her first teeth ; owing to the excess of fat on her short limbs she toddled like an infant. There was no tendency to obesity in her family. Up to the eleventh month she was nursed by her mother, and sub-

Fig. 169.—Age nine, weight 201 pounds.

sequently fed on cabbage, milk, and vegetable soup. This child, who was of Russian descent, was said never to perspire.

Cameron [b] describes a child who at birth weighed 14 pounds, at twelve months she weighed 69 pounds, and at seventeen months 98 pounds. She was not weaned until two years old and she then commenced to walk. The parents were not remarkably large. There is an instance of a boy of thirteen and a half who weighed 214 pounds.[c] Kaestner speaks of a child of four who weighed 82 pounds, and Benzenberg noted a child of the same age who weighed 137. Hildman, quoted by Picat, speaks of an infant three years and ten months old who had a girth of 30 inches. Hillairet [a] knew of a child of five which weighed 125 pounds. Botta [b] cites several instances of preternaturally stout children. One child died at the age of three weighing 90 pounds, another at the age of five weighed 100 pounds, and a third at the age of two weighed 75 pounds.

Figure 170 represents Miss " Millie Josephine " of Chicago, a recent ex-

Fig. 170.—Age thirteen, weight 422 pounds.

hibitionist, who at the reputed age of thirteen was 5 feet 6 inches tall and weighed 422 pounds.

General Remarks.—It has been chiefly in Great Britain and in Holland that the most remarkable instances of obesity have been seen, especially in the former country colossal weights have been recorded. In some countries corpulency has been considered an adornment of the female sex. Hesse-Wartegg [c] refers to the Jewesses of Tunis, who when scarcely ten years old are subjected to systematic treatment by confinement in narrow, dark rooms, where they are fed on farinaceous foods and the flesh of young puppies until

[a] 233, 1881.　　　[b] Cincin. Med. News, 1877, 321.　　　[c] Tunis, Vienna, 1881.

they are almost a shapeless mass of fat.   According to Ebstein, the Moorish women reach with astonishing rapidity the desired embonpoint on a diet of dates and a peculiar kind of meal.

In some nations and families **obesity** is **hereditary**, and generations come and go without a change in the ordinary conformation of the representatives.   In other people slenderness is equally persistent, and efforts to overcome this peculiarity of nature are without avail.

Treatment of Obesity.—Many persons, the most famous of whom was Banting, have advanced theories to reduce corpulency and to improve slenderness ; but they have been uniformly unreliable, and the whole subject of stature-development presents an almost unexplored field for investigation. Recently, Leichtenstein,[a] observing in a case of myxedema treated with the **thyroid gland** that the subcutaneous fat disappeared with the continuance of the treatment, was led to adopt this treatment for obesity itself and reports striking results.   The diet of the patient remained the same, and as the appetite was not diminished by the treatment the loss of weight was evidently due to other causes than altered alimentation.   He holds that the observations in myxedema, in obesity, and psoriasis warrant the belief that the thyroid gland eliminates a material having a regulating influence upon the constitution of the panniculus adiposus and upon the nutrition of the skin in general.   There were 25 patients in all ; in 22 the effect was entirely satisfactory, the loss of weight amounting to as much as 9.5 kilos (21 pounds).   Of the three cases in which the result was not satisfactory, one had nephritis with severe Graves' disease, and the third psoriasis.   Charrin [b] has used the injections of thyroid extract with decided benefit.   So soon as the administration of the remedy was stopped the loss of weight ceased, but with the renewal of the remedy the loss of weight again ensued to a certain point, beyond which the extract seemed powerless to act.   Ewald also reports good results from this treatment of obesity.

Remarkable Instances of Obesity.—From time immemorial fat men and women have been the object of curiosity and the number who have exhibited themselves is incalculable.   Nearly every circus and dime museum has its example, and some of the most famous have in this way been able to accumulate fortunes.

Athenæus [c] has written quite a long discourse on persons of note who in the olden times were distinguished for their obesity.   He quotes a description of Denys, the tyrant of Heraclea, who was so enormous that he was in constant danger of suffocation ; most of the time he was in a stupor or asleep, a peculiarity of very fat people.   His doctors had needles put in the back of his chairs to keep him from falling asleep when sitting up and thus incurring the danger of suffocation.   In the same work Athenæus [d] speaks of

---

[a] 300, No. 50, 1894.   [b] Compt. rend. de la Soc. de Biol., Dec. 29, 1894.
[c] "Banquet des savants," edition of Lefebvre, etc.   [d] L. xii., chap. 12.

several sovereigns noted for their obesity ; among others he says that Ptolemy VII., son of Alexander, was so fat that, according to Posidonius, when he walked he had to be supported on both sides. Nevertheless, when he was excited at a repast, he would mount the highest couch and execute with agility his accustomed dance.

According to old chronicles the cavaliers at Rome who grew fat were condemned to lose their horses and were placed in retirement. During the Middle Ages, according to Guillaume in his " Vie de Suger," obesity was considered a grace of God.

Among the prominent people in the olden time noted for their embonpoint were Agesilas, the orator C. Licinius Calvus, who several times opposed Cicero, the actor Lucius, and others. Among men of more modern times we can mention William the Conqueror ; Charles le Gros ; Louis le Gros ; Humbert II., Count of Maurienne ; Henry I., King of Navarre ; Henry III., Count of Champagne ; Conan III., Duke of Brittany ; Sancho I., King of Leon ; Alphonse II., King of Portugal ; the Italian poet Bruni, who died in 1635 ; Vivonne, a general under Louis XIV. ; the celebrated German botanist Dillenius ; Haller ; Frederick I., King of Würtemberg, and Louis XVIII.

Probably the most famous of all the fat men was **Daniel Lambert**, born March 13, 1770, in the parish of Saint Margaret, Leicester. He did not differ from other youths until fourteen. He started to learn the trade of a die-sinker and engraver in Birmingham. At about nineteen he began to believe he would be very heavy and developed great strength. He could lift 500 pounds with ease and could kick seven feet high while standing on one leg. In 1793 he weighed 448 pounds ; at this time he became sensitive as to his appearance. In June, 1809, he weighed 52 stone 11 pounds (739 pounds), and measured over 3 yards around the body and over 1 yard around the leg. He had many visitors, and it is said that once, when the dwarf Borwilaski came to see him, he asked the little man how much cloth he needed for a suit. When told about ¾ of a yard, he replied that one of his sleeves would be ample. Another famous fat man was **Edward Bright**, sometimes called " the fat man of Essex." He weighed 616 pounds.[a] In the same journal that records Bright's weight is an account of a man exhibited in Holland who weighed 503 pounds.

Wadd, a physician, himself an enormous man, wrote a treatise on obesity and used his own portrait for a frontispiece. He speaks of Doctor Beddoes, who was so uncomfortably fat that a lady of Clifton called him a " walking feather bed." He mentions Doctor Stafford, who was so enormous that this epitaph was ascribed to him :—

> "Take heed, O good traveler ! and do not tread hard,
> For here lies Dr. Stafford, in all this churchyard."

Wadd has gathered some instances, a few of which will be cited. At

[a] 476, 1827, 361.

Staunton, January 2, 1816, there died Samuel Sugars, Gent., who weighed with a single wood coffin 50 stone (700 pounds). Jacob Powell died in 1754, weighing 560 pounds. It took 16 men to carry him to his grave.[a] Mr. Baker of Worcester, supposed to be larger than Bright, was interred in a coffin that was larger than an ordinary hearse. In 1797 there was buried Philip Hayes, a professor of music, who was as heavy as Bright (616 pounds).

Mr. Spooner, an eminent farmer of Warwickshire, who died in 1775, aged fifty-seven, weighed 569 pounds and measured over 4 feet across the shoulders. The two brothers Stoneclift of Halifax, Yorkshire, together weighed 980 pounds.[b]

Keysler in his travels speaks of a corpulent Englishman who in passing through Savoy had to use 12 chairmen ; he says that the man weighed 550 pounds. It is recorded on the tombstone of James Parsons, a fat man of Teddington, who died March 7, 1743, that he had often eaten a whole shoulder of mutton and a peck of hasty pudding. Keysler mentions a young Englishman living in Lincoln who was accustomed to eat 18 pounds of meat daily. He died in 1724 at the age of twenty-eight, weighing 530 pounds. In 1815 there died in Trenaw, in Cornwall, a person known as " Giant Chillcot." He measured at the breast 6 feet 9 inches and weighed 460 pounds. One of his stockings held 6 gallons of wheat. In 1822 there was reported to be a Cambridge student who could not go out in the daytime without exciting astonishment. The fat of his legs overhung his shoes like the fat in the legs of Lambert and Bright. Dr. Short mentions a lady who died of corpulency in her twenty-fifth year weighing over 50 stone (700 pounds). Catesby speaks of a man who weighed 500 pounds, [c] and Coe mentions another who weighed 584 pounds.[d] Fabricius and Godart speak of obesity so excessive as to cause death. There is a case reported from the French of a person who weighed 800 pounds.[e] Smetius [f] speaks of George Fredericus, an office-holder in Brandenburgh, who weighed 427 pounds.

Dupuytren [g] gives the history of Marie Françoise-Clay, who attained such celebrity for her obesity. She was born in poverty, reached puberty at thirteen, and married at twenty-five, at which age she was already the stoutest woman of her neighborhood notwithstanding her infirmity. She followed her husband, who was an old-clothes dealer, afoot from town to town. She bore six children, in whom nothing extraordinary was noticed. The last one was born when she was thirty-five years old. Neither the births, her travels, nor her poverty, which sometimes forced her to beg at church doors, arrested the progress of the obesity. At the age of forty she was 5 feet 1 inch high and one inch greater about the waist. Her head was small and her neck was entirely obliterated. Her breasts were over a yard in circumference and

a 374, vol. xxiv., 483.   b 629, vol. xliv., 100.   c 629, No. 479.
d 629, vol. xlvii., 75.   e 462, vol. xiii., 65.   f 730, 579.   g 302, vol. iv.

hung as low as the umbilicus. Her arms were elevated and kept from her body by the fat in her axillæ. Her belly was enormous and was augmented by six pregnancies. Her thighs and haunches were in proportion to her general contour. At forty she ceased to menstruate and soon became afflicted with organic heart disease.

Fournier [a] quotes an instance of a woman in Paris who at twenty-four, the time of her death, weighed 486 pounds. Not being able to mount any conveyance or carriage in the city, she walked from place to place, finding difficulty not in progression, but in keeping her equilibrium. Roger Byrne, who lived in Rosenalis, Queen's County, Ireland, died of excessive fatness at the age of fifty-four, weighing 52 stone. Percy and Laurent speak of a young German of twenty who weighed 450 pounds. At birth he weighed 13 pounds, at six months 42, and at four years 150 pounds. He was 5 feet 5 inches tall and the same in circumference. William Campbell, the landlord of the Duke of Wellington in Newcastle-on-Tyne, was 6 feet 4 inches tall and weighed 728 pounds. He measured 96 inches around the shoulders, 85 inches around the waist, and 35 inches around the calf. He was born at Glasgow in 1856, and was not quite twenty-two when last measured. To illustrate the rate of augmentation, he weighed 4 stone at nine months and at ten years 18 stone. He was one of a family of seven children. His appetite was not more than the average, and he was moderate as regards the use of liquors, but a great smoker. Notwithstanding his corpulency, he was intelligent and affable.[b]

Miss Conley, a member of an American traveling circus, who weighed 479 pounds,[c] was smothered in bed by rolling over on her face; she was unable to turn on her back without assistance.

There was a girl who died at Plaisance near Paris in 1890 who weighed 470 pounds or more. In 1889 an impresario undertook to exhibit her; but eight men could not move her from her room, and as she could not pass through the door the idea was abandoned.[d]

There was a colored woman who died near Baltimore[e] who weighed 850 pounds, exceeding the great Daniel Lambert by 120 pounds. The journal reporting this case quotes the Medical Record as saying that there was a man in North Carolina, who was born in 1798, who was 7 feet 8 inches tall and weighed over 1000 pounds, probably the largest man that ever lived. Hutchison[f] says that he saw in the Infirmary at Kensington, under Porter's care, a remarkable example of obesity. The woman was only just able to walk about and presented a close resemblance to Daniel Lambert. Obesity forced her to leave her occupation. The accumulation of fat on the abdomen, back, and thighs was enormous.

According to a recent number of La Liberté, a young woman of Penn-

a 302, iv., 196.   b 476, 1878, i 297.   c 224, 1883, ii., 284.
d 536, 1890, ii., 112.   e 536, 1888, ii., 587.   f 166, vol. iv., 358.

sylvania, although only sixteen years old, weighs 450 pounds. Her waist measures 61 inches in circumference and her neck 22 inches. The same paper says that on one of the quays of Paris may be seen a wine-shop keeper with whom this Pennsylvania girl could not compare. It is said that this curiosity of the Notre-Dame quarter uses three large chairs while sitting behind her specially constructed bar. There is another Paris report of a man living in Switzerland who weighs more than 40 stone (560 pounds) and eats five times as much as an ordinary person. When traveling he finds the greatest difficulty in entering an ordinary railway carriage, and as a rule contents himself in the luggage van. Figure 171 represents an extremely fat woman with a well-developed beard. To end this list of obese individuals, we mention an old gentleman living in San Francisco who, having previously been thin, gained 14 pounds in his seventieth year and 14 pounds each of seven succeeding years.

Fig. 171.—An example of obesity with hirsuties.

Simulation of Obesity.— General dropsy, elephantiasis, lipomata, myxedema, and various other affections in which there is a hypertrophic change of the connective tissues may be mistaken for general obesity ; on the other hand, a fatty, pendulous abdomen may simulate the appearances of pregnancy or even of ovarian cyst (Fig. 172).

Dercum of Philadelphia [a] has described a variety of obesity which he has called " **adiposis dolorosa,**" in which there is an enormous growth of fat, sometimes limited, sometimes spread all over the body, this condition differing from that of general lipomatosis in its rarity, in the mental symptoms, in the headache, and the generally painful condition complained of. In some of the cases examined by Dercum he found that the thyroid was indurated and infiltrated by calcareous deposits. The disease is not myxedema because there is no peculiar physiognomy, no spade-like hands nor infiltrated skin, no alteration of the speech, etc. Dercum considers it a connective-tissue dystrophy—a fatty metamorphosis of various stages, possibly a neuritis. The first of Dercum's cases (Fig. 173) was a widow of Irish birth, who died

[a] 124, Nov. 1892.

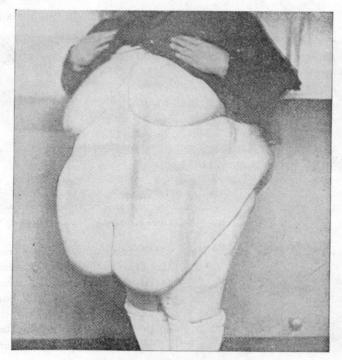

Fig. 172.—Fatty abdominal wall simulating ovarian cyst (Baldy).

Fig. 173.—" Adiposis dolorosa ' (Dercum).

both alcoholic and syphilitic. When forty-eight or forty-nine her arms began to enlarge. In June, 1887, the enlargement affected the shoulders.

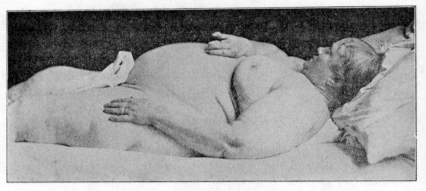

Fig. 174.—" Adiposis dolorosa" (Dercum).

arms, back, and sides of the chest. The parts affected were elastic, and there was no pitting. In some places the fat was lobulated, in others it appeared as though filled with bundles of worms. The skin was not thickened and the muscles were not involved. In the right arm there was unendurable pain to the touch, and this was present in a lesser degree in the left arm. Cutaneous sensibility was lessened. On June 13th a chill was followed by herpes over the left arm and chest, and later on the back and on the front of the chest. The temperature was normal. The second case was a married Englishwoman of sixty-four (Fig. 174). The enlarged tissue was very unevenly distributed, and sensibility was the same as in the previous case. At the woman's death she weighed 300 pounds, and the fat over the abdomen was three inches thick. The third case was a German woman in whom were seen soft, fat-like masses in various situations over either biceps, over the outer and posterior aspect of either arm, and two large masses over the belly; there was excessive prominence of the mons veneris. At the

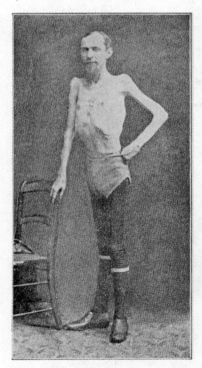

Fig. 175.—J. W. Coffey, the "living skeleton."

autopsy the heart weighed 8½ ounces, and the fat below the umbilicus was seven inches thick.

Abnormal Leanness.—In contrast to the fat men are the so-called "living skeletons," or men who have attained notice by reason of absence of the

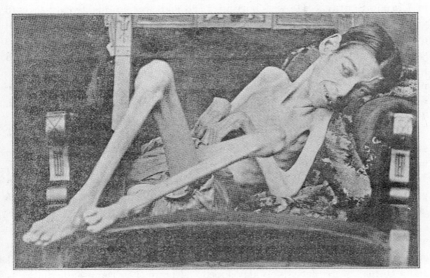

Fig. 176.—Rosa Lee Plemons.

normal adipose tissue. The semimythical poet Philotus was so thin that it was said that he fastened lead on his shoes to prevent his being blown away,— a condition the opposite of that of Dionysius of Heraclea, who, after choking to death from his fat, could hardly be moved to his grave.

Fig. 177.—Muscular atrophy associated with nondevelopment.

In March, 1754, there died in Glamorganshire of mere old age and gradual decay a little Welshman, Hopkin Hopkins, aged seventeen years. He had been recently exhibited in London as a natural curiosity; he had never weighed over 17 pounds, and for the last three years of his life never more than 12 pounds. His parents still had six children left, all of whom were normal and healthy except a girl of twelve, who only weighed 18 pounds and bore marks of old age.[a]

There was a "living skeleton" brought to England in 1825 by the name of **Claude Seurat.** He was born in 1798 and was in his twenty-seventh year. He usually ate in the course of a day a penny roll and drank a small quantity of wine. His skeleton was plainly visible, over which the skin was stretched tightly. The distance from the chest to the spine was less than 3 inches, and internally this distance was less. The pulsations of the heart were plainly visible. He was in good health and slept well. His voice was very weak and shrill. The circumference of this man's biceps was only 4 inches. The artist Cruikshank has made several drawings of Seurat.

Calvin Edson was another living skeleton. In 1813 he was in the army at the battle of Plattsburg, and had lain down in the cold and become benumbed. At this time he weighed 125 pounds and was twenty-five years old. In 1830 he weighed but 60 pounds, though 5 feet 4 inches tall. He was in perfect health and could chop a cord of wood without fatigue; he was the father of four children.

Salter[b] speaks of a man in 1873 who was thirty-two years of age and only weighed 49 pounds. He was 4 feet 6 inches tall: his forehead measured in circumference $20\frac{1}{2}$ inches and his chest 27 inches. His genitals, both internal and external, were defectively developed. Figure 175 represents the well-known Ohio "living skeleton," J. W. Coffey, who has been exhibited all over the Continent. His good health and appetite were proverbial among his acquaintances.

In some instances the so-called "living skeletons" are merely cases of extreme muscular atrophy. As a prominent example of this class the exhibitionist, Rosa Lee Plemons (Fig. 176) at the age of eighteen weighed only 27 pounds. Figure 177 shows another case of extraordinary atrophic condition of all the tissues of the body associated with nondevelopment. These persons are always sickly and exhibit all the symptoms of progressive muscular atrophy, and cannot therefore be classed with the true examples of thinness, in which the health is but slightly affected or possibly perfect health is enjoyed.

a 374, vol. xxiv., 191.   b 476, 1873, ii., 903.

CHAPTER VIII.

LONGEVITY.

Scope of the Present Article.—The limits of space in this work render impossible a scientific discussion upon the most interesting subject of longevity, and the reader is referred to some of the modern works devoted exclusively to this subject. In reviewing the examples of extreme age found in the human race it will be our object to lay before the reader the most remarkable instances of longevity that have been authentically recorded, to cite the source of the information, when possible to give explanatory details, and to report any relative points of value and interest. Throughout the article occasional facts will be given to show in what degree character, habit, and temperament influence longevity, and in what state of mind and body and under what circumstances man has obtained the highest age.

General Opinions.—There have been many learned authorities who invariably discredit all accounts of extraordinary age, and contend that there has never been an instance of a man living beyond the century mark whose age has been substantiated by satisfactory proof. Such extremists as Sir G. Cornewall Lewis and Thoms contend that since the Christian era no person of royal or noble line mentioned in history whose birth was authentically recorded at its occurrence has reached one hundred years. They have taken the worst station in life in which to find longevity as their field of observation. Longevity is always most common in the middle and lower classes, in which we cannot expect to find the records preserved with historical correctness.

The Testimony of Statistics.—Walford[813] in his wonderful "Encyclopedia of Insurance" says that in England the "Royal Exchange" for a period of one hundred and thirty-five years had insured no life which survived ninety-six. The "London Assurance" for the same period had no clients who lived over ninety, and the "Equitable" had only one at ninety-six. In an English Tontine there was in 1693 a person who died at one hundred; and in Perth there lived a nominee at one hundred and twenty-two and another at one hundred and seven. On the other hand, a writer in the Strand Magazine points out that an insurance investigator some years ago gathered a list of 225 centenarians of almost every social rank and many nationalities, but the majority of them Britons or Russians.

In reviewing Walford's statistics we must remember that it has only been in recent years that the middle and lower classes of people have taken insurance on their lives. Formerly only the wealthy and those exposed to early demise were in the habit of insuring.

Dr. Ogle of the English Registrar-General's Department gives tables of expectancy that show that 82 males and 225 females out of 1,000,000 are alive at one hundred years. The figures are based on the death-rates of the years 1871–80.

The researches of Hardy in the thirteenth, fourteenth, fifteenth, and sixteenth centuries are said to indicate that three-score-and-ten was considered old age ; yet many old tombstones and monuments contain inscriptions recording age far beyond this, and even the pages of ordinary biographies disprove the alleged results of Hardy's research.

In all statistical work of an individual type the histories of the lower classes are almost excluded ; in the olden times only the lives and movements of the most prominent are thought worthy of record. The reliable parish register is too often monopolized by the gentry, inferior births not being thought worth recording.

Many eminent scientists say that **the natural term of the life** of an animal is five times the period needed for its development. Taking twenty-one as the time of maturity in man, the natural term of human life would be one hundred and five. Sir Richard Owen fixes it at one hundred and three and a few months.

Censuses of Centenarians.—Dr. Farr, the celebrated English Registrar-General, is credited with saying that out of every 1,000,000 people in England only 223 live to be one hundred years old, making an average of one to 4484. French[a] says that during a period of ten years, from 1881 to 1890, in Massachusetts, there were 203 deaths of persons past the age of one hundred, making an average, with a population of 394,484, of one in 1928. Of French's centenarians 165 were between one hundred and one hundred and five ; 35 were between one hundred and five and one hundred and ten ; five were between one hundred and ten and one hundred and fifteen ; and one was one hundred and eighteen. Of the 203, 153 were females and 50 males. There are 508 people in Iowa who are more than ninety years of age. There are 21 who are more than one hundred years old. One person is one hundred and fifteen years old, two are one hundred and fourteen, and the remaining 18 are from one hundred to one hundred and seven.

In the British Medical Journal for 1886 there is an account of a report of centenarians. Fifty-two cases were analyzed. One who doubts the possibility of a man reaching one hundred would find this report of interest.

The Paris correspondent to the London Telegraph is accredited with the following :—

" A census of centenarians has been taken in France, and the results, which

[a] 638, Oct., 1894.

have been published, show that there are now alive in this country 213 persons who are over one hundred years old. Of these 147 are women, the alleged stronger sex being thus only able to show 66 specimens who are managing to still " husband out life's taper " after the lapse of a century. The preponderance of centenarians of the supposed weaker sex has led to the revival of some amusing theories tending to explain this phenomenon. One cause of the longevity of women is stated to be, for instance, their propensity to talk much and to gossip, perpetual prattle being highly conducive, it is said, to the active circulation of the blood, while the body remains unfatigued and undamaged. More serious theorists or statisticians, while commenting on the subject of the relative longevity of the sexes, attribute the supremacy of woman in the matter to the well-known cause, namely, that in general she leads a more calm and unimpassioned existence than a man, whose life is so often one of toil, trouble, and excitement. Setting aside these theories, however, the census of French centenarians is not devoid of interest in some of its details. At Rocroi an old soldier who fought under the First Napoleon in Russia passed the century limit last year. A wearer of the St. Helena medal—a distinction awarded to survivors of the Napoleonic campaigns, and who lives at Grand Fayt, also in the Nord—is one hundred and three years old, and has been for the last sixty-eight years a sort of rural policeman in his native commune. It is a rather remarkable fact in connection with the examples of longevity cited that in almost every instance the centenarian is a person in the humblest rank of life. According to the compilers of these records, France can claim the honor of having possessed the oldest woman of modern times. This venerable dame, having attained one hundred and fifty years, died peacefully in a hamlet in the Haute Garonne, where she had spent her prolonged existence, subsisting during the closing decade of her life on goat's milk and cheese. The woman preserved all her mental faculties to the last, but her body became attenuated to an extraordinary degree, and her skin was like parchment."

In the last ten years the St. James' Gazette has kept track of 378 centenarians, of whom 143 were men and 235 were women. A writer to the Strand Magazine tells of 14 centenarians living in Great Britain within the last half-dozen years.

It may be interesting to review the statistics of Haller, who has collected the greatest number of instances of extreme longevity. He found :—

1000 persons who lived from 100 to 110	15 persons who lived from 130 to 140
60 " " " " 110 to 120	6 " " " " 140 to 150
29 " " " " 120 to 130	1 person " " to 169

Effect of Class-Influences, Occupation, etc.

Effect of Class-Influences, Occupation, etc.—Unfortunately for the sake of authenticity, all the instances of extreme age in this country have been from persons in the lower walks of life or from obscure parts of the country, where little else than hearsay could be procured to verify them. It must also be said that it is only among people of this class that we can expect to find parallels of the instances of extreme longevity of former times. The inhabitants of the higher stations of life, the population of thickly settled communities, are living in an age and under conditions almost incompatible with longevity. In fact, the strain of nervous energy made necessary by the changed conditions of business and mode of living really predisposes to premature decay.

Those who object to the reliability of reports of postcentenarianism seem to lose sight of these facts, and because absolute proof and parallel cannot be obtained they deny the possibility without giving the subject full thought and reason. As tending to substantiate the multitude of instances are the opinions of such authorities as Hufeland, Buffon, Haller, and Flourens. Walter Savage Landor on being told that a man in Russia was living at one hundred and thirty-two replied that he was possibly older, as people when they get on in years are prone to remain silent as to the number of their years—a statement that can hardly be denied. One of the strongest disbelievers in extreme age almost disproved in his own life the statement that there were no centenarians.

It is commonly believed that in **the earliest periods of the world's history** the lives of the inhabitants were more youthful and perfect ; that these primitive men had gigantic size, incredible strength, and most astonishing duration of life. It is to this tendency that we are indebted for the origin of many romantic tales. Some have not hesitated to ascribe to our forefather Adam the height of 900 yards and the age of almost a thousand years ; but according to Hufeland acute theologians have shown that the chronology of the early ages was not the same as that used in the present day. According to this same authority Hensler has proved that the year at the time of Abraham consisted of but three months, that it was afterward extended to eight, and finally in the time of Joseph to twelve. Certain Eastern nations, it is said, still reckon but three months to the year ; this substantiates the opinion of Hensler, and, as Hufeland says, it would be inexplicable why the life of man should be shortened nearly one-half immediately after the flood.

Accepting these conclusions as correct, the highest recorded age, that of Methuselah, nine hundred years, will be reduced to about two hundred, an age that can hardly be called impossible in the face of such an abundance of reports, to which some men of comparatively modern times have approached, and which such substantial authorities as Buffon, Hufeland, and Flourens believed possible.

Alchemy and the " Elixir of Life."—The desire for long life and the acquisition of wealth have indirectly been the stimulus to medical and physical investigation, eventually evolving science as we have it now. The fundamental principles of nearly every branch of modern science were the gradual metamorphoses of the investigations of the old searchers after the " philosopher's stone " and " elixir of life." The long hours of study and experiment in the chase for this will-o'-the-wisp were of vast benefit to the coming generations ; and to these deluded philosophers of the Middle Ages, and even of ancient times, we are doubtless indebted for much in this age of advancement.

With a credulous people to work upon, many of the claimants of the discovery of the coveted secret of eternal life must be held as rank impostors claiming ridiculous ages for themselves. In the twelfth century Artephius claimed that by the means of his discovery he had attained one thousand and twenty-five years. Shortly after him came Alan de Lisle of Flanders with a reputed fabulous age. In 1244 Albertus Magnus announced himself as the discoverer. In 1555 the celebrated Doctor Dee appeared on the scene and had victims by the score. Then came the Rosicrucians. Count Saint-Germain claimed the secret of the " philosopher's stone " and declared to the Court of Louis XV. that he was two thousand years old, and a precursor of the mythical " Wandering Jew," who has been immortalized in prose and rhyme and in whose existence a great mass of the people recently believed. The last of the charlatans who claimed possession of the secret of perpetual life was Joseph Balsamo, who called himself " Count of Cagliostro." He was born in Italy in 1743 and acquired a world-wide reputation for his alleged occult powers and acquisition of the " philosopher's stone." He died in 1795, and since then no one has generally inspired the superstitious with credence in this well-worn myth. The ill-fated Ponce de Leon when he discovered Florida, in spite of his superior education, announced his firm belief in the land of the " Fountain of Perpetual Youth," in the pursuit of which he had risked his fortune and life.

We wish to emphasize that we by no means assume the responsibility of the authenticity of the cases to be quoted, but expressing belief in their possibility, we shall mention some of the **extraordinary instances of longevity** derived from an exhaustive research of the literature of all times. This venerable gallery of Nestors will include those of all periods and nations, but as the modern references are more available greater attention will be given to them.

Turning first to the history of the earlier nations, we deduce from **Jewish history** that Abraham lived to one hundred and seventy-five ; Isaac, likewise a tranquil, peaceful man, to one hundred and eighty ; Jacob, who was crafty and cunning, to one hundred and forty-seven ; Ishmael, a warrior, to one hundred and thirty-seven ; and Joseph, to one hundred and ten. Moses, a man of extraordinary vigor, which, however, he exposed to great cares and fatigues, attained the advanced age of one hundred and twenty ; and the warlike and ever-active Joshua lived to one hundred and ten. Lejoucourt[a] gives the following striking parallels : John Gower lived to one hundred and seventy-two, and Abraham to one hundred and seventy-five ; Susan, the wife of Gower, lived to one hundred and sixty-four, and Sarah, the wife of Abraham,

a " Galerie des Centenaires."

to one hundred and twenty-seven. The eldest son of the Gower couple was one hundred and fifteen when last seen, and Isaac, the son of Abraham and Sarah, lived to one hundred and eighty.

However replete with fables may be the history of the Kings of **Egypt,** none attained a remarkable age, and the record of the common people is incomplete or unavailable.

If we judge from the accounts of Lucian we must form a high idea of the great age of the Seres, or **ancient Chinese.** Lucian ascribes this longevity to their habit of drinking excessive quantities of water.

Among **the Greeks** we find several instances of great age in men of prominence. Hippocrates divided life into seven periods, living himself beyond the century mark. Aristotle made three divisions,—the growing period, the stationary period, and the period of decline. Solon made ten divisions of life, and Varro made five. Ovid ingeniously compares life to the four seasons. Epimenides of Crete is said to have lived one hundred and fifty-seven years, the last fifty-seven of which he slept in a cavern at night. Gorgias, a teacher, lived to one hundred and eight ; Democritus, a naturalist, attained one hundred and nine ; Zeno, the founder of the Stoics, lived to one hundred ; and Diogenes, the frugal and slovenly, reached ninety years. Despite his life of exposure, Hippocrates lived to one hundred and nine ; and Galen, the prince of physicians after him, who was naturally of a feeble constitution, lived past eighty, and few of the followers of his system of medicine, which stood for thirteen centuries, surpassed him in point of age.

Among **the Romans,** Orbilis, Corvinus, Fabius, and Cato, the enemy of the physicians, approximated the century mark.

A valuable collection relative to the duration of life in the time of the Emperor Vespasian has been preserved for us by Pliny from the records of a census, a perfectly reliable and creditable source. In 76 A. D. there were living in that part of Italy which lies between the Apennines and the Po 124 persons who had attained the age of one hundred and upward. There were 54 of one hundred ; 57 of one hundred and ten ; 2 of one hundred and twenty-five ; 4 of one hundred and thirty ; 4 of from one hundred and thirty-five to one hundred and thirty-seven, and 3 of one hundred and forty. In Placentia there was a man of one hundred and thirty and at Faventia a woman of one hundred and thirty-two. According to Hufeland,[427] the bills of mortality of Ulpian agree in the most striking manner with those of our great modern cities.

Among **hermits and ecclesiastics,** as would be the natural inference from their regular lives, many instances of longevity are recorded. John was supposed to be ninety-three ; Paul the hermit was one hundred and thirteen ; Saint Anthony lived to one hundred and five ; James the hermit to one hundred and four ; Saint Epithanius lived to one hundred and fifteen ; Simeon Stylites to one hundred and twelve ; Saint Mungo was accredited with one hundred and eighty-five years (Spottiswood), and Saint David attained one hundred and forty-six. Saint Polycarpe suffered martyrdom at over one hundred, and Simon Cleophas was Bishop of Jerusalem at one hundred and twenty.

Brahmin priests of India are known to attain incredible age, and one of the secrets of the adepts of the Buddhist faith is doubtless the knowledge of the best means of attaining very old age. Unless cut off by violence or accident the priests invariably become venerable patriarchs.

Influence of Mental Culture.—Men of thought have at all times been distinguished for their age. Among the venerable sages are Appolonius of Tyana, a follower of Pythagoras, who lived to over one hundred; Xenophilus, also a Pythagorean, was one hundred and six; Demonax, a Stoic, lived past one hundred; Isocrates was ninety-eight, and Solon, Sophocles, Pindar, Anacreon, and Xenophon were octogenarians.

In more modern times we find men of science and literature who have attained advanced age. Kant, Buffon, Goethe, Fontenelle, and Newton were all over eighty. Michael Angelo and Titian lived to eighty-nine and ninety-nine respectively. Harvey, the discoverer of the circulation; Hans Sloane, the celebrated president of the Royal Society in London; Plater, the Swiss physician; Duverney, the anatomist, as well as his confrére, Tenon, lived to be octogenarians. Many men have displayed activity when past four score. Brougham at eighty-two and Lyndhurst at eighty-eight could pour forth words of eloquence and sagacity for hours at a time. Landor wrote his " Imaginary Conversations " when eighty-five, and Somerville his " Molecular Science " at eighty-eight; Isaac Walton was active with his pen at ninety; Hahnemann married at eighty and was working at ninety-one.

J. B. Bailey has published a biography of " Modern Methusalehs," [183] which includes histories of the lives of Cornaro, Titian, Pletho, Herschell, Montefiore, Routh, and others. Chevreul, the centenarian chemist, has only lately died. Gladstone, Bismarck, and von Moltke exemplify vigor in age. In the Senate of the United States, Senators Edmunds, Sherman, Hoar, Morrill, and other elderly statesmen display as much vigor as their youthful colleagues. Instances of vigor in age could be cited in every profession and these few examples are only mentioned as typical. At a recent meeting of the Society of English Naturalists, Lord Kelvin announced that during the last year 26 members had died at an average age of seventy-six and a half years; one reached the age of ninety-nine years, another ninety-seven, a third ninety-five, etc.

In commenting on the perfect compatibility of activity with longevity, the National Popular Review says :—

" Great men usually carry their full mental vigor and activity into old age. M. Chevreul, M. De Lesseps, Gladstone, and Bismarck are evidences of this anthropologic fact. Pius IX., although living in tempestuous times, reached a great age in full possession of all his faculties, and the dramatist Crebillon composed his last dramatic piece at ninety-four, while Michael Angelo was still painting his great canvases at ninety-eight, and Titian at ninety still worked with all the vigor of his earlier years. The Austrian General Melas was still in the saddle and active at eighty-nine, and would have probably won Marengo but for the inopportune arrival of Desaix. The Venetian Doge Henry Dandolo, born at the beginning of the eleventh century, who lost his eyesight when a young man, was nevertheless subsequently raised to the highest office in the republic, managed successfully to conduct various wars, and at the advanced age of eighty-three, in alliance with the French, besieged and captured Constantinople. Fontenelle was as gay-spirited at ninety-eight as in his fortieth year, and the philosopher Newton worked away at his tasks at the age of eighty-three with the same ardor that animated his middle age. Cornaro was as happy at ninety as at fifty, and in far better health at the age of ninety-five than he had enjoyed at thirty.

" These cases all tend to show the value and benefits to be derived from an actively cultivated brain in making a long life one of comfort and of usefulness to its owner. The brain and spirits need never grow old, even if our bodies will insist on getting rickety and in falling by the wayside. But an abstemious life will drag even the old body along to centenarian limits in a tolerable state of preservation and usefulness. The foregoing list can be lengthened out with an indefinite number of names, but it is sufficiently long to show what good spirits and an active brain will do to lighten up the weight of old age. When we contemplate the Doge Dandolo at eighty-three animating his troops from the deck of his galley, and the brave old blind King of Bohemia falling in the thickest of the fray at Crécy, it would seem as if there was no excuse for either physical, mental, or moral decrepitude short of the age of four score and ten."

Emperors and kings, in short, the great ones of the earth, pay the penalty of their power by associate worriment and care. In ancient history we can only find a few rulers who attained four score, and this is equally the case in modern times. In the whole catalogue of the Roman and German Emperors, reckoning from Augustus to William I., only six have attained eighty years. Gordian, Valerian, Anastasius, and Justinian were octogenarians, Tiberius was eighty-eight at his death, and Augustus Cæsar was eighty-six. Frederick the Great, in spite of his turbulent life, attained a rare age for a king, seventy-six. William I. seems to be the only other exception.

Of 300 Popes who may be counted, no more than five attained the age of eighty. Their mode of life, though conducive to longevity in the minor offices of the Church, seems to be overbalanced by the cares of the Pontificate.

Personal Habits.—According to Hufeland and other authorities on longevity, sobriety, regular habits, labor in the open air, exercise short of fatigue, calmness of mind, moderate intellectual power, and a family life are among the chief aids to longevity. For this reason we find the extraordinary instances of longevity among those people who amidst bodily labor and in the open air lead a simple life, agreeable to nature. Such are farmers, gardeners, hunters, soldiers, and sailors. In these situations man may still maintain the age of one hundred and fifty or even one hundred and sixty.

Possibly **the most celebrated case of longevity** on record is that of **Henry Jenkins.** This remarkable old man was born in Yorkshire in 1501 and died in 1670, aged one hundred and sixty-nine. He remembered the battle of Flodden Field in 1513, at which time he was twelve years old. It was proved from the registers of the Chancery and other courts that he had appeared in evidence one hundred and forty years before his death and had had an oath administered to him. In the office of the King's Remembrancer is a record of a deposition in which he appears as a witness at one hundred and fifty-seven. When above one hundred he was able to swim a rapid stream.

Thomas Parr (or Parre), among Englishmen known as " old Parr," was a poor farmer's servant, born in 1483. He remained single until eighty. His first wife lived thirty-two years, and eight years after her death, at the age of one hundred and twenty, he married again. Until his one hundred and thirtieth year he performed his ordinary duties, and at this age was even accustomed to thresh. He was visited by Thomas, Earl of Arundel and Surrey, and was persuaded to visit the King in London. His intelligence and venerable demeanor impressed every one, and crowds thronged to see him and pay him homage. The journey to London, together with the excitement and change of mode of living, undoubtedly hastened his death, which occurred in less than a year. He was one hundred and fifty-two years and nine months old, and had lived under nine Kings of England. Harvey[a] examined his body, and at the necropsy his internal organs were found in a most perfect state. His cartilages were not even ossified, as is the case generally with the very aged. The slightest cause of death could not be discovered, and the general impression was that he died from being over-fed and too-well treated in London. His great-grandson was said to have died in this century in Cork at the age of one hundred and three. Parr is celebrated by a monument reared to his memory in Westminster Abbey.

The author of the Dutch dictionary entitled " Het algemen historish Vanderbok " says that there was a peasant in Hungary named **Jean Korin** who was one hundred and seventy-two and his wife was one hundred and sixty-four ; they had lived together one hundred and forty-eight years, and had a son at the time of their death who was one hundred and sixteen.

Setrasch Czarten, or, as he is called by Baily,[184] Petratsh Zartan, was also born in Hungary at a village four miles from Teneswaer in 1537. He

a 629, 1731, iii., 306, 4th ed.

lived for one hundred and eighty years in one village and died at the age of one hundred and eighty-seven, or, as another authority has it, one hundred and eighty-five. A few days before his death he had walked a mile to wait at the post-office for the arrival of travelers and to ask for succor, which, on account of his remarkable age, was rarely refused him. He had lost nearly all his teeth and his beard and hair were white. He was accustomed to eat a little cake the Hungarians call *kalatschen*, with which he drank milk. After each repast he took a glass of *eau-de-vie*. His son was living at ninety-seven and his descendants to the fifth generation embellished his old age. Shortly before his death Count Wallis had his portrait painted. Comparing his age with that of others, we find that he was five years older than the Patriarch Isaac, ten more than Abraham, thirty-seven more than Nahor, sixteen more than Henry Jenkins, and thirty-three more than "old Parr."

Sundry Instances of Great Age.—In a churchyard near Cardiff, Glamorganshire, is the following inscription : "Here lieth the body of William Edwards, of Cacreg, who departed this life 24th February, Anno Domini 1668, anno ætatis suæ one hundred and sixty-eight."

Jonas Warren of Balydole died in 1787 aged one hundred and sixty-seven. He was called the "father of the fishermen" in his vicinity, as he had followed the trade for ninety-five years.

The Journal de Madrid, 1775, contains the account of a South American negress living in Spanish possessions who was one hundred and seventy-four years of age. The description is written by a witness, who declares that she told of events which confirmed her age. This is possibly the oft-quoted case that was described in the London Chronicle, October 5, 1780, Louisa Truxo, who died in South America at the age of one hundred and seventy-five.

Hufeland speaks of Joseph Surrington, who died near Bergen, Norway, at the age of one hundred and sixty. Marvelous to relate, he had one living son of one hundred and three and another of nine. There has been recently reported from Vera Cruz, Mexico, in the town of Teluca, where the registers are carefully and efficiently kept, the death of a man one hundred and ninety-two years old—almost a modern version of Methuselah.[a] Buffon describes a man who lived to be one hundred and sixty-five. Martin[b] mentions a man of one hundred and eighty. There was a Polish peasant who reached one hundred and fifty-seven and had constantly labored up to his one hundred and forty-fifth year, always clad lightly, even in cold weather.[c] Voigt[d] admits the extreme age of one hundred and sixty.

There was a woman living in Moscow in 1848 who was said to be one hundred and sixty-eight ; she had been married five times and was one hundred and twenty-one at her last wedding. D'Azara[e] records the age of one hundred and eighty, and Rocquefort[f] speaks of two cases at one hundred and fifty.

a Quoted in "Practical Medicine." N.Y., 1895.   b 629, No. 233.   c 302, xxix.   d 503, i., 141.
e "Voyages dans l'Amerique Meridian," ii., 142.   f "Hist. des Antilles," i., 431.

There are stories of an Englishman who lived in the sixteenth century to be two hundred and seven, and there is a parallel case cited.[a]

Van Owen tabulates 331 cases of deaths between 110 and 120, 91 between 120 and 130, 37 between 130 and 140, 11 at 150, and 17 beyond this age. While not vouching for the authenticity in each case, he has always given the sources of information.

Quite celebrated in English history by Raleigh and Bacon was the venerable Countess Desmond, who appeared at Court in 1614, being one hundred and forty years old and in full possession of all her powers, mental and physical. There are several portraits of her at this advanced age still to be seen. Lord Bacon also mentions a man named Marcus Appenius, living in Rimini, who was registered by a Vespasian tax-collector as being one hundred and fifty.

There are records of Russians who have lived to one hundred and twenty-five, one hundred and thirty, one hundred and thirty-five, one hundred and forty-five, and one hundred and fifty.[b] Nemnich[583] speaks of Thomas Newman living in Bridlington at one hundred and fifty-three years. Nemnich is confirmed in his account of Thomas Newman by his tombstone in Yorkshire, dated 1542.

In the chancel of the Honington Church, Wiltshire, is a black marble monument to the memory of G. Stanley, gent., who died in 1719, aged one hundred and fifty-one.

There was a Dane named Draakenburg, born in 1623, who until his ninety-first year served as a seaman in the royal navy, and had spent fifteen years of his life in Turkey as a slave in the greatest misery. He was married at one hundred and ten to a woman of sixty, but outlived her a long time; in his one hundred and thirtieth year he again fell in love with a young country girl, who, as may well be supposed, rejected him. He died in 1772 in his one hundred and forty-sixth year. Jean Effingham died in Cornwall in 1757 in his one hundred and forty-fourth year. He was born in the reign of James I. and was a soldier at the battle of Hochstadt; he never drank strong liquors and rarely ate meat; eight days before his death he walked three miles.[302]

Bridget Devine, the well-known inhabitant of Olean Street, Manchester, died at the age of one hundred and forty-seven in 1845.[184] On the register of the Cheshire Parish is a record of the death of Thomas Hough of Frodsam in 1591 at the age of one hundred and forty-one.

Peter Garden of Auchterless died in 1775 at the age of one hundred and thirty-one. He had seen and talked with Henry Jenkins about the battle of Flodden Field, at which the latter was present when a boy of twelve. It seems almost incredible that a man could say that he had heard the story of an event which had happened two hundred and sixty-three years before related by the lips of an eye-witness to that event; nevertheless, in this case it

a 708, 1724, 636.   b 118, 1803, 57 ; 1805, 264 ; 1807, 384.

was true. A remarkable instance of longevity in one family has recently been published in the St. Thomas's Hospital Gazette. Mrs. B., born in 1630 (five years after the accession of Charles I.), died March 13, 1732. She was tended in her last illness by her great-granddaughter, Miss Jane C., born 1718, died 1807, and Miss Sarah C., born 1725, died 1811. A great-niece of one of these two ladies, Mrs. W., who remembers one of them, was born in 1803, and is at the present time alive and well. It will be seen from the above facts that there are three lives only to bridge over the long period between 1630 and 1896, and that there is at present living a lady who personally knew Miss C., who had nursed a relative born in 1630. The last lady of this remarkable trio is hale and hearty, and has just successfully undergone an operation for cataract. Similar to the case of the centenarian who had seen Henry Jenkins was that of James Horrocks, who was born in 1744 and died in 1844. His father was born in 1657, one year before the death of the Protector, and had issue in early life. He married again at eighty-four to a woman of twenty-six, of which marriage James was the offspring in 1744. In 1844 this man could with verity say that he had a brother born during the reign of Charles II., and that his father was a citizen of the Commonwealth.

Among the Mission Indians of Southern California there are reported instances of longevity ranging from one hundred and twenty to one hundred and forty. Lieutenant Gibbons found in a village in Peru one hundred inhabitants who were past the century mark, and another credible explorer in the same territory records a case of longevity of one hundred and forty. This man was very temperate and always ate his food cold, partaking of meat only in the middle of the day. In the year of 1840 in the town of Banos, Ecuador, died "Old Morales," a carpenter, vigorous to his last days. He was an elderly man and steward of the Jesuits when they were expelled from their property near this location in 1767. In the year 1838 there was a witness in a judicial trial in South America who was born on the night of the great earthquake which destroyed the town of Ambato in 1698. How much longer this man who was cradled by an earthquake lived is not as yet reported. In the State of Vera Cruz, Mexico, as late as 1893 a man died at the age of one hundred and thirty-seven. The census of 1864 for the town of Pilaguin, Ecuador, lying 11,000 feet above the level of the sea and consisting of about 2000 inhabitants, gives 100 above seventy, 30 above ninety, five above one hundred, and one at one hundred and fifteen years.

Francis Augé died in Maryland in 1767 at the age of one hundred and thirty-four. He remembered the execution of Charles I. and had a son born to him after he was one hundred.[184]

There are several other instances in which men have displayed **generative ability in old age.** John Gilley,[a] who died in Augusta, Maine, in 1813, was born in Ireland in 1690. He came to this country at the age of sixty, and continued in single blessedness until seventy-five, when he married a girl of eighteen, by whom he had eight children. His wife survived him and stated that he was virile until his one hundred and twentieth year. Baron Baravicino de Capelis died at Meran in 1770 at the age of one hundred and four, being the oldest man in Tyrol. His usual food was eggs, and he rarely tasted meat. He habitually drank tea and a well-sweetened cordial of his own recipe. He was married four times during his life, taking his fourth wife when he was eighty-four. By her he had seven children and at his death she was pregnant with the eighth child.

Pliny mentions cases of men begetting sons when past the age of eighty, and Plot [637] speaks of John Best of the parish of Horton, who when one hundred and four married a woman of fifty-six and begat a son. There are also records of a man in Stockholm of one hundred who had several children by a wife of thirty.

On August 7, 1776, Mary, the wife of Joseph Yates, at Lizard Common, not far from London, was buried at the age of one hundred and twenty-seven. She had walked to London in 1666, and was hearty and strong at one hundred and twenty, and had married a third husband at ninety-two.

A case without parallel, of long survival of a **deaf mute,** is found in Mrs. Gray of Northfleet, Kent, who died in 1770, one hundred and twenty-one years old. She was noted for her cheerful disposition, and apparently enjoyed life in spite of her infirmity, which lasted one hundred and twenty-one years.

Macklin the **actor** was born in 1697 and died in 1797. Several years before his death he played " Shylock," displaying great vigor in the first act, but in the second his memory failed him, and with much grace and solemnity he advanced to the foot-lights and apologized for his inability to continue. It is worthy of remark that several instances of longevity in Roman actresses have been recorded. One Luceja, who came on the stage very young, performed a whole century, and even made her public appearance in her one hundred and twelfth year. Copiola was said to have danced before Augustus when past ninety.

Influence of Stimulants, etc.—There have been men who have attributed their long lives to their excesses in stimulants. Thomas Wishart of Annandale, Dumfries, died in 1760 at one hundred and twenty-four. He had chewed tobacco one hundred and seventeen years, contracting the habit when a child ; his father gave it to him to allay hunger while shepherding in the mountains. John de la Somet of Virginia died in 1766 aged one hundred and thirty. He was a great smoker, and according to Eaton the habit agreed with his constitution, and was not improbably the cause of his long health and longevity. William Riddell, who died at one hundred and sixteen, carefully avoided water all his life and had a love for brandy.

Possession of Faculties.—Eglebert Hoff was a lad driving a team in Norway when the news was brought that Charles I. was beheaded. He died in Fishkill, N. Y., in 1764 at the age of one hundred and twenty-eight. He never used spectacles, read fluently, and his memory and senses were retained until his death, which was due to an accident. Nicolas Petours, curate of the parish of Baleene and afterward canon of the Cathedral of Constance, died at the age of one hundred and thirty-seven ; he was always a healthy, vigorous man, and celebrated mass five days before his death. Mr. Evans of Spital Street, Spitalfields, London, died in 1780 aged one hundred and thirty-nine, having full possession of his mental faculties. Of interest to Americans is the case of David Kinnison, who, when one hundred and eleven, related to Lossing the historian the tale of the Boston Tea Party, of which he had been a member. He died in good mental condition at the age of one hundred and fifteen. Anthony Senish, a farmer of the village of Limoges, died in 1770 in his one hundred and eleventh year. He labored until two weeks before his death, had still his hair, and his sight had not failed him. His usual food was chestnuts and Turkish corn ; he had never been bled or used any medicine. Not very long ago there was alive in Tacony, near Philadelphia, a shoemaker named R. Glen in his one hundred and fourteenth year. He had seen King William III., and all his faculties were perfectly retained ; he enjoyed good health, walking weekly to Philadelphia to church. His third wife was but thirty years old.

Longevity in Ireland.—Lord Bacon said that at one time there was not a village in all Ireland in which there was not a man living upward of eighty. In Dunsford, a small village, there were living at one time 80 persons above the age of four score. Colonel Thomas Winslow was supposed to have died in Ireland on August 26, 1766, aged one hundred and forty-six. There was a man by the name of Butler who died at Kilkenny in 1769 aged one hundred and thirty-three. He rode after the hounds while yet a centenarian. Mrs. Eckelston, a widow in Phillipstown, Kings County, Ireland, died in 1690 at one hundred and forty-three.

There are a number of instances in which there is extraordinary **renovation of the senses** or even of the body in old age,—a new period of life, as it were, is begun. A remarkable instance is an old magistrate known to Hufeland, who lived at Rechingen and who died in 1791 aged one hundred and twenty. In 1787, long after he had lost all his teeth, eight new ones appeared, and at the end of six months they again dropped out, but their place was supplied by other new ones, and Nature, unwearied, continued this process until his death. All these teeth he had acquired and lost without pain, the whole number amounting to 150. Alice, a slave born in Philadelphia, and living in 1802 at the age of one hundred and sixteen, remembered William Penn and Thomas Story. Her faculties were well preserved, but she partially lost her eyesight at ninety-six, which, strange to say, returned in part at one hundred and two. There was a woman by the name of Helen Gray who died in her one hundred and fifth year, and who but a few years before her death had acquired a new set of teeth.

In Wilson's " Healthy Skin " are mentioned several instances of very old persons in whom the natural color of the hair returned after they had been gray for years. One of them was John Weeks, whose hair became brown again at one hundred and fourteen. Sir John Sinclair [a] mentions a similar case in a Scotchman who lived to one hundred and ten. Susan Edmonds when in her ninety-fifth year recovered her black hair, but previously to her death at one hundred and five again became gray. There was a Dr. Slave who at the age of eighty had a renewal of rich brown hair, which he maintained until his death at one hundred.[b] There was a man in Vienna, aged one hundred and five, who had black hair long after his hair had first become white. This man is mentioned as a parallel to Dr. Slave. Similar examples are mentioned in Chapter VI.

It is a remarkable fact that many persons who have reached an old age have lived on the smallest **diet** and the most frugal fare. Many of the instances of longevity were in people of Scotch origin who subsisted all their lives on porridges. Saint Anthony is said to have maintained life to one hundred and five on twelve ounces of bread daily. In 1792 in the Duchy of Holstein there was an industrious laborer named Stender who died at one hundred and three, his food for the most part of his life having been oatmeal and buttermilk. Throughout his life he had been particularly free from thirst, drinking little water and no spirits.

Heredity.—There are some very interesting instances of successive longevity. Lister speaks of a son and a father, from a village called Dent, who were witnesses before a jury at York in 1664. The son was above one hundred and the father above one hundred and forty. John Moore died in 1805 aged one hundred and seven. His father died at one hundred and five and his grandfather at one hundred and fifteen, making a total of three hundred and twenty-seven years for the three generations. [184] Recently, Wynter [c] mentions four sisters,—of one hundred, one hundred and three, one hundred and five, and one hundred and seven years respectively. On the register of Bremhill, 1696, is the following remarkable entry : " Buried, September 29th, Edith Goldie, Grace Young, and Elizabeth Wiltshire, their united ages making three hundred." As late as 1886 in the district of Campinos there was a strong, active man named Joseph Joachim de Prado, of good family, who was one hundred and seven years old. His mother died by accident at one hundred and twelve, and his maternal grandmother died at one hundred and twenty-two.

Longevity in Active Military Service.—One of the most remarkable proofs that under fickle fortune, constant danger, and the most destructive influences the life of man may be long preserved is exemplified in the case of an old soldier named Mittelstedt, who died in Prussia in 1792, aged one hundred and twelve. He was born at Fissalm in June, 1681. He entered the army,

a Essay on "Longevity.'   b 302, iv., 176.   c 222, 1867, ii., 470.

served under three Kings, Frederick I., Frederick William I., and Frederick II., and did active service in the Seven Years' War, in which his horse was shot under him and he was taken prisoner by the Russians. In his sixty-eight years of army service he participated in 17 general engagements, braved numerous dangers, and was wounded many times. After his turbulent life he married, and at last in 1790, in his one hundred and tenth year, he took a third wife. Until shortly before his death he walked every month to the pension office, a distance of two miles from his house.[184]

Longevity in Physicians.—It may be of interest to the members of our profession to learn of some instances of longevity among confrères. Dr. R. Baynes of Rockland, Maine, has been mentioned in the list of " grand old men " in medicine; following in the footsteps of Hippocrates and Galen, he was practising at ninety-nine. He lives on Graham's diet, which is a form of vegetarianism; he does not eat potatoes, but does eat fruit. His drink is almost entirely water, milk, and chocolate, and he condemns the use of tea, coffee, liquors, and tobacco. He has almost a perfect set of natural teeth and his sight is excellent. Like most men who live to a great age, Dr. Baynes has a " fad," to which he attributes a chief part in prolonging his life. This is the avoidance of beds, and except when away from home he has not slept on a bed or even on a mattress for over fifty years. He has an iron reclining chair, over which he spreads a few blankets and rugs.

The British Medical Journal speaks of Dr. Boisy of Havre, who is one hundred and three. It is said he goes his rounds every day, his practice being chiefly among the poor. At one time he practised in India. He has taken alcoholic beverages and smoked tobacco since his youth, although in moderation. His father, it is added, died at the age of one hundred and eight. Mr. William R. Salmon, living near Cowbridge, Glamorganshire, recently celebrated his one hundred and sixth birthday. Mr. Salmon was born at Wickham Market in 1790, and became a member of the Royal College of Surgeons in 1809, the year in which Gladstone was born. He died April 11, 1896. In reference to this wonderful old physician the Journal of the American Medical Association, 1896, page 995, says :—

" William Reynold Salmon, M.R.C.S., of Penllyn Court, Cowbridge, Glamorganshire, South Wales, completed his one hundred and sixth year on March 16th, and died on the 11th of the present month—at the time of his death the oldest known individual of indisputably authenticated age, the oldest physician, the oldest member of the Royal College of Surgeons, England, and the oldest Freemason in the world. His age does not rest upon tradition or repute. He was the son of a successful and esteemed practising physician of Market Wickham, Suffolk, England, and there is in the possession of his two surviving relatives, who cared for his household for many years, his mother's diary, in which is inscribed in the handwriting of a lady of the eighteenth century, under the date, Tuesday, March 16, 1790, a prayer of thankfulness to God that she had passed her 'tryall,' and that a son was born, who she hoped ' would prosper, be a support to his parents, and make virtue his chief pursuit.' The Royal College of Surgeons verified this record many years ago, and it was subsequently again authenticated by the authorities of the Freemasons, who thereupon enshrined his portrait in their gallery as the oldest living Freemason. The Salmon family moved to Cowbridge in 1796, so that the doctor had lived exactly a century in the lovely and poetic Vale of Glamorgan, in the very heart of which Penllyn Court is situated. Here on his one hundred and sixth birthday—a man of over middle height, with still long, flowing hair, Druidical beard and mustache, and bushy eyebrows—Dr. Salmon was visited by one who writes :—

" 'Seen a few days ago, the Patriarch of Penllyn Court was hale and hearty. He eats well and sleeps well and was feeling better than he had felt for the last five years. On that day he rose at noon, dined at six, and retired at nine. Drank two glasses of port with his dinner, but did not smoke. He abandoned his favorite weed at the age of ninety, and had to discontinue his drives over his beautiful estate in his one hundredth year. One day is much the same as another, for he gives his two relatives little trouble in attending upon his wants. Dr. Salmon has not discovered the elixir of life, for the shadows of life's evening are stealing slowly over him. He cannot move about, his hearing is dulled, and the light is almost shut out from the " windows of his soul." Let us think of this remarkable man waiting for death uncomplainingly in his old-fashioned mansion, surrounded by the beautiful foliage and the broad expanse of green fields that he loved so much to roam when a younger man, in that sylvan Sleepy Hollow in the Vale of Glamorgan.'

" Eight weeks later he, who in youth had been ' the youngest surgeon in the army,' died, the oldest physician in the world."

Dr. William Hotchkiss,[a] said to have reached the age of one hundred and forty years, died in St. Louis April 1, 1895. He went to St. Louis forty years ago, and has always been known as the " color doctor." In his peculiar practice of medicine he termed his patients members of his " circles," and claimed to treat them by a magnetic process. Dr. A. J. Buck says that his Masonic record has been traced back one hundred years, showing conclusively that he was one hundred and twenty-one years old. A letter received from his old home in Virginia, over a year ago, says that he was born there in 1755.

It is comforting to the members of our profession, in which the average of life is usually so low, to be able to point out exceptions. It has been aptly said of physicians in general : " Aliis inserviendo consumuntur ; aliis medendo moriuntur," or " In serving others they are consumed ; in healing others they are destroyed."

[a] Nat. Pop. Review, Aug., 1895.

Recent Instances of Longevity.—There was a man who died in Spain at the advanced age of one hundred and fifty-one,[a] which is the most extraordinary instance from that country. It is reported that quite recently a Chinese centenarian passed the examination for the highest place in the Academy of Mandarins. Chevreul, born in 1786, at Angers, has only recently died after an active life in chemical investigation. Sir Moses Montefiore is a recent example of an active centenarian.

In the New York Herald of April 21, 1895, is a description and a portrait of Noah Raby of the Piscataway Poor Farm of New Jersey, to whom was ascribed one hundred and twenty-three years. He was discharged from active duty on the "Brandywine," U. S. N., eighty-three years ago. He relates having heard George Washington speak at Washington and at Portsmouth while his ship was in those places. The same journal also says that at Wichita, Kansas, there appeared at a municipal election an old negress named Mrs. Harriet McMurray, who gave her age as one hundred and fifteen. She had been a slave, and asserted that once on a visit to Alexandria with her master she had seen General Washington. From the Indian Medical Record we learn that Lieutenant Nicholas Lavin of the Grand Armée died several years ago at the age of one hundred and twenty-five, leaving a daughter of seventy-eight. He was born in Paris in 1768, served as a hussar in several campaigns, and was taken a prisoner during the retreat from Moscow. After his liberation he married and made his residence in Saratoff.

[a] Siglo Méd., Madrid, 1851.

CHAPTER IX.

PHYSIOLOGIC AND FUNCTIONAL ANOMALIES.

In considering the **anomalies of the secretions,** it must be remembered that the ingestion of certain kinds of food and the administration of peculiar drugs in medicine have a marked influence in coloring secretions. Probably the most interesting of all these anomalies is the class in which, by a compensatory process, metastasis of the secretions is noticed.

Colored Saliva.—Among the older writers the Ephemerides contains an account of blue saliva; Huxham [a] speaks of green saliva; Marcellus Donatus [b] of yellow, and Peterman [c] relates the history of a case of yellow saliva. Dickinson [d] describes a woman of sixty whose saliva was blue; besides this nothing was definitely the matter with her. It seemed, however, that the color was due to some chemic-pencil poisoning rather than to a pathologic process. A piece of this aniline pencil was caught in the false teeth. Paget cites an instance of blue saliva due to staining the tongue in the same manner. Most cases of anomalous coloring of this kind can be subsequently traced to artificial substances unconsciously introduced. Crocker mentions a woman who on washing her hands constantly found that the water was stained blue, but this was subsequently traced to the accidental introduction of an orchid leaf. In another instance there was a woman whose linen was at every change stained brown; this, however, was found to be due to a hair-wash that she was in the habit of using.

Among the older writers who have mentioned **abnormal modes of exit of the urine** is Baux,[e] who mentions urine from the nipples; Paullini [f] and the Ephemerides describe instances of urination from the eyes. Blancard, the Ephemerides, Sorbalt, and Vallisneri [g] speak of urination by the mouth. Arnold relates the history of a case of dysuria in which urine was discharged from the nose, breasts, ears, and umbilicus;[h] the woman was twenty-seven years old, and the dysuria was caused by a prolapsed uterus. There was an instance of anomalous discharge of urine from the body reported in Philadelphia many years ago which led to animated discussion.[i] A case of dysuria in which the patient discharged urine from the stomach was reported early in

a 428, iii., 12 and 14. b 306, L. i., cap. 9.   c " Diss. de Ictero." Lipsæ, 1696.
d 779, 1884.   e 462, T. viii., 59.   f 620, cent. i., obs. 79.
g 796, iii., 338.   h Jour. Universal des Sciences, 1829.   i 768, i.

this century from Germany.[a] The patient could feel the accumulation of urine by burning pain in the epigastrium. Suddenly the pain would move to the soles of the feet, she would become nauseated, and large quantities of urine would soon be vomited. There was reported the case of an hysterical female who had convulsions and mania, alternating with anuria of a peculiar nature and lasting seven days. There was not a drop of urine passed during this time, but there were discharges through the mouth of alkaline waters with a strong ammoniacal odor.[b]

Senter [c] reports in a young woman a singular case of ischuria which continued for more than three years; during this time if her urine was not drawn off with the catheter she frequently voided it by vomiting; for the last twenty months she passed much gravel by the catheter; when the use of the instrument was omitted or unsuccessfully applied the vomitus contained gravel. Carlisle [d] mentions a case in which there was vomiting of a fluid containing urea and having the sensible properties of urine. Curious to relate, a cure was effected after ligature of the superior thyroid arteries and sloughing of the thyroid gland. Vomiting of urine is also mentioned by Coley, Domine, Liron, Malagò, Zéviani, and Yeats. Marsden [e] reports a case in which, following secondary papular syphilis and profuse spontaneous ptyalism, there was vicarious secretion of the urinary constituents from the skin.

Instances of the anomalous exit of urine caused by congenital malformation or fistulous connections are mentioned in another chapter. **Black urine** is generally caused by the ingestion of pigmented food or drugs, such as carbolic acid and the anilines. Amatus Lusitanus, Bartholinus, and the Ephemerides speak of black urine after eating grapes or damson plums. The Ephemerides speaks of black urine being a precursor of death, but Piso, Rhodius, and Schenck say it is anomalous and seldom a sign of death. **White urine**, commonly known as chyluria, is frequently seen, and sometimes results from purulent cystitis. Though containing sediment, the urine looks as if full of milk. A case of this kind was seen in 1895 at the Jefferson Medical College Hospital, Philadelphia, in which the chyluria was due to a communication between the bladder and the thoracic duct.

Ackerman has spoken of **metastasis of the tears,** and Dixon [f] gives an instance in which crying was not attended by the visible shedding of tears. Salomon [g] reports a case of congenital deficiency of tears. Blood-stained tears were frequently mentioned by the older writers. Recently Cross [h] has written an article on this subject, and its analogy is seen in the next chapter under hemorrhages from the eyes through the lacrimal duct.

The Semen.—The older writers spoke of metastasis of the seminal flow, the issue being by the skin (perspiration) and other routes. This was espe-

a Allgem. Medic. Annal., Jan., 1815.   b 222, 1860, i., 27.
c 768, 1793, i., 96.   d 476, 1832–1833, ii., 704.   e 476, 1857, ii., 519.
f 548, 1860, ii., 80.   g 175, 1854.   h 476, 1891, i., 21.

cially supposed to be the case in satyriasis, in which the preternatural exit was due to superabundance of semen, which could be recognized by its odor. There is no doubt that some people have a distinct seminal odor, a fact that will be considered in the section on "Human Odors."

The Ephemerides, Schurig,[a] and Hoffman report instances of what they call fetid semen (possibly a complication of urethral disease). Paaw speaks of black semen in a negro, and the Ephemerides and Schurig mention instances of dark semen. Blancard[b] records an instance of preternatural exit of semen by the bowel. Heers [409] mentions a similar case caused by urethral fistula. Ingham[c] mentions the escape of semen through the testicle by means of a fistula. Demarquay[d] is the authority on bloody semen.

Andouard[e] mentions an instance of **blue bile** in a woman, blue flakes being found in her vomit. There was no trace of copper to be found in this case. Andouard says that the older physicians frequently spoke of this occurrence.

Rhodius[f] speaks of **the sweat** being sweet after eating honey ; the Ephemerides and Paullini also mention it. **Chromidrosis,** or colored sweat, is an interesting anomaly exemplified in numerous reports. Black sweat has been mentioned by Bartholinus,[g] who remarked that the secretion resembled ink ; in other cases Galeazzi[h] and Zacutus Lusitanus[i] said the perspiration resembled sooty water. Phosphorescent sweat has been recorded.[j] Paullini[k] and the Ephemerides mention perspiration which was of a leek-green color, and Borellus[l] has observed deep green perspiration. Marcard mentions green perspiration of the feet, possibly due to stains from colored footgear. The Ephemerides and Paullini[m] speak of violet perspiration, and Bartholinus[n] has described perspiration which in taste resembled wine.

Sir Benjamin Brodie[o] has communicated the history of a case of a young girl of fifteen on whose face was a black secretion. On attempting to remove it by washing, much pain was caused. The quantity removed by soap and water at one time was sufficient to make four basins of water as black as if with India ink. It seemed to be physiologically analogous to melanosis. The cessation of the secretion on the forehead was followed by the ejection of a similar substance from the bowel, stomach, and kidney. The secretion was more abundant during the night, and at one time in its course an erysipelas-eruption made its appearance. A complete cure ultimately followed.

Purdon[p] describes an Irish married woman of forty, the subject of rheumatic fever, who occasionally had a blue serous discharge or perspiration that literally flowed from her legs and body, and accompanied by a miliary eruption. It was on the posterior portions, and twelve hours previous was usually

a "Spermatologia," 22.
b "Op. Med. et Chirurg," T. ii.
c Med. Obs. and Inquiries, ii., No. 22.
d 363, xxxviii., 217 ; 374.
e 349, quoted in 476, i., 1878, 248.
f 680, cent. iii., obs. 68.
g 110, i., obs. 70.
h "Comment. Bonon.," vi., 60.
i 831, L. iii., obs. 73.
j 105, x., obs. 95.
k 620, cent. i., obs. 38.
l 841, cent. ii., obs. 54.
m 620, cent. i., obs. 21.
n 190, cent. iv., 62.
o 550, 1845, 611.
p Jour. Cutan. Med., London, 1868, ii., 247.

preceded by a moldy smell and a prickly sensation. On the abdomen and the back of the neck there was a yellowish secretion. In place of catamenia there was a discharge reddish-green in color. The patient denied having taken any coloring matter or chemicals to influence the color of her perspiration, and no remedy relieved her cardiac or rheumatic symptoms.

The first English case of chromidrosis, or colored sweat, was published by Yonge of Plymouth in 1709. In this affection the colored sweating appears symmetrically in various parts of the body, the parts commonly affected being the cheeks, forehead, side of the nose, whole face, chest, abdomen, backs of the hands, finger-tips, and the flexors, flexures at the axillæ, groins, and popliteal spaces. Although the color is generally black, nearly every color has been recorded. Colcott Fox [a] reported a genuine case, and Crocker speaks of a case at Shadwell in a woman of forty-seven of naturally dark complexion. The bowels were habitually sluggish, going three or four days at least without action, and latterly the woman had suffered from articular pains. The discolored sweat came out gradually, beginning at the sides of the face, then spreading to the cheeks and forehead. When seen, the upper half of the forehead, the temporal regions, and the skin between the ear and malar eminence were of a blackish-brown color, with slight hyperemia of the adjacent parts; the woman said the color had been almost black, but she had cleaned her face some. There was evidently much fat in the secretion; there was also seborrhea of the scalp. Washing with soap and water had very little effect upon it; but it was removed with ether, the skin still looking darker and redder than normal. After a week's treatment with saline purgatives the discoloration was much less, but the patient still had articular pains, for which alkalies were prescribed; she did not again attend. Crocker also quotes the case of a girl of twenty, originally under Mackay of Brighton. Her affection had lasted a year and was limited to the left cheek and eyebrow. Six months before the patch appeared she had a superficial burn which did not leave a distinct scar, but the surface was slightly granular. The deposit was distinctly fatty, evidently seborrheic and of a sepia-tint. The girl suffered from obstinate constipation, the bowels acting only once a week. The left side flushed more than the right. In connection with this case may be mentioned one by White of Harvard, a case of unilateral yellow chromidrosis in a man.[b] Demons gives the history of a case of yellow sweat in a patient with three intestinal calculi.

Wilson says that cases of green, yellow, and blue perspiration have been seen, and Hebra, Rayer, and Fuchs mention instances. Conradi records a case of blue perspiration on one-half the scrotum. Chojnowski [c] records a case in which the perspiration resembled milk.

Hyperidrosis occurs as a symptom in many nervous diseases, organic and functional, and its presence is often difficult of explanation. The following

a 767, lxvi.   b 455, ii., Nov. 10, 1884.   c 657, 1863, ii., 387.

are recent examples : [843] Kustermann reports a case of acute myelitis in which there was profuse perspiration above the level of the girdle-sensation and none at all below. Sharkey reports a case of tumor of the pons varolii and left crus cerebri, in which for months there was excessive generalized perspiration ; it finally disappeared without treatment. Hutchinson describes the case of a woman of sixty-four who for four years had been troubled by excessive sweating on the right side of the face and scalp. At times she was also troubled by an excessive flow of saliva, but she could not say if it was unilateral. There was great irritation of the right side of the tongue, and for two years taste was totally abolished. It was normal at the time of examination. The author offered no explanation of this case, but the patient gave a decidedly neurotic history, and the symptoms seem to point with some degree of probability to hysteria. Pope reports a peculiar case in which there were daily attacks of neuralgia preceded by sweating confined to a bald spot on the head. Rockwell reports a case of unilateral hyperidrosis in a feeble old man which he thought due to organic affection of the cervical sympathetic.

Dupont [a] has published an account of a curious case of chronic general hyperidrosis or profuse sweating which lasted upward of six years. The woman thus affected became pregnant during this time and was happily delivered of an infant, which she nursed herself. According to Dupont, this hyperidrosis was independent of any other affection, and after having been combated fruitlessly by various remedies, yielded at last to fluid extract of aconitin.

Myrtle [b] relates the case of a man of seventy-seven, who, after some flying pains and fever, began to sweat profusely and continued to do so until he died from exhaustion at the end of three months from the onset of the sweating. Richardson [c] records another case of the same kind. Crocker quotes the case of a tailor of sixty-five in whom hyperidrosis had existed for thirty-five years. It was usually confined to the hands and feet, but when worst affected the whole body. It was absent as long as he preserved the horizontal posture, but came on directly when he rose ; it was always increased in the summer months. At the height of the attack the man lost appetite and spirit, had a pricking sensation, and sometimes minute red papules appeared all over the hand. He had tried almost every variety of treatment, but sulphur did the most good, as it had kept the disease under for twelve months. Latterly, even that failed.

Bachman [d] reports the history of a case of hyperidrosis cured by hypnotism. **Unilateral and localized sweating** accompanies some forms of nervous disturbance. Mickle [e] has discussed unilateral sweating in the general paralysis of the insane. Ramskill [f] reports a case of sweating on one side of the face in a patient who was subject to epileptic convulsions. Takács [g] describes a

a 458, 1807, T. xxx., 33.   b 536, Feb. 25, 1885.   c 173, 1885, 191.
d Soc. de Biolog., Jan., 1894.   e 465, xxiii., 196 ; xxix., 396.
f 548, 1866, i., 367.   g 614, xxiv., 1141.

case of unilateral sweating with proportionate nervous prostration.   Bartholow and Bryan report unilateral sweating of the head.   Cason speaks of unilateral sweating of the head, face, and neck.   Elliotson [a] mentions sweat from the left half of the body and the left extremities only.   Lewis [b] reports a case of unilateral perspiration with an excess of temperature of 3.5° F. in the axilla of the perspiring side.   Mills, White, Dow, and Duncan also cite instances of unilateral perspiration.   Boquis [c] describes a case of unilateral perspiration of the skin of the head and face, and instances of complete unilateral perspiration have been frequently recorded by the older writers,— Tebure, Marcellus Donatus, Paullini, and Hartmann [d] discussing it.   Hyperidrosis confined to the hands and feet is quite common.

Instances of bloody sweat and " stigmata " have been known through the ages and are most interesting anomalies.   In the olden times there were people who represented that in their own persons they realized at certain periods the agonies of Gethsemane, as portrayed in medieval art, *e. g.*, by pictures of Christ wearing the crown of thorns in Pilate's judgment hall. Some of these instances were, perhaps, of the nature of compensatory hemorrhage, substituting the menses or periodic hemorrhoids, hemoptysis, epistaxis, etc., or possibly purpura.   Extreme religious frenzy or deep emotions might have been the indirect cause of a number of these bleeding zealots. There are instances on record in which fear and other similar emotions have caused a sweating of blood, the expression " sweating blood " being not uncommon.

Among the older writers, Ballonius,[e] Marcolini, and Riedlin mention bloody sweat.   The Ephemerides speaks of it in front of the hypochondrium.   Paullini observed a sailor of thirty, who, falling speechless and faint during a storm on the deck of his ship, sweated a red perspiration from his entire body and which stained his clothes.   He also mentions bloody sweat following coitus. Aristotle speaks of bloody sweat, and Pellison describes a scar which periodically opened and sweated blood.   There were many cases like this, the scars being usually in the location of Christ's wounds.

De Thou mentions an Italian officer who in 1552, during the war between Henry II. of France and Emperor Charles V., was threatened with public execution ; he became so agitated that he sweated blood from every portion of the body.   A young Florentine about to be put to death by an order of Pope Sixtus V. was so overcome with grief that he shed bloody tears and sweated blood.   The Ephemerides contains many instances of bloody tears and sweat occasioned by extreme fear, more especially fear of death.   Mezeray [f] mentions that the detestable Charles IX. of France, being under constant agitation and emotion, sank under a disorder which was accompanied by an exudation

a 548, 1857, 291.

c 462, T. lxxiii., 49.

e " Paradigmata," 193.

b 809, 1878–79, 284.

d "Diss. sudore unius lateris." Hal., 1751.

f " Histoire de France," iii., 306.

of blood from every pore of his body. This was taken as an attempt of nature to cure by bleeding according to the theory of the venesectionists. Fabricius Hildanus[334] mentions a child who, as a rule, never drank anything but water, but once, contrary to her habit, drank freely of white wine, and this was soon followed by hemorrhage from the gums, nose, and skin.

There is a case also related of a woman of forty-five who had lost her only son. One day she fancied she beheld him beseeching her to release his soul from purgatory by prayers and fasting every Friday. The following Friday, which was in the month of August, and for five succeeding Fridays she had a profuse bloody perspiration, the disorder disappearing on Friday, March 8th, of the following year. Pooley[a] says that Maldonato, in his "Commentaries of Four Gospels," mentions a healthy and robust man who on hearing of his sentence of death sweated blood, and Zacchias noted a similar phenomenon in a young man condemned to the flames. Allusion may also be made to St. Luke, who said of Christ that in agony He prayed more earnestly, "and His sweat was, as it were, great drops of blood falling down to the ground."[b]

Pooley quotes the case of a young woman of indolent habit who in a religious fanatical trance sweated blood. The stigmatists were often imposters who artificially opened their scars, and set the example for the really peculiar cases of bloody sweat, which among ignorant people was considered evidence of sympathy with the agony of the Cross.

Probably the best studied case on record is that of **Louise Lateau** of Bois d'Haine, which, according to Gray, occurred in 1869 in a village of Belgium when the girl was at the age of twenty-three; her previous life had offered nothing remarkable. The account is as follows: " One Friday Louise Lateau noticed that blood was flowing from one side of her chest, and this recurred every Friday. On each Thursday morning an oval surface about one inch in length on the back of each hand became pink in color and smooth, whilst a similar oval surface on the palm of each hand became of the same hue, and on the upper surface of each foot a pinkish-white square appeared. Examined under a magnifying glass, the epidermis appeared at first without solution of continuity and delicate. About noon on Thursday a vesicle formed on the pink surfaces containing clear serum. In the night between Thursday and Friday, usually between midnight and one o'clock, the flow of blood began, the vesicle first rupturing. The amount of blood lost during the so-called stigmata varied, and some observers estimated it at about one and three-quarter pints. The blood itself was of a reddish color, inclining to violet, about the hue, therefore, of capillary blood, coagulating in the usual way, and the white and red corpuscles being normal in character and relative proportion. The flow ceased on Saturdays. During the flow of the blood the patient was in a rapt, ecstatic condition. The facial expression was one of absorption and far-off contemplation, changing often to melancholy, terror, to an attitude of prayer or contrition.   The patient herself stated that at the beginning of the ecstasy she imagined herself surrounded by a brilliant light; figures then passed before her, and the successive scenes of the crucifixion were panoramically progressive.   She saw Christ in person—His clothing, His wounds, His crown of thorns, His cross—as well as the Apostles, the holy women, and the assembled Jews.   During the ecstasy the circulation of the skin and heart was regular, although at times a sudden flash or pallor overspread the face, according with the play of the expression.   From midday of Thursdays, when she took a frugal meal, until eight o'clock on Saturday mornings the girl took no nourishment, not even water, because it was said that she did not feel the want of it and could not retain anything upon her stomach.   During this time the ordinary secretions were suspended."

Fournier [a] mentions a statesman of forty-five who, following great Cabinet labors during several years and after some worriment, found that the day after indulging in sexual indiscretions he would be in a febrile condition, with pains in the thighs, groins, legs, and penis. The veins of these parts became engorged, and subsequently blood oozed from them, the flow lasting several days. The penis was the part most affected.   He was under observation for twenty months and presented the same phenomena periodically, except that during the last few months they were diminished in every respect.   Fournier also mentions a curious case of diapedesis in a woman injured by a cow.   The animal struck her in the epigastric region, she fell unconscious, and soon after vomited great quantities of blood, and continued with convulsive efforts of expulsion to eject blood periodically from every eight to fifteen days, losing possibly a pound at each paroxysm.   There was no alteration of her menses. A physician gave her astringents, which partly suppressed the vomiting, but the hemorrhage changed to the skin, and every day she sweated blood from the chest, back of the thighs, feet, and the extremities of the fingers.   When the blood ceased to flow from her skin she lost her appetite, became oppressed, and was confined to her bed for some days.   Itching always preceded the appearance of a new flow.   There was no dermal change that could be noticed.

Fullerton [b] mentions a girl of thirteen who had occasional oozing of blood from her brow, face, and the skin under the eyes.   Sometimes a pound of clots was found about her face and pillow.   The blood first appeared in a single clot, and, strange to say, lumps of fleshy substance and minute pieces of bone were discharged all day.   This latter discharge became more infrequent, the bone being replaced by cartilaginous substance.   There was no pain, discoloration, swelling, or soreness, and after this strange anomaly disappeared menstruation regularly commenced.   Van Swieten [c] mentions a young lady who from her twelfth year at her menstrual periods had hemorrhages from pustules in the skin, the pustules disappearing in the interval.

a 302, iv., 189.   b Philadelphia Jour. of Med. and Physical Sciences, 1825.   c 755, xii., 86.

Schmidt's Jahrbücher for 1836 gives an account of a woman who had diseased ovaries and a rectovesicovaginal fistula, and though sometimes catamenia appeared at the proper place it was generally arrested and hemorrhage appeared on the face. Chambers [a] mentions a woman of twenty-seven who suffered from bloody sweat after the manner of the stigmatists, and Pétrone [b] mentions a young man of healthy antecedents, the sweat from whose axillæ and pubes was red and very pungent. Pétrone believes it was due to a chromogenic micrococcus, and relieved the patient by the use of a five per cent. solution of caustic potash. Chloroform, ether, and phenol had been tried without success. Hebra [407] mentions a young man in whom the blood spurted from the hand in a spiral jet corresponding to the direction of the duct of the sweat-gland. Wilson [826] refers to five cases of bloody sweat.

There is a record [c] of a patient who once or twice a day was attacked with swelling of the scrotum, which at length acquired a deep red color and a stony hardness, at which time the blood would spring from a hundred points and flow in the finest streams until the scrotum was again empty.

Hill [d] describes a boy of four who during the sweating stage of malaria sweated blood from the head and neck. Two months later the skin-hemorrhages ceased and the boy died, vomiting blood and with bloody stools.

Postmortem sweating is described in the Ephemerides and reported by Hasenest [e] and Schneider. Bartholinus [f] speaks of bloody sweat in a cadaver.

In considering the **anomalies of lactation** we shall first discuss those of color and then the extraordinary places of secretion. Black milk is spoken of by the Ephemerides and Paullini. Red milk has been observed by Cramer and Viger.[g] Green milk has been observed by Lanzonius, Riverius,[687] and Paullini.[620] The Ephemerides also contains an account of green milk. Yellow milk has been mentioned in the Ephemerides and its cause ascribed to eating rhubarb.

It is a well-known fact that some cathartics administered to nursing mothers are taken from the breast by their infants, who, notwithstanding its indirect mode of administration, exhibit the effects of the original drug. The same is the case with some poisons, and instances of lead-poisoning and arsenic-poisoning have been seen in children who have obtained the toxic substance in the mother's milk. There is one singular case on record in which a child has been poisoned from the milk of its mother after she had been bitten by a serpent.[h]

Paullini and the Ephemerides give instances of milk appearing in the perspiration, and there are numerous varieties of **milk-metastasis** recorded. Dolæus and Nuck [i] mention the appearance of milk in the saliva. Autenreith mentions metastasis of milk through an abdominal abscess to the thigh,

a 476, 1861.   b 747, Nov., 1884.   c 504, xviii.

d 809, 1879–80.   e 406, iii., 44.   f 189, Epis. i., 718.

g 462, T. xxxii., 222, and T. xxv., 62.   h 463, xii., 455.   i "Sialographia," 49.

and Balthazaar also mentions excretion of milk from the thigh.   Bourdon [470] mentions milk from the thigh, labia, and vulva.   Klein [a] speaks of the metastasis of the milk to the lochia.   Gardane [367] speaks of metastasis to the lungs, and there is another case on record in which this phenomenon caused asphyxia.   Schenck [b] describes excretion of milk from the bladder and uterus. Jaeger in 1770 at Tübingen describes the metastasis of milk to the umbilicus, Haen [395] to the back, and Schurig [724] to a wound in the foot.   Knackstedt has seen an abscess of the thigh which contained eight pounds of milk. Hauser [c] gives the history of a case in which the kidneys secreted milk vicariously.

There is the history of a woman who suffered from metastasis of milk to the stomach, and who, with convulsive action of the chest and abdomen, vomited it daily.[d]   A peculiar instance of milk in a tumor is that of a Mrs. Reed, who, when pregnant with twins, developed an abdominal tumor from which 25 pounds of milk was drawn off.[e]

There is a French report [f] of secretion of milk in the scrotum of a man of twenty-one.   The scrotum was tumefied, and to the touch gave the sensation of a human breast, and the parts were pigmented similar to an engorged breast.   Analysis showed the secretion to have been true human milk.

Cases of **lactation in the new-born** are not infrequent.   Bartholinus, Baricelli, Muraltus, Deusingius, Rhodius, Schenck, and Schurig mention instances of it.   Cardanus describes an infant of one month whose breasts were swollen and gave milk copiously.   Battersby [g] cites a description of a male child three weeks old whose breasts were full of a fluid, analysis proving it to have been human milk ; Darby, in the same journal, mentions a child of eight days whose breasts were so engorged that the nurse had to milk it. Faye [h] gives an interesting paper in which he has collected many instances of milk in the breasts of the new-born.   Jonston [i] details a description of lactation in an infant.   Variot [j] mentions milk-secretion in the new-born and says that it generally takes place from the eighth to the fifteenth day and not in the first week.   He also adds that probably mammary abscesses in the new-born could be avoided if the milk were squeezed out of the breasts in the first days. Variot says that out of 32 children of both sexes, aged from six to nine months, all but six showed the presence of milk in the breasts.   Gibb [k] mentions copious milk-secretion in an infant, and Sworder [l] and Menard [m] have seen young babes with abundant milk-secretion.

Precocious Lactation.—Bochut [n] says that he saw a child whose breasts were large and completely developed, offering a striking contrast to the slight development of the thorax.   They were as large as a stout man's fist, pear-

---

a 490, L. v., 202.   b 718, L. ii., No. 285.

c Oglethorpe, Med. and Surg. Jour.. Savannah, Ga., 1859–60, ii., 408.

d Allgem. Medic. Annal., Jan., 1815.   e 218, 1833, vii., 13.   f 368, 1835.

g 312, 1850.   h 602, 1876, viii., 1–10.   i 447, 461.   j 237, July 25, 1890.

k 476, 1859.   l 536, 1877, 348.   m 233, 1839, iv., 77.   n 363, 1878.

shaped, with a rosy areola, in the center of which was a nipple. These precocious breasts increased in size at the beginning of the menstrual epoch (which was also present) and remained enlarged while the menses lasted. The vulva was covered with thick hair and the external genitalia were well developed. The child was reticent, and with a doll was inclined to play the role of mother.

Baudelocque mentions a girl of eight who suckled her brother with her extraordinarily developed breasts. In 1783 this child milked her breasts in the presence of the Royal Academy at Paris. Belloc spoke of a similar case. There is another of a young negress who was able to nourish an infant;[a] and among the older writers we read accounts of young virgins who induced lactation by applying infants to their breasts. Bartholinus, Benedictus, Hippocrates, Lentilius, Salmuth, and Schenck mention lactation in virgins.

De la Coide describes a case in which lactation was present, though menstruation had always been deficient. Dix, at the Derby Infirmary,[b] has observed two females in whom there was continued lactation, although they had never been pregnant. The first was a chaste female of twenty-five, who for two years had abundant and spontaneous discharge of milk that wetted the linen ; and the other was in a prostitute of twenty, who had never been pregnant, but who had, nevertheless, for several months an abundant secretion of healthy milk. Zoologists know that a nonpregnant bitch may secrete milk in abundance. Delafond and de Sinnéty have cited instances.

Lactation in the aged has been frequently noticed. Amatus Lusitanus[119] and Schenck have observed lactation in old women ; in recent years Dunglison has collected some instances. Semple[c] relates the history of an elderly woman who took charge of an infant the mother of which had died of puerperal infection. As a means of soothing the child she allowed it to take the nipple, and, strange to say, in thirty-six hours milk appeared in her breasts, and soon she had a flow as copious as she had ever had in her early married life. The child thrived on this production of a sympathetic and spontaneous lactation. Sir Hans Sloane mentions a lady of sixty-eight who, though not having borne a child for twenty years, nursed her grandchildren, one after another.

Montegre[367] describes a woman in the Department of Charente who bore two male children in 1810. Not having enough milk for both, and being too poor to secure the assistance of a midwife, in her desperation she sought an old woman named Laverge, a widow of sixty-five, whose husband had been dead twenty-nine years. This old woman gave the breast to one of the children, and in a few days an abundant flow of milk was present. For twenty-two months she nursed the infant, and it thrived as well as its brother, who was nursed by their common mother—in fact, it was even the stronger of the two.

Dargan[d] tells of a case of remarkable rejuvenated lactation in a woman of

a 302, xxx., 386.   b 548, 1856, i., 89.   c 629, ix., 1674.   d 264, 1874.

sixty, who, in play, placed the child to her breast, and to her surprise after three weeks' nursing of this kind there appeared an abundant supply of milk, even exceeding in amount that of the young mother.

Blanchard [a] mentions milk in the breasts of a woman of sixty, and Krane [b] cites a similar instance. In the Philosophical Transactions [c] there is an instance of a woman of sixty-eight having abundant lactation.

Warren, Boring, Buzzi, Stack, Durston, Egan, Scalzi, Fitzpatrick, and Gillespie mention rejuvenation and renewed lactation in aged women. Ford [d] has collected several cases in which lactation was artificially induced by women who, though for some time not having been pregnant themselves, nursed for others.

Prolonged lactation and galactorrhea may extend through several pregnancies. Green [e] reports the case of a woman of forty-seven, the mother of four children, who after each weaning had so much milk constantly in her breasts that it had to be drawn until the next birth. At the time of report the milk was still secreting in abundance. A similar and oft-quoted case was that of Gomez Pamo,[f] who described a woman in whom lactation seemed indefinitely prolonged ; she married at sixteen, two years after the establishment of menstruation. She became pregnant shortly after marriage, and after delivery had continued lactation for a year without any sign of returning menstruation. Again becoming pregnant, she weaned her first child and nursed the other without delay or complication. This occurrence took place fourteen times. She nursed all 14 of her children up to the time that she found herself pregnant again, and during the pregnancies after the first the flow of milk never entirely ceased ; always after the birth of an infant she was able to nurse it. The milk was of good quality and always abundant, and during the period between her first pregnancy to seven years after the birth of her last child the menses had never reappeared. She weaned her last child five years before the time of report, and since then the milk had still persisted in spite of all treatment. It was sometimes so abundant as to necessitate drawing it from the breast to relieve painful tension.

Kennedy [g] describes a woman of eighty-one who persistently menstruated through lactation, and for forty-seven years had uninterruptedly nursed many children, some of which were not her own. Three years of this time she was a widow. At the last reports she had a moderate but regular secretion of milk in her eighty-first year.

In regard to profuse lacteal flow, Remy is quoted [h] as having seen a young woman in Japan from whom was taken $12\frac{1}{2}$ pints of milk each day, which is possibly one of the most extreme instance of continued **galactorrhea** on record.

Galen refers to **gynecomastia or gynecomazia** ; Aristotle says he has

a 213, cent. ii., No. 83.   b 452, L. v., 243.   c 629, No. 453.   d 579, 1869, 39.
e 594, 1844, 188.   f Quoted 494, Aug. 4, 1883.   g 549, 1832.   h 548, 1883 ii., 581.

seen men with mammæ [a] which were as well developed as those of a woman, and Paulus Ægineta recognized the fact in the ancient Greeks. Subsequently Albucasis discusses it in his writings. Bartholinus, Behr, Benedictus, Borellus, Bonet, the Ephemerides, Marcellus Donatus, Schenck, Vesalius, Schacher, Martineau, and Buffon all discuss the anomalous presence of milk in the male breast. Puech says that this condition is found in one out of 13,000 conscripts.

To Bédor, a marine surgeon,[b] we owe the first scientific exposition of this subject, and a little later Villeneuve published his article in the French dictionary.[302] Since then many observations have been made on this subject, and quite recently Laurent [479] has published a most exhaustive treatise upon it.

Robert [c] describes an old man who suckled a child, and Meyer discusses the case of a castrated man who was said to suckle children. It is said that a Bishop of Cork, who gave one-half crown to an old Frenchman of seventy, was rewarded by an exhibition of his breasts, which were larger than the Bishop had ever seen in a woman. Pétrequin speaks of a male breast 18 inches long which he amputated, and Laurent gives the photograph of a man whose breasts measured 30 cm. in circumference at the base, and hung like those of a nursing woman (Fig. 178).

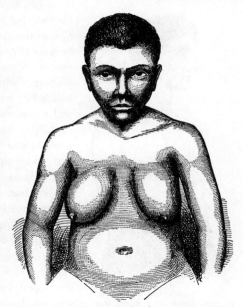

Fig. 178.—Man with fully-developed mammæ (Laurent).

In some instances whole families with supernumerary breasts are seen. Handyside gives two instances of quadruple breasts in brothers. Blanchard [d] speaks of a father who had a supernumerary nipple on each breast and his seven sons had the same deformities ; it was not noticed in the daughters. The youngest son transmitted this anomaly to his four sons. Pétrequin [e] describes a man with three mammæ, two on the left side, the third being beneath the others. He had three sons with accessory mammæ on the right side and two daughters with the same anomaly on the left side. Savitzky [f] reports a case of gynecomazia in a peasant of twenty-one whose father, elder brother, and a cousin were similarly endowed. The patient's breasts were 33 cm. in circum-

a 169, "Hist. animal.," lib. iii., chap. xx. b 461, Oct., 1812. c 629, No. 461.
d 243, 1886, 485. e 368, 1837, 195. f 703, Feb., 1894.

ference and 15 cm. from the nipple to the base of the gland; they resembled normal female mammæ in all respects. The penis and the other genitalia were normal, but the man had a female voice and absence of facial hair. There was an abundance of subcutaneous fat and a rather broad pelvis.

Wiltshire [a] said that he knew a gynecomast in the person of a distinguished naturalist who since the age of puberty observed activity in his breasts, accompanied with secretion of milky fluid which lasted for a period of six weeks and occurred every spring. This authority also mentions that the French call husbands who have well-developed mammæ " la couvade ; " the Germans call male supernumerary breasts " bauchwärze," or ventral nipples. Hutchinson [b]

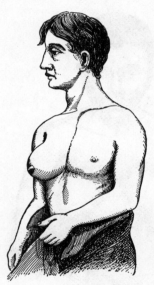

Fig. 179.—Abnormal development of right breast in a young man (Morgan).

describes several cases of gynecomazia, in which the external genital organs decreased in proportion to the size of the breast and the manners became effeminate. Cameron, quoted by Snedden, speaks of a fellow-student who had a supernumerary nipple, and also says he saw a case in a little boy who had an extra pair of nipples much wider than the ordinary ones. Ansiaux, surgeon of Liège, saw a conscript of thirteen whose left mamma was well developed like that of a woman, and whose nipple was surrounded by a large areola. He said that this breast had always been larger than the other, but since puberty had grown greatly ; the genital organs were well formed. Morgan [c] examined a seaman of twenty-one, admitted to the Royal Naval Hospital at Hong Kong, whose right mamma, in size and conformation, had the appearance of the well-developed breast of a full-grown woman. It was lobulated and had a large, brown-colored areola ; the nipple, however, was of the same size as that on the left breast (Fig. 179). The man stated that he first observed the breast to enlarge at sixteen and a half years ; since that time it had steadily increased, but there was no milk at any time from the nipple ; the external genital organs were well and fully developed. He complained of no pain or uneasiness except when in drilling aloft his breast came in contact with the ropes.

Gruger of St. Petersburg [d] divides gynecomazia into three classes :—

(1) That in which the male generative organs are normal ;

(2) In which they are deformed ;

(3) In which the anomaly is spurious, the breast being a mass of fat or a new growth.

a 224, 1884, i., 654.   b 166, iii., 326.   c 476, 1875, ii., 767.   d Quoted 224, 1886, ii., 172.

The same journal quotes an instance (possibly Morgan's case) in a young man of twenty-one with a deep voice, excellent health, and genitals well developed, and who cohabited with his wife regularly. When sixteen his right breast began to enlarge, a fact that he attributed to the pressure of a rope. Glandular substance could be distinctly felt, but there was no milk-secretion. The left breast was normal. Schuchardt has collected 272 cases of gynecomazia.

Instances of Men Suckling Infants.—These instances of gynecomazia are particularly interesting when the individuals display ability to suckle infants. Hunter refers to a man of fifty who shared equally with his wife the suckling of their children. There is an instance of a sailor who, having lost his wife, took his son to his own breast to quiet him, and after three or four days was able to nourish him.[a] Humboldt describes a South American peasant of thirty-two who, when his wife fell sick immediately after delivery, sustained the child with his own milk, which came soon after the application to the breast ; for five months the child took no other nourishment. In Franklin's " Voyages to the Polar Seas " he quotes the instance of an old Chippewa who, on losing his wife in childbirth, had put his infant to his breast and earnestly prayed that milk might flow ; he was fortunate enough to eventually produce enough milk to rear the child. The left breast, with which he nursed, afterward retained its unusual size. According to Mehliss some missionaries in Brazil in the sixteenth century asserted that there was a whole Indian nation whose women had small and withered breasts, and whose children owed their nourishment entirely to the males. Hall exhibited to his class in Baltimore a negro of fifty-five who had suckled all his mistress' family. Dunglison reports this case in 1837, and says that the mammæ projected seven inches from the chest, and that the external genital organs were well developed. Paullini and Schenck cite cases of men suckling infants, and Blumenbach has described a male-goat which, on account of the engorgement of the mammæ, it was necessary to milk every other day of the year.

Ford[b] mentions the case of a captain who in order to soothe a child's cries put it to his breast, and who subsequently developed a full supply of milk. He also quotes an instance of a man suckling his own children, and mentions a negro boy of fourteen who secreted milk in one breast. Hornor and Pulido y Fernandez[c] also mention similar instances of gynecomazia.

Human Odors.—Curious as it may seem, each individual as well as each species is in life enveloped with an odor peculiarly its own, due to its exhaled breath, its excretions, and principally to its insensible perspiration. The faculty of recognizing an odor in different individuals, although more developed in savage tribes, is by no means unknown in civilized society. Fournier quotes the instance of a young man who, like a dog, could smell the enemy by scent, and who by smell alone recognized his own wife from other persons.[d]

a 302, xxx., 384.

c Independ. méd., Barcel., xi., 274, 297, 309.

b 579, 169, 39.

d 302, iv.

Fournier also[a] mentions a French woman, an inhabitant of Naples, who had an extreme supersensitiveness of smell. The slightest odor was to her intolerable; sometimes she could not tolerate the presence of certain individuals. She could tell in a numerous circle which women were menstruating. This woman could not sleep in a bed which any one else had made, and for this reason discharged her maid, preparing her own toilet and her sleeping apartments. Cadet de Gassicourt witnessed this peculiar instance, and in consultation with several of the physicians of Paris attributed this excessive sensitiveness to the climate. There is a tale told of a Hungarian monk[469] who affirmed that he was able to decide the chastity of females by the sense of smell alone. It is well known that some savage tribes with their large, open nostrils not only recognize their enemies but also track game the same as hounds.

Individual Odors.—Many individuals are said to have exhaled particularly strong odors, and history is full of such instances. We are told by Plutarch that Alexander the Great exhaled an odor similar to that of violet flowers, and his undergarments always smelled of this natural perfume. It is said that Cujas offered a particular analogy to this. On the contrary, there are certain persons spoken of who exhaled a sulphurous odor. Martial[509] said that Thais was an example of the class of people whose odor was insupportable. Schmidt has inserted in the Ephemerides an account of a journeyman saddler, twenty-three years of age, of rather robust constitution, whose hands exhaled a smell of sulphur so powerful and penetrating as to rapidly fill any room in which he happened to be. Rayer was once consulted by a valet-de-chambre who could never keep a place in consequence of the odor he left behind him in the rooms in which he worked.

Hammond[b] is quoted with saying that when the blessed Venturni of Bergamons officiated at the altar people struggled to come near him in order to enjoy the odor he exhaled. It was said that St. Francis de Paul, after he had subjected himself to frequent disciplinary inflictions, including a fast of thirty-eight to forty days, exhaled a most sensible and delicious odor. Hammond attributes the peculiar odors of the saints of earlier days to neglect of washing and, in a measure, to affections of the nervous system. It may be added that these odors were augmented by aromatics, incense, etc., artifically applied. In more modern times Malherbe and Haller were said to diffuse from their bodies the agreeable odor of musk. These "human flowers," to use Goethe's expression, are more highly perfumed in Southern latitudes.

Modifying Causes.—According to Brieude, sex, age, climate, habits, ailments, the passions, the emotions, and the occupations modify the difference in the humors exhaled, resulting in necessarily different odors. Nursing infants have a peculiar sourish smell, caused by the butyric acid of the milk, while bottle-fed children smell like strong butter. After being weaned the odors of the

a 302, iv., 96.   b 491, 1878, 279.

babies become less decided. Boys when they reach puberty exhibit peculiar
odors which are similar to those of animals when in heat. These odors are
leading symptoms of what Borden calls "seminal fever" and are more
strongly marked in those of a voluptuous nature. They are said to be caused
by the absorption of spermatic fluid into the circulation and its subsequent
elimination by the skin. This peculiar circumstance, however, is not seen
in girls, in whom menstruation is sometimes to be distinguished by an odor
somewhat similar to that of leather. Old age produces an odor similar to that
of dry leaves, and there have been persons who declared that they could tell
approximately the age of individuals by the sense of smell.

Certain tribes and races of people have characteristic odors. Negroes have a rank ammoniacal odor, unmitigated by cleanliness; according
to Pruner-Bey it is due to a volatile oil set free by the sebaceous follicles.
The Esquimaux and Greenlanders have the odors of their greasy and oily
foods, and it is said that the Cossacks, who live much with their horses, and
who are principally vegetarians, will leave the atmosphere charged with odors
several hours after their passage in numbers through a neighborhood. The
lower race of Chinamen are distinguished by a peculiar musty odor, which
may be noticed in the laundry shops of this country. Some people, such as
the low grade of Indians, have odors, not distinctive, and solely due to the
filth of their persons. Food and drink, as have been mentioned, markedly
influence the odor of an individual, and those perpetually addicted to a special
diet or drink have a particular odor.

Odor after Coitus.—Preismann in 1877 makes the statement that for
six hours after coitus there is a peculiar odor noticeable in the breath, owing
to a peculiar secretion of the buccal glands. He says that this odor is most
perceptible in men of about thirty-five, and can be discerned at a distance of
from four to six feet. He also adds that this fact would be of great medicolegal value in the early arrest of those charged with rape. In this connection
the analogy of the breath immediately after coitus to the odor of chloroform
has been mentioned.[a] The same article states that after coitus naturally foul
breath becomes sweet.

The emotions are said to have a decided influence on the odor of an
individual. Gambrini, quoted by Monin,[b] mentions a young man, unfortunate
in love and violently jealous, whose whole body exhaled a sickening, pernicious,
and fetid odor. Orteschi met a young lady who, without any possibility of
fraud, exhaled the strong odor of vanilla from the commissures of her fingers.

Rayer speaks of a woman under his care at the Hôpital de la Charité
affected with chronic peritonitis, who some time before her death exhaled a very
decided **odor of musk.** The smell had been noticed several days, but was
thought to be due to a bag of musk put purposely into the bed to overpower
other bad smells. The woman, however, gave full assurance that she had no

a 536, 1883, i., 374.　　　b "Sur les Odeurs du Corps Humain." Paris, 1885.

kind of perfume about her and that her clothes had been frequently changed. The odor of musk in this case was very perceptible on the arms and other portions of the body, but did not become more powerful by friction. After continuing for about eight days it grew fainter and nearly vanished before the patient's death. Speranza [a] relates a similar case.

Complexion.—Paré[618] states that persons of red hair and freckled complexion have a noxious exhalation; the odor of prussic acid is said to come from dark individuals, while blondes exhale a secretion resembling musk. Fat persons frequently have an oleaginous smell.

The **disorders of the nervous system** are said to be **associated with peculiar odors.** Févre says the odor of the sweat of lunatics resembles that of yellow deer or mice, and Knight remarks that the absence of this symptom would enable him to tell whether insanity was feigned or not. Burrows declares that in the absence of further evidence he would not hesitate to pronounce a person insane if he could perceive certain associate odors. Sir William Gull and others are credited with asserting that they could detect syphilis by smell. Weir Mitchell has observed that in lesions of nerves the corresponding cutaneous area exhaled the odor of stagnant water. Hammond refers to three cases under his notice in which specific odors were the results of affections of the nervous system. One of these cases was a young woman of hysterical tendencies who exhaled the odor of violets, which pervaded her apartments. This odor was given off the left half of the chest only and could be obtained concentrated by collecting the perspiration on a handkerchief, heating it with four ounces of spirit, and distilling the remaining mixture. The administration of the salicylate of soda modified in degree this violaceous odor. Hammond also speaks of a young lady subject to chorea whose insensible perspiration had an odor of pineapples; a hypochondriac gentleman under his care smelled of violets. In this connection he mentions a young woman who, when suffering from intense sick headache, exhaled an odor resembling that of Limburger cheese.

Barbier met a case of disordered innervation in a captain of infantry, the upper half of whose body was subject to such offensive perspiration that despite all treatment he had to finally resign his commission.

In lethargy and catalepsy the perspiration very often has a cadaverous odor, which has probably occasionally led to a mistaken diagnosis of death. Schaper and de Meara[517] speak of persons having a cadaveric odor during their entire life.

Various **ingesta** readily give evidence of themselves by their influence upon the breath. It has been remarked that the breath of individuals who have recently performed a prolonged necropsy smells for some hours of the odor of the cadaver. Such things as copaiba, cubebs, sandalwood, alcohol, coffee, etc., have their recognizable fragrance. There is an instance of a young woman taking Fowler's solution who had periodic offensive axillary sweats that ceased when the medicine was discontinued.

Henry of Navarre was a victim of bromidrosis ; proximity to him was insufferable to his courtiers and mistresses, who said that his odor was like that of carrion. Tallemant says that when his wife, Marie de Médicis, approached the bridal night with him she perfumed her apartments and her person with the essences of the flowers of her country in order that she might be spared the disgusting odor of her spouse. Some persons are afflicted with an excessive perspiration of the feet which often takes a disgusting odor. The inguinoscrotal and inguinovulvar perspirations have an aromatic odor like that of the genitals of either sex.

During menstruation, hyperidrosis of the axillæ diffuses an aromatic odor similar to that of acids or chloroform, and in suppression of menses, according to the Ephemerides, the odor is as of hops.

Odors of Disease.—The various diseases have their own peculiar odors. The "hospital odor," so well known, is essentially variable in character and chiefly due to an aggregation of cutaneous exhalations. The wards containing women and children are perfumed with butyric acid, while those containing men are influenced by the presence of alkalies like ammonia.

Gout, icterus, and even cholera (Drasch and Porker) have their own odors. Older observers, confirmed by Döppner, say that all the plague-patients at Vetlianka diffused an odor of honey. In diabetes there is a marked odor of apples. The sweat in dysentery unmistakably bears the odor of the dejecta. Béhier calls the odor of typhoid that of the blood, and Berard says that it attracts flies even before death. Typhus has a mouse-like odor, and the following diseases have at different times been described as having peculiar odors,—measles, the smell of freshly plucked feathers ; scarlatina, of bread hot from the oven ; eczema and impetigo, the smell of mold ; and rupia, a decidedly offensive odor.

The hair has peculiar odors, differing in individuals. The hair of the Chinese is known to have the odor of musk, which cannot be washed away by the strongest of chemicals. Often the distinctive odor of a female is really due to the odor of great masses of hair. It is said that wig-makers simply by the sense of smell can tell whether hair has been cut from the living head or from combings, as hair loses its odor when it falls out. In the paroxysms of hysteroepilepsy the hair sometimes has a specific odor of ozone. Tænia favosa gives to the scalp an odor resembling that of cat's urine.

Sexual Influence of Odors.—In this connection it may be mentioned that there is a peculiar form of sexual perversion, called by Binet "**fetichism,**" in which the subject displays a perverted taste for the odors of handkerchiefs, shoes, underclothing, and other articles of raiment worn by the opposite sex. Binet maintains that these articles play the part of the "fetich" in early theology. It is said that the favors given by the ladies to the knights in the Middle Ages were not only tokens of remembrance and appreciation, but sexual excitants as well. In his remarkable "Osphrésiologie," Cloquet calls attention to the sexual pleasure excited by the odors of flowers, and tells how Richelieu excited his sexual functions by living in an atmosphere loaded with these perfumes. In the Orient the harems are perfumed with intense extracts and flowers, in accordance with the strong belief in the aphrodisiac effect of odors.

Krafft-Ebing[a] quotes several interesting cases in which the connection between the olfactory and sexual functions is strikingly verified.

"The case of Henry III. shows that contact with a person's perspiration may be the exciting cause of passionate love. At the betrothal feast of the King of Navarre and Margaret of Valois he accidentally dried his face with a garment of Maria of Cleves which was moist with her perspiration. Although she was the bride of the Prince of Condé, Henry immediately conceived such a passion for her that he could not resist it, and, as history shows, made her very unhappy. An analogous instance is related of Henry IV., whose passion for the beautiful Gabrielle is said to have originated at the instant when, at a ball, he wiped his brow with her handkerchief."

Krafft-Ebing also says that "one learns from reading the work of Ploss ('Das Weib') that attempts to attract a person of the opposite sex by means of the perspiration may be discerned in many forms in popular psychology. In reference to this a custom is remarkable which holds among the natives of the Philippine Islands when they become engaged. When it becomes necessary for the engaged pair to separate they exchange articles of wearing apparel, by means of which each becomes assured of faithfulness. These objects are carefully preserved, covered with kisses, and smelled."

The love of perfumes by libertines and prostitutes, as well as sensual women of the higher classes, is quite marked. Heschl reported a case of a man of forty-five in whom absence of the olfactory sense was associated with imperfect development of the genitals; it is also well known that olfactory hallucinations are frequently associated with psychoses of an erotic type.

Garnier[b] has recently collected a number of observations of fetichism, in which he mentions individuals who have taken sexual satisfaction from the odors of shoes, night-dresses, bonnets, drawers, menstrual napkins, and other objects of the female toilet. He also mentions creatures who have gloated over the odors of the blood and excretions from the bodies of women, and gives instances of fetichism of persons who have been arrested in the streets of Paris for clipping the long hair from young girls. There are also on record instances of homosexual fetichism, a type of disgusting inversion of the sexual instinct, which, however, it is not in the province of this work to discuss.

Among animals the influence of the olfactory perceptions on the sexual sense is unmistakable. According to Krafft-Ebing, Althaus shows that ani-

<hr>

[a] "Psychopathia Sexualis."   [b] "Les Fétichistes," etc. Paris, 1896.

mals of opposite sexes are drawn to each other by means of olfactory perceptions, and that almost all animals at the time of rutting emit a very strong odor from their genitals. It is said that the dog is attracted in this way to the bitch several miles away. An experiment by Schiff is confirmatory. He extirpated the olfactory nerves of puppies, and found that as they grew the male was unable to distinguish the female. Certain animals, such as the musk-ox, civet-cat, and beaver, possess glands on their sexual organs that secrete materials having a very strong odor. Musk, a substance possessing the most penetrating odor and used in therapeutics, is obtained from the preputial follicles of the musk-deer of Thibet; and castor, a substance less penetrating, is obtained from the preputial sacs of the beaver. Virgin moths (Bombyx) carried in boxes in the pockets of entomologists will on wide commons cause the appearance of males of the same species.

Bulimia is excessive morbid hunger, also called canine appetite. While sometimes present in healthy people, it is most often seen in idiots and the insane, and is a symptom of diabetes mellitus. Mortimer [a] mentions a boy of twelve who, while laboring under this affliction, in six days devoured food to the extent of 384 pounds and two ounces. He constantly vomited, but his craving for food was so insatiable that if not satisfied he would devour the flesh off his own bones. Martyn,[b] Professor of Botany at Cambridge in the early part of the last century, tells of a boy ten years old whose appetite was enormous. He consumed in one week 373 pounds of food and drink. His urine and stools were voided in normal quantities, the excess being vomited. A pig was fed on what he vomited, and was sold in the market. The boy continued in this condition for a year, and at last reports was fast failing. Burroughs [c] mentions a laborer at Stanton, near Bury, who ate an ordinary leg of veal at a meal, and fed at this extravagant rate for many days together. He would eat thistles and other similar herbs greedily. At times he would void worms as large as the shank of a clay-pipe, and then for a short period the bulimia would disappear.

Johnston [d] mentions a case of bulimia in a man who devoured large quantities of raw flesh. There is an instance on record [e] of a case of canine appetite in which nearly 400 pounds of solid and fluid elements were taken into the body in six days and again ejected. A recovery was effected by giving very concentrated food, frequently repeated in small quantities. Mason [f] mentions a woman in St. Bartholomew's Hospital in London in the early part of this century who was wretched unless she was always eating. Each day she consumed three quartern-loaves, three pounds of beef-steak, in addition to large quantities of vegetables, meal, etc., and water. Smith [g] describes a boy of fourteen who ate continuously fifteen hours out of the twenty-four, and who had eight bowel movements each day. One year previous his weight

a 629, 1743, 1066.   b 629, 1743.   c 629, No. 598.   d 535, 1800, iii., 209.
e 564, iii., 501.   f 476, 1870, i., 701.   g 545, 1880, xlii., 385.

was 105 pounds, but when last seen he weighed 284 pounds and was increasing a half pound daily. Despite his continuous eating, this boy constantly complained of hunger.

Polydipsia is an abnormal thirst; it may be seen in persons otherwise normal, or it may be associated with diseases—such as diabetes mellitus or diabetes insipidus. Mackenzie [a] quotes a case from Trousseau, in which an individual afflicted with diabetes insipidus passed 32 liters of urine daily and drank enormous quantities of water. This patient subjected himself to severe regimen for eight months,—although one day, in his agonies, he seized the chamber-pot and drank its contents at once. Mackenzie also mentions an infant of three who had polydipsia from birth and drank daily nearly two pailfuls of water. At the age of twenty-two she married a cobbler, unaware of her propensity, who found that his earnings did not suffice to keep her in water alone, and he was compelled to melt ice and snow for her. She drank four pailfuls a day, the price being 12 sous; water in the community was scarce and had to be bought. This woman bore 11 children. At the age of forty she appeared before a scientific commission and drank in their presence 14 quarts of water in ten hours and passed ten quarts of almost colorless urine. Dickinson mentions that he has had patients in his own practice who drank their own urine. Mackenzie also quotes Trousseau's history of a man who drank a liter of strong French brandy in two hours, and habitually drank the same quantity daily. He stated that he was free from the effects of alcohol; on several occasions on a wager he took 20 liters of wine, gaining his wager without visibly affecting his nervous system.

There is an instance of a man of fifty-eight [b] who could not live through the night without a pail of water, although his health was otherwise good. Atkinson in 1856 reported a young man who in childhood was a dirt-eater, though at that time complaining of nothing but excessive thirst. He was active, industrious, enjoyed good health, and was not addicted to alcoholics. His daily ration of water was from eight to twelve gallons. He always placed a tub of water by his bed at night, but this sometimes proved insufficient. He had frequently driven hogs from mudholes to slake his thirst with the water. He married in 1829 and moved into Western Tennessee, and in 1854 he was still drinking the accustomed amount; and at this time he had grown-up children. Ware [c] mentions a young man of twenty who drank six gallons of water daily. He was tormented with thirst, and if he abstained he became weak, sick, and dizzy. Throughout a long life he continued his habit, sometimes drinking a gallon at one draught; he never used spirits. There are three cases of polydipsia reported from London in 1792. [d]

Field [e] describes a boy with bilious remittent fever who would drink until

a 548, 1878, ii., 268.   b 218, 1856.   c 589, 1815.
d 528, 1792.   e Western Jour. Med., 1869, iv., 714.

his stomach was completely distended and then call for more. Emesis was followed by cries for more water. Becoming frantic, he would jump from his bed and struggle for the water bucket; failing in this, he ran to the kitchen and drank soapsuds, dish-water, and any other liquid he could find. He had swallowed a mass of mackerel which he had not properly masticated, a fact proved later by ejection of the whole mass. There is a case on record [a] in which there was intolerable thirst after retiring, lasting for a year. There was apparently no polydipsia during the daytime.

The amount of water drunk by **glass-blowers** in a day is almost incredible. McElroy [b] has made observations in the glass-factories in his neighborhood, and estimates that in the nine working hours of each day a glass-blower drinks from 50 to 60 pints of water. In addition to this many are addicted to the use of beer and spirits after working hours and at lunch-time. The excreta and urine never seem to be perceptibly increased. When not working these men do not drink more than three or four pints of water. Occasionally a man becomes what is termed " blown-up with water ;" that is, the perspiration ceases, the man becomes utterly helpless, has to be carried out, and is disabled until the sweating process is restored by vigorously applied friction. There is little deleterious change noticed in these men ; in fact, they are rarely invalids.

Hydroadipsia is a lack of thirst or absence of the normal desire for water. In some of these cases there is a central lesion which accounts for the symptoms. McElroy, among other cases, speaks of one in a patient who was continually dull and listless, eating little, and complaining of much pain after the least food. This, too, will be mentioned under abstinence.

Perverted appetites are of great variety and present many interesting as well as disgusting examples of anomalies. In some cases the tastes of people differ so that an article considered by one race as disgusting would be held as a delicacy by another class. The ancients used asafetida as a seasoning ; and what we have called "stercus diaboli," the Asiatics have named the "food of the gods." The inhabitants of Greenland drink the oil of the whale with as much avidity as we would a delicate wine, and they eat blubber the mere smell of which nauseates an European. In some nations of the lower grade, insects, worms, serpents, etc., are considered edible. The inhabitants of the interior of Africa are said to relish the flesh of serpents and eat grubs and worms. The very earliest accounts of the Indians of Florida and Texas show that " for food, they dug roots, and that they ate spiders, ants' eggs, worms, lizards, salamanders, snakes, earth, wood, the dung of deer, and many other things." [c] Gomara, in his " Historia de les Indias," says this loathsome diet was particular to one tribe, the Yaguaces of Florida. It is said that a Russian peasant prefers a rotten egg to a fresh one ; and there are persons who prefer game partly spoiled.

[a] 476, 1869, i., 285, etc.   [b] 272, 1877, 9 *et seq.*   [c] "De Vaca in Ternaux," vii., 144.

Bourke [a] recalls that the drinking of human urine has often been a religious rite, and describes the urine-dance of the Zuñis of New Mexico, in which the participants drink freely of their urine; he draws an analogy to the Feast of the Fools, a religious custom of Pagan origin which did not disappear in Europe until the time of the Reformation. It is still a practice in some parts of the United States to give children fresh urine for certain diseases. It is said that the ordure of the Grand Lama of Thibet was at one time so venerated that it was collected and worn as amulets.

The disgusting habit of eating human excrement is mentioned by Schurig,[b] who gives numerous examples in epileptics, maniacs, chlorotic young women, pregnant women, children who have soiled their beds and, dreading detection, have swallowed their ejecta, and finally among men and women with abnormal appetites. The Indians of North America consider a broth made from the dung of the hare and caribou a dainty dish, and according to Abbe Domenech, as a means of imparting a flavor, the bands near Lake Superior mix their rice with the excrement of rabbits. De Bry mentions that the negroes of Guinea ate filthy, stinking elephant-meat and buffalo-flesh infested with thousands of maggots, and says that they ravenously devoured dogs' guts raw. Spencer, in his "Descriptive Sociology," describes a "Snake savage" of Australia who devoured the contents of entrails of an animal. Some authors have said that within the last century the Hottentots devoured the flesh and the entrails of wild beasts, uncleansed of their filth and excrement, and whether sound or rotten. In a personal letter to Captain Bourke, the Reverend J. Owen Dorsey reports that while among the Ponkas he saw a woman and child devour the entrails of a beef with their contents. Bourke also cites instances in which human ordure was eaten by East Indian fanatics. Numerous authorities are quoted by Bourke to prove the alleged use of ordure in food by the ancient Israelites. Pages of such reference are to be found in the works on Scatology, and for further reference the reader is referred to books on this subject, of which prominent in English literature is that of Bourke.[c]

Probably the most revolting of all the perverted tastes is that for human flesh. This is called **anthropophagy or cannibalism,** and is a time-honored custom among some of the tribes of Africa. This custom is often practised more in the spirit of vengeance than of real desire for food. Prisoners of war were killed and eaten, sometimes cooked, and among some tribes raw. In their religious frenzy the Aztecs ate the remains of the human beings who were sacrificed to their idols. At other times cannibalism has been a necessity. In a famine in Egypt, as pictured by the Arab Abdallatif, the putrefying debris of animals, as well as their excrement, was used as food, and finally the human dead were used; then infants were killed and devoured, so great was the distress. In many sieges, shipwrecks, etc., cannibalism has been

---

[a] "Scatologic Rites of All Nations."   [b] "Chylologia." Dresden, 1725.
[c] "Scatologic Rites of All Nations."

practised as a last resort for sustaining life. When supplies have given out several Arctic explorers have had to resort to eating the bodies of their comrades. In the famous Wiertz Museum in Brussels is a painting by this eccentric artist in which he has graphically portrayed a woman driven to insanity by hunger, who has actually destroyed her child with a view to cannibalism. At the siege of Rochelle it is related that, urged by starvation, a father and mother dug up the scarcely cold body of their daughter and ate it. At the siege of Paris by Henry IV. the cemeteries furnished food for the starving. One mother in imitation of what occurred at the siege of Jerusalem roasted the limbs of her dead child and died of grief under this revolting nourishment.

St. Jerome states that he saw Scotchmen in the Roman armies in Gaul whose regular diet was human flesh, and who had "double teeth all around."

Cannibalism, according to a prominent New York journal, has been recently made a special study by the Bureau of Ethnology at Washington, D. C. Data on the subject have been gathered from all parts of the world, which are particularly interesting in view of discoveries pointing to the conclusion that this horrible practice is far more widespread than was imagined. Stanley claims that 30,000,000 cannibals dwell in the basin of the Congo to-day—people who relish human flesh above all other meat. Perah, the most peculiar form of cannibalism, is found in certain mountainous districts of northeast Burmah, where there are tribes that follow a life in all important respects like that of wild beasts. These people eat the congealed blood of their enemies. The blood is poured into bamboo reeds, and in the course of time, being corked up, it hardens. The filled reeds are hung under the roofs of the huts, and when a person desires to treat his friends very hospitably the reeds are broken and the contents devoured.

"The black natives of Australia are all professed cannibals. Dr. Carl Lumholtz, a Norwegian scientist, spent many months in studying them in the wilds of the interior. He was alone among these savages, who are extremely treacherous. Wearing no clothing whatever, and living in nearly every respect as monkeys do, they know no such thing as gratitude, and have no feeling that can be properly termed human. Only fear of the traveler's weapons prevented them from slaying him, and more than once he had a narrow escape. One of the first of them whom he employed looked more like a brute than a man. 'When he talked,' says the doctor, 'he rubbed his belly with complacency, as if the sight of me made his mouth water.' This individual was regarded with much respect by his fellows because of his success in procuring human flesh to eat. These aborigines say that the white man's flesh is salt and occasions nausea. A Chinaman they consider as good for eating as a black man, his food being chiefly vegetable.

"The most horrible development of cannibalism among the Australian blacks is the eating of defunct relatives. When a person dies there follows an elaborate ceremony, which terminates with the lowering of the corpse into the grave. In the grave is a man not related to the deceased, who proceeds to cut off the fat adhering to the muscles of the face, thighs, arms, and stomach, and passes it around to be swallowed by some of the near relatives. All those who have eaten of the cadaver have a black ring of charcoal powder and fat drawn around the mouth. The order in which the mourners partake of their dead relatives is duly prescribed. The mother eats of her children and the children of their mother. A man eats of his sister's husband and of his brother's wife. Mothers' brothers, mothers' sisters, sisters' children, mothers' parents, and daughters' children are also eaten by those to whom the deceased person stands in such relation. But the father does not eat of his children, nor the children of their sire.

"The New Zealanders, up to very recent times, were probably the most anthropophagous race that ever existed. As many as 1000 prisoners have been slaughtered by them at one time after a successful battle, the bodies being baked in ovens underground. If the individual consumed had been a redoubtable enemy they dried his head as a trophy and made flutes of his thigh bones.

"Among the Monbuttos of Africa human fat is commonly employed for a variety of purposes. The explorer Schweinfurth speaks of writing out in the evenings his memoranda respecting these people by the light of a little oil-lamp contrived by himself, which was supplied with some questionable-looking grease furnished by the natives. The smell of this grease, he says, could not fail to arouse one's worst suspicions against the negroes. According to his account the Monbuttos are the most confirmed cannibals in Africa. Surrounded as they are by a number of peoples who are blacker than themselves, and who, being inferior to them in culture, are held in contempt, they carry on expeditions of war and plunder which result in the acquisition of a booty especially coveted by them—namely, human flesh. The bodies of all foes who fall in battle are distributed on the field among the victors, and are prepared by drying for transportation. The savages drive their prisoners before them, and these are reserved for killing at a later time. During Schweinfurth's residence at the Court of Munza it was generally understood that nearly every day a little child was sacrificed to supply a meal for the ogre potentate. For centuries past the slave trade in the Congo Basin has been conducted largely for the purpose of furnishing human flesh to consumers. Slaves are sold and bought in great numbers for market, and are fattened for slaughter.

"The Mundurucus of the Upper Amazon, who are exceedingly ferocious, have been accused of cannibalism. It is they who preserve human heads in such a remarkable way. When one of their warriors has killed an enemy he cuts off the head with his bamboo knife, removes the brain, soaks the head in a vegetable oil, takes out bones of the skull, and dries the remaining parts by putting hot pebbles inside of it. At the same time care is taken to preserve all the features and the hair intact. By repeating the process with the hot pebbles many times the head finally becomes shrunken to that of a small doll, though still retaining its human aspect, so that the effect produced is very weird and uncanny. Lastly, the head is decorated with brilliant feathers, and the lips are fastened together with a string, by which the head is suspended from the rafters of the council-house."

Ancient Customs.—According to Herodotus the ancient Lydians and Medes, and according to Plato the islanders in the Atlantic, cemented friendship by drinking human blood. Tacitus speaks of Asian princes swearing allegiance with their own blood, which they drank. Juvenal says that the Scythians drank the blood of their enemies to quench their thirst.

Occasionally a religious ceremony has given sanction to cannibalism. It is said that in the Island of Chios there was a rite by way of sacrifice to Dionysius in which a man was torn limb from limb, and Faber tells us that the Cretans had an annual festival in which they tore a living bull with their teeth. Spencer quotes that among the Bacchic orgies of many of the tribes of North America, at the inauguration of one of the Clallum chiefs on the northwest coast of British America, the chief seized a small dog and began to devour it alive, and also bit the shoulders of bystanders. In speaking of these ceremonies, Boas, quoted by Bourke, says that members of the tribes practising Hamatsa ceremonies show remarkable scars produced by biting, and at certain festivals ritualistic cannibalism is practised, it being the duty of the Hamatsa to bite portions of flesh out of the arms, legs, or breast of a man.

Another cause of cannibalism, and the one which deserves discussion here, is genuine perversion or depravity of the appetite for human flesh among civilized persons,—the desire sometimes being so strong as to lead to actual murder. Several examples of this anomaly are on record. Gruner of Jena speaks of a man by the name of Goldschmidt, in the environs of Weimar, who developed a **depraved appetite for human flesh.** He was married at twenty-seven, and for twenty-eight years exercised his calling as a cow-herd. Nothing extraordinary was noticed in him, except his rudeness of manner and his choleric and gross disposition. In 1771, at the age of fifty-five, he met a young traveler in the woods, and accused him of frightening his cows; a discussion arose, and subsequently a quarrel, in which Goldschmidt killed his antagonist by a blow with a stick which he used. To avoid detection he dragged the body to the bushes, cut it up, and took it home in sections. He then washed, boiled, and ate each piece. Subsequently, he developed a further taste for human flesh, and was finally detected in eating a child which he had enticed into his house and killed. He acknowledged his appetite before his trial.

Hector Boetius says that a Scotch brigand and his wife and children were condemned to death on proof that they killed and ate their prisoners. The extreme youth of one of the girls excused her from capital punishment; but at twelve years she was found guilty of the same crime as her father and suffered capital punishment. This child had been brought up in good surroundings, yet her inherited appetite developed. Gall tells of an individual who, instigated by an irresistible desire to eat human flesh, assassinated many persons; and his daughter, though educated away from him, yielded to the same craving.

At Bicêtre[a] there was an individual who had a horribly depraved appetite for decaying human flesh. He would haunt the graveyards and eat the putrefying remains of the recently buried, preferring the intestines. Having regaled himself in a midnight prowl, he would fill his pockets for future use. When interrogated on the subject of his depravity he said it had existed since childhood. He acknowledged the greatest desire to devour children he would meet playing; but he did not possess the courage to kill them.

Prochaska quotes the case of a woman of Milan who attracted children to her home in order that she might slay, salt, and eat them. About 1600, there is the record of a boy named Jean Granier, who had repeatedly killed and devoured several young children before he was discovered. Rodericus à Castro[257] tells of a pregnant woman who so strongly desired to eat the shoulder of a baker that she killed him, salted his body, and devoured it at intervals.

There is a record of a woman who in July, 1817, was discovered in cooking an amputated leg of her little child. Gorget in 1827 reported the celebrated case of Leger the vine dresser, who at the age of twenty-four wandered about a forest for eight days during an attack of depression. Coming across a girl of twelve, he violated her, and then mutilated her genitals, and tore out her heart, eating of it, and drinking the blood. He finally confessed his crime with calm indifference. After Leger's execution Esquirol found morbid adhesions between the brain and the cerebral membranes. Mascha relates a similar instance in a man of fifty-five who violated and killed a young girl, eating of her genitals and mammæ. At the trial he begged for execution, saying that the inner impulse that led him to his crime constantly persecuted him.

A modern example of lust-murder and anthropophagy is that of Menesclou, who was examined by Brouardel, Motet, and others, and declared to be mentally sound; he was convicted. This miscreant was arrested with the forearm of a missing child in his pocket, and in his stove were found the head and entrails in a half-burnt condition. Parts of the body were found in the water-closet, but the genitals were missing; he was executed, although he made no confession, saying the deed was an accident. Morbid changes were found in his brain. Krafft-Ebing cites the case of Alton, a clerk in England, who lured a child into a thicket, and after a time returned to his office, where he made an entry in his note-book: "Killed to-day a young girl; it was fine and hot." The child was missed, searched for, and found cut into pieces. Many parts, and among them the genitals, could not be found. Alton did not show the slightest trace of emotion, and gave no explanation of the motive or circumstances of his horrible deed; he was executed.

D'Amador[b] tells of persons who went into slaughter-houses and waste-places to dispute with wolves for the most revolting carrion. It is also mentioned that patients in hospitals have been detected in drinking the blood of patients after venesections, and in other instances frequenting dead-houses and sucking the blood of the recently deceased. Du Saulle[a] quotes the case of a chlorotic girl of fourteen who eagerly drank human blood. She preferred that flowing fresh from a recent wound.

Further Examples of Depraved Appetites.—Bijoux[b] speaks of a porter or garçon at the Jardin des Plantes in Paris who was a prodigious glutton. He had eaten the body of a lion that had died of disease at the menagerie. He ate with avidity the most disgusting things to satiate his depraved appetite. He showed further signs of a perverted mind by classifying the animals of the menagerie according to the form of their excrement, of which he had a collection. He died of indigestion following a meal of eight pounds of hot bread.

Percy[c] saw the famous Tarrare, who died at Versailles, at about twenty-six years of age. At seventeen he weighed 100 pounds. He ate a quarter of beef in twenty-four hours. He was fond of the most revolting things. He particularly relished the flesh of serpents and would quickly devour the largest. In the presence of Lorenze he seized a live cat with his teeth, eventrated it, sucked its blood, and ate it, leaving the bare skeleton only. In about thirty minutes he rejected the hairs in the manner of birds of prey and carnivorous animals. He also ate dogs in the same manner. On one occasion it was said that he swallowed a living eel without chewing it ; but he had first bitten off its head. He ate almost instantly a dinner that had been prepared for 15 vigorous workmen and drank the accompanying water and took their aggregate allowance of salt at the same time. After this meal his abdomen was so swollen that it resembled a balloon. He was seen by Courville, a surgeon-major in a military hospital, where he had swallowed a wooden box wrapped in plain white paper. This he passed the next day with the paper intact. The General-in-chief had seen him devour thirty pounds of raw liver and lungs. Nothing seemed to diminish his appetite. He waited around butcher-shops to eat what was discarded for the dogs. He drank the bleedings of the hospital and ate the dead from the dead-houses. He was suspected of eating a child of fourteen months, but no proof could be produced of this. He was of middle height and was always heated and sweating. He died of a purulent diarrhea, all his intestines and peritoneum being in a suppurating condition.

Fulton[d] mentions a girl of six who exhibited a marked taste for feeding on slugs, beetles, cockroaches, spiders, and repulsive insects. This child had been carefully brought up and was one of 13 children, none of whom displayed any similar depravity of appetite. The child was of good disposition and slightly below the normal mental standard for her age. At the age of fourteen her appetite became normal.

In the older writings many curious instances of abnormal appetite are

[a] Med. Critic, 1862, ii., 711.   [b] 302, iv., 199.   [c] 302, iv., 200   [d] 180, 1879.

seen.   Borellus speaks of individuals swallowing stones, horns, serpents, and toads.   Plater [a] mentions snail-eating and eel-eating, two customs still extant. Rhodius is accredited with seeing persons who swallowed spiders and scorpions.   Jonston[447] says that Avicenna, Rufus, and Gentilis relate instances of young girls who acquired a taste for poisonous animals and substances, who could ingest them with impunity.   Colonia Agrippina was supposed to have eaten spiders with impunity.   Van Woensel [b] is said to have seen persons who devoured live eels.

The habit of **dirt-eating or clay-eating**, called pica, is well authenticated in many countries.   The Ephemerides contains mention of it; Hunter speaks of the blacks who eat potters' clay; Bartholinus[190] describes dirt-eating as does also à Castro.[c]   Properly speaking, dirt-eating should be called geophagism; it is common in the Antilles and South America, among the low classes, and is seen in the negroes and poorest classes of some portions of the Southern United States.   It has also been reported from Java, China, Japan, and is said to have been seen in Spain and Portugal.   Peat-eating or bog-eating is still seen in some parts of Ireland.

There were a number of people in the sixteenth and seventeenth centuries who had formed the habit of eating small pebbles after each meal.   They formed the habit from seeing birds swallowing gravel after eating.   A number of such cases are on record.[d]

There is on record the account of a man living in Würtemberg who with much voracity had eaten a suckling pig, and sometimes devoured an entire sheep.   He swallowed dirt, clay, pebbles, and glass, and was addicted to intoxication by brandy.   He lived sixty years in this manner and then he became abstemious; he died at seventy-nine.   His omentum was very lean, but the liver covered all his abdominal viscera.   His stomach was very large and thick, but the intestines were very narrow.

Ely [e] had a patient who was addicted to **chalk-eating**; this he said invariably relieved his gastric irritation.   In the twenty-five years of the habit he had used over $\frac{1}{2}$ ton of chalk; but notwithstanding this he always enjoyed good health.   The Ephemerides contains a similar instance, and Verzascha mentions a lime-eater.   Adams [f] mentions a child of three who had an instinctive desire to eat mortar.   This baby was rickety and had carious teeth. It would pick its preferred diet out of the wall, and if prevented would cry loudly.   When deprived of the mortar it would vomit its food until this substance was given to it again.   At the time of report part of the routine duties of the sisters of this boy was to supply him with mortar containing a little sand.   Lime-water was substituted, but he insisted so vigorously on the solid form of food that it had to be replaced in his diet.   He suffered from small-pox; on waking up in the night with a fever, he always cried for

a 635, L. i. and L. ii.   b 105, 1748, viii., 62-64.   c 257, L. iii., 399.
d 629, 1700.   e 218, 1868, 101.   f 476, 1885, i., 235.

a piece of mortar. The quantity consumed in twenty-four hours was about ½ teacupful. The child had never been weaned.

Arsenic Eaters.—It has been frequently stated that the peasants of Styria are in the habit of taking from two to five grains of arsenious acid daily for the purpose of improving the health, avoiding infection, and raising the whole tone of the body. It is a well-substantiated fact that the quantities taken habitually are quite sufficient to produce immediate death ordinarily. But the same might be easily said of those addicted to opium and chloral, a subject that will be considered later. Perverted appetites during pregnancy have been discussed on pages 80 and 81.

Glass-eaters, penknife-swallowers, and sword-swallowers, being exhibitionists and jugglers, and not individuals with perverted appetites, will be considered in Chapter XII.

Fasting.—The length of time which a person can live with complete abstinence from food is quite variable. Hippocrates admits the possibility of fasting more than six days without a fatal issue; but Pliny and others allow a much longer time, and both the ancient and modern literature of medicine are replete with examples of abstinence to almost incredible lengths of time. Formerly, and particularly in the Middle Ages when religious frenzy was at its highest pitch, prolonged abstinence was prompted by a desire to do penance and to gain the approbation of Heaven.

In many religions fasting has become a part of worship or religious ceremony, and from the earliest times certain sects have carried this custom to extremes. It is well known that some of the priests and anchorites of the East now subsist on the minimum amount of food, and from the earliest times before the advent of Christianity we find instances of prolonged fasting associated with religious worship. The Assyrians, the Hebrews, the Egyptians, and other Eastern nations, and also the Greeks and Romans, as well as feasting days, had their times of fasting, and some of these were quite prolonged.

At the present day religious fervor accounts for but few of our remarkable instances of abstinence, most of them being due to some form of nervous disorder, varying from hysteria and melancholia to absolute insanity. The ability seen in the Middle Ages to live on the Holy Sacrament and to resist starvation may possibly have its analogy in some of the fasting girls of the present day. In the older times these persons were said to have been nourished by angels or devils; but according to Hammond many cases both of diabolical abstinence from food and of holy fasting exhibited manifest signs of hysteric symptoms. Hammond, in his exhaustive treatise on the subject of "Fasting Girls," also remarks that some of the chronicles detail the exact symptoms of hysteria and without hesitation ascribe them to a devilish agency. For instance, he speaks of a young girl in the valley of Calepino who had all her limbs twisted and contracted and had a sensation in her esophagus as if a ball was sometimes rising in her throat or falling into the stomach—a rather lay description of the characteristic hysteric "lump in the throat," a frequent sign of nervous abstinence.

Abstinence, or rather anorexia, is naturally associated with numerous diseases, particularly of the febrile type ; but in all of these the patient is maintained by the use of nutrient enemata or by other means, and the abstinence is never complete.

A peculiar type of anorexia is that striking and remarkable digestive disturbance of hysteria which Sir William Gull has called **anorexia nervosa.** In this malady there is such annihilation of the appetite that in some cases it seems impossible ever to eat again.   Out of it grows an antagonism to food which results at last, and in its worst forms, in spasm on the approach of food, and this in its turn gives rise to some of those remarkable cases of survival for long periods without food.   As this goes on there may be an extreme degree of muscular restlessness, so that the patients wander about until exhausted. According to Osler, who reports a fatal case in a girl who, at her death, only weighed 49 pounds, nothing more pitiable is to be seen in medical practice than an advanced case of this malady.   The emaciation and exhaustion are extreme, and the patient is as miserable as one with carcinoma of the esophagus, food either not being taken at all or only upon urgent compulsion.

Gull [a] mentions a girl of fourteen, of healthy, plump appearance,who in the beginning of February, 1887, without apparent cause evinced a great repugnance to food and soon afterward declined to take anything but a half cup of tea or coffee.   Gull saw her in April, when she was much emaciated ; she persisted in walking through the streets, where she was the object of remark of passers-by.   At this time her height was five feet four inches, her weight 63 pounds, her temperature 97° F., her pulse 46, and her respiration from 12 to 14.   She had a persistent wish to be moving all the time, despite her emaciation and the exhaustion of the nutritive functions.

There is another class of abstainers from food exemplified in the **exhibitionists** who either for notoriety or for wages demonstrate their ability to forego eating, and sometimes drinking, for long periods.   Some have been clever frauds, who by means of artifices have carried on skilful deceptions ; others have been really interesting physiologic anomalies.

Older Instances.—Democritus in 323 B. C. is said to have lived forty days by simply smelling honey and hot bread.   Hippocrates remarks that most of those who endeavored to abstain five days died within that period, and even if they were prevailed upon to eat and drink before the termination of their fast they still perished.   There is a possibility that some of these cases of Hippocrates were instances of pyloric carcinoma or of stenosis of the pylorus.   In the older writings there are instances reported in which the period of abstinence has varied from a short time to endurance beyond the

a 476, 1888, i., 321.

bounds of credulity. Hufeland mentions total abstinence from food for seventeen days, and there is a contemporary case of abstinence for forty days in a maniac who subsisted solely on water and tobacco. Bolsot [a] speaks of abstinence for fourteen months, and Consbruch [b] mentions a girl who fasted eighteen months. Müller [c] mentions an old man of forty-five who lived six weeks on cold water. There is an instance of a person living in a cave twenty-four days without food or drink,[d] and another of a man who survived five weeks' burial under ruins.[e] Ramazzini speaks of fasting sixty-six days; Willian, sixty days (resulting in death); von Wocher, thirty-seven days (associated with tetanus); Lantana, sixty days; Hobbes,[f] forty days; Marcardier,[g] six months; Cruikshank,[h] two months; the Ephemerides, thirteen months; Gerard,[i] sixty-nine days (resulting in death); and in 1722 there was recorded an instance of abstinence lasting twenty-five months.[j]

Desbarreaux-Bernard [k] says that Guillaume Granié died in the prison of Toulouse in 1831, after a voluntary suicidal abstinence of sixty-three days.

Haller [l] cites a number of examples of long abstinence, but most extraordinary was that of a girl of Confolens, described by Citois of Poitiers, who published a history of the case in the beginning of the seventeenth century. This girl is said to have passed three entire years, from eleven to fourteen, without taking any kind of aliment. In the " Harleian Miscellanies " is a copy of a paper humbly offered to the Royal Society by John Reynolds, containing a discourse upon prodigious abstinence, occasioned by the twelve months' fasting of a woman named Martha Taylor, a damsel of Derbyshire. Plot [637] gives a great variety of curious anecdotes of prolonged abstinence. Ames [m] refers to " the true and admirable history of the maiden of Confolens," mentioned by Haller. In the Annual Register, vol. i., is an account of three persons who were buried five weeks in the snow; and in the same journal, in 1762, is the history of a girl who is said to have subsisted nearly four years on water. In 1684 four miners were buried in a coal-pit in Horstel, a half mile from Liège, Belgium, and lived twenty-four days without food, eventually making good recoveries. An analysis of the water used during their confinement showed an almost total absence of organic matter and only a slight residue of calcium salts.[n]

Joanna Crippen lay six days in the snow without nutriment, being overcome by the cold while on the way to her house; she recovered despite her exposure.[o] Somis, physician to the King of Sardinia, gives an account of three women of Piedmont, Italy, who were saved from the ruins of a stable

[a] 470, 1685. [b] 452, L. ix., 115. [c] 452, L. xxiv. [d] 629, 158.

[e] 586, xv., 45. [f] 629, 1668. [g] 462. T. xxiii.

[h] "Anat. of the Absorbent Vessels," 101. [i] 462, T. vi., 147.

[j] 708, 1722. [k] 789, 1880, xxx., 350. [l] 400, T. vi., 171 *et seq.*

[m] "Topographical Antiquities." [n] 629, 1684. [o] 629, 1700-20, v., 358.

where they had been buried by an avalanche of snow, March 19, 1755. thirty-seven days before.   Thirty houses and 22 inhabitants were buried in this catastrophe, and these three women, together with a child of two, were sheltered in a stable over which the snow lodged 42 feet deep.   They were in a manger 20 inches broad and upheld by a strong arch.   Their enforced position was with their backs to the wall and their knees to their faces.   One woman had 15 chestnuts, and, fortunately, there were two goats near by, and within reach some hay, sufficient to feed them for a short time.   By milking one of the goats which had a kid, they obtained about two pints daily, upon which they subsisted for a time.   They quenched their thirst with melted snow liquefied by the heat of their hands.   Their sufferings were greatly increased by the filth, extreme cold, and their uncomfortable positions ; their clothes had rotted.   When they were taken out their eyes were unable to endure the light, and their stomachs at first rejected all food.

While returning from Cambridge, February 2, 1799, Elizabeth Woodcock dismounted from her horse, which ran away, leaving her in a violent snowstorm.   She was soon overwhelmed by an enormous drift six feet high.   The sensation of hunger ceased after the first day and that of thirst predominated, which she quenched by sucking snow.   She was discovered on the 10th of February, and although suffering from extensive gangrene of the toes, she recovered.   Hamilton[a] says that at a barracks near Oppido, celebrated for its earthquakes, there were rescued two girls, one sixteen and the other eleven : the former had remained under the ruins without food for eleven days. This poor creature had counted the days by a light coming through a small opening.   The other girl remained six days under the ruin in a confined and distressing posture, her hands pressing her cheek until they had almost made a hole in it.   Two persons were buried under earthquake ruins at Messina for twenty-three and twenty-two days each.

Thomas Creaser[b] gives the history of Joseph Lockier of Bath, who, while going through a woods between 6 and 7 P. M., on the 18th of August, was struck insensible by a violent thunderbolt.   His senses gradually returned and he felt excessively cold.   His clothes were wet, and his feet so swollen that the power of the lower extremities was totally gone and that of the arms was much impaired.   For a long time he was unable to articulate or to summon assistance.   Early in September he heard some persons in the wood and, having managed to summon them in a feeble voice, told them his story.   They declared him to be an impostor and left him.   On the evening of the same day his late master came to his assistance and removed him to Swan Inn.   He affirmed that during his exposure in the woods he had nothing to eat ; though distressing at first, hunger soon subsided and yielded to thirst, which he appeased by chewing grass having beads of water thereon.   He slept during the warmth of the day, but the cold kept him

a 629, lxxiii.   b " Case Joseph Lockier." 8°, Bath, 1806.

awake at night. During his sleep he dreamt of eating and drinking. On November 17, 1806, several surgeons of Bath made an affidavit, in which they stated that this man was admitted to the Bath City Dispensary on September 15th, almost a month after his reputed stroke, in an extremely emaciated condition, with his legs and thighs shriveled as well as motionless. There were several livid spots on his legs and one toe was grangrenous. After some time they amputated the toe. The power in the lower extremities soon returned.

In relating his travels in the Levant, Hasselquist mentions 1000 Abyssinians who became destitute of provisions while en route to Cairo, and who lived two months on gum arabic alone, arriving at their destination without any unusual sickness or mortality. Dr. Franklin lived on bread and water for a fortnight, at the rate of ten pounds per week, and maintained himself stout and healthy. Sir John Pringle knew a lady of ninety who lived on pure fat meat. Gower of Chelmsford had a patient who lived ten years on a pint of tea daily, only now or then chewing a half dozen raisins or almonds, but not swallowing them. Once in long intervals she took a little bread.

Brassavolus describes a younger daughter of Frederick King of Naples, who lived entirely without meat, and could not endure even the taste of it ; as often as she put any in her mouth she fell fainting. The monks of Monte Santo (Mount Athos) never touched animal food, but lived on vegetables, olives, and cheese. In 1806 one of them at the age of one hundred and twenty was healthy.

Sometimes in the older writings we find records of incredible abstinence. Jonston[a] speaks of a man in 1460 who, after an unfortunate matrimonial experience, lived alone for fifteen years, taking neither food nor drink. Petrus Aponensis cites the instance of a girl fasting for eight years. According to Jonston, Hermolus lived forty years on air alone. This same author has also collected cases of abstinence lasting eleven, twenty-two, and thirty years, and cites Aristotle as an authority in substantiating his instances of fasting girls.

Wadd, the celebrated authority on corpulence, quotes Pennant in mentioning a woman in Rosshire who lived one and three-quarters years without meat or drink. Granger had under observation a woman by the name of Ann Moore, fifty-eight years of age, who fasted for two years. Fabricius Hildanus[334] relates of Apollonia Schreiera that she lived three years without meat or drink. He also tells of Eva Flegen, who began to fast in 1596, and from that time on, for sixteen years, lived without meat or drink. According to the Rev. Thos. Steill, Janet Young fasted sixteen years and partially prolonged her abstinence for fifty years. The Edinburgh Medical and Surgical Journal,[b] which contains a mention of the foregoing case, also describes the case of Janet Macleod, who fasted for four years, showing no signs of emaciation. Benja-

[a] 447, 444.   [b] 318, 1813, ix., 157.

min Rush speaks of a case mentioned in a letter to St. George Tucker, from J. A. Stuart, of a man who, after receiving no benefit from a year's treatment for hemiplegia, resolved to starve himself to death. He totally abstained from food for sixty days, living on water and chewing apples, but spitting out the pulp; at the expiration of this time he died. Eccles [a] relates the history of a beautiful young woman of sixteen, who upon the death of a most indulgent father refused food for thirty-four days, and soon afterward for fifty-four days, losing all her senses but that of touch.

There is an account [b] of a French adventurer, the Chevalier de Saint-Lubin, who had a loathing for food and abstained from every kind of meat and drink for fifty-eight days. Saint-Sauver, at that time Lieutenant of the Bastille, put a close watch on this man and certified to the verity of the fast. The European Magazine in 1783 contained an account of the Calabria earthquake, at which time a girl of eighteen was buried under ruins for six days. The edge of a barrel fell on her ankle and partly separated it, the dust and mortar effectually stopping the hemorrhage. The foot dropped off and the wound healed without medical assistance, the girl making a complete recovery. There is an account taken from a document in the Vatican of a man living in 1306, in the reign of Pope Clement V., who fasted for two years.[c] McNaughton [d] mentions Rubin Kelsey, a medical student afflicted with melancholia, who voluntarily fasted for fifty-three days, drinking copiously and greedily of water. For the first six weeks he walked about, and was strong to the day of his death.

Hammond has proved many of the reports of "fasting girls" to have been untrustworthy. The case of Miss Faucher of Brooklyn, who was supposed to have taken no food for fourteen years, was fraudulent. He says that Ann Moore was fed by her daughter in several ways; when washing her mother's face she used towels wet with gravy, milk, or strong arrow-root meal. She also conveyed food to her mother by means of kisses. One of the "fasting girls," Margaret Weiss, although only ten years old, had such powers of deception that after being watched by the priest of the parish, Dr. Bucoldianus, she was considered free from juggling, and, to everybody's astonishment, she grew, walked, and talked like other children of her age, still maintaining that she used neither food nor drink. In several other cases reported all attempts to discover imposture failed. As we approach more modern times the detection is more frequent. Sarah Jacobs, the Welsh fasting girl who attained such celebrity among the laity, was taken to Guy's Hospital on December 9, 1869, and after being watched by eight experienced nurses for eight days she died of starvation. A postmortem examination of Anna Garbero of Racconis, in Piedmont,[e] who died on May 19, 1828, after having endured a supposed fast of two years, eight months, and eleven days,

a 527, 1774, v., part ii., 471 et seq.   b 328, 1790, 124.
c Journal de Pharmacia, etc., de Lisboa.   d 763, 1830, i., 113.   e 151, 1828.

revealed remarkable intestinal changes. The serous membranes were all callous and thickened, and the canal of the sigmoid flexure was totally obliterated. The mucous membranes were all soft and friable, and presented the appearance of incipient gangrene.

Modern Cases.—Turning now to modern literature, we have cases of marvelous abstinence well substantiated by authoritative evidence. Dickson [a] describes a man of sixty-two, suffering from monomania, who refused food for four months, but made a successful recovery. Richardson [b] mentions a case, happening in 1848, of a man of thirty-three who voluntarily fasted for fifty-five days. His reason for fasting, which it was impossible to combat, was that he had no gastric juice and that it was utterly useless for him to take any nutrition, as he had no means of digesting it. He lived on water until the day of his death. Richardson gives an interesting account of the changes noticed at the necropsy. There is an account of a religious mendicant of the Jain caste [c] who as a means of penance fasted for ninety-one days. The previous year he had fasted eighty-six days. He had spent his life in strict asceticism, and during his fasting he was always engrossed in prayer.

Collins [d] describes a maiden lady of eighty, always a moderate eater, who was attacked by bronchitis, during which she took food as usual. Two days after her recovery, without any known cause, she refused all food and continued to do so for thirty-three days, when she died. She was delirious throughout this fast and slept daily seven or eight hours. As a rule, she drank about a wineglassful of water each day and her urine was scanty and almost of the consistency of her feces. There is a remarkable case of a girl of seventeen [e] who, suffering with typhoid fever associated with engorgement of the abdomen and suppression of the functions of assimilation, fasted for four months without visible diminution in weight. Pierce [f] reports the history of a woman of twenty-six who fasted for three months and made an excellent recovery.

Grant [g] describes the "Market Harborough fasting-girl," a maiden of nineteen, who abstained from food from April, 1874, until December, 1877, although continually using morphia. Throughout her fast she had periodic convulsions, and voided no urine or feces for twelve months before her death. There was a middle-aged woman in England in 1860 who for two years lived on opium, gin, and water. Her chief symptoms were almost daily sickness and epileptic fits three times a week. She was absolutely constipated, and at her death her abdomen was so distended as to present the appearance of ascites. After death, the distention of the abdomen was found to be due to a coating of fat, four inches thick, in the parietes. There was no obstruction to the intestinal canal and no fecal or other accumulation within it.

a 476, 1853, i., 512.   b 173, 1890.   c 536, 1882, i., 11.   d 224, 1880, ii., 214.

e 276, 1828–9, iii., 283.   f 124, 1852, 571.   g 224, 1878, i., 152.

Christina Marshall,[a] a girl of fourteen, went fifteen and one-half months without taking solid nourishment. She slept very little, seldom spoke, but occasionally asked the time of day. She took sweets and water, with beef tea at intervals, and occasionally a small piece of orange. She died April 18, 1882, after having been confined to her bed for a long while.

King,[b] a surgeon, U. S. A., gives an account of the deprivation of a squad of cavalry numbering 40. While scouting for Indians on the plains they went for eighty-six hours without water ; when relieved their mouths and throats were so dry that even brown sugar would not dissolve on their tongues. Many were delirious, and all had drawn fresh blood from their horses. Despite repeated vomiting, some drank their own urine. They were nearly all suffering from overpowering dyspnea, two were dead, and two were missing. The suffering was increased by the acrid atmosphere of the dry plains ; the slightest exercise in this climate provoked a thirst. MacLoughlin,[c] the surgeon in charge of the S. S. City of Chester, speaks of a young stow-away found by the stevedores in an insensible condition after a voyage of eleven days. The man was brought on deck and revived sufficiently to be sent to St. Vincent's Hospital, N. Y., about one and one-half hours after discovery, in an extremely emaciated, cold, and nearly pulseless condition. He gave his name as John Donnelly, aged twenty, of Dumbarton, Scotland. On the whole voyage he had nothing to eat or drink. He had found some salt, of which he ate two handfuls, and he had in his pocket a small flask, empty. Into this flask he voided his urine, and afterward drank it. Until the second day he was intensely hungry, but after that time was consumed by a burning thirst ; he shouted four or five hours every day, hoping that he might be heard. After this he became insensible and re-membered nothing until he awakened in the hospital where, under careful treatment, he finally recovered.

Fodere mentions some workmen who were buried alive fourteen days in a cold, damp cavern under a ruin, and yet all lived. There is a modern instance of a person being buried thirty-two days beneath snow, without food.[d] The Lancet[e] notes that a pig fell off Dover Cliff and was picked up alive one hundred and sixty days after, having been partially imbedded in debris. It was so surrounded by the chalk of the cliff that little motion was possible, and warmth was secured by the enclosing material. This animal had there-fore lived on its own fat during the entire period.

Among the **modern exhibitionists** may be mentioned Merlatti, the fast-ing Italian, and Succi, both of whom fasted in Paris ; Alexander Jacques, who fasted fifty days ; and the American, Dr. Tanner, who achieved great notoriety by a fast of forty days, during which time he exhibited progressive emaciation. Merlatti, who fasted in Paris in 1886, lost 22 pounds in a

a 224, 1882, i., 631.   b 124, April, 1878.   c 476, 1878, ii., 646.
d 556, 1861, i., 67.   e 476, 1890, i., 978.

month ; during his fast of fifty days he drank only pure filtered water. Prior to the fast his farewell meal consisted of a whole fat goose, including the bones, two pounds of roast beef, vegetables for two, and a plate of walnuts, the latter eaten whole. Alexander Jacques [a] fasted fifty days and Succi fasted forty days. Jacques lost 28 pounds and 4 ounces (from 142 pounds, 8 ounces to 114 pounds, 4 ounces), while Succi's loss was 34 pounds and 3 ounces. Succi diminished in height from $65\frac{3}{4}$ to $64\frac{1}{2}$ inches, while Jacques increased from $64\frac{1}{2}$ to $65\frac{1}{2}$ inches. Jacques smoked cigarettes incessantly, using 700 in the fifty days, although, by professional advice, he stopped the habit on the forty-second day. Three or four times a day he took a powder made of herbs, to which he naturally attributed his power of prolonging life without food. Succi remained in a room in which he kept the temperature at a very high point. In speaking of Succi's latest feat a recent report says : " It has come to light in his latest attempt to go for fifty days without food that he privately regaled himself on soup, beefsteak, chocolate, and eggs. It was also discovered that one of the ' committee,' who were supposed to watch and see that the experiment was conducted in a bona fide manner, ' stood in ' with the faster and helped him deceive the others. The result of the Vienna experiment is bound to cast suspicion on all previous fasting accomplishments of Signor Succi, if not upon those of his predecessors."

Although all these modern fasters have been accused of being jugglers and deceivers, throughout their fasts they showed constant decrease in weight, and inspection by visitors was welcomed at all times. They invariably invited medical attention, and some were under the closest surveillance ; although we may not implicitly believe that the fasts were in every respect bona fide, yet we must acknowledge that these men displayed great endurance in their apparent indifference for food, the deprivation of which in a normal individual for one day only causes intense suffering.

Anomalies of Temperature.—In reviewing the reports of the highest recorded temperatures of the human body, it must be remembered that no matter how good the evidence or how authentic the reference there is always chance for malingering. It is possible to send the index of an ordinary thermometer up to the top in ten or fifteen seconds by rubbing it between the slightly moistened thumb and the finger, exerting considerable pressure at the time. There are several other means of artificially producing enormous temperatures with little risk of detection, and as the sensitiveness of the thermometer becomes greater the easier is the deception.

Mackenzie [b] reports the temperature-range of a woman of forty-two who suffered with erysipelatous inflammation of a stump of the leg. Throughout a somewhat protracted illness, lasting from February 20 to April 22, 1879, the temperature many times registered between 108° and 111° F. About a year later she was again troubled with the stump, and this time the tempera-

a 224, 1890, i., 1444.   b 476, 1881, ii., 796.

ture reached as high as 114°. Although under the circumstances, as any rational physician would, Mackenzie suspected fraud, he could not detect any method of deception. Finally the woman confessed that she had produced the temperature artificially by means of hot-water bottles, poultices, etc.

MacNab [a] records a case of rheumatic fever in which the temperature was 111.4° F. as indicated by two thermometers, one in the axilla and the other in the groin. This high degree of temperature was maintained after death. Before the Clinical Society of London, Teale [b] reported a case in which, at different times, there were recorded temperatures from 110° to 120° F. in the mouth, rectum, and axilla. According to a comment in the Lancet, there was no way that the patient could have artificially produced this temperature, and during convalescence the thermometer used registered normal as well as subnormal temperatures. Cæsar [c] speaks of a girl of fifteen with enteric fever, whose temperature, on two occasions 110° F., reached the limit of the mercury in the thermometer.

There have been instances mentioned in which, in order to escape duties, prisoners have artificially produced high temperatures, and the same has occasionally been observed among conscripts in the army or navy. There is an account [d] of a habit of prisoners of introducing tobacco into the rectum, thereby reducing the pulse to an alarming degree and insuring their exemption from labor. In the Adelaide Hospital in Dublin [e] there was a case in which the temperature in the vagina and groin registered from 120° to 130°, and one day it reached 130.8° F.; the patient recovered. Ormerod [f] mentions a nervous and hysteric woman of thirty-two, a sufferer with acute rheumatism, whose temperature rose to 115.8° F. She insisted on leaving the hospital when her temperature was still 104°.

Wunderlich mentions a case of tetanus in which the temperature rose to 46.40° C. (115.5° F.), and before death it was as high as 44.75° C. Obernier [g] mentions 108° F. in typhoid fever. Kartulus [h] speaks of a child of five, with typhoid fever, who at different times had temperatures of 107°, 108°, and 108.2° F.; it finally recovered. He also quotes a case of pyemia in a boy of seven, whose temperature rose to 107.6° F. He also speaks of Wunderlich's case of remittent fever, in which the temperature reached 107.8° F. Wilson Fox, in mentioning a case of rheumatic fever, says the temperature reached 110° F.

Philipson [i] gives an account of a female servant of twenty-three who suffered from a neurosis which influenced the vasomotor nervous system, and caused hysteria associated with abnormal temperatures. On the evening of July 9th her temperature was 112° F.; on the 16th, it was 111°; on the 18th, 112°; on the 24th, 117° (axilla); on the 28th, in the left axilla it

a 476, 1873, ii., 341.	b 476, 1875, ii., 107.	c 476, 1879, i., 868.
d 476, 1876, i., 28.	e 548, 1880, i., 585.	f 476, 1878, ii., 658.
g 199, 1867.	h 476, 1879, i., 609.	i 476, 1880, i., 641.

was 117°, in the right axilla, 114°, and in the mouth, 112°; on the 29th, it was 115° in the right axilla, 110° in the left axilla, and 116° in the mouth. The patient was discharged the following September. Steel of Manchester [a] speaks of a hysteric female of twenty, whose temperature was 116.4°. Mahomed [b] mentions a hysteric woman of twenty-two at Guy's Hospital, London, with phthisis of the left lung, associated with marked hectic fevers. Having registered the limit of the ordinary thermometers, the physicians procured one with a scale reaching to 130° F. She objected to using the large thermometers, saying they were "horse thermometers." On October 15, 1879, however, they succeeded in obtaining a temperature of 128° F. with the large thermometer. In March of the following year she died, and the necropsy revealed nothing indicative of a cause for these enormous temperatures. She was suspected of fraud, and was closely watched in Guy's Hospital, but never, in the slightest way, was she detected in using artificial means to elevate the temperature record.

In cases of insolation it is not at all unusual to see a patient whose temperature cannot be registered by an ordinary thermometer. Any one who has been resident at a hospital in which heat-cases are received in the summer will substantiate this. At the Emergency Hospital in Washington, during recent years, several cases have been brought in which the temperatures were above the ordinary registering point of the hospital thermometers, and one of the most extraordinary cases recovered.

At a meeting of the Association of American Physicians in 1895, Jacobi of New York reported a **case of hyperthermy reaching 148° F.** This instance occurred in a profoundly hysteric fireman, who suffered a rather severe injury as the result of a fall between the revolving rods of some machinery, and was rendered unconscious for four days. Thereafter he complained of various pains, bloody expectoration, and had convulsions at varying intervals, with loss of consciousness, rapid respiration, unaccelerated pulse, and excessively high temperature, the last on one occasion reaching the height of 148° F. The temperature was taken carefully in the presence of a number of persons, and all possible precautions were observed to prevent deception. The thermometer was variously placed in the mouth, anus, axilla, popliteal space, groin, urethra, and different instruments were from time to time employed. The behavior of the patient was much influenced by attention and by suggestion. For a period of five days the temperature averaged continuously between 120° and 125° F.

In the discussion of the foregoing case, Welch of Baltimore referred to a case that had been reported in which it was said that the temperature reached as high as 171° F. These extraordinary elevations of temperature, he said, appear physically impossible when they are long continued, as they are fatal to the life of the animal cell.

a 476, 1881, ii., 790.   b 476, 1881, ii., 790.

In the same connection Shattuck of Boston added that he had observed a temperature of 117° F. ; every precaution had been taken to prevent fraud or deception.   The patient was a hysteric young woman.

Jacobi closed the discussion by insisting that his observations had been made with the greatest care and precautions and under many different circumstances.   He had at first viewed the case with skepticism, but he could not doubt the results of his observation.   He added, that although we cannot explain anomalies of this kind, this constitutes no reason why we should deny their occurrence.

Duffy[a] records one of the **lowest temperatures** on record in a negress of thirty-five who, after an abortion, showed only 84° F. in the mouth and axillæ.   She died the next day.

The amount of external heat that a human being can endure is sometimes remarkable, and the range of temperature compatible with life is none the less extraordinary.   The Esquimaux and the inhabitants of the extreme north at times endure a temperature of —60° F., while some of the people living in equatorial regions are apparently healthy at a temperature as high as 130° F., and work in the sun, where the temperature is far higher. In the engine-rooms of some steamers plying in tropical waters temperatures as high as 150° F. have been registered, yet the engineers and the stokers become habituated to this heat and labor in it without apparent suffering.   In Turkish baths, by progressively exposing themselves to graduated temperatures, persons have been able to endure a heat considerably above the boiling point, though having to protect their persons from the furniture and floors and walls of the rooms.   The hot air in these rooms is intensely dry, provoking profuse perspiration.   Sir Joseph Banks remained some time in a room the temperature of which was 211° F., and his own temperature never mounted above normal.

There have been exhibitionists who claimed particular ability to endure intense heats without any visible disadvantage.   These men are generally styled **" human salamanders,"** and must not be confounded with the " fire-eaters," who, as a rule, are simply jugglers.   Martinez,[b] the so-called " French Salamander," was born in Havana.   As a baker he had exposed himself from boyhood to very high temperatures, and he subsequently gave public exhibitions of his extraordinary ability to endure heat.   He remained in an oven erected in the middle of the Gardens of Tivoli for fourteen minutes when the temperature in the oven was 338° F.   His pulse on entering was 76 and on coming out 130.   He often duplicated this feat before vast assemblages, though hardly ever attaining the same degree of temperature, the thermometer generally varying from 250° F. upward.   Chamouni was the celebrated " Russian Salamander," assuming the title of " The Incombustible." [c] His great feat was to enter an oven with a raw leg of mutton, not retiring

a 681, 1874, vii., 365.   b 226, 1827, 276.   c 476, 1827-8, 585.

until the meat was well baked. This person eventually lost his life in the performance of this feat; his ashes were conveyed to his native town, where a monument was erected over them. Since the time of these two contemporaneous salamanders there have been many others, but probably none have attained the same notoriety.

In this connection Tillet speaks of some servant girls to a baker who for fifteen minutes supported a temperature of 270° F.; for ten minutes, 279° F.; and for several minutes, 364° F., thus surpassing Martinez. In the Glasgow Medical Journal, 1859, there is an account of a baker's daughter who remained twelve minutes in an oven at 274° F. Chantrey, the sculptor, and his workman are said to have entered with impunity a furnace of over 320° F.

In some of the savage ceremonies of **fire worship** the degree of heat endured by the participants is really remarkable, and even if the rites are performed by skilful juggling, nevertheless, the ability to endure intense heat is worthy of comment. A recent report says :—

" The most remarkable ceremonial of fire worship that survives in this country is practised by the Navajos. They believe in purification by fire, and to this end they literally wash themselves in it. The feats they perform with it far exceed the most wonderful acts of fire-eating and fire-handling accomplished by civilized jugglers. In preparation for the festival a gigantic heap of dry wood is gathered from the desert. At the appointed moment the great pile of inflammable brush is lighted and in a few moments the whole of it is ablaze. Storms of sparks fly 100 feet or more into the air, and ashes fall about like a shower of snow. The ceremony always takes place at night and the effect of it is both weird and impressive.

" Just when the fire is raging at its hottest a whistle is heard from the outer darkness and a dozen warriors, lithe and lean, dressed simply in narrow white breech-cloths and moccasins and daubed with white earth so as to look like so many living statues, come bounding through the entrance to the corral that incloses the flaming heap. Yelping like wolves, they move slowly toward the fire, bearing aloft slender wands tipped with balls of eagle-down. Rushing around the fire, always to the left, they begin thrusting their wands toward the fire, trying to burn off the down from the tips. Owing to the intensity of the heat this is difficult to accomplish. One warrior dashes wildly toward the fire and retreats ; another lies as close to the ground as a frightened lizard, endeavoring to wriggle himself up to the fire ; others seek to catch on their wands the sparks that fly in the air. At last one by one they all succeed in burning the downy balls from the wands. The test of endurance is very severe, the heat of the fire being so great.

" The remarkable feats, however, are performed in connection with another dance that follows. This is heralded by a tremendous blowing of horns. The noise grows louder and louder until suddenly ten or more men run into the corral, each of them carrying two thick bundles of shredded cedar bark.

Four times they run around the fire waving the bundles, which are then lighted. Now begins a wild race around the fire, the rapid running causing the brands to throw out long streamers of flames over the hands and arms of the dancers. The latter apply the brands to their own nude bodies and to the bodies of their comrades in front. A warrior will seize the flaming mass as if it were a sponge, and, keeping close to the man he is pursuing, will rub his back with it as if bathing him. The sufferer in turn catches up with the man in front of him and bathes him in flame. From time to time the dancers sponge their own backs with the flaming brands. When a brand is so far consumed that it can no longer be held it is dropped and the dancers disappear from the corral. The spectators pick up the flaming bunches thus dropped and bathe their own hands in the fire.

" No satisfactory explanation seems to be obtainable as to the means by which the dancers in this extraordinary performance are able to escape injury. Apparently they do not suffer from any burns. Doubtless some protection is afforded by the earth that is applied to their bodies."

Spontaneous combustion of the human body, although doubted by the medical men of this day, has for many years been the subject of much discussion ; only a few years ago, among the writers on this subject, there were as many credulous as there were skeptics. There is, however, no reliable evidence to support the belief in the spontaneous combustion of the body. A few apochryphal cases only have been recorded. The opinion that the tissues of drunkards might be so saturated with alcohol as to render the body combustible is disproved by the simple experiment of placing flesh in spirits for a long time and then trying to burn it. Liebig and others found that flesh soaked in alcohol would burn only until the alcohol was consumed. That various substances ignite spontaneously is explained by chemic phenomena, the conditions of which do not exist in the human frame. Watkins [a] in speaking of the inflammability of the human body remarks that on one occasion he tried to consume the body of a pirate given to him by a U. S. Marshal. He built a rousing fire and piled wood on all night, and had not got the body consumed by the forenoon of the following day. Quite a feasible reason for supposed spontaneous human combustion is to be found in several cases quoted by Taylor,[757] in which persons falling asleep, possibly near a fire, have been accidentally ignited, and becoming first stupefied by the smoke, and then suffocated, have been burned to charcoal without awaking. Drunkenness or great exhaustion may also explain certain cases. In substantiation of the possibility of Taylor's instances several prominent physiologists have remarked that persons have endured severe burns during sleep and have never wakened. There is an account of a man who lay down on the top of a lime kiln, which was fired during his sleep, and one leg was burned entirely off without awaking the man, a fact explained by the very slow and gradual increase of temperature.

a 593, 1870.

The **theories** advanced by the advocates of spontaneous human combustion are very ingenious and deserve mention here. An old authority has said : " Our blood is of such a nature, as also our lymph and bile : all of which, when dried by art, flame like spirit of wine at the approach of the least fire and burn away to ashes." Lord Bacon mentions spontaneous combustion, and Marcellus Donatus [306] says that in the time of Godefroy of Bouillon there were people of a certain locality who supposed themselves to have been burning of an invisible fire in their entrails, and he adds that some cut off a hand or a foot when the burning began, that it should go no further. What may have been the malady with which these people suffered must be a matter of conjecture.

Overton,[a] in a paper on this subject, remarks that in the " Memoirs of the Royal Society of Paris," 1751, there is related an account of a butcher who, opening a diseased beef, was burned by a flame which issued from the maw of the animal ; there was first an explosion which rose to a height of five feet and continued to blaze several minutes with a highly offensive odor. Morton saw a flame emanate from beneath the skin of a hog at the instant of making an incision through it. Ruysch, the famous Dutch physician, remarks that he introduced a hollow bougie into a woman's stomach he had just opened, and he observed a vapor issuing from the mouth of the tube, and this lit on contact with the atmosphere. This is probably an exaggeration of the properties of the hydrogen sulphid found in the stomach. There is an account [b] of a man of forty-three, a gross feeder, who was particularly fond of fats and a victim of psoriasis palmaria, who on going to bed one night, after extinguishing the light in the room, was surprised to find himself enveloped in a phosphorescent halo ; this continued for several days and recurred after further indiscretions in diet. It is well known that there are insects and other creatures of the lower animal kingdom which possess the peculiar quality of phosphorescence.

There are numerous cases of spontaneous combustion of the human body reported by the older writers. Bartholinus mentions an instance after the person had drunk too much wine. Fouquet [c] mentions a person ignited by lightning. Schrader [d] speaks of a person from whose mouth and fauces after a debauch issued fire. Schurig [e] tells of flames issuing from the vulva, and Moscati [f] records the same occurrence in parturition ; Sinibaldus,[737] Borellus, [841] and Bierling [211] have also written on this subject, and the Ephemerides contains a number of instances.

In 1763 Bianchini, Prebendary of Verona, published an account of the death of Countess Cornelia Bandi of Cesena, who in her sixty-second year was consumed by a fire kindled in her own body. In explanation Bianchini

a 774, 1835, 9 *et seq.* b 476, 1842, ii., 2, 374.
c 462, T. lxviii., 436. d " Observat. rar.," fasc. i., No. 10.
e "Chylologia," 524. f " Mem. di Matem. e di Fisica della di Modena," x.

said that the fire was caused in the entrails by the inflamed effluvia of the blood, by the juices and fermentation in the stomach, and, lastly, by fiery evaporations which exhaled from the spirits of wine, brandy, etc. In the Gentleman's Magazine, 1763, there is recorded an account of three noblemen who, in emulation, drank great quantities of strong liquor, and two of them died scorched and suffocated by a flame forcing itself from the stomach. There is an account of a poor woman in Paris in the last century who drank plentifully of spirits, for three years taking virtually nothing else. Her body became so combustible that one night while lying on a straw couch she was spontaneously burned to ashes and smoke. The evident cause of this combustion is too plain to be commented on. In the Lancet, 1845, there are two cases reported in which shortly before death luminous breath has been seen to issue from the mouth.[a]

There is an instance reported of a professor of mathematics [b] of thirty-five years of age and temperate, who, feeling a pain in his left leg, discovered a pale flame about the size of a ten-cent piece issuing therefrom. As recent as March, 1850, in a Court of Assizes in Darmstadt during the trial of John Stauff, accused of the murder of the Countess Goerlitz, the counsel for the defense advanced the theory of spontaneous human combustion, and such eminent doctors as von Siebold, Graff, von Liebig, and other prominent members of the Hessian medical fraternity were called to comment on its possibility ; principally on their testimony a conviction and life-imprisonment was secured. In 1870 [c] there was a woman of thirty-seven, addicted to alcoholic liquors, who was found in her room with her viscera and part of her limbs consumed by fire, but the hair and clothes intact. According to Walford,[813] in the Scientific American for 1870, there was a case reported by Flowers of Louisiana of a man, a hard drinker, who was sitting by a fire surrounded by his Christmas guests, when suddenly flames of a bluish tint burst from his mouth and nostrils and he was soon a corpse. Flowers states that the body remained extremely warm for a much longer period than usual.

Statistics.—From an examination of 28 cases of spontaneous combustion, Jacobs [d] makes the following summary :—

(1) It has always occurred in the human living body.

(2) The subjects were generally old persons.

(3) It was noticed more frequently in women than in men.

(4) All the persons were alone at the time of occurrence.

(5) They all led an idle life.

(6) They were all corpulent or intemperate.

(7) Most frequently at the time of occurrence there was a light and some ignitible substance in the room.

(8) The combustion was rapid and was finished in from one to seven hours.

a 476, 1845, ii., 274 ; 1845, i., 11.   b 124, xvii., 266.

c 789, 1870.   d 235, May 15 and 30, 1841.

(9) The room where the combustion took place was generally filled with a thick vapor and the walls covered with a thick, carbonaceous substance.

(10) The trunk was usually the part most frequently destroyed ; some part of the head and extremities remained.

(11) With but two exceptions, the combustion occurred in winter and in the northern regions.

Magnetic, Phosphorescent, and Electric Anomalies.—There have been certain persons who have appeared before the public under such names as the " human magnet," the " electric lady," etc. There is no doubt that some persons are supercharged with magnetism and electricity. For instance, it is quite possible for many persons by drawing a rubber comb through the hair to produce a crackling noise, and even produce sparks in the dark. Some exhibitionists have been genuine curiosities of this sort, while others by skilfully arranged electric apparatus are enabled to perform their feats. A curious case was reported in this country many years ago,[a] which apparently emanates from an authoritative source. On the 25th of January, 1837, a certain lady became suddenly and unconsciously charged with electricity. Her newly acquired power was first exhibited when passing her hand over the face of her brother ; to the astonishment of both, vivid electric sparks passed from the ends of each finger. This power continued with augmented force from the 25th of January to the last of February, but finally became extinct about the middle of May of the same year.

Schneider[b] mentions a strong, healthy, dark-haired Capuchin monk, the removal of whose head-dress always induced a number of shining, crackling sparks from his hair or scalp. Bartholinus observed a similar peculiarity in Gonzaga, Duke of Mantua. In another case luminous sparks were given out whenever the patient passed urine. Marsh relates two cases of phthisis in which the heads of the patients were surrounded by phosphorescent lights. Kaster mentions an instance in which light was seen in the perspiration and on the body linen after violent exertion. After exertion Jurine,[c] Guyton, and Driessen observed luminous urine passed by healthy persons, and Nasse mentions the same phenomenon in a phthisical patient. Percy and Stokes have observed phosphorescence in a carcinomatous ulcer.

There is a description of a Zulu boy exhibited in Edinburgh in 1882[d] whose body was so charged with electricity that he could impart a shock to any of his patrons. He was about six and a-half years of age, bright, happy, and spoke English thoroughly well. From infancy he had been distinguished for this faculty, variable with the state of the atmosphere. As a rule, the act of shaking hands was generally attended by a quivering sensation like that produced by an electric current, and contact with his tongue gave a still sharper shock.

[a] 124, Jan., 1838.
[c] 458, 1813, 48.

[b] Casper's Wochenschrift, No. 15, 1849.
[d] 536, 1882, ii., 360.

Sir Charles Bell has made extensive investigation of the subject of human magnetism and is probably the best authority on the subject, but many celebrated scientists have studied it thoroughly. In the Pittsburg Medical Review [a] there is a description of a girl of three and a half, a blonde, and extremely womanly for her age, who possessed a wonderful magnetic power. Metal spoons would adhere to her finger-tips, nose, or chin. The child, however, could not pick up a steel needle, an article generally very sensitive to the magnet; nor would a penny stick to any portion of her body.

Only recently there was exhibited through this country a woman named Annie May Abbott, who styled herself the " Georgia Electric Lady." This person gave exhibitions of wonderful magnetic power, and invited the inspection and discussion of medical men. Besides her chief accomplishment she possessed wonderful strength and was a skilled equilibrist. By placing her hands on the sides of a chair upon which a heavy man was seated, she would raise it without apparent effort. She defied the strongest person in the audience to take from her hand a stick which she had once grasped. Recent reports say that Miss Abbott is amusing herself now with the strong men of China and Japan. The Japanese wrestlers, whose physical strength is celebrated the world over, were unable to raise Miss Abbott from the floor, while with the tips of her fingers she neutralized their most strenuous efforts to lift even light objects, such as a cane, from a table. The possibilities, in this advanced era of electric mechanism, make fraud and deception so easy that it is extremely difficult to pronounce on the genuineness of any of the modern exhibitions of human electricity.

The Effects of Cold.—Gmelin, the famous scientist and investigator of this subject, says that man has lived where the temperature falls as low as —157° F. Habit is a marked factor in this endurance. In Russia men and women work with their breasts and arms uncovered in a temperature many degrees below zero and without attention to the fact. In the most rigorous winter the inhabitants of the Alps work with bare breasts and the children sport about in the snow. Wrapping himself in his *pelisse* the Russian sleeps in the snow. This influence of habit is seen in the inability of intruders in northern lands to endure the cold, which has no effect on the indigenous people. On their way to besiege a Norwegian stronghold in 1719, 7000 Swedes perished in the snows and cold of their neighboring country. On the retreat from Prague in 1742, the French army, under the rigorous sky of Bohemia, lost 4000 men in ten days. It is needless to speak of the thousands lost in Napoleon's campaign in Russia in 1812.

Pinel has remarked that the insane are less liable to the effects of cold than their normal fellows, and mentions the escape of a naked maniac, who, without any visible after-effect, in January, even, when the temperature was —4° F., ran into the snow and gleefully rubbed his body with ice. In the French journals in 1814 there is the record of the rescue of a naked crazy woman who was found in the Pyrenees, and who had apparently suffered none of tne ordinary effects of cold.

Psychologic Effects of Cold.—Lambert says that the mind acts more quickly in cold weather, and that there has been a notion advanced that the emotion of hatred is much stronger in cold weather, a theory exemplified by the assassination of Paul of Russia, the execution of Charles of England, and that of Louis of France. Emotions, such as love, bravery, patriotism, etc., together with diverse forms of excitement, seem to augment the ability of the human body to endure cold.

Cold seems to have little effect on the generative function. In both Sweden, Norway, and other Northern countries the families are as large, if not larger, than in other countries. Cold undoubtedly imparts vigor, and, according to DeThou, Henry III. lost his effeminacy and love of pleasure in winter and reacquired a spirit of progress and reformation. Zimmerman has remarked that in a rigorous winter the lubberly Hollander is like the gayest Frenchman. Cold increases appetite, and Plutarch says Brutus experienced intense bulimia while in the mountains, barely escaping perishing. With full rations the Greek soldiers under Xenophon suffered intense hunger as they traversed the snow-clad mountains of Armenia.

Beaupré remarks that those who have the misfortune to be buried under the snow perish less quickly than those who are exposed to the open air, his observations having been made during the retreat of the French army from Moscow. In Russia it is curious to see fish frozen stiff, which, after transportation for great distances, return to life when plunged into cold water.

Sudden death from cold baths and cold drinks has been known for many centuries. Mauriceau [a] mentions death from cold baptism on the head, and Graseccus,[385] Scaliger, Rush,[696] Schenck,[718] and Velschius [798] mention deaths from cold drinks. Aventii, Fabricius Hildanus, [334] the Ephemerides, and Curry relate instances of a fatal issue following the ingestion of cold water by an individual in a superheated condition. Cridland [b] describes a case of sudden insensibility following the drinking of a cold fluid. It is said that Alexander the Great narrowly escaped death from a constrictive spasm, due to the fact that while in a copious sweat he plunged into the river Cydnus. Tissot gives an instance of a man dying at a fountain after a long draught on a hot day. Hippocrates mentions a similar fact, and there are many modern instances.

The ordinary effects of cold on the skin locally and the system generally will not be mentioned here, except to add the remark of Captain Wood that in Greenland, among his party, could be seen ulcerations, blisters, and other painful lesions of the skin. In Siberia the Russian soldiers cover their noses and ears with greased paper to protect them against the cold. The Lap-

[a] 513, ii., 348.

[b] 476, 1843, i., 70.

landers and Samoïedes, to avoid the dermal lesions caused by cold (possibly augmented by the friction of the wind and beating of snow), anoint their skins with rancid fish oil, and are able to endure temperatures as low as —40° F. In the retreat of the 10,000 Xenophon ordered all his soldiers to grease the parts exposed to the air.

Effects of Working in Compressed Air.—According to a writer in Cassier's Magazine,[a] the highest working pressures recorded have been close to 50 pounds per square inch, but with extreme care in the selection of men, and corresponding care on the part of the men, it is very probable that this limit may be considerably exceeded. Under average conditions the top limit may be placed at about 45 pounds, the time of working, according to conditions, varying from four to six hours per shift. In the cases in which higher pressures might be used, the shifts for the men should be restricted to two of two hours each, separated by a considerable interval. As an example of heavy pressure work under favorable conditions as to ventilation, without very bad effects on the men, Messrs. Sooysmith & Company had an experience with a work on which men were engaged in six-hour shifts, separated into two parts by half-hour intervals for lunch. This work was excavation in open, seamy rock, carried on for several weeks under about 45 pounds pressure. The character of the material through which the caisson is being sunk or upon which it may be resting at any time bears quite largely upon the ability of the men to stand the pressure necessary to hold back the water at that point. If the material be so porous as to permit a considerable leakage of air through it, there will naturally result a continuous change of air in the working chamber, and a corresponding relief of the men from the deleterious effects which are nearly always produced by over-used air.

From Strasburg in 1861 Bucuoy reports that during the building of a bridge at Kehl laborers had to work in compressed air, and it was found that the respirations lost their regularity; there were sometimes intense pains in the ears, which after a while ceased. It required a great effort to speak at $2\frac{1}{2}$ atmospheres, and it was impossible to whistle. Perspiration was very profuse. Those who had to work a long time lost their appetites, became emaciated, and congestion of the lung and brain was observed. The movements of the limbs were easier than in normal air, though afterward muscular and rheumatic pains were often observed.

The peculiar and extraordinary development of the remaining special senses when one of the number is lost has always been a matter of great interest. Deaf people have always been remarkable for their acuteness of vision, touch, and smell. Blind persons, again, almost invariably have the sense of hearing, touch, and what might be called the senses of location and temperature exquisitely developed. This substitution of the senses is but an example of the great law of compensation which we find throughout nature.

a Scientific American, May, 18, 1885, 307.

Jonston [a] quotes a case in the seventeenth century of a blind man who, it is said, could tell black from white by touch alone; several other instances are mentioned in a chapter entitled "De compensatione naturæ monstris facta." It must, however, be held impossible that blind people can thus distinguish colors in any proper sense of the words.   Different colored yarns, for example, may have other differences of texture, etc., that would be manifest to the sense of touch.   We know of one case in which the different colors were accurately distinguished by a blind girl, but only when located in customary and definite positions.   Le Cat [b] speaks of a blind organist, a native of Holland, who still played the organ as well as ever.   He could distinguish money by touch, and it is also said that he made himself familiar with colors.   He was fond of playing cards, but became such a dangerous opponent, because in shuffling he could tell what cards and hands had been dealt, that he was never allowed to handle any but his own cards.

It is not only in those who are congenitally deficient in any of the senses that the remarkable **examples of compensation** are seen, but sometimes **late in life** these are developed.   The celebrated sculptor, Daniel de Volterre, became blind after he had obtained fame, and notwithstanding the deprivation of his chief sense he could, by touch alone, make a statue in clay after a model. Le Cat also mentions a woman, perfectly deaf, who without any instruction had learned to comprehend anything said to her by the movements of the lips alone.   It was not necessary to articulate any sound, but only to give the labial movements.   When tried in a foreign language she was at a loss to understand a single word.

Since the establishment of the modern high standard of blind asylums and deaf-and-dumb institutions, where so many ingenious methods have been developed and are practised in the education of their inmates, feats which were formerly considered marvelous are within the reach of all those under tuition. To-day, those born deaf-mutes are taught to speak and to understand by the movements of the lips alone, and the blind read, become expert workmen, musicians, and even draughtsmen.   D. D. Wood of Philadelphia, although one of the finest organists in the country, has been totally blind for years.   It is said that he acquires new compositions with almost as great facility as one not afflicted with his infirmity.   " Blind Tom," a semi-idiot and blind negro, achieved world-wide notoriety by his skill upon the piano.

In some extraordinary cases in which both sight and hearing, and sometimes even taste and smell, are wanting, the individuals in a most wonderful way have developed the sense of touch to such a degree that it almost replaces the absent senses.   The extent of this compensation is most beautifully illustrated in the cases of Laura Bridgman and Helen Keller.   No better examples could be found of the compensatory ability of differentiated organs to replace absent or disabled ones.

[a] 447, 469.   [b] " Traité des Sens."

Laura Dewey Bridgman[a] was born December 21, 1829, at Hanover. N. H. Her parents were farmers and healthy people. They were of average height, regular habits, slender build, and of rather nervous dispositions. Laura inherited the physical characteristics of her mother. In her infancy she was subject to convulsions, but at twenty months had improved, and at this time had learned to speak several words. At the age of two years, in common with two of the other children of the family, she had an attack of severe scarlet fever. Her sisters died, and she only recovered after both eyes and ears had suppurated; taste and smell were also markedly impaired. Sight in the left eye was entirely abolished, but she had some sensation for large, bright objects in the right eye up to her eighth year; after that time she became totally blind. After her recovery it was two years before she could sit up all day, and not until she was five years old had she entirely regained her strength. Hearing being lost, she naturally never developed any speech; however, she was taught to sew, knit, braid, and perform several other minor household duties. In 1837 Dr. S. W. Howe, the Director of the Massachusetts Asylum for the Blind, took Laura in charge, and with her commenced the ordinary deaf-mute education. At this time she was seven years and ten months old. Two years later she had made such wonderful progress and shown such ability to learn that, notwithstanding her infirmities, she surpassed any of the pupils of her class. Her advancement was particularly noticed immediately after her realization that an idea could be expressed by a succession of raised letters. In fact, so rapid was her progress, that it was deemed advisable by the authorities to hold her back. By her peculiar sensibility to vibration she could distinguish the difference between a whole and a half note in music, and she struck the notes on the piano quite correctly. During the first years of her education she could not smell at all, but later she could locate the kitchen by this sense. Taste had developed to such an extent that at this time she could distinguish the different degrees of acidity. The sense of touch, however, was exceedingly delicate and acute. As to her moral habits, cleanliness was the most marked. The slightest dirt or rent in her clothes caused her much embarrassment and shame, and her sense of order, neatness, and propriety was remarkable. She seemed quite at home and enjoyed the society of her own sex, but was uncomfortable and distant in the society of males. She quickly comprehended the intellectual capacity of those with whom she was associated, and soon showed an affiliation for the more intelligent of her friends. She was quite jealous of any extra attention shown to her fellow scholars, possibly arising from the fact that she had always been a favorite. She cried only from grief, and partially ameliorated bodily pain by jumping and by other excessive muscular movements. Like most mutes, she articulated a number of noises,—50 or more,

a "Anatomy and Observations on the Brain and Several Sense Organs of the Blind Deaf-mute, Laura Dewey Bridgman," by H. H. Donaldson.

all monosyllabic; she laughed heartily, and was quite noisy in her play. At this time it was thought that she had been heard to utter the words doctor, pin, ship, and others. She attached great importance to orientation, and seemed quite ill at ease in finding her way about when not absolutely sure of directions. She was always timid in the presence of animals, and by no persuasion could she be induced to caress a domestic animal. In common with most maidens, at sixteen she became more sedate, reserved, and thoughtful; at twenty she had finished her education. In 1878 she was seen by G. Stanley Hall, who found that she located the approach and departure of people through sensation in her feet, and seemed to have substituted the cutaneous sense of vibration for that of hearing. At this time she could distinguish the odors of various fragrant flowers and had greater susceptibility to taste, particularly to sweet and salty substances. She had written a journal for ten years, and had also composed three autobiographic sketches, was the authoress of several poems, and some remarkably clever letters. She died at the Perkins Institute, May 24, 1889, after a life of sixty years, burdened with infirmities such as few ever endure, and which, by her superior development of the remnants of the original senses left her, she had overcome in a degree nothing less than marvelous. According to a well-known observer, in speaking of her mental development, although she was eccentric she was not defective. She necessarily lacked certain data of thought, but even this fact was not very marked, and was almost counterbalanced by her exceptional power of using what remained.

In the present day there is a girl as remarkable as Laura Bridgman, and who bids fair to attain even greater fame by her superior development. This girl, **Helen Keller,** is both deaf and blind; she has been seen in all the principal cities of the United States, has been examined by thousands of persons, and is famous for her victories over infirmities. On account of her wonderful power of comprehension special efforts have been made to educate Helen Keller, and for this reason her mind is far more finely developed than in most girls of her age. It is true that she has the advantage over Laura Bridgman in having the senses of taste and smell, both of which she has developed to a most marvelous degree of acuteness. It is said that by odor alone she is always conscious of the presence of another person, no matter how noiseless his entrance into the room in which she may be. She cannot be persuaded to take food which she dislikes, and is never deceived in the taste. It is, however, by the means of what might be called "touch-sight" that the most miraculous of her feats are performed. By placing her hands on the face of a visitor she is able to detect shades of emotion which the normal human eye fails to distinguish, or, in the words of one of her lay observers, " her sense of touch is developed to such an exquisite extent as to form a better eye for her than are yours or mine for us; and, what is more, she forms judgments of character by this sight." According to a recent report of a conversation with one of the principals of the school in which her education is being completed, it is said that since the girl has been under his care he has been teaching her to sing with great success. Placing the fingers of her hands on the throat of a singer, she is able to follow notes covering two octaves with her own voice, and sings synchronously with her instructor. The only difference between her voice and that of a normal person is in its resonant qualities. So acute has this sense become, that by placing her hand upon the frame of a piano she can distinguish two notes not more than half a tone apart. Helen is expected to enter the preparatory school for Radcliffe College in the fall of 1896.

At a meeting of the American Association to Promote the Teaching of Speech to the Deaf, in Philadelphia, July, 1896, this child appeared, and in a well-chosen and distinct speech told the interesting story of her own progress. Miss Sarah Fuller, principal of the Horace Mann School for the Deaf, Boston, is credited with the history of Helen Keller, as follows :—

"Helen Keller's home is in Tuscumbia, Ala. At the age of nineteen months she became deaf, dumb, and blind after convulsions lasting three days. Up to the age of seven years she had received no instruction. Her parents engaged Miss Sullivan of the Perkins Institute for the Blind, South Boston, to go to Alabama as her teacher. She was familiar with methods of teaching the blind, but knew nothing about instructing deaf children. Miss Sullivan called upon Miss Fuller for some instruction on the subject. Miss Fuller was at that time experimenting with two little deaf girls to make them speak as hearing children do, and called Miss Sullivan's attention to it. Miss Sullivan left for her charge, and from time to time made reports to Dr. Anagnos, the principal of the Perkins School, which mentioned the remarkable mind which she found this little Alabama child possessed. The following year Miss Sullivan brought the child, then eight years old, to Boston, and Mrs. Keller came with her. They visited Miss Fuller's school. Miss Sullivan had taught the child the manual alphabet, and she had obtained much information by means of it. Miss Fuller noticed how quickly she appreciated the ideas given to her in that way.

"It is interesting to note that before any attempt had been made to teach the child to speak or there had been any thought of it, her own quickness of thought had suggested it to her as she talked by hand alphabet to Miss Fuller. Her mother, however, did not approve Miss Fuller's suggestion that an attempt should be made to teach her speech. She remained at the Perkins School, under Miss Sullivan's charge, another year, when the matter was brought up again, this time by little Helen herself, who said she must speak. Miss Sullivan brought her to Miss Fuller's school one day and she received her first lesson, of about two hours' length.

"The child's hand was first passed over Miss Fuller's face, mouth, and neck, then into her mouth, touching the tongue, teeth, lips, and hard palate, to give her an idea of the organs of speech. Miss Fuller then arranged her mouth, tongue, and teeth for the sound of i as in it. She took the child's finger and placed it upon the windpipe so that she might feel the vibration there, put her finger between her teeth to show her how wide apart they were, and one finger in the mouth to feel the tongue, and then sounded the vowel. The child grasped the idea at once. Her fingers flew to her own mouth and throat, and she produced the sound so nearly accurate that it sounded like an echo. Next the sound of ah was made by dropping the jaw a little and letting the child feel that the tongue was soft and lying in the bed of the jaw, with the teeth more widely separated. She in the same way arranged her own, but was not so successful as at first, but soon produced the sound perfectly.

"Eleven such lessons were given, at intervals of three or four days, until she had acquired all the elements of speech, Miss Sullivan in the meantime practising with the child on the lessons received. The first word spoken was arm, which was at once associated with her arm ; this gave her great delight. She soon learned to pronounce words by herself, combining the elements she had learned, and used them to communicate her simple wants. The first connected language she used was a description she gave Miss Fuller of a visit she had made to Dr. Oliver Wendell Holmes, in all over 200 words. They were, all but two or three, pronounced correctly. She now, six years afterward, converses quite fluently with people who know nothing of the manual alphabet by placing a couple of fingers on the speaker's lips, her countenance showing great intentness and brightening as she catches the meaning. Anybody can understand her answers."

In a beautiful eulogy of Helen Keller in a recent number of Harper's Magazine, Charles Dudley Warner expresses the opinion that she is the purest-minded girl of her age in the world.

Edith Thomas, a little inmate of the Perkins Institute for the Blind, at South Boston, is not only deaf and dumb but also blind. She was a fellow-pupil with Helen Keller, and in a measure duplicated the rapid progress of her former playmate. In commenting on progress in learning to talk the Boston Herald says : "And as the teacher said the word 'Kitty' once or twice she placed the finger-tips of one hand upon the teacher's lips and with the other hand clasped tightly the teacher's throat ; then, guided by the muscular action of the throat and the position of the teeth, tongue, and lips, as interpreted by that marvelous and delicate touch of hers, she said the word 'Kitty' over and over again distinctly in a very pretty way. She can be called dumb no longer, and before the summer vacation comes she will have mastered quite a number of words, and such is her intelligence and patience, in spite of the loss of three senses, she may yet speak quite readily.

"Her history is very interesting. She was born in Maplewood, and up to the time of contracting diphtheria and scarlet fever, which occurred when she was four years old, had been a very healthy child of more than ordinary quickness and ability. She had attained a greater command of language than most children of her age. What a contrast between these 'other days,' as she calls them, and the days which followed, when hearing and sight were completely gone, and gradually the senses of speech and smell went, too! After the varied instruction of the blind school the little girl had advanced so far as to make the rest of her study comparatively easy. The extent of her vocabulary is not definitely known, but it numbers at least 700 words. Reading, which was once an irksome task, has become a pleasure to her. Her ideas of locality and the independence of movement are remarkable, and her industry and patience are more noticeable from day to day. She has great ability, and is in every respect a very wonderful child."

According to recent reports, in the vicinity of Rothesay, on the Clyde, there resides a lady totally deaf and dumb, who, in point of intelligence, scholarship, and skill in various ways, far excels many who have all their faculties. Having been educated partly in Paris, she is a good French scholar, and her general composition is really wonderful. She has a short-hand system of her own, and when writing letters, etc., she uses a peculiar machine, somewhat of the nature of a typewriter.

Among the deaf persons who have acquired fame in literature and the arts have been Dibil Alkoffay, an Arabian poet of the eighth century; the tactician, Folard; the German poet, Engelshall; Le Sage; La Condamine, who composed an epigram on his own infirmity; and Beethoven, the famous musician. Fernandez, a Spanish painter of the sixteenth century, was a deaf-mute.

All the world pities **the blind,** but despite their infirmities many have achieved the highest glory in every profession. Since Homer there have been numerous blind poets. Milton lost none of his poetic power after he had become blind. The Argovienne, Louise Egloff, and Daniel Leopold, who died in 1753, were blind from infancy. Blacklock, Avisse, Koslov, and La Motte-Houdart are among other blind poets. Asconius Pedianus, a grammarian of the first century; Didyme, the celebrated doctor of Alexandria; the Florentine, Bandolini, so well versed in Latin poetry; the celebrated Italian grammarian, Pontanus; the German, Griesinger, who spoke seven languages; the philologist, Grassi, who died in 1831, and many others have become blind at an age more or less advanced in their working lives.

Probably the most remarkable of the blind scientists was the Englishman, Saunderson, who in 1683, in his first year, was deprived of sight after an attack of small-pox. In spite of his complete blindness he assiduously studied the sciences, and graduated with honor at the University of Cambridge in mathematics and optics. His sense of touch was remarkable. He had a collection of old Roman medals, all of which, without mistake, he could distinguish by their impressions. He also seemed to have the ability to judge distance, and was said to have known how far he had walked, and by the velocity he could even tell the distance traversed in a vehicle. Among other blind mathematicians was the Dutchman, Borghes (died in 1652); the French astronomer, the Count de Pagan, who died in 1655 ; Galileo ; the astronomer, Cassini, and Bérard, who became blind at twenty-three years, and was for a long time Professor of Mathematics at the College of Briançon.

In the seventeenth century the sculptor, Jean Gonnelli, born in Tuscany, became blind at twenty years ; but in spite of his infirmity he afterward executed what were regarded as his masterpieces. It is said that he modeled a portrait of Pope Urban VIII., using as a guide his hand, passed from time to time over the features. Lomazzo, the Italian painter of the eighteenth century, is said to have continued his work after becoming blind.

Several men distinguished for their bravery and ability in the art of war have been blind. Jean de Troczow, most commonly known by the name of Ziska, in 1420 lost his one remaining eye, and was afterward known as the " old blind dog," but, nevertheless, led his troops to many victories. Froissart beautifully describes the glorious death of the blind King of Bohemia at the battle of Crécy in 1346. Louis III., King of Provence ; Boleslas III., Duke of Bohemia ; Magnus IV., King of Norway, and Bela II., King of Hungary, were blind. Nathaniel Price, a librarian of Norwich in the last century, lost his sight in a voyage to America, which, however, did not interfere in any degree with his duties, for his books were in as good condition, and their location as directly under his knowledge, during his blindness as they were in his earlier days. At the present day in New York there is a blind billiard expert who occasionally gives exhibitions of his prowess.

Feats of Memory.—From time to time there have been individuals, principally children, who gave wonderful exhibitions of memory, some for dates, others for names, and some for rapid mental calculation. Before the Anthropological Society in 1880 Broca exhibited a lad of eleven, a Piedmontese, named **Jacques Inaudi.** This boy, with a trick monkey, had been found earning his livelihood by begging and by solving mentally in a few minutes the most difficult problems in arithmetic. A gentleman residing in Marseilles had seen him while soliciting alms perform most astonishing feats of memory, and brought him to Paris. In the presence of the Society Broca gave him verbally a task in multiplication, composed of some trillions to be multiplied by billions. In the presence of all the members he accomplished his task in less than ten minutes, and without the aid of pencil and paper, solving the whole problem mentally. Although not looking intelligent, and not being able to read or write, he perhaps could surpass any one in the world in his particular feat. It was stated that he proceeded from left to right in his calculations, instead of from right to left in the usual manner. In his personal appearance the only thing indicative of his wonderful abilities was his high forehead.

An infant prodigy named **Oscar Moore** was exhibited to the physicians of Chicago at the Central Music Hall in 1888, and excited considerable comment at the time. The child was born of mulatto parents at Waco, Texas, on August 19, 1885, and when only thirteen months old manifested remarkable mental ability and precocity. S. V. Clevenger, a physician of Chicago, has described the child as follows :—

" Oscar was born blind and, as frequently occurs in such cases, the touch-sense compensatingly developed extraordinarily. It was observed that after touching a person once or twice with his stubby baby fingers, he could thereafter unfailingly recognize and call by name the one whose hand he again felt. The optic sense is the only one defective, for tests reveal that his hearing, taste, and smell are acute, and the tactile development surpasses in refinement. But his memory is the most remarkable peculiarity, for when his sister conned her lessons at home, baby Oscar, less than two years old, would recite all he heard her read. Unlike some idiot savants, in which category he is *not* to be included, who repeat parrot-like what they have once heard, baby Oscar seems to digest what he hears, and requires at least more than one repetition of what he is trying to remember, after which he possesses the information imparted and is able to yield it at once when questioned. It is not necessary for him to commence at the beginning, as the possessors of some notable memories were compelled to do, but he skips about to any required part of his repertoire.

" He sings a number of songs and counts in different languages, but it is not supposable that he understands every word he utters. If, however, his understanding develops as it promises to do, he will become a decided polyglot. He has mastered an appalling array of statistics, such as the areas in square miles of hundreds of countries, the population of the world's principal cities, the birthdays of all the Presidents, the names of all the cities of the United States of over 10,000 inhabitants, and a lot of mathematical data. He is greatly attracted by music, and this leads to the expectation that when more mature he may rival Blind Tom.

" In disposition he is very amiable, but rather grave beyond his years. He shows great affection for his father, and is as playful and as happy as the ordinary child. He sleeps soundly, has a good childish appetite, and appears to be in perfect health. His motions are quick but not nervous, and are as well coordinated as in a child of ten. In fact, he impresses one as having the intelligence of a much older child than three years (now five years), but his height, dentition, and general appearance indicate the truthfulness of the age assigned. An evidence of his symmetrical mental development appears in his extreme inquisitiveness. He wants to understand the meaning of what he is taught, and some kind of an explanation must be given him for what he learns. Were his memory alone abnormally great and other faculties defective this would hardly be the case ; but if so, it cannot at present be determined

" His complexion is yellow, with African features, flat nose, thick lips, but not prognathous, superciliary ridges undeveloped, causing the forehead to protrude a little. His head measures 19 inches in circumference, on a line with the upper ear-tips, the forehead being much narrower than the occipito-parietal portion, which is noticeably very wide. The occiput protrudes backward, causing a forward sweep of the back of the neck. From the nose-root to the nucha over the head he measures 13½ inches, and between upper ear-tips across and over the head 11 inches, which is so close to the eight- and ten-inch standard that he may be called mesocephalic. The bulging in the vicinity of the parietal region accords remarkably with speculations upon the location of the auditory memory in that region, such as those in the American Naturalist, July, 1888, and the fact that injury of that part of the brain may cause loss of memory of the meaning of words. It may be that the premature death of the mother's children has some significance in connection with Oscar's phenomenal development. There is certainly a hypernutrition of the parietal brain with atrophy of the optic tract, both of which conditions could arise from abnormal vascular causes, or the extra growth of the auditory memory region may have deprived of nutrition, by pressure, the adjacent optic centers in the occipital brain. The otherwise normal motion of the eyes indicates the nystagmus to be functional.

" Sudden exaltation of the memory is often the consequence of grave brain disease, and in children this symptom is most frequent. Pritchard, Rush, and other writers upon mental disorders record interesting instances of remarkable memory-increase before death, mainly in adults, and during fever and insanity. In simple mania the memory is often very acute. Romberg tells of a young girl who lost her sight after an attack of small-pox, but acquired an extraordinary memory. He calls attention to the fact that the scrofulous and rachitic diatheses in childhood are sometimes accompanied by this disorder. Winslow notes that in the incipient state of the brain disease of early life connected with fevers, disturbed conditions of the cerebral circulation and vessels, and in affections of advanced life, there is often witnessed a remarkable exaltation of the memory, which may herald death by apoplexy.

" Not only has the institution of intelligence in idiots dated from falls upon the head, but extra mentality has been conferred by such an event. Pritchard tells of three idiot brothers, one of whom, after a severe head injury, brightened up and became a barrister, while his brothers remained idiotic. ' Father Mabillon,' says Winslow, ' is said to have been an idiot until twenty-six years of age, when he fractured his skull against a stone staircase. He was trepanned. After recovering, his intellect fully developed itself in a mind endowed with a lively imagination, an amazing memory, and a zeal for study rarely equaled.' Such instances can be accounted for by the brain having previously been poorly nourished by a defective blood supply, which defect was remedied by the increased circulation afforded by the head-injury.

" It is a commonly known fact that activity of the brain is attended with a greater head-circulation than when the mind is dull, within certain limits. Anomalous development of the brain through blood-vessels, affording an extra nutritive supply to the mental apparatus, can readily be conceived as occurring before birth, just as aberrant nutrition elsewhere produces giants from parents of ordinary size.

" There is but one sense-defect in the child Oscar, his eyesight-absence, and that is atoned for by his hearing and touch-acuteness, as it generally is in the blind. Spitzka and others demonstrate that in such cases other parts of the brain enlarge to compensate for the atrophic portion which is connected with the functionless nerves. This, considered with his apparently perfect mental and physical health, leaves no reason to suppose that Oscar's extravagant memory depends upon disease any more than we can suspect all giants of being sickly, though the anomaly is doubtless due to pathologic conditions. Of course, there is no predicting what may develop later in his life, but in any event science will be benefited.

" It is a popular idea that great vigor of memory is often associated with low-grade intelligence, and cases such as Blind Tom and other ' idiot *savants,*' who could repeat the contents of a newspaper after a single reading, justify the supposition. Fearon, on ' Mental Vigor,' tells of a man who could remember the day that every person had been buried in the parish for thirty-five years, and could repeat with unvarying accuracy the name and age of the deceased and the mourners at the funeral. But he was a complete fool. Out of the line of burials he had not one idea, could not give an intelligible reply to a single question, nor be trusted even to feed himself. While memory-development is thus apparent in some otherwise defective intellects, it has probably as often or oftener been observed to occur in connection with full or great intelligence. Edmund Burke, Clarendon, John Locke, Archbishop Tillotson, and Dr. Johnson were all distinguished for having great strength of memory. Sir W. Hamilton observed that Grotius, Pascal, Leibnitz, and Euler were not less celebrated for their intelligence than for their memory. Ben Jonson could repeat all that he had written and whole books he had read. Themistocles could call by name the 20,000 citizens of Athens. Cyrus is said to have known the name of every soldier in his army. Hortensius, a great Roman orator, and Seneca had also great memories. Niebuhr, the Danish historian, was remarkable for his acuteness of memory. Sir James Mackintosh, Dugald Stewart, and Dr. Gregory had similar reputations.

" Nor does great mental endowment entail physical enfeeblement; for, with temperance, literary men have reached extreme old age, as in the cases of Klopstock, Goethe, Chaucer, and the average age attained by all the signers of the American Declaration of Independence was sixty-four years, many of them being highly gifted men intellectually. Thus, in the case of the phenomenal Oscar it cannot be predicted that he will not develop, as he now promises to do, equal and extraordinary powers of mind, even though it would be rare in one of his racial descent, and in the face of the fact that precocity gives no assurance of adult brightness, for it can be urged that John Stuart Mill read Greek when four years of age.

" The child is strumous, however, and may die young. His exhibitors, who are coining him into money, should seek the best medical care for him and avoid surcharging his memory with rubbish. Proper cultivation of his special senses, especially the tactile, by competent teachers, will give Oscar the best chance of developing intellectually and acquiring an education in the proper sense of the word."

By long custom many men of letters have developed wonderful feats of memory ; and among illiterate persons, by means of points of association, the power of memory has been little short of marvelous. At a large hotel in Saratoga there was at one time a negro whose duty was to take charge of the hats and coats of the guests as they entered the dining-room and return to each his hat after the meal. It was said that, without checks or the assistance of the owners, he invariably returned the right articles to the right persons on request, and no matter how large the crowd, his limit of memory never seemed to be reached. Many persons have seen expert players at draughts and chess who, blindfolded, could carry on numerous games with many competitors and win most of the matches. To realize what a wonderful feat of memory this performance is, one need only see the absolute exhaustion of one of these men after a match. In whist, some experts have been able to detail the succession of the play of the cards so many hands back that their competitors had long since forgotten it.

There is reported to be in Johnson County, Missouri, a mathematical wonder by the name of Rube Fields. At the present day he is between forty and fifty years of age, and his external appearance indicates poverty as well as indifference. His temperament is most sluggish ; he rarely speaks unless spoken to, and his replies are erratic.

The boyhood of this strange character was that of an overgrown country lout with boorish manners and silly mind. He did not and would not go to school, and he asserts now that if he had done so he " would have become as big a fool as other people." A shiftless fellow, left to his own devices, he performed some wonderful feats, and among the many stories connected with this period of his life is one which describes how he actually ate up a good-sized patch of sugar cane, simply because he found it good to his taste.

Yet from this clouded, illiterate mind a wonderful mathematical gift shines. Just when he began to assert his powers is not known ; but his feats have been remembered for twenty years by his neighbors. A report says :—

" Give Rube Fields the distance by rail between any two points, and the dimensions of a car-wheel, and almost as soon as the statement has left your lips he will tell you the number of revolutions the wheel will make in traveling over the track. Call four or five or any number of columns of figures down a page, and when you have reached the bottom he will announce the sum. Given the number of yards or pounds of articles and the price, and at once he will return the total cost—and this he will do all day long, without apparent effort or fatigue.

"A gentleman relates an instance of Fields' knowledge of figures. After having called several columns of figures for addition, he went back to the first column, saying that it was wrong, and repeating it, purposely miscalling the next to the last figure. At once Fields threw up his hand, exclaiming: 'You didn't call it that way before.'

"Fields' answers come quick and sharp, seemingly by intuition. Calculations which would require hours to perform are made in less time than it takes to state the question. The size of the computations seems to offer no bar to their rapid solution, and answers in which long lines of figures are reeled off come with perfect ease. In watching the effort put forth in reaching an answer, there would seem to be some process going on in the mind, and an incoherent mumbling is often indulged in, but it is highly probable that Fields does not himself know how he derives his answers. Certain it is that he is unable to explain the process, nor has any one ever been able to draw from him anything concerning it. Almost the only thing he knows about the power is that he possesses it, and, while he is not altogether averse to receiving money for his work, he has steadily refused to allow himself to be exhibited." In reviewing the peculiar endowment of Fields, the Chicago Record says:—

"How this feat is performed is as much a mystery as the process by which he solves a problem in arithmetic. He answers no questions. Rapid mathematicians, men of study, who by intense application and short methods have become expert, have sought to probe these two mysteries, but without results. Indeed, the man's intelligence is of so low an order as to prevent him from aiding those who seek to know. With age, too, he grows more surly. Of what vast value this 'gift' might be to the world of science, if coupled with average intelligence, is readily imagined. That it will ever be understood is unlikely. As it is, the power staggers belief and makes modern psychology, with its study of brain-cells, stand aghast. As to poor Fields himself, he excites only sympathy. Homeless, unkempt, and uncouth, traveling aimlessly on a journey which he does not understand, he hugs to his heart a marvelous power, which he declares to be a gift from God. To his weak mind it lifts him above his fellow-men, and yet it is as useless to the world as a diamond in a dead man's hand."

Wolf-Children.—It is interesting to know to what degree a human being will resemble a beast when deprived of the association with man. We seem to get some insight to this question in the investigation of so-called cases of "wolf-children."

Saxo Grammaticus speaks of a bear that kidnapped a child and kept it a long time in his den. The tale of the Roman she-wolf is well known, and may have been something more than a myth, as there have been several apparently authentic cases reported in which a child has been rescued from its associations with a wolf who had stolen it some time previously. Most of the stories of wolf-children come from India. According to Oswald[a] in Ball's "Jungle Life in India," there is the following curious account of two children in the Orphanage of Sekandra, near Agra, who had been discovered among wolves: "A trooper sent by a native Governor of Chandaur to demand payment of some revenue was passing along the bank of the river about noon when he saw a large female wolf leave her den, followed by three whelps and a little boy. The boy went on all-fours, and when the trooper tried to catch him he ran as fast as the whelps, and kept up with the old one. They all entered the den, but were dug out by the people and the boy was secured. He struggled hard to rush into every hole or gully they came near. When he saw a grown-up person he became alarmed, but tried to fly at children and bite them. He rejected cooked meat with disgust, but delighted in raw flesh and bones, putting them under his paws like a dog." The other case occurred at Chupra, in the Presidency of Bengal. In March, 1843, a Hindoo mother went out to help her husband in the field, and while she was cutting rice her little boy was carried off by a wolf. About a year afterward a wolf, followed by several cubs and a strange, ape-like creature, was seen about ten miles from Chupra. After a lively chase the nondescript was caught and recognized (by the mark of a burn on his knee) as the Hindoo boy that had disappeared in the rice-field. This boy would not eat anything but raw flesh, and could never be taught to speak, but expressed his emotions in an inarticulate mutter. His elbows and the pans of his knees had become horny from going on all-fours with his foster mother. In the winter of 1850 this boy made several attempts to regain his freedom, and in the following spring he escaped for good and disappeared in the jungle-forest of Bhangapore.

The Zoologist for March, 1888, reproduced a remarkable pamphlet printed at Plymouth in 1852, which has been epitomized in the Lancet.[b] This interesting paper gives an account of wolves nurturing small children in their dens. Six cases are given of boys who have been rescued from the maternal care of wolves. In one instance the lad was traced from the moment of his being carried off by a lurking wolf while his parents were working in the field, to the time when, after having been recovered by his mother six years later, he escaped from her into the jungle. In all these cases certain marked features reappear. In the first, the boy was very inoffensive, except when teased, and then he growled surlily. He would eat anything thrown to him, but preferred meat, which he devoured with canine

a "Zoological Sketches," Philadelphia, 1883, p. 195.   b 476, 1888, i., 593.

voracity.   He drank a pitcher of buttermilk at one gulp, and could not be induced to wear clothing even in the coldest weather.   He showed the greatest fondness for bones, and gnawed them contentedly, after the manner of his adopted parents.   This child had coarse features, a repulsive countenance, was filthy in his habits, and could not articulate a word.

In another case the child was kidnapped at three and recovered at nine. He muttered, but could not articulate.   As in the other case, he could not be enticed to wear clothes.   From constantly being on all-fours the front of this child's knees and his elbows had become hardened.   In the third case the father identified a son who had been carried away at the age of six, and was found four years afterward.   The intellectual deterioration was not so marked.   The boy understood signs, and his hearing was exceedingly acute ; when directed by movements of the hands to assist the cultivators in turning out cattle, he readily comprehended what was asked of him ; yet this lad, whose vulpine career was so short, could neither talk nor utter any decidedly articulate sound.

The author of the pamphlet expressed some surprise that there was no case on record in which a grown man had been found in such association. This curious collection of cases of wolf-children is attributed to Colonel Sleeman, a well-known officer, who is known to have been greatly interested in the subject, and who for a long time resided in the forests of India.   A copy, now a rarity, is in the South Kensington Museum.

An interesting case of a wolf-child was reported many years ago in Chambers' Journal.   In the Etwah district, near the banks of the river Jumna, a boy was captured from the wolves.   After a time this child was restored to his parents, who, however, " found him very difficult to manage for he was most fractious and troublesome—in fact, just a caged wild beast Often during the night for hours together he would give vent to mos unearthly yells and moans, destroying the rest and irritating the tempers o his neighbors and generally making night hideous.   On one occasion hi people chained him by the waist to a tree on the outskirts of the village Then a rather curious incident occurred.   It was a bright moonlight nigh and two wolf cubs (undoubtedly those in whose companionship he had bee captured), attracted by his cries while on the prowl, came to him, and wer distinctly seen to gambol around him with as much familiarity and affectio as if they considered him quite one of themselves.   They only left him (the approach of morning, when movement and stir again arose in the villag This boy did not survive long.   He never spoke, nor did a single ray (human intelligence ever shed its refining light over his debased features."

Recently a writer in the Badmington Magazine, in speaking of the authe ticity of wolf-children, says :—

" A jemidar told me that when he was a lad he remembered going, wi others, to see a wolf-child which had been netted.   Some time after this, wh staying at an up-country place called Shaporeooundie, in East Bengal, it was my fortune to meet an Anglo-Indian gentleman who had been in the Indian civil service for upward of thirty years, and had traveled about during most of that time ; from him I learned all I wanted to know of wolf-children, for he not only knew of several cases, but had actually seen and examined, near Agra, a child which had been recovered from the wolves. The story of Romulus and Remus, which all schoolboys and the vast majority of grown people regard as a myth, appears in a different light when one studies the question of wolf-children, and ascertains how it comes to pass that boys are found living on the very best terms with such treacherous and rapacious animals as wolves, sleeping with them in their dens, sharing the raw flesh of deer and kids which the she-wolf provides, and, in fact, leading in all essentials the actual life of a wolf.

" A young she-wolf has a litter of cubs, and after a time her instinct tells her that they will require fresh food. She steals out at night in quest of prey. Soon she espies a weak place in the fence (generally constructed of thatching grass and bamboos) which encloses the compound, or 'unguah,' of a poor villager. She enters, doubtless, in the hope of securing a kid ; and while prowling about inside looks into a hut where a woman and infant are soundly sleeping. In a moment she has pounced on the child, and is out of reach before its cries can attract the villagers. Arriving safely at her den under the rocks, she drops the little one among her cubs. At this critical time the fate of the child hangs in the balance. Either it will be immediately torn to pieces and devoured, or in a most wonderful way remain in the cave unharmed. In the event of escape, the fact may be accounted for in several ways. Perhaps the cubs are already gorged when the child is thrown before them, or are being supplied with solid food before their carnivorous instinct is awakened, so they amuse themselves by simply licking the sleek, oily body (Hindoo mothers daily rub their boy babies with some native vegetable oil) of the infant, and thus it lies in the nest, by degrees getting the odor of the wolf cubs, after which the mother wolf will not molest it. In a little time the infant begins to feel the pangs of hunger, and hearing the cubs sucking, soon follows their example. Now the adoption is complete, all fear of harm to the child from wolves has gone, and the foster-mother will guard and protect it as though it were of her own flesh and blood.

" The mode of progression of these children is on all fours—not, as a rule, on the hands and feet, but on the knees and elbows. The reason the knees are used is to be accounted for by the fact that, owing to the great length of the human leg and thigh in proportion to the length of the arm, the knee would naturally be brought to the ground, and the instep and top of the toes would be used instead of the sole and heel of the almost inflexible foot. Why the elbow should be employed instead of the hand is less easy to understand, but probably it is better suited to give support to the head and fore-part of the body.

"Some of these poor waifs have been recovered after spending ten or more years in the fellowship of wolves, and, though wild and savage at first, have in time become tractable in some degree. They are rarely seen to stand upright, unless to look around, and they gnaw bones in the manner of a dog, holding one end between the forearms and hands, while snarling and snapping at everybody who approaches too near. The wolf-child has little except his outward form to show that it is a human being with a soul. It is a fearful and terrible thing, and hard to understand, that the mere fact of a child's complete isolation from its own kind should bring it to such a state of absolute degradation. Of course, they speak no language, though some, in time, have learned to make known their wants by signs. When first taken they fear the approach of adults, and, if possible, will slink out of sight; but should a child of their own size, or smaller, come near, they will growl, and even snap and bite at it. On the other hand, the close proximity of "pariah" dogs or jackals is unresented, in some cases welcomed; for I have heard of them sharing their food with these animals, and even petting and fondling them. They have in time been brought to a cooked-meat diet, but would always prefer raw flesh. Some have been kept alive after being reclaimed for as long as two years, but for some reason or other they all sicken and die, generally long before that time. One would think, however, that, having undoubtedly robust constitutions, they might be saved if treated in a scientific manner and properly managed."

Rudyard Kipling, possibly inspired by accounts of these wolf-children in India, has ingeniously constructed an interesting series of fabulous stories of a child who was brought up by the beasts of the jungles and taught their habits and their mode of communication. The ingenious way in which the author has woven the facts together and interspersed them with his intimate knowledge of animal-life commends his "Jungle-Book" as a legitimate source of recreation to the scientific observer.

Among observers mentioned in the "Index Catalogue" who have studied this subject are Giglioli,[a] Mitra,[b] and Ornstein.[c]

The artificial manufacture of "wild men" or "wild boys" in the Chinese Empire is shown by recent reports. Macgowan[d] says the traders kidnap a boy and skin him alive bit by bit, transplanting on the denuded surface the hide of a bear or dog. This process is most tedious and is by no mean complete when the hide is completely transplanted, as the subject must be rendered mute by destruction of the vocal cords, made to use all fours in walking and submitted to such degradation as to completely blight all reason. It is said that the process is so severe that only one in five survive. A "wild boy" exhibited in Kiangse had the entire skin of a dog substituted and walked on a fours. It was found that he had been kidnapped. His proprietor was decap-

a "Arch. per l'Antrop.," Firenze, 1882, xii., 49.   b J. Anthrop. Soc., Bombay, 1893, iii., 10
c "Verhandl. d. Berl. Gesselsch. f. Anthrop.," 1891, 817.   d 616, 1893, viii., 3

tated on the spot. Macgowan says that parasitic monsters are manufactured in China by a similar process of transplantation. He adds that the deprivation of light for several years renders the child a great curiosity, if in conjunction its growth is dwarfed by means of food and drugs, and its vocal apparatus destroyed. A certain priest subjected a kidnapped boy to this treatment and exhibited him as a sacred deity. Macgowan mentions that the child looked like wax, as though continually fed on lardaceous substances. He squatted with his palms together and was a driveling idiot. The monk was discovered and escaped, but his temple was razed.

Equilibrists.—Many individuals have cultivated their senses so acutely that by the eye and particularly by touch they are able to perform almost incredible feats of maintaining equilibrium under the most difficult circumstances. Professional **rope-walkers** have been known in all times. The Greeks had a particular passion for equilibrists, and called them " neurobates," " oribates," and " stænobates." Blondin would have been one of the latter. Antique medals showing equilibrists making the ascent of an inclined cord have been found. The Romans had walkers both of the slack-rope and tight-rope. Many of the Fathers of the Church have pronounced against the dangers of these exercises. Among others, St. John Chrysostom speaks of men who execute movements on inclined ropes at unheard-of heights. In the ruins of Herculaneum there is still visible a picture representing an equilibrist executing several different exercises, especially one in which he dances on a rope to the tune of a double flute, played by himself. The Romans particularly liked to witness ascensions on inclined ropes, and sometimes these were attached to the summits of high hills, and while mounting them the acrobats performed different pantomimes. It is said that under Charles VI. a Genoese acrobat, on the occasion of the arrival of the Queen of France, carried in each hand an illuminated torch while descending a rope stretched from the summit of the towers of Notre Dame to a house on the Pont au Change. According to Guyot-Daubès, a similar performance was seen in London in 1547. In this instance the rope was attached to the highest pinnacle of St. Paul's Cathedral. Under Louis XII. an acrobat named Georges Menustre, during a passage of the King through Mâcon, executed several performances on a rope stretched from the grand tower of the Chateau and the clock of the Jacobins, at a height of 156 feet. A similar performance was given at Milan before the French Ambassadors, and at Venice under the Doges and the Senate on each St. Mark's Day, rope-walkers performed at high altitudes. In 1649 a man attempted to traverse the Seine on a rope placed between the Tour de Nesles and the Tour du Grand-Prévost. The performance, however, was interrupted by the fall of the mountebank into the Seine. At subsequent fairs in France other acrobats have appeared. At the commencement of this century there was a person named Madame Saqui who astonished the public with her nimbleness and extraordinary skill in rope-walking. Her specialty was military maneuvers. On a cord 20 meters from the ground she executed all sorts of military pantomimes without assistance, shooting off pistols, rockets, and various colored fires. Napoleon awarded her the title of the first acrobat of France. She gave a performance as late as 1861 at the Hippodrome of Paris.

In 1814 there was a woman called " La Malaga," who, in the presence of the allied sovereigns at Versailles, made an ascension on a rope 200 feet above the Swiss Lake.

In the present generation probably the most famous of all the equilibrists was **Blondin.** This person, whose real name was Emile Gravelet, acquired a universal reputation ; about 1860 he traversed the Niagara Falls on a cable at an elevation of nearly 200 feet. Blondin introduced many novelties in his performances. Sometimes he would carry a man over on his shoulders ; again he would eat a meal while on his wire ; cook and eat an omelet, using a table and ordinary cooking utensils, all of which he kept balanced. In France Blondin was almost the patron saint of the rope-walkers ; and at the present day the performers imitate his feats, but never with the same grace and perfection.

In 1882 an acrobat bearing the natural name of Arsens Blondin traversed one river after another in France on a wire stretched at high altitudes. With the aid of a balancing-rod he walked the rope blindfolded ; with baskets on his feet ; sometimes he wheeled persons over in a wheelbarrow. He was a man of about thirty, short, but wonderfully muscled and extremely supple.

It is said [394] that a negro equilibrist named Malcom several times traversed the Meuse at Sedan on a wire at about a height of 100 feet. Once while attempting this feat, with his hands and feet shackled with iron chains, allowing little movement, the support on one side fell, after the cable had parted, and landed on the spectators, killing a young girl and wounding many others. Malcom was precipitated into the river, but with wonderful presence of mind and remarkable strength he broke his bands and swam to the shore, none the worse for his high fall ; he immediately helped in attention to his wounded spectators. A close inspection of all the exhibitionists of this class will show that they are of superior physique and calm courage. They only acquire their ability after long gymnastic exercise, as well as actual practice on the rope. Most of these persons used means of balancing themselves, generally a long and heavy pole ; but some used nothing but their outstretched arms. In 1895, at the Royal Aquarium in London, there was an individual who slowly mounted a long wire reaching to the top of this huge structure, and, after having made the ascent, without the aid of any means of balancing but his arms, slid the whole length of the wire, landing with enormous velocity into an outstretched net.

The equilibrists mentioned thus far have invariably used a tightly stretched rope or wire; but there are a number of persons who perform feats, of course not of such magnitude, on a slack wire, in which they have to defy not only the force of gravity, but the to-and-fro motion of the cable as well. It is particularly with the Oriental performers that we see this exhibition. Some use open parasols, which, with their Chinese or Japanese costumes, render the performance more picturesque; while others seem to do equally well without such adjuncts. There have been performers of this class who play with sharp daggers while maintaining themselves on thin and swinging wires.

Another class of equilibrists are those who maintain the upright position, resting on their heads with their feet in the air. At the Hippodrome in Paris some years since there was a man who remained in this position seven minutes and ate a meal during the interval. There were two clowns at the Cirque Franconi who duplicated this feat, and the program called their dinner " *Un déjeuner en tête-à-tête.*" Some other persons perform wonderful feats of a similar nature on an oscillating trapeze, and many similar performances have been witnessed by the spectators of our large circuses.

The " **human pyramids** " are interesting, combining, as they do, wonderful power of maintaining equilibrium with agility and strength. The rapidity with which they are formed and are tumbled to pieces is marvelous; they sometimes include as many as 16 persons—men, women, and children.

The exhibitions given by the class of persons commonly designated as " **jugglers** " exemplify the perfect control that by continual practice one may obtain over his various senses and muscles. The most wonderful feats of dexterity are thus reduced into mere automatic movements. Either standing, sitting, mounted on a horse, or even on a wire, they are able to keep three, four, five, and even six balls in continual motion in the air. They use articles of the greatest difference in specific gravity in the same manner. A juggler called " Kara," appearing in London and Paris in the summer of 1895, juggled with an open umbrella, an eye-glass, and a traveling satchel, and received each after its course in the air with unerring precision. Another man called " Paul Cinquevalli," well known in this country, does not hesitate to juggle with lighted lamps or pointed knives. The tricks of the clowns with their traditional pointed felt hats are well known. Recently there appeared in Philadelphia a man who received six such hats on his head, one on top of the other, thrown by his partner from the rear of the first balcony of the theater. Others will place a number of rings on their fingers, and with a swift and dexterous movement toss them all in the air, catching them again all on one finger. Without resorting to the fabulous method of Columbus, they balance eggs on a table, and in extraordinary ways defy all the powers of gravity.

In India and China we see the most marvelous of the knife-jugglers.

With unerring skill they keep in motion many pointed knives, always receiving them at their fall by the handles. They throw their implements with such precision that one often sees men, who, placing their partner against a soft board, will stand at some distance and so pen him in with daggers that he cannot move until some are withdrawn, marking a silhouette of his form on the board,—yet never once does one as much as graze the skin. With these same people the foot-jugglers are most common. These persons, both male and female, will with their feet juggle substances and articles that it requires several assistants to raise.

A curious trick is given by Rousselet in his magnificent work entitled "*L'Inde des Rajahs*," and quoted by Guyot-Daubés. It is called in India the "dance of the eggs." The dancer, dressed in a rather short skirt, places on her head a large wheel made of light wood, and at regular intervals having hanging from it pieces of thread, at the ends of which are running knots kept open by beads of glass. She then brings forth a basket of eggs, and passes them around for inspection to assure her spectators of their genuineness. The monotonous music commences and the dancer sets the wheel on her head in rapid motion; then, taking an egg, with a quick movement she puts it on one of the running knots and increases the velocity of the revolution of the wheel by gyrations until the centrifugal force makes each cord stand out in an almost horizontal line with the circumference of the wheel. Then one after another she places the eggs on the knots of the cord, until all are flying about her head in an almost horizontal position. At this moment the dance begins, and it is almost impossible to distinguish the features of the dancer. She continues her dance, apparently indifferent to the revolving eggs. At the velocity with which they revolve the slightest false movement would cause them to knock against one another and surely break. Finally, with the same lightning-like movements, she removes them one by one, certainly the most delicate part of the trick, until they are all safely laid away in the basket from which they came, and then she suddenly brings the wheel to a stop; after this wonderful performance, lasting possibly thirty minutes, she bows herself out.

A unique Japanese feat is to tear pieces of paper into the form of butterflies and launch them into the air about a vase full of flowers; then with a fan to keep them in motion, making them light on the flowers, fly away, and return, after the manner of several living butterflies, without allowing one to fall to the ground.

Marksmen.—It would be an incomplete paper on the acute development of the senses that did not pay tribute to the men who exhibit marvelous skill with firearms. In the old frontier days in the Territories, the woodsmen far eclipsed Tell with his bow or Robin Hood's famed band by their unerring aim with their rifles. It is only lately that there disappeared in this country the last of many woodsmen, who, though standing many paces away and without the aid of the improved sights of modern guns, could by means of a rifle-ball, with marvelous precision, drive a nail "home" that had been placed partly in a board. The experts who shoot at glass balls rarely miss, and when we consider the number used each year, the proportion of inaccurate shots is surprisingly small. Ira Paine, Doctor Carver, and others have been seen in their marvelous performances by many people of the present generation. The records made by many of the competitors of the modern army-shooting matches are none the less wonderful, exemplifying as they do the degree of precision that the eye may attain and the control which may be developed over the nerves and muscles. The authors know of a country-man who successfully hunted squirrels and small game by means of pebbles thrown with his hand.

Physiologic wonders are to be found in all our modern sports and games. In billiards, base-ball, cricket, tennis, etc., there are experts who are really physiologic curiosities. In the trades and arts we see development of the special senses that is little less than marvelous. It is said that there are workmen in Krupp's gun factory in Germany who have such control over the enormous trip hammers that they can place a watch under one and let the hammer fall, stopping it with unerring precision just on the crystal. An expert tool juggler in one of the great English needle factories, in a recent test of skill, performed one of the most delicate mechanical feats imaginable. He took a common sewing needle of medium size (length $1\frac{3}{8}$ inches) and drilled a hole through its entire length from eye to point—the opening being just large enough to admit the passage of a very fine hair. Another workman in a watch-factory of the United States drilled a hole through a hair of his beard and ran a fiber of silk through it.

Ventriloquists, or "two-voiced men," are interesting anomalies of the present day ; it is common to see a person who possesses the power of speaking with a voice apparently from the epigastrium. Some acquire this faculty, while with others it is due to a natural resonance, formed, according to Dupont, in the space between the third and fourth ribs and their cartilaginous union and the middle of the first portion of the sternum. Examination of many of these cases proves that the vibration is greatest here. It is certain that ventriloquists have existed for many centuries. It is quite possible that some of the old Pagan oracles were simply the deceptions of priests by means of ventriloquism.

Dupont, Surgeon-in-chief of the French Army about a century since, examined minutely an individual professing to be a ventriloquist. With a stuffed fox on his lap near his epigastrium, he imitated a conversation with the fox. By lying on his belly, and calling to some one supposed to be below the surface of the ground, he would imitate an answer seeming to come from the depths of the earth. With his belly on the ground he not only made the illusion more complete, but in this way he smothered " the epigastric voice."

He was always noticed to place the inanimate objects with which he held conversations near his umbilicus.

Ventriloquists must not be confounded with persons who by means of skilful mechanisms, creatures with movable fauces, etc., imitate ventriloquism. The latter class are in no sense of the word true ventriloquists, but simulate the anomaly by quickly changing the tones of their voice in rapid succession, and thus seem to make their puppets talk in many different voices. After having acquired the ability to suddenly change the tone of their voice, they practise imitations of the voices of the aged, of children, dialects, and feminine tones, and, with a set of mechanical puppets, are ready to appear as ventriloquists. By contraction of the pharyngeal and laryngeal muscles they also imitate tones from a distance. Some give their performance with little labial movement, but close inspection of the ordinary performer of this class shows visible movements of his lips. The true ventriloquist pretends only to speak from the belly and needs no mechanical assistance.

The wonderful powers of mimicry displayed by expert ventriloquists are marvelous; they not only imitate individuals and animals, but do not hesitate to imitate a conglomeration of familiar sounds and noises in such a manner as to deceive their listeners into believing that they hear the discussions of an assemblage of people. The following description of an imitation of a domestic riot by a Chinese ventriloquist is given by the author of "The Chinaman at Home" and well illustrates the extent of their abilities: "The ventriloquist was seated behind a screen, where there were only a chair, a table, a fan, and a ruler. With this ruler he rapped on the table to enforce silence, and when everybody had ceased speaking there was suddenly heard the barking of a dog. Then we heard the movements of a woman. She had been waked by the dog and was shaking her husband. We were just expecting to hear the man and wife talking together when a child began to cry. To pacify it the mother gave it food; we could hear it drinking and crying at the same time. The mother spoke to it soothingly and then rose to change its clothes. Meanwhile another child had wakened and was beginning to make a noise. The father scolded it, while the baby continued crying. By-and-by the whole family went back to bed and fell asleep. The patter of a mouse was heard. It climbed up some vase and upset it. We heard the clatter of the vase as it fell. The woman coughed in her sleep. Then cries of "Fire! fire!" were heard. The mouse had upset the lamp; the bed curtains were on fire. The husband and wife waked up, shouted, and screamed, the children cried, people came running and shouting. Children cried, dogs barked, squibs and crackers exploded. The fire brigade came racing up. Water was pumped up in torrents and hissed in the flames. The representation was so true to life that every one rose to his feet and was starting away when a second blow of the ruler on the table commanded silence. We rushed behind the screen, but there was nothing there except the ventriloquist, his table, his chair, and his ruler."

Athletic Feats.—The ancients called athletes those who were noted for their extraordinary agility, force, and endurance. The history of athletics is not foreign to that of medicine, but, on the contrary, the two are in many ways intimately blended. The instances of feats of agility and endurance are in every sense of the word examples of physiologic and functional anomalies, and have in all times excited the interest and investigation of capable physicians.

The Greeks were famous for their love of athletic pastimes ; and classical study serves powerfully to strengthen the belief that no institution exercised greater influence than **the public contests of Greece** in molding national character and producing that admirable type of personal and intellectual beauty that we see reflected in her art and literature. These contests were held at four national festivals, the Olympian, the Pythian, the Nemean, and the Isthmean games. On these occasions every one stopped labor, truce was declared between the States, and the whole country paid tribute to the contestants for the highly-prized laurels of these games. Perhaps the enthusiasm shown in athletics and interest in physical development among the Greeks has never been equaled by any other people. Herodotus and all the Greek writers to Plutarch have elaborated on the glories of the Greek athlete, and tell us of the honors rendered to the victors by the spectators and the vanquished, dwelling with complacency on the fact that in accepting the laurel they cared for nothing but honor. The Romans in " ludi publici," as they called their games, were from first to last only spectators ; but in Greece every eligible person was an active participant. In the regimen of diet and training the physicians from the time of Hippocrates, and even before, have been the originators and professional advisers of the athlete. The change in the manner of living of athletes, if we can judge from the writings of Hippocrates, was anterior to his time ; for in Book V. of the " Epidemics " we read of Bias, who, " suapte natura vorax, in choleram-morbum incidit ex carnium esu, præcipueque suillarum crudarum, etc."

From the time of the well-known fable of the hero who, by practising daily from his birth, was able to lift a full-grown bull, thus gradually accustoming himself to the increased weight, physiologists and scientists have collaborated with the athlete in evolving the present ideas and system of training. In his aphorisms Hippocrates bears witness to the dangers of over-exercise and superabundant training, and Galen is particularly averse to an art which so preternaturally develops the constitution and nature of man ; many subsequent medical authorities believed that excessive development of the human frame was necessarily followed by a compensatory shortening of life.

The foot-race was the oldest of the Greek institutions, and in the first of the Olympiads the " dromos," a course of about 200 yards, was the only contest ; but gradually the " dialos," in which the course was double that of the dromos, was introduced, and, finally, tests of endurance as well as speed were instituted in the long-distance races and the contests of racing in heavy armor, which were so highly commended by Plato as preparation for the arduous duties of a soldier. Among the Greeks we read of Lasthenes the Theban, who vanquished a horse in the course; of Polymnestor, who chased and caught a hare; and Philonides, the courier of Alexander the Great, who in nine hours traversed the distance between the Greek cities Sicyone and Elis, a distance of over 150 miles. We read of the famous soldier of Marathon, who ran to announce the victory to the Magistrates of Athens and fell dead at their feet. In the Olympian games at Athens in 1896 this distance (about 26 miles) was traversed in less than three hours.

It is said of Euchidas, who carried the fire necessary for the sacrifices which were to replace those which the Persians had spoiled, that he ran a thousand stadia (about 125 miles) and fell dead at the end of his mission. The Roman historians have also recited the extraordinary feats of the couriers of their times. Pliny speaks of an athlete who ran 235 kilometers (almost 150 miles) without once stopping. He also mentions a child who ran almost half this distance.

In the Middle Ages the Turks had **couriers** of almost supernatural agility and endurance. It is said that the distance some of them would traverse in twenty-four hours was 120 miles, and that it was common for them to make the round trip from Constantinople to Adrianople, a distance of 80 leagues, in two days. They were dressed very lightly, and by constant usage the soles of their feet were transformed into a leathery consistency. In the last century in the houses of the rich there were couriers who preceded the carriages and were known as "Basques," who could run for a very long time without apparent fatigue. In France there is a common proverb, "Courir comme un Basque." Rabelais says: "Grand-Gousier dépêche le Basque son laquais pour quérir Gargantua en toute hâte."

In the olden times the English nobility maintained running footmen who, living under special regimen and training, were enabled to traverse unusual distances without apparent fatigue. There is an anecdote of a nobleman living in a castle not far from Edinburgh, who one evening charged his courier to carry a letter to that city. The next morning when he arose he found this valet sleeping in his antechamber. The nobleman waxed wroth but the courier gave him a response to the letter. He had traveled 70 mile during the night. It is said that one of the noblemen under Charles II. in preparing for a great dinner perceived that one of the indispensable piece of his service was missing. His courier was dispatched in great haste t another house in his domain, 15 miles distant, and returned in two hour with the necessary article, having traversed a distance of over 30 miles. is also said [394] that a courier carrying a letter to a London physician returne with the potion prescribed within twenty-four hours, having traversed 14 miles. There is little doubt of the ability of these couriers to tire out any horse. The couriers who accompany the diligences in Spain often fatigue the animals who draw the vehicles.

At the present time in this country **the Indians** furnish examples of marvelous feats of running. The Tauri-Mauri Indians, who live in the heart of the Sierra Madre Mountains, are probably the most wonderful long-distance runners in the world. Their name in the language of the mountain Mexicans means foot-runners; and there is little doubt that they perform athletic feats which equal the best in the days of the Olympian games. They are possibly the remnants of the wonderful runners among the Indian tribes in the beginning of this century. There is an account of one of the Tauri-Mauri who was mail carrier between Guarichic and San Jose de los Cruces, a distance of 50 miles of as rough, mountainous road as ever tried a mountaineer's lungs and limbs. Bareheaded and barelegged, with almost no clothing, this man made this trip each day, and, carrying on his back a mail-pouch weighing 40 pounds, moved gracefully and easily over his path, from time to time increasing his speed as though practising, and then again more slowly to smoke a cigarette. The Tauri-Mauri are long-limbed and slender, giving the impression of being above the average height. There is scarcely any flesh on their puny arms, but their legs are as muscular as those of a greyhound. In short running they have the genuine professional stride, something rarely seen in other Indian racers. In traversing long distances they leap and bound like deer.

"Deerfoot," the famous Indian long-distance runner, died on the Cattaraugus Reservation in January, 1896. His proper name was Louis Bennett, the name "Deerfoot" having been given to him for his prowess in running. He was born on the reservation in 1828. In 1861 he went to England, where he defeated the English champion runners. In April, 1863, he ran 11 miles in London in fifty-six minutes fifty-two seconds, and 12 miles in one hour two minutes and two and one-half seconds, both of which have stood as world's records ever since.

In Japan, at the present day, the popular method of conveyance, both in cities and in rural districts, is the two-wheeled vehicle, looking like a baby-carriage, known to foreigners as the jinrickisha, and to the natives as the kuruma. In the city of Tokio there is estimated to be 38,000 of these little carriages in use. They are drawn by coolies, of whose endurance remarkable stories are told. These men wear light cotton breeches and a blue cotton jacket bearing the license number, and the indispensable umbrella hat. In the course of a journey in hot weather the **jinrickisha man** will gradually remove most of his raiment and stuff it into the carriage. In the rural sections he is covered with only two strips of cloth, one wrapped about his head and the other about his loins. It is said that when the roadway is good, these "human horses" prefer to travel bare-footed; when working in the mud they wrap a piece of straw about each big toe, to prevent slipping and to give them a firmer grip. For any of these men a five-mile spurt on a good road without a breathing spell is a small affair. A pair of them will roll a jinrickisha along a country road at the rate of four miles an hour, and they will do this eight hours a day. The general average of the distance traversed in a day is 25 miles. Cockerill, who has recently described these men, says that the majority of them die early. The terrible physical strain brings on hypertrophy and valvular diseases of the heart, and many of them suffer from hernia. Occasionally one sees a veteran jinrickisha man, and it is interesting to note how tenderly he is helped by his confrères. They give him preference as regards wages, help push his vehicle up heavy grades, and show him all manner of consideration.

Figure 180 represents two Japanese porters and their usual load, which is much more difficult to transport than a jinrickisha carriage. In other Eastern countries, palanquins and other means of conveyance are still borne on the

Fig. 180.—Japanese porters.

shoulders of couriers, and it is not so long since our ancestors made their calls in Sedan-chairs borne by sturdy porters.

Some of the **letter-carriers of India** make a daily journey of 30 miles. They carry in one hand a stick, at the extremity of which is a ring containing several little plates of iron, which, agitated during the course, produce a loud noise designed to keep off ferocious beasts and serpents. In the other hand they carry a wet cloth, with which they frequently refresh themselves by wiping the countenance. It is said that a regular Hindustanee carrier, with a weight of 80 pounds on his shoulder,—carried, of course, in two divisions, hung on his neck by a yoke,—will, if properly paid, lope along over 100 miles in twenty-four hours—a feat which would exhaust any but the best trained runners.

The " go-as-you-please " pedestrians, whose powers during the past years have been exhibited in this country and in England, have given us marvelous examples of endurance, over 600 miles having been accomplished in a six-days' contest. Hazael, the professional pedestrian, has run over 450 miles in ninety-nine hours, and Albert has traveled over 500 miles in one hundred and ten hours. Rowell, Hughes, and Fitzgerald have astonishingly high records for long-distance running, comparing favorably with the older, and presumably mythical, feats of this nature. In California, C. A. Harriman of

Truckee in April, 1883, walked twenty-six hours without once resting, traversing 122 miles.

For the purpose of comparison we give the **best modern records for running :—**

100 Yards.—$9\frac{3}{5}$ seconds, made by Edward Donavan, at Natick, Mass., September 2, 1895.

220 Yards.—$21\frac{3}{5}$ seconds, made by Harry Jewett, at Montreal, September 24, 1892.

Quarter-Mile.—$47\frac{3}{4}$ seconds, made by W. Baker, at Boston, Mass., July 1, 1886.

Half-Mile.—1 minute $53\frac{2}{5}$ seconds, made by C. J. Kirkpatrick, at Manhattan Field, New York, September 21, 1895.

1 Mile.—4 minutes $12\frac{3}{4}$ seconds, made by W. G. George, at London, England, August 23, 1886.

5 Miles.—24 minutes 40 seconds, made by J. White, in England, May 11, 1863.

10 Miles.—51 minutes $6\frac{3}{5}$ seconds, made by William Cummings, at London, England. September 18, 1895.

25 Miles.—2 hours 33 minutes 44 seconds, made by G. A. Dunning, at London, England, December 26, 1881.

50 Miles.—5 hours 55 minutes $4\frac{1}{2}$ seconds, made by George Cartwright, at London, England, February 21, 1887.

75 Miles.—8 hours 48 minutes 30 seconds, made by George Littlewood, at London, England, November 24, 1884.

100 Miles.—13 hours 26 minutes 30 seconds, made by Charles Rowell, at New York, February 27, 1882.

In instances of **long-distance traversing,** rapidity is only a secondary consideration, the remarkable fact being in the endurance of fatigue and the continuity of the exercise. William Gale [a] walked 1500 miles in a thousand consecutive hours, and then walked 60 miles every twenty-four hours for six weeks on the Lillie Bridge cinder path. He was five feet five inches tall, forty-nine years of age, and weighed 121 pounds, and was but little developed muscularly. He was in good health during his feat; his diet for the twenty-four hours was $1\frac{1}{2}$ pounds of meat, five or six eggs, some cocoa, two quarts of milk, a quart of tea, and occasionally a glass of bitter ale, but never wine nor spirits. Strange to say, he suffered from constipation, and took daily a compound rhubarb pill. He was examined at the end of his feat by Gant. His pulse was 75, strong, regular, and his heart was normal. His temperature was 97.25° F., and his hands and feet warm; respirations were deep and averaged 15 a minute. He suffered from frontal headache and was drowsy. During the six weeks he had lost only seven pounds, and his appetite maintained its normal state.

Zeuner of Cincinnati [b] refers to John Snyder of Dunkirk, whose walking feats were marvelous. He was not an impostor. During forty-eight hours he was watched by the students of the Ohio Medical College, who stated that he walked constantly; he assured them that it did not rest him to sit down, but made him uncomfortable. The celebrated Weston walked 5000 miles in one hundred days, but Snyder was said to have traveled

[a] 224, 1881, i., 63. [b] 224, 1887, 321.

25,000 miles in five hundred days and was apparently no more tired than when he began.

Recently there was a person who pushed a wheelbarrow from San Francisco to New York in one hundred and eighteen days. In 1809 the celebrated Captain Barclay wagered that he could walk 1000 miles in one thousand consecutive hours, and gained his bet with some hours to spare. In 1834 Ernest Mensen astonished all Europe by his pedestrian exploits. He was a Norwegian sailor, who wagered that he could walk from Paris to Moscow in fifteen days. On June 25, 1834, at ten o'clock A. M., he entered the Kremlin, after having traversed 2500 kilometers (1550 miles) in fourteen days and eighteen hours. His performances all over Europe were so marvelous as to be almost incredible. In 1836, in the service of the East India Company, he was dispatched from Calcutta to Constantinople, across Central Asia. He traversed the distance in fifty-nine days, accomplishing 9000 kilometers (5580 miles) in one-third less time than the most rapid caravan. He died while attempting to discover the source of the Nile, having reached the village of Syang.

A most marvelous feat of endurance is recorded in England in the first part of this century. It is said that on a wager Sir Andrew Leith Hay and Lord Kennedy walked two days and a night under pouring rain, over the Grampian range of mountains, wading all one day in a bog. The distance traversed was from a village called Banchory on the river Dee to Inverness. This feat was accomplished without any previous preparation, both men starting shortly after the time of the wager.

Riders.—The feats of endurance accomplished by the couriers who ride great distances with many changes of horses are noteworthy. According to a contemporary medical journal [a] there is, in the Friend of India, an account of the Thibetan couriers who ride for three weeks with intervals of only half an hour to eat and change horses. It is the duty of the officials at the Dak bungalows to see that the courier makes no delay, and even if dying he is tied to his horse and sent to the next station. The celebrated English huntsman, "Squire" Osbaldistone, on a wager rode 200 miles in seven hours ten minutes and four seconds. He used 28 horses; and as one hour twenty-two minutes and fifty-six seconds were allowed for stoppages, the whole time, changes and all, occupied in accomplishing this wonderful feat was eight hours and forty-two minutes. The race was ridden at the Newmarket Houghton Meeting over a four-mile course. It is said that a Captain Horne of the Madras Horse Artillery rode 200 miles on Arab horses in less than ten hours along the road between Madras and Bangalore. When we consider the slower speed of the Arab horses and the roads and climate of India, this performance equals the 200 miles in the shorter time about an English race track and on thoroughbreds. It is said that this wonderful horseman lost

a 548, 1868, i., 515.

his life in riding a horse named "Jumping Jenny" 100 miles a day for eight days. The heat was excessive, and although the horse was none the worse for the performance, the Captain died from the exposure he encountered. There is a record of a Mr. Bacon of the Bombay Civil Service, who rode one camel from Bombay to Allygur (perhaps 800 miles) in eight days.

As regards the **physiology of the runners and walkers,** it is quite interesting to follow the effects of training on the respiration, whereby in a measure is explained the ability of these persons to maintain their respiratory function, although excessively exercising. A curious discussion, persisted in since antiquity, is as to the supposed **influence of the spleen** on the ability of couriers. For ages runners have believed that the spleen was a hindrance to their vocation, and that its reduction was followed by greater agility on the course. With some, this opinion is perpetuated to the present day. In France there is a proverb, "Courir comme un dérate." To reduce the size of the spleen, the Greek athletes used certain beverages, the composition of which was not generally known ; the Romans had a similar belief and habit. Pliny speaks of a plant called *equisetum,* a decoction of which taken for three days after a fast of twenty-four hours would effect absorption of the spleen. The modern pharmacopeia does not possess any substance having a similar virtue, although quinin has been noticed to diminish the size of the spleen when engorged in malarial fevers. Strictly speaking, however, the facts are not analogous. Hippocrates advises a moxa of mushrooms applied over the spleen for melting or dissolving it. Godefroy Mœbius is said to have seen in the village of Halberstadt a courier whose spleen had been cauterized after incision ; and about the same epoch (seventeenth century) some men pretended to be able to successfully extirpate the spleen for those who desired to be couriers. This operation we know to be one of the most delicate in modern surgery, and as we are progressing with our physiologic knowledge of the spleen we see nothing to justify the old theory in regard to its relations to agility and coursing.

Swimming.—The instances of endurance that we see in the aquatic sports are equally as remarkable as those that we find among the runners and walkers. In the ancient days the Greeks, living on their various islands and being in a mild climate, were celebrated for their prowess as swimmers. Socrates relates the feats of swimming among the inhabitants of Delos. The journeys of Leander across the Hellespont are well celebrated in verse and prose, but this feat has been easily accomplished many times since, and is hardly to be classed as extraordinary. Herodotus says that the Macedonians were skilful swimmers ; and all the savage tribes about the borders of waterways are found possessed of remarkable dexterity and endurance in swimming.

In 1875 the celelebrated Captain Webb swam from Dover to Calais.[a] On

a 476, 1875, ii., 359.

landing he felt extremely cold, but his body was as warm as when he started. He was exhausted and very sleepy, falling in deep slumber on his way to the hotel.   On getting into bed his temperature was 98° F. and his pulse normal. In five hours he was feverish, his temperature rising to 101° F.   During the passage he was blinded from the salt water in his eyes and the spray beating against his face.   He strongly denied the newspaper reports that he was delirious, and after a good rest was apparently none the worse for the task. In 1876 he again traversed this passage with the happiest issue.   In 1883 he was engaged by speculators to swim the rapids at Niagara, and in attempting this was overcome by the powerful currents, and his body was not recovered for some days after.   The passage from Dover to Calais has been duplicated.

In 1877 Cavill, another Englishman, swam from Cape Griz-Nez to South Forland in less than thirteen hours.   In 1880 Webb swam and floated at Scarborough for seventy-four consecutive hours—of course, having no current to contend with and no point to reach.   This was merely a feat of staying in the water.   In London in 1881, Beckwith, swimming ten hours a day over a 32-lap course for six days, traversed 94 miles.   Since the time of Captain Webb, who was the pioneer of modern long-distance swimming, many men have attempted and some have duplicated his feats ; but these foolhardy performances have in late years been diminishing, and many of the older feats are forbidden by law.

Jumpers and acrobatic tumblers have been popular from the earliest time.   By the aid of springing boards and weights in their hands, the old jumpers covered great distances.   Phayllus of Croton is accredited with jumping the incredible distance of 55 feet, and we have the authority of Eustache and Tzetzes [a] that this jump is genuine.   In the writings of many Greek and Roman historians are chronicled jumps of about 50 feet by the athletes ; if they are true, the modern jumpers have greatly degenerated.   A jump of over 20 feet to-day is considered very clever, the record being 29 feet seven inches with weights, and 23 feet eight inches without weights, although much greater distances have been jumped with the aid of apparatus, but never an approximation to 50 feet.   The most surprising of all these athletes are the tumblers, who turn somersaults over several animals arranged in a row.   Such feats are not only the most amusing sights of a modern circus, but also the most interesting as well.   The agility of these men is marvelous, and the force with which they throw themselves in the air apparently enables them to defy gravity.   In London, Paris, or New York one may see these wonderful tumblers and marvel at the capabilities of human physical development.

In September, 1895, M. F. Sweeney, an American amateur, at Manhattan Field in New York jumped six feet 5⅝ inches high in the running high jump without weights.   With weights, J. H. Fitzpatrick at Oak Island, Mass., jumped six feet six inches high. The record for the running high kick is nine feet eight inches, a marvelous performance, made by C. C. Lee at New Haven, Conn., March 19, 1887.

Extraordinary physical development and strength has been a grand means of natural selection in the human species. As Guyot-Daubès remarks, in prehistoric times, when our ancestors had to battle against hunger, savage beasts, and their neighbors, and when the struggle for existence was so extremely hard, the strong man alone resisted and the weak succumbed. This natural selection has been perpetuated almost to our day ; during the long succession of centuries, the chief or the master was selected on account of his being the strongest, or the most valiant in the combat. Originally, the cavaliers, the members of the nobility, were those who were noted for their courage and strength, and to them were given the lands of the vanquished. Even in times other than those of war, disputes of succession were settled by jousts and tourneys. This fact is seen in the present day among the lower animals, who in their natural state live in tribes ; the leader is usually the strongest, the wisest, and the most courageous.

The strong men of all times have excited the admiration of their fellows and have always been objects of popular interest. The Bible celebrates the exploits of Samson of the tribe of Dan. During his youth he, single handed, strangled a lion ; with the jaw-bone of an ass he is said to have killed 1000 Philistines and put the rest to flight. At another time during the night he transported from the village of Gaza enormous burdens and placed them on the top of a mountain. Betrayed by Delilah, he was delivered into the hands of his enemies and employed in the most servile labors. When old and blind he was attached to the columns of an edifice to serve as an object of public ridicule ; with a violent effort he overturned the columns, destroying himself and 3000 Philistines.

In the Greek mythology we find a great number of heroes, celebrated for their feats of strength and endurance. Many of them have received the name of Hercules ; but the most common of these is the hero who was supposed to be the son of Jupiter and Alcmena. He was endowed with prodigious strength by his father, and was pursued with unrelenting hatred by Juno. In his infancy he killed with his hands the serpents which were sent to devour him. The legends about him are innumerable. He was said to have been armed with a massive club, which only he was able to carry. The most famous of his feats were the twelve labors, with which all readers of mythology are familiar. Hercules, personified, meant to the Greeks physical force as well as strength, generosity, and bravery, and was equivalent to the Assyrian Hercules. The Gauls had a Hercules-Pantopage, who, in addition to the ordinary qualities attributed to Hercules, had an enormous appetite.

As late as the sixteenth century, and in a most amusing and picturesque manner, Rabelais has given us the history of Gargantua, and even to this day, in some regions, there are groups of stones which are believed by ignorant people to have been thrown about by Gargantua in his play. In their citations the older authors often speak of battles, and in epic ballads of heroes with marvelous strength. In the army of Charlemagne, after Camerarius, and quoted by Guyot-Daubès.(who has made an extensive collection of the literature on this subject and to whom the authors are indebted for much information), there was found a giant named Oenother, a native of a village in Suabia, who performed marvelous feats of strength. In his history of Bavaria Aventin speaks of this monster. To Roland, the nephew of Charlemagne, the legends attributed prodigious strength ; and, dying in the valley of Roncesveaux, he broke his good sword "Durandal" by striking it against a rock, making a breach, which is stilled called the "Brèche de Roland." Three years before his death, on his return from Palestine, Christopher, Duke of Bavaria, was said to have lifted to his shoulders a stone which weighed more than 340 pounds. Louis de Boufflers, surnamed the "Robust," who lived in 1534, was noted for his strength and agility. When he placed his feet together, one against the other, he could find no one able to disturb them. He could easily bend and break a horseshoe with his hands, and could seize an ox by the tail and drag it against its will. More than once he was said to have carried a horse on his shoulders. According to Guyot-Daubès [394] there was, in the last century, a Major Barsaba who could seize the limb of a horse and fracture its bone. There was a tale of his lifting an iron anvil, in a blacksmith's forge, and placing it under his coat.

To the Emperor Maximilian I. was ascribed enormous strength ; even in his youth, when but a simple patriot, he vanquished, at the games given by Severus, 16 of the most vigorous wrestlers, and accomplished this feat without stopping for breath. It is said that this feat was the origin of his fortune. Among other celebrated persons in history endowed with uncommon strength were Edmund "Ironsides," King of England ; the Caliph Mostasem-Billah ; Baudouin, "Bras-de-Fer," Count of Flanders ; William IV., called by the French "Fier-a-Bras," Duke of Aquitaine ; Christopher, son of Albert the Pious, Duke of Bavaria ; Godefroy of Bouillon ; the Emperor Charles IV. ; Scanderbeg ; Leonardo da Vinci ; Marshal Saxe ; and the recently deceased Czar of Russia, Alexander III.

Turning now to the authentic **modern Hercules,** we have a man by the name of Eckeberg, born in Anhalt, and who traveled under the name of "**Samson.**" He was exhibited in London, and performed remarkable feats of strength. He was observed by the celebrated Désaguliers (a pupil of Newton) in the commencement of the last century, who at that time was interested in the physiologic experiments of strength and agility. Désaguliers believed that the feats of this new Samson were more due to agility than strength. One day, accompanied by two of his confrères, although a man of ordinary strength, he duplicated some of Samson's feats, and followed his performance by a communication to the Royal Society. One of his tricks was to resist the strength of five or six men or of two horses. Désaguliers claimed that this was entirely due to the position taken. This person would lift a man by one foot, and bear a heavy weight on his chest when resting with his head and two feet on two chairs. By supporting himself with his arms he could lift a piece of cannon attached to his feet.

A little later Désaguliers studied an individual in London named Thomas Topham, who used no ruse in his feats and was not the skilful equilibrist that the German Samson was, his performances being merely the results of abnormal physical force. He was about thirty years old, five feet ten inches in height and well proportioned, and his muscles well developed, the strong ligaments showing under the skin. He ignored entirely the art of appearing supernaturally strong, and some of his feats were rendered difficult by disadvantageous positions. In the feat of the German—resisting the force of several men or horses—Topham exhibited no knowledge of the principles of physics, like that of his predecessor, but, seated on the ground and putting his feet against two stirrups, he was able to resist the traction of a single horse ; when he attempted the same feat against two horses he was severely strained and wounded about the knees. According to Désaguliers, if Topham had taken the advantageous positions of the German Samson, he could have resisted not only two, but four horses. On another occasion, with the aid of a bridle passed about his neck, he lifted three hogsheads full of water, weighing 1386 pounds. If he had utilized the force of his limbs and his loins, like the German, he would have been able to perform far more difficult feats. With his teeth he could lift and maintain in a horizontal position a table over six feet long, at the extremity of which he would put some weight. Two of the feet of the table he rested on his knees. He broke a cord five cm. in diameter, one part of which was attached to a post and the other to a strap passed under his shoulder. He was able to carry in his hands a rolling-pin weighing 800 pounds, about twice the weight a strong man is considered able to lift.

Tom Johnson was another strong man who lived in London in the last century, but he was not an exhibitionist, like his predecessors. He was a porter on the banks of the Thames, his duty being to carry sacks of wheat and corn from the wharves to the warehouses. It was said that when one of his comrades was ill, and could not provide support for his wife and children, Johnson assumed double duty, carrying twice the load. He could seize a sack of wheat, and with it execute the movements of a club-swinger, and with as great facility. He became quite a celebrated boxer, and, besides his strength, he soon demonstrated his powers of endurance, never seeming fatigued after a lively bout. The porters of Paris were accustomed to lift and carry on their shoulders bags of flour weighing 159 kilograms (350 pounds) and to mount stairs with them.   Johnson, on hearing this, duplicated the feat with three sacks, and on one occasion attempted to carry four, and resisted this load some little time.   These four sacks weighed 1400 pounds.

Some years since there was a female Hercules who would get on her hands and knees under a carriage containing six people, and, forming an arch with her body, she would lift it off the ground, an attendant turning the wheels while in the air to prove that they were clear from the ground.

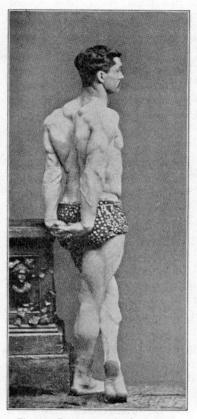

Fig. 181.—Extreme muscular development.   Fig. 182.—Sandow (after a photograph by Falk).

Guyot-Daubès considers that one of the most remarkable of all the men noted for their strength was a butcher living in the mountains of Margeride, known as Lapiada (the extraordinary).   This man, whose strength was legendary in the neighboring country, one day seized a mad bull that had escaped from his stall and held nim by the horns until his attendants could bind him.   For amusement he would lie on his belly and allow several men to get on his back ; with this human load he would rise to the erect position.

One of Lapiada's great feats was to get under a cart loaded with hay and, forming an arch with his body, raise it from the ground, then little by little he would mount to his haunches, still holding the cart and hay.   Lapiada terminated his Herculean existence in attempting a mighty effort.   Having charged himself alone with the task of placing a heavy tree-trunk in a cart, he seized it, his muscles stiffened, but the blood gushed from his mouth and nostrils, and he fell, overcome at last.   The end of Lapiada presents an analogue to that of the celebrated athlete, Polydamas, who was equally the victim of too great confidence in his muscular force, and who died crushed by the force that he hoped to maintain.   Figures 181 and 183 portray the muscular development of an individual noted for his feats of strength, and who exhibited not long since.

In recent years we have had S e b a s t i a n Miller, whose specialty was wrestling and stone-breaking ; Samson, a recent English exhibition-ist, Louis Cyr, and **Sandow,** who, in addition to his remarkable strength and control over his muscles, is a very clever gymnast.   Sandow gives an excellent exposition of the so-called " checker-board" arrangement of the muscular fibers of the lower thoracic and abdominal regions, and in a brilliant light demon-strates his extraordinary power over his muscles, contracting muscles ordinarily involuntary in time with music, a feat really more remarkable than his exhibition of strength.   Figures 182 and 184 show the beautiful muscular development of this remarkable man.

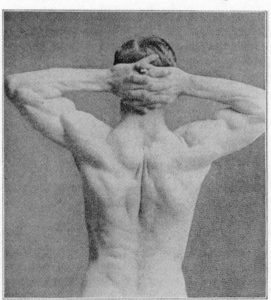

Fig. 183.—Marked development of the muscles of the back.

Joseph Pospischilli, a convict recently imprisoned in the Austrian fortress of Olen, surprised the whole Empire by his wonderful feats of strength. One of his tricks was to add a fifth leg to a common table (placing the useless addition in the exact center) and then balance it with his teeth while two full-grown gipsies danced on it, the music being furnished by a violinist seated in the middle of the well-balanced platform.   One day when the prison in which this Hercules was confined was undergoing repairs, he picked up a large carpenter's bench with his teeth and held it balanced aloft for nearly a minute. Since being released from the Olen prison, Pospischilli and his cousin, another local "strong man" named Martenstine, have formed a combination and are now starring Southern Europe, performing all kinds of startling feats of strength. Among other things they have had a 30-foot bridge made of strong timbers, which is used in one of their great muscle acts. This bridge has two living piers—Pospischilli acting as one and Martenstine the other. Besides supporting this monstrous structure (weight, 1866 pounds) upon their shoulders, these freaks of superhuman strength allow a team of horses and a wagon loaded with a ton of cobble-stones to be driven across it.

It is said that Selig Whitman, known as "Ajax," a New York policeman, has lifted 2000 pounds with his hands and has maintained 450 pounds with his teeth. This man is five feet $8\frac{1}{2}$ inches tall and weighs 162 pounds. His chest measurement is 40 inches, the biceps 17 inches, that of his neck $16\frac{1}{2}$ inches, the forearm 11, the wrist $9\frac{1}{2}$, the thigh 23, and the calf 17.

Fig. 184.—Sandow (after a photograph by Sarony).

One of the strongest of the **" strong women "** is Madame Elise, a Frenchwoman, who performs with her husband. Her greatest feat is the lifting of eight men weighing altogether about 1700 pounds. At her performances she supports across her shoulders a 700-pound dumb-bell, on each side of which a person is suspended.

Miss Darnett, the "singing strong lady," extends herself upon her hands and feet, face uppermost, while a stout platform, with a semicircular groove for her neck, is fixed upon her chest, abdomen, and thighs by means of a waist-belt which passes through brass receivers on the under side of the board. An ordinary upright piano is then placed on the platform by four men ; a performer mounts the platform and plays while the " strong lady " sings a love song while supporting possibly half a ton.

Strength of the Jaws.—There are some persons who exhibit extraordinary power of the jaw. In the ·curious experiments of Regnard and

Blanchard at the Sorbonne, it was found that a crocodile weighing about 120 pounds exerted a force between its jaws at a point corresponding to the insertion of the masseter muscles of 1540 pounds ; a dog of 44 pounds exerted a similar force of 363 pounds.

It is quite possible that in animals like the tiger and lion the force would equal 1700 or 1800 pounds. The anthropoid apes can easily break a cocoa-nut with their teeth, and Guyot-Daubès thinks that possibly a gorilla has a jaw-force of 200 pounds. A human adult is said to exert a force of from 45 to 65 pounds between his teeth, and some individuals exceed this average as much as 100 pounds. In Buffon's experiments he once found a Frenchman who could exert a force of 534 pounds with his jaws.

In several American circuses there have been seen women who hold themselves by a strap between their teeth while they are being hauled up to a trapeze some distance from the ground. A young mulatto girl by the name of " Miss Kerra" exhibited in the Winter Circus in Paris ; suspended from a trapeze, she supported a man at the end of a strap held between her teeth, and even permitted herself to be turned round and round.

Fig. 185.—Signor Lawonda, "the iron-jawed man."

She also held a cannon in her teeth while it was fired. This feat has been done by several others. According to Guyot-Daubès, at Épernay in 1882, while a man named Bucholtz, called " the human cannon," was performing this feat, the cannon, which was over a yard long and weighed nearly 200 pounds, burst and wounded several of the spectators.

There was another Hercules in Paris, who with his teeth lifted and held a heavy cask of water on which was seated a man and varying weights, according to the size of his audience, at the same time keeping his hands occupied with other weights. Figure 185 represents a well-known modern exhibitionist lifting with his teeth a cask on which are seated four men.

The celebrated Mlle. Gauthier, an actress of the Comédie-Français, had marvelous **power of her hands,** bending coins, rolling up silver plate, and performing divers other feats. Major Barsaba had enormous powers of hand and fingers. He could roll a silver plate into the shape of a goblet. Being challenged by a Gascon, he seized the hand of his unsuspecting adversary in the ordinary manner of salutation and crushed all the bones of the fingers, thus rendering unnecessary any further trial of strength.

It is said that Marshal Saxe once visited a blacksmith ostensibly to have his horse shod, and seeing no shoe ready he took a bar of iron, and with his hands fashioned it into a horseshoe. There are Japanese dentists who extract teeth with their wonderfully developed fingers. There are stories of a man living in the village of Cantal who received the sobriquet of "La Coupia" (The Brutal). He would exercise his function as a butcher by strangling with his fingers the calves and sheep, instead of killing them in the ordinary manner. It is said that one day, by placing his hands on the shoulders of the strong man of a local fair, he made him faint by the pressure exerted by his fingers.

Manual strangulation is a well-known crime and is quite popular in some countries. The Thugs of India sometimes murdered their victims in this way. Often such force is exerted by the murderer's fingers as to completely fracture the cricoid cartilage.

In viewing the feats of strength of the exhibitionist we must bear in consideration the numerous **frauds** perpetrated. A man of extraordinary strength sometimes finds peculiar stone, so stratified that he is able to break it with the force he can exert by a blow from the hand alone, although a man of ordinary strength would try in vain. In most of these instances, if one were to take a piece of the exhibitionist's stone, he would find that a slight tap of the hammer would break it. Again, there are many instances in which the stone has been found already separated and fixed quite firmly together, placing it out of the power of an ordinary man to break, but which the exhibitionist finds within his ability. This has been the solution of the feats of many of the individuals who invite persons to send them marked stones to use at their performances. By skilfully arranging stout twine on the hands, it is surprising how easily it is broken, and there are many devices and tricks to deceive the public, all of which are more or less used by "strong men."

The recent **officially recorded feats of strength** that stand unequaled in the last decade are as follows :—

Weight-lifting.—Hands alone, 1571¼ pounds, done by C. G. Jefferson, an amateur, at Clinton, Mass., December 10, 1890 ; with harness, 3239 pounds, by W. B. Curtis, at New York, December 20, 1868 ; Louis Cyr, at Berthierville, Can., October 1, 1888, pushed up 3536 pounds of pig-iron with his back, arms, and legs.

Dumb-bells.— H. Pennock, in New York, 1870, put up a 10-pound dumb-bell 8431 times in four hours thirty-four minutes ; by using both hands to raise it to the

PLATE 6.

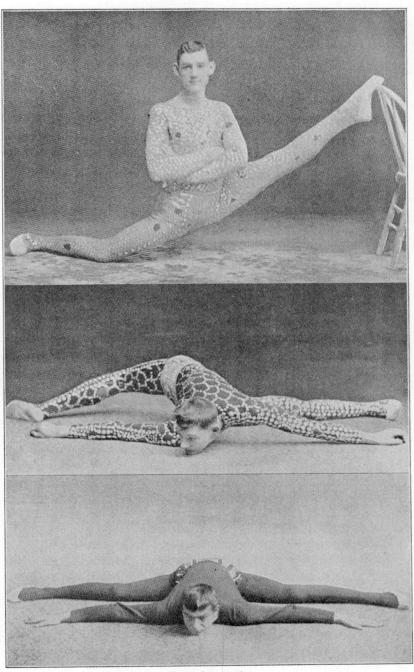

Feats of contortion.

shoulder, and then using one hand alone, R. A. Pennell, in New York, January 31, 1874, managed to put up a bell weighing 201 pounds 5 ounces; and Eugene Sandow, at London, February 11, 1891, surpassed this feat with a 250-pound bell.

Throwing 16-pound Hammer.— J. S. Mitchell, at Travers Island, N. Y., October 8, 1892, made a record-throw of 145 feet ¾ inch.

Putting 16-pound Shot.—George R. Gray, at Chicago, September 16, 1893, made the record of 47 feet.

Throwing 56-pound Weight.—J. S. Mitchell, at New York, September 22, 1894, made the distance record of 35 feet 10 inches; and at Chicago, September 16, 1893, made the height record of 15 feet 4½ inches.

The class of people commonly known as **contortionists** by the laxity of their muscles and ligaments are able to dislocate or preternaturally bend their joints. In entertainments of an arena type and even in what are now called " variety performances" are to be seen individuals of this class. These persons can completely straddle two chairs, and do what they call " the split ;" they can place their foot about their neck while maintaining the upright position ; they can bend almost double at the waist in such a manner that the back of the head will touch the calves, while the legs are perpendicular with the ground ; they can bring the popliteal region over their shoulders and in this position walk on their hands ; they can put themselves in a narrow barrel ; eat with a fork attached to a heel while standing on their hands, and perform divers other remarkable and almost incredible feats. Their performances are genuine, and they are real physiologic curiosities. Plate 6 represents two well-known contortionists in their favorite feats.

Wentworth, the oldest living contortionist, is about seventy years of age, but seems to have lost none of his earlier sinuosity. His chief feat is to stow himself away in a box 23 × 29 × 16 inches. When inside, six dozen wooden bottles of the same size and shape as those which ordinarily contain English soda water are carefully stowed away, packed in with him, and the lid slammed down. He bestows upon this act the curious and suggestive name of " Packanatomicalization."

Another class of individuals are those who can either partially or completely dislocate the major articulations of the body. Many persons exhibit this capacity in their fingers. Persons vulgarly called " double jointed" are quite common.

Charles Warren, an American contortionist, has been examined by several medical men of prominence and descriptions of him have appeared from time to time in prominent medical journals.[a] When he was but a child he was constantly tumbling down, due to the heads of the femurs slipping from the acetabula, but reduction was always easy. When eight years old he joined a company of acrobats and strolling performers, and was called by the euphonious title of " the Yankee dish-rag." His muscular system was well-developed, and, like Sandow, he could make muscles act in concert or separately.

[a] 224, 1882, i., 650, and 476, 1882, i., 576.

He could throw into energetic single action the biceps, the supinator longus, the radial extensors, the platysma myoides, and many other muscles. When he "strings," as he called it, the sartorius, that ribbon muscle shows itself as a tight cord, extending from the front of the iliac spine to the inner side of the knee.   Another trick was to leave flaccid that part of the serratus magnus which is attached to the inferior angle of the scapula whilst he roused energetic contraction in the rhomboids.   He could displace his muscles so that the lower angles of the scapulæ projected and presented the appearance historically attributed to luxation of the scapula.

Warren was well informed on surgical landmarks and had evidently been a close student of Sir Astley Cooper's classical illustrations of disloca-

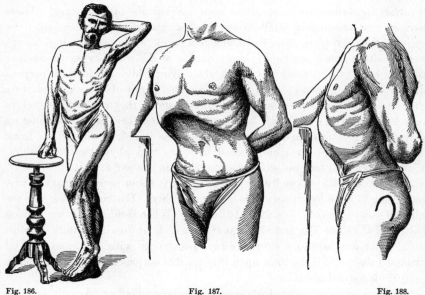

Fig. 186.   Fig. 187.   Fig. 188.
Charles Warren, the celebrated dislocationist.

tions.   He was able so to contract his abdominal muscles that the aorta could be distinctly felt with the fingers.   In this feat nearly all the abdominal contents were crowded beneath the diaphragm (Fig. 187).   On the other hand, he could produce a phantom abdominal tumor by driving the coils of the intestine within a peculiar grasp of the rectus and oblique muscles.   The "growth" (Fig. 188) was rounded, dull on percussion, and looked as if an exploratory incision or puncture would be advisable for diagnosis.

By extraordinary muscular power and extreme laxity of his ligaments, he simulated all the dislocations about the hip joint (Fig. 186).   Sometimes he produced actual dislocation, but usually he said he could so distort his muscles as to imitate in the closest degree the dislocations.   He could imitate the various forms of talipes, in such a way as to deceive an expert. He dislocated nearly every joint in the body with great facility. It was said that he could contract at will both pillars of the fauces. He could contract his chest to 34 inches and expand it to 41 inches.

Warren weighed 150 pounds, was a total abstainer, and was the father of two children, both of whom could readily dislocate their hips.

In France in 1886 there was shown a man who was called "**l'homme protée,**" or protean man. He had an exceptional power over his muscles. Even those muscles ordinarily involuntary he could exercise at will. He could produce such rigidity of stature that a blow by a hammer on his body fell as though on a block of stone. By his power over his abdominal muscles he could give himself different shapes, from the portly alderman to the lean and haggard student, and he was even accredited with assuming the shape of a "living skeleton." Quatrefages, the celebrated French scientist, examined him, and said that he could shut off the blood from the right side and then from the left side of the body, which feat he ascribed to unilateral muscular action.

In 1893 there appeared in Washington, giving exhibitions at the colleges there and at the Emergency Hospital, a man named Fitzgerald, claiming to reside in Harrisburg, Pa., who made his living by exhibiting at medical colleges over the country. He simulated all the dislocations, claiming that they were complete, using manual force to produce and reduce them. He exhibited a thorough knowledge of the pathology of dislocations and of the anatomy of the articulations. He produced the different forms of talipes, as well as all the major hip-dislocations. When interrogated as to the cause of his enormous saphenous veins, which stood out like huge twisted cords under the skin and were associated with venous varicosity on the leg, he said he presumed they were caused by his constantly compressing the saphenous vein at the hip in giving his exhibitions, which in some large cities were repeated several times a day.

Endurance of Pain.—The question of the endurance of pain is, necessarily, one of comparison. There is little doubt that in the lower classes the sensation of pain is felt in a much less degree than in those of a highly intellectual and nervous temperament. If we eliminate the element of fear, which always predominates in the lower classes, the result of general hospital observation will show this distinction. There are many circumstances which have a marked influence on pain. Patriotism, enthusiasm, and general excitement, together with pride and natural obstinacy, prove the power of the mind over the body. The tortures endured by prisoners of war, religious martyrs and victims, exemplify the power of a strong will excited by deep emotion over the sensation of pain. The flagellants, persons who expiated their sins by voluntarily flaying themselves to the point of exhaustion, are modern examples of persons who in religious enthusiasm inflict pain on themselves. In the ancient times in India the frenzied zealots struggled for positions from which they could throw themselves under the car of the Juggernaut, and their intense emotions turned the pains of their wounds into a pleasure. According to the reports of her Majesty's surgeons, there are at the present time in India native Brahmins who hang themselves on sharp hooks placed in the flesh between the scapulæ, and remain in this position without the least visible show of pain. In a similar manner they pierce the lips and cheeks with long pins and bore the tongue with a hot iron. From a reliable source the authors have an account of a man in Northern India who as a means of self-inflicted penance held his arm aloft for the greater part of each day, bending the fingers tightly on the palms. After a considerable time the nails had grown or been forced through the palms of the hands, making their exit on the dorsal surfaces. There are many savage rites and ceremonies calling for the severe infliction of pain on the participants which have been described from time to time by travelers. The Aztecs willingly sacrificed even their lives in the worship of their Sun-god.

By means of singing and dancing **the Aïssaoui,** in the Algerian town of Constantine, throw themselves into an ecstatic state in which their bodies seem to be insensible even to severe wounds. Hellwald says they run sharp-pointed irons into their heads, eyes, necks, and breasts without apparent pain or injury to themselves. Some observers claim they are rendered insensible to pain by self-induced hypnotism.

An account by Carpenter of the Algerian Aïssaoui contained the following lucid description of the performances of these people :—

" The center of the court was given up to the Aïssaoui. These were 12 hollow-cheeked men, some old and some young, who sat cross-legged in an irregular semicircle on the floor. Six of them had immense flat drums or tambours, which they presently began to beat noisily. In front of them a charcoal fire burned in a brazier, and into it one of them from time to time threw bits of some sort of incense, which gradually filled the place with a thin smoke and a mildly pungent odor.

" For a long time—it seemed a long time—this went on with nothing to break the silence but the rhythmical beat of the drums. Gradually, however, this had become quicker, and now grew wild and almost deafening, and the men began a monotonous chant which soon was increased to shouting. Suddenly one of the men threw himself with a howl to the ground, when he was seized by another, who stripped him of part of his garments and led him in front of the fire. Here, while the pounding of the drums and the shouts of the men became more and more frantic, he stood swaying his body backward and forward, almost touching the ground in his fearful contortions, and wagging his head until it seemed as if he must dislocate it from his shoulders. All at once he drew from the fire a red-hot bar of iron, and with a yell of horror, which sent a shiver down one's back, held it up before his eyes.

More violently than ever he swayed his body and wagged his head, until he had worked himself up to a climax of excitement, when he passed the glowing iron several times over the palm of each hand and then licked it repeatedly with his tongue. He next took a burning coal from the fire, and, placing it between his teeth, fanned it by his breath into a white heat. He ended his part of the performance by treading on red-hot coals scattered on the floor, after which he resumed his place with the rest. Then the next performer, with a yell as before, suddenly sprang to his feet and began again the same frantic contortions, in the midst of which he snatched from the fire an iron rod with a ball on one end, and after winding one of his eyelids around it until the eyeball was completely exposed, he thrust its point in behind the eye, which was forced far out on his cheek. It was held there for a moment, when it was withdrawn, the eye released, and then rubbed vigorously a few times with the balled end of the rod.

" The drums all the time had been beaten lustily, and the men had kept up their chant, which still went unceasingly on. Again a man sprang to his feet and went through the same horrid motions. This time the performer took from the fire a sharp nail and, with a piece of the sandy limestone common to this region, proceeded with a series of blood-curdling howls to hammer it down into the top of his head, where it presently stuck upright, while he tottered dizzily around until it was pulled out with apparent effort and with a hollow snap by one of the other men.

" The performance had now fairly begun, and, with short intervals and always in the same manner, the frenzied contortions first, another ate up a glass lamp-chimney, which he first broke in pieces in his hands and then crunched loudly with his teeth. He then produced from a tin box a live scorpion, which ran across the floor with tail erect, and was then allowed to attach itself to the back of his hand and his face, and was finally taken into his mouth, where it hung suspended from the inside of his cheek and was finally chewed and swallowed. A sword was next produced, and after the usual preliminaries it was drawn by the same man who had just given the scorpion such unusual opportunities several times back and forth across his throat and neck, apparently deeply imbedded in the flesh. Not content with this, he bared his body at his waist, and while one man held the sword, edge upward, by the hilt and another by the point, about which a turban had been wrapped, he first stood upon it with his bare feet and then balanced himself across it on his naked stomach, while still another of the performers stood upon his back, whither he had sprung without any attempt to mollify the violence of the action. With more yells and genuflections, another now drew from the fire several iron skewers, some of which he thrust into the inner side of his cheeks and others into his throat at the larynx, where they were left for a while to hang.

" The last of the actors in this singular entertainment was a stout man with a careworn face, who apparently regarded his share as a melancholy duty which he was bound to perform, and the last part of it, I have no doubt, was particularly painful. He first took a handful of hay, and, having bared the whole upper part of his body, lighted the wisp at the brazier and then passed the blazing mass across his chest and body and over his arms and face. This was but a preliminary, and presently he began to sway backward and forward until one grew dazed with watching him. The drums grew noisier and noisier and the chant louder and wilder. The man himself had become maudlin, his tongue hung from his mouth, and now and then he ejaculated a sound like the inarticulate cry of an animal. He could only totter to the fire, out of which he snatched the balled instrument already described, which he thereupon thrust with a vicious stab into the pit of his stomach, where it was left to hang. A moment after he pulled it out again, and, picking up the piece of stone used before, he drove it with a series of resounding blows into a new place, where it hung, drawing the skin downward with its weight, until a companion pulled it out and the man fell in a heap on the floor."

To-day it is only through the intervention of the United States troops that some of the barbarous ceremonies of the North American Indians are suppressed. The episode of the "Ghost-dance" is fresh in every mind. Instances of self-mutilation, although illustrating this subject, will be discussed at length in Chapter XIV.

Malingerers often endure without flinching the most arduous tests. Supraorbital pressure is generally of little avail, and pinching, pricking, and even incision are useless with these hospital impostors. It is reported that in the City Hospital of St. Louis a negro submitted to the ammonia-test, inhaling this vapor for several hours without showing any signs of sensibility, and made his escape the moment his guard was absent. A contemporary journal says :—

"The obstinacy of resolute impostors seems, indeed, capable of emulating the torture-proof perseverance of religious enthusiasts and such martyrs of patriotism as Mucius Scævola or Grand Master Ruediger of the Teutonic Knights, who refused to reveal the hiding place of his companion even when his captors belabored him with red-hot irons.

"One Basil Rohatzek, suspected of fraudulent enlistment (bounty-jumping, as our volunteers called it), pretended to have been thrown by his horse and to have been permanently disabled by a paralysis of the lower extremities. He dragged himself along in a pitiful manner, and his knees looked somewhat bruised, but he was known to have boasted his ability to procure his discharge somehow or other. One of his tent mates had also seen him fling himself violently and repeatedly on his knees (to procure those questionable bruises), and on the whole there seemed little doubt that the fellow was shamming. All the surgeons who had examined him concurred in that view, and the case was finally referred to his commanding officer, General Colloredo. The impostor was carried to a field hospital in a little Bohemian border town and watched for a couple of weeks, during which he had been twice seen moving his feet in his sleep. Still, the witnesses were not prepared to swear that those changes of position might not have been effected by a movement of the whole body. The suspect stuck to his assertion, and Colloredo, in a fit of irritation, finally summoned a surgeon, who actually placed the feet of the professed paralytic in " aqua fortis," but even this rigorous method availed the cruel surgeon nothing, and he was compelled to advise dismissal from the service.

" The martyrdom of Rohatzek, however, was a mere trifle compared with the ordeal by which the tribunal of Paris tried in vain to extort a confession of the would-be regicide, Damiens. Robert Damiens, a native of Arras, had been exiled as an habitual criminal, and. returning in disguise made an attempt upon the life of Louis XV., January 5, 1757. His dagger pierced the mantle of the King, but merely grazed his neck. Damiens, who had stumbled, was instantly seized and dragged to prison, where a convocation of expert torturers exhausted their ingenuity in the attempt to extort a confession implicating the Jesuits, a conspiracy of Huguenots, etc. But Damiens refused to speak. He could have pleaded his inability to name accomplices who did not exist, but he stuck to his resolution of absolute silence. They singed off his skin by shreds, they wrenched out his teeth and finger-joints, they dragged him about at the end of a rope hitched to a team of stout horses, they sprinkled him from head to foot with acids and seething oil, but Damiens never uttered a sound till his dying groan announced the conclusion of the tragedy."

The apparent indifference to the pain of a major operation is sometimes marvelous, and there are many interesting instances on record. When at the battle of Dresden in 1813 Moreau, seated beside the Emperor Alexander, had both limbs shattered by a French cannon-ball, he did not utter a groan, but asked for a cigar and smoked leisurely while a surgeon amputated one of his members. In a short time his medical attendants expressed the danger and questionability of saving his other limb, and consulted him. In the calmest way the heroic General instructed them to amputate it, again remaining unmoved throughout the operation.

Crompton[a] records a case in which during an amputation of the leg not a sound escaped from the patient's lips, and in three weeks, when it was found necessary to amputate the other leg, the patient endured the operation without an anesthetic, making no show of pain, and only remarking that he thought the saw did not cut well. Crompton quotes another case, in which the patient held a candle with one hand while the operator amputated his other arm at the shoulder-joint. Several instances of self-performed major operations are mentioned in Chapter XIV.

[a] 392, 1887, 143.

Supersensitiveness to Pain.—Quite opposite to the foregoing instances are those cases in which such influences as expectation, naturally inherited nervousness, and genuine supersensitiveness make the slightest pain almost unendurable. In many of these instances the state of the mind and occasionally the time of day have a marked influence. Men noted for their sagacity and courage have been prostrated by fear of pain. Sir Robert Peel, a man of acknowledged superior physical and intellectual power, could not even bear the touch of Brodie's finger to his fractured clavicle. The authors know of an instance of a pugilist who had elicited admiration by his ability to stand punishment and his indomitable courage in his combats, but who fainted from the puncture of a small boil on his neck.

The relation of pain to shock has been noticed by many writers.[846] Before the days of anesthesia, such cases as the following, reported by Sir Astley Cooper, seem to have been not unusual : A brewer's servant, a man of middle age and robust frame, suffered much agony for several days from a thecal abscess, occasioned by a splinter of wood beneath the thumb. A few seconds after the matter was discharged by an incision, the man raised himself by a convulsive effort from his bed and instantly expired.

It is a well-known fact that powerful nerve-irritation, such as produces shock, is painless, and this accounts for the fact that wounds received during battle are not painful.

Leyden of Berlin showed to his class at the Charité Hospital a number of hysteric women with a **morbid desire for operation without an anesthetic.** Such persons do not seem to experience pain, and, on the contrary, appear to have genuine pleasure in pain. In illustration, Leyden showed a young lady who during a hysteric paroxysm had suffered a serious fracture of the jaw, injuring the facial artery, and necessitating quite an extensive operation. The facial and carotid arteries had to be ligated and part of the inferior maxilla removed, but the patient insisted upon having the operations performed without an anesthetic, and afterward informed the operator that she had experienced great pleasure throughout the whole procedure.

Pain as a Means of Sexual Enjoyment.—There is a form of sexual perversion in which the pervert takes delight in being subjected to degrading, humiliating, and cruel acts on the part of his or her associate. It was named **masochism** from Sacher-Masoch, an Austrian novelist, whose works describe this form of perversion. The victims are said to experience peculiar pleasure at the sight of a rival who has obtained the favor of their mistress, and will even receive blows and lashes from the rival with a voluptuous mixture of pain and pleasure. Masochism corresponds to the passivism of Stefanowski, and is the opposite of sadism, in which the pleasure is derived from inflicting pain on the object of affection. Krafft-Ebing cites several instances of masochism.

Although the enjoyment and frenzy of **flagellation** are well known, its pleasures are not derived from the pain but by the undoubted stimulation offered to the sexual centers by the castigation. The delight of the heroines of flagellation, Maria Magdalena of Pazzi and Elizabeth of Genton, in being whipped on the naked loins, and thus calling up sensual and lascivious fancies, clearly shows the significance of flagellation as a sexual excitant. It is said that when Elizabeth of Genton was being whipped she believed herself united with her ideal and would cry out in the loudest tones of the joys of love.

There is undoubtedly a sympathetic communication between the ramifying nerves of the skin of the loins and the lower portion of the spinal cord which contains the sexual centers. Recently, in cases of dysmenorrhea, amenorrhea, dysmenorrhagia, and like sexual disorders, massage or gentle flagellation of the parts contiguous with the genitalia and pelvic viscera has been recommended. Taxil is the authority for the statement that just before the sexual act rakes sometimes have themselves flagellated or pricked until the blood flows in order to stimulate their diminished sexual power. Rhodiginus, Bartholinus, and other older physicians mention individuals in whom severe castigation was a prerequisite of copulation. As a ritual custom flagellation is preserved to the present day by some sects.

Before leaving the subject of flagellation it should be stated that among the serious after-results of this practice as a disciplinary means, fatal emphysema, severe hemorrhage, and shock have been noticed. There are many cases of death from corporal punishment by flogging. Ballingal[a] records the death of a soldier from flogging; Davidson[b] has reported a similar case, and there is a death from the same cause cited in the Edinburgh Medical and Surgical Journal for 1846.

Idiosyncrasy is a peculiarity of constitution whereby an individual is affected by external agents in a different manner from others. Begin[c] defines idiosyncrasy as the predominance of an organ, of a viscus, or a system of organs. This definition does not entirely grasp the subject. An idiosyncrasy is something inherent in the organization of the individual, of which we only see the manifestation when proper causes are set in action. We do not attempt to explain the susceptibility of certain persons to certain foods and certain exposures. We know that such is the fact. According to Begin's idea, there is scarcely any separation between idiosyncrasy and temperament, whereas from what would appear to be sound reasoning, based on the physiology of the subject, a very material difference exists.

Idiosyncrasies may be congenital, hereditary, or acquired, and, if acquired, may be only temporary. Some, purely of mental origin, are often readily cured. One individual may synchronously possess an idiosyncrasy of the digestive, circulatory, and nervous systems. Striking examples of transitory or temporary idiosyncrasies are seen in pregnant women.

a Monthly Journal of Medical Sciences, London, 1846.   b 548, 1853.
c "Physiologie Pathologique." Paris, 1828.

There are certain so-called antipathies that in reality are idiosyncrasies, and which are due to peculiarities of the ideal and emotional centers. The organ of sense in question and the center that takes cognizance of the image brought to it are in no way disordered. In some cases the antipathy or the idiosyncrasy develops to such an extent as to be in itself a species of mono-mania. The fear-maladies, or "phobias," as they are called, are examples of this class, and, belonging properly under temporary mental derangements, the same as hallucinations or delusions, will be spoken of in another chapter.

Possibly the most satisfactory divisions under which to group the material on this subject collected from literature are into examples of idiosyncrasies in which, although the effect is a mystery, the sense is perceptible and the cause distinctly defined and known, and those in which sensibility is latent. The former class includes all the peculiar antipathies which are brought about through the special senses, while the latter groups all those strange instances in which, without the slightest antipathy on the part of the subject, a certain food or drug, after ingestion, produces an untoward effect.

The first examples of idiosyncrasies to be noticed will be those manifested through **the sense of smell.** On the authority of Spigelius, whose name still survives in the nomenclature of the anatomy of the liver, Mackenzie quotes an extraordinary case in a Roman Cardinal, Oliver Caraffa, who could not endure the smell of a rose. This is confirmed from personal observation by another writer, Pierius,[a] who adds that the Cardinal was obliged every year to shut himself up during the rose season, and guards were stationed at the gates of his palace to stop any visitors who might be wearing the dreadful flower. It is, of course, possible that in this case the rose may not have caused the disturbance, and as it is distinctly stated that it was the smell to which the Cardinal objected, we may fairly conclude that what annoyed him was simply a manifestation of rose-fever excited by the pollen. There is also an instance of a noble Venetian who was always confined to his palace during the rose season. However, in this connection Sir Kenelm Digby relates that so obnoxious was a rose to Lady Heneage, that she blistered her cheek while accidentally lying on one while she slept. Ledelius [b] records the description of a woman who fainted before a red rose, although she was accustomed to wear white ones in her hair. Cremer describes a Bishop who died of the smell of a rose from what might be called "aromatic pain."

The organ of smell is in intimate relation with the brain and the organs of taste and sight; and its action may thus disturb that of the esophagus, the stomach, the diaphragm, the intestines, the organs of generation, etc. Odorous substances have occasioned syncope, stupor, nausea, vomiting, and sometimes death. It is said that the Hindoos, and some classes who eat nothing but vegetables, are intensely nauseated by the odors of European tables, and for this reason they are incapable of serving as dining-room servants.

a "Hieroglyphica." Francofurti, 1678.   b 104, dec., ii., and ann. x., obs. 8.

Fabricius Hildanus [334] mentions a person who fainted from the odor of vinegar. The Éphemerides contains an instance of a soldier who fell insensible from the odor of a peony. Wagner knew a man who was made ill by the odor of bouillon of crabs. The odors of blood, meat, and fat are repugnant to herbivorous animals. It is a well-known fact that horses detest the odor of blood.

Schneider,[a] the father of rhinology, mentions a woman in whom the odor of orange-flowers produced syncope. Odier has known a woman who was affected with aphonia whenever exposed to the odor of musk, but who immediately recovered after taking a cold bath. Dejean has mentioned a man who could not tolerate an atmosphere of cherries. Highmore knew a man in whom the slightest smell of musk caused headache followed by epistaxis. Lanzonius [570] gives an account of a valiant soldier who could neither bear the sight nor smell of an ordinary pink. There is an instance on record in which the odor coming from a walnut tree excited epilepsy. It is said that one of the secretaries of Francis I. was forced to stop his nostrils with bread if apples were on the table. He would faint if one was held near his nose. Schenck [718] says that the noble family of Fystates in Aquitaine had a similar peculiarity—an innate hatred of apples. Bruyerinus knew a girl of sixteen who could not bear the smell of bread, the slightest particle of which she would detect by its odor. She lived almost entirely on milk. Bierling [210] mentions an antipathy to the smell of musk, and there is a case on record in which it caused convulsions. Boerhaave bears witness that the odor of cheese caused nasal hemorrhage. Whytt mentions an instance in which tobacco became repugnant to a woman each time she conceived, but after delivery this aversion changed to almost an appetite for tobacco fumes. Panaroli [617] mentions an instance of sickness caused by the smell of sassafras, and there is also a record of a person who fell helpless at the smell of cinnamon. Wagner had a patient who detested the odor of citron. Ignorant of this repugnance, he prescribed a potion in which there was water of balm-mint, of an odor resembling citron. As soon as the patient took the first dose he became greatly agitated and much nauseated, and this did not cease until Wagner repressed the balm-mint. There is reported [b] the case of a young woman, rather robust, otherwise normal, who always experienced a desire to go to stool after being subjected to any nasal irritation sufficient to excite sneezing.

It has already been remarked that individuals and animals have their special odors, certain of which are very agreeable to some people and extremely unpleasant to others. Many persons are not able to endure the emanations from cats, rats, mice, etc., and the mere fact of one of these animals being in their vicinity is enough to provoke distressing symptoms. Mlle. Contat, the celebrated French actress, was not able to endure the odor

a "De osse cribriformi," 367.   b 302, xxiii., 501.

of a hare. Stanislaus, King of Poland and Duke of Lorraine, found it impossible to tolerate the smell of a cat. The Ephemerides mentions the odor of a little garden-frog as causing epilepsy. Ab Heers [409] mentions a similar anomaly, fainting caused by the smell of eels. Habit had rendered Haller insensible to the odor of putrefying cadavers, but according to Zimmerman the odor of the perspiration of old people, not perceptible to others, was intolerable to him at a distance of ten or twelve paces. He also had an extreme aversion for cheese. According to Dejan, Gaubius knew a man who was unable to remain in a room with women, having a great repugnance to the female odor. Strange as it may seem, some individuals are incapable of appreciating certain odors. Blumenbach mentions an Englishman whose sense of smell was otherwise very acute, but he was unable to perceive the perfume of the mignonette.

The impressions which come to us through the **sense of hearing** cause sensations agreeable or disagreeable, but even in this sense we see marked examples of idiosyncrasies and antipathies to various sounds and tones. In some individuals the sensations in one ear differ from those of the other. Everard Home [629] has cited several examples, and Heidmann of Vienna has treated two musicians, one of whom always perceived in the affected ear, during damp weather, tones an octave lower than in the other ear. The other musician perceived tones an octave higher in the affected ear. Cheyne [a] is quoted as mentioning a case in which, when the subject heard the noise of a drum, blood jetted from the veins with considerable force. Sauvages [b] has seen a young man in whom intense headache and febrile paroxysm were only relieved by the noise from a beaten drum. Esparron has mentioned an infant in whom an ataxic fever was established by the noise of this instrument. Ephemerides contains an account of a young man who became nervous and had the sense of suffocation when he heard the noise made by sweeping. Zimmerman speaks of a young girl who had convulsions when she heard the rustling of oiled silk. Boyle, the father of chemistry, could not conquer an aversion he had to the sound of water running through pipes. A gentleman of the Court of the Emperor Ferdinand suffered epistaxis when he heard a cat mew. La Mothe Le Vayer could not endure the sounds of musical instruments, although he experienced pleasurable sensations when he heard a clap of thunder. It is said that a chaplain in England [629] always had a sensation of cold at the top of his head when he read the 53d chapter of Isaiah and certain verses of the Kings. There was an unhappy wight who could not hear his own name pronounced without being thrown into convulsions.[c] Marguerite of Valois, sister of Francis I., could never utter the words "mort" or "petite verole," such a horrible aversion had she to death and small-pox. According to Campani, the Chevalier Alcantara could never say "lana," or words pertaining to woolen clothing. Hippo-

a 302, xxiii., 503.   b "Nosol. Method." Paris, 1771.   c 110 v., obs. 15, 60.

crates says that a certain Nicanor had the greatest horror of the sound of the flute at night, although it delighted him in the daytime. Rousseau[a] reports a Gascon in whom incontinence of urine was produced by the sound of a bagpipe. Frisch, Managetta, and Rousse speak of a man in whom the same effect was produced by the sound of a hurdy-gurdy. Even Shakespeare alludes to the effects of the sound of bagpipes. Tissot mentions a case in which music caused epileptic convulsions, and Forestus[348] mentions a beggar who had convulsions at the sound of a wooden trumpet similar to those used by children in play. Rousseau mentions music as causing convulsive laughter in a woman. Bayle mentions a woman who fainted at the sound of a bell. Paullini cites an instance of vomiting caused by music, and Marcellus Donatus mentions swooning from the same cause. Many people are unable to bear the noise caused by the grating of a pencil on a slate, the filing of a saw, the squeak of a wheel turning about an axle, the rubbing of pieces of paper together, and certain similar sounds. Some persons find the tones of music very disagreeable, and some animals, particularly dogs, are unable to endure it. In Albinus the younger the slightest perceptible tones were sufficient to produce an inexplicable anxiety. There was a certain woman of fifty[b] who was fond of the music of the clarionet and flute, but was not able to listen to the sound of a bell or tambourine. Frank knew a man who ran out of church at the beginning of the sounds of an organ, not being able to tolerate them. Pope could not imagine music producing any pleasure. The harmonica has been noticed to produce fainting in females. Fischer[c] says that music provokes sexual frenzy in elephants. Gutfeldt[d] speaks of a peculiar idiosyncrasy of sleep produced by hearing music. Delisle[e] mentions a young person who during a whole year passed pieces of ascarides and tenia, during which time he could not endure music.

Autenreith[f] mentions the vibrations of a loud noise tickling the fauces to such an extent as to provoke vomiting. There are some emotional people who are particularly susceptible to certain expressions. The widow of Jean Calas always fell in a faint when she heard the words of the death-decree sounded on the street. There was a Hanoverian officer in the Indian war against Typoo-Saib, a good and brave soldier, who would feel sick if he heard the word "tiger" pronounced. It was said that he had experienced the ravages of this beast.

The therapeutic value of music has long been known. For ages warriors have been led to battle to the sounds of martial strains. David charmed away Saul's evil spirit with his harp. Horace in his 32d Ode, Book 1, concludes his address to the lyre :—

> " O laborum.
> Dulce lenimen, mihicumque salve,
> Rite vocanti ;"

[a] " Dict. de Musique."   [b] 302, xxiii.   [c] 559, 1803, 7.
[d] 159, 1806.   [e] 476, 1828-9, 720.   [f] 181, 1023.

or, as Kiessling of Berlin interprets :—

" O laborum,
Dulce lenimen medicumque, salve,
Rite vocanti.''

—" O, of our troubles the sweet, the healing sedative, etc." Homer, Plutarch, Theophrastus, and Galen say that music cures rheumatism, the pests, and stings of reptiles, etc.   Diemerbroeck,[304] Bonet, Baglivi, Kercher, and Desault mention the efficacy of melody in phthisis, gout, hydrophobia, the bites of venomous reptiles, etc.   There is a case in the Lancet[a] of a patient in convulsions who was cured in the paroxysm by hearing the tones of music. Before the French Academy of Sciences in 1708, and again in 1718, there was an instance of a dancing-master stricken with violent fever and in a condition of delirium, who recovered his senses and health on hearing melodious music.   There is little doubt of the therapeutic value of music, but particularly do we find its value in instances of neuroses.   The inspiration offered by music is well-known, and it is doubtless a stimulant to the intellectual work.   Bacon, Milton, Warburton, and Alfieri needed music to stimulate them in their labors, and it is said that Bourdaloue always played an air on the violin before preparing to write.

According to the American Medico-Surgical Bulletin, " Professor Tarchanoff of Saint Petersburg has been investigating the influence of music upon man and other animals.   The subject is by no means a new one.   In recent times Dagiel and Féré have investigated the effect of music upon the respirations, the pulse, and the muscular system in man.   Professor Tarchanoff made use of the ergograph of Mosso, and found that if the fingers were completely fatigued, either by voluntary efforts or by electric excitation, to the point of being incapable of making any mark except a straight line on the registering cylinder, music had the power of making the fatigue disappear, and the finger placed in the ergograph again commenced to mark lines of different heights, according to the amount of excitation.   It was also found that music of a sad and lugubrious character had the opposite effect, and could check or entirely inhibit the contractions.   Professor Tarchanoff does not profess to give any positive explanation of these facts, but he inclines to the view that ' the voluntary muscles, being furnished with excitomotor and depressant fibers, act in relation to the music similarly to the heart—that is to say, that joyful music resounds along the excitomotor fibers, and sad music along the depressant or inhibitory fibers.'   Experiments on dogs showed that music was capable of increasing the elimination of carbonic acid by 16.7 per cent., and of increasing the consumption of oxygen by 20.1 per cent.   It was also found that music increased the functional activity of the skin.   Professor Tarchanoff claims as the result of these experiments that music may fairly be regarded as a serious therapeutic agent, and that it exer-

a 476, 1828–9, 720.

cises a genuine and considerable influence over the functions of the body. Facts of this kind are in no way surprising, and are chiefly of interest as presenting some physiologic basis for phenomena that are sufficiently obvious. The influence of the war-chant upon the warrior is known even to savage tribes. We are accustomed to regard this influence simply as an ordinary case of psychic stimuli producing physiologic effects.

" Professor Tarchanoff evidently prefers to regard the phenomena as being all upon the same plane, namely, that of physiology ; and until we know the difference between mind and body, and the principles of their interaction, it is obviously impossible to controvert this view successfully. From the immediately practical point of view we should not ignore the possible value of music in some states of disease. In melancholia and hysteria it is probably capable of being used with benefit, and it is worth bearing in mind in dealing with insomnia. Classical scholars will not forget that the singing of birds was tried as a remedy to overcome the insomnia of Mæcenas. Music is certainly a good antidote to the pernicious habit of introspection and self-analysis, which is often a curse both of the hysteric and of the highly cultured. It would seem obviously preferable to have recourse to music of a lively and cheerful character."

Idiosyncrasies of the **visual organs** are generally quite rare. It is well-known that among some of the lower animals, *e. g.*, the turkey-cocks, buffaloes, and elephants, the color red is unendurable. Buchner[a] and Tissot[b] mention a young boy who had a paroxysm if he viewed anything red. Certain individuals become nauseated when they look for a long time on irregular lines or curves, as, for examples, in caricatures. Many of the older examples of idiosyncrasies of color are nothing more than instances of color-blindness, which in those times was unrecognized. Prochaska[c] knew a woman who in her youth became unconscious at the sight of beet-root, although in her later years she managed to conquer this antipathy, but was never able to eat the vegetable in question. One of the most remarkable forms of idiosyncrasy on record is that of a student who was deprived of his senses by the very sight of an old woman. On one occasion he was carried out from a party in a dying state, caused, presumably, by the abhorred aspect of the chaperons. The Count of Caylus[d] was always horror-stricken at the sight of a Capuchin friar. He cured himself by a wooden image dressed in the costume of this order placed in his room and constantly before his view. It is common to see persons who faint at the sight of blood. Analogous are the individuals who feel nausea in an hospital ward.

All Robert Boyle's philosophy could not make him endure the sight of a spider, although he had no such aversion to toads, venomous snakes, etc. Paré mentions a man who fainted at the sight of an eel, and another who had convulsions at the sight of a carp. There is a record of a young lady

---

[a] " De rachitide perfecta." 1754.   [b] "De l'épilepsie."   [c] "Annot. Acad."   [d] 302, xxiii.

in France who fainted on seeing a boiled lobster.   Millingen [a] cites the case of a man who fell into convulsions whenever he saw a spider.   A waxen one was made, which equally terrified him.   When he recovered, his error was pointed out to him, and the wax figure was placed in his hand without caus- ing dread, and henceforth the living insect no longer disturbed him.   Amatus Lusitanus [119] relates the case of a monk who fainted when he beheld a rose, and never quitted his cell when that flower was in bloom.   Scaliger, the great scholar, who had been a soldier a considerable portion of his life, confesses that he could not look on a water-cress without shuddering, and remarks: " I, who despise not only iron, but even thunderbolts, who in two sieges (in one of which I commanded) was the only one who did not com- plain of the food as unfit and horrible to eat, am seized with such a shudder- ing horror at the sight of a water-cress that I am forced to go away." [b] One of his children was in the same plight as regards the inoffensive vegetable, cabbage.   Scaliger [c] also speaks of one of his kinsmen who fainted at the sight of a lily.   Vaughheim, a great huntsman of Hanover, would faint at the sight of a roasted pig.   Some individuals have been disgusted at the sight of eggs.   There is an account of a sensible man who was terrified at the sight of a hedgehog, and for two years was tormented by a sensation as though one was gnawing at his bowels.   According to Boyle, Lord Barry- more, a veteran warrior and a person of strong mind, swooned at the sight of tansy.   The Duke d'Épernon swooned on beholding a leveret, although a hare did not produce the same effect.   Schenck tells of a man who swooned at the sight of pork.   The Ephemerides contains an account of a person who lost his voice at the sight of a crab, and also cites cases of antipathy to partridges, a white hen, to a serpent, and to a toad.   Lehman speaks of an antipathy to horses ; and in his observations Lyser [498] has noticed aversion to the color purple.   It is a strange fact that the three greatest generals of recent years, Wellington, Napoleon, and Roberts, could never tolerate the sight of a cat, and Henry III. of France could not bear this animal in his room.   We learn [d] of a Dane of herculean frame who had a horror of cats. He was asked to a supper at which, by way of a practical joke, a live cat was put on the table in a covered dish.   The man began to sweat and shudder with- out knowing why, and when the cat was shown he killed his host in a paroxysm of terror.   Another man could not even see the hated form even in a picture without breaking into a cold sweat and feeling a sense of oppres- sion about the heart.   Quercetanus [658] and Smetius mention fainting at the sight of cats.   Marshal d'Abret was supposed to be in violent fear of a pig.

As to **idiosyncrasies of the sense of touch,** it is well known that some people cannot handle velvet or touch the velvety skin of a peach without

---

a " Curiosities of Medical Experience," London, 1837, ii., 246.
b " De Subtilat. Exercit." Hanover, 1634.   c " Exercit.," 142.
d 570, dec. i., ann. iii., obs. 46.

having disagreeable and chilly sensations come over them.   Prochaska knew a man who vomited the moment he touched a peach, and many people, otherwise very fond of this fruit, are unable to touch it.   The Ephemerides speaks of a peculiar idiosyncrasy of skin in the axilla of a certain person, which if tickled would provoke vomiting.   It is occasionally stated in the older writings that some persons have an idiosyncrasy as regards the phases of the sun and moon.   Baillou speaks of a woman who fell unconscious at sunset and did not recover till it reappeared on the horizon.   The celebrated Chancellor Bacon, according to Mead, was very delicate, and was accustomed to fall into a state of great feebleness at every moon-set without any other imaginable cause.   He never recovered from his swooning until the moon reappeared.

Nothing is more common than the **idiosyncrasy** which certain people display **for certain foods**.   The trite proverb, " What is one man's meat is another man's poison," is a genuine truth, and is exemplified by hundreds of instances.   Many people are unable to eat fish without subsequent disagreeable symptoms.   Prominent among the causes of urticaria are oysters, crabs, and other shell fish, strawberries, raspberries, and other fruits.   The abundance of literature on this subject makes an exhaustive collection of data impossible, and only a few of the prominent and striking instances can be reported.

Amatus Lusitanus [119] speaks of vomiting and diarrhea occurring each time a certain Spaniard ate meat.   Haller knew a person who was purged violently by syrup of roses.   The son of one of the friends of Wagner would vomit immediately after the ingestion of any substance containing honey.   Bayle [a] has mentioned a person so susceptible to honey that by a plaster of this substance placed upon the skin this untoward effect was produced.   Whytt knew a woman who was made sick by the slightest bit of nutmeg.   Tissot [b] observed vomiting in one of his friends after the ingestion of the slightest amount of sugar.   Ritte [452] mentions a similar instance.   Roose [c] has seen vomiting produced in a woman by the slightest dose of distilled water of linden.   There is also mentioned a person in whom orange-flower water produced the same effect.   Dejean cites a case in which honey taken internally or applied externally acted like poison.   It is said that the celebrated Haen [d] would always have convulsions after eating half a dozen strawberries.   Earle and Halifax attended a child for kidney-irritation produced by strawberries, and this was the invariable result of the ingestion of this fruit.   The authors personally know of a family the male members of which for several generations could not eat strawberries without symptoms of poisoning.   The female members were exempt from the idiosyncrasy.   A little boy of this family was killed by eating a single berry.   Whytt mentions a woman of delicate constitution and great sensibility of the digestive tract in whom foods difficult

a " De utilitat. physic. experiment."   b " Maladies des Nerfs."
c " Ueber die Krankheiten der Gesunden."   d 302, xxiii., 499.

of digestion provoked spasms, which were often followed by syncopes. Bayle describes a man who vomited violently after taking coffee. Wagner mentions a person in whom a most insignificant dose of manna had the same effect. Preslin speaks of a woman who invariably had a hemorrhage after swallowing a small quantity of vinegar. According to Zimmerman, some people are unable to wash their faces on account of untoward symptoms. According to Gaubius, the juice of a citron applied to the skin of one of his acquaintances produced violent rigors.

Brasavolus says that Julia, wife of Frederick, King of Naples, had such an aversion to meat that she could not carry it to her mouth without fainting. The anatomist Gavard was not able to eat apples without convulsions and vomiting. It is said that Erasmus was made ill by the ingestion of fish ; but this same philosopher, who was cured of a malady by laughter, expressed his appreciation by an elegy on the folly. There is a record of a person who could not eat almonds without a scarlet rash immediately appearing upon the face. Marcellus Donatus knew a young man who could not eat an **egg** without his lips swelling and purple spots appearing on his face. Smetius [a] mentions a person in whom the ingestion of fried eggs was often followed by syncope. Brunton [b] has seen a case of violent vomiting and purging after the slightest bit of egg. On one occasion this person was induced to eat a small morsel of cake on the statement that it contained no egg, and, although fully believing the words of his host, he subsequently developed prominent symptoms, due to the trace of egg that was really in the cake. A letter from a distinguished *littérateur* to Sir Morell Mackenzie gives a striking example of the idiosyncrasy to eggs transmitted through four generations. Being from such a reliable source, it has been deemed advisable to quote the account in full : " My daughter tells me that you are interested in the ill-effects which the eating of eggs has upon her, upon me, and upon my father before us. I believe my grandfather, as well as my father, could not eat eggs with impunity. As to my father himself, he is nearly eighty years old ; he has not touched an egg since he was a young man ; he can, therefore, give no precise or reliable account of the symptoms the eating of eggs produce in him. But it was not the mere ' stomach-ache ' that ensued, but much more immediate and alarming disturbances. As for me, the peculiarity was discovered when I was a spoon-fed child. On several occasions it was noticed (that is my mother's account) that I felt ill without apparent cause ; afterward it was recollected that a small part of a yolk of an egg had been given to me. Eclaircissement came immediately after taking a single spoonful of egg. I fell into such an alarming state that the doctor was sent for. The effect seems to have been just the same that it produces upon my daughter now,—something that suggested brain-congestion and convulsions. From time to time, as a boy and a young man, I have eaten an egg by way of try-

a "Miscellan.," etc., 566.   b 643, 1885, ii., 113.

ing it again, but always with the same result—a feeling that I had been poisoned; and yet all the while I liked eggs. Then I never touched them for years. Later I tried again, and I find the ill-effects are gradually wearing off. With my daughter it is different; she, I think, becomes more susceptible as time goes on, and the effect upon her is more violent than in my case at any time. Sometimes an egg has been put with coffee unknown to her, and she has been seen immediately afterward with her face alarmingly changed—eyes swollen and wild, the face crimson, the look of apoplexy. This is her own account: 'An egg in any form causes within a few minutes great uneasiness and restlessness, the throat becomes contracted and painful, the face crimson, and the veins swollen. These symptoms have been so severe as to suggest that serious consequences might follow.' To this I may add that in her experience and my own, the newer the egg, the worse the consequences."

Hutchinson [a] speaks of a Member of Parliament who had an idiosyncrasy as regards **parsley**. After the ingestion of this herb in food he always had alarming attacks of sickness and pain in the abdomen, attended by swelling of the tongue and lips and lividity of the face. This same man could not take the smallest quantity of honey, and certain kinds of fruit always poisoned him. There was a collection of instances of idiosyncrasy in the British Medical Journal, 1859, which will be briefly given in the following lines: One patient could not eat **rice** in any shape without extreme distress. From the description given of his symptoms, spasmodic asthma seemed to be the cause of his discomfort. On one occasion when at a dinner-party he felt the symptoms of rice-poisoning come on, and, although he had partaken of no dish ostensibly containing rice, was, as usual, obliged to retire from the table. Upon investigation it appeared that some white soup with which he had commenced his meal had been thickened with ground rice. As in the preceding case there was another gentleman who could not eat rice without a sense of suffocation. On one occasion he took lunch with a friend in chambers, partaking only of simple bread and cheese and bottled beer. On being seized with the usual symptoms of rice-poisoning he informed his friend of his peculiarity of constitution, and the symptoms were explained by the fact that a few grains of rice had been put into each bottle of beer for the purpose of exciting a secondary fermentation. The same author speaks of a gentleman under treatment for stricture who could not eat **figs** without experiencing the most unpleasant formication of the palate and fauces. The fine dust from split **peas** caused the same sensation, accompanied with running at the nose; it was found that the father of the patient suffered from hay-fever in certain seasons. He also says a certain young lady after eating eggs suffered from swelling of the tongue and throat, accompanied by "alarming illness," and there is recorded in the same paragraph a history of another young girl in

a 166, iv., 78.

whom the ingestion of honey, and especially honey-comb, produced swelling of the tongue, frothing of the mouth, and blueness of the fingers. The authors know of a gentleman in whom sneezing is provoked on the ingestion of chocolate in any form. There was another instance—in a member of the medical profession—who suffered from urticaria after eating **veal**. Veal has the reputation of being particularly indigestible, and the foregoing instance of the production of urticaria from its use is doubtless not an uncommon one.

Overton [a] cites a striking case of constitutional peculiarity or idiosyncrasy in which **wheat flour** in any form, the staff of life, an article hourly prayed for by all Christian nations as the first and most indispensable of earthly blessings, proved to one unfortunate individual a prompt and dreadful poison. The patient's name was David Waller, and he was born in Pittsylvania County, Va., about the year 1780. He was the eighth child of his parents, and, together with all his brothers and sisters, was stout and healthy. At the time of observation Waller was about fifty years of age. He had dark hair, gray eyes, dark complexion, was of bilious and irascible temperament, well formed, muscular and strong, and in all respects healthy as any man, with the single exception of his peculiar idiosyncrasy. He had been the subject of but few diseases, although he was attacked by the epidemic of 1816. From the history of his parents and an inquiry into the health of his ancestry, nothing could be found which could establish the fact of heredity in his peculiar disposition. Despite every advantage of stature, constitution, and heredity, David Waller was through life, from his cradle to his grave, the victim of what is possibly a unique idiosyncrasy of constitution. In his own words he declared : "Of two equal quantities of tartar and wheat flour, not more than a dose of the former, he would rather swallow the tartar than the wheat flour." If he ate flour in any form or however combined, in the smallest quantity, in two minutes or less he would have painful itching over the whole body, accompanied by severe colic and tormina in the bowels, great sickness in the stomach, and continued vomiting, which he declared was ten times as distressing as the symptoms caused by the ingestion of tartar emetic. In about ten minutes after eating the flour the itching would be greatly intensified, especially about the head, face, and eyes, but tormenting all parts of the body, and not to be appeased. These symptoms continued for two days with intolerable violence, and only declined on the third day and ceased on the tenth. In the convalescence, the lungs were affected, he coughed, and in expectoration raised great quantities of phlegm, and really resembled a phthisical patient. At this time he was confined to his room with great weakness, similar to that of a person recovering from an asthmatic attack. The mere smell of wheat produced distressing symptoms in a minor degree, and for this reason he could not, without suffering, go into a mill or house where the smallest quantity of wheat flour was kept. His condition was the same from the earliest times, and he was laid out for dead when an infant at the breast, after being fed with " pap " thickened with wheat flour. Overton remarks that a case of constitutional peculiarity so little in harmony with the condition of other men could not be received upon vague or feeble evidence, and it is therefore stated that Waller was known to the society in which he lived as an honest and truthful man. One of his female neighbors, not believing in his infirmity, but considering it only a whim, put a small quantity of flour in the soup which she gave him to eat at her table, stating that it contained no flour, and as a consequence of the deception he was bed-ridden for ten days with his usual symptoms. It was also stated that Waller was never subjected to militia duty because it was found on full examination of his infirmity that he could not live upon the rations of a soldier, into which wheat flour enters as a necessary ingredient. In explanation of this strange departure from the condition of other men, Waller himself gave a reason which was deemed equivalent in value to any of the others offered. It was as follows: His father being a man in humble circumstances in life, at the time of his birth had no wheat with which to make flour, although his mother during gestation "longed" for wheat-bread. The father, being a kind husband and responsive to the duty imposed by the condition of his wife, procured from one of his opulent neighbors a bag of wheat and sent it to the mill to be ground. The mother was given much uneasiness by an unexpected delay at the mill, and by the time the flour arrived her strong appetite for wheat-bread had in a great degree subsided. Notwithstanding this, she caused some flour to be immediately baked into bread and ate it, but not so freely as she had expected. The bread thus taken caused intense vomiting and made her violently and painfully ill, after which for a considerable time she loathed bread. These facts have been ascribed as the cause of the lamentable infirmity under which the man labored, as no other peculiarity or impression in her gestation was noticed. In addition it may be stated that for the purpose of avoiding the smell of flour Waller was in the habit of carrying camphor in his pocket and using snuff, for if he did not smell the flour, however much might be near him, it was as harmless to him as to other men.

The authors know of a case in which the eating of any raw fruit would produce in a lady symptoms of asthma ; cooked fruit had no such effect.

Food-Superstitions.—The superstitious abhorrence and antipathy to various articles of food that have been prevalent from time to time in the history of the human race are of considerable interest and well deserve some mention here. A writer in a prominent journal has studied this subject with the following result :—

" From the days of Adam and Eve to the present time there has been not only forbidden fruit, but forbidden meats and vegetables. For one reason or another people have resolutely refused to eat any and all kinds of flesh, fish, fowl, fruits, and plants. Thus, the apple, the pear, the strawberry, the quince, the bean, the onion, the leek, the asparagus, the woodpecker, the pigeon, the goose, the deer, the bear, the turtle, and the eel—these, to name only a few eatables, have been avoided as if unwholesome or positively injurious to health and digestion.

"As we all know, the Jews have long had an hereditary antipathy to **pork.** On the other hand, swine's flesh was highly esteemed by the ancient Greeks and Romans. This fact is revealed by the many references to pig as a dainty bit of food. At the great festival held annually in honor of Demeter, roast pig was the *pièce de résistance* in the bill of fare, because the pig was the sacred animal of Demeter. Aristophanes in 'The Frogs' makes one of the characters hint that some of the others 'smell of roast pig.' These people undoubtedly had been at the festival (known as the Thesmophoria) and had eaten freely of roast pig. Those who took part in another Greek mystery or festival (known as the Eleusinia) abstained from certain food, and above all from beans.

"Again, as we all know, mice are esteemed in China and in some parts of India. But the ancient Egyptians, Greeks, and Jews abhorred mice and would not touch mouse-meat. Rats and field-mice were sacred in Old Egypt, and were not to be eaten on this account. So, too, in some parts of Greece, the mouse was the sacred animal of Apollo, and mice were fed in his temples. The chosen people were forbidden to eat 'the weasel, and the mouse, and the tortoise after his kind.' These came under the designation of unclean animals, which were to be avoided.

"But people have abstained from eating kinds of flesh which could not be called unclean. For example, the people of Thebes, as Herodotus tells us, abstained from sheep. Then, the ancients used to abstain from certain vegetables. In his 'Roman Questions' Plutarch asks: 'Why do the Latins abstain strictly from the flesh of the woodpecker?' In order to answer Plutarch's question correctly it is necessary to have some idea of the peculiar custom and belief called '**totemism.**' There is a stage of society in which people claim descent from and kinship with beasts, birds, vegetables, and other objects. This object, which is a 'totem,' or family mark, they religiously abstain from eating. The members of the tribe are divided into clans or stocks, each of which takes the name of some animal, plant, or object, as the bear, the buffalo, the woodpecker, the asparagus, and so forth. No member of the bear family would dare to eat bear-meat, but he has no objection to eating buffalo steak. Even the marriage law is based on this belief, and no man whose family name is Wolf may marry a woman whose family name is also Wolf.

"In a general way it may be said that almost all our food prohibitions spring from the extraordinary custom generally called totemism. Mr. Swan, who was missionary for many years in the Congo Free State, thus describes the custom : ' If I were to ask the Yeke people why they do not eat zebra flesh, they would reply, '*Chijila,*' *i.e.,* ' It is a thing to which we have an antipathy ; ' or better, ' It is one of the things which our fathers taught us not to eat.' So it seems the word ' Bashilang ' means ' the people who have an antipathy to the leopard ; ' the ' Bashilamba,' ' those who have an antipathy to the dog,' and the ' Bashilanzefu,' ' those who have an antipathy to the elephant.' In other words, the members of these stocks refuse to eat their totems, the zebra, the leopard, or the elephant, from which they take their names.

" The survival of antipathy to certain foods was found among people as highly civilized as the Egyptians, the Greeks, and the Romans. Quite a list of animals whose flesh was forbidden might be drawn up. For example, in Old Egypt the sheep could not be eaten in Thebes, nor the goat in Mendes, nor the cat in Bubastis, nor the crocodile at Ombos, nor the rat, which was sacred to Ra, the sun-god. However, the people of one place had no scruples about eating the forbidden food of another place. And this often led to religious disputes.

" Among the vegetables avoided as food by the Egyptians may be mentioned the onion, the garlic, and the leek. Lucian says that the inhabitants of Pelusium adored the onion. According to Pliny the Egyptians relished the leek and the onion. Juvenal exclaims : ' Surely a very religious nation, and a blessed place, where every garden is overrun with gods ! ' The survivals of totemism among the ancient Greeks are very interesting. Families named after animals and plants were not uncommon. One Athenian *gens,* the Ioxidæ, had for its ancestral plant the asparagus. One Roman *gens,* the Piceni, took a woodpecker for its totem, and every member of this family refused, of course, to eat the flesh of the woodpecker. In the same way as the nations of the Congo Free State, the Latins had an antipathy to certain kinds of food. However, an animal or plant forbidden in one place was eaten without any compunction in another place. ' These local rites in Roman times,' says Mr. Lang, ' caused civil brawls, for the customs of one town naturally seemed blasphemous to neighbors with a different sacred animal. Thus when the people of dog-town were feeding on the fish called oxyrrhyncus, the citizens of the town which revered the oxyrrhyncus began to eat dogs. Hence arose a riot.' The antipathy of the Jews to pork has given rise to quite different explanations. The custom is probably a relic of totemistic belief. That the unclean animals—animals not to be eaten— such as the pig, the mouse, and the weasel, were originally totems of the children of Israel, Professor Robertson Smith believes is shown by various passages in the Old Testament.

" When animals and plants ceased to be held sacred they were endowed with sundry magical or mystic properties. The apple has been supposed to possess peculiar virtues, especially in the way of health. ' The relation of the apple to health,' says Mr. Conway, ' is traceable to Arabia. Sometimes it is regarded as a bane. In Hessia it is said an apple must not be eaten on, New Year's Day, as it will produce an abscess. But generally it is curative. In Pomerania it is eaten on Easter morning against fevers ; in Westphalia (mixed with saffron) against jaundice ; while in Silesia an apple is scraped from top to stalk to cure diarrhea, and upward to cure costiveness.' According to an old English fancy, if any one who is suffering from a wound in the head should eat strawberries it will lead to fatal results. In the South of England the folk say that the devil puts his cloven foot upon the blackberries on Michaelmas Day, and hence none should be gathered or eaten after that day. On the other hand, in Scotland the peasants say that the devil throws his cloak over the blackberries and makes them unwholesome after that day, while in Ireland he is said to stamp on the berries. Even that humble plant, the cabbage, has been invested with some mystery. It was said that the fairies were fond of its leaves, and rode to their midnight dances on cabbage-stalks. The German women used to say that ' Babies come out of the cabbage-heads.' The Irish peasant ties a cabbage-leaf around the neck for sore throat. According to Gerarde, the Spartans ate watercress with their bread, firmly believing that it increased their wit and wisdom. The old proverb is, ' Eat cress to learn more wit.'

" There is another phase to food-superstitions, and that is the theory that the qualities of the eaten pass into the eater. Mr. Tylor refers to the habit of the Dyak young men in abstaining from deer-meat lest it should make them timid, while the warriors of some South American tribes eat the meat of tigers, stags, and boars for courage and speed. He mentions the story of an English gentleman at Shanghai who at the time of the Taeping attack met his Chinese servant carrying home the heart of a rebel, which he intended to eat to make him brave. There is a certain amount of truth in the theory that the quality of food does affect the mind and body. Buckle in his ' History of Civilization' took this view, and tried to prove that the character of a people depends on their diet."

Idiosyncrasies to Drugs.—In the absorption and the assimilation of drugs idiosyncrasies are often noted ; in fact, they are so common that we can almost say that no one drug acts in the same degree or manner on different individuals. In some instances the untoward action assumes such a serious aspect as to render extreme caution necessary in the administration of the most inert substances. A medicine ordinarily so bland as cod-liver oil may give rise to disagreeable eruptions. Christison speaks of a boy ten years old who was said to have been killed by the ingestion of two ounces of Epsom salts without inducing purgation ; yet this common purge is universally used without the slightest fear or caution. On the other hand, the extreme tolerance exhibited by certain individuals to certain drugs offers a new phase of this subject. There are well-authenticated cases on record in which death has been caused in children by the ingestion of a small fraction of a grain of opium. While exhibiting especial tolerance from peculiar disposition and long habit, Thomas De Quincey, the celebrated English litterateur, makes a statement in his "Confessions" that with impunity he took as much as 320 grains of opium a day, and was accustomed at one period of his life to call every day for "a glass of laudanum negus, warm, and without sugar," to use his own expression, after the manner a toper would call for a "hot-Scotch."

The individuality noted in the assimilation and the ingestion of drugs is functional as well as anatomic. Numerous cases have been seen by all physicians. The severe toxic symptoms from a whiff of cocain-spray, the acute distress from the tenth of a grain of morphin, the gastric crises and profuse urticarial eruptions following a single dose of quinin,—all are proofs of it. The "personal equation" is one of the most important factors in therapeutics, reminding us of the old rule, "Treat the patient, not the disease."

The idiosyncrasy may be either temporary or permanent, and there are many conditions that influence it. The time and place of administration; the degree of pathologic lesion in the subject; the difference in the physiologic capability of individual organs of similar nature in the same body; the degree of human vitality influencing absorption and resistance; the peculiar epochs of life; the element of habituation, and the grade and strength of the drug, influencing its virtue,—all have an important bearing on untoward action and tolerance of poisons.

It is not in the province of this work to discuss at length the explanations offered for these individual idiosyncrasies. Many authors have done so, and Lewin [a] has devoted a whole volume to this subject, of which, fortunately, an English translation has been made by Mulheron,[b] and to these the interested reader is referred for further information. In the following lines examples of idiosyncrasy to the most common remedial substances will be cited, taking the drugs up alphabetically.

Acids.—Ordinarily speaking, the effect of **boric acid** in medicinal doses on the human system is nil, an exceptionally large quantity causing diuresis. Binswanger, according to Lewin, took eight gm. in two doses within an hour, which was followed by nausea, vomiting, and a feeling of pressure and fulness of the stomach which continued several hours. Molodenkow [c] mentions two fatal cases from the external employment of boric acid as an antiseptic. In one case the pleural cavity was washed out with a five per cent. solution of boric acid and was followed by distressing symptoms, vomiting, weak pulse, erythema, and death on the third day. In the second case, in a youth of sixteen, death occurred after washing out a deep abscess of the nates with the same solution. The autopsy revealed no change or signs indicative of the cause of death. Hogner [d] mentions two instances of death from the employ-

a "Die Nebenwirkungen der Arzneimittel."
b "The Untoward Effect of Drugs." Detroit, 1884.   c 704, 1881, No. 42.   d 720, ccii., 38.

ment of $2\frac{1}{2}$ per cent. solution of boric acid in washing out a dilated stomach. The symptoms were quite similar to those mentioned by Molodenkow.

In recent years the medical profession has become well aware that in its application to wounds it is possible for **carbolic acid** or **phenol** to exercise exceedingly deleterious and even fatal consequences. In the earlier days of antisepsis, when operators and patients were exposed for some time to an atmosphere saturated with carbolic spray, toxic symptoms were occasionally noticed. Von Langenbeck [a] spoke of severe carbolic-acid intoxication in a boy in whom carbolic paste had been used in the treatment of abscesses. The same author reports two instances of death following the employment of dry carbolized dressings after slight operations. Kohler [b] mentions the death of a man suffering from scabies who had applied externally a solution containing about a half ounce of phenol. Rose spoke of gangrene of the finger after the application of carbolized cotton to a wound thereon. In some cases phenol acts with a rapidity equal to any poison. Taylor speaks of a man who fell unconscious ten seconds after an ounce of phenol had been ingested, and in three minutes was dead. There is recorded an account of a man of sixty-four who was killed by a solution containing slightly over a dram of phenol. A half ounce has frequently caused death; smaller quantities have been followed by distressing symptoms, such as intoxication (which Olshausen has noticed to follow irrigation of the uterus), delirium, singultus, nausea, rigors, cephalalgia, tinnitus aurium, and anasarca. Hind [c] mentions recovery after the ingestion of nearly six ounces of crude phenol of 14 per cent. strength. There was a case at the Liverpool Northern Hospital [d] in which recovery took place after the ingestion with suicidal intent of four ounces of crude carbolic acid. Quoted by Lewin, Busch accurately describes a case which may be mentioned as characteristic of the symptoms of carbolism. A boy, suffering from abscess under the trochanter, was operated on for its relief. During the few minutes occupied by the operation he was kept under a two per cent. carbolic spray, and the wound was afterward dressed with carbolic gauze. The day following the operation he was seized with vomiting, which was attributed to the chloroform used as an anesthetic. On the following morning the bandages were removed under the carbolic spray; during the day there was nausea, in the evening there was collapse, and carbolic acid was detected in the urine. The pulse became small and frequent and the temperature sank to 35.5° C. The frequent vomiting made it impossible to administer remedies by the stomach, and, in spite of hypodermic injections and external application of analeptics, the boy died fifty hours after operation.

Recovery has followed the ingestion of an ounce of officinal **hydrochloric acid**.[e] Black [f] mentions a man of thirty-nine who recovered after swallow-

a 199, 1878, No. 48.   b 720, clv., 276.   c 476, 1884, i., 659.
d 548, 1875, ii., 597.   e 218, xv.   f 476, 1886, ii., 14.

ing 1½ ounces of commercial hydrochloric acid. Johnson [a] reports a case of poisoning from a dram of hydrochloric acid. Tracheotomy was performed, but death resulted.

Burman [b] mentions recovery after the ingestion of a dram of dilute **hydrocyanic acid** of Scheele's strength (2.4 gm. of the acid). In this instance insensibility did not ensue until two minutes after taking the poison, the retarded digestion being the means of saving life.

Quoting Taafe, in 1862 Taylor speaks of the case of a man who swallowed the greater part of a solution containing an ounce of **potassium cyanid.** In a few minutes the man was found insensible in the street, breathing stertorously, and in ten minutes after the ingestion of the drug the stomach-pump was applied. In two hours vomiting began, and thereafter recovery was rapid.

Mitscherlich speaks of erosion of the gums and tongue with hemorrhage at the slightest provocation, following the long administration of **dilute nitric acid.** This was possibly due to the local action.

According to Taylor, the smallest quantity of **oxalic acid** causing death is one dram. Ellis [c] describes a woman of fifty who swallowed an ounce of oxalic acid in beer. In thirty minutes she complained of a burning pain in the stomach and was rolling about in agony. Chalk and water was immediately given to her and she recovered. Woodman [d] reports recovery after taking ½ ounce of oxalic acid.

Salicylic acid in medicinal doses frequently causes untoward symptoms, such as dizziness, transient delirium, diminution of vision, headache, and profuse perspiration; petechial eruptions and intense gastric symptoms have also been noticed.

Sulphuric acid causes death from its corrosive action, and when taken in excessive quantities it produces great gastric disturbance; however, there are persons addicted to taking oil of vitriol without any apparent untoward effect. There is mentioned a boot-maker [e] who constantly took ½ ounce of the strong acid in a tumbler of water, saying that it relieved his dyspepsia and kept his bowels open.

Antimony.—It is recorded that ¾ grain of tartar emetic has caused death in a child and two grains in an adult. Falot [f] reports three cases in which after small doses of tartar emetic there occurred vomiting, delirium, spasms, and such depression of vitality that only the energetic use of stimulants saved life. Beau [g] mentions death following the administration of two doses of 1½ gr. of tartar emetic. Preparations of antimony in an ointment, applied locally have caused necrosis, particularly of the cranium, and Hebra [407] has long since denounced the use of tartar emetic ointment in affections of the scalp. Carpenter [h] mentions recovery after ingestion of two

a 224, 1871, i., 221.   b 476, 1854, i., 39.   c 476, 1864, 265.   d 548, 1864, ii., 386.
e 548, 1861, i., 295.   f 789, 1852, 245.   g 548, 1857, i., 320.   h 491, 1893, 514.

drams of tartar emetic. Behrends [a] describes a case of catalepsy with mania, in which a dose of 40 gr. of tartar emetic was tolerated, and Morgagni speaks of a man who swallowed two drams, immediately vomited, and recovered. Instances like the last, in which an excessive amount of a poison by its sudden emetic action induces vomiting before there is absorption of a sufficient quantity to cause death, are sometimes noticed. McCreery [b] mentions a case of accidental poisoning with half an ounce of tartar emetic successfully treated with green tea and tannin. Mason [c] reports recovery after taking 80 gr. of tartar emetic.

Arsenic.—The **sources of arsenical poisoning** are so curious as to deserve mention. Confectionery, wall-paper, dyes, and the like are examples. In other cases we note money-counting,[d] the colored candles of a Christmas tree,[e] paper collars,[f] ball-wreaths of artificial flowers,[g] ball-dresses made of green tarlatan,[h] playing cards,[i] hat-lining,[j] and fly-papers.[k]

Bazin has reported a case in which erythematous pustules appeared after the exhibition during fifteen days of the $\frac{5}{6}$ gr. of arsenic. Macnal [l] speaks of an eruption similar to that of measles in a patient to whom he had given but three drops of Fowler's solution for the short period of three days. Pareira says that in a gouty patient for whom he prescribed $\frac{1}{6}$ gr. of potassium arseniate daily, on the third day there appeared a bright red eruption of the face, neck, upper part of the trunk and flexor surfaces of the joints, and an edematous condition of the eyelids. The symptoms were preceded by restlessness, headache, and heat of the skin, and subsided gradually after the second or third day, desquamation continuing for nearly two months. After they had subsided entirely, the exhibition of arsenic again aroused them, and this time they were accompanied by salivation. Charcot and other French authors have noticed the frequent occurrence of suspension of the sexual instinct during the administration of Fowler's solution. Jackson [m] speaks of recovery after the ingestion of two ounces of arsenic by the early employment of an emetic. Walsh [n] reports a case in which 600 gr. of arsenic were taken without injury. The remarkable tolerance of arsenic eaters is well known. Taylor asserts that the smallest lethal dose of arsenic has been two gr., but Tardieu mentions an instance in which ten cgm. ($1\frac{1}{2}$ gr.) has caused death. Mackenzie [o] speaks of a man who swallowed a large quantity of arsenic in lumps, and received no treatment for sixteen hours, but recovered. It is added that from two masses passed by the anus 105 gr. of arsenic were obtained.

In speaking of the tolerance of **belladonna,** in 1859 Fuller mentioned a

[a] 587, ix., 199.   [b] 124, 1853.   [c] 224, 1877, i., 674.   [d] 491, 1883, 526.

[e] 536, 1889, i., 287.   [f] 224, 1880, ii., 240.   [g] 548, 1862, i., 137.

[h] 476, 1875, ii., 758.   [i] 224, 1879, ii., 630.   [j] 224, 1879, ii., 746.

[k] 476, 1884, i., 408.   [l] 548, 1868.   [m] 124, July, 1858.

[n] Annalist, N. Y., 1849, 136.   [o] 435, 1872.

child of fourteen who in eighteen days took 37 grains of atropin ; a child of ten who took seven grains of extract of belladonna daily, or more than two ounces in twenty-six days ; and a man who took 64 grains of the extract of belladonna daily, and from whose urine enough atropin was extracted to kill two white mice and to narcotize two others. Bader has observed grave symptoms following the employment of a vaginal suppository containing three grains of the extract of belladonna. The dermal manifestations, such as urticaria and eruptions resembling the exanthem of scarlatina, are too well known to need mention here. An enema containing 80 grains of belladonna root has been followed in five hours by death, and Taylor[757] has mentioned recovery after the ingestion of three drams of belladonna. In 1864 Chambers reported to the Lancet the recovery of a child of four years who took a solution containing $\frac{1}{2}$ grain of the alkaloid. In some cases the idiosyncrasy to belladonna is so marked that violent symptoms follow the application of the ordinary belladonna plaster. Maddox[a] describes a case of poisoning in a music teacher by the belladonna plaster of a reputable maker. She had obscure eye-symptoms, and her color-sensations were abnormal. Locomotor equilibration was also affected. Golden[b] mentions two cases in which the application of belladonna ointment to the breasts caused suppression of the secretion of milk. Goodwin[c] relates the history of a case in which an infant was poisoned by a belladonna plaster applied to its mother's breast and died within twenty-four hours after the first application of the plaster. In 1881 Betancourt spoke of an instance of inherited susceptibility to belladonna, in which the external application of the ointment produced all the symptoms of belladonna poisoning. Cooper[d] mentions the symptoms of poisoning following the application of extract of belladonna to the scrotum. Davison reports poisoning by the application of belladonna liniment. Jenner and Lyman also record belladonna poisoning from external applications.

Rosenthal[e] reports a rare case of poisoning in a child eighteen months old who had swallowed about a teaspoonful of **benzin.** Fifteen minutes later the child became unconscious. The stomach-contents, which were promptly removed, contained flakes of bloody mucus. At the end of an hour the radial pulse was scarcely perceptible, respiration was somewhat increased in frequency and accompanied with a rasping sound. The breath smelt of benzin. The child lay in quiet narcosis, occasionally throwing itself about as if in pain. The pulse gradually improved, profuse perspiration occurred, and normal sleep intervened. Six hours after the poisoning the child was still stupefied. The urine was free from albumin and sugar, and the next morning the little one had perfectly recovered.

There is an instance mentioned[f] of a robust youth of twenty who by a mistake took a half ounce of **cantharides.** He was almost immediately

a 124, 1893.   b 476, 1856.   c 545, 1871, 346.

d 224, 1877, i., 164.   e Therap. Gaz., July 16, 1894.   f 476, 1825, 233.

seized with violent heat in the throat and stomach, pain in the head, and intense burning on urination.   These symptoms progressively increased, were followed by intense sickness and almost continual vomiting.   In the evening he passed great quantities of blood from the urethra with excessive pain in the urinary tract.   On the third day all the symptoms were less violent and the vomiting had ceased.   Recovery was complete on the fifteenth day.

Digitalis has been frequently observed to produce dizziness, fainting, disturbances of vision, vomiting, diarrhea, weakness of the pulse, and depression of temperature.   These phenomena, however, are generally noticed after continued administration in repeated doses, the result being doubtless due to cumulative action caused by abnormally slow elimination by the kidneys.   Traube[a] observed the presence of skin-affection after the use of digitalis in a case of pericarditis.   Tardieu has seen a fluid-dram of the tincture of digitalis cause alarming symptoms in a young woman who was pregnant. He also quotes cases of death on the tenth day from ingestion of 20 grains of the extract, and on the fifth day from $2\frac{1}{2}$ grams of the infusion.   Köhnhorn[b] mentions a death from what might be called chronic digitalis poisoning.

There is a deleterious practice of some of the Irish peasantry connected with their belief in fairies, which consists of giving a cachetic or rachitic child large doses of a preparation of fox-glove (Irish—luss-more, or great herb), to drive out or kill the fairy in the child.   It was supposed to kill an unhallowed child and cure a hallowed one.   In the Hebrides, likewise, there were many cases of similar poisoning.

Epidemics of **ergotism** have been recorded from time to time since the days of Galen, and were due to poverty, wretchedness, and famine, resulting in the feeding upon ergotized bread.   According to Wood,[829] gangrenous ergotism, or "Ignis Sacer" of the Middle Ages, killed 40,000 persons in Southwestern France in 922 A. D., and in 1128–29, in Paris alone, 14,000 persons perished from this malady.   It is described as commencing with itchings and formications in the feet, severe pain in the back, contractions in the muscles, nausea, giddiness, apathy, with abortion in pregnant women, in suckling women drying of milk, and in maidens with amenorrhea.   After some time, deep, heavy aching in the limbs, intense feeling of coldness, with real coldness of the surfaces, profound apathy, and a sense of utter weariness develop ; then a dark spot appears on the nose or one of the extremities, all sensibility is lost in the affected part, the skin assumes a livid red hue, and adynamic symptoms in severe cases deepen as the gangrene spreads, until finally death ensues.   Very generally the appetite and digestion are preserved to the last, and not rarely there is a most ferocious hunger.   Wood also mentions a species of ergotism characterized by epileptic paroxysms, which he calls "spasmodic ergotism."   Prentiss[c] mentions a brunette of forty-two, under the influence of ergot, who exhibited a peculiar depression of

a 263, i., 622.   b 476, 1876, i., 583.   c 450, 1889, No. 26, 912.

spirits with hysteric phenomena, although deriving much benefit from the administration of the drug from the hemorrhage caused by uterine fibroids. After taking ergot for three days she felt like crying all the time, became irritable, and stayed in bed, being all day in tears. The natural disposition of the patient was entirely opposed to these manifestations, as she was even-tempered and exceptionally pleasant.

In addition to the instance of the fatal ingestion of a dose of **Epsom salts** already quoted, Lang [a] mentions a woman of thirty-five who took four ounces of this purge. She experienced burning pain in the stomach and bowels, together with a sense of asphyxiation. There was no purging or vomiting, but she became paralyzed and entered a state of coma, dying fifteen minutes after ingestion.

Iodin Preparations.—The eruptions following the administration of small doses of **potassium iodid** are frequently noticed (Fig. 189), and at the same time large quantities of albumin have been seen in the urine. Potassium iodid, although generally spoken of as a poisonous drug, by gradually increasing the dose can be given in such enormous quantities as to be almost beyond the bounds of credence, several drams being given at a dose. On the other hand, eight grains have produced alarming symptoms.[b] In the extensive use of **iodoform** as a dressing instances of untoward

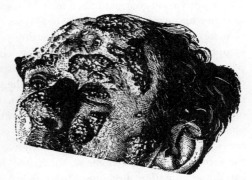

Fig. 189.—A somewhat rare form of eruption from the ingestion of iodin compounds (after J. C. McGuire).

effects, and even fatal ones, have been noticed, the majority of them being due to careless and injudicious application. In a French journal [c] there is mentioned the history of a man of twenty-five, suspected of urethral ulceration, who submitted to the local application of one gram of iodoform. Deep narcosis and anesthesia were induced, and two hours after awakening his breath smelled strongly of iodoform. There are two similar instances recorded in England.[d]

Pope [e] mentions two fatal cases of **lead-poisoning** from diachylon plaster, self-administered for the purpose of producing abortion. Lead water-pipes, the use of cosmetics and hair-dyes, coloring matter in confectionery and in pastry, habitual biting of silk threads, imperfectly burnt pottery, and cooking bread with painted wood [f] have been mentioned as causes of chronic lead-poisoning.

a 476, 1891.   b 133, xxvi., 197.   c Le Practicien, Mar. 17, 1879.

d 476, May 31, 1879.   e 224, 1893.   f 653, 1877, 349.

Mercury.—Armstrong[a] mentions recovery after ingestion of $1\frac{1}{2}$ drams of corrosive sublimate, and Lodge[b] speaks of recovery after a dose containing 100 grains of the salt. It is said[c] that a man swallowed 80 grains of mercuric chlorid in whiskey and water, and vomited violently about ten minutes afterward. A mixture of albumin and milk was given to him, and in about twenty-five minutes a bolus of gold-leaf and reduced iron; in eight days he perfectly recovered. Severe and even fatal poisoning may result from the external application of mercury. Meeres[d] mentions a case in which a solution (two grains to the fluid-ounce) applied to the head of a child of nine for the relief of tinea tonsurans caused diarrhea, profuse salivation, marked prostration, and finally death. Washing out the vagina with a solution of corrosive sublimate, 1 : 2000, has caused severe and even fatal poisoning.[e] Bonet[216] mentions death after the inunction of a mercurial ointment, and instances of distressing salivation from such medication are quite common. There are various dermal affections which sometimes follow the exhibition of mercury and assume an erythematous type. The susceptibility of some persons to calomel, the slightest dose causing profuse salivation and painful oral symptoms, is so common that few physicians administer mercury to their patients without some knowledge of their susceptibility to this drug. Blundel[f] relates a curious case occurring in the times when mercury was given in great quantities, in which to relieve obstinate constipation a half ounce of crude mercury was administered and repeated in twelve hours. Scores of globules of mercury soon appeared over a vesicated surface, the result of a previous blister applied to the epigastric region. Blundel, not satisfied with the actuality of the phenomena, submitted his case to Dr. Lister, who, after careful examination, pronounced the globules metallic.

Oils.—Mauvezin[g] tells of the ingestion of three drams of **croton oil** by a child of six, followed by vomiting and rapid recovery. There was no diarrhea in this case. Wood quotes Cowan in mentioning the case of a child of four, who in two days recovered from a teaspoonful of croton oil taken on a full stomach. Adams saw recovery in an adult after ingestion of the same amount. There is recorded[h] an instance of a woman who took about an ounce, and, emesis being produced three-quarters of an hour afterward by mustard, she finally recovered. There is a record in which so small a dose as three minims is supposed to have killed a child of thirteen months.[i] According to Wood, Giacomini mentions a case in which 24 grains of the drug proved fatal in as many hours.

Castor oil is usually considered a harmless drug, but the castor bean, from which it is derived, contains a poisonous acrid principle, three such beans having sufficed to produce death in a man. Doubtless some of the in-

a 491, 1887, 120.   b 224, 1888, ii., 720.   c 124, 1863, 340.
d 476, Sept. 16, 1871.   e 261, 1887, No. 47.   f 476, 1830, 767.
g 363, 1869, 290.   h 218, 1868, i., 294.   i 548, 1870, i.

stances in which castor oil has produced symptoms similar to cholera are the results of the administration of contaminated oil.

The untoward effects of **opium and its derivatives** are quite numerous. Gaubius treated an old woman in whom, after three days, a single grain of opium produced a general desquamation of the epidermis ; this peculiarity was not accidental, as it was verified on several other occasions. Hargens [452] speaks of a woman in whom the slightest bit of opium in any form produced considerable salivation. Gastric disturbances are quite common, severe vomiting being produced by minimum doses ; not infrequently, intense mental confusion, vertigo, and headache, lasting hours and even days, sometimes referable to the frontal region and sometimes to the occipital, are seen in certain nervous individuals after a dose of from $\frac{1}{4}$ to $\frac{5}{6}$ gr. of opium. These symptoms were familiar to the ancient physicians, and, according to Lewin, Tralles reports an observation with reference to this in a man, and says regarding it in rather unclassical Latin : " . . . per multos dies ponderosissimum caput circumgestasse." Convulsions are said to be observed after medicinal doses of opium. Albers [a] states that twitching in the tendons, tremors of the hands, and even paralysis, have been noticed after the ingestion of opium in even ordinary doses. The " pruritus opii," so familiar to physicians, is spoken of in the older writings. Dioscorides, Paulus Aegineta, and nearly all the writers of the last century describe this symptom as an annoying and unbearable affection. In some instances the ingestion of opium provokes an eruption in the form of small, isolated red spots, which, in their general character, resemble roseola. Rieken [b] remarks that when these spots spread over all the body they present a scarlatiniform appearance, and he adds that even the mucous membranes of the mouth and throat may be attacked with erethematous inflammation. Behrend [c] observed an opium exanthem, which was attended by intolerable itching, after the exhibition of a quarter of a grain. It was seen on the chest, on the inner surfaces of the arms, on the flexor surfaces of the forearms and wrists, on the thighs, and posterior and inner surfaces of the legs, terminating at the ankles in a stripe-like discoloration about the breadth of three fingers. It consisted of closely disposed papules of the size of a pin-head, and several days after the disappearance of the eruption a fine, bran-like desquamation of the epidermis ensued. Brand [d] has also seen an eruption on the trunk and flexor surfaces, accompanied with fever, from the ingestion of opium. Billroth [e] mentions the case of a lady in whom appeared a feeling of anxiety, nausea, and vomiting after ingestion of a small fraction of a grain of opium ; she would rather endure her intense pain than suffer the untoward action of the drug. According to Lewin, Brochin [f] reported a case in which the idiosyncrasy to morphin was so great that $\frac{1}{25}$ of a grain of the drug administered

a 161, xxvi., 225.   b 720, cvii., 22.   c 199, 1879, 626.
d 199, 1879, 718.   e 611, 1868, 763.   f 363, 1877, 226.

hypodermically caused irregularity of the respiration, suspension of the heart-beat, and profound narcosis. According to the same authority, Wernich has called attention to paresthesia of the sense of taste after the employment of morphin, which, according to his observation, is particularly prone to supervene in patients who are much reduced and in persons otherwise healthy who have suffered from prolonged inanition.   These effects are probably due to a central excitation of a similar nature to that produced by santonin.   Persons thus attacked complain, shortly after the injection, of an intensely sour or bitter taste, which for the most part ceases after elimination of the morphin.   Von Graefe and Sommerfrodt speak of a spasm of accommodation occurring after ingestion of medicinal doses of morphin.   There are several cases on record [a] in which death has been produced in an adult by the use of $\frac{1}{2}$ to $\frac{1}{6}$ grain of morphin.   According to Wood, the maximum doses from which recovery has occurred without emesis are 55 grains of solid opium, and six ounces of laudanum.   According to the same authority, in 1854 there was a case in which a babe one day old was killed by one minim of laudanum, and in another case a few drops of paregoric proved fatal to a child of nine months.   Doubtful instances of death from opium are given, one in an adult female [b] after 30 grains of Dover's powder given in divided doses, and another [c] after a dose of $\frac{1}{4}$ grain of morphin.   Yavorski [d] cites a rather remarkable instance of morphin-poisoning with recovery : a female took 30 grains of acetate of morphin, and as it did not act quickly enough she took an additional dose of $\frac{1}{2}$ ounce of laudanum.   After this she slept a few hours, and awoke complaining of being ill.   Yavorski saw her about an hour later, and by producing emesis, and giving coffee, atropin, and tincture of musk, he saved her life.   Pyle [e] describes a pugilist of twenty-two who, in a fit of despondency after a debauch (in which he had taken repeated doses of morphin sulphate), took with suicidal intent three teaspoonfuls of morphin ; after rigorous treatment he revived and was discharged on the next day perfectly well.   Potassium permanganate was used in this case.   Chaffee [f] speaks of recovery after the ingestion of 18 grains of morphin without vomiting.

In **chronic opium eating** the amount of this drug which can be ingested with safety assumes astounding proportions. In his "Confessions" De Quincey remarks : " Strange as it may sound, I had a little before this time descended suddenly and without considerable effort from 320 grains of opium (8000 drops of laudanum) per day to 40 grains, or $\frac{1}{8}$ part.   Instantaneously, and as if by magic, the cloud of profoundest melancholy which rested on my brain, like some black vapors that I have seen roll away from the summits of the mountains, drew off in one day,—passed off with its murky banners as simultaneously as a ship that has been stranded and is floated off by a spring-tide—

' That moveth altogether, if it move at all.'

a 829, 168.	b 269, July, 1882.	c 218, Jan. 3, 1885.
d 812, 1885.	e 533, May 12, 1894.	f 545, 1882, xlvii., 697.

Now, then, I was again happy ; I took only a thousand drops of laudanum per day, and what was that ? A latter spring had come to close up the season of youth ; my brain performed its functions as healthily as ever before ; I read Kant again, and again I understood him, or fancied that I did." There have been many authors who, in condemning De Quincey for unjustly throwing about the opium habit a halo of literary beauty which has tempted many to destruction, absolutely deny the truth of his statements. No one has any stable reason on which to found denial of De Quincey's statements as to the magnitude of the doses he was able to take ; and his frankness and truthfulness is equal to that of any of his detractors. William Rosse Cobbe, in a volume entitled " Dr. Judas, or Portrayal of the Opium Habit," gives with great frankness of confession and considerable purity of diction a record of his own experiences with the drug. One entire chapter of Mr. Cobbe's book and several portions of other chapters are devoted to showing that De Quincey was wrong in some of his statements, but notwithstanding his criticism of De Quincey, Mr. Cobbe seems to have experienced the same adventures in his dreams, showing, after all, that De Quincey knew the effects of opium, even if he seemed to idealize it. According to Mr. Cobbe, there are in the United States upward of two millions of victims of enslaving drugs entirely exclusive of alcohol. Cobbe mentions several instances in which De Quincey's dose of 320 grains of opium daily has been surpassed. One man, a resident of Southern Illinois, consumed 1072 grains a day ; another in the same State contented himself with 1685 grains daily ; and still another is given whose daily consumption amounted to 2345 grains per day. In all cases of laudanum-takers it is probable that analysis of the commercial laudanum taken would show the amount of opium to be greatly below that of the official proportion, and little faith can be put in the records of large amounts of opium taken when the deduction has been made from the laudanum used. Dealers soon begin to know opium victims, and find them ready dupes for adulteration. According to Lewin, Samter mentions a case of morphin-habit which was continued for three years, during which, in a period of about three hundred and twenty-three days, upward of $2\frac{1}{2}$ ounces of morphin was taken daily. According to the same authority, Eder reports still larger doses. In the case observed by him the patient took laudanum for six years in increasing doses up to one ounce per day ; for eighteen months, pure opium, commencing with 15 grains and increasing to $2\frac{1}{4}$ drams daily ; and for eighteen months morphin, in commencing quantities of six grains, which were later increased to 40 grains a day. When deprived of their accustomed dose of morphin the sufferings which these patients experience are terrific, and they pursue all sorts of deceptions to enable them to get their enslaving drug. Patients have been known to conceal tubes in their mouths, and even swallow them, and the authors know of a fatal instance in which a tube of hypodermic tablets of the drug was found concealed in the rectum.

The administration of such an inert substance as the infusion of **orange-peel** has been sufficient to invariably produce nervous excitement in a patient afflicted with carcinoma.

Sonnenschein refers to a case of an infant of five weeks who died from the effects of one **phosphorous** match head containing only $\frac{1}{100}$ grain of phosphorus. There are certain people who by reason of a special susceptibility cannot tolerate phosphorus, and the exhibition of it causes in them nausea, oppression, and a feeling of pain in the epigastric region, tormina and tenesmus, accompanied with diarrhea, and in rare cases jaundice, sometimes lasting several months. In such persons $\frac{1}{30}$ grain is capable of causing the foregoing symptoms. In 1882 a man was admitted to Guy's Hospital, London, after he had taken half of a sixpenny pot of phosphorous paste in whiskey, and was subsequently discharged completely recovered.

A peculiar feature of phosphorus-poisoning is necrosis of the jaw. This affection was first noticed in 1838, soon after the introduction of the manufacture of phosphorous matches. In late years, owing to the introduction of precautions in their manufacture, the disease has become much less common. The tipping of the match sticks is accomplished by dipping their ends in a warm solution of a composition of phosphorus, chlorate of potassium, with particles of ground flint to assist friction, some coloring agent, and Irish glue. From the contents of the dipping-pans fumes constantly arise into the faces of the workmen and dippers, and in cutting the sticks and packing the matches the hands are constantly in contact with phosphorus. The region chiefly affected in this poisoning is the jaw-bone, but the inflammation may spread to the adjoining bones and involve the vomer, the zygoma, the body of the sphenoid bone, and the basilar process of the occipital bone. It is supposed that conditions in which the periosteum is exposed are favorable to the progress of the disease, and, according to Hirt, workmen with diseased teeth are affected three times as readily as those with healthy teeth, and are therefore carefully excluded from some of the factories in America.

Prentiss of Washington, D. C., in 1881[a] reported a remarkable case of **pilocarpin** idiosyncrasy in a blonde of twenty-five. He was consulted by the patient for constipation. Later on symptoms of cystitis developed, and an ultimate diagnosis of pyelitis of the right kidney was made. Uremic symptoms were avoided by the constant use of pilocarpin. Between December 16, 1880, and February 22, 1881, the patient had 22 sweats from pilocarpin. The action usually lasted from two to six hours, and quite a large dose was at length necessary. The idiosyncrasy noted was found in the hair, which at first was quite light, afterward chestnut-brown, and May 1, 1881, almost pure black. The growth of the hair became more vigorous and thicker than formerly, and as its color darkened it became coarser in proportion. In March, 1889, Prentiss saw his patient, and at that time her hair was

a 547, July 2, 1881.

dark brown, having returned to that color from black. Prentiss also reported the following case [a] as adding another to the evidence that jaborandi will produce the effect mentioned under favorable circumstances : Mrs. L., aged seventy-two years, was suffering from Bright's disease (contracted kidney). Her hair and eyebrows had been snow-white for twenty years. She suffered greatly from itching of the skin, due to the uremia of the kidney-disease ; the skin was harsh and dry. For this symptom fluid extract of jaborandi was prescribed with the effect of relieving the itching. It was taken in doses of 20 or 30 drops several times a day, from October, 1886, to February, 1888. During the fall of 1887 it was noticed by the nurse that the eyebrows were growing darker, and that the hair of the head was darker in patches. These patches and the eyebrows continued to become darker, until at the time of her death they were quite black, the black tufts on the head presenting a very curious appearance among the silver-white hairs surrounding them.

Quinin being such a universally used drug, numerous instances of idiosyncrasy and intolerance have been recorded. Chevalier [b] mentions that through contact of the drug workmen in the manufacture of quinin are liable to an affection of the skin which manifests itself in a vesicular, papular, or pustular eruption on different parts of the body. Vépan [c] mentions a lady who took $1\frac{1}{2}$ grains and afterward $2\frac{1}{2}$ grains of quinin for neuralgia, and two days afterward her body was covered with purpuric spots, which disappeared in the course of nine days but reappeared after the administration of the drug was resumed. Lewin says that in this case the severity of the eruption was in accordance with the size of the dose, and during its existence there was bleeding at the gums ; he adds that Gouchet also noticed an eruption of this kind in a lady who after taking quinin expectorated blood. The petechiæ were profusely spread over the entire body, and they disappeared after the suspension of the drug. Daubœuf, Garraway,[d] Hemming,[e] Skinner,[f] and Cöbner [g] mention roseola and scarlatiniform erythema after minute doses of quinin. In nearly all these cases the accompanying symptoms were different. Heusinger [h] speaks of a lady who, after taking $\frac{1}{2}$ grain of quinin, experienced headache, nausea, intense burning, and edema, together with nodular erythema on the eyelids, cheeks, and portion of the forehead. At another time $1\frac{1}{2}$ grains of the drug gave rise to herpetic vesicles on the cheeks, followed by branny desquamation on elimination of the drug. In other patients intense itching is experienced after the ingestion of quinin. Peters [i] cites an instance of a woman of sixty-five who, after taking one grain of quinin, invariably exhibited after an hour a temperature of from 104° to 105° F., accelerated pulse, rigors, slight delirium, thirst, and all the appearances of

a 727, Oct. 3, 1890.   b 141, 1851, T. lxviii., 5.   c 369, 1865.
d 224, 1869, ii., 388.   e 224, 1869, ii., 533.   f 224, 1870, i., 103.
g 199, 1877, 305.   h 199, 1877, 361.   i 476, 1889, ii., 727.

ill-defined fever, which would pass off in from twelve to twenty-four hours. Peters witnessed this idiosyncrasy several times and believed it to be permanent.   The most unpleasant of the untoward symptoms of quinin exhibition are the disturbances of the organs of special sense.   Photophobia, and even transient amblyopia, have been observed to follow small doses.   In the examination of cases of the untoward effects of quinin upon the eye, Knapp of New York found the power of sight diminished in various degrees, and rarely amaurosis and immobility of the pupils.   According to Lewin, the perceptions of color and light are always diminished, and although the disorder may last for some time the prognosis is favorable.   The varieties of the disturbances of the functions of the ear range from tinnitus aurium to congestion causing complete deafness.   The gastro-intestinal and genito-urinary tracts are especially disposed to untoward action by quinin.   There is a case recorded in which, after the slightest dose of quinin, tingling and burning at the meatus urinarius were experienced.   According to Lewin, there is mentioned in the case reported by Gauchet a symptom quite unique in the literature of quinin, viz., hemoptysis.   Simon de Ronchard [a] first noted the occurrence of several cases of hemoptysis following the administration of doses of eight grains daily. In the persons thus attacked the lungs and heart were healthy.   Hemoptysis promptly ceased with the suspension of the drug.   When it was renewed, blood again appeared in the sputa.   Taussig [b] mentions a curious mistake, in which an ounce of quinin sulphate was administered to a patient at one dose ; the only symptoms noticed were a stuporous condition and complete deafness.   No antidote was given, and the patient perfectly recovered in a week. In malarious countries, and particularly in the malarial fevers of the late war, enormous quantities of quinin were frequently given.   In fact, at the present day in some parts of the South quinin is constantly kept on the table as a prophylactic constituent of the diet.

Skinner [c] noticed the occurrence of a scarlatiniform eruption in a woman after the dose of $\frac{1}{165}$ grain of **strychnin**, which, however, disappeared with the discontinuance of the drug.   There was a man in London in 1865 [d] who died in twenty minutes after the ingestion of $\frac{1}{2}$ grain of strychnin.   Wood speaks of a case in which the administration of $\frac{1}{100}$ grain killed a child three and one-half months old.   Gray [e] speaks of a man who took 22 grains and was not seen for about an hour.   He had vomited some of it immediately after taking the dose, and was successfully treated with chloral hydrate.   A curious case is mentioned in which three mustard plasters, one on the throat, one on the back of the neck, and another on the left shoulder of a woman, produced symptoms similar to strychnin poisoning.   They remained in position for about thirty minutes, and about thirty hours afterward a painful stinging sensation commenced in the back of the neck, followed by violent

a 363, Jan., 1861.   b 548, 1864, i., 461.   c 224, 1870, i., 303.
d 392, 1865, xi., 208.   e 224, 1880, i., 476.

twitching of the muscles of the face, arms, and legs, which continued in regular succession through the whole of the night, but after twelve hours yielded to hot fomentations of poppy-heads applied to the back of the neck. It could not be ascertained whether any medicine containing strychnin had been taken, but surely, from the symptoms, such must have been the case.

Tobacco.—O'Neill [a] gives the history of a farmer's wife, aged forty, who wounded her leg against a sewing-machine, and by lay advice applied a handful of chopped wet tobacco to it, from which procedure, strange to say, serious **nicotin-poisoning** ensued. The pupils were dilated, there were dimness of vision, confusion of thought, and extreme prostration. The pulse was scarcely apparent, the skin was white and wet with clammy perspiration. Happily, strychnin was given in time to effect recovery, and without early medical assistance she would undoubtedly have succumbed. There are several similar cases on record.

Although not immediately related to the subject of idiosyncrasy, the following case may be mentioned here: Ramadge [b] speaks of a young Frenchman, suffering from an obstinate case of gonorrhea, who was said to have been completely cured by living in a newly painted house in which he inhaled the odors or vapors of turpentine.

White [c] speaks of a case of exanthematous eruption similar to that of ivy-poison in mother and child, which was apparently caused by playing with and burning the toy called " Pharaoh's serpent egg."

The **idiosyncrasies noticed in some persons during coitus** are quite interesting. The Ephemerides mentions a person in whom coitus habitually caused vomiting, and another in whom excessive sexual indulgence provoked singultus. Sometimes exaggerated tremors or convulsions, particularly at the moment of orgasm, are noticed. Females especially are subject to this phenomenon, and it is seen sometimes in birds.

Winn [d] reports the case of a man who, when prompted to indulge in sexual intercourse, was immediately prior to the act seized with a fit of sneezing. Even the thought of sexual pleasure with a female was sufficient to provoke this peculiar idiosyncrasy.

Sullivan [e] mentions a bride of four weeks, who called at the doctor's office, saying that in coitus her partner had no difficulty until the point of culmination or orgasm, when he was seized with complete numbness and lost all pleasurable sensation in the penis. The numbness was followed by a sensation of pain, which was intensified on the slightest motion, and which was at times so excruciating as to forbid separation for upward of an hour, or until the penis had become flaccid. The woman asked for advice for her unfortunate husband's relief, and the case was reported as a means of obtaining suggestions from the physicians over the country. In response, one

[a] 476, 1879, i., 296.   [b] 476, 1829–30, i., 415.   [c] 331, 1867.

[d] 703, 1873, x., 318.   [e] 569, 1879, ii., 225.

theory was advanced that this man had been in the habit of masturbating and had a stricture of the membranous portion of the urethra, associated with an ulcer of the prostate involving the ejaculatory ducts, or an inflammatory condition of all the tissues compressed by the ejaculatory muscles.

Hendrichsen[a] quotes a case in which a spasmodic contraction of the levator ani occurred during coitus, and the penis could not be withdrawn while this condition lasted ; and in support of this circumstance Hendrichsen mentions that Marion Sims, Beigel, and Budin describe spasmodic contractions of the levator ani, constricting the vagina ; he also cites an instance under his personal observation in which this spasm was excited by both vaginal and rectal examination, although on the following day no such condition could be produced. In this connection, among the older writers, Borellus[841] gives the history of a man who before coitus rubbed his virile member with musk, and, similar to the connection of a dog and bitch, was held fast in his wife's vagina ; it was only after the injection of great quantities of water to soften the parts that separation was obtained. Diemerbroeck[304] confirms this singular property of musk by an analogous observation, in which the ludicrous method of throwing cold water on the persons was practised. Schurig also relates the history of a similar instance.

Among the peculiar effects of coitus is its deteriorating effect on the healing process of wounds. Boerhaave, Paré, and Fabricius Hildanus all speak of this untoward effect of venery, and in modern times Poncet has made observations at a hospital in Lyons which prove that during the process of healing wounds are unduly and harmfully influenced by coitus, and cites confirmatory instances. Poncet also remarks that he found on nine occasions, by placing a thermometer in the rectum, that the temperature was about 1° F. lower just before than after coitus, and that during the act the temperature gradually rose above normal.

There are many associate conditions which, under the exciting influence of coitus, provoke harmful effects and even a fatal issue. Deguise[b] mentions a man who had coitus 18 times in ten hours with most disastrous effects. Cabrolius[245] speaks of a man who took a potion of aphrodisiac properties, in which, among other things, he put an enormous dose of cantharides. The anticipation of the effect of his dose, that is, the mental influence, in addition to the actual therapeutic effect, greatly distressed and excited him. Almost beyond belief, it is said that he approached his wife eighty-seven times during the night, spilling much sperm on the sleeping-bed. Cabrolius was called to see this man in the morning, and found him in a most exhausted condition, but still having the supposed consecutive ejaculations. Exhaustion progressed rapidly, and death soon terminated this erotic crisis. Lawson is accredited with saying that among the Marquesan tribe he knew of a woman who during a single night had intercourse with 103 men.

Among the older writers there are instances reported in which erection and ejaculation took place without the slightest pleasurable sensation. Claudius exemplifies this fact in his report of a Venetian merchant who had vigorous erections and ejaculations of thick and abundant semen without either tingling or pleasure.

Attila, King of the Huns, and one of the most celebrated leaders of the German hosts which overran the Roman Empire in its decline, and whose enormous army and name inspired such terror that he was called the "Scourge of God," was supposed to have died in coitus. Apoplexy, organic heart disorders, aneurysms, and other like disorders are in such cases generally the direct cause of death, coitus causing the death indirectly by the excitement and exertion accompanying the act.

Bartholinus, Benedictus, Borellus, Pliny, Morgagni, Plater, à Castro, Forestus, Marcellus Donatus, Schurig, Sinibaldus, Schenck, the Ephemerides, and many others mention death during coitus; the older writers in some cases attributed the fatal issue to excessive sexual indulgence, not considering the possibility of the associate direct cause, which most likely would have been found in case of a necropsy.

Suspended Animation.—Various opinions have been expressed as to the length of time compatible with life during which a person can stay under water. Recoveries from drowning furnish interesting examples of the suspension of animation for a protracted period, but are hardly ever reliable, as the subject at short intervals almost invariably rises to the surface of the water, allowing occasional respiration. Taylor[757] mentions a child of two who recovered after ten minutes' submersion; in another case a man recovered after fourteen minutes' submersion. There is a case reported in this country [a] of a woman who was said to have been submerged twenty minutes. Guérard [b] quotes a case happening in 1774, in which there was submersion for an hour with subsequent recovery; but there hardly seems sufficient evidence of this.

Green [c] mentions submersion for fifteen minutes; Douglass,[d] for fourteen minutes; Laub,[e] for fifteen minutes; Povall [f] gives a description of three persons who recovered after a submersion of twenty-five minutes. There is a case in French literature,[g] apparently well authenticated, in which submersion for six minutes was followed by subsequent recovery.

There have been individuals who gave exhibitions of **prolonged submersion** in large glass aquariums, placed in full view of the audience. Taylor remarks that the person known some years ago in London as "Lurline" could stay under water for three minutes. There have been several exhibitionists of this sort. Some of the more enterprising seat themselves on an artificial coral, and surrounded by fishes of divers hues complacently eat a meal while thus submerged. It is said that quite recently in Detroit there

a 124, 1853, 348. b 141, 1850, ii., 306. c 629, 1732–44. d 490, 1842, i., 448.
e 425, 1868. f 819, 1828. g 789, 1871, 3 s. xii., 293.

was a performer who accomplished the feat of remaining under water four minutes and eight seconds in full view of the audience. Miss Lurline swam about in her aquarium, which was brilliantly illuminated, ate, reclined, and appeared to be taking a short nap during her short immersion. In Paris, some years since, there was exhibited a creature called " l'homme-poisson," who performed feats similar to Lurline, including the smoking of a cigarette held entirely in his mouth. In all these exhibitions all sorts of artificial means are used to make the submersion appear long. Great ceremony, music, and the counting of the seconds in a loud voice from the stage, all tend to make the time appear much longer than it really is. However, James Finney in London, April 7, 1886, stayed under water four minutes, twenty-nine and one-fourth seconds, and one of his feats was to pick up 70 or 80 gold-plated half-pennies with his mouth, his hands being securely tied behind his back, and never emerging from his tank until his feat was fully accomplished. In company with his sister he played a game of " nap " under water, using porcelain cards and turning them to the view of the audience. " Professor Enochs " recently stayed under water at Lowell, Mass., for four minutes, forty-six and one-fifth seconds. The best previous record was four minutes, thirty-five seconds, made by " Professor Beaumont " at Melbourne on December 16, 1893.

For the most satisfactory examples of prolonged submersion we must look to the **divers**, particularly the natives who trade in coral, and the pearl fishers. Diving is an ancient custom, and even legendary exploits of this nature are recorded. Homer compares the fall of Hector's chariot to the action of a diver ; and specially trained men were employed at the Siege of Syracuse, their mission being to laboriously scuttle the enemy's vessels. Many of the old historians mention diving, and Herodotus speaks of a diver by the name of Scyllias who was engaged by Xerxes to recover some articles of value which had been sunk on some Persian vessels in a tempest. Egyptian divers are mentioned by Plutarch, who says that Anthony was deceived by Cleopatra in a fishing contest by securing expert divers to place the fish upon the hooks. There was a historical or rather legendary character by the name of Didion, who was noted for his exploits in the river Meuse. He had the ability to stay under water a considerable length of time, and even to catch fish while submerged.

There was a famous diver in Sicily at the end of the fifteenth century whose feats are recorded in the writings of Alexander ab Alexandro, Pontanus, and Father Kircher, the Jesuit savant. This man's name was Nicolas, born of poor parents at Catania. From his infancy he showed an extraordinary power of diving and swimming, and from his compatriots soon acquired various names indicative of his capacity. He became very well known throughout Sicily, and for his patron had Frederick, King of Naples. In the present day, the sponge-fishers and pearl-fishers in the West Indies, the

Mediterranean, the Indian Seas, and the Gulf of Mexico invite the attention of those interested in the anomalies of suspended animation. There are many marvelous tales of their ability to remain under water for long periods. It is probable that none remain submerged over two minutes, but, what is more remarkable, they are supposed to dive to extraordinary depths, some as much as 150 to 200 feet. Ordinarily they remain under water from a minute to one and a half minutes. Remaining longer, the face becomes congested, the eyes injected, the sputum bloody, due to rupture of some of the minute vessels in the lung. It is said by those who have observed them carefully that few of these divers live to an advanced age. Many of them suffer apoplectic attacks, and some of them become blind from congestion of the ocular vessels. The Syrian divers are supposed to carry weights of considerable size in their hands in order to facilitate the depth and duration of submersion. It is also said that the divers of Oceanica use heavy stones. According to Guyot-Daubès,[394] in the Philippine Isles the native pearl-fishers teach their children to dive to the depth of 25 meters. The Tahitians, who excited the admiration of Cook, are noted for their extraordinary diving. Speaking of the inhabitants of the island of Fakaraya, near Tahiti, de la Quesnerie says that the pearl-fishers do not hesitate to dive to the depth even of 100 feet after their coveted prizes. On the Ceylon coast the mother-of-pearl fishers are under the direction of the English Government, which limits the duration and the practice of this occupation. These divers are generally Cingalese, who practise the exercise from infancy. As many as 500 small boats can be seen about the field of operation, each equipped with divers. A single diver makes about ten voyages under the water, and then rests in the bottom of the boat, when his comrade takes his place. Among other native divers are the Arabs of Algeria and some of the inhabitants of the Mexican coast.

It might be well to mention here the divers who work by means of apparatus. The ancients had knowledge of contrivances whereby they could stay under water some time. Aristotle speaks of an instrument by which divers could rest under water in communication with the air, and compares it with the trunk of an elephant wading a stream deeper than his height. In the presence of Charles V. diving bells were used by the Greeks in 1540. In 1660 some of the cannon of the sunken ships of the Spanish Armada were raised by divers in diving bells. Since then various improvements in submarine armor have been made, gradually evolving into the present perfected diving apparatus of to-day, by which men work in the holds of vessels sunk in from 120 to 200 feet of water. The enormous pressure of the water at these great depths makes it necessary to have suits strong enough to resist it. Lambert, a celebrated English diver, recovered £90,000 in specie from the steamer Alphonso XII., a Spanish mail boat belonging to the Lopez line, which sank off Point Gando, Grand Canary, in 26½ fathoms of water. For nearly six months the salvage party, despatched by the underwriters in May,

1885, persevered in the operations; two divers lost their lives, the golden bait being in the treasure-room beneath the three decks, but Lambert finished the task successfully.

Deep-sea divers only acquire proficiency after long training. It is said that as a rule divers are indisposed to taking apprentices, as they are afraid of their vocation being crowded and their present ample remuneration diminished. At present there are several schools. At Chatham, England, there is a school of submarine mining, in which men are trained to lay torpedoes and complete harbor defense. Most of these divers can work six hours at a time in from 35 to 50 feet of water. Divers for the Royal Navy are trained at Sheerness. When sufficiently trained to work at the depth of 150 feet seamen-divers are fully qualified, and are drafted to the various ships. They are connected with an air-pump in charge of trustworthy men; they signal for their tools and material, as well as air, by means of a special line for this purpose. At some distance below the water the extraordinary weight of the suits cannot be felt, and the divers work as well in armor as in ordinary laboring clothes. One famous diver says that the only unpleasant experience he ever had in his career as a diver, not excepting the occasion of his first dive, was a drumming in the ears, as a consequence of which, after remaining under water at a certain work for nine hours, he completely lost the use of one ear for three months, during which time he suffered agony with the earache. These men exhibit absolute indifference to the dangers attached to their calling, and some have been known to sleep many fathoms beneath the surface. Both by means of their signal lines and by writing on a slate they keep their associates informed of the progress of their work.

Suspension of the Pulse.—In some cases the pulse is not apparent for many days before actual death, and there have been instances in which, although the pulse ceased for an extended period, the patient made an ultimate recovery. In reviewing the older literature we find that Ballonius[185] mentions an instance in which the pulse was not apparent for fourteen days before complete asphyxia. Ramazzini[660] describes a case of cessation of the pulse four days before death. Schenck[718] details the history of a case in which the pulse ceased for three days and asphyxia was almost total, but the patient eventually recovered. There is a noteworthy observation[a] in which there was cessation of the pulse for nine days without a fatal issue.

Some persons seem to have a preternatural control over their circulatory system, apparently enabling them to produce **suspension of cardiac movement at will.** Cheyne speaks of a Colonel Townshend who appeared to possess the power of dying, as it were, at will,—that is, so suspending the heart's action that no pulsation could be detected. After lying in this state of lifelessness for a short period, life would become slowly established without any consciousness or volition on the man's part. The longest period in

a 282, 1732, 287.

which he remained in this death-like condition was about thirty minutes. A postmortem examination of this person was awaited with great interest; but after his death nothing was found to explain the power he possessed over his heart.

Saint Augustin knew of a priest named Rutilut who had the power of voluntarily simulating death. Both the pulsation and respiration was apparently abolished when he was in his lifeless condition. Burning and pricking left visible effects on the skin after his recovery, but had no apparent effect on his lethargy. Chaillé [a] reports an instance of voluntary suspension of the pulse.

Relative to **hibernation,** it is well-known that mice, snakes, and some reptiles, as well as bees, sometimes seem to entirely suspend animation for an extended period, and especially in the cold weather. In Russia fish are transported frozen stiff, but return to life after being plunged into cold water. A curious tale is told by Harley, from Sir John Lubbock, of a snail brought from Egypt and thought to be dead. It was placed on a card and put in position on a shelf in the British Museum in March, 1845. In March, 1850, after having been gummed to a label for five years, it was noticed to have an apparent growth on its mouth and was taken out and placed in water, when it soon showed signs of life and ate cabbage leaves offered to it. It has been said, we think with credible evidence, that cereal seeds found in the tombs with mummies have grown when planted, and Harley quotes an instance of a gentleman who took some berries, possibly the remnants of Pharaoh's daughter's last meal, coming as they did from her mummified stomach after lying dormant in an Egyptian tomb many centuries, and planted them in his garden, where they soon grew, and he shortly had a bush as flourishing as any of those emanating from fresh seeds.

Human hibernation is an extremely rare anomaly. Only the **fakirs of India** seem to have developed this power, and even the gifted ones there are seldom seen. Many theories have been advanced to explain this ability of the fakirs, and many persons have discredited all the stories relative to their powers; on the other hand, all who have witnessed their exhibitions are convinced of their genuineness. Furthermore, these persons are extremely scarce and are indifferent to money; none has been enticed out of his own country to give exhibitions. When one dies in a community, his place is never filled—proving that he had no accomplices who knew any fraudulent secret practices, otherwise the accomplice would soon step out to take his place. These men have undoubtedly some extraordinary mode of sending themselves into a long trance, during which the functions of life are almost entirely suspended. We can readily believe in their ability to fast during their periods of burial, as we have already related authentic instances of fasting for a great length of time, during which the individual exercised his normal functions.

[a] 593, xvi., 388.

To the fakir, who neither visibly breathes nor shows circulatory movements, and who never moves from his place of confinement, fasting should be comparatively easy, when we consider the number of men whose minds were actively at work during their fasts, and who also exercised much physical power.

Harley [a] says that the fakirs begin their performances by taking a large dose of the powerfully stupefying " bang," thus becoming narcotized. In this state they are lowered into a cool, quiet tomb, which still further favors the prolongation of the artificially induced vital lethargy ; in this condition they rest for from six to eight weeks. When resurrected they are only by degrees restored to life, and present a wan, haggard, debilitated, and wasted appearance. Braid [b] is credited, on the authority of Sir Claude Wade, with stating that a fakir was buried in an unconscious state at Lahore in 1837, and when dug up, six weeks later, he presented all the appearances of a dead person. The legs and arms were shrunken and stiff, and the head reclined on the shoulder in a manner frequently seen in a corpse. There was no pulsation of the heart or arteries of the arm or temple—in fact, no really visible signs of life. By degrees this person was restored to life. Every precaution had been taken in this case to prevent the possibility of fraud, and during the period of interment the grave was guarded night and day by soldiers of the regiment stationed at Lahore.

Honigberger,[c] a German physician in the employ of Runjeet Singh, has an account of a fakir of Punjaub who allowed himself to be buried in a well-secured vault for such a long time that grain sown in the soil above the vault sprouted into leaf before he was exhumed. Honigberger affirms that the time of burial was over 40 days, and that on being submitted to certain processes the man recovered and lived many years after. Sir Henry Lawrence verified the foregoing statements. The chest in which the fakir was buried was sealed with the Runjeet stamp on it, and when the man was brought up he was cold and apparently lifeless. Honigberger also states that this man, whose name was Haridas, was four months in a grave in the mountains ; to prove the absolute suspension of animation, the chin was shaved before burial, and at exhumation this part was as smooth as on the day of interment. This latter statement naturally calls forth comment when we consider the instances that are on record of the growth of beard and hair after death.

There is another account of a person of the same class who had the power of suspending animation,[d] and who would not allow his coffin to touch the earth for fear of worms and insects, from which he is said to have suffered at a previous burial.

It has been stated that the fakirs are either eunuchs or hermaphrodites,

a 548, 1881, ii., 733.   b " Treatise on Human Hibernation," 1850.
c 548, 1870, i., 21.   d Calcutta Med. Jour., 1835.

social outcasts, having nothing in common with the women or men of their neighborhood ; but Honigberger mentions one who disproved this ridiculous theory by eloping to the mountains with his neighbor's wife.

Instances of **recovery after asphyxia from hanging** are to be found, particularly among the older references of a time when hanging was more common than it is to-day. Bartholinus,[189] Blegny,[215] Camerarius,[247] Morgagni,[576] Pechlin,[621] Schenck,[718] Stoll,[751] and Wepfer[a] all mention recovery after hanging. Forestus[348] describes a case in which a man was rescued by provoking vomiting with vinegar, pepper, and mustard seed. There is a case on record[b] in which a person was saved after hanging nineteen minutes. There was a case of a man brought into the Hôpital Saint-Louis[c] asphyxiated by strangulation, having been hung for some time. His rectal temperature was only 93.3° F., but six hours after it rose to 101.6° F., and he subsequently recovered. Taylor[d] cites the instance of a stout woman of forty-four who recovered from hanging. When the woman was found by her husband she was hanging from the top of a door, having been driven to suicide on account of his abuse and intemperance. When first seen by Taylor she was comatose, her mouth was surrounded by white froth, and the swollen tongue protruded from it. Her face was bloated, her lips of a darkened hue, and her neck of a brown parchment-color. About the level of the larynx, the epidermis was distinctly abraded, indicating where the rope had been. The conjunctiva was insensible and there was no contractile response of the pupil to the light of a candle. The reflexes of the soles of the feet were tested, but were quite in abeyance. There was no respiratory movement and only slight cardiac pulsation. After vigorous measures the woman ultimately recovered. Recovery is quite rare when the asphyxiation has gone so far, the patients generally succumbing shortly after being cut down or on the following day. Chevers[266] mentions a most curious case, in which cerebral congestion from the asphyxiation of strangling was accidentally relieved by an additional cut across the throat. The patient was a man who was set upon by a band of **Thugs** in India, who, pursuant to their usual custom, strangled him and his fellow-traveler. Not being satisfied that he was quite dead, one of the band returned and made several gashes across his throat. This latter action effectually relieved the congestion caused by the strangulation and undoubtedly saved his life, while his unmutilated companion was found dead. After the wounds in his throat had healed this victim of the Thugs gave such a good description of the murderous band that their apprehension and execution soon followed.

Premature Burial.—In some instances simulation of death has been so exact that it has led to premature interment. There are many such cases on record, and it is a popular superstition of the laity that all the gruesome tales

a "Exercit. in Apoplex.," 181.
b 200, x., 242.
c 476, 1870, i., 446.
d 381, 1880, ii., 387.

are true of persons buried alive and returning to life, only to find themselves hopelessly lost in a narrow coffin many feet below the surface of the earth. Among the lower classes the dread of being buried before life is extinct is quite generally felt, and for generations the medical profession have been denounced for their inability to discover an infallible sign of death. Most of the instances on record, and particularly those from lay journals, are vivid exaggerations, drawn from possibly such a trivial sign as a corpse found with the fist tightly clenched or the face distorted, which are the inspiration of the horrible details of the dying struggles of the person in the coffin. In the works of Fontenelle there are 46 cases recorded of the premature interment of the living, in which apparent has been mistaken for real death. None of these cases, however, are sufficiently authentic to be reliable. Moreover, in all modern methods of burial, even if life were not extinct, there could be no possibility of consciousness or of struggling. Absolute asphyxiation would soon follow the closing of the coffin lid.

We must admit, however, that the mistake has been made, particularly in instances of catalepsy or trance, and during epidemics of malignant fevers or plagues, in which there is an absolute necessity of hasty burial for the prevention of contagion. In a few instances on the battle-field sudden syncope, or apparent death, has possibly led to premature interment; but in the present day this is surely a very rare occurrence. There is also a danger of mistake from cases of asphyxiation, drowning, and similar sudden suspensions of the vital functions.

It is said that in the eighty-fourth Olympiad, Empedocles restored to life a woman who was about to be buried, and that this circumstance induced the Greeks, for the future protection of the supposed dead, to establish laws which enacted that no person should be interred until the sixth or seventh day. But even this extension of time did not give satisfaction, and we read that when Hephestion, at whose funeral obsequies Alexander the Great was present, was to be buried his funeral was delayed until the tenth day. There is also a legend that when Acilius Aviola fell a victim to disease he was burned alive, and although he cried out, it was too late to save him, as the fire had become so widespread before life returned.

While returning to his country house Asclepiades, a physician denominated the "God of Physic," and said to have been a descendant of Æsculapius, saw during the time of Pompey the Great a crowd of mourners about to start a fire on a funeral pile. It is said that by his superior knowledge he perceived indications of life in the corpse and ordered the pile destroyed, subsequently restoring the supposed deceased to life. These examples and several others of a similar nature induced the Romans to delay their funeral rites, and laws were enacted to prevent haste in burning, as well as in interment. It was not until the eighth day that the final rites were performed, the days immediately subsequent to death having their own special ceremonies. The

Turks were also fearful of premature interment and subjected the defunct to every test; among others, one was to examine the contractility of the sphincter ani, which shows their keen observation of a well-known modern medical fact.

According to the Memoirs of Amelot de la Houssaye, Cardinal Espinola, Prime Minister to Philip II., put his hand to the embalmer's knife with which he was about to be opened. 'It is said that Vesalius, sometimes called the "Father of Anatomy," having been sent for to perform an autopsy on a woman subject to hysteric convulsions, and who was supposed to be dead, on making the first incision perceived by her motion and cries that she was still alive. This circumstance, becoming known, rendered him so odious that he had to leave the community in which he practised, and it is believed that he never entirely recovered from the shock it gave him. The Abbé Prévost, so well known by his works and the singularities of his life, was seized by apoplexy in the Forest of Chantilly on October 23, 1763. His body was carried to the nearest village, and the officers of justice proceeded to open it, when a cry he sent forth frightened all the assistants and convinced the surgeon in charge that the Abbé was not dead; but it was too late to save him, as he had already received a mortal wound.

Massien speaks of a woman living in Cologne in 1571 who was interred living, but was not awakened from her lethargy until a grave-digger opened her grave to steal a valuable ring which she wore. This instance has been cited in nearly every language. There is another more recent instance, coming from Poitiers, of the wife of a goldsmith named Mernache who was buried with all her jewels. During the night a beggar attempted to steal her jewelry, and made such exertion in extracting one ring that the woman recovered and was saved. After this resurrection she is said to have had several children. This case is also often quoted. Zacchias [830] mentions an instance which, from all appearances, is authentic. It was that of a young man, pest-stricken and thought to be dead, who was placed with the other dead for burial. He exhibited signs of life, and was taken back to the pest-hospital. Two days later he entered a lethargic condition simulating death, and was again on his way to the sepulcher, when he once more recovered.

It is said that when the body of William, Earl of Pembroke,[a] who died April 10, 1630, was opened to be embalmed, the hand raised when the first incision was made. There is a story of an occurrence which happened on a return voyage from India.[b] The wife of one of the passengers, an officer in the army, to all appearances died. They were about to resort to sea-burial, when, through the interposition of the husband, who was anxious to take her home, the ship-carpenters started to construct a coffin suitable for a long voyage, a process which took several days, during which time she lay in her berth, swathed in robes and ready for interment. When the coffin was at last ready the husband went to take his last farewell, and removed the wed-

a 536, 1887, i., 586.   b 548, 1866, i., 287.

ding-ring, which was quite tightly on her finger. In the effort to do this she was aroused, recovered, and arrived in England perfectly well.

It is said that when a daughter of Henry Laurens, the first President of the American Congress, died of small-pox, she was laid out as dead, and the windows of the room were opened for ventilation. While left alone in this manner she recovered. This circumstance so impressed her illustrious father that he left explicit directions that in case of his death he should be burned. [a] The same journal also contains the case of a maid-servant who recovered thrice on her way to the grave, and who, when really dead, was kept a preposterous length of time before burial.

The literature on this subject is very exhaustive, volumes having been written on the uncertainty of the signs of death, with hundreds of examples cited illustrative of the danger of premature interment. The foregoing instances have been given as indicative of the general style of narration ; for further information the reader is referred to the plethora of material on this subject.

Postmortem Anomalies.—Among the older writers startling **movements of a corpse** have given rise to much discussion, and possibly often led to suspicion of premature burial. Bartholinus [190] describes motion in a cadaver. Barlow [b] says that movements were noticed after death in the victims of Asiatic cholera. The bodies were cold and expressions were death-like, but there were movements simulating natural life. The most common was flexion of the right leg, which would also be drawn up toward the body and resting on the left leg. In some cases the hand was moved, and in one or two instances a substance was grasped as if by reflex action. Some observers have stated that reflex movements of the face were quite noticeable. These movements continued sometimes for upward of an hour, occurring mostly in muscular subjects who died very suddenly, and in whom the muscular irritability or nervous stimulus or both had not become exhausted at the moment of dissolution. Richardson [173] doubts the existence of postmortem movements of respiration.

Snow is accredited [c] with having seen a girl in Soho who, dying of scarlet fever, turned dark at the moment of death, but in a few hours presented such **a life-like appearance and color** as to almost denote the return of life. The center of the cheeks became colored in a natural fashion, and the rest of the body resumed the natural flesh color. The parents refused to believe that death had ensued. Richardson remarks that he had seen two similar cases, and states that he believes the change is due to oxidation of the blood surcharged with carbon dioxid. The moist tissues suffuse carbonized blood, and there occurs an osmotic interchange between the carbon dioxid and the oxygen of the air resulting in an oxygenation of the blood, and modification of the color from dark venous to arterial red.

---

[a] 548, 1866, i., 287.   [b] 173, 1889, 5.   [c] Richardson, 173, 1889.

A peculiar postmortem anomaly is **erection of the penis.** The Ephemerides and Morgagni [576] discuss postmortem erection, and Guyon mentions that on one occasion he saw 14 negroes hanged, and states that at the moment of suspension erection of the penis occurred in each ; in nine of these blacks traces of this erectile state were perceived an hour after death.

Cadaveric perspiration has been observed and described by several authors, and Paullini [620] has stated that he has seen tears flow from the eyes of a corpse.

The retardation of putrefaction of the body after death sometimes presents interesting changes. **Petrifaction or mummification** of the body are quite well known, and not being in the province of this work, will be referred to collateral books on this subject ; but sometimes an unaccountable preservation takes place. In a tomb recently opened at Canterbury Cathedral, [a] for the purpose of discovering what Archbishop's body it contained, the corpse was of an extremely offensive and sickening odor, unmistakably that of putrefaction. The body was that of Hubert Walter, who died in 1204 A. D., and the decomposition had been retarded, and was actually still in progress, several hundred years after burial.

Retardation of the putrefactive process has been noticed in bodies some years **under water.** König of Hermannstadt mentions a man who, forty years previous to the time of report, had fallen under the waters of Echoschacht, and who was found in a complete state of preservation.

Postmortem Growth of Hair and Nails.—The hair and beard may grow after death, and even change color. Bartholinus recalls a case of a man who had short, black hair and beard at the time of interment, but who, some time after death, was found to possess long and yellowish hair. Aristotle discusses postmortem growth of the hair, and Garmanus cites an instance in which the beard and hair were cut several times from the cadaver. We occasionally see evidences of this in the dissecting-rooms. Caldwell [b] mentions a body buried four years, the hair from which protruded at the points where the joints of the coffin had given away. The hair of the head measured 18 inches, that of the beard eight inches, and that on the breast from four to six inches. Rosse of Washington mentions an instance in which after burial the hair turned from dark brown to red, and also cites a case in a Washington cemetery of a girl, twelve or thirteen years old, who when exhumed was found to have a new growth of hair all over her body. The Ephemerides contains an account of hair suddenly turning gray after death.

Nails sometimes grow several inches after death, and there is on record the account of an idiot who had an idiosyncrasy for long nails, and after death the nails were found to have grown to such an extent that they curled up under the palms and soles.

The untoward effects of the emotions on the vital functions are

[a] 476, 1890, i., 1105.   [b] 538, 1877.

quite well exemplified in medical literature.   There is an abundance of cases reported in which joy, fear, pride, and grief have produced a fatal issue.   In history we have the old story of the Lacedemonian woman who for some time had believed her son was dead, and who from the sudden joy occasioned by seeing him alive, herself fell lifeless.   There is a similar instance in Roman history. Aristotle, Pliny, Livy, Cicero, and others cite instances of death from sudden or excessive joy.   Fouquet died of excessive joy on being released from prison. A niece of the celebrated Leibnitz immediately fell dead on seeing a casket of gold left to her by her deceased uncle.

Galen mentions **death from joy,** and in comment upon it he says that the emotion of joy is much more dangerous than that of anger.   In discussing this subject, Haller says that the blood is probably sent with such violence to the brain as to cause apoplexy.   There is one case on record in which after a death from sudden joy the pericardium was found full of blood.[a]   The Ephemerides, Marcellus Donatus,[306] Martini, and Struthius all mention death from joy.

Death from violent laughter has been recorded, but in this instance it is very probable that death was not due to the emotion itself, but to the extreme convulsion and exertion used in the laughter.   The Ephemerides mentions a death from laughter, and also describes the death of a pregnant woman from violent mirth.   Roy,[b] Swinger,[c] and Camerarius[247] have recorded instances of death from laughter.   Strange as it may seem, Saint-Foix[d] says that the Moravian brothers, a sect of Anabaptists having great horror of bloodshed, executed their condemned brethren by tickling them to death.

Powerfully depressing emotions, which are called by Kant "asthenic," such as **great and sudden sorrow,** grief, or fright, have a pronounced effect on the vital functions, at times even **causing death.**   Throughout literature and history we have examples of this anomaly.   In Shakespeare's "Pericles," Thaisa, the daughter to Simonides and wife of Pericles, frightened when pregnant by a threatened shipwreck, dies in premature childbirth.

In Scott's "Guy Mannering," Mrs. Bertram, on suddenly learning of the death of her little boy, is thrown into premature labor, followed by death. Various theories are advanced in explanation of this anomaly.   A very plausible one is, that the cardiac palsy is caused by energetic and persistent excitement of the inhibitory cardiac nerves.   Strand[e] is accredited with saying that agony of the mind produces rupture of the heart.   It is quite common to hear the expression, "Died of a broken heart;" and, strange to say, in some cases postmortem examination has proved the actual truth of the saying. Bartholinus, Fabricius Hildanus, Pliny, Rhodius, Schenck, Marcellus Donatus, Riedlin, and Garengeot speak of death from fright and fear, and the

---

a "Anecdotes de Médecine," 117.   b 462, 1812, Oct., 199.
c "Theatre vitæ human," 2656.   d "Essais historiques sur Paris," T. v., 54.
e "Treatise on the Physical Cause of the Death of Christ."

Ephemerides describes a death the direct cause of which was intense shame. Deleau,[a] a celebrated doctor of Paris, while embracing his favorite daughter, who was in the last throes of consumption, was so overcome by intense grief that he fell over her corpse and died, and both were buried together.

The **fear of child-birth** has been frequently cited as a cause of death. McClintock quotes a case from Travers of a young lady, happily married, who entertained a fear of death in child-birth ; although she had been safely delivered, she suddenly and without apparent cause died in six hours. Every region of the body was examined with minutest care by an eminent physician, but no signs indicative of the cause of death were found. Mordret cites a similar instance of death from fear of labor. Morgagni[576] mentions a woman who died from the disappointment of bearing a girl baby when she was extremely desirous of a boy.

The following case, quoted from Lauder Brunton,[b] shows the extent of shock which may be produced by fear : Many years ago a janitor of a college had rendered himself obnoxious to the students, and they determined to punish him. Accordingly they prepared a block and an axe, which they conveyed to a lonely place, and having appropriately dressed themselves, some of them prepared to act as judges, and sent others of their company to bring him before them. He first affected to treat the whole affair as a joke, but was solemnly assured by the students that they meant it in real earnest. He was told to prepare for immediate death. The trembling janitor looked all around in the vain hope of seeing some indication that nothing was really meant, but stern looks met him everywhere. He was blindfolded, and made to kneel before the block. The executioner's axe was raised, but, instead of the sharp edge, a wet towel was brought sharply down on the back of the neck. The bandage was now removed from the culprit's eyes, but to the horror and astonishment of the students they found that he was dead. Such a case may be due to heart-failure from fear or excitement.

It is not uncommon that **death ensues from the shock alone following blows that cause no visible injury,** but administered to vital parts. This is particularly true of blows about the external genital region, or epigastrium, where the solar plexus is an active factor in inhibition. Ivanhoff of Bulgaria in 1886 speaks of a man of forty-five who was dealt a blow on the testicle in a violent street fight, and staggering, he fell insensible. Despite vigorous medical efforts he never regained consciousness and died in forty-five minutes. Postmortem examination revealed everything normal, and death must have been caused by syncope following violent pain. Watkins[c] cites an instance occurring in South Africa. A native shearing sheep for a farmer provoked his master's ire by calling him by some nickname. While the man was in a squatting posture the farmer struck him in the epigastrium. He followed this up by a kick in the side and a blow on the head, neither of

a 224, 1878, ii., 381. b 846, 292. c 476, 1884, i., 916.

which, however, was as severe as the first blow.   The man fell unconscious and died.   At the autopsy there were no signs indicative of death, which must have been due to the shock following the blow on the epigastrium.

As illustrative of the sensitiveness of the epigastric region, Vincent relates the following case : " A man received a blow by a stick upon the epigastrium. He had an anxious expression and suffered from oppression.   Irregular heart-action and shivering were symptoms that gradually disappeared during the day.   In the evening his appetite returned and he felt well ; during the night he died without a struggle, and at the autopsy there was absolutely nothing abnormal to be found."   Blows upon the neck often produce sudden collapse. Prize-fighters are well aware of the effects of a blow on the jugular vein. Maschka, quoted by Warren,[846] reports the case of a boy of twelve, who was struck on the anterior portion of the larynx by a stone.   He fell lifeless to the ground, and at autopsy no local lesion was found nor any lesion elsewhere. The sudden death may be attributed in this case partly to shock and partly to cerebral anemia.

Soldiers have been seen to drop lifeless on the battle-field without apparent injury or organic derangement ; in the olden times this death was attributed to fear and fright, and later was supposed to be caused by what is called " the wind of a cannon-ball."   Tolifree [a] has written an article on this cause of sudden death and others have discussed it.   By some it is maintained that the momentum acquired by a cannon-ball generates enough force in the neighboring air to prostrate a person in the immediate vicinity of its path of flight.

<hr>

[a] 187, 1834, ii., 151.

CHAPTER X.

SURGICAL ANOMALIES OF THE HEAD AND NECK.

Injuries of such a delicate organ as **the eye,** in which the slightest accident can produce such disastrous consequences, naturally elicit the interest of all. Examples of **exophthalmos,** or protrusion of the eye from the orbit from bizarre causes, are of particular interest. Among the older writers we find Ficker[a] and the Ephemerides giving instances of exophthalmos from vomiting. Fabricius Hildanus[b] mentions a similar instance. Salmuth,[706] Verduc,[799] and others mention extrusion of the eyeball from the socket, due to excessive coughing. Ab Heers[409] and Sennert[732] mention instances in which after replacement the sight was uninjured. Tyler relates the case of a man who, after arising in the morning, blew his nose violently, and to his horror his left eye extruded from the orbit. With the assistance of his wife it was immediately replaced and a bandage placed over it. When Tyler saw him the upper lid was slightly swollen and discolored, but there was no hemorrhage.

Hutchinson[c] describes extrusion of the eyeball from the orbit caused by a thrust with a stick. There was paraphymotic strangulation of the globe, entirely preventing replacement and necessitating excision. Reyssie[d] speaks of a patient who, during a fire, was struck in the right eye by a stream of water from a hose, violently thrusting the eye backward. Contracting under the double influence of shock and cold, the surrounding tissues forced the eyeball from the orbit, and an hour later Reyssie saw the patient with the eye hanging by the optic nerve and muscles. Its reduction was easy, and after some minor treatment vision was perfectly restored in the injured organ. Thirty months after the accident the patient had perfect vision, and the eye had never in the slightest way discommoded him.

Bodkin[e] mentions the case of a woman of sixty who fell on the key in a door and completely avulsed her eye. In von Graefe's Archiv there is a record of a man of seventy-five who suffered complete avulsion of the eye by a cart-wheel passing over his head. Verhaeghe records[f] complete avulsion of the eye caused by a man falling against the ring of a sharp-worn key. Hamill[g]

[a] 452, 1809, xi., 63. [b] 334, cent. i., obs. i. [c] 693, 1866.
[d] 363, 1859, No. 65. [e] 312, 1854. [f] 145, xxvi., 99. [g] 224, 1878, i., 894.

describes the case of a young girl whose conjunctiva was pierced by one of the rests of an ordinary gas-bracket. Being hooked at one of its extremities the iron became entangled in either the inferior oblique or external rectus muscles, and completely avulsed the eyeball upon the cheek. The real damage could not be estimated, as the patient never returned after the muscle was clipped off close to its conjunctival insertion. Calhoun [a] mentions an instance of a little Esquimaux dog whose head was seized between the jaws of a large Newfoundland with such force as to press the left eyeball from the socket. The ball rested on the cheek, held by the taut optic nerve ; the cornea was opaque. The ball was carefully and gently replaced, and sight soon returned to the eye.

In former days there was an old-fashioned manner of fighting called "gouging." In this brutal contest the combatant was successful who could, with his thumb, press his opponent's eyeball out. Strange to say, little serious or permanently bad results followed such inhuman treatment of the eye. Von Langenbeck of Berlin mentions an instance of fracture of the superior maxilla, in which the eyeball was so much displaced as to lodge in the antrum of Highmore. Von Becker of Heidelberg reports the history of a case in which a blow from the horn of a cow dislocated the eye so far back in the orbit as to present the appearance of enucleation. The conjunctiva hid the organ from view, but when it was pulled aside the eyeball was exposed, and in its remote position still possessed the power of vision. In some cases in which exophthalmos has been seemingly spontaneous, extreme laxity of the lids may serve as an explanation. There is an instance on record in which a Polish Jew appeared in a Continental hospital, saying that while turning in bed, without any apparent cause, his eyeball was completely extruded. There have been people who prided themselves on their ability to produce partial exophthalmos.

Rupture of the Eyeball.—Jessop mentions the case of a child of eight who suffered a blow on the eye from a fall against a bedpost, followed by compound rupture of the organ. The wound in the sclerotic was three or four lines in length, and the rent in the conjunctiva was so large that it required three sutures. The chief interest in this case was the rapid and complete recovery of vision.

Adler [b] reports a case of fracture of the superior maxillary in which the dislocated bone-fragment of the lower orbital border, through pressure on the inferior maxillary and counter pressure on the skull, caused rupture of the conjunctiva of the left eye.

Serious Sequelæ of Orbital Injuries.—In some instances injuries primarily to the orbit either by extension or implication of the cerebral contents provoke the most serious issues. Pointed instruments thrust into the orbital cavity may by this route reach the brain. There is a record [c] of death

a 176, 1876.   b Wien. Med. Woch., No. 6, 1895.   c 476, 1831.

caused by a wound of a cavernous sinus through the orbit by the stem of a tobacco-pipe. Bower[a] saw a woman at the Gloucester Infirmary who had been stabbed in the eye by the end of an umbrella. There was profuse hemorrhage from the nostrils and left eye, but no signs indicative of its origin. Death shortly ensued, and at the necropsy a fracture through the roof of the orbit was revealed, the umbrella point having completely severed the optic nerve and divided the ophthalmic artery. The internal carotid artery was wounded in one-half of its circumference at its bend, just before it passes up between the anterior clinoid process and the optic nerve. The cavernous sinus was also opened. In this rare injury, although there was a considerable quantity of clotted blood at the base of the brain, there was no wound to the eyeball nor to the brain itself.

Pepper records a case in which a knife was thrust through the sphenoidal fissure, wounding a large meningeal vein, causing death from intracranial hemorrhage. Nélaton describes an instance in which the point of an umbrella wounded the cavernous sinus and internal carotid artery of the opposite side, causing the formation of an arteriovenous aneurysm which ultimately burst, and death ensued. Polaillon[b] saw a boy of eighteen who was found in a state of coma. It was stated that an umbrella stick had been thrust up through the roof of the orbit and had been withdrawn with much difficulty. The anterior lobe of the brain was evidently much wounded ; an incision was made in the forehead and a portion of the frontal bone chiseled away ; entrance being thus effected, the dura was incised, and some blood and cerebrospinal fluid escaped. Five splinters were removed and a portion of the damaged brain-substance, and a small artery was tied with catgut. The debris of the eyeball was enucleated and a drain was placed in the frontal wound, coming out through the orbit. The patient soon regained consciousness and experienced no bad symptoms afterward. The drains were gradually withdrawn, the process of healing advanced rapidly, and recovery soon ensued.

Annandale[c] mentions an instance in which a knitting-needle penetrated the brain through the orbit. Hewett[d] speaks of perforation of the roof of the orbit and injury to the brain by a lead-pencil.

Gunshot Injuries of the Orbit.—Barkan[e] recites the case in which a leaden ball $\frac{32}{100}$ inch in diameter was thrown from a sling into the left orbital cavity, penetrating between the eyeball and osseous wall of the orbit without rupturing the tunics of the eye or breaking the bony wall of the cavity. It remained lodged two weeks without causing any pain or symptoms, and subsequently worked itself forward, contained in a perfect conjunctival sac, in which it was freely movable.

Buchanan[f] recites the case of a private in the army who was shot at a

a 476, 1879, i., 547.   b 233, Aug., 1891.   c 318, 1877, xii.
d 779, 1848–50, i., 188.   e 616, 1874–5, 444.   f 545, 1862–3, ix., 274.

distance of three feet away, the ball entering the inner canthus of the right eye and lodging under the skin of the opposite side. The eye was not lost, and opacity of the lower part of the cornea alone resulted. Cold water and purging constituted the treatment.

It is said [a] that an old soldier of one of Napoleon's armies had a musket-ball removed from his left orbit after twenty-four years' lodgment. He was struck in the orbit by a musket-ball, but as at the same time a companion fell dead at his side he inferred that the bullet rebounded from his orbit and killed his comrade. For twenty-four years he had suffered from cephalalgia and pains and partial exophthalmos of the left eye. After removal of the ball the eye partially atrophied.

Warren reports a case of a man of thirty-five whose eyeball was destroyed by the explosion of a gun, the breech-pin flying off and penetrating the head. The orbit was crushed ; fourteen months afterward the man complained of soreness on the hard palate, and the whole breech-pin, with screw attached, was extracted. The removal of the pin was followed by fissure of the hard palate, which, however, was relieved by operation. The following is an extract [b] of a report by Wenyon of Fatshan, South China :—

" Tang Shan, Chinese farmer, thirty-one years of age, was injured in the face by the bursting of a shot-gun. After being for upward of two months under the treatment of native practitioners, he came to me on December 4, 1891. I observed a cicatrix on the right side of his nose, and above this a sinus, still unhealed, the orifice of which involved the inner canthus of the right eye, and extended downward and inward for about a centimeter. The sight of the right eye was entirely lost, and the anterior surface of the globe was so uniformly red that the cornea could hardly be distinguished from the surrounding conjunctiva. There was no perceptible enlargement or protrusion of the eyeball, and it did not appear to have sustained any mechanical injury or loss of tissue. The ophthalmia and keratitis were possibly caused by the irritating substances applied to the wound by the Chinese doctors. The sinus on the side of the nose gave exit to a continuous discharge of slightly putrid pus, and the patient complained of continuous headache and occasional dizziness, which interfered with his work. The pain was referred to the right frontal and temporal regions, and the skin on this part of the head had a slight blush, but there was no superficial tenderness. The patient had been told by his native doctors, and he believed it himself, that there was no foreign body in the wound ; but on probing it I easily recognized the lower edge of a hard metallic substance at a depth of about one inch posteriorly from the orifice of the sinus. Being unable to obtain any reliable information as to the probable size or shape of the object, I cautiously made several attempts to remove it through a slightly enlarged opening, but without success. I therefore continued the incision along the side of the nose to the nostril,

a 222, 1846.   b 224, Oct. 12, 1895.

thus laying open the right nasal cavity ; then, seizing the foreign body with a pair of strong forceps, I with difficulty removed the complete breech-pin of a Chinese gun. Its size and shape are accurately represented by the accompanying drawing (Fig. 190). The breech-pin measures a little over three inches in length, and weighs $2\frac{2}{3}$ ounces, or 75.6 grams. It had evidently lain at the back of the orbit, inclined upward and slightly backward from its point of entrance, at an angle of about 45 degrees. On its removal the headache was at once relieved and did not return. In ten days the wound was perfectly healed and the patient went back to his work. A somewhat similar case, but which terminated fatally, is recorded in the American Journal of the Medical Sciences of July, 1882."

The extent of permanent injury done by **foreign bodies in the orbit** is variable. In some instances the most extensive wound is followed by the happiest result, while in others vision is entirely destroyed by a minor injury.

Carter[a] reports a case in which a hat-peg $3\frac{3}{10}$ inches long and about $\frac{1}{4}$ inch in diameter (upon one end of which was a knob nearly $\frac{1}{2}$ inch in diameter) was impacted in the orbit for from ten to twenty days, and during this

Fig. 190.—Breech-pin removed from the orbit. (Actual size.)

time the patient was not aware of the fact. Recovery followed its extraction, the vision and movements of the eye being unimpaired.

According to the Philosophical Transactions[b] a laborer thrust a long lath with great violence into the inner canthus of the left eye of his fellow workman, Edward Roberts. The lath broke off short, leaving a piece two inches long, $\frac{1}{2}$ inch wide, and $\frac{1}{4}$ inch thick, in situ. Roberts rode about a mile to the surgery of Mr. Justinian Morse, who extracted it with much difficulty ; recovery followed, together with restoration of the sight and muscular action. The lath was supposed to have passed behind the eyeball. Collette[c] speaks of an instance in which 186 pieces of glass were extracted from the left orbit, the whole mass weighing 186 Belgian grains. They were blown in by a gust of wind that broke a pane of glass ; after extraction no affection of the brain or eye occurred. Watson[d] speaks of a case in which a chip of steel $\frac{3}{8}$ inch long was imbedded in cellular tissue of the orbit for four days, and was removed without injury to the eye. Wordsworth[e] reports a case in which a foreign body was deeply imbedded in the orbit for six weeks, and was re-

a Ophth. Rev., No. 4, p. 337.   b 629, 1743, 945.   c 145, 1850, 217.
d 224, 1876, i., 506.   e 548, 1861, ii., 452.

moved with subsequent recovery. Chisholm[a] has seen a case in which for five weeks a fly was imbedded in the culdesac between the lower lid and the eyeball.

Foreign bodies are sometimes contained **in the eyeball** for many years. There is an instance on record[b] in which a wooden splinter, five mm. long and two mm. broad, remained in the eye forty-seven years. It was extracted, with the lens in which it was lodged, to relieve pain and other distressing symptoms. Snell[c] reports a case in which a piece of steel was imbedded and encapsulated in the ciliary process twenty-nine years without producing sympathetic irritation of its fellow, but causing such pain as to warrant enucleation of this eye. Gunning[d] speaks of a piece of thorn ⅜ inch long, imbedded in the left eyeball of an old man for six years, causing total loss of vision ; he adds that, after its removal, some improvement was noticed.

Williams mentions a stone-cutter whose left eye was put out by a piece of stone. Shortly after this his right eye was wounded by a knife, causing traumatic cataract, which was extracted by Sir William Wilde, giving the man good sight for twelve years, after which iritis attacked the right eye and produced a false membrane over the pupil so that the man could not work. It was in this condition that he consulted Williams, fourteen years after the loss of the left eye. The eye was atrophied, and on examination a piece of stone was seen projecting from it directly between the lids. The visible portion was ¼ inch long, and the end in the shrunken eye was evidently longer than the end protruding. The sclera was incised, and, after fourteen years' duration in the eye, the stone was removed.

Taylor[e] reports the removal of a piece of bone which had remained quiescent in the eye for fourteen years ; after the removal of the eye the bone was found adherent to the inner tunics. It resembled the lens in size and shape. Williams[f] mentions continual tolerance of foreign bodies in the eyeball for fifteen and twenty-two years ; and Chisholm[g] reports the lodgment of a fragment of metal in the iris for twenty-three years. Liebreich[h] extracted a piece of steel from the interior of the eye where it had been lodged twenty-two years. Barkar[i] speaks of a piece of steel which penetrated through the cornea and lens, and which, five months later, was successfully removed by the extraction of the cataractous lens. Critchett[j] gives an instance of a foreign body being loose in the anterior chamber for sixteen years. Rider[k] speaks of the lodgment of a fragment of a copper percussion cap in the left eye, back of the inner ciliary margin of the iris, for thirty-five years ; and Bartholinus[l] mentions a thorn in the canthus for thirty years. Jacob[m] reports a case in which a chip of iron remained in the eyeball twenty-eight years

a 186, 1870. b 548, 1880, i., 280. c 476, 1880, i., 749. d 476, 1880, i., 749.

e 809, 1878. f 218, 1881, 84. g 476, April 3, 1880. h 224, 1873, ii., 651.

i Archiv. of Opthal. and Otol., N Y., 1874, iv., 231. j 693, 1857-8, i., 264.

k 773, 1872, 160. l 188, iv., obs. 64. m 476, 1880, i., 667.

without giving indications for removal. It was clearly visible, protruding into the anterior surface of the iris, and although it was rusted by its long lodgment, sight in the eye was fairly good, and there was no sign of irritation.

Snell [a] gives an instance in which a piece of steel was imbedded close to the optic disc with retention of sight. It was plainly visible by the opthalmoscope eighteen months after the accident, when as yet no diminution of sight was apparent. Smyly [b] speaks of a portion of a tobacco pipe which was successfully removed from the anterior chamber by an incision through the cornea. Clark [c] mentions a case in which molten lead in the eye caused no permanent injury ; and there are several cases mentioned in confirmation of the statement that the eye seems to be remarkably free from disastrous effects after this injury.

Williamson [d] mentions eyelashes in the anterior chamber of the eye, the result of a stab wound of this organ.

Contusion of the eyeball may cause **dislocation of the lens** into the anterior chamber, and several instances have been recorded. We regret our inability to give the reference or authority for a report that we have seen, stating that by one kick of a horse the lenses of both eyes of a man were synchronously knocked through the eyeballs by the calkins of the horseshoe. Oliver mentions extraction of a lens by a thrust of a cow's horn.

Lowe [e] speaks of rupture of the anterior capsule of the lens from violent sneezing, with subsequent absorption of the lenticular substance and restoration of vision. Trioen [f] mentions a curious case of expulsion of the crystalline lens from the eye in ophthalmia, through the formation of a corneal fissure. The authors have personal knowledge of a case of spontaneous extrusion of the lens through a corneal ulcer, in a case of ophthalmia of the new-born.

Injury of the Eyeball by Birds.—There are several instances in which birds have pierced the eyeball with their bills, completely destroying vision. Not long since a prominent taxidermist winged a crane, picked it up, and started to examine it, when it made one thrust with its bill and totally destroyed his eyeball. In another instance a man was going from the railroad station to his hotel in a gale of wind, when, as he turned the corner of the street, an English sparrow was blown into his face. Its bill penetrated his eyeball and completely ruined his sight. There are several instances on record in which game fowls have destroyed the eyes of their owners. In one case a game cock almost completed the enucleation of the eye of his handler, by striking him with his gaff while preparing in a cock-pit.

Moorehead [g] explains a **rare accident** to an eye as follows :—

" Mr. S. B. A., while attending to his bees, was stung by one upon the right upper eyelid near its center. An employee, who was assisting in the work, immediately discovered the sting driven in the lid and cautiously ex-

[a] 693, ix., part iii.   [b] 310, 1876, 181.   [c] 591, 1852, 303.

[d] 476, 1882, ii., 448.   [e] 476, 1861, i., 530.   [f] 784, 98.   [g] 533, May 27, 1893.

tracted it, stating that he made sufficient traction to lift the lid well away from the globe. In a few hours the lid became much swollen, but the pain experienced at first had disappeared. Before retiring for the night he began gentle massage of the lid, stroking it horizontally with his finger. The edematous condition was by this means much reduced in a short time. While thus engaged in stroking the lid he suddenly experienced intense pain in the eye as if it had been pierced by a sharp instrument. The suffering was very severe, and he passed a wretched night, constantly feeling 'something in his eye.'

"The next morning, the trouble continuing, he came to me for relief. Upon examination of the lid, no opening could be made out where the sting had penetrated, and a minute inspection of the conjunctival surface with a good glass failed to reveal any foreign substance. Cleansing the lid thoroughly, and carefully inspecting with a lens under strong light, a minute dark point was made out about the center of the lid. Feeling that this might be the point of the sting, I had recourse to several expedients for its removal, but without success. Finally, with a fine knife, I succeeded in cutting down by the side of the body and tilting it out. Examination with a $\frac{1}{5}$ inch objective confirmed my opinion that it was the point of the bee-sting.

" The barbed formation of the point explains how, under the stroking with the finger, it was forced through the dense tarsal cartilage and against the cornea of the eye."

There is a story told in La Médecine Moderne [a] of a seamstress of Berlin who was in the habit of allowing her dog to lick her face. She was attacked with a severe inflammation of the right eye, which had to be enucleated, and was found full of tenia echinococcus, evidently derived from the dog's tongue.

Gabb [b] mentions a case of epistaxis in which the blood welled up through the lacrimal ducts and suffused into the eye so that it was constantly necessary to wipe the lower eyelid, and the discharge ceased only when the nose stopped bleeding. A brief editorial note on **epistaxis through the eyes,** referring to a case in the Medical News of November 30, 1895, provoked further reports from numerous correspondents. Among others, the following :—

" Dr. T. L. Wilson of Bellwood, Pa., relates the case of an old lady of seventy-eight whom he found with the blood gushing from the nostrils. After plugging the nares thoroughly with absorbent cotton dusted with tannic acid he was surprised to see the blood ooze out around the eyelids and trickle down the cheeks. This oozing continued for the greater part of an hour, being controlled by applications of ice to both sides of the nose."

" Dr. F. L. Donlon of New York City reports the case of a married woman, about fifty years old, in whom epistaxis set in suddenly at 11 P. M., and had continued for several hours, when the anterior nares were plugged.

a 545, June 6, 1896.   b 224, 1883, i., 715.

In a short time the woman complained that she could scarcely see, owing to the welling up of blood in the eyes and trickling down her face. The bleeding only ceased when the posterior nares also were plugged."

"Dr. T. G. Wright of Plainville, Conn., narrates the case of a young man whom he found in the night, bleeding profusely, and having already lost a large amount of blood. Shortly after plugging both anterior and posterior nares the blood found its way through the lacrimal ducts to the eyes and trickled down the cheeks."

"Dr. Charles W. Crumb cites the case of a man, sixty-five years old, with chronic nephritis, in whom a slight bruise of the nose was followed by epistaxis lasting twenty-four hours. When the nares were plugged blood escaped freely from the eyes. A cone-shaped bit of sponge, saturated with ferrous sulphate, was passed into each anterior naris, and another piece of sponge, similarly medicated, into either posterior naris. The patient had been taking various preparations of potassium, and it was thought that his blood contained a deficiency of fibrin. Upon removal of the nasal plugs a catarrhal inflammation developed which lasted a long time and was attended with considerable purulent discharge."

Late Restoration of Sight.—There are some marvelous cases on record in which, after many years of blindness, the surgeon has been able, by operation, to restore the sight. McKeown [a] gives the history of a blind fiddler of sixty-three, who, when one and a half years old, had lost the sight of both eyes after an attack of small-pox. Iridectomy was performed, and after over sixty years of total blindness his sight was restored; color-perception was good. Berncastle [b] mentions a case of extraction of double cataract and double iridectomy for occluded pupils, which, after thirty years of blindness, resulted in the recovery of good sight. The patient was a blind beggar of Sydney.

To those interested in this subject, Jauffret [c] has a most interesting description of a man by the name of Garin, who was born blind, who talked at eight or nine months, showed great intelligence, and who was educated at a blind asylum. At the age of twenty-four he entered the hospital of Forlenze, to be operated upon by that famous oculist. Garin had never seen, but could distinguish night or darkness by one eye only, and recognized orange and red when placed close to that eye. He could tell at once the sex and age of a person approximately by the voice and tread, and formed his conclusions more rapidly in regard to females than males. Forlenze diagnosed cataract, and, in the presence of a distinguished gathering, operated with the happiest result. The description that follows, which is quoted by Fournier [d] and is readily accessible to any one, is well worth reading, as it contains an account of the first sensations of light, objects, distance, etc., and minor analogous

[a] 476, 1888, i., 14.   [b] 179, Oct. 15, 1869.
[c] "Experience metaphysique ou Developpement de la lumière et des sensations."
[d] 302, iv.

thoughts, of an educated and matured mind experiencing its first sensations of sight.

Hansell and Clark [843] say that the perplexities of learning to see after twenty-six years of blindness from congenital disease, as described by a patient of Franke, remind one of the experience of Shelley's Frankenstein. Franke's patient was successfully operated on for congenital double cataract, at twenty-six years of age. The author describes [a] the difficulties the patient had of recognizing by means of vision the objects he had hitherto known through his other senses, and his slowness in learning to estimate distances and the comparative size of objects.

Sight is popularly supposed to be occasionally **restored without the aid of art,** after long years of blindness. Benjamin Rush saw a man of forty-five who, twelve years before, became blind without ascertainable cause, and recovered his sight equally without reason. St. Clair mentions Marshal Vivian, who at the age of one hundred regained sight that for nearly forty years had gradually been failing almost to blindness, and preserved this new sight to the time of his death.

There are many superstitions prevalent among uneducated people as to "second sight," recovery of vision, etc., which render their reports of such things untrustworthy. The real explanations of such cases are too varied for discussion here.

Nyctalopia etymologically means night-blindness, but the general usage, making the term mean night-vision, is so strongly intrenched that it is useless and confusing to attempt any reinstatement of the old significance. The condition in which one sees better by night, relatively speaking, than by day is due to some lesion of the macular region, rendering it blind. At night the pupil dilates more than in the day-time, and hence vision with the extramacular or peripheral portions of the retina is correspondingly better. It is, therefore, a symptom of serious retinal disease. All night-prowling animals have widely dilatable pupils, and in addition to this they have in the retina a special organ called the *tapetum lucidum*, the function of which is to reflect to a focus in front of them the relatively few rays of light that enter the widely-dilated pupil and thus enable them the better to see their way. Hence the luminous appearance of the eyes of such animals in the dark.

Hemeralopia (etymologically day-blindness, but by common usage meaning day-vision or night-blindness) is a symptom of a peculiar degenerative disease of the retina, called *retinitis pigmentosa*. It also occurs in some cases of extreme denutrition, numerous cases having been reported among those who make the prolonged fasts customary in the Russian church. In *retinitis pigmentosa* the peripheral or extramacular portions of the retina are subject to a pigmentary degeneration that renders them insensitive to light, and patients so afflicted are consequently incapable of seeing at night as well as others. They stumble and run against objects easily seen by the normal eye.

[a] Beit. zur Augenh., Heft xvi., 1894.

Snow-blindness occurs from prolonged exposure of the eyes to snow upon which the sun is shining. Some years ago, some seventy laborers, who were clearing away snow-drifts in the Caucasus, were seized, and thirty of them could not find their way home, so great was the photophobia, conjunctivitis, and lacrimation. Graddy [a] reports six cases, and many others are constantly occurring.

Other forms of **retinal injury from too great or too prolonged exposure to light** are "moon-blindness," due to sleeping with the eyes exposed to bright moonlight, and that due to lightning—a case, *e. g.*, being reported by Knies.[b] Silex [c] also reports such a case and reviews the reported cases, 25 in number, in ten of which cataract ensued. In the Annual of the Universal Medical Sciences, 1888, there is a report of seven cases of retinal injury with central scotoma, amblyopia, etc., in Japanese medical students, caused by observation of the sun in eclipse.

In discussing the question of **electric-light injuries of the eyes** Gould [d] reviews the literature of the subject and epitomizes the cases reported up to that time. They numbered 23. No patient was seriously or permanently injured, and none was in a person who used the electric light in a proper manner as an illuminant. All were in scientific investigators or workmen about the light, who approached it too closely or gazed at it too long and without the colored protecting spectacles now found necessary by such workers.

Injuries to the Ear.—The folly of the practice of **boxing children's ears,** and the possible disastrous results subsequent to this punishment, are well exemplified throughout medical literature. Stewart [e] quotes four cases of rupture of the tympanum from boxing the ears, and there is an instance [f] of a boy of eight, who was boxed on the ear at school, in whom subsequent brain-disease developed early, and death followed. Roosa of New York mentions the **loss of hearing following a kiss on the ear.**[g]

Dalby,[h] in a paper citing many different **causes of rupture of the tympanic membrane,** mentions the following : A blow in sparring ; violent sneezing ; blowing the nose ; forcible dilatation of the Eustachian canal ; a thorn or twig of a tree accidentally thrust into the head ; picking the ear with a toothpick. In time of battle soldiers sometimes have their tympanums ruptured by the concussion caused by the firing of cannon. Dalby mentions an instance of an officer who was discharged for deafness acquired in this manner during the Crimean War. He was standing beside a mortar which, unexpectedly to him, was fired, causing rupture of the tympanic membrane, followed by hemorrhage from the ear. Similar cases were reported in the recent naval engagements between the Chinese and Japanese. Wilson [i] reports two

a 124, 1887.   b Graefe's Archiv, 1887.   c Arch. f. Augenheilk., 1887.
d 533, Dec. 8, 1888.   e 476, 1889, i., 574.   f 476, 1879, i., 23.
g Archives of Otology, 1880, ix., 16.   h 476, 1875, i., 752.   i 533, xli., 173.

cases of rupture of the membrana tympani caused by diving. Roosa [a] divides the causes into traumatic, hemorrhagic, and inflammatory, and primary lesions of the labyrinth, exemplifying each by numerous instances. Under traumatic causes he mentions severe falls, blows about the head or face, constant listening to a telegraphic instrument, cannonading, and finally eight cases of boiler-makers' deafness. Roosa cites a curious case of **sudden** and profound **deafness** in a young man in perfect health, while calling upon the parents of his lady-love to ask her hand in marriage. Strange to say that after he had had a favorable reply he gradually recovered his hearing ! In the same paper there is an instance of a case of deafness due to the sudden cessation of perspiration, and an instance of tinnitus due to the excessive use of tobacco ; Roosa also mentions a case of deafness due to excessive mental employment.

Perforation of the Tympanum.—Kealy [b] relates an instance in which a pin was introduced into the left ear to relieve an intolerable itching. It perforated the tympanum, and before the expiration of twenty-four hours was coughed up from the throat with a small quantity of blood. The pin was bent at an angle of about 120 degrees. Another similar case [c] was that of a girl of twenty-two who, while pricking her ear with a hair-pin, was jerked or struck on the arm by a child, and the pin forced into the ear ; great pain and deafness followed, together with the loss of taste on the same side of the tongue ; after treatment both of the disturbed senses were restored. A man of twenty [d] was pricked in the ear by a needle entering the meatus. He uttered a cry, fell senseless, and so continued until the fourth day when he died. The whole auditory meatus was destroyed by suppuration. Gamgee [e] tells of a constable who was stabbed in the left ear, severing the middle meningeal artery, death ensuing. In this instance, after digital compression, ligature of the common carotid was practised as a last resort. There is an account [f] of a provision-dealer's agent who fell asleep at a public house at Tottenham. In sport an attendant tickled his ear with a wooden article used as a pipe light. A quick, unconscious movement forced the wooden point through the tympanum, causing cerebral inflammation and subsequent death. There is a record [g] of death, in a child of nine, caused by the passage of a knitting-needle into the auditory meatus.

Kauffmann [h] reports a case of what he calls **objective tinnitus aurium,** in which the noise originating in the patient's ears was distinctly audible by others. The patient was a boy of fourteen, who had fallen on the back of his head and had remained unconscious for nearly two weeks. The noises were bilateral, but more distinct on the left than on the right side. The sounds were described as crackling, and seemed to depend on movements of

a 124, Oct., 1874, 376.

b 548, 1859, 602.

c 476, 1889, i., 574.

d 566, Jan. 20, 1829.

e 476, 1875, i., 535.

f 476, 1895, ii., 222.

g 224, 1869, ii., 470.

h Deutsche Med. Zeitung, Jan. 6, 1896.

the arch of the palate. Kauffmann expresses the opinion that the noises were due to clonic spasm of the tensor velum palati, and states that under appropriate treatment the tinnitus gradually subsided.

The introduction of **foreign bodies in the ear** is usually accidental, although in children we often find it as a result of sport or curiosity. There is an instance on record of a man who was accustomed to catch flies and put them in his ear, deriving from them a pleasurable sensation from the tickling which ensued. There have been cases in which children, and even adults, have held grasshoppers, crickets, or lady-birds to their ears in order to more attentively listen to the noise, and while in this position the insects have escaped and penetrated the auditory canal. **Insects** often enter the ears of persons reposing in the fields with the ear to the ground. Fabricius Hildanus speaks of a cricket penetrating the ear during sleep. Calhoun [a] mentions an instance of disease of the ear which he found was due to the presence of several living maggots in the interior of the ear. The patient had been sleeping in a horse stall in which were found maggots similar to those extracted from his ear. An analogous instance was seen in a negro in the Emergency Hospital, Washington, D. C., in the summer of 1894 ; and many others are recorded. The insects are frequently removed only after a prolonged lodgment.

D'Aguanno [b] gives an account of two instances of living larvæ of the musca sarcophaga in the ears of children. In one of the cases the larvæ entered the drum-cavity through a rupture in the tympanic membrane. In both cases the maggots were removed by forceps. Haug [c] has observed a tic (ixodes ricinus) in the ear of a lad of seventeen. The creature was killed by a mercuric-chlorid solution, and removed with a probe.

There is a common superstition that centipedes have the faculty of entering the ear and penetrating the brain, causing death. The authors have knowledge of an instance in which three small centipedes were taken from the ear of a policeman after remaining there three days ; during this time they caused excruciating pain, but there was no permanent injury. The Ephemerides contains instances in which, while yet living, worms, crickets, ants, and beetles have all been taken from the ear. In one case the entrance of a cricket in the auditory canal was the cause of death. Martin [d] gives an instance in which larvæ were deposited in the ear. Stalpart van der Wiel [750] relates an instance of the lodgment of a living spider in the ear.

Far more common than insects are **inanimate objects as foreign bodies** in the ear, and numerous examples are to be found in literature. Fabricius Hildanus [334] tells of a glass ball introduced into the auditory canal of a girl of ten, followed by headache, numbness on the left side, and after four or five years epileptic seizures, and atrophy of the arm. He extracted it and the symptoms immediately ceased. Sabatier speaks of an abscess of the brain caused by a ball of paper in the ear ; and it is quite common for persons in

[a] 176, 1873, x., 665. [b] 843, 836. [c] Ibid. [d] 462, T. xxxi., 179.

the habit of using a tampon of cotton in the meatus to mistake the deep entrance of this substance for functional derangement, and many cases of temporary deafness are simply due to forgetfulness of the cause. A strange case is reported in a girl of fourteen, who lost her tympanum from a profuse otorrhea, and who substituted an artificial tympanum which was, in its turn, lost by deep penetration, causing augmentation of the symptoms, of the cause of which the patient herself seemed unaware.[a] Sometimes artificial otoliths are produced by the insufflation of various powders which become agglutinated, and are veritable foreign bodies. Holman[b] tells of a negro, aged thirty-five. whose wife poured molten pewter in his ear while asleep. It was removed, but total deafness was the result.

Alley[c] mentions a New Orleans wharf laborer, in whose ear was poured some molten lead ; seventeen months afterward the lead was still occupying the external auditory meatus. It is quite remarkable that the lead should have remained such a length of time without causing meningeal inflammation. There was deafness and palsy of that side of the face. A fungous growth occupied the external portion of the ear ; the man suffered pain and discharge from the ear, and had also great difficulty in closing his right eyelid. Morrison[d] mentions an alcoholic patient of forty who, on June 6, 1833, had nitric acid poured in her right ear. There were no headache, febrile symptoms, stupor, or vertigo. Debility alone was present. Two weeks after the injury paralysis began on the right side, and six weeks from the injury the patient died. This case is interesting from the novel mode of death, the perfect paralysis of the arm, paralysis agitans of the body (occurring as hemorrhage from the ear came on, and subsiding with it), and extensive caries of the petrous bone, without sensation of pain or any indicative symptoms.

There is an instance in a young girl in which a piece of pencil remained in the right ear for seven years.[e] Haug speaks of two beads lying in the auditory canal for twenty-eight years without causing any harm.

A boy of six introduced a carob-nut kernel into each ear. On the next day incompetent persons attempted to extract the kernel from the left side, but only caused pain and hemorrhage. The nut issued spontaneously from the right side. In the afternoon the auditory canal was found excoriated and red, and deep in the meatus the kernel was found, covered with blood. The patient had been so excited and pained by the bungling attempts at extraction that the employment of instruments was impossible ; prolonged employment of injections was substituted. Discharge from the ear commenced, intense fever and delirium ensued, and the patient had to be chloroformed to facilitate the operation of extraction. The nut, when taken out, was found to have a consistency much larger than originally, caused by the agglutination of wax and blood. Unfortunately the symptoms of meningitis increased ; three days

a 720, 1877, 210.   b 744, 1888.   c 124, April, 1852, 377.
d 310, 1836, ix., 99.   e 554, 1842, No. 32.

after the operation coma followed, and on the next day death ensued.[a] In 75 cases collected by Mayer, and cited by Poulet [641] (whose work on " Foreign Bodies " is the most extensive in existence), death as a consequence of meningitis was found in three.

Fleury de Clermont [b] mentions a woman of twenty-five who consulted him for removal of a pin which was in her right ear. Vain attempts by some of her lay-friends to extract the pin had only made matters worse. The pin was directed transversely, and its middle part touched the membrana tympanum. The mere touching of the pin caused the woman intense pain ; even after etherization it was necessary to construct a special instrument to extract it. She suffered intense cephalalgia and other signs of meningitis ; despite vigorous treatment she lost consciousness and died shortly after the operation.

Winterbotham [c] reports an instance in which a cherry-stone was removed from the meatus auditorius after lodgment of upward of sixty years. Marchal de Calvi mentions intermittent deafness for forty years, caused by the lodgment of a small foreign body in the auditory canal. There is an instance in which a carious molar tooth has been tolerated in the same location for forty years.[d]

Albucasius, Fabricius Hildanus, Paré, and others, have mentioned the fact that seeds and beans have been frequently seen to increase in volume while lodged in the auditory canal. Tulpius [842] speaks of an infant, playing with his comrades, who put a cherry-seed in his ear which he was not able to extract. The seed increased in volume to such an extent that it was only by surgical interference that it could be extracted, and then such serious consequences followed that death resulted. Albers [e] reports an instance in which a pin introduced into the ear issued from the pharynx.

Confusion of diagnosis is occasionally noticed in terrified or hysteric persons. Lowenberg was called to see a child of five who had introduced a button into his left ear. When he saw the child it complained of all the pain in the right ear, and he naturally examined this ear first but found nothing to indicate the presence of a foreign body. He examined the ear supposed to be healthy and there found the button lying against the tympanum. This was explained by the fact that the child was so pained and terrified by the previous explorations of the affected ear that rather than undergo them again he presented the well ear for examination. In the British Medical Journal for 1877 is an account of an unjustified exploration of an ear for a foreign body by an incompetent physician, who spent a half hour in exploration and manipulation, and whose efforts resulted in the extraction of several pieces of bone. The child died in one and a half hours afterward from extreme hemorrhage, and the medical bungler was compelled to appear before a coroner's jury in explanation of his ignorance.

In the external ear of a child Tansley observed a diamond which he

a 720, 1800, 230.   b 363, 1870, 58.   c 548, 1866, ii., 496.   d 641, 695.   e 456, i., 151.

removed under chloroform.[a]   The mother of the child had pushed the body further inward in her endeavors to remove it and had wounded the canal. Schmiegelow [b] reports a foreign body forced into the drum-cavity, followed by rough extraction, great irritation, tetanus, and death ; and there are on record several cases of fatal meningitis, induced by rough endeavors to extract a body from the external ear.

In the Therapeutic Gazette, August 15, 1896, there is a translation of the report of a case by Voss, in which a child of five pushed a dry pea in his ear.   Four doctors spent several days endeavoring to extract it, but only succeeded in pushing it in further.   It was removed by operation on the fifth day, but suppuration of the tympanic cavity caused death on the ninth day.

Barclay[c] reports a rare case of ensnared aural foreign body in a lady, aged about forty years, who, while " picking " her left ear with a so-called "invisible hair-pin " several hours before the consultation, had heard a sudden " twang " in the ear, as if the **hair-pin** had broken.   And so, indeed, it had ; for on the instant she had attempted to jerk it quickly from the ear the sharp extremity of the inner portion of its lower prong sprang away from its fellow, penetrated the soft tissues of the floor of the external auditory canal, and remained imbedded there, the separated end of this prong only coming away in her grasp.   Every attempt on her part to remove the hair-pin by traction on its projecting prong—she durst not force it *inward* for fear of wounding the drumhead—had served but to bury the point of the broken prong more deeply into the flesh of the canal, thereby increasing her suffering.   Advised by her family physician not to delay, she forthwith sought advice and aid.   On examination, it was found that the lower prong of the "invisible hair-pin " had broken at the outer end of its wavy portion, and seemed firmly imbedded in the floor of the auditory canal, now quite inflamed, at a point about one-third of its depth from the outlet of the canal.   The loop or turn of the hair-pin was about $\frac{1}{2}$ inch from the flaccid portion of the drumhead, and, together with the unbroken prong, it lay closely against the roof of the canal. Projecting from the meatus there was enough of this prong to be easily grasped between one's thumb and finger.   Removal of the hair-pin was effected by first inserting within the meatus a Gruber speculum, encircling the unbroken projecting prong, and then raising the end of the broken one with a long-shanked aural hook, when the hair-pin was readily withdrawn.   The wound of the canal-floor promptly healed.

In the severest forms of **scalp-injuries,** such as avulsion of the scalp from the entangling of the hair in machinery, skin-grafting or replantation is of particular value.   Ashhurst [d] reports a case which he considers the severest case of scalp-wound that he had ever seen, followed by recovery.   The patient was a girl of fifteen, an operative in a cotton-mill, who was caught by

a 165, Aug., 1894.   b 843, 836.   c 533, Jan. 11, 1896.   d 174, 324.

her hair between two rollers which were revolving in opposite directions ; her scalp being thus, as it were, squeezed off from her head, forming a large horseshoe flap. The linear extent of the wound was 14 inches, the distance between the two extremities being but four inches. This large flap was thrown backward, like the lid of a box, the skull being denuded of its pericranium for the space of 2½ by one inch in extent. The anterior temporal artery was divided and bled profusely, and when admitted to the hospital the patient was extremely depressed by shock and hemorrhage. A ligature was applied to the bleeding vessel, and after it had been gently but carefully cleansed the flap was replaced and held in place with gauze and collodion dressing. A large compress soaked in warm olive oil was then placed over the scalp, covered with oiled silk and with a recurrent bandage. A considerable portion of the wound healed by adhesions, and the patient was discharged, cured, in fifty-four days. No exfoliation of bone occurred. Reverdin, a relative of the discoverer of transplantation of skin,[a] reported the case of a girl of twenty-one whose entire scalp was detached by her hair being caught in machinery, leaving a wound measuring 35 cm. from the root of the nose to the nape of the neck, 28 cm. from one ear to the other, and 57 cm. in circumference. Grafts from the rabbit and dog failed, and the skin from the amputated stump of a boy was employed, and the patient was able to leave the hospital in seven months. Cowley [b] speaks of a girl of fourteen whose hair was caught in the revolving shaft of a steam-engine, which resulted in the tearing off of her whole scalp. A triangular portion of the skin was hanging over her face, the apex of the triangle containing short hair, from which the long hair had been detached. Both ears were hanging down the neck, having been detached above. The right pinna was entire, and the upper half of the left pinna had disappeared. The whole of the head and back of the neck was denuded of skin. One of the temporal arteries was ligated, and the scalp cleansed and reapplied. The hanging ears and the skin of the forehead were successfully restored to their proper position. The patient had no bad symptoms and little pain, and the shock was slight. Where the periosteum had sloughed the bone was granulating, and at the time of the report skin-grafting was shortly to be tried.

Schaeffer [c] has presented quite an extensive article on scalp-injuries in which grafting and transplantation has been used, and besides reporting his own he mentions several other cases. One was that of a young lady of twenty-four. While at work under a revolving shaft in a laundry the wind blew her hair and it was caught in the shaft. The entire skull was laid bare from the margin of the eyelids to the neck. The nasal bones were uncovered and broken, exposing the superior nasal meatus. The skin of the eyelids was removed from within three mm. of their edges. The lower margin of the wound

[a] Deutsche Zeitschrift für Chirurg., Feb., 1876. [b] 476, 1879, ii., 421.
[c] 782, 1887, iii., 166 et seq.

was traceable from the lower portion of the left external process of the frontal bone, downward and backward below the left ear (which was entirely removed), thence across the neck, five cm. below the superior curved line of the occipital bone, and forward through the lower one-third of the right auricle to the right external angular process of the frontal bone and margin of the right upper eyelid, across the lid, nose, and left eyelid, to the point of commencement. Every vessel and nerve supplying the scalp was destroyed, and the pericranium was torn off in three places, one of the denuded spots measuring five by seven cm. and another five by six cm. The neck flap of the wound fell away from the muscular structures beneath it, exposing the trapezius muscle almost one-half the distance to the shoulder blade. The right ear was torn across in its lower third, and hung by the side of the neck by a piece of skin less than five mm. wide. The exposed surface of the wound measured 40 cm. from before back, and 34 cm. in width near the temporal portion. The cranial sutures were distinctly seen in several places, and only a few muscular fibers of the temporal were left on each side. Hemorrhage was profuse from the temporal, occipital, and posterior auricular arteries, which were tied. The patient was seen three-quarters of an hour after the injury, and the mangled scalp was thoroughly washed in warm carbolized water, and stitched back in position, after the hair was cut from the outer surface. Six weeks after the injury suppuration was still free, and skin-grafting was commenced. In all, 4800 grafts were used, the patient supplying at different times 1800 small grafts. Her own skin invariably did better than foreign grafts. In ten months she had almost completely recovered, and sight and hearing had returned. Figure 191 shows the extent of the injury, and the ultimate results of the treatment.

Schaeffer also reports the case of a woman working in a button factory at Union City, Conn., in 1871, who placed her head under a swiftly turning shaft to pick up a button, when her hair caught in the shaft, taking off her scalp from the nape of the neck to the eyebrows. The scalp was cleansed by her physician, Dr. Bartlett, and placed on her head about two hours after the accident, but it did not stay in position. Then the head was covered twice by skin-grafts, but each time the grafts were lost; but the third time a successful grafting was performed and she was enabled to work after a period of two years. The same authority also quotes Wilson and Way of Bristol, Conn., in an account of a complete avulsion of the scalp, together with tearing of the eyelid and ear. The result of the skin-grafting was not given. Powell of Chicago gives an account of a girl of nineteen who lost her scalp while working in the Elgin Watch Factory at Elgin, Illinois. The wound extended across the forehead above the eyebrows, but the ears were untouched. Skin-grafting was tried in this case but with no result, and the woman afterward lost an eve by exposure, from retraction of the eyelid.

In some cases **extensive wounds of the scalp heal without artificial**

aid by simply cicatrizing over. Gross [387] mentions such a case in a young lady, who, in 1869, lost her scalp in a factory. There is reported [a] an account of a conductor on the Union Pacific Railroad, who, near Cheyenne, in 1869, was scalped by Sioux Indians. He suffered an elliptic wound, ten by eight cm., a portion of the outer table of the cranium being removed, yet the wound healed over.

Cerebral Injuries.—The recent advances in brain-surgery have, in a measure, diminished the interest and wonder of some of the older instances of

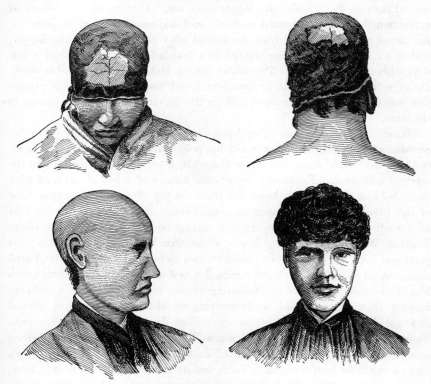

Fig. 191.—Scalp-injury and skin-graft (Schaeffer).

major injuries of the cerebral contents with unimportant after-results, and in reviewing the older cases we must remember that the recoveries were made under the most unfavorable conditions, and without the slightest knowledge of all important asepsis and antisepsis.

Penetration or even complete **transfixion of the brain** is not always attended with serious symptoms. Dubrisay [b] is accredited with the description of a man of forty-four, who, with suicidal intent, drove a dagger ten cm. long and one cm. wide into his brain. He had deliberately held the dagger

a 544, surgical portion, part i., 315.   b 476, 1881, ii., 845.

in his left hand, and with a mallet in his right hand struck the steel several blows.   When seen two hours later he claimed that he experienced no pain, and the dagger was sticking out of his head.   For half an hour efforts at extraction were made, but with no avail.   He was placed on the ground and held by two persons while traction was made with carpenter's pliers.   This failing, he was taken to a coppersmith's, where he was fastened by rings to the ground, and strong pinchers were placed over the dagger and attached to a chain which was fastened to a cylinder revolved by steam force.   At the second turn of the cylinder the dagger came out.   During all the efforts at extraction the patient remained perfectly cool and complained of no pain.   A few drops of blood escaped from the wound after the removal of the dagger, and in a few minutes the man walked to a hospital where he remained a few days without fever or pain.   The wound healed, and he soon returned to work. By experiments on the cadaver Dubrisay found that the difficulty in extraction was due to rust on the steel, and by the serrated edges of the wound in the bone.

Warren describes a case of epilepsy of seven months' standing, from depression of the skull caused by a red hot poker thrown at the subject's head. Striking the frontal bone just above the orbit, it entered three inches into the cerebral substance.   Kesteven [a] reports the history of a boy of thirteen who, while holding a fork in his hand, fell from the top of a load of straw.   One of the prongs entered the head one inch behind and on a line with the lobe of the left ear and passed upward and slightly backward to almost its entire length.   With some difficulty it was withdrawn by a fellow workman ; the point was bent on itself to the extent of two inches.   The patient lived nine days.   Abel and Colman [b] have reported a case of puncture of the brain with loss of memory, of which the following extract is an epitome : " A railway-fireman, thirty-six years old, while carrying an oil-feeder in his hand, slipped and fell forward, the spout of the can being driven forcibly into his face. There was transitory loss of consciousness, followed by twitching and jerking movements of the limbs, most marked on the left side, the legs being drawn up and the body bent forward.   There was no hemorrhage from mouth, nose, or ears.   The metallic spout of the oil-can was firmly fixed in the base of the skull, and was only removed from the grasp of the bone by firm traction with forceps.   It had passed upward and toward the middle line, with its concavity directed from the middle line.   Its end was firmly plugged by bone from the base of the skull.   No hemorrhage followed its removal.   The wound was cleansed and a simple iodoform-dressing applied.   The violent jerking movements were replaced by a few occasional twitchings.   It was now found that the left side of the face and the left arm were paralyzed, with inability to close the left eye completely.   The man became drowsy and confused, and was unable to give replies to any but the simplest questions.   The temperature rose to 102°; the pupils became contracted, the right in a greater degree than the left; both reacted to light. The left leg began to lose power. There was complete anesthesia of the right eyebrow and of both eyelids and of the right cheek for an uncertain distance below the lower eyelid. The conjunctiva of the right eye became congested, and a small ulcer formed on the right cornea, which healed without much trouble. In the course of a few days power began to return, first in the left leg and afterward, though to a much less extent, in the left arm. For two weeks there was drowsiness, and the man slept considerably. He was apathetic, and for many days passed urine in bed. He could not recognize his wife or old comrades, and had also difficulty in recognizing common objects and their uses. The most remarkable feature was the loss of all memory of his life for twenty years before the accident. As time went on, the period included in this loss of memory was reduced to five years preceding the accident. The hemi-

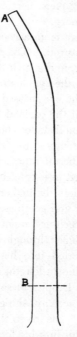

Fig. 192.—Diagram indicating the probable course of the spout; the direction was not vertical, but inclined backward (Abel and Colman).

Fig. 193.—Exact outline of spout after removal; the dotted line represents position of cheek-wound; from A to B, natural size, measured 6⅛ inches.

plegia persisted, although the man was able to get about. Sensibility was lost to all forms of stimuli in the right upper eyelid, forehead, and anterior part of the scalp, corresponding with the distribution of the supraorbital and nasal nerves. The cornea was completely anesthetic, and the right cheek, an inch and a half external to the angle of the nose, presented a small patch of anesthesia. There was undue emotional mobility, the patient laughing or crying on slight provocation. The condition of mind-blindness remained. It is believed that the spout of the oil-can must have passed under the zygoma to the base of the skull, perforating the great wing of the sphenoid bone and penetrating the centrum ovale, injuring the anterior fibers of the motor tract in the internal capsule near the genu."

Figures 192 and 193 show the outline and probable course of the spout.

Beaumont [a] reports the history of an injury in a man of forty-five, who, standing but 12 yards away, was struck in the orbit by a rocket, which penetrated through the sphenoidal fissure into the middle and posterior lobes of the left hemisphere. He did not fall at the time he was struck, and fifteen minutes after the stick was removed he arose without help and walked away. Apparently no extensive cerebral lesion had been caused, and the man suffered no subsequent cerebral symptoms except, three years afterward, impairment of memory.

There is an account given by Chelius [b] of an extraordinary wound caused by a ramrod. The rod was accidentally discharged while being employed in loading, and struck a person a few paces away. It entered the head near the root of the zygomatic arch, about a finger's breadth from the outer corner of the right eye, passed through the head, emerging at the posterior superior angle of the parietal bone, a finger's breadth from the sagittal suture, and about the same distance above the superior angle of the occipital bone. The wounded man attempted to pull the ramrod out, but all his efforts were ineffectual. After the tolerance of this foreign body for some time, one of his companions managed to extract it, and when it was brought out it was as straight as the day it left the maker's shop. Little blood was lost, and the wound healed rapidly and completely ; in spite of this major injury the patient recovered.

Carpenter [c] reports the curious case of an insane man who deliberately bored holes through his skull, and at different times, at a point above the ear, he inserted into his brain five pieces of No. 20 broom wire from $2\frac{1}{16}$ to $6\frac{3}{4}$ inches in length, a fourpenny nail $2\frac{1}{4}$ inches long, and a needle $1\frac{5}{8}$ inches long. Despite these desperate attempts at suicide he lived several months, finally accomplishing his purpose by taking an overdose of morphin. Mac-Queen [d] has given the history of a man of thirty-five, who drove one three-inch nail into his forehead, another close to his occiput, and a third into his vertex an inch in front and $\frac{1}{4}$ inch to the left of the middle line. He had used a hammer to effect complete penetration, hoping that death would result from his injuries. He failed in this, as about five weeks later he was discharged from the Princess Alice Hospital at Eastbourne, perfectly recovered. There is a record [e] of a man by the name of Bulkley who was found, by a police officer in Philadelphia, staggering along the streets, and was taken to the inebriate ward of the Blockley Hospital, where he subsequently sank and died, after having been transferred from ward to ward, his symptoms appearing inexplicable. A postmortem examination revealed the fact that an ordinary knife-blade had been driven into his brain on the right side, just above

a 476, 1862, i., 626.   b 265, i.   c 124, 1876, 426.
d 476, 1890, ii., 721.   e 547, Nov. 1, 1871.

the ear, and was completely hidden by the skin. It had evidently become loosened from the handle when the patient was stabbed, and had remained in the brain several days. No clue to the assailant was found.

Thudicum [a] mentions the case of a man who walked from Strafford to Newcastle, and from Newcastle to London, where he died, and in his brain was found the breech-pin of a gun. Neiman [b] describes a severe gunshot wound of the frontal region, in which the iron breech-block of an old-fashioned muzzle-loading gun was driven into the substance of the brain, requiring great force for its extraction. The patient, a young man of twenty-eight, was unconscious but a short time, and happily made a good recovery. A few pieces of bone came away, and the wound healed with only a slight depression of the forehead. Wilson [c] speaks of a child who fell on an upright copper paper-file, which penetrated the right side of the occipital bone, below the external orifice of the ear, and entered the brain for more than three inches ; and yet the child made a speedy recovery.

Baron Larrey knew of a man whose head was completely transfixed by a ramrod, which extended from the middle of the forehead to the left side of the nape of the neck ; despite this serious injury the man lived two days.

Jewett [d] records the case of an Irish drayman who, without treatment, worked for forty-seven days after receiving a penetrating wound of the skull ¼ inch in diameter and four inches deep. Recovery ensued in spite of the delay in treatment.

Gunshot Injuries.—Swain [e] mentions a patient who stood before a looking glass, and, turning his head far around to the left, fired a pistol shot into his brain behind the right ear. The bullet passed into his mouth, and he spat it out. Some bleeding occurred from both the internal and external wounds ; the man soon began to suffer with a troublesome cough, with bloody expectoration ; his tongue was coated and drawn to the right ; he became slightly deaf in his right ear and dragged his left leg in walking. These symptoms, together with those of congestion of the lung, continued for about a week, when he died, apparently from his pulmonary trouble.

Ford [f] quotes the case of a lad of fifteen who was shot in the head, ¾ inch anterior to the summit of the right ear, the ball escaping through the left os frontis, 1¼ inch above the center of the brow. Recovery ensued, with a cicatrix on the forehead, through which the pulsations of the brain could be distinctly seen. The senses were not at all deteriorated.

Richardson [g] tells of a soldier who was struck by a Minié ball on the left temporal bone ; the missile passed out through the left frontal bone ½ inch to the left of the middle of the forehead. He was only stunned, and twenty-four hours later his intellect was undisturbed. There was no operation ; free

[a] 536. 1884, ii., 419.   [b] 520, Oct. 20, 1891.   [c] 224, 1887, ii., 278.
[d] Hosp. Gaz., London, 1879, 39.   [e] 224, Feb. 7, 1891.
[f] Monthly Jour. Med. Sciences, 1845, v., 653.   [g] 593, 1866–67, xix., 52.

suppuration with discharges of fragments of skull and broken-down substance ensued for four weeks, when the wounds closed kindly, and recovery followed.

Angle [a] records the case of a cowboy who was shot by a comrade in mistake. The ball entered the skull beneath the left mastoid process and passed out of the right eye. The man recovered.

Rice [b] describes the case of a boy of fourteen who was shot in the head, the ball directly traversing the brain substance, some of which protruded from the wound. The boy recovered. The ball entered one inch above and in front of the right ear and made its exit through the lambdoidal suture posteriorly.

Hall of Denver, Col.,[c] in an interesting **study of gunshot wounds of the brain,** writes as follows :—

" It is in regard to injuries involving the brain that the question of the production of immediate unconsciousness assumes the greatest interest. We may state broadly that if the medulla or the great centers at the base of the brain are wounded by a bullet, instant unconsciousness must result ; with any other wounds involving the brain-substance it will, with very great probability, result. But there is a very broad area of uncertainty. Many instances have been recorded in which the entrance of a small bullet into the anterior part of the brain has not prevented the firing of a second shot on the part of the suicide. Personally, I have not observed such a case, however. But, aside from the injuries by the smallest missiles in the anterior parts of the brain, we may speak with almost absolute certainty with regard to the production of unconsciousness, for the jar to the brain from the blow of the bullet upon the skull would produce such a result even if the damage to the brain were not sufficient to do so.

" Many injuries to the brain from bullets of moderate size and low velocity do not cause more than a temporary loss of consciousness, and the subjects are seen by the surgeon, after the lapse of half an hour or more, apparently sound of mind. These are the cases in which the ball has lost its momentum in passing through the skull, and has consequently done little damage to the brain-substance, excepting to make a passage for itself for a short distance into the brain. It is apparently well established that, in the case of the rifle-bullet of high velocity, and especially if fired from the modern military weapons using nitro-powders, and giving an enormous initial velocity to the bullet, the transmission of the force from the displaced particles of brain (and this rule applies to any other of the soft organs as well) to the adjacent parts is such as to disorganize much of the tissue surrounding the original track of the missile. Under these circumstances a much slighter wound would be necessary to produce unconsciousness or death than in the case of a bullet of low velocity, especially if it were light in weight. Thus I have recorded elsewhere an

a San Francisco Med. Jour., 1856, i., 10.   b 218, 1849, 323.   c 533, 1895, ii., 478.

instance of instant death in a grizzly bear, an animal certainly as tenacious of life as any we have, from a mere furrow, less than a quarter of an inch in depth, through the cortex of the brain, without injury of the skull excepting the removal of the bone necessary for the production of this furrow. The jar to the brain from a bullet of great velocity, as in this case, was alone sufficient to injure the organ irreparably. In a similar manner I have known a deer to be killed by the impact of a heavy rifle-ball against one horn, although there was no evidence of fracture of the skull. On the other hand, game animals often escape after such injuries not directly involving the brain, although temporarily rendered unconscious, as I have observed in several instances, the diagnosis undoubtedly being concussion of the brain.

" Slight injury to the brain, and especially if it be unilateral, then, may not produce unconsciousness. It is not very uncommon for a missile from a heavy weapon to strike the skull, and be deflected without the production of such a state. Near the town in which I formerly practised, the town-marshal shot at a negro, who resisted arrest, at a distance of only a few feet, with a 44-caliber revolver, striking the culprit on the side of the head. The wound showed that the ball struck the skull and plowed along under the scalp for several inches before emerging, but it did not even knock the negro down, and no unconsciousness followed later. I once examined an express-messenger who had been shot in the occipital region by a weapon of similar size, while seated at his desk in the car. The blow was a very glancing one and did not produce unconsciousness, and probably, as in the case of the negro, because it did not strike with sufficient directness."

Head Injuries with Loss of Cerebral Substance.—The brain and its membranes may be severely wounded, portions of the cranium or cerebral substance destroyed or lost, and yet recovery ensue. Possibly the most noted injury of this class was that reported by Harlow [a] and commonly known as " **Bigelow's Case** " or the " **American Crow-bar Case.** " Phineas P. Gage, aged twenty-five, a foreman on the Rutland and Burlington Railroad, was employed September 13, 1847, in charging a hole with powder preparatory to blasting. A premature explosion drove a tamping-iron, three feet seven inches long, $1\frac{1}{4}$ inches in diameter, weighing $13\frac{1}{4}$ pounds, completely through the man's head. The iron was round and comparatively smooth ; the pointed end entered first. The iron struck against the left side of the face, immediately anterior to the inferior maxillary and passed under the zygomatic arch, fracturing portions of the sphenoid bone and the floor of the left orbit ; it then passed through the left anterior lobe of the cerebrum, and, in the median line, made its exit at the junction of the coronal and sagittal sutures, lacerating the longitudinal sinus, fracturing the parietal and frontal bones, and breaking up considerable of the brain ; the globe of the left eye protruded nearly one-half of its diameter. The patient was thrown backward and gave a few convulsive movements of

a 218, 1848.

the extremities. He was taken to a hotel ¾ mile distant, and during the transportation seemed slightly dazed, but not at all unconscious. Upon arriving at the hotel he dismounted from the conveyance, and without assistance walked up a long flight of stairs to the hall where his wound was to be dressed. Harlow saw him at about six o'clock in the evening, and from his condition could hardly credit the story of his injury, although his person and his bed were drenched with blood. His scalp was shaved, the coagula and debris removed, and among other portions of bone was a piece of the anterior superior angle of each parietal bone and a semicircular piece of the frontal bone, leaving an opening 3½ inches in diameter. At 10 P. M. on the day of the injury Gage was perfectly rational and asked about his work and after his friends. After a while delirium set in for a few days, and on the eleventh day he lost the vision in the left eye. His convalescence was rapid and uneventful. It was said that he discharged pieces of bone and cerebral substance from his mouth for a few days. The iron when found was smeared with blood and cerebral substance.

As was most natural such a wonderful case of cerebral injury attracted much notice. Not only was the case remarkable in the apparent innocuous loss of cerebral substance, but in the singular chance which exempted the brain from either concussion or compression, and subsequent inflammation. Professor Bigelow examined the patient in January, 1850, and made a most excellent report of the case,[a] and it is due to his efforts that the case attained world-wide notoriety. Bigelow found the patient quite recovered in his faculties of body and mind, except that he had lost the sight of the injured eye. He exhibited a linear cicatrix one inch long near the angle of the ramus of the left lower jaw. His left eyelid was involuntarily closed and he had no power to overcome his ptosis. Upon the head, well covered by the hair, was a large unequal depression and elevation. In order to ascertain how far it might be possible for a bar of the size causing the injury to traverse the skull in the track assigned to it, Bigelow procured a common skull in which the zygomatic arches were barely visible from above, and having entered a drill near the left angle of the inferior maxilla, he passed it obliquely upward to the median line of the cranium just in front of the junction of the sagittal and coronal sutures. This aperture was then enlarged until it allowed the passage of the bar in question, and the loss of substance strikingly corresponded with the lesion said to have been received by the patient. From the coronoid process of the inferior maxilla there was removed a fragment measuring about ¾ inch in length. This fragment, in the patient's case, might have been fractured and subsequently reunited. The iron bar, together with a cast of the patient's head, was placed in the Museum of the Massachusetts Medical College.

Bigelow appends an engraving (Fig. 194) to his paper. In the illustration the parts are as follows :—

[a] 124, July, 1850.

(1) Lateral view of a prepared cranium representing the iron bar traversing its cavity.

(2) Front view of same.

(3) Plan of the base seen from within. In these three figures the optic foramina are seen to be intact and are occupied by small white rods.

(4) Cast taken from the shaved head of the patient representing the appearance of the fracture in 1850, the anterior fragment being considerably elevated in the profile view.

(5) The iron bar with length and diameter in proportion to the size of the other figures.

Heaton [a] reports a case in which, by an explosion, a tamping-iron was driven through the chin of a man into the cerebrum. Although there was loss of brain-substance, the man recovered with his mental faculties unim-

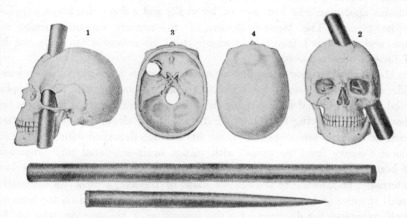

Fig. 194.—Dr. Harlow's case of recovery after the passage of an iron bar through the head.

paired. A second case was that of a man who, during an explosion, was wounded in the skull. There was visible a triangular depression, from which, possibly, an ounce of brain-substance issued. This man also recovered.

Jewett mentions a case in which an injury somewhat similar to that in Bigelow's case was produced by a gas-pipe.

Among older writers, speaking of loss of brain-substance with subsequent recovery, Brasavolus saw as much brain evacuated as would fill an egg shell; the patient afterward had an impediment of speech and grew stupid. Franciscus Arcæus gives the narrative of a workman who was struck on the head by a stone weighing 24 pounds falling from a height. The skull was fractured; fragments of bone were driven into the brain. For three days the patient was unconscious and almost lifeless. After the eighth day a cranial

[a] Trans. Detroit Med. and Library Assoc., 1879, i., 4.

abscess spontaneously opened, from the sinciput to the occiput, and a large quantity of "corruption" was evacuated. Speech returned soon after, the eyes opened, and in twenty days the man could distinguish objects. In four months recovery was entire. Bontius relates a singular accident to a sailor, whose head was crushed between a ship and a small boat; the greater part of the occipital bone was taken away in fragments, the injury extending almost to the foramen magnum. Bontius asserts that the patient was perfectly cured by another surgeon and himself. Galen mentions an injury to a youth in Smyrna, in whom the brain was so seriously wounded that the anterior ventricles were opened; and yet the patient recovered. Glandorp [380] mentions a case of fracture of the skull out of which his father took large portions of brain and some fragments of bone. He adds that the man was afterward paralyzed on the opposite side and became singularly irritable. In his "Chirurgical Observations," Job van Meek'ren tells the story of a Russian nobleman who lost part of his skull, and a dog's skull was supplied in its place. The bigoted divines of the country excommunicated the man, and would not annul his sentence until he submitted to have the bit of foreign bone removed.

Mendenhall [a] reports the history of an injury to a laborer nineteen years old. While sitting on a log a few feet from a comrade who was chopping wood, the axe glanced and, slipping from the woodman's grasp, struck him just above the ear, burying the "bit" of the axe in his skull. Two hours afterward he was seen almost pulseless, and his clothing drenched with blood which was still oozing from the wound with mixed brain-substance and fragments of bone. The cut was horizontal on a level with the orbit, $5\frac{1}{2}$ inches long externally, and, owing to the convex shape of the axe, a little less internally. Small spicules of bone were removed, and a cloth was placed on the battered skull to receive the discharges for the inspection of the surgeon, who on his arrival saw at least two tablespoonfuls of cerebral substance on this cloth. Contrary to all expectation this man recovered, but, strangely, he had a marked and peculiar change of voice, and this was permanent. From the time of the reception of the injury his whole mental and moral nature had undergone a pronounced change. Before the injury, the patient was considered a quiet, unassuming, and stupid boy, but universally regarded as honest. Afterward he became noisy, self-asserting, sharp, and seemingly devoid of moral sense or honesty. These new traits developed immediately, and more strikingly so soon as convalescence was established.

Bergtold [b] quotes a case reported in 1857 [545] of extreme injury to the cranium and its contents. While sleeping on the deck of a canal boat, a man at Highspire was seriously injured by striking his head against a bridge. When seen by the surgeon his hair was matted and his clothes saturated with blood. There was a terrible gap in the scalp from the superciliary ridge to the occip-

a 124, 1869.   b Medical Press of Western New York, 1888, 317.

ital bone, and, though full of clots, the wound was still oozing. In a cloth on a bench opposite were rolled up a portion of the malar bone, some fragments of the os frontis, one entire right parietal bone, detached from its fellow along the sagittal suture, and from the occipital along the lambdoidal suture, perhaps taking with it some of the occipital bone together with some of the squamous portion of the temporal bone. This bone was as clean of soft parts as if it had been removed from a dead subject with a scalpel and saw. No sight of the membranes or of the substance of the brain was obtained. The piece of cranium removed was $6\frac{3}{4}$ inches in the longitudinal diameter, and $5\frac{3}{4}$ inches in the short oval diameter. The dressing occupied an hour, at the end of which the patient arose to his feet and changed his clothes as though nothing had happened. Twenty-six years after the accident there was slight unsteadiness of gait, and gradual paralysis of the left leg and arm and the opposite side of the face, but otherwise the man was in good condition. In place of the parietal bone the head presented a marked deficiency as though a slice of the skull were cut out (Fig. 195). The depressed area measured five by six inches. In 1887 the man left the hospital in Buffalo with the paralysis improved, but his mental equilibrium could be easily disturbed. He became hysteric and sobbed when scolded.

Fig. 195.—Skull injury with extensive loss of cranial and cerebral substance.

Buchanan [a] mentions the history of a case in a woman of twenty-one, who, while working in a mill, was struck by a bolt. Her skull was fractured and driven into the brain comminuted. Hanging from the wound was a bit of brain-substance, the size of a finger, composed of convolution as well as white matter. The wound healed, there was no hernia, and at the time of report the girl was conscious of no disturbance, not even a headache. There was nothing indicative of the reception of the injury except a scar near the edge of the hair on the upper part of the right side of the forehead. Steele,[b] in a school-boy of eight, mentions a case of very severe injury to the bones of the face and head, with escape of cerebral substance, and recovery. The injury was caused by falling into machinery.

There was a seaman aboard of the U. S. S. "Constellation," [c] who fell through a hatchway from the masthead, landing on the vertex of the head. There was copious bleeding from the ears, 50 to 60 fluid-ounces of blood oozing in a few hours, mingled with small fragments of brain-tissue. The next day the discharge became watery, and in it were found small pieces of true brain-

a 381, 1879.   b 476, 1889, i., 1083.   c 124, April, 1859.

substance. In five weeks the man returned to duty complaining only of giddiness and of a "stuffed-up" head. In 1846 there is a record of a man of forty who fell from a scaffold, erected at a height of 20 feet, striking on his head. He was at first stunned, but on admission to the hospital recovered consciousness. A small wound was found over the right eyebrow, protruding from which was a portion of brain-substance. There was slight hemorrhage from the right nostril, and some pain in the head, but the pulse and respiration were undisturbed. On the following day a fragment of the cerebral substance, about the size of a hazel-nut, together with some blood-clots, escaped from the right nostril. In this case the inner wall of the frontal sinus was broken, affording exit for the lacerated brain.

Fig. 196.—Skull injury with extensive destruction of brain-substance around the Rolandic area (Cooke and Laycock).

Cooke and Laycock [a] mention a case of intracranial injury with extensive destruction of brain-substance around the Rolandic area; there was recovery but with loss of the so-called muscular sense. The patient, a workman of twenty-nine, while cutting down a gum-tree, was struck by a branch as thick as a man's arm, which fell from 100 feet overhead, inflicting a compound comminuted fracture of the cranium. The right eye was contused but the pupils equal; the vertex-wound was full of brain-substance and pieces of bone, ten of which were removed, leaving an oval opening four by three inches. The base of the skull was fractured behind the orbits; a fissure $\frac{1}{4}$ inch wide was discernible, and the right frontal bone could be easily moved. The lacerated and contused brain-substance was removed. Consciousness returned six days after the operation. The accompanying illustrations (Figs. 196 and 197) show the extent of the injury. The lower half of the ascending frontal convolution, the greater half of the sigmoid gyrus, the posterior third of the lower and middle frontal convolutions, the base and posterior end of the upper convolution, and the base of the corresponding portion of the falciform lobe were involved. The sensory and motor functions of the arm were retained in a relative degree. There was power of simple movements, but complex movements were awkward. The tactile localization was almost lost.

a 180, July 13, 1893.

Morton [a] mentions a patient of forty-seven, who was injured in a railroad accident near Phœnixville, Pa.; there was a compound comminuted fracture of the skull involving the left temporal, sphenoid, and superior maxillary bones. The side of the head and the ear were considerably lacerated; several teeth were broken, and besides this there was injury to the dura and cerebral substance. There was profound coma for ten days and paralysis of the 1st, 2d, 3d, 4th, 6th, and 7th cranial nerves, particularly affecting the left side of the face. There was scarcely enough blood-supply left to the orbit to maintain life in the globe. The man primarily recovered, but ninety-one days from the injury he died of cerebral abscess.

There is the record [b] of a curious brain-injury in a man of twenty-two, who was struck on the skull by a circular saw. The saw cut directly down into the brain, severing the superior longitudinal sinus, besides tearing a branch of the meningeal artery. The wound was filled with sawdust left by the saw while it was tearing through the parts. After ordinary treatment the man recovered.

Bird [c] reports a compound comminuted fracture of the left temporal region, with loss of bone, together with six drams of brain-substance, which, however, was followed by recovery. Tagert [d] gives an instance of compound depressed fracture of the skull, with loss of brain-substance, in which recovery was effected without operative interference. Ballou,[e] Bartlett,[f] Buckner, Capon,[g] Carmichael,[h] Corban,[i] Maunder,[j] and many others, cite instances of

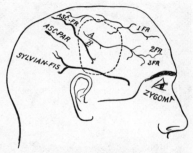

Fig. 197.—Diagrammatic sketch of injury seen in figure 196.

cranial fracture and loss of brain-substance, with subsequent recovery. Halsted [k] reports the history of a boy of seventeen, who, while out fowling, had the breech-pin of a shot-gun blown out, the sharp point striking the forehead in the frontal suture, crushing the os frontis, destroying $1\frac{3}{4}$ inches of the longitudinal sinus, and causing severe hemorrhage from both the longitudinal and frontal sinuses. The pin was pulled out by the boy, who washed his own face, and lay down; he soon became semi-comatose, in which condition he remained for some days; but, after operation, he made complete recovery.

Loss of Brain-substance from Cerebral Tumor.—Koser is accredited with reporting results of a postmortem held on a young man of twenty who suffered from a cerebral tumor of considerable duration. It was stated that, although there was a cavity in the brain at least five inches

a 547, Oct. 3, 1874.   b 130, 1861, 165.   c 124, 1865, 552.   d 548, 1852, 268.

e 298, 1883.   f 647, 1878.   g 548, 1879.   h 312, 1841.

i 535, 1825.   j 548, 1870.   k 703, 1870, 131.

in length, the patient, almost up to the time of death, was possessed of the senses of touch, taste, hearing, and smell, showed considerable control over his locomotor muscles, and could talk. In fact, he was practically discommoded in no other way than by loss of vision, caused by pressure on the optic centers. It was also stated that the retention of memory was remarkable, and, up to within two weeks of his death, the patient was able to memorize poems. The amount of involvement discovered post-mortem in cases similar to the preceding is astonishing. At a recent pathologic display in London [619] several remarkable specimens were shown.

Extensive Fractures of the Skull.—Jennings [a] mentions an instance of extensive fracture of the skull, 14 pieces of the cranium being found (Fig. 198). The patient lived five weeks and two days after the injury, the immediate cause of death being edema of the lungs. His language was incoherent and full of oaths. Belloste, in his " Hospital Surgeon," states that he had under his care a most dreadful case of a girl of eleven or twelve

Fig. 198.—Cranial fracture (14 fragments) (Jennings).

years, who received 18 or 19 cutlass wounds of the head, each so violent as to chip out pieces of bone ; but, notwithstanding her severe injuries, she made recovery. At the Emergency Hospital in Washington, D. C., there was received a negress with at least six gaping wounds of the head, in some cases denuding the periosteum and cutting the cranium. During a debauch the night before she had been engaged in a quarrel with a negro with whom she lived, and was struck by him several times on the head with an axe. She lay all night unconscious, and was discovered the next morning with her hair and clothes and the floor on which she lay drenched with blood. The ambulance was summoned to take her to the morgue, but on the arrival of the police it was seen that feeble signs of life still existed. On admission to the hospital she was semi-comatose, almost pulseless, cold, and exhibiting all the signs of extreme hemorrhage and shock. Her head was cleaned up, but her condition would not permit of any other treatment than a corrosive-sublimate compress and a bandage of Scultetus. She was taken to the hospital ward, where warmth and stimulants were applied, after which she completely reacted. She progressed so well that it was not deemed advisable to remove the head-bandage until the fourth day, when it was seen that the wounds had almost entirely healed and suppuration was virtually absent. The patient rapidly and completely recovered, and her neighbors, on

a 124, May, 1891.

her return home, could hardly believe that she was the same woman whom, a few days before, they were preparing to take to the morgue.

A serious injury, which is not at all infrequent, is that caused by **diving into shallow water,** or into a bath from which water has been withdrawn. Curran [a] mentions a British officer in India who, being overheated, stopped at a station bath in which the previous night he had had a plunge, and without examining, took a violent " header " into the tank, confidently expecting to strike from eight to ten feet of water. He dashed his head against the concrete bottom 12 feet below (the water two hours previously having been withdrawn) and crushed his brain and skull into an indistinguishable mass.

There are many cases on record in which an injury, particularly a gunshot wound of the skull, though showing no external wound, has caused death by producing a **fracture of the internal table of the cranium.**   Paré [618] gives details of the case of a nobleman whose head was guarded by a helmet and who was struck by a ball, leaving no external sign of injury, but it was subsequently found that there was an internal fracture of the cranium. Tulpius [842] and Scultetus are among the older writers reporting somewhat similar instances, and there are several analogous cases reported as having occurred during the War of the Rebellion. Boling [b] reports a case in which the internal table was splintered to a much greater extent than the external.

Fracture of the base of the skull is ordinarily spoken of as a fatal injury, reported instances of recovery being extremely rare, but Battle,[c] in a paper on this subject, has collected numerous statistics of nonfatal fracture of the base of the brain, viz.:—

	Male.	Female.
Anterior fossa,	16	5
Middle fossa,	50	6
Posterior fossa,	10	1
Middle and anterior fossæ,	15	5
Middle and posterior fossæ,	4	1
Anterior, middle, and posterior fossæ,	1	.
	96	18 Total, 114.

In a paper on nonmortal fractures of the base of the skull, Lidell [d] gives an account of 135 cases.   MacCormac [e] reports a case of a boy of nine who was run over by a carriage drawn by a pair of horses.   He suffered fracture of the base of the skull, of the bones of the face, and of the left ulna, and although suppuration at the points of fracture ensued, followed by an optic neuritis, an ultimate recovery was effected. Ball, an Irish surgeon, has collected several instances in which the base of the skull has been driven in and the condyle of the jaw impacted in the opening by force transmitted through the lower maxilla.

The tolerance of foreign bodies in the brain is most marvelous. In the ancient chronicles of Kœnigsberg there is recorded the history of a man

a 476, 1886, ii., 579.   b 817, 1844.   c 476, 1890, ii., 1.
d 124, lxxxi., 1881, 335.   e 476, 1886, ii., 209.

who for fourteen years carried in his head a piece of iron as large as his finger. After its long lodgment, during which the subject was little discommoded, it finally came out by the palatine arch. There is also an old record of a ball lodging near the sella turcica for over a year, the patient dying suddenly of an entirely different accident. Fabricius Hildanus [334] relates the history of an injury, in which, without causing any uncomfortable symptoms, a ball rested between the skull and dura for six months.

Amatus Lusitanus [119] speaks of a drunken courtesan who was wounded in a fray with a long, sharp-pointed knife which was driven into the head. No apparent injury resulted, and death from fever took place eight years after the reception of the injury. On opening the head a large piece of knife was found between the skull and dura. It is said that Benedictus mentions a Greek who was wounded, at the siege of Colchis, in the right temple by a dart and taken captive by the Turks ; he lived for twenty years in slavery, the wound having completely healed. Obtaining his liberty, he came to Sidon, and five years after, as he was washing his face, he was seized by a violent fit of sneezing, and discharged from one of his nostrils a piece of the dart having an iron point of considerable length.

In about 1884 there died in the Vienna Hospital [a] a bookbinder of forty-five, who had always passed as an intelligent man, but who had at irregular intervals suffered from epileptic convulsions. An iron nail covered with rust was discovered in his brain ; from the history of his life and from the appearances of the nail it had evidently been lodged in the cerebrum since childhood.

Slee [b] mentions a case in which, after the death of a man from septic peritonitis following a bullet-wound of the intestines, he found postmortem a knife-blade $\frac{5}{16}$ inch in width projecting into the brain to the depth of one inch. The blade was ensheathed in a strong fibrous capsule $\frac{1}{2}$ inch thick, and the adjacent brain-structure was apparently normal. The blade was black and corroded, and had evidently passed between the sutures during boyhood as there was no depression or displacement of the cranial bones. The weapon had broken off just on a level with the skull, and had remained in situ until the time of death without causing any indicative symptoms. Slee does not state the man's age, but remarks that he was a married man and a father at the time of his death, and had enjoyed the best of health up to the time he was shot in the abdomen. Callaghan, quoted in Erichsen's "Surgery," remarks that he knew of an officer who lived seven years with a portion of a gun-breech weighing three ounces lodged in his brain.

Lawson [c] mentions the impaction of a portion of a breech of a gun in the forehead of a man for twelve years, with subsequent removal and recovery. Waldon [d] speaks of a similar case in which a fragment of the breech weighing three ounces penetrated the cranium, and was lodged in the brain for two months previous to the death of the patient.

a 545, Nov. 1, 1884.   b 533, July 25, 1891.   c 224, 1869.   d 564, 1799.

Huppert[a] tells of the lodgment of a slate-pencil three inches long in the brain during lifetime, death ultimately being caused by a slight head-injury. Larry mentions a person who for some time carried a six ounce ball in the brain and ultimately recovered. Peter[b] removed a musket-ball from the frontal sinus after six years' lodgment, with successful issue. Mastin[c] has given an instance in which the blade of a pen-knife remained in the brain six months, recovery following its removal. Camden[d] reports a case in which a ball received in a gunshot wound of the brain remained in situ for thirteen years ; Cronyn[e] mentions a similar case in which a bullet rested in the brain for eight years. Doyle[f] successfully removed an ounce Minié ball from the brain after a fifteen years' lodgment.

Pipe-stems, wires, shot, and other foreign bodies, are from time to time recorded as remaining in the brain for some time. Wharton[g] has compiled elaborate statistics on this subject, commenting on 316 cases in which foreign bodies were lodged in the brain, and furnishing all the necessary information to persons interested in this subject.

Fig. 199.—Warren's apparatus for resorting to the method of Taliacotius.

Injuries of the nose, with marked deformity, are in a measure combated by devices invented for restoring the missing portions of the injured member. Taliacotius, the distinguished Italian surgeon of the sixteenth century, devised an operation which now bears his name, and consists in fashioning a nose from the fleshy tissues of the arm. The arm is approximated to the head and held in this position by an apparatus or system of bandages for about ten days, at which time it is supposed that it can be severed, and further trimming and paring of the nose is then practised. A column is subsequently made from the upper lip. In the olden days there was a humorous legend representing Taliacotius making noses for his patients from the gluteal regions of other persons, which statement, needless to say, is not founded on fact. Various **modifications and improvements on the Taliacotian method** have been made (Fig. 199); but in recent years the Indian method, introduced by Carpue into England in 1816, is generally preferred. Syme of Edinburgh, Wood, and Ollier have devised methods of restoring the nose, which bear their names.

Ohmann-Dumesnil[h] reports a case of rhinophyma in a man of seventy-two, an alcoholic, who was originally affected with acne rosacea, on whom he performed a most successful operation for restoration. The accompanying

[a] 155, 1875.
[b] 133, 1870, ii.
[c] 681, 1873.
[d] Trans. Med. Soc. W. Va., 1877.
[e] 230, 1871-2, xi., 194.
[f] South. Med. Rec., Atlanta, 1878, 323.
[g] 547, 1879, ix., 493.
[h] International Med. Mag., Phila., Feb., 1894.

illustration (Fig. 200) shows the original deformity--a growth weighing two pounds—and also pictures the appearance shortly after the operation. This case is illustrative of the possibilities of plastic surgery in the hands of a skilful and ingenious operator.

About 1892 Dr. J. P. Parker then of Kansas City, Mo., restored the missing bridge of a patient's nose by laying the sunken part open in two long flaps, denuding the distal extremity of the little finger of the patient's right hand of nail, flesh, tendons, etc., and binding it into the wound of the nose until firm union had taken place. The finger was then amputated at the second joint and the plastic operation completed, with a result pleasing both to patient and operator.

There is a case quoted [a] of a young man who, when first seen by his medical attendant, had all the soft parts of the nose gone, except one-third of the left ala

Fig. 200.—Case of rhinophyma before and after operation (Ohmann-Dumesnil).

and a thin flap of the septum which was lying on the upper lip. The missing member was ferreted out and cleansed, and after an hour's separation sutured on. The nostrils were daily syringed with a corrosive sublimate solution, and on the tenth day the dressing was removed ; the nose was found active and well, with the single exception of a triangular notch on the right side, which was too greatly bruised by the violence of the blow to recover. When we consider the varicosity of this organ we can readily believe the possibility of the foregoing facts, and there is little doubt that more precaution in suturing severed portions of the nose would render the operation of nose-making a very rare one.

Maxwell [b] mentions a curious case of attempted suicide in which the ball, passing through the palatine process of the superior maxillary bone, crushing the vomer to the extent of its own diameter, fell back through the right nostril into the pharynx, was swallowed, and discharged from the anus.

a 536, 1890, ii., 240.   b 246, 1869.

Deformities of the nose causing enormous development, or the condition called " **double-nose** " by Bartholinus, Borellus, Bidault, and others, are ordinarily results of a pathologic development of the sebaceous glands. In some cases tumors develop from the root of the nose, forming what appears to be a second nose. In other cases monstrous vegetations divide the nose into many tumors. In the early portion of this century much was heard about a man who was a daily habitue of the Palais-Royal Gardens. His nose was divided into unequally sized tumors, covering nearly his entire face. Similar instances have been observed in recent years. Hey mentions a case in which the tumor extended to the lower part of the under lip, which compressed the patient's mouth and nostrils to such an extent that while sleeping, in order to insure sufficient respiration, he had to insert a tin-tube into one of his nostrils. Imbert de Lannes [a] is quoted as operating on a former Mayor of Angoulême. This gentleman's nose was divided into five lobes by sarcomatous tumors weighing two pounds, occupying the external surface of the face, adherent to the buccinator muscles to which they extended, and covering the chin. In the upright position the tumors sealed the nostrils and mouth, and the man had to bend his head before and after respiration. In eating, this unfortunate person had to lift his tumors away from his mouth, and during sleep the monstrous growths were supported in a sling attached to his night-cap. He presented such a hideous aspect that he was virtually ostracized from society. The growth had been in progress for twelve years, but during twenty-two months' confinement in Revolutionary prisons the enlargement had been very rapid. Fournier says that the most beautiful result followed the operation, which was considered quite hazardous.

Foreign bodies in the nose present phenomena as interesting as wounds of this organ. Among the living objects which have been found in the nose may be mentioned flies, maggots, worms, leeches, centipedes, and even lizards. Zacutus Lusitanus tells of a person who died in two days from the effects of a leech which was inadvertently introduced into the nasal fossa, and there is a somewhat similar case [b] of a military pharmacist, a member of the French army in Spain, who drank some water from a pitcher and exhibited, about a half hour afterward, a persistent hemorrhage from the nose. Emaciation progressively continued, although his appetite was normal. Three doctors, called in consultation, prescribed bleeding, which, however, proved of no avail. Three weeks afterward he carried in his nostril a tampon of lint, wet with an astringent solution, and, on the next day, on blowing his nose, there fell from the right nostril a body which he recognized as a leech. Healey [c] gives the history of four cases in which medicinal leeches were removed from the mouth and posterior nares of persons who had, for some days previously, been drinking turbid water. Sinclair [d] mentions the removal of a leech from the posterior nares.

[a] 302, iv., 209.
[c] Trans. Med. and Phys. Soc., Calcutta, 1842.
[b] 662, 1st series, T. x., 406.
[d] 224, 1885, i., 1246.

In some regions, more particularly tropical ones, there are certain **flies** that crawl into the nostrils of the inhabitants and deposit eggs in the cavities. The larvæ develop and multiply with great rapidity, and sometimes gain admission into the frontal sinus, causing intense cephalalgia, and even death.

Dempster [a] reports an instance of the lodgment of numerous live **maggots** within the cavity of the nose, causing sloughing of the palate and other complications. Nicholson [b] mentions a case of ulceration and abscess of the nostrils and face from which maggots were discharged. Jarvis [c] gives the history of a strange and repeated hemorrhage from the nose and adjacent parts that was found to be due to maggots from the ova of a fly, which had been deposited in the nose while the patient was asleep. Tomlinson [d] gives a case in which maggots traversed the Eustachian tube, some being picked out of the nostrils, while others were coughed up. Packard [e] records the accidental entrance of a **centipede** into the nostril. There is an account [f] of a native who was admitted to the Madras General Hospital, saying that a small **lizard** had crawled up his nose. The urine of these animals is very irritating, blistering any surface it touches. Despite vigorous treatment the patient died in consequence of the entrance of this little creature.

There have been instances among the older writers in which a **pea** has remained in the nose for such a length of time as to present evidences of sprouting. The Ephemerides renders an instance of this kind, and Breschet cites the history of a young boy, who, in 1718, introduced a pea into his nostril ; in three days it had swollen to such an extent as to fill the whole passage. It could not be extracted by an instrument, so tobacco snuff was used, which excited sneezing, and the pea was ejected.

Vidal and the Ephemerides report several instances of **tolerance of foreign bodies in the nasal cavities** for from twenty to twenty-five years. Wiesman, in 1893, reported a rhinolith, which was composed of a cherrystone enveloped in chalk, that had been removed after a sojourn of sixty years, with intense ozena as a consequence of its lodgment. Waring [g] mentions the case of a housemaid who carried a rhinolith, with a cherry-stone for a nucleus, which had been introduced twenty-seven years before, and which for twenty-five years had caused no symptoms. Grove [h] describes a necrosed inferior turbinated bone, to which was attached a coffee-grain which had been retained in the nostril for twenty years. , Hickman [i] gives an instance of a steel ring which for thirteen and a half years had been impacted in the nasopharyngeal fossa of a child. It was detected by the rhinoscope and was removed. Parker [j] speaks of a gunbreech bolt which was removed from the

a 434, 1836, i., 449.   b 500, 1842, iv., 345.   c 594, 1847, ix., 315.
d 272, 1872.   e 545, xxix., 100.   f 548, 1876, ii., 717.   g 224, 1893.
h Trans. Path. Soc., Phila., 1874, 25.   i 224, 1867, ii., 266.   j 476, 1885, i., 378.

nose after five years' lodgment. Major [a] mentions the removal of a foreign body from the nose seven years after its introduction.

Howard [b] removed a large thimble from the posterior nares, although it had remained in its position for some time undetected. Eve reports a case in which a thimble was impacted in the right posterior nares. Gazdar [c] speaks of a case of persistent neuralgia of one-half of the face, caused by a foreign body in the nose. The obstruction was removed after seven years' lodgment, and the neuralgia disappeared. Molinier [d] has an observation on the extraction of a fragment of a knife-blade which had rested four years in the nasal fossæ, where the blade had broken off during a quarrel.

A peculiar habit, sometimes seen in nervous individuals, is that of " **swallowing the tongue.**" Cohen claims that in some cases of supposed laryngeal spasm the tongue is swallowed, occluding the larynx, and sometimes with fatal consequences. There are possibly a half score of cases recorded, but this anomaly is very rare, and Major [e] is possibly the only one who has to a certainty demonstrated the fact by a laryngoscopic examination. By the laryngoscope he was enabled to observe a paroxysm in a woman, in which the tongue retracted and impinged on the epiglottis, but quickly recovered its position. Pettit mentions suffocation from " tongue swallowing," both with and without section of the frenum. Schobinger [f] cites a similar instance, due to loosening of the frenum.

Analogous to the foregoing phenomenon is the habit of " **tongue sucking.**" Morris [g] mentions a young lady of fifteen who spontaneously dislocated her jaw, owing indirectly to this habit. Morris says that from infancy the patient was addicted to this habit, which was so audible as to be heard in all parts of the room. The continued action of the pterygoid muscles had so preternaturally loosened the ligaments and muscular structures supporting the joint as to render them unable to resist the violent action of " tongue sucking" even during sleep.

Injuries to the Tongue.—Hobbs [h] describes a man of twenty-three who, while working, had a habit of protruding his tongue. One day he was hit under the chin by the chain of a crane on a pier, his upper teeth inflicting a wound two inches deep, three inches from the tip, and dividing the entire structure of the tongue except the arteries. The edges of the wound were brought into apposition by sutures, and after the removal of the latter perfect union and complete restoration of the sensation of taste ensued. Franck [350] mentions **regeneration of a severed tongue ;** and Van Wy has seen union of almost entirely severed parts of the tongue. De Fuisseaux [i] reports reunion of the tongue by suture after almost complete transverse division.

[a] 252, xv. [b] 612, 1852-3, v., 215. [c] 435, xviii., 341.
[d] 662, 1854, xiv., 291. [e] 252, 1884-5, 611. [f] 401, v.
[g] 224, 1872, ii., 242. [h] 536, 1887, 78. [i] Arch. Belges de Méd. Milt., 1851.

There is an account [a] of a German soldier who, May 2, 1813, was wounded at the battle of Gross-Görschen by a musket ball which penetrated the left cheek, carrying away the last four molars of the upper jaw and passing through the tongue, making exit on the left side, and forcing out several teeth of the left lower jaw. To his surprise, thirty years afterward, one of the teeth was removed from an abscess of the tongue. Baker [b] speaks of a boy of thirteen who was shot at three yards distance. The bullet knocked out two teeth and passed through the tongue, although it produced no wound of the pharynx, and was passed from the anus on the sixth day. Stevenson [c] mentions a case of an organist who fell forward when stooping with a pipe in his mouth, driving its stem into the roof of the pharynx. He complained of a sore throat for several days, and, after explanation, Stevenson removed from the soft palate a piece of clay pipe nearly $1\frac{1}{4}$ inches long. Herbert tells of a case resembling carcinoma of the tongue, which was really due to the lodgment of a piece of tooth in that organ.

Articulation Without the Tongue.—Total or partial destruction of the tongue does not necessarily make articulation impossible. Banon [d] mentions a man who had nothing in his mouth representing a tongue. When he was young, he was attacked by an ulceration destroying every vestige of this member. The epiglottis, larynx, and pharynx, in fact the surrounding structures were normal, and articulation, which was at first lost, became fairly distinct, and deglutition was never interfered with. Paré gives a description of a man whose tongue was completely severed, in consequence of which he lost speech for three years, but was afterward able to make himself understood by an ingenious bit of mechanism. He inserted under the stump of the tongue a small piece of wood, in a most marvelous way replacing the missing member. Articulation with the absence of some constituent of the vocal apparatus has been spoken of on page 254.

Hypertrophy of the Tongue.—It sometimes happens that the tongue is so large that it is rendered not only useless but a decided hindrance to the performance of the ordinary functions into which it always enters. Ehrlich, Ficker, Klein,[e] Rodtorffer, and the Ephemerides, all record instances in which a large tongue was removed either by ligation or amputation. Von Siebold [f] records an instance in which death was caused by the ligature of an abnormally sized tongue. There is a modern record of three cases of enormous tongues, the result of simple hypertrophy.[g] In one case the tongue measured $6\frac{1}{4}$ inches from the angle of the mouth about the sides and tip to the opposite angle, necessitating amputation of the protruding portion.

Carnochan [h] reports a case in which hypertrophy of the tongue was reduced to nearly the normal size by first tying the external carotid, and

a 476, 1846, i., 173. b 224, 1883, i., 457. c 224, 1890, ii., 205.

d 312, 1864, iii., 60. e 735, i., 665. f 735, i., 651.

g 548, 1853, i., 202. h Am. Med. Gaz. and Jour. Health, N. Y., 1856, vii., 1.

six weeks later the common carotid artery. Chalk [a] mentions partial dislocation of the lower jaw from an enlarged tongue. Lyford [b] speaks of enlargement of the tongue causing death.

The above conditions are known as **macroglossia**, which is a congenital hypertrophy of the tongue analogous to elephantiasis. It is of slow growth, and as the organ enlarges it interferes with deglutition and speech. It may protrude over the chin and reach even as far down as the sternum (Fig. 201).

The great enlargement may cause deformities of the teeth and lower jaw, and even present itself as an enormous tumor in the neck (Fig. 202). The protruding tongue itself may ulcer-

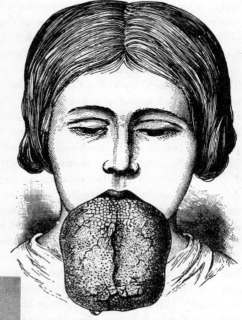

Fig. 201.—Macroglossia in a girl eleven years old (after Humphrey).

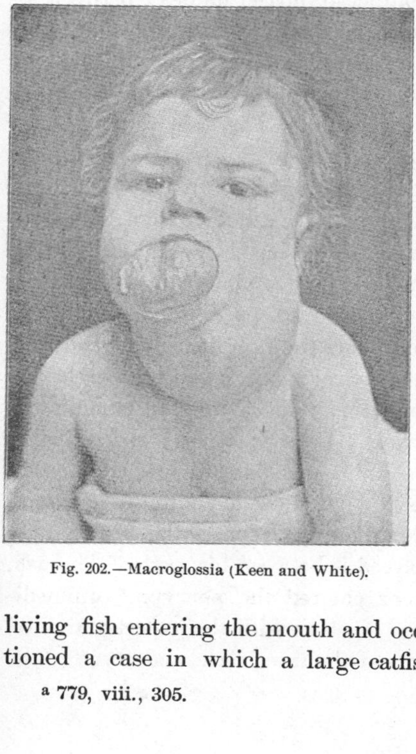

ate, possibly bleed, and there is constant dribbling of saliva. The disease is probably due to congenital defect aggravated by frequent attacks of glossitis, and the treatment consists in the removal of the protruding portions by the knife, ligation, the cautery, or écraseur.

Living Fish in the Pharynx.—Probably the most interesting cases of foreign bodies are those in which living fish enter the pharynx and esophagus. Chevers [266] has collected five cases in which death was caused by living fish entering the mouth and occluding the air-passages. He has mentioned a case in which a large catfish jumped into the mouth of a Madras

Fig. 202.—Macroglossia (Keen and White).

bheestie.   An operation on the esophagus was immediately commenced, but abandoned, and an attempt made to push the fish down with a probang, which was, in a measure, successful.   However, the patient gave a convulsive struggle, and, to all appearances, died.   The trachea was immediately opened, and respiration was restored.   During the course of the night the man vomited up pieces of fish bone softened by decomposition.   In 1863 White mentions that the foregoing accident is not uncommon among the natives of India, who are in the habit of swimming with their mouths open in tanks abounding with fish. There is a case [a] in which a fisherman, having both hands engaged in drawing a net, and seeing a sole-fish about eight inches long trying to escape through the meshes of the net, seized it with his teeth.   A sudden convulsive effort of the fish enabled it to enter the fisherman's throat, and he was asphyxiated before his boat reached the shore.   After death the fish was found in the cardiac end of the stomach.   There is another case of a man named Durand, who held a mullet between his teeth while rebaiting his hook.   The fish, in the convulsive struggles of death, slipped down the throat, and because of the arrangement of its scales it could be pushed down but not up ; asphyxiation, however, ensued.   Stewart [b] has extensively described the case of a native "Puckally" of Ceylon who was the victim of the most distressing symptoms from the impaction of a living fish in his throat.   The native had caught the fish, and in order to extract it placed its head between his teeth, holding the body with the left hand and the hook with the right.   He had hardly extracted the hook, when the fish pricked his palm with his long and sharp dorsal fin, causing him suddenly to release his grasp on the fish and voluntarily open his mouth at the same time.   The fish quickly bolted into his mouth, and, although he grasped the tail with his right hand, and squeezed his pharynx with his left, besides coughing violently, the fish found its way into the esophagus.   Further attempts at extraction were dangerous and quite likely to fail ; his symptoms were distressing, he could not hold his head erect without the most agonizing pain and he was almost prostrated from fright and asphyxia ; it was thought advisable to push the fish into the stomach, and after an impaction of sixteen hours the symptoms were relieved. The fish in this instance was the *Anabas scandens* or "walking perch" of Ceylon, which derives its name from its power of locomotion on land and its ability to live out of water for some time.   It is from four to five inches long and has a dorsal fin as sharp as a knife and directed toward the tail, and pectoral fins following the same direction ; these would admit of entrance, but would interfere with extraction.   MacLauren [c] reports the history of a young man who, after catching a fish, placed it between his teeth.   The fish, three inches long, by a sudden movement, entered the pharynx.   Immediately ensued suffocation, nausea, vomiting, together with the expectoration of blood and mucus.   There was emphysema of the face, neck, and chest.   The fish could be easily felt impacted in the tissues, but, after swallowing much water and vinegar, together with other efforts at extraction, the fins were loosened—about twenty-four hours after the accident. By this time the emphysema had extended to the scrotum. There was much expectoration of muco-purulent fluid, and on the third day complete aphonia, but the symptoms gradually disappeared, and recovery was complete in eight days. Dantra is accredited [a] with describing asphyxiation, accompanied by great agony, in a man who, while swimming, had partially swallowed a live fish. The fish was about three inches in length and one in breadth, and was found lying on the dorsum of his tongue and, together with numerous clots of blood, filled his mouth. Futile attempts to extract the fish by forceps were made. Examination showed that the fish had firmly grasped the patient's uvula, which it was induced to relinquish when its head was seized by the forceps and pressed from side to side. After this it was easily extracted and lived for some time. There was little hemorrhage after the removal of the offending object, and the blood had evidently come from the injuries to the sides of the mouth, caused by the fins. The uvula was bitten, not torn. There is an interesting account of a native of India, who, while fishing in a stream, caught a flat eel-like fish from fifteen to sixteen inches long. After the fashion of his fellows he attempted to kill the eel by bitting off its head ; in the attempt the fish slipped into his gullet, and owing to its sharp fins could not be withdrawn. The man died one hour later in the greatest agony ; so firmly was the eel impacted that even after death it could not be extracted, and the man was buried with it protruding from his mouth.

A Leech in the Pharynx.—Granger, a surgeon in Her Majesty's Indian Service,[b] writes :—" Several days ago I received a note from the political sirdar, asking me if I would see a man who said he had a leech in his throat which he was unable to get rid of. I was somewhat sceptical, and thought that possibly the man might be laboring under a delusion. On going outside the fort to see the case, I found an old Pathan graybeard waiting for me. On seeing me, he at once spat out a large quantity of dark, half-clotted blood to assure me of the serious nature of his complaint. His history—mostly made out with the aid of interpreters—was that eleven days ago he was drinking from a rain-water tank and felt something stick in his throat, which he could not reject. He felt this thing moving, and it caused difficulty in swallowing, and occasionally vomiting. On the following day he began to spit up blood, and this continued until he saw me. He stated that he once vomited blood, and that he frequently felt that he was going to choke. On examining his throat, a large clot of blood was found to be adherent to the posterior wall of the pharynx. On removing this clot of blood, no signs of the presence of a leech could be detected. However, on account of the symptoms complained of by the patient I introduced a polypus forceps

a 548, 1878, ii., 504.   b 224, 1895, ii., 695.

into the lower part of the pharynx and toward the esophagus, where a body, distinctly moving, was felt. This body I seized with the forceps, and with considerable force managed to remove it. It was a leech between $2\frac{1}{2}$ and three inches in length, and with a body of the size of a Lee-Metford bullet. No doubt during the eleven days it had remained in the man's throat the leech had increased in size. Nevertheless it must have been an animal of considerable size when the man attempted to swallow it. I send this case as a typical example of the carelessness of natives of the class from which we enlist our Sepoys, as to the nature of the water they drink. This man had drunk the pea-soup like water of a tank dug in the side of the hill, rather than go a few hundred yards to a spring where the water is perfectly clear and pure. Though I have not met with another case of leeches being taken with drinking water, I am assured that such cases are occasionally met with about Agra and other towns in the North-West Provinces. This great carelessness as to the purity or impurity of their drinking water shows the difficulty medical officers must experience in their endeavors to prevent the Sepoys of a regiment from drinking water from condemned or doubtful sources during a cholera or typhoid epidemic."

Foreign Bodies in the Pharynx and Esophagus.—Aylesbury [a] mentions a boy who swallowed a fish-hook while eating gooseberries. He tried to pull it up, but it was firmly fastened, and a surgeon was called. By ingeniously passing a leaden bullet along the line, the weight of the lead loosened the hook, and both bullet and hook were easily drawn up. Babbit and Battle [b] report an ingenious method of removing a piece of meat occluding the esophagus—the application of trypsin. Henry [c] speaks of a German officer who accidentally swallowed a piece of beer bottle, $\frac{3}{8}$ x $\frac{1}{8}$ inch, which subsequently penetrated the esophagus, and in its course irritated the recurrent laryngeal and vagi, giving rise to the most serious phlegmonous inflammation and distressing respiratory symptoms. A peculiar case [d] is that of the man who died after a fire at the Eddystone Lighthouse. He was endeavoring to extinguish the flames which were at a considerable distance above his head, and was looking up with his mouth open, when the lead of a melting lantern dropped down in such quantities as not only to cover his face and enter his mouth, but run over his clothes. The esophagus and tunica in the lower part of the stomach were burned, and a great piece of lead, weighing over $7\frac{1}{2}$ ounces, was taken from the stomach after death.

Evans [e] relates the history of a girl of twenty-one who swallowed four artificial teeth, together with their gold plate ; two years and eight days afterward she ejected them after a violent attack of retching. Gauthier [f] speaks of a young girl who, while eating soup, swallowed a fragment of bone. For a long time she had symptoms simulating phthisis, but fourteen years afterward the

a 374, 1738, viii., 380.   b 604, 1887.   c 178, 1882.

d 629, 1756, part ii.   e 476, 1879, ii., 75.   f 663, T., xxxiv., 13.

bone was dislodged, and, although the young woman was considered in the last stages of phthisis, she completely recovered in six weeks. Gastellier [a] has reported the case of a young man of sixteen who swallowed a crown piece, which became lodged in the middle portion of the esophagus and could not be removed. For ten months the piece of money remained in this position, during which the young man was never without acute pain and often had convulsions. He vomited material, sometimes alimentary, sometimes mucus, pus, or blood, and went into the last stage of marasmus. At last, after this long-continued suffering, following a strong convulsion and syncope, the coin descended to the stomach, and the young man expectorated great quantities of pus. After thirty-five years, the coin had not been passed by the rectum.

Instances of **migration of foreign bodies from the esophagus** are repeatedly recorded. There is an instance [b] of a needle which was swallowed and lodged in the esophagus, but twenty-one months afterward was extracted by an incision at a point behind the right ear. Kerckring speaks of a girl who swallowed a needle which was ultimately extracted from the muscles of her neck. Poulet [641] remarks that Vigla has collected the most interesting of these cases of migration of foreign bodies. Hévin mentions several cases of grains of wheat abstracted from abscesses of the thoracic parietes, from thirteen to fifteen days after ingestion. Bonnet and Helmontius have reported similar facts. Volgnarius has seen a grain of wheat make its exit from the axilla, and Polisius mentions an abscess of the back from which was extracted a grain of wheat three months after ingestion. Bally [c] reports a somewhat similar instance, in which, three months after ingestion, during an attack of peripneumonia, a foreign body was extracted from an abscess of the thorax, between the 2d and 3d ribs. Ambrose [d] found a needle encysted in the heart of a negress. She distinctly stated that she had swallowed it at a time calculated to have been nine years before her death. Planque speaks of a small bone perforating the esophagus and extracted through the skin.

Abscess or ulceration, consequent upon periesophagitis, caused by the lodgment of foreign bodies in the esophagus, often leads to the most serious results. There is an instance [662] of a soldier who swallowed a bone while eating soup, who died on the thirty-first day from the rupture internally of an esophageal abscess. Grellois [e] has reported the history of a case of a child twenty-two months old, who suffered for some time with impaction of a small bone in the esophagus. Less than three months afterward the patient died with all the symptoms of marasmus, due to difficult deglutition, and at the autopsy an abscess was seen in the posterior wall of the pharynx, opposite the 3d cervical vertebra ; extensive caries was also noticed in the bodies of the 2d, 3d, and 4th cervical vertebræ. Guattani [f] mentions a curious instance in which a man playing with a chestnut threw it in the air, catching it in his

a 458, T. xxiii., 147.   b 641, 113.   c Acad. de Médecine, 1824.
d 538, 1870.   e 458, T. xiii., 1807.   f 641, 119.

mouth. The chestnut became lodged in the throat and caused death on the nineteenth day. At the autopsy it was found that an abscess communicating with the trachea had been formed in the pharynx and esophagus.

A peculiarly fatal accident in this connection is that in which a foreign body in the esophagus ulcerates, and penetrates one of the neighboring major vessels. Colles[a] mentions a man of fifty-six who, while eating, perceived a sensation as of a rent in the chest. The pain was augmented during degluti- tion, and almost immediately afterward he commenced to expectorate great quantities of blood. On the following day he vomited a bone about an inch long and died on the same day. At the autopsy it was found that there was a rent in the posterior wall of the esophagus, about $\frac{1}{2}$ inch long, and a cor- responding wound of the aorta. There was blood in the pleura, pericardium, stomach, and intestines. There is one case in which a man of forty-seven sud- denly died, after vomiting blood, and at the autopsy it was demonstrated that a needle had perforated the posterior wall of the esophagus and wounded the aorta.[b] Poulet has collected[c] 31 cases in which ulceration caused by foreign bodies in the esophagus has resulted in perforation of the walls of some of the neighboring vessels. The order of frequence was as follows: aorta, 17; carotids, four; vena cava, two; and one case each of perforation of the in- ferior thyroid artery, right coronary vein, demi-azygos vein, the right sub- clavicular artery (abnormal), and the esophageal artery. In three of the cases collected there was no autopsy and the vessel affected was not known.

In a child of three years that had swallowed a half-penny, Atkins[d] re- ports rupture of the innominate artery. No symptoms developed, but six weeks later, the child had an attack of ulcerative stomatitis, from which it seemed to be recovering nicely, when suddenly it ejected two ounces of bright red blood in clots, and became collapsed out of proportion to the loss of blood. Under treatment, it rallied somewhat, but soon afterward it ejected four ounces more of blood and died in a few minutes. At the autopsy $\frac{3}{4}$ pint of blood was found in the stomach, and a perforation was discovered on the right side of the esophagus, leading into a cavity, in which a blackened half- penny was found. A probe passed along the aorta into the innominate pro- truded into the same cavity about the bifurcation of the vessel.

Denonvilliers has described a perforation of the esophagus and aorta by a five-franc piece. A preserved preparation of this case, showing the coin in situ, is in the Musée Dupuytren (Fig. 203). Blaxland[e] relates the instance of a woman of forty-five who swallowed a fish bone, was seized with violent hematemesis, and died in eight hours. The necropsy revealed a penetration of the aorta through the thoracic portion of the esophagus. There is also in the Musée Dupuytren a preparation described by Bousquet, in which the aorta and the esophagus were perforated by a very irregular piece of bone

a 313, 1855, T. xix., 25.   b 476, 1877, ii., 789.   c 641, 122.
d 224, May 4, 1895.   e 490, 1847, iv., 647.

(Fig. 204). Mackenzie mentions an instance of death from perforation of the aorta by a fish-bone.

In some cases penetration of the esophagus allows the further penetration of some neighboring membrane or organ in the same manner as the foregoing cases. Dudley [a] mentions a case in which fatal hemorrhage was caused by penetration of the esophagus and lung by a chicken-bone. Buist [b] speaks of a patient who swallowed two artificial teeth. On the following day there was pain in the epigastrium, and by the fourth day the pain extended to the vertebræ, with vomiting, delirium, and death on the fifth day. At the autopsy it was found that a foreign body, seven cm. long had perforated the

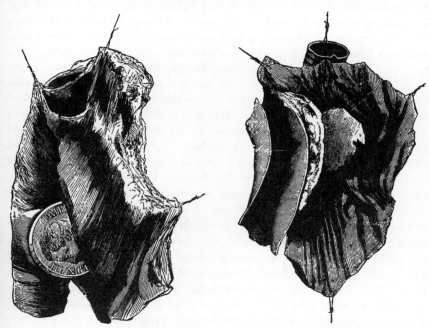

Fig. 203.—Perforation of esophagus and aorta by a five-franc piece (coin in situ) (after Poulet).

Fig. 204.—Perforation of aorta by a piece of bone (after Poulet).

pericardium, causing a suppurative pericarditis. Dagron [242] reports a unique instance of death by purulent infection arising from perforation of the esophagus by a pin. The patient was a man of forty-two, and, some six weeks before he presented himself for treatment, before swallowing had experienced a severe pain low down in the neck. Five days before admission he had had a severe chill, followed by sweating and delirium. He died of a supraclavicular abscess on the fifth day; a black steel pin was found against the esophagus and trachea.

In connection with foreign bodies in the esophagus, it might be interesting

[a] 648, 1858.   [b] 264, 1858.

to remark that Ashhurst [a] has collected 129 cases of esophagotomy for the removal of foreign bodies, resulting in 95 recoveries and 34 deaths. Gaudolphe [b] collected 142 cases with 110 recoveries.

Injuries of the neck are usually inflicted with suicidal intent or in battle. Cornelius Nepos says that while fighting against the Lacedemonians, Epaminondas was sensible of having received a mortal wound, and apprehending that the lance was stopping a wound in an important vessel, remarked that he would die when it was withdrawn. When he was told that the Bœotians had conquered, exclaiming " I die unconquered," he drew out the lance and perished. Petrus de Largenta speaks of a man with an arrow in one of his carotids, who was but slightly affected before its extraction, but who died immediately after the removal of the arrow. Among the remarkable recoveries from injuries of the neck is that mentioned by Boerhaave, of a young man who lived nine or ten days after receiving a sword-thrust through the neck between the 4th and 5th vertebræ, dividing the vertebral artery. Benedictus, Bonacursius, and Monroe, all mention recovery after cases of cutthroat in which the esophagus as well as the trachea was wounded, and food protruded from the external cut. Warren [c] relates the history of a case in which the vertebral artery was wounded by the discharge of a pistol loaded with pebbles. The hemorrhage was checked by compression and packing, and after the discharge of a pebble and a piece of bone from the wound, the man was seen a month afterward in perfect health. Corson of Norristown, Pa., has reported the case of a quarryman who was stabbed in the neck with a shoemaker's knife, severing the left carotid one inch below its division. He was seen thirty minutes later in an apparently lifeless condition, but efforts at resuscitation were successfully made. The hemorrhage ceased spontaneously, and at the time of report, the man presented the symptoms of one who had had his carotid ligated (facial atrophy on one side, no pulse, etc.). Baron Larrey [478] mentions a case of gunshot wound in which the carotid artery was open at its division into internal and external branches, and says that the wound was plugged by an artilleryman until ligation, and in this primitive manner the patient was saved. Sale [d] reports the case of a girl of nineteen, who fell on a china bowl that she had shattered, and wounded both the right common carotid artery and internal jugular vein. There was profuse and continuous hemorrhage for a time, and subsequently a false aneurysm developed, which ruptured in about three months, giving rise to enormous momentary hemorrhage ; notwithstanding the severity of the injury and the extent of the hemorrhage, complete recovery ensued. Amos [e] relates the instance of a woman named Mary Green who, after complete division of all the vessels of the neck, walked 23 yards and climbed over an ordinary bar-gate nearly four feet high.

a 174, 385.   b 497, Jan. 20, 1895.   c 218, 1862, lxvi., 389.
d 124, 1879, 281.   e 490, 1832, x., 183.

Cholmeley reports the instance of a Captain of the First Madras Fusil-eers, who was wounded at Pegu by a musket-ball penetrating his neck. The common carotid was divided and for five minutes there was profuse hemor-rhage which, however, strange to say, spontaneously ceased. The patient died in thirty-eight hours, supposedly from spinal concussion or shock.[a]

Relative to **ligature of the common carotid artery,** Ashhurst mentions the fact that the artery has been ligated in 228 instances, with 94 recoveries. Ellis[b] mentions ligature of both carotids in four and a half days, as a treat-ment for a gunshot wound, with subsequent recovery. Lewtas[c] reports a case of ligation of the innominate and carotid arteries for traumatic aneurysm (likely a hematoma due to a gunshot injury of the subclavian artery). The patient was in profound collapse, but steadily reacted and was discharged cured on the forty-fifth day, with no perceptible pulse at the wrist and only a feeble beat in the pulmonary artery.

Garengeot, Wirth, Fine, and Evers, all mention **perforating wounds of the trachea and esophagus with recoveries.** Van Swieten and Hiester mention cases in which part of the trachea was carried away by a ball, with recovery. Monro, Tulpius, Bartholinus, and Paré report severance of the trachea with the absence of oral breathing, in which the divided portions were sutured, with successful results. In his "Theatro Naturæ" Bodinus says that William, Prince of Orange, lost the sense of taste after receiving a wound of the larynx; according to an old authority, a French soldier became mute after a similar accident. Davies-Colley[d] mentions a boy of eighteen who fell on a stick about the thickness of the index finger, transfixing his neck from right to left; he walked to a doctor's house, 250 yards away, with the stick in situ. In about two weeks he was discharged completely well. During treatment he had no hemorrhage of any importance, and his voice was not affected, but for a while he had slight dysphagia.

Barker[e] gives a full account of a barber who was admitted to a hospital two and a half hours after cutting his throat. He had a deep wound running transversely across the neck, from one angle of the jaw to the other, cutting open the floor of the mouth and extending from the inner border of the sterno-cleido-mastoid to the other, leaving the large vessels of the neck untouched. The razor had passed through the glosso-epiglottidean fold, a tip of the epi-glottis, and through the pharynx down to the spinal column. There was little hemorrhage, but the man could neither swallow nor speak. The wound was sutured, tracheotomy done, and the head kept fixed on the chest by a copper splint. He was ingeniously fed by esophageal tubes and rectal enemata; in three weeks speech and deglutition were restored. Shortly afterward the esopha-geal tube was removed and recovery was virtually complete. Little[f] men-tions an extraordinary case of a woman of thirty-six who was discharged

a 548, 1855, 538.	b 594, 1845.	c 224, 1889.
d 476, 1882.	e 436, May 16, 1894.	f 476, 1889, ii., 91.

from Garland's asylum, where she had been an inmate for three months. This unfortunate woman had attempted suicide by **self-decapitation from behind forward.** She was found, knife in hand, with a huge wound in the back of the neck and her head bobbing about in a ghastly manner. The incision had severed the skin, subcutaneous tissues and muscles, the ligaments and bone, opening the spinal canal, but not cutting the cord. The instrument used to effect this major injury was a blunt potato-peeling knife. Despite this terrible wound the patient lived to the sixth day.

Hislop[a] records a case of cut-throat in a man of seventy-four. He had a huge gaping wound of the neck, extending to within a half inch of the carotids on each side. The trachea was almost completely severed, the band left was not more than ¼ inch wide. Hislop tied four arteries, brought the ends of the trachea together with four strong silk sutures, and, as the operation was in the country, he washed the big cavity of the wound out with cold spring-water. He brought the superficial surfaces together with ten interrupted sutures, and, notwithstanding the patient's age, the man speedily recovered. This emphasizes the fact that the old theory of leaving wounds of this nature open was erroneous. Solly[b] reports the case of a tailor of twenty-two who attempted suicide by cutting through the larynx, entirely severing the epi-glottis and three-fourths of the pharynx. No bleeding point was found, and recovery ensued.

Cowles[c] describes the case of a soldier of thirty-five who, while escaping from the patrols, was shot by the Officer of the Day with a small bullet from a pistol. The ball entered the right shoulder, immediately over the supra-scapular notch, passed superficially upward and forward into the neck, wounding the esophagus posteriorly at a point opposite the thyroid cartilage, and lodged in the left side of the neck. The patient had little hemor-rhage, but had expectorated and swallowed much blood. He had a constant desire to swallow, which continued several days. The treat-ment was expectant; and in less than three weeks the soldier was returned to duty. From the same authority there is a condensation of five reports of gunshot wounds of the neck, from all of which the patients recovered and returned to duty.

Braman[d] describes the case of a man on whom several injuries were inflicted by a drunken companion. The first wound was slight; the second a deep flesh-wound over the trapezius muscle; the third extended from the right sterno-cleido-mastoid midway upward to the middle of the jaw and down to the raphe of the trachea. The external jugular, the external thyroid, and the facial arteries were severed. Braman did not find it necessary to ligate, but was able to check the hemorrhage with lint and persulphate of iron, in powder, with pressure. After fourteen hours the wound was closed; the patient recovered, and was returned to duty in a short time.

a 476, June 30, 1894.   b 476, 1864, i., 94.   c 847, 23.   d 847, 90.

Thomas[a] has reported the case of a man sixty-five years old whc, in an attempt at suicide with a penknife, had made a deep wound in the left side of the neck. The sternohyoid and omohyoid muscles were divided; the internal jugular vein was cut through, and its cut ends were collapsed and ¾ inch apart; the common carotid artery was cut into, but not divided; the thyroid cartilage was notched, and the external and anterior jugular veins were severed. Clamp-forceps were immediately applied to the cut vessels and one on each side the aperture in the common carotid from which a small spurt of blood, certainly not half a teaspoonful, came out. The left median basilic vein was exposed by an incision, and 20 ounces of warm saline solution were slowly perfused, an ordinary glass syringe with a capacity of five ounces, with an India-rubber tubing attached to a canula in the vein, being employed. After seven ounces of fluid had been injected, the man made a short, distinct inspiration; at ten ounces a deeper one (the radial pulse could now be felt beating feebly); at 15 ounces the breathing became regular and deep; at 18 ounces the man opened his eyes, but did not appear to be conscious. The clamped vessels were now tied with catgut and the wound cleansed with phenol lotion and dressed with cyanid-gauze. The man was surrounded by hot-water bottles and the foot of the bed elevated 18 inches. In the course of an hour the patient had recovered sufficiently to answer in a squeaky voice to his name when called loudly. Improvement proceeded rapidly until the twenty-second day, when violent hemorrhage occurred, preceded a few hours previously by a small trickle, easily controlled by pressure. The wound was at once opened and blood found oozing from the distal extremities of the carotid artery and jugular vein, which were promptly clamped. The common carotid artery was not sound, so that ligatures were applied to the internal and external carotids and to the internal jugular with a small branch entering into it. The patient was in great collapse, but quickly rallied, only to suffer renewed hemorrhage from the internal carotid nine days later. This was controlled by pressure with sponges, and a quart of hot water was injected into the rectum. From this time on the patient made a slow recovery, a small sinus in the lower part of the neck disappearing on the removal of the catgut ligature.

Adams[b] describes the case of a woman who attempted suicide with a common table-knife, severing the thyroid, cricoid, and first three rings of the trachea, and lacerating the sternohyoid and thyroid arteries; she finally recovered.

There is a curious case of suicide[c] of a woman who, while under the effects of opium, forced the handle of a mirror into her mouth. From all appearances, the handle had broken off near the junction and she had evidently fallen forward with the remaining part in her mouth, driving it forcibly against the spine, and causing the point of the handle to run downward in

[a] 224, No. 1823, p. 1420. [b] 476, 1850, i., 699. [c] 476, 1889, ii., 608.

front of the cervical vertebræ. On postmortem examination, a sharp piece of wood about two inches long, corresponding to the missing portion of the broken mirror handle, was found lying between the posterior wall of the esophagus and the spine. Hennig [a] mentions a case of gunshot wound of the neck in which the musket ball was lodged in the posterior portion of the neck and was subsequently discharged by the anus.

Injuries of the cervical vertebræ, while extremely grave, and declared by some authors to be inevitably fatal, are, however, not always followed by death or permanently bad results. Barwell [b] mentions a man of sixty-three who, in a fit of despondency, threw himself from a window, having fastened a rope to his neck and to the window-sill. He fell 11 or 12 feet, and in doing so suffered a subluxation of the 4th cervical vertebra. It slowly resumed the normal position by the elasticity of the intervertebral fibrocartilage, and there was complete recovery in ten days. Lazzaretto [c] reports the history of the case of a seaman whose atlas was dislocated by a blow from a falling sail-yard. The dislocation was reduced and held by adhesive strips, and the man made a good recovery. Vanderpool of Bellevue Hospital, N. Y., [d] describes a fracture of the odontoid process caused by a fall on the back of the head ; death, however, did not ensue until six months later. According to Ashhurst, [e] Philips, the elder Cline, Willard Parker, Bayard, Stephen Smith, May, and several other surgeons, have recorded complete recovery after fracture of the atlas and axis. The same author also adds that statistic investigation shows that as large a proportion as 18 per cent. of injuries of the cervical vertebræ occurring in civil practice, recover. However, the chances of a fatal issue in injuries of the vertebræ vary inversely with the distance of the point of injury from the brain. Keen has recorded a case in which a conoidal ball lodged in the body of the third cervical vertebra, from which it was extracted six weeks later. The paralysis, which, up to the time of extraction, had affected all four limbs, rapidly diminished. In about five weeks after the removal of the bullet nearly the entire body of the 3d cervical vertebra, including the anterior half of the transverse process and vertebral foramen, was spontaneously discharged. Nearly eight years afterward Keen saw the man still living, but with his right shoulder and arm diminished in size and partly paralyzed.

Doyle [f] reports a case of dislocated neck with recovery. During a runaway the patient was thrown from his wagon, and was soon after found on the roadside apparently dead. Physicians who were quickly summoned from the immediate neighborhood detected faint signs of life ; they also found a deformity of the neck, which led them to suspect dislocation. An ambulance was called, and without any effort being made to relieve the deformity the man was placed in it and driven to his home about a mile distant. The jolting

a 316, 1817.   b 224, 1882, 369.   c 318, 1813, ix., 165.
d Archives of Clinical Surgery, N. Y., 1877, ii., 116.   e 174, 353.   f 231, Jan., 1896.

over the rough roads greatly aggravated his condition. When Doyle saw the patient, his general appearance presented a hopeless condition, but being satisfied that a dislocation existed, Doyle immediately prepared to reduce it. Two men were told to grasp the feet and two more the head, and were directed to make careful but strong extension. At the same time the physician placed his right hand against the neck just over the pomum Adami, and his left against the occiput, and, while extension was being made, he flexed the head forward until the chin nearly touched the breast, after which the head was returned to its normal position. The manipulation was accompanied by a clicking sensation, caused by the replacement of the dislocated vertebra.

The patient immediately showed signs of relief and improved rapidly. Perceptible but feeble movements were made by all the limbs except the right arm. The patient remained in a comatose condition for eight or nine days, during which he had enuresis and intestinal torpor. He suffered from severe concussion of the brain, which accounted for his prolonged coma. Delirium was present, but he was carefully watched and not allowed to injure himself. His recovery was tedious and was delayed by several relapses. His first complaint after consciousness returned (on the tenth day) was of a sense of constriction about the neck, as if he were being choked. This gradually passed off, and his improvement went on without development of any serious symptoms.

Fig. 205.—B. Baldwin, "the switchman with the broken neck."

At the time of report he appeared in the best of health and was quite able to attend to his daily avocations. Doyle appends to his report the statement that among 394 cases embraced in Ashhurst's statistics, in treatment of dislocations in the cervical region, the mortality has been nearly four times greater when constitutional or general treatment has been relied on exclusively than when attempts had been made to reduce the dislocation by extension, rotation, etc. Doyle strongly advocates attempts at reduction in such cases.

Figure 205 represents a photograph of Barney Baldwin, a switchman of the Louisville and Nashville Railroad, who, after recovery from cervical dislocation, exhibited himself about the country, never appearing without his suspensory apparatus.

Acheson[a] records a case of luxation of the cervical spine with recovery after the use of a jury-mast. The patient was a man of fifty-five, by trade a train-conductor. On July 10, 1889, he fell backward in front of a train, his head striking between the ties; the brake-body caught his body, pushing it forward on his head, and turned him completely over. Three trucks passed over him. When dragged from beneath the train, his upper extremities were paralyzed. At noon the next day, nineteen hours after the accident, examination revealed bruises over the body, and he suffered intense pain at the back of the neck and base of the skull. Posteriorly, the neck presented a natural appearance; but anteriorly, to use the author's description, his neck resembled a combined case of mumps and goiter. The sternomastoid muscle bulged at the angle of the jaw, and was flaccid, and his "Adam's apple" was on a level with the chin. Sensation in the upper extremities was partially restored, and, although numb, he now had power of movement in the arms and hands, but could not rotate his neck. A diagnosis of cervical dislocation was made, and violent extension, with oscillation forward and backward, was practised, and the abnormal appearance subsided at once. No crepitus was noticed. On the fourth day there was slight hemorrhage from the mouth, which was more severe on the fifth and sixth days. The lower jaw had been forced past the upper, until the first molar had penetrated the tissues beneath the tongue. A plaster-of-Paris apparatus was applied, and in two months was exchanged for one of sole-leather. In rising from the recumbent position the man had to lift his head with his hands. Fifty days after the accident he suffered excruciating pain at the change of the weather, and at the approach of a storm the joints, as well as the neck, were involved. It was believed (one hundred and seven days after the accident) that both fracture and luxation existed. His voice had become guttural, but examination of the fauces was negative. The only evidence of paralysis was in the fingers, which, when applied to anything, experienced the sensation of touching gravel. The mottling of the tissues of the neck, which appeared about the fiftieth day, had entirely disappeared.

According to Thorburn,[b] Hilton had a patient who lived fourteen years with paraplegia due to fracture of the 5th, 6th, and 7th cervical vertebræ. Shaw is accredited with a case in which the patient lived fifteen months, the fracture being above the 4th cervical vertebra.

In speaking of **foreign bodies in the larynx and trachea,** the first to be considered will be liquids. There is a case on record[c] of an infant who was eating some coal, and being discovered by its mother was forced to rapidly swallow some water. In the excitement, part of the fluid swallowed fell into the trachea, and death rapidly ensued. It is hardly necessary to mention the instances in which pus or blood from ruptured abscesses entered the trachea and caused subsequent asphyxiation. A curious instance is

a 124, March, 1890.   b 224, Oct. 27, 1894.   c 641, 365.

reported by Gaujot of Val-de-Grâce of a soldier who was wounded in the Franco-Prussian war, and into whose wound an injection of the tincture of iodin was made. The wound was of such an extent as to communicate with a bronchus, and by this means the iodin entered the respiratory tract, causing suffocation. According to Poulet, Vidal de Cassis mentions an inmate of the Charité Hospital, in Paris, who, full of wine, had started to vomit ; he perceived Corvisart, and knew he would be questioned, therefore he quickly closed his mouth to hide the proofs of his forbidden ingestion. The materials in his mouth were forced into the larynx, and he was immediately asphyxiated. Laënnec, Mérat, and many other writers have mentioned death caused by the entrance of vomited materials into the air-passages. Parrot [a] has observed a child who died by the penetration of chyme into the air-passages. The bronchial mucous and underlying membrane were already in a process of digestion. Behrend, Piégu, and others cite analogous instances.

The presence of a foreign body in the larynx is at all times the cause of distressing symptoms, and, sometimes, a substance of the smallest size will cause death. There is a curious accident recorded [b] that happened to a young man of twenty-three, who was anesthetized in order to extract a tooth. A cork had been placed between the teeth to keep the mouth open. The tooth was extracted but slipped from the forceps, and, together with the cork, fell into the pharynx. The tooth was ejected in an effort at vomiting, but the cork entered the larynx, and, after violent struggles, asphyxiation caused death in an hour. The autopsy demonstrated the presence of the cork in the larynx. A somewhat analogous case, though not ending fatally, was reported by Hertz [c] of a woman of twenty-six, who was anesthetized for the extraction of the right second inferior molar. The crown broke off during the operation, and immediately after the extraction she had a fit of coughing. About fifteen days later she experienced pain in the lungs. Her symptoms increased to the fifth week, when she became so feeble as to be confined to her bed. A body seemed to be moving in the trachea, synchronously with respiration. At the end of the fifth week the missing crown of the tooth was expelled after a violent fit of coughing ; the symptoms immediately ameliorated, and recovery was rapid thereafter. Aronsohn [d] speaks of a child who was playing with a toy wind-instrument, and in his efforts to forcibly aspirate air through it, the child drew the detached reed into the respiratory passages, causing asphyxiation. At the autopsy the foreign body was found at the superior portion of the left bronchus. There are other cases in which, while sucking oranges or lemons, seeds have been aspirated ; and there is a case in which, in a like manner, the claw of a crab was drawn into the air-passages. There are two cases mentioned [e] in which children playing with toy balloons, which they inflated with their breath, have, by inspiration, reversed them and

a 789, 1885, ii., 167.   b 272, 1867.   c 296, 1873.
d Thèse de Strasbourg, 1856.   e 476, 1886, i., 758.

drawn the rubber of the balloon into the opening of the glottis, causing death. Aronsohn, who has already been quoted, and whose collection of instances of this nature is probably the most extensive, speaks of a child in the street who was eating an almond; a carriage threw the child down and he suddenly inspired the nut into the air-passages, causing immediate asphyxia. The same author also mentions a soldier walking in the street eating a plum, who, on being struck by a horse, suddenly started and swallowed the seed of the fruit. After the accident he had little pain or oppression, and no coughing, but twelve hours afterward he rejected the seed in coughing.

A curious accident is that in which a foreign body thrown into the air and caught in the mouth has caused immediate asphyxiation. Suetonius [754] transmits the history of a young man, a son of the Emperor Claudius, who, in sport, threw a small pear into the air and caught it in his mouth, and, as a consequence, was suffocated. Guattani [563] cites a similar instance of a man who threw up a chestnut, which, on being received in the mouth, lodged in the air-passages; the man died on the nineteenth day. Brodie reported the classic observation of the celebrated engineer, Brunel, who swallowed a piece of money thrown into the air and caught in his mouth. It fell into the open larynx, was inspired, causing asphyxiation, but was removed by inversion of the man's body.

Sennert says that Pope Adrian IV. died from the entrance of a fly into his respiratory passages; and Remy and Gautier record instances of the penetration of small fish into the trachea. There are, again, instances of leeches in this location.

Occasionally the **impaction of artificial teeth in the** neighborhood of the **larynx** has been **unrecognized** for many years. Lennox Browne [a] reports the history of a woman who was supposed to have either laryngeal carcinoma or phthisis, but in whom he found, impacted in the larynx, a plate with artificial teeth attached, which had remained in this position twenty-two months unrecognized and unknown. The patient, when questioned, remembered having been awakened in the night by a violent attack of vomiting, and finding her teeth were missing assumed they were thrown away with the ejections. From that time on she had suffered pain and distress in breathing and swallowing, and became the subject of progressive emaciation. After the removal of the impacted plate and teeth she soon regained her health. Paget [b] speaks of a gentleman who for three months, unconsciously, carried at the base of the tongue and epiglottis, very closely fitted to all the surface on which it rested, a full set of lost teeth and gold palate-plate. From the symptoms and history it was suspected that he had swallowed his set of false teeth, but, in order to prevent his worrying, he was never informed of this suspicion, and he never once suspected the causes of his symptoms.

Wrench [c] mentions a case illustrative of the extent to which imagination

a 536, 1860, ii., 588.   b 548, 1862, i., 59.   c 476, 1880, i., 71.

may produce symptoms simulating those ordinarily caused by the swallowing of false teeth. This man awoke one morning with his nose and throat full of blood, and noticed that his false teeth, which he seldom removed at night, were missing. He rapidly developed great pain and tumor in the larynx, together with difficulty in deglutition and speech. After a fruitless search, with instrumental and laryngoscopic aid, the missing teeth were found—in a chest of drawers; the symptoms immediately subsided when the mental illusion was relieved.

There is a curious case of a man drowned near Portsmouth.[a] After the recovery of his body it was seen that his false teeth were impacted at the anterior opening of the glottis, and it was presumed that the shock caused by the plunge into the cold water had induced a violent and deep inspiration which carried the teeth to the place of impaction.

Perrin[b] reports a case of an old man of eighty-two who lost his life from the impaction of a small piece of meat in the trachea and glottis. In the Musée Val-de-Grâce is a prepared specimen of this case showing the foreign body in situ (Fig. 206). In the same museum Perrin has also deposited a preparation from the body of a man of sixty-two, who died from the entrance of a morsel of beef into the respiratory passages. At the postmortem a mobile mass of food about the size

Fig. 206.—Foreign body in trachea and glottis.

Fig. 207.—Foreign body in trachea.

of a hazel-nut was found at the base of the larynx at the glossoepiglottic fossa. About the 5th ring of the trachea the caliber of this organ was obstructed by a cylindric alimentary bolus about six inches long, extending almost to the bronchial division (Fig. 207). Ashhurst shows a fibrinous cast, similar to that found in croup, caused by a foreign body removed by Wharton, together with a shawl-pin, from a patient at the Children's Hospital seven hours after the performance of tracheotomy. Search for the foreign body at the time of the operation was prevented by profuse hemorrhage.

The ordinary instances of foreign bodies in the larynx and trachea are so common that they will not be mentioned here. Their variety is innumerable and it is quite possible for more than two to be in the same location simultaneously. In his treatise on this subject Gross says that he has seen two, three, and even four substances simultaneously or successively penetrate the

a 476, 1882, i., 964.   b 641, 403.

same location.   Bérard [a] presented a stick of wood extracted from the vocal cords of a child of ten, and a few other similar instances are recorded.

The Medical Press and Circular [b] finds in an Indian contemporary some curious instances of misapplied ingenuity on the part of certain habitual criminals in that country.   The discovery on a prisoner of a heavy leaden bullet about ¾ inch in diameter led to an inquiry as to the object to which it was applied.   It was ascertained that it served to aid in the formation of a pouch-like recess at the base of the epiglottis.   The ball is allowed to slide down to the desired position, and it is retained there for about half an hour at a time.   This operation is repeated many times daily until a pouch the desired size results, in which criminals contrive to secrete jewels, money, etc., in such a way as to defy the most careful search, and without interfering in any way with speech or respiration.   Upward of 20 prisoners at Calcutta were found to be provided with this pouch-formation.   The resources of the professional malingerer are exceedingly varied, and testify to no small amount of cunning. The taking of internal irritants is very common, but would-be in-patients very frequently overshoot the mark and render recovery impossible.   Castor-oil seeds, croton beans, and sundry other agents are employed with this object in view, and the medical officers of Indian prisons have to be continually on the lookout for artificially induced diseases that baffle diagnosis and resist treatment.   Army surgeons are not altogether unfamiliar with these tricks, but compared with the artful Hindoos the British soldier is a mere child in such matters.

Excision of the larynx has found its chief indication in carcinoma, but has been employed in sarcoma, polypi, tuberculosis, enchondroma, stenosis, and necrosis.   Whatever the procedure chosen for the operation, preliminary tracheotomy is a prerequisite.   It should be made well below the isthmus of the thyroid gland, and from three to fifteen days before the laryngectomy. This affords time for the lungs to become accustomed to the new manner of breathing, and the trachea becomes fixed to the anterior wall of the neck.

Powers and White [c] have gathered 69 cases of either total or partial extirpation of the larynx, to which the 240 cases collected and analyzed by Eugene Kraus, in 1890, have been added.   The histories of six new cases are given. Of the 309 operations, 101, or 32 per cent. of the patients, died within the first eight weeks from shock, hemorrhage, pneumonia, septic infection, or exhaustion.   The cases collected by these authors show a decrease in the death ratio in the total excision,—29 per cent. as against 36 per cent. in the Kraus tables.   The mortality in the partial operation is increased, being 38 per cent. as opposed to 25 per cent.   Cases reported as free from the disease before the lapse of three years are of little value, except in that they diminish, by so much, the operative death-rate.   Of 180 laryngectomies for carcinoma prior to January 1, 1892, 72, or 40 per cent., died as a result of the operation ; 51 of

a 242, 1833, viii., 60.   b 536, 1889, ii., 189.   c 538, March 23, 1895.

the remaining 108 had recurrence during the first year, and 11, or ten per cent. of the survivors, were free from relapse three or more years after operation. In 77 cases of partial laryngectomy for cancer, 26, or 33 per cent., died during the first two months ; of the remaining 51, seven cases, or 13 per cent., are reported as free from the disease three or more years after the operation.

Injuries destroying great portions of the face or jaw, but not causing death, are seldom seen, except on the battle-field, and it is to military surgery that we must look for the most striking instances of this kind. Ribes [a] mentions a man of thirty-three who, in the Spanish campaign in 1811, received an injury which carried away the entire body of the lower jaw, half of each ramus, and also mangled in a great degree the neighboring soft parts. He was transported from the field of battle, and, despite enormous hemorrhage and suppuration, in two months recovered. At the time of report the wounded man presented no trace of the inferior maxillary bone, but by carrying the finger along the side of the pharynx in the direction of the superior dental arch the coronoid apophyses could be recognized, and about six lines nearer the temporal extremity the ramus could be discovered. The tongue was missing for about one-third its length, and was thicker than natural and retracted on the hyoid bone. The sublingual glands were adherent to the under part of the tongue and were red and over-developed. The inferior parts of the cheeks were cicatrized with the lateral and superior regions of the neck, and with the base of the tongue and the hyoid bone. The tongue was free under and in front of the larynx. The patient used a gilded silver plate to fix the tongue so that deglutition could be carried on. He was not able to articulate sounds, but made himself understood through the intervention of this plate, which was fixed to a silver chin. The chin he used to maintain the tongue-plate, to diminish the deformity, and to retain the saliva, which was constantly dribbling on the neck (Fig. 208). The same author quotes the instance of a man of fifty, who, during the siege of Alexandria in 1801, was struck in the middle of his face, obliquely, by a cannon-ball, from below upward and from right to left. A part of the right malar bone, the two superior maxillary bones, the nasal bones, the cartilage, the vomer, the middle lamina of the ethmoid, the left maxillary bone, a portion of the left zygomatic arch, and a great portion of the inferior maxilla were carried away, or comminuted, and all the soft parts correspondingly lacerated. Several hours afterward this soldier was counted among the number of dead, but Larrey, the surgeon-in-chief of the army, with his typical vigilance and humanity, remarked that the patient gave signs of life, and that, despite the magnitude of his wound, he did not despair of his recovery. Those portions in which attrition was very great were removed, and the splinters of bone taken out, showing an enormous wound. Three months were

a 302, xxix., 424.

necessary for cicatrization, but it was not until the capitulation of Marabou, at which place he was wounded, that the patient was returned to France. At this time he presented a hideous aspect. There were no signs of nose, nor cartilage separating the entrance of the nostrils, and the vault of the nasal fossa could be easily seen. There was a part of the posterior region of the right superior maxilla, but the left was entirely gone—in fact, the man presented an enormous triangular opening in the center of the face, as shown by the accompanying illustration (Fig. 209). The tongue and larynx were severely involved, and the sight in the left eye was lost. This patient continually wore a gilded silver mask, which covered his deformity and rendered articulation a little less difficult. The saliva continually dribbled from the mouth and from the inferior internal portion of his mask, compelling him to carry some substance to receive the dribblings. Whymper[a] mentions an

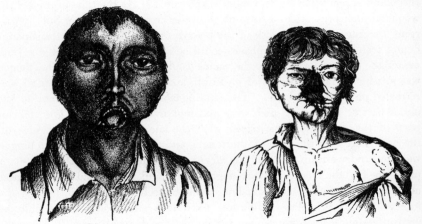

Fig. 208.—Gunshot injury of the lower jaw.   Fig. 209.—Gunshot injury of the face.

analogous instance of a gunner who had his whole lower jaw torn away by a shell, but who recovered and used an ingenious contrivance in the shape of a silver mask for remedying the loss of the parts. Steiner[b] mentions a wound from a cannon-ball, which carried away the left half of the inferior maxilla, stripping the soft parts as high as the malar, and on the left side of the neck to within $1\frac{1}{2}$ inches of the clavicle, laying bare the transverse processes of the 2d and 3d vertebræ, and exposing the external carotid and most of its branches.

It sometimes happens that a foreign body, such as the breech of a gun, may be imbedded for some time in the face, with subsequent safe removal. Keith[c] mentions an instance of the successful removal of the breech of a fowling-piece from the face, at the root of the nose, after a lodgment of four months; and Fraser[d] cites an analogous instance in which the breech

a 490, 1833.   b 526, 1849.   c 548, 1858, 416.   d 218, 1863, 470.

was imbedded in the bones of the face for eight years. Smith [a] records an instance in which a broken piece of tobacco-pipe penetrated the cheek, remained there for seven months, but was successfully extracted.

Before leaving accidents to the head and neck, a most curious case, cited by O'Neill,[b] will be briefly reviewed. A boy of twelve was entrusted to carry a new iron pot to the destination of its purchaser. Probably to facilitate transportation, the boy removed his hat and placed the pot obliquely on the back part of his head, but a sudden movement caused it to slip forward and downward over the head. Unavailing efforts were made at the time and after he reached home, to remove the pot from his head, but in vain, and he continued all the night greatly prostrated by fright, hunger, and thirst, together with the efforts at removal. The next morning he was taken to a neighboring blacksmith, who, by greasing one of his fingers, managed to insinuate it between the head and pot. Placing the other side of the pot against an anvil, he struck over the location of his finger a quick, heavy tap with a hammer, and the pot fell to pieces. The little patient was much exhausted by all his treatment and want of sleep, and, in fact, could hardly have endured his situation much longer.

a 476, 1864, i., 490.   b 476, 1889, i., 156.

CHAPTER XI.

SURGICAL ANOMALIES OF THE EXTREMITIES.

Reunion of Digits.—An interesting phenomenon noticed in relation to severed digits is their wonderful capacity for reunion. Restitution of a severed part, particularly if one of considerable function, naturally excited the interest of the older writers. Locher [a] has cited an instance of avulsion of the finger with restitution of the avulsed portion; and Brulet, [b] Van Esh, Farmer, [338] Ponteau, Regnault, and Rosenberg cite instances of reunion of a digit after amputation or severance. Eve's "Remarkable Cases in Surgery" contains many instances of reunion of both fingers and thumbs, and in more recent years several other similar cases have been reported. [c] At the Emergency Hospital in Washington, D. C., there was a boy brought in who had completely severed one of his digits by a sharp bread-cutter. The amputated finger was wrapped up in a piece of brown paper, and, being apparently healthy and the wound absolutely clean, it was fixed in the normal position on the stump, and covered by a bichlorid dressing. In a short time complete function was restored. In this instance no joint was involved, the amputation being in the middle of the 2d phalanx. Staton [d] has described a case in which the hand was severed from the arm by an accidental blow from an axe. The wound extended from the styloid process directly across to the trapezium, dividing all the muscles and blood-vessels, cutting through bones. A small portion of the skin below the articulation, with the ulna, remained intact. After an unavoidable delay of an hour, Staton proceeded to replace the hand with silver sutures, adhesive plaster, and splints. On the third day pulsation was plainly felt in the hand, and on the fourteenth day the sutures were removed. After some time the patient was able to extend the fingers of the wounded member, and finally to grasp with all her wonted strength.

The **reproduction or accidental production of nails** after the original part has been torn away by violence or destroyed by disease, is quite interesting. Sometimes when the whole last phalanx has been removed, the nail regrows at the tip of the remaining stump. Tulpius [842] seems to have met with this remarkable condition. Maréchal de Rougères, [e] Voigtel, and Ormançey [f] have related instances of similar growths on the 2d phalanx

a 456, ii., 405.   b 297, No. 223.   c 313, Aug., 1865 ; 224, Jan., 1862.

d 604, 1880.   e 462, T. xxvii., 177.   f 461, March, 1809.

after the loss of the 1st. For several months a woman had suffered from an ulcer of the middle finger of the right hand, in consequence of a whitlow; there was loss of the 3d phalanx, and the whole of the articular surface and part of the compact bony structure of the 2d. On examining the sore, Ormançey saw a bony sequestrum which appeared to keep it open. He extracted this, and, until cicatrization was complete, he dressed the stump with saturnine cerate. Some months afterward Ormançey saw with astonishment that the nail had been reproduced; instead of following the ordinary direction, however, it lay directly over the face of the stump, growing from the back toward the palmar aspect of the stump digit, as if to cover and protect the stump. Blandin has observed a case of the same description.[a] A third occurred at the Hôpital de la Charité, in a woman, who, in consequence of a whitlow, had lost the whole of the 3d phalanx of one of the forefingers. The soft and fleshy cushion which here covered the 2d phalanx was terminated by a small, blackish nail, like a grain of spur rye. It is probable that in these cases the soft parts of the 3d phalanx, and especially the ungual matrix, had not been wholly destroyed. In his lectures Chevalier speaks of analogous cases.

In some instances **avulsion of a finger** is effected in a peculiar manner. In 1886 Anche reported to his confrères in Bordeaux a rare accident of this nature that occurred to a carpenter. The man's finger was caught between a rope and the block of a pulley. By a sudden and violent movement on his part he disengaged the hand but left the 3d finger attached to the pulley. At first examination the wound looked like that of an ordinary amputation by the usual oval incision; from the center of the wound the proximal fragment of the 1st phalanx projected. Polaillon[b] has collected 42 similar instances, in none of which, however, was the severance complete.

It occasionally happens that in avulsion of the finger an entire tendon is stripped up and torn off with the detached member. Vogel[c] describes an instance of this nature, in which the long flexor of the thumb was torn off with that digit. In the Surgical Museum at Edinburgh there is preserved a thumb and part of the flexor longus pollicis attached, which were avulsed simultaneously. Nunnely[d] has seen the little finger together with the tendon and body of the longer flexor muscle avulsed by machinery. Stone[e] details the description of the case of a boy named Lowry, whose left thumb was caught between rapidly twisting strands of a rope, and the last phalanx, the neighboring soft parts, and also the entire tendon of the flexor longus pollicis were instantly torn away. There was included even the tendinous portion of that small slip of muscle taking its origin from the anterior aspect of the head and upper portion of the ulna, and which is so delicate and insignificant as to

---

a "Anatomie Topographique," p. 558, Paris.   b Quoted 476, 1886, ii., 641.
c Med.-Chir. Beobachtungen, 353.   d 779, 1859.   e 124, 1854.

be generally overlooked by anatomists. There was great pain along the course of the tract of abstraction of the tendon.

Pinkerton[a] describes a carter of thirty-one who was bitten on the thumb by a donkey. The man pulled violently in one direction, and the donkey, who had seized the thumb firmly with his teeth, pulled forcibly in the other direction until the tissues gave way and the man ran off, leaving his thumb in the donkey's mouth. The animal at once dropped the thumb, and it was picked up by a companion who accompanied the man to the hospital. On examination the detached portion was found to include the terminal phalanx of the thumb, together with the tendon of the flexor longus pollicis measuring ten inches, about half of which length had a fringe of muscular tissue hanging from the free borders, indicating the extent and the penniform arrangement of the fibers attached to it. Meyer[b] cites a case in which the index finger was torn off and the flexor muscle twisted from its origin. The authors know of an unreported case in which a man running in the street touched his hand to a hitching block he was passing; a ring on one of his fingers caught in the hook of the block, and tore off the finger with the attached tendon and muscle. There is a similar instance of a Scotch gentleman who slipped, and, to prevent falling, he put out his hand to catch the railing. A ring on one of his fingers became entangled in the railing and the force of the fall tore off the soft parts of the finger together with the ring.

The older writers mentioned as a curious fact that **avulsion of the arm,** unaccompanied by hemorrhage, had been noticed. Belchier,[629] Carmichael,[524] and Clough[c] report instances of this nature, and, in the latter case, the progress of healing was unaccompanied by any uncomfortable symptoms. In the last century Hunczoysky observed complete avulsion of the arm by a cannon-ball, without the slightest hemorrhage. The Ephemerides contains an account of the avulsion of the hand without any bleeding, and Woolcomb[d] has observed a huge wound of the arm from which hemorrhage was similarly absent. Later observations have shown that in this accident absence of hemorrhage is the rule and not the exception. The wound is generally lacerated and contused and the mouths of the vessels do not gape, but are twisted and crushed. The skin usually separates at the highest point and the muscles protrude, appearing to be tightly embraced and almost strangulated by the skin, and also by the tendons, vessels, and nerves which, crushed and twisted with the fragments of bone, form a conical stump. Cheselden reports the history of a case, which has since become classic, that he observed in St. Thomas' Hospital in London, in 1837. A miller had carelessly thrown a slip-knot of rope about his wrist, which became caught in a revolving cog, drawing him from the ground and violently throwing his body against a beam. The force exerted by the cog drawing on the rope was sufficient to avulse his whole arm and shoulder-blade. There was comparatively little hemorrhage

a 381, 1887, 43.   b 701, 1879.   c 564, iii.   d 629, lx.

and the man was insensible to pain; being so dazed and surprised he really was unconscious of the nature of his injury until he saw his arm in the wheel.

According to Billroth the avulsion of an arm is usually followed by fatal shock. Fischer, however, relates the case of a lion-tamer whose whole left arm was torn from the shoulder by a lion; the loss of blood being very slight and the patient so little affected by shock that he was able to walk to the hospital.

Mussey[a] describes a boy of sixteen who had his left arm and shoulder-blade completely torn from his body by machinery. The patient became so involved in the bands that his body was securely fastened to a drum, while his legs hung dangling. In this position he made about 15 revolutions around the drum before the motion of the machinery could be effectually stopped by cutting off the water to the great wheel. When he was disentangled from the bands and taken down from the drum a huge wound was seen at the shoulder, but there was not more than a pint of blood lost. The collar-bone projected from the wound about half an inch, and hanging from the wound were two large nerves (probably the median and ulnar) more than 20 inches long. He was able to stand on his feet and actually walked a few steps; as his frock was opened, his arm, with a clot of blood, dropped to the floor. This boy made an excellent recovery. The space between the plastered ceiling and the drum in which the revolutions of the body had taken place was scarcely 7½ inches wide. Horsbeck's case was of a negro of thirty-five who, while pounding resin on a 12-inch leather band, had his hand caught between the wheel and band. His hand, forearm, arm, etc., were rapidly drawn in, and he was carried around until his shoulder came to a large beam, where the body was stopped by resistance against the beam, fell to the floor, and the arm and scapula were completely avulsed and carried on beyond the beam. In this case, also, the man experienced little pain, and there was comparatively little hemorrhage. Maclean[b] reports the history of an accident to a man of twenty-three who had both arms caught between a belt and the shaft while working in a woolen factory, and while the machinery was in full operation. He was carried around the shaft with great velocity until his arms were torn off at a point about four inches below the shoulder-joint on each side. The patient landed on his feet, the blood spurting from each brachial artery in a large stream. His fellow-workmen, without delay, wound a piece of rope around each bleeding member, and the man recovered after primary amputation of each stump. Will[c] gives an excellent instance of avulsion of the right arm and scapula in a girl of eighteen, who was caught in flax-spinning machinery. The axillary artery was seen lying in the wound, pulsating feebly, but had been efficiently closed by the torsion of the machinery. The girl recovered.

Additional cases of avulsion of the upper extremity are reported by

[a] 124, 1837, xxi., 385.   [b] 632, 1880.   [c] 224, 1884, i., 1135.

Aubinais,[a] Bleynie,[b] Charles,[c] George,[d] James,[e] Jones,[f] Marcano,[g] Belchier,[575] Braithwaite,[h] and Hendry.[i]

Avulsion of the Lower Extremity.—The symptoms following avulsion of the upper extremity are seen as well in similar accidents to the leg and thigh, although the latter are possibly the more fatal. Horlbeck[j] quotes Benomont's description of a small boy who had his leg torn off at the knee by a carriage in motion; the child experienced no pain, and was more concerned about the punishment he expected to receive at home for disobedience than about the loss of his leg. Carter[k] speaks of a boy of twelve who incautiously put the great toe of his left foot against a pinion wheel of a mill in motion. The toe was fastened and drawn into the mill, the leg following almost to the thigh. The whole left leg and thigh, together with the left side of the scrotum, were torn off; the boy died as a result of his injuries.

Ashhurst reported to the Pathological Society of Philadelphia the case of a child of nine who had its right leg caught in the spokes of a carriage wheel. The child was picked up unconscious, with its thigh entirely severed, and the bone broken off about the middle third; about three inches higher the muscles were torn from the sheaths and appeared as if cut with a knife. The great sciatic nerve was found hanging 15 inches from the stump, having given way from its division in the popliteal space. The child died in twelve hours. One of the most interesting features of the case was the rapid cooling of the body after the accident and prolongation of the coolness with slight variations until death ensued. Ashhurst remarks that while the cutaneous surface of the stump was acutely sensitive to the touch, there was no manifestation of pain evinced upon handling the exposed nerve.

With reference to **injuries to the sciatic nerve,** Küster[l] mentions the case of a strong man of thirty, who in walking slipped and fell on his back. Immediately after rising to his feet he felt severe pain in the right leg and numbness in the foot. He was unable to stand, and was carried to his house, where Küster found him suffering great pain. The diagnosis had been fracture of the neck of the femur, but as there was no crepitation and passive movements caused but little pain, Küster suspected rupture of the sciatic nerve. The subsequent history of the case confirmed this diagnosis. The patient was confined to bed six weeks, and it was five months afterward before he was able to go about, and then only with a crutch and a stick.

Park[m] mentions an instance of rupture of the sciatic nerve caused by a patient giving a violent lurch during an operation at the hip-joint.

The instances occasionally observed of **recovery of an injured leg after**

a Soc. Acad. Loire inf., 1862.　　b 673, 1867–8, i., 11.　　c 476, 1872, i., 216.

d 315, 1879, xxxix., 69.　　e 180, 1868, xiii., 117.　　f 224, 1870, i., 545.

g 242, 1875, 228.　　h 490, 1832.　　i 299, 1875.　　j 264, 1859, 433.

k 528, 1792, ii., 17.　　l 199, March 26, 1883.　　m 450, 1884, 323.

extensive severance and loss of substance are most marvelous. Morton [a] mentions a boy of sixteen, who was struck by one of the blades of a reaping machine, and had his left leg cut through about 1¼ inches above the ankle-joint. The foot was hanging by the portion of skin corresponding to the posterior quarter of the circumference of the leg, together with the posterior tibial vessels and nerves. These were the only structures escaping division, although the ankle-joint itself was intact. There was comparatively little hemorrhage and no shock ; a ligature was applied to the vessels, the edges of the wound were drawn together by wire sutures, and the cut surfaces of the tibia were placed in as good apposition as possible, although the lower fragment projected slightly in front of the upper. The wound was dressed and healing progressed favorably ; in three months the wound had filled up to such an extent that the man was allowed to go on crutches. The patient was discharged in five months, able to walk very well, but owing to the loss of the function of the extensor tendons the toes dragged.

Washington [b] reports in full the case of a boy of eleven, who, in handing a fowling piece across a ditch, was accidentally shot. The contents of the gun were discharged through the leg above the ankle, carrying away five-sixths of the structure—at the time of the explosion the muzzle of the gun was only two feet away from his leg. The portions removed were more than one inch of the tibia and fibula (irregular fractures of the ends above and below), a corresponding portion of the posterior tibial muscle, and the long flexors of the great and small toes, as well as the tissue interposed between them and the Achilles tendon. The anterior tibial artery was fortunately uninjured. The remaining portions consisted of a strip of skin two inches in breadth in front of the wound, the muscles which it covered back of the wound, the Achilles tendon, and another piece of skin, barely enough to cover the tendon. The wound was treated by a bran-dressing, and the limb was saved with a shortening of but 1½ inches.

There are several **anomalous injuries** which deserve mention. Markoe [c] observed a patient of seventy-two, who ruptured both the quadriceps tendons of each patella by slipping on a piece of ice, one tendon first giving way, and followed almost immediately by the other. There was the usual depression immediately above the upper margin of the patella, and the other distinctive signs of the accident. In three months both tendons had united to such an extent that the patient was able to walk slowly. Gibney [d] records a case in which the issue was not so successful, his patient being a man who, in a fall ten years previously, had ruptured the right quadriceps tendon, and four years later had suffered the same accident on the opposite side. As a result of his injuries, at the time Gibney saw him, he had completely lost all power of extending the knee-joint. Partridge [e] mentions an instance, in a

a 476, 1873.   b 124, 1877, i., 332.   c 597, 1884.
d 597, Dec. 29, 1884.   e 548, 1868, i., 175.

strong and healthy man, of rupture of the tendon of the left triceps cubiti, caused by a fall on the pavement. There are numerous cases in which the tendo Achillis has recovered after rupture,—in fact, it is unhesitatingly severed when necessity demands it, sufficient union always being anticipated. None of these cases of rupture of the tendon are unique, parallel instances existing in medical literature in abundance.

Marshall [a] had under his observation a case in which the femoral artery was ruptured by a cart-wheel passing over the thigh, and death ensued although there were scarcely any external signs of contusion and positively no fracture. Boerhaave cites a curious instance in which a surgeon attempted to stop hemorrhage from a wounded radial artery by the application of a caustic, but the material applied made such inroads as to destroy the median artery and thus brought about a fatal hemorrhage.

Spontaneous fractures are occasionally seen, but generally in advanced age, although muscular action may be the cause. There are several cases on record in which the muscular exertion in throwing a stone or ball, or in violently kicking the leg, has fractured one or both of the bones of an extremity. In old persons intracapsular fracture may be caused by such a trivial thing as turning in bed, and even a sudden twist of the ankle has been sufficient to produce this injury. In a boy of thirteen Storrs [b] has reported fracture of the femur within the acetabulum. In addition to the causes enumerated, inflammation of osseous tissue, or osteoid carcinoma, has been found at the seat of a spontaneous fracture.

One of the most interesting subjects in the history of surgery is the gradual **evolution of the rational treatment of dislocations.** Possibly no portion of the whole science was so backward as this. Thirty-five centuries ago Darius, son of Hydaspis, suffered a simple luxation of the foot; it was not diagnosed in this land of Apis and of the deified discoverer of medicine. Among the wise men of Egypt, then in her acme of civilization, there was not one to reduce the simple luxation which any student of the present day would easily diagnose and successfully treat. Throughout the dark ages and down to the present century, the hideous and unnecessary apparatus employed, each decade bringing forth new types, is abundantly pictured in the older books on surgery; in some almost recent works there are pictures of windlasses and of individuals making superhuman efforts to pull the luxated member back—all of which were given to the student as advisable means of treatment.

Relative to **anomalous dislocations** the field is too large to be discussed here, but there are two recent ones worthy of mention. Bradley [c] relates an instance of death following a subluxation of the right humerus backward on the scapula. It could not be reduced because the tendon of the biceps lay between the head of the humerus and a piece of the bone which was chipped off.

a 224, 1870, ii., 116.   b 656, 1843.   c 224, 1877, i., 544.

Baxter-Tyrie[a] reports a dislocation of the shoulder-joint, of unusual origin, in a man who was riding a horse that ran away up a steep hill. After going a few hundred yards the animal abated its speed, when the rider raised his hand to strike. Catching sight of the whip, the horse sprang forward, while the man felt an acute pain and a sense of something having given way at his shoulder. He did not fall off, but rode a little further and was helped to dismount. On examination a subcoracoid dislocation of the head of the humerus was found. The explanation is that as the weight of the whip was inconsiderable (four ounces) the inertia of the arm converted it into a lever of the first order. Instead of fulfilling its normal function of preventing dis-

placement, the coraco-acro-mial arch acted as a fulcrum. The limb from the fingers to that point acted as the "long arm," and the head and part of the neck of the humerus served as the "short arm." The inertia of the arm, left behind as it were, supplied the power, while the ruptured capsular ligament and displacement of the head of the bone would represent the work done.

Congenital Disloca-tions.—The extent and ac-curacy of the knowledge pos-sessed by Hippocrates on the subject of congenital disloca-tions have excited the admir-ation of modern writers, and until a comparatively recent

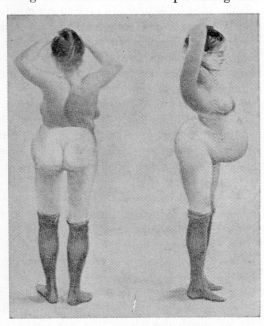

Fig. 210.—Case of congenital luxation of the femora (Hirst).

time examples of certain of the luxations described by him had not been recorded. With regard, for instance, to congenital dislocations at the shoulder-joint, little or nothing was known save what was contained in the writings of Hippocrates, till R. M. Smith and Guérin discussed the lesion in their works.

Among congenital dislocations, those of the hips are most common—in fact, 90 per cent. of all. They are sometimes not recognizable until after the lapse of months and sometimes for years, but their causes—faulty develop-ments of the joint, paralysis, etc.—are supposed to have existed at birth. One or both joints may be involved, and according to the amount of involvement the gait is peculiar. As to the reduction of such a dislocation, the most that

[a] 476, No. 3767, 1165.

can be done is to diminish the deformity and functional disability by traction and palliative measures with apparatus. The normal structure of the joint does not exist, and therefore the dislocation admits of no reduction. Congenital dislocations of the shoulder are also seen, owing to faulty development of the glenoid fossa ; and at the knee, the leg generally being in extreme hyperextension, the foot sometimes resting on the abdomen. Congenital luxation of the femora, when it appears in adult women (Fig. 210) is a prominent factor in dystocia. There is a dislocation found at birth, or occurring shortly after, due to dropsy of the joint in utero ; and another form due to succeeding paralysis of groups of muscles about the joint.

The interesting instances of **major amputations** are so numerous and so well known as to need no comment here. **Amputation of the hip** with recovery is fast becoming an ordinary operation ; at Westminster Hospital in London, there is preserved the right humerus and scapula, presenting an enormous bulk, which was removed by **amputation at the shoulder-joint,** for a large lymphosarcoma growing just above the clavicle. The patient was a man of twenty-two, and made a good recovery. Another similar preparation is to be seen in London at St. Bartholomew's Hospital.

Simultaneous, synchronous, or consecutive amputations of all the limbs have been repeatedly performed. Champenois[a] reports the case of a Sumatra boy of seven, who was injured to such an extent by an explosion as to necessitate the amputation of all his extremities, and, despite his tender age and the extent of his injuries, the boy completely recovered. Jackson, quoted by Ashhurst,[b] had a patient from whom he simultaneously amputated all four limbs for frost-bite.

Muller[c] reports a case of amputation of all four limbs for frost-bite, with recovery. The patient, aged twenty-six, while traveling to his home in Northern Minnesota, was overtaken by a severe snow storm, which continued for three days ; on December 13th he was obliged to leave the stage in a snow-drift on the prairie, about 110 miles distant from his destination. He wandered over the prairie that day and night, and the following four days, through the storm, freezing his limbs, nose, ears, and cheeks, taking no food or water until, on December 16th, he was found in a dying condition by Indian scouts, and taken to a station-house on the road. He did not reach the hospital at Fort Ridgely until the night of December 24th—eleven days after his first exposure. He was almost completely exhausted, and, after thawing the ice from his clothes, stockings, and boots,—which had not been removed since December 13th,—it was found that both hands and forearms were completely mortified up to the middle third, and both feet and legs as far as the upper third ; both knees over and around the patellæ, and the alæ and tip of the nose all presented a dark bluish appearance and fairly circumscribed swelling. No evacuation of the bowels had taken place for over two weeks,

a 662, 1869, 507.   b 174, 107.   c 847, 216.

and as the patient suffered from singultus and constant pain over the epigastric region, a light cathartic was given, which, in twenty-four hours, gave relief. The four frozen limbs were enveloped in a solution of zinc chlorid. The frozen ears and cheeks healed in due time, and the gangrenous parts of the nose separated and soon healed, with the loss of the tip and parts of the alæ, leaving the septum somewhat exposed. On January 10th the lines of demarcation were distinct and deep on all four limbs, though the patient, seconded by his wife, at first obstinately opposed operative interference; on January 13th, after a little hesitancy, the man consented to an amputation of the arms. This was successfully carried out on both forearms, at the middle third, the patient losing hardly any blood and complaining of little pain. The great relief afforded by this operation so changed his aversion to being operated upon that on the next day he begged to have both legs amputated in the same manner, which was done, three days afterward, with the same favorable result. After some minor complications the patient left for his home, perfectly recovered, June 9, 1866.

Begg of Dundee[a] successfully performed quadruple amputation on a woman, the victim of idiopathic gangrene. With artificial limbs she was able to earn a livelihood by selling fancy articles which she made herself. This woman died in 1885, and the four limbs, mounted on a lay figure, were placed in the Royal College of Surgeons, in London. Wallace, of Rock Rapids, Iowa, has successfully removed both forearms, one leg, and half of the remaining foot, for frost-bite. Allen[b] describes the case of a boy of eight who was run over by a locomotive, crushing his right leg, left foot, and left forearm to such an extent as to necessitate **primary triple amputation** at the left elbow, left foot, and right leg, the boy recovering. Ashhurst remarks that Luckie, Alexander, Koehler, Lowman, and Armstrong have successfully removed both legs and one arm simultaneously for frost-bite, all the patients making excellent recoveries in spite of their mutilations; he adds that he himself has successfully resorted to synchronous amputation of the right hip-joint and left leg for a railroad injury occurring in a lad of fifteen, and has twice synchronously amputated three limbs from the same patient, one case recovering.

Wharton[c] reports a case of triple major amputation on a negro of twenty-one, who was run over by a train (Fig. 211). His right leg was crushed at the knee, and the left leg crushed and torn off in the middle third; the right forearm and hand were crushed. In order to avoid chill and exposure, he was operated on in his old clothes, and while one limb was being amputated the other was being prepared. The most injured member was removed first. Recovery was uninterrupted.

There are two cases of **spontaneous amputation** worthy of record. Boerhaave mentions a peasant near Leyden, whose axillary artery was divided

[a] 224, 1886, i., 81.   [b] 476, 1889, i., 730.   [c] 533, March 31, 1894.

with a knife, causing great effusion of blood, and the patient fainted. The mouth of the vessel was retracted so far as to render ligature impossible, and the poor man was abandoned to what was considered an inevitable fate by his unenlightened attendants. Expecting to die every moment, he continued several days in a languid state, but the hemorrhage ceased spontaneously, and the arm decayed, shrunk, and dried into a mummified stump, which he carried about for quite a while. Rooker [a] speaks of a fracture of the forearm, near the lower part of the middle third, in a patient aged fourteen. Incipient gangrene below the seat of fracture, with associate inflammation, developed ; but on account of the increasing gangrene it was determined to amputate. On the fifth day the line of demarcation extended to the spine

Fig. 211.—Synchronous triple amputation (Wharton).

of the scapula, laying bare the bone and exposing the acromion process and involving the pectoral muscles. It was again decided to let Nature continue her work. The bones exfoliated, the spine and the acromial end of the scapula came away, and a good stump was formed. Figure 212 represents the patient at the age of twenty-eight.

By ingenious mechanical contrivances persons who have lost an extremity are enabled to perform the ordinary functions of the missing member with but slight deterioration. **Artificial arms, hands, and legs** have been developed to such a degree of perfection that the modern mechanisms of this nature are very unlike the cumbersome and intricate contrivances formerly used.

Le Progrés Médical [b] contains an interesting account of a curious contest held between **dismembered athletes** at Nogent-Sur-Marne, a small town in the Department of the Seine, in France.

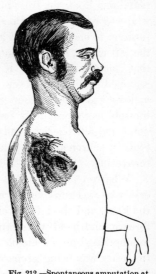

Fig. 212.—Spontaneous amputation at the shoulder (Rooker).

Responding to a general

a 133, 1879, xx., 210.   b Quoted 476, 1895, ii., 220.

invitation, no less than seven individuals who had lost either leg or thigh, competed in running races for prizes. The enterprising cripples were divided into two classes : the *cuissards*, or those who had lost a thigh, and *jambards*, or those who had lost a leg ; and, contrary to what might have been expected, the grand champion came from the former class. The distance in each race was 200 meters. M. Roullin, whose thigh, in consequence of an accident, was amputated in 1887, succeeded in traversing the course in the remarkable time of thirty seconds (about 219 yards) ; whereas M. Florrant, the speediest jambard, required thirty-six seconds to run the same distance ; and was, moreover, defeated by two other cuissards besides the champion. The junior race was won in thirty-five seconds, and this curious day's sport was ended by a *course de consolation*, which was carried off in thirty-three seconds by M. Mausire, but whether he was a cuissard or a jambard was not stated.

On several occasions in England, cricket matches have been organized between armless and legless men. In Charles Dickens' paper, "All the Year Round," October 5, 1861, there is a reference to a cricket match between a one-armed eleven and a one-legged eleven. There is a recent report from De Kalb, Illinois, of a boy of thirteen who had lost both legs and one arm, but who was nevertheless enabled to ride a bicycle specially constructed for him by a neighboring manufacturer. With one hand he guided the'handle bar, and bars of steel attached to his stumps served as legs. He experienced no trouble in balancing the wheel ; it is said that he has learned to dismount, and soon expects to be able to mount alone ; although riding only three weeks, he has been able to traverse one-half a mile in two minutes and ten seconds. While the foregoing instance is an exception, it is not extraordinary in the present day to see persons with artificial limbs riding bicycles, and even in Philadelphia, May 30, 1896, there was a special bicycle race for one-legged contestants.

The instances of interesting cases of **foreign bodies in the extremities** are not numerous. In some cases the foreign body is tolerated many years in this location. There are to-day many veterans who have bullets in their extremities. Girdwood[a] speaks of the removal of a foreign body after twenty-five years' presence in the forearm. Pike[b] mentions a man in India, who, at the age of twenty-two, after killing a wounded hare in the usual manner by striking it on the back of the neck with the side of the hand, noticed a slight cut on the hand which soon healed but left a lump under the skin. It gave him no trouble until two months before the time of report, when he asked to have the lump removed, thinking it was a stone. It was cut down upon and removed, and proved to be the spinous process of the vertebra of a hare. The bone was living and healthy and had formed a sort of arthrodial joint on the base of the phalanx of the little finger and had remained in this position for nearly twenty-two years.

a 251, 1866.   b 224, 1889, ii., 1331.

White [a] has described a case in which a nail broken off in the foot, separated into 26 splinters, which, after intense suffering, were successfully removed. There was a case recently reported of a man admitted to the Bellevue Hospital, New York, whose arm was supposed to have been fractured by an explosion, but instead of which **11 feet of lead wire** were found in it by the surgeons. The man was a machinist in the employ of the East River Lead Co., and had charge of a machine which converted molten lead into wire. This machine consists of a steel box into which the lead is forced, being pressed through an aperture $\frac{1}{8}$ inch in diameter by hydraulic pressure of 600 tons. Reaching the air, the lead becomes hard and is wound on a large wheel in the form of wire. Just before the accident this small aperture had become clogged, and the patient seized the projecting wire in his hand, intending to free the action of the machine, as he had previously done on many occasions, by a sharp, strong pull; but in so doing an explosion occurred, and he was hurled to the floor unconscious. While on the way to the hospital in the ambulance, he became conscious and complained of but little pain except soreness of the left arm about the elbow. The swelling, which had developed very rapidly, made it impossible for the surgeons to make an examination, but on the following day, when the inflammation had subsided sufficiently, a diagnosis of fracture of the bones of the arm was made. There was no external injury of the skin of any magnitude, and the surgeons decided to cut down on the trifling contusion, and remove what appeared to be a fragment of bone, lodged slightly above the wrist. An anesthetic was administered, and an incision made, but to the amazement of the operators, instead of bone, a piece of wire one inch in length and $\frac{1}{8}$ inch in diameter was removed. On further exploration piece after piece of the wire was taken out until finally the total length thus removed aggregated 11 feet, the longest piece measuring two feet and the shortest $\frac{1}{4}$ inch. The wire was found imbedded under the muscles of the arm, and some of it had become wedged between the bones of the forearm. Probably the most remarkable feature of this curious accident was the fact that there was no fracture or injury to the bone, and it was thought possible that the function of the arm would be but little impaired.

Tousey [b] reports a case of foreign body in the axilla that was taken for a necrotic fragment of the clavicle. The patient was a boy of sixteen, who climbed up a lamp-post to get a light for his bicycle lamp; his feet slipped off the ornamental ledge which passed horizontally around the post about four feet from the ground, and he fell. In the fall a **lead pencil** in his waistcoat pocket caught on the ledge and was driven into the axilla, breaking off out of sight. This was supposed to be a piece of the clavicle, and was only discovered to be a pencil when it was removed six weeks after.

There are several diseases of the bone having direct bearing on the anomalies of the extremities which should have mention here. **Osteomalacia**

[a] 647, 1860.   [b] 597, Jan. 12, 1895.

is a disease of the bones in adult life, occurring most frequently in puerperal women, but also seen in women not in the puerperal state, and in men. It is characterized by a progressive softening of the bone-substance, from a gradual absorption of the lime-salts, and gives rise to considerable deformity, and occasionally to spontaneous fracture.

Rachitis or rickets is not a disease of adult life, but of infancy and childhood, and never occurs after the age of puberty. It seldom begins before six months or after three years. There are several theories as to its causation, one being that it is due to an abnormal development of acids. There is little doubt that defective nutrition and bad hygienic surroundings are prominent factors in its production. The principal pathologic change is seen in the epiphyseal lines of long bones and

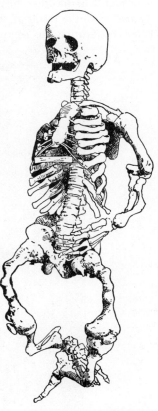

Fig. 213.—Appearance during life of the highest grade of rachitis: pseudoosteomalacia (Pippingskjöld).

Fig. 214.—Extreme deformity of skeleton due to rickets, showing enlargement of the ends of the bones (Sp. 1545, Warren Museum).

beneath the periosteum. Figure 213 shows the appearance during life of a patient with the highest grade of rachitis, and it can be easily understood what a barrier to natural child-birth it would produce. In rachitis epiphyseal swellings are seen at the wrists and ankle-joints, and in superior cases at the ends of the phalanges of the fingers and toes. When the shaft of a long bone is affected, not only deformity, but even fracture may occur. Under these circumstances the humerus and femur appear to be the bones most likely to break ; there is an associate deformity of the head, known as " craniotabes," together with pigeon-breast and various spinal curvature. The accompanying illustration (Fig. 214) is from a drawing of a skeleton in the Warren Museum in Boston. The subject was an Indian, twenty-one years of age, one of the Six Nations. His mode of locomotion was by a large wooden bowl, in which he sat and moved forward by advancing first one side of the bowl and then the other, by means of his hands. The nodules or " adventitious joints " were the result of imperfect ossification, or, in other words, of motion before ossification was completed.

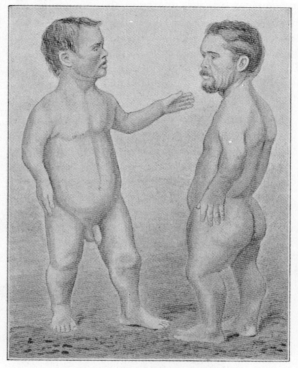

Fig. 215.—Two adult cases of achondroplasia (Thomson).

Analogous to rachitis is **achondroplasia,** or the so-called fetal rickets—a disease in which deformity results from an arrest, absence, or perversion of the normal process of enchondral ossification. It is decidedly an intrauterine affection, and the great majority of fetuses die in utero. Thomson [a] reports three living cases of achondroplasia. The first was a child five months of age, of pale complexion, bright and intelligent, its head measuring 23 inches in length. There was a narrow thorax showing the distinct beads of rickets ; the upper and lower limbs were very short, but improved under antirachitic

[a] 318, June, 1893.

treatment. The child died of pneumonia. The other two cases (Fig. 215) were in adults, one thirty-nine and the other thirty-six. The men were the same height, 49 inches, and resembled each other in all particulars. They both enjoyed good health, and, though somewhat dwarfed, were of considerable intelligence. Neither had married. Both the upper and lower limbs showed exaggerations of the normal curves ; the hands and feet were broad and short ; the gait of both of these little men was waddling, the trunk swaying when they attempted to make any rapid progress.

Osteitis deformans is a hyperplasia of bone described by Paget in 1856. Paget's patient was a gentleman of forty-six who had always enjoyed good health ; without assignable cause he began to be subject to aching pains in the thighs and legs. The bones of the left leg began to increase in size, and a year or two later the left femur also enlarged considerably. During a period of twenty years these changes were followed by a growth of other bones. The spine became firm and rigid, the head increased $5\frac{1}{4}$ inches in circumference. The bones of the face were not affected. When standing, the patient had a peculiar bowed condition of the legs, with marked flexure at the knees. He finally died of osteosarcoma, originating in the left radius. Paget collected eight cases, five of whom died of malignant disease. The postmortem of Paget's case showed extreme thickening in the bones affected, the femur and cranium particularly showing osteosclerosis. Several cases have been recorded in this country ; according to Warren, Thieberge analyzed 43 cases ; 21 were men, 22 women ; the disease appeared usually after forty.

Acromegaly is distinguished from osteitis deformans in that it is limited to hypertrophy of the hands, feet, and face, and it usually begins earlier. In gigantism the so-called " giant growth of bones " is often congenital in character, and is unaccompanied by inflammatory symptoms.

The deformities of the articulations may be congenital but in most cases are acquired. When these are of extreme degree, locomotion is effected in most curious ways. Ankylosis at unnatural angles and even complete reversion of the joints has been noticed. Paré gives a case of reversion, and of crooked hands and feet ; and Barlow [a] speaks of a child of two and three-quarter years with kyphosis, but mobility of the lumbar region, which walked on its elbows and knees. The pathology of this deformity is obscure, but there might have been malposition in utero. Wilson presented a similar case before the Clinical Society of London, in 1888. The " Camel-boy," exhibited some years ago throughout the United States, had reversion of the joints, which resembled those of quadrupeds. He walked on all fours, the mode of progression resembling that of a camel.

Figure 216 represents Orloff, " the transparent man," an exhibitionist, showing curious deformity of the long bones and atrophy of the extremities. He derived his name from the remarkable transparency of his deformed members

[a] 476, 1890, ii.

to electric light, due to porosity of the bones and deficiency of the overlying tissues.

Figure 217, taken from Hutchinson's " Archives of Surgery," [a] represents an extreme case of deformity of the knee-joints in a boy of seven, the result of severe osteoarthritis. The knees and elbows were completely ankylosed.

Fig. 216.—Extreme deformity of the bones and joints.

Fig. 217.—Deformed knee-joints from severe osteoarthritis (Hutchinson).

Infantile spinal paralysis is often the cause of distressing deformities, forbidding locomotion in the ordinary manner. In a paper on the surgical and mechanical treatment of such deformities Willard[b] mentions a boy of fourteen, the victim of infantile paralysis, who at the age of eleven had never walked, but dragged his legs along (Fig. 218). His legs were greatly twisted, and there was flexion at right angles at the hips and knees. There was equinovarus in the left foot and equinovalgus in the right. By an operation of

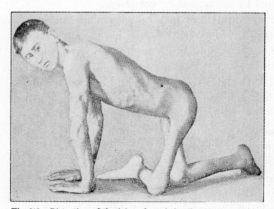

Fig. 218.—Distortion of the joints from infantile spinal paralysis (Willard).

subcutaneous section at the hips, knees, and feet, with application of plaster-of-Paris and extension, this hopeless cripple walked with crutches in two months, and with an apparatus consisting of elastic straps over the quadriceps femoris, peroneals, and weakened muscles, the valgus-foot being supported beneath the sole. In six months he was walking long distances; in one year he moved speedily on crutches. Willard also mentions another case of a girl of eleven who was totally unable to support the body in the erect position, but could move on all fours, as shown in figure 219. There was equino-varus in the right foot and valgus in the left. The left hip was greatly distorted, not only in the direction of flexion, but there was also twisting of the femoral neck, simulating dislocation. This patient was also operated on in the same manner as the preceding one.

Fig. 219.—Mode of locomotion in a case of deformity from infantile spinal paralysis (Willard).

Relative to **anomalous increase or hypertrophy of the bones of the extremities,** Fischer shows that an increase in the length of bone may follow slight injuries. He mentions a boy of twelve, who was run over by a wagon and suffered a contusion of the bones of the right leg. In the course of a year this leg became $4\frac{1}{2}$ cm. longer than the other, and the bones were also much thicker than in the other. Fischer also reports several cases of abnormal growth of bone following necrosis. A case of shortening $3\frac{3}{4}$ cm., after a fracture, was reduced to one cm. by compensatory growth. Elongation of the bone is also mentioned as the result of the inflammation of the joint. Warren also quotes Taylor's case of a lady who fell, injuring, but not fracturing, the thigh. Gradual enlargement, with an outward curving of the bone, afterward took place.

CHAPTER XII.

SURGICAL ANOMALIES OF THE THORAX AND ABDOMEN.

Injuries of the lung or bronchus are always serious, but contrary to the general idea, recovery after extensive wound of the lung is quite a common occurrence. Even the older writers report many instances of remarkable recoveries from lung-injuries, despite the primitive and dirty methods of treatment. A review of the literature previous to this century shows the names of Arcæus, Brunner, Collomb, Fabricius Hildanus, Vogel, Rhodius, Petit, Guérin, Köler, Peters, Flebbe, and Stalpart,[750] as authorities for instances of this nature. In one of the journals[108] there is a description of a man who was wounded by a broad-sword thrust in the mediastinum. After death it was found that none of the viscera were wounded, and death was attributed to the fact that the in-rush of air counterbalancing the pressure within the lungs left them to their own contractile force, with resultant collapse, obstruction to the circulation, and death. It is said that Vesalius demonstrated this condition on the thorax of a pig.

Gooch[382] gives an instance of a boy of thirteen who fell from the top of a barn upon the sharp prow of a plough, inflicting an oblique wound from the axilla to below the sternum, slightly above the insertion of the diaphragm. Several ribs were severed, and the left thoracic cavity was wholly exposed to view, showing the lungs, diaphragm, and pericardium all in motion. The lungs soon became gangrenous, and in this horrible state the patient lived twelve days. One of the curious facts noticed by the ancient writers was the amelioration of the symptoms caused by thoracic wounds after hemorrhage from other locations; and naturally, in the treatment of such injuries, this circumstance was used in advocacy of depletion. Monro speaks of a gentleman who was wounded in a duel, and who had all the symptoms of hemothorax; his condition was immediately relieved by the evacuation of a considerable quantity of bloody matter with the urine. Swammerdam records a similar case, and Fabricius ab Aquapendente noticed a case in which the opening in the thorax showed immediate signs of improvement after the patient voided large quantities of bloody urine. Glandorp also calls attention to the foregoing facts. Nicolaus Novocomensis narrates the details of the case of one of his friends, suffering from a penetrating wound of the thorax, who was relieved and ultimately cured by a bloody evacuation with the stool.

There is an extraordinary recovery reported [a] in a boy of fifteen who, by falling into the machinery of an elevator, was severely injured about the chest. There were six extensive lacerations, five through the skin about six inches long, and one through the chest about eight inches long. The 3d, 4th, 5th, and 6th ribs were fractured and torn apart, and about an inch of the substance of the 4th rib was lost. Several jagged fragments were removed ; a portion of the pleura, two by four inches, had been torn away, exposing the pericardium and the left lung, and showing the former to have been penetrated and the latter torn. The lung collapsed completely, and for three or four months no air seemed to enter it, but respiration gradually returned. The lacerated integument could only be closed approximately by sutures. It is worthy of remark that, although extremely pale, the patient complained of but little pain, and exhibited only slight symptoms of shock. The pleural cavity subsequently filled with a dirty serum, but even this did not interfere with the healing of the wound and the restoration of the lung ; the patient recovered without lateral curvature.

Bartholf reports a case of rapid recovery after perforating wound of the lung. The pistol-ball entered the back $1\frac{1}{2}$ inches to the right of the spinous process of the 6th dorsal vertebra, and passed upward and very slightly inward toward the median line. Its track could be followed only $1\frac{1}{4}$ inches. Emphysema appeared fifteen minutes after the reception of the wound, and soon became pronounced throughout the front and side of the neck, a little over the edge of the lower jaw, and on the chest two inches below the sternum and one inch below the clavicle. In four hours respiration became very frequent, short, and gasping, the thoracic walls and the abdomen scarcely moving. The man continued to improve rapidly, the emphysema disappeared on the seventh day, and eighteen days after the reception of the wound he was discharged. There was slight hemorrhage from the wound at the time, but the clot dried and closed the wound, and remained there until it was removed on the morning of his discharge, leaving a small, dry, white cicatrix.

Loss of Lung-tissue.—The old Amsterdam authority, Tulpius,[842] has recorded a case in which a piece of lung of about three fingers' breadth protruded through a large wound of the lung under the left nipple. This wound received no medical attention for forty-eight hours, when the protruding portion of lung was thought to be dead, and was ligated and cut off; it weighed about three ounces. In about two weeks the wound healed with the lung adherent to it and this condition was found six years later at the necropsy of this individual. Tulpius quoted Celsus and Hippocrates as authorities for the surgical treatment of this case. In 1787 Bell gave an account of a case in which a large portion of the lung protruded and was strangulated by the

a Annual of the Universal Medical Sciences, 1892.

edges of the thoracic wound, yet the patient made a good recovery. Fabricius Hildanus [334] and Ruysch [699] record instances of recovery in which large pieces of lung have been cut off; and it is said that with General Wolfe at Quebec there was another officer who was shot through the thorax and who recovered after the removal of a portion of the lung. In a letter to one of his medical friends Roscius says that he succeeded in cutting off part of a protruding, livid, and gangrenous lung, after a penetrating wound of the chest, with a successful result. Hale [a] reports a case of a penetrating stab-wound in which a piece of lung was removed from a man of twenty-five.

Tait [b] claims that **surgical treatment**, as exemplified by Biondi's experiment in removing portions of lung from animals, such as dogs, sheep, cats, etc., is not practical; he adds that his deductions are misleading, as the operation was done on healthy tissue and in deep and narrow-chested animals. **Excision of diseased portions of the lung** has been practised by Krönlein (three cases), Ruggi of Bologna (two cases), Block, Milton, Weinlechner; one of Krönlein's patients recovered and Milton's survived four months, but the others promptly succumbed after the operation. Tuffier [c] is quoted as showing a patient, aged twenty-nine, upon whom, for beginning tuberculosis, he had performed pneumonectomy four years before. At the operation he had removed the diseased area at the apex of the right lung, together with sound tissue for two cm. in every direction. Tuffier stated that the result of his operation had been perfectly successful and the patient had shown no suspicious symptoms since.

Rupture of the Lung Without Fracture.—It is quite possible for the lung to be ruptured by external violence without fracture of the ribs; there are several such cases on record. The mechanism of this rare and fatal form of injury has been very aptly described by Gosselin as due to a sudden pressure exerted on the thoracic wall at the moment of full inspiration, there being a spasm of the glottis or obstruction of the larynx, in consequence of which the lung bursts. An extravasation of air occurs, resulting in the development of emphysema, pneumothorax, etc. Subsequently pleurisy, pneumonia, or even pus in the pleural cavity often result. Hemoptysis is a possible, but not a marked symptom. The mechanism is identical with that of the bursting of an inflated paper bag when struck by the hand. Other observers discard this theory of M. Gosselin and claim that the rupture is due to direct pressure, as in the cases in which the heart is ruptured without fracture of the ribs. The theory of Gosselin would not explain these cardiac ruptures from external violence on the thoracic walls, and, therefore, was rejected by some. Paré, Morgagni, Portal, Hewson Smith, Dupuytren, Laënnec, and others mention this injury. Gosselin reports two cases terminating in recovery. Ashhurst reports having seen three cases, all of which terminated fatally before the fifth day; he has collected the histories of 39

a 526, 1851.   b 224, 1884, i., 1178.   c 533, Nov. 23, 1895.

cases, of which 12 recovered. Otis has collected reports of 25 cases of this form of injury from military practice exclusively. These were generally caused by a blow on the chest, by a piece of shell, or other like missile. Among the 25 cases there were 11 recoveries. As Ashhurst very justly remarks, this injury appears more fatal in civil than in military life.

Pyle[a] reports a case successfully treated, as follows :—

"Lewis W., ten years old, white, born in Maryland, and living now in the District of Columbia, was brought in by the Emergency Hospital ambulance, on the afternoon of November 10th, with a history of having been run over by a hose-cart of the District Fire Department. The boy was in a state of extreme shock, having a weak, almost imperceptible pulse ; his respirations were shallow and rapid, and his temperature subnormal. There were no signs of external injury about his thoracic cavity and no fracture of the ribs could be detected, although carefully searched for ; there was marked emphysema ; the neck and side of the face were enormously swollen with the extravasated air ; the tissues of the left arm were greatly infiltrated with air, which enabled us to elicit the familiar crepitus of such infiltration when an attempt at the determination of the radial pulse was made. Consciousness was never lost. There were several injuries to the face and scalp ; and there was hemorrhage from the nose and mouth, which was attributed to the fact that the patient had fallen on his face, striking both nose and lip. This was confirmed subsequently by the absence of any evidences of hemoptysis during the whole period of convalescence. The saliva was not even blood-streaked ; therefore, it can be said with verity that there was no hemoptysis. Shortly after admission the patient reacted to the stimulating treatment, his pulse became stronger, and all evidences of threatened collapse disappeared. He rested well the first night and complained of no pain, then or subsequently. The improvement was continuous. The temperature remained normal until the evening of the fifth day, when it rose to 102.2°, and again, on the evening of the sixth, to 102.3°. This rise was apparently without significance as the patient at no time seemed disturbed by it. On the eighth day the temperature again reached the normal and has since remained there. The boy is apparently well now, suffers no inconvenience, and has left the hospital, safe from danger and apparently free from any pulmonary embarrassment. He uses well-developed diaphragmatic breathing which is fully sufficient."

Pollock[b] reports the case of a boy of seven, whose lung was ruptured by a four-wheeled cab which ran over him. He was discharged well in thirty-two days. Bouilly[c] speaks of recovery in a boy of seventeen, after a rupture of the lung without fracture. There are several other interesting cases of recovery on record.

There are instances of **spontaneous rupture of the lung,** from severe cough. Hicks[d] speaks of a child of ten months suffering with a severe cough

a 533, Feb. 24, 1894.   b 700, 1877–8, 246.   c 368, Oct. 15, 1881.   d 490, April 22, 1837, 119.

resembling pertussis, whose lung ruptured about two weeks after the beginning of the cough, causing death on the second day. Ferrari [a] relates a curious case of rupture of the lung from deep inspiration.

Complete penetration or transfixion of the thoracic cavity is not necessarily fatal, and some marvelous instances of recovery after injuries of this nature, are recorded. Eve [b] remarks that General Shields was shot through the body by a discharge of a cannon at Cerro Gordo, and was given up as certain to die. The General himself thought it was grape-shot that traversed his chest. He showed no signs of hemoptysis, and although in great pain, was able to give commands after reception of the wound. In this case, the ball had evidently entered within the right nipple, had passed between the lungs, through the mediastinum, emerging slightly to the right of the spine. Guthrie [c] has mentioned a parallel instance of a ball traversing the thoracic cavity, the patient completely recovering after treatment. Girard, Weeds, Meacham, Bacon, Fryer and others [d] report cases of perforating gunshot wounds of the chest with recovery.

Sewell [e] describes a case of transfixion of the chest in a youth of eighteen. After mowing and while carrying his scythe home, the patient accidentally fell on the blade ; the point passed under the right axilla, between the 3d and 4th right ribs, horizontally through the chest, and came out through corresponding ribs of the opposite side, making a small opening. He fell to the ground and lay still until his brother came to his assistance ; the latter with great forethought and caution carefully calculated the curvature of the scythe blade, and thus regulating his direction of tension, successfully withdrew the instrument. There was but little hemoptysis and the patient soon recovered. Chelius [f] records an instance of penetration of the chest by a carriage shaft, with subsequent recovery. Hoyland [g] mentions a man of twenty-five who was discharging bar-iron from the hold of a ship ; in a stooping position, preparatory to hoisting a bundle on deck, he was struck by one of the bars which pinned him to the floor of the hold, penetrating the thorax, and going into the wood of the flooring to the extent of three inches, requiring the combined efforts of three men to extract it. The bar had entered posteriorly between the 9th and 10th ribs of the left side, and had traversed the thorax in an upward and outward direction, coming out anteriorly between the 5th and 6th ribs, about an inch below and slightly external to the nipple. There was little constitutional disturbance, and the man was soon discharged cured. Brown [h] records a case of impalement in a boy of fourteen. While running to a fire, he struck the point of the shaft of a carriage, which passed through his left chest, below the nipple. There was, strangely, no hemorrhage, and no symptoms of so severe an injury ; the boy recovered.

There is deposited in the Museum of the Royal College of Surgeons in

a 659, 1855.   b 744, 1848.   c 476, 1853.   d 847, 27 et seq.   e 124, 1849.

f 265, i.   g 491, 1863, ii., 241.   h Trans. Med. Soc. Pa., 1877, pt. 2, 730.

London, a mast-pivot, 15 inches in length and weighing between seven and eight pounds, which had passed obliquely through the body of a sailor. The specimen is accompanied by a colored picture of the sufferer himself in two positions. The name of the sailor was Taylor, and the accident occurred aboard a brig lying in the London docks. One of Taylor's mates was guiding the pivot of the try-sail into the main boom, when a tackle gave way. The pivot instantly left the man's hand, shot through the air point downward, striking Taylor above the heart, passing out lower down posteriorly, and then imbedded itself in the deck. The unfortunate subject was carried at once to the London Hospital, and notwithstanding his transfixion by so formidable an instrument, in five months Taylor had recovered sufficiently to walk, and ultimately returned to his duties as a seaman.

In the same museum, near to this spike, is the portion of a shaft of the carriage which passed through the body of a gentleman who happened to be standing near the vehicle when the horse plunged violently forward, with the result that the off shaft penetrated his body under the left arm, and came out from under the right arm, pinning the unfortunate man to the stable door. Immediately after the accident the patient walked upstairs and got in bed ; his recovery progressed uninterruptedly, and his wounds were practically healed at the end of nine weeks ; he is reported to have lived eleven years after this terrible accident.

In the Indian Medical Gazette [a] there is an account of a private of thirty-five, who was thrown forward and off his horse while endeavoring to mount. He fell on a lance which penetrated his chest and came out through the scapula. The horse ran for about 100 yards, the man hanging on and trying to stop him. After the extraction of the lance the patient recovered. Longmore [b] gives an instance of complete transfixion by a lance of the right side of the chest and lung, the patient recovering. Ruddock [c] mentions cases of penetrating wounds of both lungs with recovery.

There is a most remarkable instance of **recovery after major thoracic wounds** recorded by Brokaw. [d] In a brawl, a shipping clerk received a thoracic wound extending from the 3d rib to within an inch of the navel, $13\frac{1}{2}$ inches long, completely severing all the muscular and cartilaginous structures, including the cartilages of the ribs from the 4th to the 9th, and wounding the pleura and lung. In addition there was an abdominal wound $6\frac{1}{2}$ inches long, extending from the navel to about two inches above Poupart's ligament, causing almost complete intestinal evisceration. The lung was partially collapsed. The cartilages were ligated with heavy silk, and the hemorrhage checked by ligature and by packing gauze in the interchondral spaces. The patient speedily recovered, and was discharged in a little over a month, the only disastrous result of his extraordinary injuries being a small ventral hernia.

[a] 435, 1873, 44.　　[b] 476, 1871, i., 78.　　[c] 656, 1842.　　[d] 702, Dec., 1890.

In **wounds of the diaphragm,** particularly those from stabs and gun-shot injuries, death is generally due to accompanying lesions rather than to injury of the muscle itself. The older writers, particularly Glandorp,[380] Hollerius, and Alexander Benedictus, made a favorable diagnosis of wounds made in the fleshy portions of the diaphragm, but despaired of those in the tendinous portions. Bertrand, Fabricius Hildanus,[334] la Motte, Ravaton, Valentini,[794] and Glandorp, record instances of recovery from wounds of the diaphragm.

There are some peculiar causes of diaphragmatic injuries on record, laughter, prolonged vomiting, excessive eating, etc., being mentioned. On the other hand, in his " Essay on Laughter (du Ris)," Joubert quotes a case in which involuntary laughter was caused by a wound of the diaphragm ; the laughter mentioned in this instance was probably caused by convulsive move-ments of the diaphragm, due to some unknown irritation of the phrenic nerve. Bremuse [a] gives an account of a man who literally split his diaphragm in two by the ingestion of four plates of potato soup, numerous cups of tea and milk, followed by a large dose of sodium bicarbonate to aid digestion. After this meal his stomach swelled to an enormous extent and tore the dia-phragm on the right side, causing immediate death.

The diaphragm may be ruptured by external violence (a fall on the chest or abdomen), or by violent squeezing (railroad accidents, etc.), or according to Ashhurst, by spasmodic contraction of the part itself. If the injury is unaccompanied by lesion of the abdominal or thoracic viscera, the prognosis is not so unfavorable as might be supposed. Unless the laceration is ex-tremely small, protrusion of the stomach or some other viscera into the tho-racic cavity will almost invariably result, constituting the condition known as internal or **diaphragmatic hernia.** Paré[618] relates the case of a Captain who was shot through the fleshy portion of the diaphragm, and though the wound was apparently healed, the patient complained of a colicky pain. Eight months afterward the patient died in a violent paroxysm of this pain. At the postmortem by Guillemeau, a man of great eminence and a pupil of Paré, a part of the colon was found in the thorax, having passed through a wound in the diaphragm. Gooch[382] saw a similar case, but no history of the injury could be obtained. Bausch[b] mentions a case in which the omentum, stomach, and pancreas were found in the thoracic cavity, having protruded through an extensive opening in the diaphragm. Muys, Bonnet, Blancard, Schenck, Sennert, Fantoni, and Godefroy record instances in which, after rupture of the diaphragm, the viscera have been found in the thorax ; there are many modern cases on record. Internal hernia through the diaphragm is mentioned by Cooper, Bowles, Fothergill, Monro, Ballonius, Derrecagiax, and Schmidt. Sir Astley Cooper[c] mentioned a case of hernia ventriculi from external violence, wherein the diaphragm was lacerated without any fracture of the ribs. The man was aged twenty-seven, and being an outside passenger on a coach (and also intoxicated), when it broke down he was projected some distance, striking the ground with considerable force. He died on the next day, and the diagnosis was verified at the necropsy, the opening in the diaphragm causing stricture of the bowel.

Postempski[a] successfully treated a wound of the diaphragm complicated with a wound of the omentum, which protruded between the external opening between the 10th and 11th ribs; he enlarged the wound, forced the ribs apart, ligated and cut off part of the omentum, returned its stump to the abdomen, and finally closed both the wound in the diaphragm and the external wound with sutures. Quoted by Ashhurst, Hunter recorded a case of gunshot wound, in which, after penetrating the stomach, bowels, and diaphragm, the ball lodged in the thoracic cavity, causing no difficulty in breathing until shortly before death, and even then the dyspnea was mechanical—from gaseous distention of the intestines.

Peritonitis in the thoracic cavity is a curious condition which may be brought about by a penetrating wound of the diaphragm. In 1872 Sargent communicated to the Boston Society for Medical Improvement an account of a postmortem examination of a woman of thirty-seven, in whom he had observed major injuries twenty years before. At that time, while sliding down some hay from a loft, she was impaled on the handle of a pitchfork which entered the vagina, penetrated 22 inches, and was arrested by an upper left rib, which it fractured; further penetration was possibly prevented by the woman's feet striking the floor. Happily there was no injury to the bladder, uterus, or intestines. The principal symptoms were hemorrhage from the vagina and intense pain near the fractured rib, followed by emphysema. The pitchfork-handle was withdrawn, and was afterward placed in the museum of the Society, the abrupt bloody stain, 22 inches from the rounded end, being plainly shown. During twenty years the woman could never lie on her right side or on her back, and for half of this time she spent most of the night in the sitting position. Her last illness attracted little attention because her life had been one of suffering. After death it was found that the cavity in the left side of the chest was entirely filled with abdominal viscera. The opening in the diaphragm was four inches in diameter, and through it had passed the stomach, transverse colon, a few inches of the descending colon, and a considerable portion of the small intestines. The heart was crowded to the right of the sternum and was perfectly healthy, as was also the right lung. The left lung was compressed to the size of a hand. There were marked signs of peritonitis, and in the absence of sufficient other symptoms, it could be said that this woman had died of peritonitis in the left thoracic cavity.

Extended tolerance of foreign bodies loose in the thoracic cavity has been noticed. Tulpius[842] mentions a person who had a sponge shut up

a 174, 398.

in his thoracic cavity for six weeks ; it was then voided by the mouth, and the man recovered. Fabricius Hildanus [334] relates a similar instance in which a sponge-tent was expelled by coughing. Arnot [a] reports a case in which a piece of iron was found in a cyst in the thorax, where it had remained for fourteen years. Leach [b] gives a case in which a bullet was impacted in the chest for forty-two years. Snyder [c] speaks of a fragment of knife-blade which was lodged in the chest twelve years and finally coughed up.

Foreign Bodies in the Bronchi.—Walnut kernels, coins, seeds, beans, corks, and even sponges have been removed from the bronchi. In the presence of Sir Morrell Mackenzie, Johnston of Baltimore removed a **toy locomotive** from the subglottic cavity by tracheotomy and thyreotomy. The child had gone to sleep with the toy in his mouth and had subsequently swallowed it. [d] Eldredge [e] presented a hopeless consumptive, who as a child of five had swallowed an **umbrella ferrule** while whistling through it, and who expelled it in a fit of coughing twenty-three years after. Eve of Nashville [f] mentions a boy who placed a fourpenny nail in a spool to make a whistle, and, by a violent inspiration, drew the nail deep into the left bronchus. It was removed by tracheotomy. Liston removed a large piece of bone from the right bronchus of a woman, and Houston tells of a case in which a molar tooth was lodged in a bronchus causing death on the eleventh day. Warren mentions spontaneous expulsion of a horse-shoe nail from the bronchus of a boy of two and one-half years. From Dublin, in 1844, Houston reports the case of a girl of sixteen who inhaled the wooden peg of a small fiddle and in a fit of coughing three months afterward expelled it from the lungs. In 1849 Solly communicated the case of a man who inhaled a pebble placed on his tongue to relieve thirst. On removal this pebble weighed 144 grains. Watson of Murfreesboro removed a portion of an umbrella rib from a trachea, but as he failed to locate or remove the ferrule, the case terminated fatally. Brigham [g] mentions a child of five who was seized with a fit of coughing while she had a small brass nail in her mouth ; pulmonary phthisis ensued, and in one year she died. At the post-mortem examination the nail was found near the bifurcation of the right bronchus, and, although colored black, was not corroded.

Marcacci [h] reported an observation of the removal of a bean from the bronchus of a child of three and a half years. The child swallowed the bean while playing, immediately cried, and became hoarse. No one having noticed the accident, a diagnosis of croup was made and four leeches were applied to the neck. The dyspnea augmented during the night, and there

a 550, 1827, xiii., 281. b 175, 1857. c 267, 1870, xi., 401.

d Archives of Clinical Surgery, N. Y., 1876, i., 211, et seq.

e Rhode Island Med. Soc., Providence, 1860, i., 82. f 579, 1853, v., 129.

g 124, 1836, 46. h 720, 1876, clxx., p. 271.

was a whistling sound with each respiratory movement. On the next day the medical attendants suggested the possibility of a foreign body in the larynx. Tracheotomy was performed but the dyspnea continued, showing that the foreign body was lodged below the incision. The blood of one of the cut vessels entered the trachea and caused an extra paroxysm of dyspnea, but the clots of blood were removed by curved forceps. Marcacci fils practised suction, and placed the child on its head, but in vain. A feather was then introduced in the wound with the hope that it would clean the trachea and provoke respiration ; when the feather was withdrawn the bean followed. The child was much asphyxiated, however, and five or six minutes elapsed before the first deep inspiration. The wound was closed, the child recovered its voice, and was well four days afterward. Annandale saw a little patient who had swallowed a bead of glass, which had lodged in the bronchus. He introduced the handle of a scalpel into the trachea, producing sufficient irritation to provoke a brusque expiration, and at the second attempt the foreign body was expelled. Hulke [a] records the case of a woman, the victim of a peculiar accident happening during the performance of tracheotomy, for an affection of the larynx. The internal **canule of the tracheotomy-tube** fell into the right bronchus, but was removed by an ingenious instrument extemporaneously devised from silver wire. A few years ago in this country there was much public excitement and newspaper discussion over the daily reports which came from the bedside of a gentleman who had swallowed a cork, and which had become lodged in a bronchus. Tracheotomy was performed and a special corkscrew devised to extract it, but unfortunately the patient died of slow asphyxiation and exhaustion. Herrick [b] mentions the case of a boy of fourteen months who swallowed a shawl-pin two inches long, which remained in the lungs four years, during which time there was a constant dry and spasmodic cough, and corresponding depression and emaciation. When it was ultimately coughed up it appeared in one large piece and several smaller ones, and was so corroded as to be very brittle. After dislodgment of the pin there was subsidence of the cough and rapid recovery.

Lapeyre [c] mentions an elderly gentleman who received a sudden slap on the back while smoking a **cigarette,** causing him to start and take a very deep inspiration. The cigarette was drawn into the right bronchus, where it remained for two months without causing symptoms or revealing its presence. It then set up a circumscribed pneumonia and cardiac dropsy which continued two months longer, at which time, during a violent fit of coughing, the cigarette was expelled enveloped in a waxy, mucus-like matter. Louis relates the case of a man who carried a louis-d'or in his lung for six and a half years.

There is a case on record [d] of a man who received a gunshot wound, the ball entering behind the left clavicle and passing downward and across to the right clavicle. Sometime afterward this patient expectorated two pieces of

a 476, 1876. b 218, 1871. c 476, 1890, 628. d 133, 1873, 146.

bone and a piece of gum blanket in which he was enveloped at the time of the injury. Carpenter [a] describes a case of fatal pleuritis, apparently due to the presence of four artificial teeth which had been swallowed thirteen years before.

Cardiac Injuries.—For ages it has been the common opinion relative to injuries of the heart that they are necessarily fatal and that, as a rule, death immediately follows their reception. Notwithstanding this current belief a careful examination of the literature of medicine presents an astounding number of cases in which the heart has been positively wounded, and the patients have lived days, months, and even recovered ; postmortem examination, by revealing the presence of cicatrices in the heart, confirming the original diagnosis. This question is one of great interest as, in recent years, there has been constant agitation of the possibility of surgical procedures in cardiac as well as cerebral injuries. Del Vecchio [b] has reported a series of experiments on dogs with the conclusion that in case of wounds in human beings **suture of the heart** is a possible operation. In this connection he proposes the following operative procedure : Two longitudinal incisions to be made from the lower border of the 3d rib to the upper border of the 7th rib, one running along the inner margin of the sternum, the other about ten mm. inside the nipple-line. These incisions are joined by a horizontal cut made in the fourth intercostal space. The 4th, 5th, and 6th ribs and cartilages are divided and the outer cutaneous flaps turned up ; pushing aside the pleura with the finger, expose the pericardium and incise it longitudinally ; suture the heart-wound by interrupted sutures. Del Vecchio adds that Fischer has collected records of 376 cases of wounds of the heart with a mortality two to three minutes after the injury of 20 per cent. Death may occur from a few seconds to nine months after the accident. Keen and Da Costa [c] quote Del Vecchio, and, in comment on his observations, remark that death in cases of wound of the heart is due to pressure of effused blood in the pericardial sac, and, because this pressure is itself a check to further hemorrhage, there seems, as far as hemorrhage is concerned, to be rather a question whether operative interference may not be itself more harmful than beneficial. It might be added that the shock to the cardiac action might be sufficient to check it, and at present we would have no sure means of starting pulsation if once stopped. In heart-injuries, paracentesis, followed, if necessary, by incision of the pericardium, is advised by some surgeons.

Realizing the fatality of injuries of the heart, in consequence of which almost any chance by operation should be quickly seized by surgeons rather than trust the lives of patients to the infinitesimal chance of recovery, it would seem that the profession should carefully consider and discuss the feasibility of any procedure in this direction, no matter how hypothetic.

Hall [d] states that his experience in the study of cardiac wounds, chiefly

a 392, 1842.   b 684, April 4, 1895.   c 843, 337.   d 533, Nov. 2, 1895.

on game-animals, would lead him to the conclusion that transverse wounds of the lower portions of the heart, giving rise to punctures rather than extensive lacerations, do not commonly cause cessation of life for a time varying from some considerable fraction of a minute to many minutes or even hours, and especially if the puncture be valvular in character, so as to prevent the loss of much blood. However, if the wound involve the base of the organ, with extensive laceration of the surrounding parts, death is practically instantaneous. It would seem that injury to the muscular walls of the heart is much less efficient in the production of immediate death than destruction of the cardiac nervous mechanism, serious irritation of the latter producing almost instantaneous death from shock. In addition, Hall cites several of the instances on which he based his conclusions. He mentions two wild geese which flew respectively ¼ and ¾ of a mile after having been shot through the heart, each with a pellet of BB shot, the base in each instance being uninjured; in several instances antelope and deer ran several rods after being shot with a rifle ball in a similar manner; on the other hand, death was practically instantaneous in several of these animals in which the base of the heart was extensively lacerated. Again, death may result instantaneously from wounds of the precordial region, or according to Erichsen, if held directly over the heart, from the discharge of a pistol containing powder alone, a result occasionally seen after a blow on the precordial region. It is well, however, to state that in times of excitement, one may receive an injury which will shortly prove fatal, and yet not be aware of the fact for some time, perhaps even for several minutes. It would appear that the nervous system is so highly tuned at such times, that it does not respond to reflex irritations as readily as in the absence of excitement.

Instances of Survival after Cardiac Injuries.—We briefly cite the principal interesting instances of cardiac injuries in which death has been delayed for some time, or from which the patient ultimately recovered.

Paré[618] relates the case of a soldier who received a blow from a halberd, penetrating the left ventricle, and who walked to the surgeon's tent to have his wound dressed and then to his own tent 250 yards away. Diemerbroeck[a] mentions two instances of long survival after cardiac injuries, in one of which the patient ran 60 paces after receiving the wound, had complete composure of mind, and survived nine days. There is an instance[b] in which a man ran 400 paces after penetration of the left ventricle, and lived for five hours. Morand[575] gives an instance of survival for five days after wound of the right ventricle. Saucerotte[c] speaks of survival for three days after injury to the heart.

Babington[d] speaks of a case of heart-injury, caused by transfixion by a bayonet, in which the patient survived nine hours. Other older cases are as

[a] 303, L. ii., cap. vi., 266 and 381.   [b] 470, T. xxxv.

[c] Mélanges de Chirurgie, etc.   [d] Medical Records, etc., 1798, No. 4.

follows : l'Ecluse,[a] seven days ; the Ephemerides, four and six days ; Col de Vilars, twelve days ; Marcucci,[b] eighteen days ; Bartholinus,[c] five days ; Durande,[d] five days ; Boyer, five days ; Capelle,[e] twenty-six hours ; Fahner, eleven days ; Marigues,[f] thirteen days ; Morgagni, eight days ; la Motte, [g] twelve hours ; Rhodius,[h] Riedlin,[i] two days ; Saviard,[713] eleven days ; Sennert,[j] three days ; Triller,[k] fourteen days ; and Tulpius,[l] two and fifteen days ; and Zittman,[m] eight days.

The Duc de Berri, heir to the French throne, who was assassinated in 1826, lived several hours with one of his ventricles opened. His surgeon, Dupuytren, was reprimanded for keeping the wound open with a probe introduced every two hours, but this procedure has its advocates at the present day. Randall[n] mentions a gunshot wound of the right ventricle which did not cause death until the sixty-seventh day. Grant[o] describes a wound in which a ball from a revolver entered a little to the right of the sternum, between the cartilages of the 5th and 6th ribs, and then entered the right ventricle about an inch from the apex. It emerged from the lower part, passed through the diaphragm, the cardiac end of the stomach, and lodged in the left kidney. The patient remained in a state of collapse fifteen hours after being shot, and with little or no nourishment lived twenty-six days. At the postmortem examination the wounds in the organs were found to be healed, but the cicatrices were quite evident. Bowling[p] gives a case of gunshot wound of the shoulder in which death resulted eleven weeks after, the bullet being found in the left ventricle of the heart. Thompson[q] has reported a bayonet wound of the heart, after the reception of which the patient lived four days. The bayonet entered the ventricle about $1\frac{1}{2}$ inches from the left apex, traversing the left wall obliquely, and making exit close to the septum ventriculorum. Roberts[r] mentions a man who ran 60 yards and lived one hour after being shot through both lungs and the right auricle. Curran[s] mentions the case of a soldier who, in 1809, was wounded by a bullet which entered his body to the left of the sternum, between the 2d and 3d ribs. He was insensible a half hour, and was carried aboard a fighting ship crowded with sailors. There was little hemorrhage from his wound, and he survived fourteen days. At the postmortem examination some interesting facts were revealed. It was found that the right ventricle was transversely opened for about an inch, the ball having penetrated its anterior surface, near the origin of the pulmonary artery (Fig. 220). The ball was found loose in the pericardium, where it had fallen during the necropsy. There was a circular lacerated opening iñ the tricuspid valve, and the ball must have been in the right auricle during the

[a] 418, 1744.   [b] Orteschi Giornale di Medicina, Venet, 1763.   [c] 190, cent. i., hist. 77.
[d] Hufeland, N. Annalen. i., p. 301.   [e] Journal de Santé, T. i.   [f] 462, T. xlviii, 243.
[g] Chirurgie, obs. 228.   [h] 680, cent. ii., obs. 39.   [i] 683, 1700, 985.
[j] Opera chirurg., L. v., P. iv., c. 3.   [k] Diss. Viteb., 1775.   [l] 842, L. ii., c. 18.
[m] 835, cent. iii., cas. 50.   [n] 124, 1829.   [o] 124, July, 1857.   [p] 476, 1852, ii., 491.
[q] 548, 1863, ii., 487.   [r] 681, 1871, xii., 607.   [s] 476, 1887, i., 673.

fourteen days in which the man lived. Vite [a] mentions an example of remarkable tenacity of life after reception of a cardiac wound, the subject living four days after a knife-wound penetrating the chest into the pericardial sac and passing through the left ventricle of the heart into the opposite wall. Boone [b] speaks of a gunshot wound in which death was postponed until the thirteenth day. Bullock [c] mentions a case of gunshot wound in which the ball was found lodged in the cavity of the ventricle four days and eighteen hours after infliction of the wound. Carnochan [d] describes a penetrating wound of the heart in a subject in whom life had been protracted eleven days. After death the bullet was found buried and encysted in the heart. Holly [e] reports a case of pistol-shot wound through the right ventricle, septum, and aorta, with the ball in the left ventricle. There was apparent recovery in fourteen days and sudden death on the fifty-fifth day.

Hamilton [f] gives an instance of a shoemaker sixty-three years old who, while carrying a bundle, fell with rupture of the heart and lived several minutes. On postmortem examination an opening in the heart was found large enough to admit a blowpipe. Noble [g] speaks of duration of life for five and a half days after rupture of the heart; and there are instances on record in which life has been prolonged for thirteen hours [h] and for fifty-three hours [i] after a similar injury. Glazebrook [j] reports the case of a colored man of thirty, of powerful physique, who was admitted to the Freedmen's Hospital, Wash-

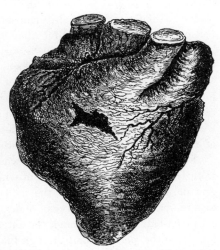

Fig. 220.—Wound of the heart; survival, fourteen days (Curran).

ington, D. C., at 12.30 A. M., on February 5, 1895. Upon examination by the surgeons, an incised wound was discovered one inch above the left nipple, $3\frac{1}{4}$ inches to the left of the median line, the incision being $2\frac{1}{4}$ inches in length and its direction parallel with the 3d rib. The man's general condition was fairly good, and the wound was examined. It was impossible to trace its depth further than the 3d rib, although probing was resorted to; it was therefore considered a simple wound, and dressed accordingly. Twelve hours later symptoms of internal hemorrhage were noticed, and at 8 A. M., February 6th, the man died after surviving his injury thirty-two hours. A necropsy was held three hours after death, and an oblique incision $\frac{3}{4}$ inch in

a 681, 1876.   b 124, 1879, 589.   c 712, 1858, i., 295.   d 128, 1855.
e 538, 1878.   f 476, 1860.   g 476, 1889, i., 774.
h 224, 1881, ii., 1051.   i 224, 1889, ii., 204.   j 533, lxvi., 508.

length was found through the cartilage-end of the 3d rib. A similar wound was next found in the pericardium, and upon examining the heart there was seen a clean, incised wound $\frac{1}{2}$ inch in length, directly into the right ventricle, the endocardial wound being $\frac{3}{8}$ inch long. Both the pericardium and left pleura were distended with fresh blood and large clots. Church [a] reports a case of gunshot wound of the heart in a man of sixty-seven who survived three hours. The wound had been made by a pistol bullet (32 caliber), was situated $1\frac{1}{4}$ inches below the mammary line, and slightly to the left of the center of the sternum; through it considerable blood had escaped. The postmortem examination showed that the ball had pierced the sternum just above the xiphoid cartilage, and had entered the pericardium to the right and at the lower part. The sac was filled with blood, both fresh and clotted. There was a ragged wound in the anterior wall $\frac{1}{2}$ inch in diameter. The wound of exit was $\frac{5}{8}$ inch in diameter. After traversing the heart the ball had penetrated the diaphragm, wounded the omentum in several places, and become lodged under the skin posteriorly between the 9th and 10th ribs. Church adds that the " Index Catalogue of the Surgeon-General's Library " at Washington contains 22 cases of direct injury to the heart, all of which lived longer than his case : 17 lived over three days ; eight lived over ten days ; two lived over twenty-five days ; one died on the fifty-fifth day, and there were three well-authenticated recoveries. Purple [b] tabulates a list of 42 cases of heart-injury which survived from thirty minutes to seventy days.

Fourteen instances of gunshot wounds of the heart have been collected from U. S. Army reports,[c] in all of which death followed very promptly, except in one instance in which the patient survived fifty hours. In another case the patient lived twenty-six hours after reception of the injury, the conical pistol-ball passing through the anterior margin of the right lobe of the lung into the pericardium, through the right auricle, and again entered the right pleural cavity, passing through the posterior margin of the lower lobe of the right lung ; at the autopsy it was found in the right pleural cavity. The left lung and cavity were perfectly normal. The right lung was engorged and somewhat compressed by the blood in the pleural cavity. The pericardium was much distended and contained from six to eight ounces of partially coagulated blood. There was a fibrinous clot in the left ventricle.

Nonfatal Cardiac Injuries.—Wounds of the heart are not necessarily fatal. Of 401 cases of cardiac injury collected by Fischer [d] there were as many as 50 recoveries, the diagnosis being confirmed in 33 instances by an autopsy in which there were found distinct signs of the cardiac injury. By a peculiar arrangement of the fibers of the heart, a wound transverse to one layer of fibers is in the direction of another layer, and to a certain extent, therefore, valvular in function ; it is probably from this fact that punctured wounds of the heart are often attended with little or no bleeding.

a 533, Oct. 27, 1894.   b 597, xiv., 411–434.   c 847, 33.   d 174, 396.

Among the older writers, several instances of nonfatal injuries to the heart are recorded.   Before the present century scientists had observed game-animals that had been wounded in the heart in the course of their lives, and after their ultimate death such direct evidence as the presence of a bullet or an arrow in their hearts was found.   Rodericus a Veiga tells the story of a deer that was killed in hunting, and in whose heart was fixed a piece of arrow that appeared to have been there some time.   Glandorp[a] experiment-ally produced a nonfatal wound in the heart of a rabbit.   Wounds of the heart, not lethal, have been reported by Benivenius,[198] Marcellus Donatus, [b] Schott,[c] Stalpart van der Wiel,[d] and Wolff.   Ollenrot reports an additional instance of recovery from heart-injury, but in his case the wound was only superficial.

There is a recent case[e] of a boy of fourteen, who was wounded in the heart by a pen-knife stab.   The boy was discharged cured from the Middle-sex Hospital, but three months after the reception of the injury he was taken ill and died.   A postmortem examination showed that the right ventricle had been penetrated in a slanting direction ; the cause of death was apoplexy, produced by the weakening and thinning of the heart's walls, the effect of the wound.   Tillaux[f] reports the case of a man of sixty-five, the victim of gen-eral paralysis, who passed into his chest a blade 16 cm. long and 2 mm. broad.   The wound of puncture was 5 cm. below the nipple and 2 cm. to the outside.   The left side of the chest was emphysematous and ecchymosed. The heart-sounds were regular, and the elevation of the skin by the blade coincided with the ventricular systole.   The blade was removed on the fol-lowing day, and the patient gradually improved.   Some thirteen months after he had expectoration of blood and pus and soon died.   At the necropsy it was seen that the wound had involved both lungs ; the posterior wall of the ventricle and the inferior lobe of the right lung were traversed from before backward, and from left to right, but the ventricular cavity was not pene-trated.   Strange to say, the blade had passed between the vertebral column and the esophagus, and to the right of the aorta, but had wounded neither of these organs.

O'Connor[490] mentions a graduate of a British University who, with suicidal intent, transfixed his heart with a darning-needle.   It was extracted by a pair of watchmaker's pliers.   In five days the symptoms had all abated, and the would-be suicide was well enough to start for the Continent.   Mühlig[g] was consulted by a mason who, ten years before, had received a blow from a stiletto near the left side of the sternum.   The cicatrix was plainly visible, but the man said he had been able to perform his daily labors, although at the present time suffering from intense dyspnea and anasarca.   A loud bel-

a 380, Obs., 83.   b 306, L. v., c. iv., 569.   c " Physic. Curios." L., iii., 576.
d 750, cent. ii., Obs., 23.   e 548, 1863, ii., 499.
f 362, No. 20, 1868.   g 645, 1860, No. 43.

lows-sound could be heard, which the man said had been audible since the
time of reception of the injury. This was a double bruit accompanying systole, and entirely obscuring the physical signs. From this time the man
speedily failed, and after his death there were cicatricial signs found, particularly on the wall of the left ventricle, together with patency of the interventricular septum, with signs of cicatrization about this rent. At the side of
the left ventricle the rent was twice as large and lined with cicatricial tissue.

Stelzner[a] mentions a young student who attempted suicide by thrusting a
darning-needle into his heart. He complained of pain and dyspnea ; in
twenty-four hours his symptoms increased to such an extent that operation
was deemed advisable on account of collapse. The 5th rib was resected and
the pleural cavity opened. When the pericardial sac was incised, a teaspoonful of turbid fluid oozed out, and the needle was felt in an oblique position in
the right ventricle. By pressure of a finger passed under the heart, the eye
of the needle was pressed through the anterior wall and fixed on the operator's finger-nail. An attempt to remove by the forceps failed, as the violent
movements of the heart drew the needle back into the cavity. About this
stage of the operation an unfortunate accident happened—the iodoform tampon, which protected the exposed pleural cavity, was drawn into this cavity
during a deep inspiration, and could not be found. Notwithstanding subsequent pneumothorax and extensive pleuritic effusion, the patient made a good
recovery at the end of the fourth week and at the time of report it was still
uncertain whether the needle remained in the heart or had wandered into the
mediastinum. During the discussion which followed the report of this case,
Hahn showed a portion of a knitting-needle which had been removed from
the heart of a girl during life. The extraction was very slow in order to
allow of coagulation along the course of the wound in the heart, and to guard
against hemorrhage into the pericardial sac, which is so often the cause of
death in punctured wounds of this organ. Hahn remarked that the pulse,
which before the removal had been very rapid, sank to 90.

Marks[b] reports the case of a stab-wound penetrating the left 9th intercostal space, the diaphragm, pleura, pericardium, and apex of the heart. It
was necessary to enlarge the wound, and, under an anesthetic, after removing
one and one-half inches of the 9th and 10th ribs, the wound was thoroughly
packed with iodoform gauze and in twenty-one days the patient recovered.
Lavender[c] mentions an incised wound of the heart penetrating the right ventricle, from which the patient recovered. Purple[d] gives an account of a recovery from a wound penetrating both ventricles. The diagnosis was confirmed
by a necropsy nine years thereafter. Stoll[e] records a nonfatal injury to the
heart.

Mastin[f] reports the case of a man of thirty-two who was shot by a 38-cali-

a 260, 1883, No. 25. b 529, 1893. c 770, 1851, 104, et seq.
d 597, xiv., 411 to 434 e 398, i., 354. f 533, 1895, i., 728.

ber Winchester, from an ambush, at a distance of 110 yards. The ball entered near the chest posteriorly on the left side just below and to the outer angle of the scapula, passed between the 7th and 8th ribs, and made its exit from the intercostal space of the 4th and 5th ribs, $2\frac{1}{4}$ inches from the nipple. A line drawn from the wound of entrance to that of exit would pass exactly through the right ventricle. After receiving the wound the man walked about twenty steps, and then, feeling very weak from profuse hemorrhage from the front of the wound, he sat down. With little or no treatment the wound closed and steady improvement set in ; the patient was discharged in three weeks. As the man was still living at last reports, the exact amount of damage done in the track of the bullet is not known, although Mastin's supposition is that the heart was penetrated.

Mellichamp [a] speaks of a gunshot wound of the heart with recovery, and Ford [b] records an instance in which a wound of the heart by a buckshot was followed by recovery. O'Connor reports a case under his observation in which a pistol-ball passed through three of the four cavities of the heart and lodged in the root of the right lung. The patient, a boy of fifteen, died of the effects of cardiac disease three years and two months later. Bell mentions a case in which, six years after the receipt of a gunshot wound of the chest, a ball was found in the right ventricle. Christison [c] speaks of an instance in which a bullet was found in the heart of a soldier in Bermuda, with no apparent signs of an opening to account for its entrance. There is a case on record [d] of a boy of fourteen who was shot in the right shoulder, the bullet entering through the right upper border of the trapezius, two inches from the acromion process. Those who examined him supposed the ball was lodged near the sternal end of the clavicle, four or five inches from where it entered. In about six weeks the boy was at his labors. Five years later he was attacked with severe pneumonia and then first noticed tumultuous action of the heart which continued to increase after his recovery. Afterward the pulsation could be heard ten or 12 feet away. He died of another attack of pneumonia fifteen years later and the heart was found to be two or three times its natural size, soft and flabby, and, on opening the right ventricle, a bullet was discovered embedded in its walls. There was no scar of entrance discernible, though the pericardium was adherent. Biffi of Milan [e] describes the case of a lunatic who died in consequence of gangrene of the tongue from a bite in a paroxysm of mania. At the necropsy a needle, six cm. in length, was found transfixing the heart, with which the relatives of the deceased said he had stabbed himself twenty-two months prior to his death. There is a collection of cases [f] in which bullets have been lodged in the heart from twenty to thirty years.

Balch [g] reports a case in which a leaden bullet remained twenty years in the walls of the heart. Hamilton [h] mentions an instance of gunshot wound

[a] 264, 1876, iv., 17.   [b] 538, 1875.   [c] 319, 1853.   [d] 548, 1861, ii., 229.
[e] 360, Oct. 16, 1869.   [f] 548, 1861, ii., 229.   [g] 124, xlii., 293.   [h] 597, 1867, iv., 379.

of the heart, in which for twenty years a ball was embedded in the wall of the right ventricle, death ultimately being caused by pneumonia. Needles have quite frequently been found in the heart after death; Graves, Leaming, Martin, Neill, Piorry, Ryerson, and others record such cases. Callender [a] mentions recovery of the patient after removal of a needle from the heart.

Garangeot mentions an aged Jesuit of seventy-two, who had in the substance of his heart a bone $4\frac{1}{2}$ inches long and possibly an inch thick. This case is probably one of ossification of the cardiac muscle; in the same connection Battolini says that the heart of Pope Urban VII. contained a bone shaped like the Arab *T.*

Among the older writers we frequently read of hairs, worms, and snakes being found in the cavities of the heart. The Ephemerides, Zacutus Lusitanus, Paré, Swinger, Riverius, and Senac are among the authorities who mention this circumstance. The deception was possibly due to the presence of loose and shaggy membrane attached to the endocardial lining of the heart, or in some cases to echinococci or trichinæ. A strange case of **foreign body in the heart** was reported [b] some time since in England. The patient had swallowed a thorn of the Prunus spinosa (Linn.), which had penetrated the esophagus and the pericardium and entered the heart. A postmortem examination one year afterward confirmed this, as a contracted cicatrix was plainly visible on the posterior surface of the heart about an inch above the apex, through which the thorn had penetrated the right ventricle and lodged in the tricuspid valve. The supposition was that the thorn had been swallowed while eating radishes. Buck [c] mentions a case of hydatid cysts in the wall of the left ventricle, with rupture of the cysts and sudden death.

It is surprising the extent of **injury to the pericardium** Nature will tolerate. In his "Comment on the Aphorisms of Hippocrates," Cardanus says that he witnessed the excision of a portion of the pericardium with the subsequent cure of the patient. According to Galen, Marulus, the son of Mimographus, recovered after a similar operation. Galen also adds, that upon one occasion he removed a portion of carious sternum and found the pericardium in a putrid state, leaving a portion of the heart naked. It is said that in the presence of Leucatel and several theologians, François Botta opened the body of a man who died after an extended illness and found the pericardium putrefied and a great portion of the heart destroyed, but the remaining portion still slightly palpitating. In this connection Young [d] mentions a patient of sixty-five who in January, 1860, injured his right thumb and lost the last joint by swelling and necrosis. Chloroform was administered to excise a portion of the necrosed bone and death ensued. Postmortem examination revealed gangrene of the heart and a remarkable tendency to gangrene elsewhere (omentum, small intestines, skin, etc.). Recently, Dalton [e] records a remarkable case of stab-wound of the pericardium with division of the inter-

a 550, lvi., 203.   b 548, 1861, ii., 119.   c 476, 1879.   d 273, 1868.   e 150, Feb., 1895.

costal artery, upon which he operated. An incision eight inches long was made over the 4th rib, six inches of the rib were resected, the bleeding intercostal artery was ligated, the blood was turned out of the pericardial cavity, this cavity being irrigated with hot water. The wound in the pericardium, which was two inches long, was sutured and the external wound was closed. Recovery followed. Harris [a] gives an instance of a man who was injured by a bar of iron falling on his shoulder, producing a compound fracture of the ribs as low as the 7th, and laying the heart and lungs bare without seriously injuring the pericardium.

Rupture of the heart from contusion of the chest is not always instantly fatal. According to Ashhurst, Gamgee has collected 28 cases of rupture of this viscus, including one observed by himself. In nine of these cases there was no fracture, and either no bruise of the parietes or a very slight one. The pericardium was intact in at least half of the cases, and in 22 in which the precise seat of lesion was noticed the right ventricle was ruptured in eight, the left in three, the left auricle in seven, the right in four. The longest period during which any patient survived the injury was fourteen hours.

Among the older writers who note this traumatic injury are Fine, who mentions concussion rupturing the right ventricle, and Ludwig, who reports a similar accident. Johnson [b] mentions rupture of the left ventricle in a paroxysm of epilepsy. There is another species of rupture of the heart which is not traumatic, in which the rupture occurs spontaneously, the predisposing cause being fatty degeneration, dilatation, or some other pathologic process in the cardiac substance. It is quite possible that the older instances of what was known as " broken-heart," which is still a by-word, were really cases in which violent emotion had produced rupture of a degenerated cardiac wall. Wright [c] gives a case of spontaneous rupture of the heart in which death did not occur for forty-eight hours. Barth has collected 24 cases of spontaneous rupture of the heart, and in every instance the seat of lesion was in the left ventricle. It was noticed that in some of these cases the rupture did not take place all at once, but by repeated minor lacerations, death not ensuing in some instances for from two to eleven days after the first manifestation of serious symptoms. A more recent analysis is given by Meyer of cases reported since 1870 : [d] Meyer collects 25 cases of rupture of the left ventricle, seven of the right ventricle, and four of the right auricle. Within the last year Collings [e] has reported a case of idiopathic rupture of the heart in a man of fifty-three, who had always lived a temperate life, and whose only trouble had been dyspepsia and a weak heart. There was no history of rheumatism or rheumatic fever. The man's father had died suddenly of heart disease. After feeling out of sorts for a time, the man experienced severe pain in the precordium and felt too ill to leave his bed. He gradually became worse and

a 218, 1871, 241.   b Medic. Bemerk. und Untersuchungen, L. ii., 103, et seq.
c "Med. Observ. and Queries," vol. vi.   d Quoted 174, 388.   e 476, 1895, No. 3738, 987.

sick after taking food. Speech became thick, the mouth was drawn to the right, and the right eye was partially closed. The left arm became paralyzed, then the right leg. The tongue deviated to the right on protrusion. The sphincters were unaffected. The heart sounds were faint and without added sounds. The man was moved to a water-bed, his body and head being kept horizontal, and great care being taken to avoid sudden movement. Later, when his pelvis was raised to allow the introduction of a bed-pan, almost instantaneous death ensued. Upon postmortem examination prolonged and careful search failed to reveal any microscopic change in the brain, its vessels, or the meninges. On opening the pericardium it was found to be filled with blood-clot, and on washing this away a laceration about $1\frac{1}{2}$ inches in length was found in the left ventricle; the aperture was closed by a recent clot. The cavities of the heart were dilated, the walls thin and in advanced stage of fatty degeneration. There was no valvular disease. The aorta and its main branches were atheromatous. Both lungs contained calcifying tubercle; the abdomen was loaded with fat; the spleen was soft; the kidneys were engorged, but otherwise healthy.

Stokes[a] gives the case of a man who was severely crushed between the arms of a water-wheel of great size and the embankment on which the axle of the wheel was supported; a peculiar factor of the injury being that his **heart** was **displaced from left to right.** At the time of report, after recovery from the injury, the patient exhibited remarkable tolerance of great doses of digitalis. When not taking digitalis, his pulse was 100 to 120, regular, and never intermittent.

Hypertrophy of the Heart.—The heart of a man of ordinary size weighs nine ounces, and that of a woman eight; in cases of hypertrophy, these weights may be doubled, although weights above 25 ounces are rare. According to Osler, Beverly Robinson describes a heart weighing 53 ounces, and Dulles has reported one weighing 48 ounces. Among other modern records are the following: Fifty and one-half ounces,[b] 57 ounces,[c] and one weighing four pounds and six ounces.[d] The Ephemerides[e] contains an incredible account of a heart that weighed 14 pounds. Favell[f] describes a heart that only weighed $3\frac{1}{2}$ ounces.

Wounds of the aorta are almost invariably fatal, although cases are recorded by Pelletan, Heil, Legouest, and others, in which patients survived such wounds for from two months to several years. Green[g] mentions a case of stab-wound in the suprasternal fossa. The patient died one month after of another cause, and at the postmortem examination the aorta was shown to have been opened; the wound in its walls was covered with a spheric, indurated coagulum. No attempt at union had been made.

Zillner[h] observed a penetrating wound of the aorta after which the patient

a 490, 1831.   b 476, 1854, ii., 332   c 548, 1884, i., 150.
d 548, 1860, ii., 644.   e 104, Dec. 3, Ann., iii., Obs., 166.
f 656, 1843, v., 358.   g 744, 1855.   h Wien. Med. Zeitung, Nov. 29, 1881.

lived sixteen days, finally dying of pericarditis. Zillner attributed this circumstance to the small size of the wound, atheroma and degeneration of the aorta and slight retraction of the inner coat, together with a possible plugging of the pericardial opening. In 1880 Chiari said that while dissecting the body of a man who died of phthisis, he found a false aneurysm of the ascending aorta with a transverse rupture of the vessel by the side of it, which had completely cicatrized. Hill [a] reports the case of a soldier who was stabbed with a bowie-knife nine inches long and three inches wide. The blade passed through the diaphragm, cut off a portion of the liver, and severed the descending aorta at a point about the 7th dorsal vertebra ; the soldier lived over three hours after complete division of this important vessel. Heil [b] reports the case of a man of thirty-two, a soldier in the Bavarian army, who, in a quarrel in 1812, received a stab in the right side. The instrument used was a common table-knife, which was passed between the 5th and 6th ribs, entering the left lung, and causing copious hemorrhage. The patient recovered in four months, but suffered from amaurosis which had commenced at the time of the stab. Some months afterward he contracted pneumonia and was readmitted to the hospital, dying in 1813. At the postmortem the cicatrix in the chest was plainly visible, and in the ascending aorta there was seen a wound, directly in the track of the knife, which was of irregular border and was occupied by a firm coagulum of blood. The vessel had been completely penetrated, as, by laying it open, an internal cicatrix was found corresponding to the other. Fatal hemorrhage had been avoided in this case by the formation of coagulum in the wound during the syncope immediately following the stab, possibly aided by extended exposure to cold.

Sundry Cases.—Sandifort [709] mentions a curious case of coalescence of the esophagus and aorta, with ulceration and consequent rupture of the aorta, the hemorrhage proceeding from the stomach at the moment of rupture.

Heath [c] had a case of injury to the external iliac artery from external violence, with subsequent obliteration of the vessel. When the patient was discharged no pulse could be found in the leg.

Dismukes [d] reports a case in which the patient had received 13 wounds, completely severing the subclavian artery, and, without any medical or surgical aid, survived the injury two hours.

Illustrative of the degree of hemorrhage which may follow an injury so slight as that of falling on a needle we cite an instance, reported by a French authority,[e] of a child who picked up a needle, and, while running with it to its mother, stumbled and fell, the needle penetrating the 4th intercostal space, the broadened end of it remaining outside of the wound. The mother seized the needle between her teeth and withdrew it, but the child died, before

a 131, 1875, ii., 389.   b 834, 1837–8.   c 548, 1874, ii., 363.

d 579, 1856, xi., 59.   e 646, 1883.

medical aid could be summoned, from internal hemorrhage, causing pulmonary pressure and dyspnea.

Rupture of the esophagus is attributable to many causes. Dryden [a] mentions vomiting as a cause, and Guersant [b] reports the case of a little girl of seven, who, during an attack of fever, ruptured her esophagus by vomiting. In 1837 Heyfelder reported the case of a drunkard, who, in a convulsion, ruptured his esophagus and died. Williams [c] mentions a case in which not only the gullet, but also the diaphragm, was ruptured in vomiting. In this country, Bailey [d] and Fitz [e] have recorded cases of rupture of the esophagus. Brewer [587] relates a parallel instance of rupture from vomiting. All the foregoing cases were linear ruptures, but there is a unique case given by Boerhaave in 1724, in which the rent was transverse. Ziemssen and Mackenzie [499] have both translated from the Latin the report of this case which is briefly as follows: The patient, Baron de Wassenaer, was fifty years of age, and, with the exception that he had a sense of fulness after taking moderate meals, he was in perfect health. To relieve this disagreeable feeling he was in the habit of taking a copious draught of an infusion of " blessed thistle " and ipecacuanha. One day, about 10.30 in the evening, when he had taken no supper, but had eaten a rather hearty dinner, he was bothered by a peculiar sensation in his stomach, and to relieve this he swallowed about three tumblerfuls of his usual infusion, but to no avail. He then tried to excite vomiting by tickling the fauces, when, in retching, he suddenly felt a violent pain ; he diagnosed his own case by saying that it was " the bursting of something near the pit of the stomach." He became prostrated and died in eighteen and one-half hours ; at the necropsy it was seen that without any previously existing signs of disease the esophagus had been completely rent across in a transverse direction.

Schmidtmuller [f] mentions separation of the esophagus from the stomach ; and Flint [g] reports the history of a boy of seven who died after being treated for worms and cerebral symptoms. After death the contents of the stomach were found in the abdominal cavity, and the esophagus was completely separated from the stomach. Flint believed the separation was postmortem, and was possibly due to the softening of the stomach by the action of the gastric acids. In this connection may be mentioned the case reported by Hanford [h] of a man of twenty-three who had an attack of hematemesis and melanema two years before death. A postmortem was made five hours after death, and there was so much destruction of the stomach by a process resembling digestion that only the pyloric and cardiac orifices were visible. Hanford suggests that this was an instance of antemortem digestion of the stomach which physiologists claim is impossible.

a 524, 1788, iii., 308.   b Bull. de la Fac. de Méd. de Paris, 1812, 73.

c 779, 1848, i., 151.   d 597, May, 1873.   e 124, Jan., 1877.

f 101, L. i., No. 6.   g 526, 1848, 715.   h 476, 1886, i., 546.

Nearly all cases of **rupture of the stomach** are due to carcinoma, ulcer, or some similar condition, although there have been instances of rupture from pressure and distention. Wunschheim [a] reports the case of a man of fifty-two who for six months presented symptoms of gastric derangement, and who finally sustained spontaneous rupture of the posterior border of the stomach due to overdistention. There was a tear two inches long, beginning near the cardiac end and running parallel to the lesser curvature. The margin of the tear showed no evidence of digestion. There were obstructing esophageal neoplasms about $10\frac{1}{3}$ inches from the teeth, which prevented vomiting. In reviewing the literature Wunschheim found only six cases of spontaneous rupture of the stomach. Arton [b] reports the case of a negro of fifty who suffered from tympanites. He was a hard drinker and had been aspirated several times, gas heavily laden with odors of the milk of asafetida being discharged with a violent rush. The man finally died of his malady, and at postmortem it was found that his stomach had burst, showing a slit four inches long. The gall bladder contained two quarts of inspissated bile.

Fulton [c] mentions a case of rupture of the esophageal end of a stomach in a child. The colon was enormously distended and the walls thickened. When three months old it was necessary to puncture the bowel for distention. Collins [d] describes spontaneous rupture of the stomach in a woman of seventy-four, the subject of lateral curvature of the spine, who had frequent attacks of indigestion and tympanites. On the day of death there was considerable distention, and a gentle purgative and antispasmodic were given. Just before death a sudden explosive sound was heard, followed by collapse. A necropsy showed a rupture two inches long and two inches from the pyloric end. Lallemand [e] mentions an instance of the rupture of the coats of the stomach by the act of vomiting. The patient was a woman who had suffered with indigestion five or six months, but had been relieved by strict regimen. After indulging her appetite to a greater extent than usual, she experienced nausea, and made violent and ineffectual efforts to discharge the contents of the stomach. While suffering great agony she experienced a sensation as if something was tearing in the lower part of her belly. The woman uttered several screams, fell unconscious, and died that night. Postmortem examination showed that the anterior and middle part of the stomach were torn obliquely to the extent of five inches. The tear extended from the smaller toward the greater curvature. The edges were thin and irregular and presented no marks of disease. The cavity of the peritoneum was full of half-digested food. The records of St. Bartholomew's Hospital, London, contain the account of a man of thirty-four who for two years had been the subject of paroxysmal pain in the stomach. The pains usually continued for several hours and subsided with vomiting. At St. Bartholomew's he had an attack of vomiting after a debauch. On the following day he was seized

[a] 644, xviii., No. 3, 21.   [b] 538, 1878, 208.   [c] 606, 1893.   [d] 134, 1894.   [e] 302, xlix.

with vomiting accompanied by nausea and flatus, and after a sudden attack of pain at the pit of the stomach which continued for two hours, he died. A ragged opening at the esophageal orifice, on the anterior surface of the stomach was found. This tear extended from below the lesser curvature to its extremity, and was four inches long. There were no signs of gastric carcinoma or ulcer.

Clarke[a] reports the case of a Hindoo of twenty-two, under treatment for ague, who, without pain or vomiting, suddenly fell into collapse and died twenty-three hours later. He also mentions a case of rupture of the stomach of a woman of uncertain history, who was supposed to have died of cholera. The examination of the bodies of both cases showed true rupture of the stomach and not mere perforation. In both cases, at the time of rupture, the stomach was empty, and the gastric juice had digested off the capsules of the spleens, thus allowing the escape of blood into the abdominal cavities. The seats of rupture were on the anterior walls. In the first case the coats of the stomach were atrophied and thin. In the second the coats were healthy and not even softened. There was absence of softening, erosion, or rupture on the posterior walls.

As illustrative of the amount of paralytic distention that is possible, Bamberger mentions a case in which 70 pounds of fluid filled the stomach.

Voluntary Vomiting.—It is an interesting fact that some persons exhibit the power of contracting the stomach at will and expeling its contents without nausea. Montégre[b] mentions a distinguished member of the Faculty of Paris, who, by his own volition and without nausea or any violent efforts, could vomit the contents of his stomach. In his translation of " Spallanzani's Experiments on Digestion " Sennebier reports a similar instance in Geneva, in which the vomiting was brought about by swallowing air.

In discussing **wounds** and other injuries **of the stomach** no chapter would be complete without a description of the celebrated case of **Alexis St. Martin,** whose accident has been the means of contributing so much to the knowledge of the physiology of digestion. This man was a French Canadian of good constitution, robust and healthy, and was employed as a voyageur by the American Fur Company. On June 16, 1822, when about eighteen years of age, he was accidentally wounded by a discharge from a musket. The contents of the weapon, consisting of powder and duck-shot, entered his left side from a distance of not more than a yard off. The charge was directed obliquely forward and inward, literally blowing off the integument and muscles for a space about the size of a man's hand, carrying away the anterior half of the 6th rib, fracturing the 5th rib, lacerating the lower portion of the lowest lobe of the left lung, and perforating the diaphragm and the stomach. The whole mass of the discharge together with fragments of clothing were driven into the muscles and cavity of the chest. When first seen

a 435, Aug., 1885.

b 302, iv., 188.

by Dr. Beaumont about a half hour after the accident, a portion of the lung, as large as a turkey's egg was found protruding through the external wound. The protruding lung was lacerated and burnt. Immediately below this was another protrusion, which proved to be a portion of the stomach, lacerated through all its coats. Through an orifice, large enough to admit a fore-finger, oozed the remnants of the food he had taken for breakfast. His injuries were dressed; extensive sloughing commenced, and the wound became considerably enlarged. Portions of the lung, cartilages, ribs, and of the ensiform process of the sternum came away. In a year from the time of the accident, the wound, with the exception of a fistulous aperture of the stomach and side, had completely cicatrized. This aperture was about $2\frac{1}{2}$ inches in circumference, and through it food and drink constantly extruded unless prevented by a tent-compress and bandage. The man had so far recovered as to be able to walk and do light work, his digestion and appetite being normal. Some months later a small fold or doubling of the stomachal coats slightly protruded until the whole aperture was filled, so as to supersede the necessity of a compress, the protruding coats acting as a valve when the stomach was filled. This valvular protrusion was easily depressed by the finger. St. Martin suffered little pain except from the depression of the skin. He took his food and drink like any healthy person, and for eleven years remained under Dr. Beaumont's own care in the Doctor's house as a servant. During this time were performed the experiments on digestion which are so well known. St. Martin was at all times willing to lend himself in the interest of physiologic science. In August, 1879, The Detroit Lancet contains advices that St. Martin was living at that time at St. Thomas, Joliette County, Province of Quebec, Canada. At the age of seventy-nine he was comparatively strong and well, and had always been a hard worker. At this time the opening in the stomach was nearly an inch in diameter, and in spite of its persistence his digestion had never failed him.

Spizharny[a] relates a remarkable case of **gastric fistula in the loin,** and collects 61 cases of gastric fistula, none of which opened in the loin. The patient was a girl of eighteen, who had previously had perityphlitis, followed by abscesses about the navel and lumbar region. Two fistulæ were found in the right loin, and were laid open into one canal, which, after partial resection of the 12th rib, was dilated and traced inward and upward, and found to be in connection with the stomach. Food was frequently found on the dressings, but with the careful use of tampons a cure was effected.

In the olden times wounds of the stomach were not always fatal. The celebrated anatomist, Fallopius, successfully treated two cases in which the stomach was penetrated so that food passed through the wound. Jacobus Orthaeus tells us that in the city of Fuldana there was a soldier who received a wound of the stomach, through which food passed immediately after being

a 704, 1893.

swallowed; he adds that two judicious surgeons stitched the edges of the wound to the integuments, thereby effecting a cure. There is another old record [570] of a gastric fistula through which some aliment passed during the period of eleven years.

Archer [a] tells of a man who was stabbed by a negro, the knife entering the cartilages of the 4th rib on the right side, and penetrating the stomach to the extent of two inches at a point about two inches below the xiphoid cartilage. The stomachal contents, consisting of bacon, cabbage, and cider, were evacuated. Shortly after the reception of the injury, an old soldier sewed up the wound with an awl, needle, and wax-thread; Archer did not see the patient until forty-eight hours afterward, at which time he cleansed and dressed the wound. After a somewhat protracted illness the patient recovered, notwithstanding the extent of injury and the primitive mode of treatment.

Travers [b] mentions the case of a woman of fifty-three who, with suicidal intent, divided her abdominal parietes below the navel with a razor, wounding the stomach in two places. Through the wound protruded the greater part of the larger curvature of the stomach; the arch of the colon and the entire greater omentum were both strangulated. A small portion of the coats of the stomach, including the wound, was nipped up, a silk ligature tied about it, and the entrails replaced. Two months afterward the patient had quite recovered, though the ligature of the stomach had not been seen in the stool. Clements [c] mentions a robust German of twenty-two who was stabbed in the abdomen with a dirk, producing an incised wound of the stomach. The patient recovered and was returned to duty the following month.

There are many cases on record in which injury of the stomach has been due to some mistake or accident in the juggling process of knife-swallowing or sword-swallowing. The records of injuries of this nature extend back many hundred years, and even in the earlier days the delicate operation of **gastrotomy,** sometimes with a successful issue, was **performed upon persons who had swallowed knives.** Gross mentions that in 1502 Florian Mathias of Bradenberg removed a knife nine inches long from the stomach of a man of thirty-six, followed by a successful recovery. Glandorp,[380] from whom, possibly, Gross derived his information, relates this memorable case as being under the direction of Florianus Matthaesius of Bradenburg. The patient, a native of Prague, had swallowed a knife eight or nine inches long, which lay pointing at the superior portion of the stomach. After it had been lodged in this position for seven weeks and two days gastrotomy was performed, and the knife extracted; the patient recovered. In 1613 Crollius reports the case of a Bohemian peasant who had concealed a knife in his mouth, thinking no one would suspect he possessed the weapon; while he was excited it slipped into the stomach, from whence it subsequently penetrated through to the skin; the man recovered. There is another old case of a man at Prague who swallowed

a 541, 1812.   b 317, 1836, i., 81.   c 847, 91.

a knife which some few weeks afterward made its exit from an abdominal abscess. Gooch [382] quotes the case of a man, belonging to the Court of Paris, who, nine months after swallowing a knife, voided it at the groin. In the sixteenth century Laurentius Joubert relates a similar case, the knife having remained in the body two years. De Diemerbroeck [304] mentions the fact that a knife ten inches long was extracted by gastrotomy, and placed among the rarities in the anatomic chamber of the University at Leyden. The operation was done in 1635 at Koenigsberg, by Schwaben, who for his surgical prowess was appointed surgeon to the King of Poland. The patient lived eight years after the operation.

It is said that in 1691, while playing tricks with a knife $6\frac{1}{2}$ inches long, a country lad of Saxony swallowed it, point first. He came under the care of Weserern, physician to the Elector of Brandenburgh, who successfully extracted it, two years and seven months afterward, from the pit of the lad's stomach. The horn haft of the knife was considerably digested. In 1720 Hubner[a] of Rastembourg operated on a woman who had swallowed an open knife. After the incision it was found that the knife had almost pierced the stomach and had excited a slight suppuration. After the operation recovery was very prompt.

Bell[b] of Davenport, Iowa, performed gastrotomy on a man, who, while attempting a feat of legerdemain, allowed a bar of lead, $10\frac{1}{8}$ inches long, $1\frac{1}{2}$ inches wide, and $9\frac{1}{2}$ ounces in weight, to slip into his stomach. The bar was removed and the patient recovered. Gussenbauer[c] gives an account of a juggler who turned his head to bow an acknowledgment of applause while swallowing a sword; he thus brought his upper incisors against the sword, which broke off and slipped into his stomach. To relieve suffocation the sword was pushed further down. Gastrotomy was performed, and the piece of sword 11 inches long was extracted; as there was perforation of the stomach before the operation, the patient died of peritonitis.

An hour after ingestion, Bernays of St. Louis successfully removed a knife $9\frac{1}{2}$ inches long. By means of an army-bullet forceps the knife was extracted easily through an incision $\frac{5}{8}$ inch long in the walls of the stomach. Gross[d] speaks of a man of thirty who was in the habit of giving exhibitions of sword-swallowing in public houses, and who injured his esophagus to such an extent as to cause abscess and death. In the Journal of the American Medical Association, March 1, 1896, there is an extensive list of gastrotomies performed for the removal of knives and other foreign bodies, from the seventeenth century to the present time.

The physiologic explanation of sword-swallowing is quite interesting. We know that when we introduce the finger, a spoon, brush, etc., into the throat of a patient, we cause extremely disagreeable symptoms. There is nausea, gagging, and considerable hindrance with the function of respira-

a 641, 218.   b Quoted 362, 1880.   c 821, Dec. 20 and 27, 1883.   d 476, 1885, i., 249.

tion.   It therefore seems remarkable that there are people whose physiologic construction is such that, without apparent difficulty, they are enabled to swallow a sword many inches long.   Many of the exhibitionists allow the visitors to touch the stomach and outline the point of the sabre through the skin.   The sabre used is usually very blunt and of rounded edges, or if

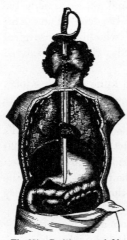

sharp, a guiding tube of thin metal is previously swallowed.   The explanation of these exhibitions is as follows : The instrument enters the mouth and pharynx, then the esophagus, traverses the cardiac end of the stomach, and enters the latter as far as the antrum of the pylorus, the small culdesac of the stomach.   In their normal state in the adult these organs are not in a straight line, but are so placed by the passage of the sword.   In the first place the head is thrown back, so that the mouth is in the direction of the esophagus, the curves of which disappear or become less as the sword proceeds (Fig. 221) ; the angle that the esophagus makes with the stomach is obliterated, and finally the stomach is distended in the vertical diameter and its internal curve disappears, thus permitting the blade to traverse the greater diameter of the stomach.   According to Guyot-

Fig. 221.—Position occupied by the blade in the body of a sword-swallower (after Guyot-Daubès).

Daubès,[394] these organs, in a straight line, extend a distance of from 55 to 62 cm., and consequently the performer is enabled to swallow an instrument of this length.   The length is divided as follows :—

Mouth and pharynx, ... 10 to 12 cm.
Esophagus, ... 25 to 28 cm.
Distended stomach, ... 20 to 22 cm.

_____

55 to 62 cm.

These acrobats with the sword have rendered important service to medicine.   It was through the good offices of a sword-swallower that the Scotch physician, Stevens, was enabled to make his experiments on digestion.   He caused this assistant to swallow small metallic tubes pierced with holes.   They were filled, according to Reaumur's method, with pieces of meat.   After a certain length of time he would have the acrobat disgorge the tubes, and in this way he observed to what degree the process of digestion had taken place. It was also probably the sword-swallower who showed the physicians to what extent the pharynx could be habituated to contact, and from this resulted the invention of the tube of Faucher, the esophageal sound, lavage of the stomach, and illumination of this organ by electric light.   Some of these individuals also have the faculty of swallowing several pebbles, as large even as hen's eggs, and of disgorging them one by one by simple contractions of the stomach.

From time to time individuals are seen who possess the power of **swallowing pebbles, knives, bits of broken glass, etc.,** and, in fact, there have been recent tricky exhibitionists who claimed to be able to swallow **poisons,** in large quantities, with impunity.   Henrion, called " Cassandra," a celebrated example of this class, was born at Metz in 1761.   Early in life he taught himself to swallow pebbles, sometimes whole and sometimes after breaking them with his teeth.   He passed himself off as an American savage ; he swallowed as many as 30 or 40 large pebbles a day, demonstrating the fact by percussion on the epigastric region.   With the aid of salts he would pass the pebbles and make them do duty the next day.   He would also swallow live mice and crabs with their claws cut.   It was said that when the mice were introduced into his mouth, they threw themselves into the pharynx where they were immediately suffocated and then swallowed.   The next morning they would be passed by the rectum flayed and covered with a mucous substance.   Henrion continued his calling until 1820, when, for a moderate sum, he was induced to swallow some nails and a plated iron spoon $5\frac{1}{2}$ inches long and one inch in breadth.   He died seven days later.[a]

According to Bonet, there was a man by the name of Pichard who swallowed a razor and two knives in the presence of King Charles II. of England, the King himself placing the articles into the man's mouth.   In 1810 Babbington and Curry [302] are accredited with citing the history of an American sailor in Guy's Hospital, London, who frequently swallowed penknives for the amusement of his audiences.   At first he swallowed four, and three days later passed them by the anus ; on another occasion he swallowed 14 of different sizes with the same result.   Finally he attempted to gorge himself with 17 penknives, but this performance was followed by horrible pains and alarming abdominal symptoms.   His excrement was black from iron.   After death the cadaver was opened and 14 corroded knives were found in the stomach, some of the handles being partly digested ; two were found in the pelvis and one in the abdominal cavity.   Paré [618] recalls the instance of a shepherd who suffered distressing symptoms after gulping a knife six inches long.   Afterward the knife was abstracted from his groin.   Fabricius Hildanus [334] cites a somewhat similar case.

Early in the century there was a man known as the " Yankee knife-swallower," whose name was John Cummings, an American sailor, who had performed his feats in nearly all the ports of the world.   One of his chief performances was swallowing a billiard ball.   Poland [b] mentions a man (possibly Cummings) who, in 1807, was admitted to Guy's Hospital with dyspeptic symptoms which he attributed to knife-swallowing.   His story was discredited at first ; but after his death, in March, 1809, there were 30 or 40 fragments of knives found in his stomach.   One of the back-springs on a knife had transfixed the colon and rectum.   In the Edinburgh Philosophical

Journal for 1825 [a] there is an account of a juggler who swallowed a knife which remained in his stomach and caused such intense symptoms that gastrotomy was advised ; the patient, however, refused operation.

Drake [b] reports a curious instance of polyphagia. The person described was a man of twenty-seven who pursued the vocation of a "sword-swallower." He had swallowed a gold watch and chain with a seal and key attached ; at another time he swallowed 34 bullets and voided them by the anus. At Poughkeepsie, N. Y., in August, 1819, in one day and night he swallowed 19 pocket-knives and 41 copper cents. This man had commenced when a lad of fifteen by swallowing marbles, and soon afterward a small penknife. After his death his esophagus was found normal, but his stomach was so distended as to reach almost to the spine of the ilium, and knives were found in the stomach weighing one pound or more. In his exhibitions he allowed his spectators to hear the click of the knives and feel them as low down as the anterior superior spine of the ilium.

The present chief of the dangerous "profession" of sword-swallowing is Chevalier Cliquot, a French Canadian by birth, whose major trick is to swallow a real bayonet sword, weighted with a cross-bar and two 18-pound dumbbells. He can swallow without difficulty a 22-inch cavalry sword ; formerly, in New York, he gave exhibitions of swallowing fourteen 19-inch bayonet swords at once. A negro, by the name of Jones, exhibiting not long since in Philadelphia, gave hourly exhibitions of his ability to swallow with impunity pieces of broken glass and china.

Foreign Bodies in the Alimentary Canal.—In the discussion of the foreign bodies that have been taken into the stomach and intestinal tract possibly the most interesting cases, although the least authentic, are those relating to **living animals,** such as fish, insects, or reptiles. It is particularly among the older writers that we find accounts of this nature. In the Ephemerides we read of a man who vomited a serpent that had crept into his mouth, and of another person who ejected a beetle that had gained entrance in a similar manner. From the same authority we find instances of the vomiting of live fish, mice, toads, and also of the passage by the anus of live snails and snakes. Frogs vomited are mentioned by Bartholinus, Dolæus, Hellwigius, Lentilus, Salmuth, and others. [708] A Vege mentions a man who swallowed a young chicken whole. Paullini speaks of a person who, after great pain, vomited a mouse which he had swallowed. Borellus, Bartholinus, Thoner, and Viridet, are among the older authorities mentioning persons who swallowed toads. Hippocrates speaks of asphyxia from a serpent which had crawled into the mouth.

Borellus states that he knew a case of a person who vomited a salamander. Plater [635] reports the swallowing of eels and snails. Rhodius mentions persons who have eaten scorpions and spiders with impunity. Planchon [c] writes of an instance in which a live spider was ejected from the bowel; and Colini[a] reports the passage of a live lizard which had been swallowed two days before, and there is another similar case on record.[b] Marcellus Donatus[c] records an instance in which a viper, which had previously crawled into the mouth, had been passed by the anus. There are also recorded instances in French literature in which persons affected with pediculosis, have, during sleep, unconsciously swallowed lice which were afterward found in the stools.

There is an abundance of cases in which leeches have been accidentally swallowed. Pliny, Aetius, Dioscorides, Scribonius-Largus, Celsus, Oribasius, Paulus Aegineta, and others, describe such cases. Bartholinus speaks of a Neapolitan prince who, while hunting, quenched his thirst in a brook, putting his mouth in the running water. In this way he swallowed a leech, which subsequently caused annoying hemorrhage from the mouth. Timaeus mentions a child of five who swallowed several leeches, and who died of abdominal pains, hemorrhage, and convulsions. Rhodius, Riverius, and Zwinger make similar observations. According to Baron Larrey the French soldiers in Napoleon's Egyptian campaign occasionally swallowed leeches. Grandchamp and Duval[d] have commented on curious observations of leeches in the digestive tract. Dumas and Marques also speak of the swallowing of leeches. Colter[e] reports a case in which beetles were vomited. Wright[f] remarks on Banon's case of fresh-water shrimps passed from the human intestine. Dalton, Dickman,[g] and others, have discussed the possibility of a slug living in the stomach of man. Pichells[h] speaks of a case in which beetles were expelled from the stomach; and Pigault[i] gives an account of a living lizard expelled by vomiting. Fontaine, Gaspard, Vetillart, Ribert, MacAlister,[j] and Waters[k] record cases in which living caterpillars have been swallowed.

Sundry Cases.—The variety of foreign bodies that have been swallowed either accidentally or for exhibitional or suicidal purposes is enormous. Nearly every imaginable article from the minutest to the most incredible size has been reported. To begin to epitomize the literature on this subject would in itself consume a volume, and only a few instances can be given here, chosen in such a way as to show the variety, the effects, and the possibilities of their passage through the intestinal canal.

Chopart[l] says that in 1774 the belly of a ravenous galley-slave was opened, and in the stomach were found **52 foreign bodies,** including a barrel-hoop 19 inches long, nails, pieces of pipe, spoons, buckles, seeds, glass, and a knife. In the intestines of a person Agnew[m] found a pair of suspenders, a mass of straw, and three roller-bandages, an inch in width and diameter. Velpeau[n] mentions

a 462, T. li., 460.   b 107, i., 22.   c 306, ii., c. xii., 222.   d 458, T. xxv. and xxvi.
e 548, 1878, i., 676.   f 312, 1864, li., 407.   g 476, 1859, ii., 337.   h 318, lxvi., 384.
i Quart. Jour. Calcutta Med. and Phys. Soc., 1837, i., 291.   j 312, liv., 478.
k 538, xxix., 93.   l "Maladies des Voies Urinaires."   m 526, 1853.   n 476, 1849, ii., 41.

a fork which was passed from the anus twenty months after it was swallowed. Wilson [a] mentions an instance of gastrotomy which was performed for the extraction of a fork swallowed sixteen years before.   There is an interesting case [b] in which, in a delirium of typhoid fever, a girl of twenty-two swallowed two iron forks, which were subsequently expelled through an abdominal abscess.   A French woman of thirty-five,[c] with suicidal intent, swallowed a four-pronged fork, which was removed four years afterward from the thigh. For two years she had suffered intense pain in both thighs.   In the Royal College of Surgeons in London there is a steel button-hook $3\frac{1}{2}$ inches in length which was accidentally swallowed, and was passed three weeks later by the anus, without having given rise to any symptom.[619]

Among the insane a favorite trait seems to be swallowing nails.   In the Philosophical Transactions [d] is an account of the contents of the stomach of an idiot who died at thirty-three.   In this organ were found nine cart-wheel nails, six screws, two pairs of compasses, a key, an iron pin, a ring, a brass pommel weighing nine ounces, and many other articles.   The celebrated Dr. Lettsom, in 1802, spoke of an idiot who swallowed **four pounds of old nails** and a pair of compasses.   A lunatic in England [e] swallowed ten ounces of screws and bits of crockery, all of which were passed by the anus.   Boardman [f] gives an account of a child affected with hernia who swallowed a nail $2\frac{1}{2}$ inches long.   In a few days the nail was felt in the hernia, but in due time it was passed by the rectum.   Blower [g] reports an account of a nail passing safely through the alimentary canal of a baby.   Armstrong [h] mentions an insane hair-dresser of twenty-three, in whose stomach after death were found **30 or more spoon handles, 30 nails,** and other minor articles.

Closmadenc [363] reported a remarkable case which was extensively quoted.[i]   The patient was an hysteric young girl, an inmate of a convent, to whom he was called to relieve a supposed fit of epilepsy.   He found her half-asphyxiated, and believed that she had swallowed a foreign body.   He was told that under the influence of exaggerated religious scruples this girl inflicted penance upon herself by swallowing earth and holy medals.   At the first dose of the emetic, the patient made a strong effort to vomit, whereupon a cross seven cm. long appeared between her teeth.   This was taken out of her mouth, and with it an enormous **rosary 220 cm.** long, and having seven medals attached to it.   Hunt[j] recites a case occurring in a pointer dog, which swallowed its **collar and chain,** only imperfectly masticating the collar.   The chain and collar were immediately missed and search made for them.   For several days the dog was ill and refused food.   Finally the gamekeeper saw the end of the chain hanging from the dog's anus, and taking hold of it, he drew out a yard of chain with links one inch long, with a

a 476, 1887, i., 1109.   b Neue Jahrbücher der deutschen Medizin und Chirurgie, 1823.
c 593, 1853.   d 629, 1700–20, v.   e 476, 1866, i., 619.   f 230, 1867.
g 224, 1870.   h 476, 1852.   i 548, 1859, ii., 273.   j 476, 1872, ii., 837.

cross bar at the end two inches in length; the dog soon recovered. The collar was never found, and had apparently been digested or previously passed.

Fear of robbery has often led to the swallowing of **money or jewelry.** Vaillant, the celebrated doctor and antiquarian, after a captivity of four months in Algiers, was pursued by Tunis pirates, and swallowed 15 medals of gold; shortly after arriving at Lyons he passed them all at stool. Fournier and Duret[a] published the history of a galley slave at Brest in whose stomach were found 52 pieces of money, their combined weight being one pound, 10¼ ounces. On receiving a sentence of three years' imprisonment, an Englishman,[b] to prevent them being taken from him, swallowed seven half-crowns. He suffered no bad effects, and the coins not appearing the affair was forgotten. While at stool some twenty months afterward, having taken a purgative for intense abdominal pain, the seven coins fell clattering into the chamber. Hévin mentions the case of a man who, on being captured by Barbary pirates, swallowed all the money he had on his person. It is said that a certain Italian swallowed 100 louis d'ors at a time.

It occasionally happens that **false teeth** are accidentally swallowed, and even passed through the intestinal tract. Easton[c] mentions a young man who accidentally swallowed some artificial teeth the previous night, and, to further their passage through the bowel, he took a dose of castor oil. When seen he was suffering with pain in the stomach, and was advised to eat much heavy food and avoid aperients. The following day after several free movements he felt a sharp pain in the lower part of his back. A large enema was given and the teeth and plate came away. The teeth were cleansed and put back in his mouth, and the patient walked out. Nine years later the same accident again happened to the man but in spite of treatment nothing was seen of the teeth for a month afterward, when a body appeared in the rectum which proved to be a gold plate with the teeth in it. In The Lancet of December 10, 1881, there is an account of a vulcanite tooth-plate which was swallowed and passed forty-two hours later. Billroth[d] mentions an instance of gastrotomy for the removal of swallowed artificial teeth, with recovery; and another case in which a successful esophagotomy was performed. Gardiner[e] mentions a woman of thirty-three who swallowed two false teeth while supping soup. A sharp angle of the broken plate had caught in a fold of the cardiac end of the stomach and had caused violent hematemesis. Death occurred seventeen hours after the first urgent symptoms.

In the Museum of the Royal College of Surgeons in London there is an intestinal concretion weighing 470 grains, which was passed by a woman of seventy who had suffered from constipation for many years. Sixteen years

---

a 462, T. xlii. b 490, May 20, 1837. c 476, 1882, i., 381.
d 476, 1885, i., 591. e 253, March, 1881.

before the concretion was passed she was known to have swallowed a tooth. At one side of the concretion a piece had been broken off exposing an incisor tooth which represented the nucleus of the formation. Manasse [199] recently reported the case of a man of forty-four whose stomach contained a stone weighing 75 grams. He was a joiner and, it was supposed, habitually drank some alcoholic solution of shellac used in his trade. Quite likely the shellac had been precipitated in the stomach and gave rise to the calculus.

Berwick [a] mentions a child of eight months who was playing with a detached **organ-handle,** and put it in its mouth. Seeing this the mother attempted to secure the handle, but it was pushed into the esophagus. A physician was called, but nothing was done, and the patient seemed to suffer little inconvenience. Three days later the handle was expelled from the anus. Teakle [b] reports the successful passage through the alimentary canal of the **handle of a music-box.** Hashimoto, Surgeon-General of the Imperial Japanese Army, tells of a woman of forty-nine who was in the habit of inducing vomiting by irritating her fauces and pharynx with a Japanese **toothbrush**—a wooden instrument six or seven inches long with bristles at one end. In May, 1872, she accidentally swallowed this brush. Many minor symptoms developed, and in eleven months there appeared in the epigastric region a fluctuating swelling, which finally burst, and from it extended the end of the brush. After vainly attempting to extract the brush the attending physician contented himself with cutting off the projecting portion. The opening subsequently healed; and not until thirteen years later did the pain and swelling return. On admission to the hospital in October, 1888, two fistulous openings were seen in the epigastric region, and the foreign body was located by probing. Finally, on November 19, 1888, the patient was anesthetized, one of the openings enlarged, and the brush extracted. Five weeks later the openings had all healed and the patient was restored to health.

Garcia [c] reports an interesting instance of foreign body in a man between forty-five and fifty. This man was afflicted with a syphilitic affection of the mouth, and he constructed a **swab ten inches long** with which to cleanse his fauces. While making the application alone one day, a spasmodic movement caused him to relinquish his grasp on the handle, and the swab disappeared. He was almost suffocated, and a physician was summoned; but before his arrival the swab had descended into the esophagus. Two weeks later, gastroperitoneal symptoms presented, and as the stick was located, gastrotomy was proposed; the patient, however, would not consent to an operation. On the twenty-sixth day an abscess formed on the left side below the nipple, and from it was discharged a large quantity of pus and blood. Four days after this, believing himself to be better, the man began to redress the wound, and from it he saw the end of a stick protruding. A physician was called, and by traction the stick was withdrawn from between the 3d and 4th ribs;

forty-nine days after the accident the wound had healed completely. Two years afterward the patient had an attack of cholera, but in the fifteen subsequent years he lived an active life of labor.

Occasionally an enormous mass of **hair** has been removed from the stomach. A girl of twenty[a] with a large abdominal swelling was admitted to a hospital. Her illness began five years previously, with frequent attacks of vomiting, and on three occasions it was noticed that she became quite bald. Abdominal section was performed, the stomach opened, and from it was removed a mass of hair which weighed five pounds and three ounces. A good recovery ensued. In the Museum of St. George's Hospital, London,[619] are masses of hair and string taken from the stomach and duodenum of a girl of ten. It is said that from the age of three the patient had been in the habit of eating these articles. There is a record in the last century of a boy of sixteen who ate all the hair he could find; after death his stomach and intestines were almost completely lined with hairy masses. In the Journal of the American Medical Association, March 1, 1896, there is a report of a case of hair-swallowing.

Foreign Bodies in the Intestines.—White[b] relates the history of a case in which a silver spoon was swallowed and successfully excised from the intestinal canal. Houston[c] mentions a maniac who swallowed a rusty iron spoon 11 inches long. Fatal peritonitis ensued and the spoon was found impacted in the last acute turn of the duodenum. In 1895, in London, [619] there was exhibited a specimen, including the end of the ileum with the adjacent end of the colon, showing a dessertspoon which was impacted in the latter. The spoon was seven inches long, and its bowl measured $1\frac{1}{2}$ inches across. There was much ulceration of the mucous membrane. This spoon had been swallowed by a lunatic of twenty-two, who had made two previous ineffectual attempts at suicide. Mason[d] describes the case of a man of sixty-five who, after death by strangulated hernia, was opened, and two inches from the ileocecal valve was found an earthen egg-cup which he had swallowed. Mason also relates the instance of a man who swallowed metal balls $2\frac{1}{2}$ inches in diameter; and the case of a Frenchman who, to prevent the enemy from finding them, swallowed a box containing despatches from Napoleon. He was kept prisoner until the despatches were passed from his bowels. Denby[e] discovered a large egg-cup in the ileum of a man. Fillion[f] mentions an instance of recovery following the perforation of the jejunum by a piece of horn which had been swallowed. Madden[g] tells of a person, dying of intestinal obstruction, in whose intestines were found several ounces of crude mercury and a plum-stone. The mercury had evidently been taken for purgative effect. Rodenbaugh[h] mentions a most interesting case of beans sprouting while in the bowel. Harrison[i] relates a curious case in which the swallowed

a 476, 1895, i., 1581.

b 541, 1807, iv., 367.

c 311, 1830, v., 319.

d 476, 1870, i., 701.

e 476, 1834.

f 462, T. lxiii., 538.

g 629, 1732.

h 613, 1876.

i 476, 1883, i., 863.

lower epiphysis of the femur of a rabbit made its way from the bowel to the bladder, and was discharged thence by the urethra.

In cases of appendicitis **foreign bodies** have been found lodged **in or about the vermiform appendix** so often that it is quite a common lay idea that appendicitis is invariably the result of the lodgment of some foreign body accidentally swallowed. In recent years the literature of this subject proves that a great variety of foreign bodies may be present. A few of the interesting cases will be cited in the following lines :—

In the New England Medical Journal, 1843, is an account of a vermiform appendix which was taken from the body of a man of eighty-eight who had died of pneumothorax. During life there were no symptoms of disease of the appendix, and after death no adhesions were found, but this organ was remarkably long, and in it were found 122 robin-shot. The old gentleman had been excessively fond of birds all his life, and was accustomed to bolt the meat of small birds without properly chewing it; to this fact was attributed the presence of these shot in the appendix. A somewhat similar case [a] was that of a man who died in the Hôtel-Dieu in 1833. The ileum of this man contained 92 shot and 120 plum stones. Buckler[b] reports a case of appendicitis in a child of twelve, in which a common-sized bird-shot was found in the appendix. Packard[c] presented a case of appendicitis in which two pieces of rusty and crooked wire, one $2\frac{1}{2}$ and the other $1\frac{1}{2}$ inches long, were found in the omentum, having escaped from the appendix. Howe[d] describes a case in which a double oat, with a hard envelope, was found in the vermiform appendix of a boy of four years and one month of age. Prescott[e] reports a case of what he calls fatal colic from the lodgment of a chocolate-nut in the appendix ; and Noyes[f] relates an instance of death in a man of thirty-one attributed to the presence of a raisin-seed in the vermiform appendix. Needles, pins, peanuts, fruit-stones, peas, grape-seeds, and many similar objects have been found in both normal and suppurative vermiform appendices.

Intestinal Injuries.—The degree of injury that the intestinal tract may sustain, and after recovery perform its functions as usual, is most extraordinary ; and even when the injury is of such an extent as to be mortal, the persistence of life is remarkable. It is a well known fact that in bull-fights, after mortal injuries of the abdomen and bowels, horses are seen to struggle on almost until the sport is finished. Fontaine[g] reports a case of a Welsh quarryman who was run over by a heavy four-horse vehicle. The stump of a glass bottle was crushed into the intestinal cavity, and the bowels protruded and were bruised by the wheels of the wagon. The grit was so firmly ground into the bowel that it was impossible to remove it ; yet the man made a complete re-

a 368, 1834.
c "Proceedings Patholog. Soc. of Phila.," 1858, i., 170.
e 589, 1815, iv., 221.   f 299, 1875, x., 30.
b 810, 1856, vii., 266.
d 218, 1860, lxiii., 231.
g 681, 1875, xix., 109.

covery. Nicolls [a] has the case of a man of sixty-nine, a workhouse maniac, who on August 20th attempted suicide by running a red-hot poker into his abdomen. His wound was dressed and he was recovering, but on September 11th he tore the cast off his abdomen, and pulled out of the wound the omentum and 32 inches of colon, which he tore off and threw between his pallet and the wall. Strange to say he did not die until eight days after this horrible injury.

Tardieu [b] relates the case of a chemist who removed a large part of the mesentery with a knife, and yet recovered. Delmas of Montpellier reports the history of a wagoner with complete rupture of the intestines and rupture of the diaphragm, and who yet finished his journey, not dying until eighteen hours after.

Successful Intestinal Resection.—In 1755 Nedham [c] of Norfolk reported the case of a boy of thirteen who was run over and eviscerated. It was found necessary to remove 57 inches of the protruding bowel, but the boy made a subsequent recovery. Koebererle [d] of Strasburg performed an operation on a woman of twenty-two for the relief of intestinal obstruction. On account of numerous strictures it was found necessary to remove over two yards of the small intestine ; the patient recovered without pain or trouble of any kind. In his dissertation on " Ruptures " Arnaud remarks that he cut away more than seven feet of gangrenous bowel, his patient surviving. Beehe [e] reports recovery after the removal of 48 inches of intestine. The case was one of strangulation of an umbilical hernia.

Sloughing of the Intestine Following Intussusception.—Lobstein [488] mentions a peasant woman of about thirty who was suddenly seized with an attack of intussusception of the bowel, and was apparently in a moribund condition when she had a copious stool, in which she evacuated three feet of bowel with the mesentery attached. The woman recovered, but died five months later from a second attack of intussusception, the ileum rupturing and peritonitis ensuing. There is a record in this country [f] of a woman of forty-five who discharged 44 inches of intestine, and who survived for forty-two days. The autopsy showed the sigmoid flexure gone, and from the caput ceci to the termination the colon only measured 14 inches. Vater [g] gives a history of a penetrating abdominal wound in which a portion of the colon hung from the wound during fourteen years, forming an artificial anus.

Among others mentioning considerable sloughing of intestine following intussusception, and usually with complete subsequent recovery, are Bare, [h] 13 inches of the ileum ; Blackton,[i] nine inches ; Bower,[j] 14 inches ; Dawson,[k] 29 inches ; Sheldon,[l] $4\frac{1}{2}$ feet ; Stanley,[m] three feet ; Tremaine,[n] 17 inches ; and Grossoli,[o] 40 cm.

[a] 312, 1854, xxxii., 214.   [b] 141, xxxix.,157.   [c] 629, 1755, xlix., part i., 238.
[d] 545, 1881.   [e] Trans. Amer. Inst. Homeop., 1870, Chicago, 871.   [f] 124, 1846.
[g] 629, 1719–33.   [h] 124, 1863.   [i] 548, 1853.   [j] 149, 1803.   [k] 817, 1840.
[l] 546, 1850.   [m] 426, 1826.   [n] 252, 1879.   [o] 746, 1875.

Rupture of the Intestines.—It is quite possible for the intestine to be ruptured by external violence, and cases of rupture of all parts of the bowel have been recorded. Titorier [a] gives the history of a case in which the colon was completely separated from the rectum by external violence. Hinder [b] reports the rupture of the duodenum by a violent kick. Eccles,[c] Ely,[d] and Pollock [e] also mention cases of rupture of the duodenum. Zimmerman,[f] Atwell,[g] and Allan [h] report cases of rupture of the colon.

Operations upon the gastrointestinal tract have been so improved in the modern era of antisepsis that at the present day they are quite common. There are so many successful cases on record that the whole subject deserves mention here.

Gastrostomy is an operation for establishing a fistulous opening in the stomach through the anterior wall. Many operations have been devised, but the results of this maneuver in malignant disease have not thus far been very satisfactory. It is quite possible that, being an operation of a serious nature, it is never performed early enough, the patient being fatally weakened by inanition. Gross and Zesas [i] have collected, respectively, 207 and 162 cases with surprisingly different rates of mortality : that of Gross being only 29.47 per cent., while that of Zesas was for cicatricial stenoses 60 per cent., and for malignant cases 84 per cent. It is possible that in Zesas's statistics the subjects were so far advanced that death would have resulted in a short time without operation. Gastrotomy we have already spoken of.

Pyloroplasty is an operation devised by Heineke and Mikulicz, and is designed to remove the mechanic obstruction in cicatricial stenoses of the pylorus, at the same time creating a new pylorus.

Gastroenterostomy and pylorectomy are operations devised for the relief of malignant disease of the pylorus, the diseased portions being removed and the parts resected.

Gastrectomy or extirpation of the stomach is considered by most surgeons entirely unjustifiable, as there is seldom hope of cure or prospect of amelioration. La Tribune Médicale for January 16, 1895,[j] gives an abstract of Langenbuch's contribution upon **total extirpation of the stomach.** Three patients were treated, of whom two died. In the first case, on opening the abdominal cavity the stomach was found very much contracted, presenting extensive carcinomatous infiltration on its posterior surface. After division of the epiploön section was made at the pylorus and at the cardiac extremities ; the portions removed represented seven-eighths of the stomach. The pylorus was stitched to the remains of the cardiac orifice, making a cavity about the size of a hen's egg. In this case a cure was accomplished in three weeks. The second case was that of a man in whom almost the entire stomach

a 463, xi.   b 435, 1866.   c 548, 1863.   d 218, 1859.   e 700, 1877.
f 827, 1840, 603.   g Indiana Jour. of Med., Indianapolis, 1875.
h 476, 1878, ii., 332.   i 845, 705.   j 843, 246.

was removed, and the pyloric and cardiac ends were stitched together in the wound of the parietes. The third case was that of a man of sixty-two with carcinoma of the pylorus. After pylorectomy, the line of suture was confined with iodoform-gauze packing. Unfortunately the patient suffered with bronchitis, and coughing caused the sutures to give way; the patient died of inanition on the twenty-third day.

Enterostomy, or the formation of a fecal fistula above the ileocecal valve, was performed for the first time by Nélaton in 1840, but the mortality since 1840 has been so great that in most cases it is deemed inadmissible.

Colostomy, an operation designed to make a fistulous opening in any portion of the rectum, was first practised by Littre. In early times the mortality of inguinal colostomy was about five per cent., but has been gradually reduced until König reports 20 cases with only one death from peritonitis, and Cripps 26 cases with only one death.[a] This will always retain its place in operative surgery as a palliative and life-saving operation for carcinomatous stenosis of the lower part of the colon, and in cases of carcinoma of the rectum in which operation is not feasible.

Intestinal anastomosis, whereby two portions of a severed or resected bowel can be intimately joined, excluding from fecal circulation the portion of bowel which has become obstructed, was originally suggested by Maisonneuve, and was studied experimentally by von Hacken. Billroth resorted to it, and Senn modified it by substituting decalcified bone-plates for sutures. [b] Since that time, Abbe, Matas, Davis, Brokaw, Robinson, Stamm, Baracz, and Dawburn, have modified the material of the plates used, substituting catgut rings, untanned leather, cartilage, raw turnips, potatoes, etc. Recently, Murphy of Chicago has invented a button, which has been extensively used all over the world, in place of sutures and rings, as a means of anastomosis. Hardly any subject has had more discussion in recent literature than the merits of this ingenious contrivance.

Foreign Bodies in the Rectum.—Probably the most celebrated case of foreign body introduced into the rectum is the classic one mentioned by Hévin.[c] Some students introduced the frozen **tail of a pig** in the anus of a French prostitute. The bristles were cut short, and having prepared the passage with oil, they introduced the tail with great force into the rectum, allowing a portion to protrude. Great pain and violent symptoms followed; there was distressing vomiting, obstinate constipation, and fever. Despite the efforts to withdraw the tail, the arrangement of the bristles which allowed entrance, prevented removal. On the sixth day, in great agony, the woman applied to Marchettis, who ingeniously adopted the simple procedure of taking a long hollow reed, and preparing one of its extremities so that it could be introduced into the rectum, he was enabled to pass the reed entirely around the tail and to withdraw both. Relief was prompt, and the removal of the

a 845, 715.   b 845, 720.   c Quoted 641, 353.

foreign body was followed by the issue of stercoraceous matter which had accumulated the six days it had remained in situ.

Tuffet[302] is quoted as mentioning a farmer of forty-six who, in masturbation, introduced a barley-head into his urethra. It was found necessary to cut the foreign body out of the side of the glans. A year later he put in his anus a cylindric snuff-box of large size, and this had to be removed by surgical methods. Finally, a drinking goblet was used, but this resulted in death, after much suffering and lay treatment. In his memoirs of the old Academy of Surgery in Paris, Morand speaks of a monk who, to cure a violent colic, introduced into his fundament a **bottle** of *l'eau de la reine de Hongrie*, with a small opening in its mouth, by which the contents, drop by drop, could enter the intestine. He found he could not remove the bottle, and violent inflammation ensued. It was at last necessary to secure a boy with a small hand to extract the bottle. There is a record of a case [a] in which a tin cup or tumbler was pushed up the rectum and then passed into the colon where it caused gangrene and death. It was found to measure $3\frac{1}{2}$ by $3\frac{1}{2}$ by two inches. There is a French case [b] in which a preserve-pot three inches in diameter was introduced into the rectum, and had to be broken and extracted piece by piece.

Cloquet [c] had a patient who put into his rectum a beer glass and a **preserving pot**. Montanari removed from the rectum of a man a **mortar pestle** 30 cm. long, and Poulet[641] mentions a pederast who accidentally killed himself by introducing a similar instrument, 55 cm. long, which perforated his intestine. Studsgaard mentions that in the pathologic collection at Copenhagen there is a long, smooth **stone,** 17 cm. long, weighing 900 gm., which a peasant had introduced into his rectum to relieve prolapsus. The stone was extracted in 1756 by a surgeon named Frantz Dyhr. Jeffreys [d] speaks of a person who, to stop diarrhea, introduced into his rectum a piece of wood measuring seven inches.

There is a remarkable case recorded [e] of a stick in the anus of a man of sixty, the superior extremity in the right hypochondrium, the inferior in the concavity of the sacrum. The stick measured 32 cm. in length; the man recovered. It is impossible to comprehend this extent of straightening of the intestine without great twisting of the mesocolon. Tompsett [f] mentions that he was called to see a workman of sixty-five, suffering from extreme rectal hemorrhage. He found the man very feeble, without pulse, pale, and livid. By digital examination he found a hard body in the rectum, which he was sure was not feces. This body he removed with a polyp-forceps, and found it to be a cylindric candle-box, which measured six inches in circumference, $2\frac{1}{4}$ in length, and $1\frac{3}{4}$ in diameter. The removal was followed by a veritable flood of fecal material, and the man recovered. Lane [g] reports

a 218, 1855. b 297, T. iii., 177. c 446, 1844. d 476, 1868.
e 365, 1868. f 476, 1869, i., 448. g 224, May 9, 1874.

perforation of the rectum by the introduction of two large pieces of soap; there was coincident strangulated hernia.

Hunter [a] mentions a native Indian, a resident of Coorla, who had introduced a **bullock's horn** high up into his abdomen, which neither he nor his friends could extract. He was chloroformed and placed in the lithotomy position, his buttocks brought to the edge of the bed, and after dilatation of the sphincter, by traction with the fingers and tooth-forceps, the horn was extracted. It measured 11 inches long. The young imbecile had picked it up on the road, where it had been rendered extremely rough by exposure, and this caused the difficulty in extraction.

In Nelson's Northern Lancet, 1852,[582] there is the record of a case of a man at stool, who slipped on a cow's horn, which entered the rectum and lodged beyond the sphincter. It was only removed with great difficulty.

A convict at Brest [b] put up his rectum a **box of tools.** Symptoms of vomiting, meteorism, etc., began, and became more violent until the seventh day, when he died. After death, there was found in the transverse colon, a cylindric or conic box, made of sheet iron, covered with skin to protect the rectum and, doubtless, to aid expulsion. It was six inches long and five inches broad and weighed 22 ounces. It contained a piece of gun-barrel four inches long, a mother-screw steel, a screw-driver, a saw of steel for cutting wood four inches long, another saw for cutting metal, a boring syringe, a prismatic file, a half-franc piece and four one-franc pieces tied together with thread, a piece of thread, and a piece of tallow, the latter presumably for greasing the instruments. On investigation it was found that these conic cases were of common use, and were always thrust up the rectum base first. In excitement this prisoner had pushed the conic end up first, thus rendering expulsion almost impossible. Ogle [c] gives an interesting case of foreign body in the rectum of a boy of seventeen. The boy was supposed to be suffering with an abdominal tumor about the size of a pigeon's egg under the right cartilages; it had been noticed four months before. On admission to the hospital the lad was suffering with pain and jaundice; sixteen days later he passed a stick ten inches long, which he reluctantly confessed that he had introduced into the anus. During all his treatment he was conscious of the nature of his trouble, but he suffered rather than confess. Studsgaard [d] mentions a man of thirty-five who, for the purpose of stopping diarrhea, introduced into his rectum a preserve-bottle nearly seven inches long with the open end uppermost. The next morning he had violent pain in the abdomen, and the bottle could be felt through the abdominal wall. It was necessary to perform abdominal section through the linea alba, divide the sigmoid flexure, and thus remove the bottle. The intestine was sutured and the patient recovered. The bottle measured 17 cm. long, five cm. in diameter at its lower end, and three cm. at its upper end.

[a] 777, 1860.   [b] 548, 1861, ii., 564.   [c] 548, 1863, ii., 599.   [d] 425, 1878.

Briggs [a] reports a case in which a **wine glass** was introduced into the rectum, and although removed twenty-four hours afterward, death ensued. Hockenhull [b] extracted 402 stones from the rectum of a boy of seven. Landerer [c] speaks of a curious case in which the absorptive power of the rectum was utilized in the murder of a boy of fifteen. In order to come into the possession of a large inheritance the murderess poisoned the boy by introducing the ends of some **phosphorous matches** into his rectum, causing death that night; there was intense inflammation of the rectum. The woman was speedily apprehended, and committed suicide when her crime was known.

Complete transfixion of the abdomen does not always have a fatal issue. In fact, two older writers, Wisemann and Muys, testify that it is quite possible for a person to be transfixed without having any portion of the intestines or viscera wounded. In some nations in olden times, the extremest degree of punishment was transfixion by a stake. In his voyages and travels,[d] in describing the death of the King of Demaa at the hands of his page, Mendez Pinto says that instead of being reserved for torture, as were his successors Ravaillac, and Gerard, the slayer of William the Silent, the assassin was impaled alive with a long stake which was thrust in at his fundament and came out at the nape of his neck. There is a record [e] of a man of twenty-five, a soldier in the Chinese war of 1860, who, in falling from his horse, was accidentally transfixed by a bayonet. The steel entered his back two inches to the left of the last dorsal vertebra, and reappeared two inches to the left and below the umbilicus; as there was no symptom of visceral wound there were apparently no injuries except perforation of the parietes and the peritoneum. The man recovered promptly.

Ross [f] reports a case of transfixion in a young male aborigine, a native of New South Wales, who had received a spear-wound in the epigastrium during a quarrel; extraction was impossible because of the sharp-pointed barbs; the spear was, therefore, sawed off, and was removed posteriorly by means of a small incision. The edges of the wound were cleansed, stitched, and a compress and bandage applied. During the night the patient escaped and joined his comrades in the camp, and on the second day was suffering with radiating pains and distention. The following day it was found that the stitches and plaster had been removed, and the anterior wound was gaping and contained an ichorous discharge. The patient was bathing the wound with a decoction of the leaves of the red-gum tree. Notwithstanding that the spear measured seven inches, and the interference of treatment, the abdominal wound closed on the sixth day, and recovery was uninterrupted. Gilkrist [g] mentions an instance in which a ramrod was fired into a soldier's abdomen, its extremity lodging in the spinal column, without causing the slightest evidence of wounds of the intestines or viscera. A minute postmor-

a 579, 1880.   b 176, 1886–87, iii., 547.   c 156; and quoted 224, 1882, i., 498.
d London, 1663, 264.   e 548, March 30, 1861.   f 476, 1891.   g 476, 1832, ii., 147.

tem examination was held some time afterward, the soldier having died by drowning, but the results were absolutely negative as regards any injury done by the passage of the ramrod.

Humphreys[a] says that a boy of eleven, while "playing soldier" with another boy, accidentally fell on a rick-stake. The stake was slightly curved at its upper part, being 43 inches long and three inches in circumference, and sharp-pointed at its extremity. As much as $17\frac{1}{2}$ inches entered the body of the lad. The stake entered just in front of the right spermatic cord, passed beneath Poupart's ligament into the cavity of the abdomen, traversed the whole cavity across to the left side ; it then entered the thorax by perforating the diaphragm, displaced the heart by pushing it to the right of the sternum, and pierced the left lung. It then passed anteriorly under the muscles and integument in the axillary space, along the upper third of the humerus, which was extended beyond the head, the external skin not being ruptured. The stick remained in situ for four hours before attempts at extraction were made. On account of the displacement of the heart it was decided not to give chloroform. The boy was held down by four men, and Humphreys and his assistant made all the traction in their power. After removal not more than a teaspoonful of blood followed. The heart still remained displaced, and a lump of intestine about the size of an orange protruded from the wound and was replaced. The boy made a slow and uninterrupted recovery, and in six weeks was able to sit up. The testicle sloughed, but five months later, when the boy was examined, he was free from pain and able to walk. There was a slight enlargement of the abdomen and a cicatrix of the wound in the right groin. The right testicle was absent, and the apex of the heart was displaced about an inch.

Woodbury[b] reports the case of a girl of fourteen, who fell seven or eight feet directly upon an erect stake in a cart ; the tuberosity was first struck, and then the stake passed into the anus, up the rectum for two inches, thence through the rectal wall, and through the body in an obliquely upward direction. Striking the ribs near the left nipple it fractured three, and made its exit. The stake was three inches in circumference, and 27 inches of its length passed into the body, six or seven inches emerging from the chest. This girl recovered so rapidly that she was able to attend school six weeks afterward. In a case reported by Bailey[c] a middle-aged woman, while sliding down a hay-stack, struck directly upon a pitchfork handle which entered the vagina ; the whole weight of the woman was successfully maintained by the cellular tissue of the uterovaginal culdesac.

Minot[d] speaks of the passage of one prong of a pitchfork through the body of a man of twenty-one, from the perineum to the umbilicus ; the man recovered.

Hamilton[e] reports a case of laceration of the perineum with penetration

a 548, 1871, ii., 392. b 579, 1874, xiv., 151. c Ibid
d 218, 1861, 80. e Trans. Belmont M. Soc., Bridgeport, Ohio, 1849–50, 55.

of the pelvic cavity to the depth of ten inches by a stick $\frac{3}{4}$ inch thick. Prowse [a] mentions the history of a case of impalement in a man of thirty-four, who, coming down a hay-stack, alighted on the handle of a pitchfork which struck him in the middle of the scrotum, and passed up between the skin and fascia to the 10th rib. Recovery was prompt.

There are several cases on record in which extensive wounds of the abdominal parietes with protrusion and injury to the intestine have not been followed by death. Injuries to the intestines themselves have already been spoken of, but there are several cases of **evisceration** worthy of record.

Doughty [b] says that at midnight on June 7, 1868, he was called to see a man who had been stabbed in a street altercation with a negro. When first seen in the street, the patient was lying on his back with his abdomen exposed, from which protruded an enormous mass of intestines, which were covered with sand and grit ; the small intestine (ileum) was incised at one point and scratched at another by the passing knife. The incision, about an inch in length, was closed with a single stitch of silk thread, and after thorough cleansing the whole mass was returned to the abdominal cavity. In this hernial protrusion were recognized four or five feet of the ileum, the cecum with its appendix, part of the ascending colon with corresponding portions of the mesentery ; the distribution of the superior mesentery, made more apparent by its living pulsation, was more beautifully displayed in its succession of arches than in any dissection that Doughty had ever witnessed. Notwithstanding the extent of his injuries the patient recovered, and at last reports was doing finely.

Barnes [c] reports the history of a negro of twenty-five who was admitted to the Freedmen's Hospital, New Orleans, May 15, 1867, suffering from an incised wound of the abdomen, from which protruded eight inches of colon, all of the stomach, and nearly the whole of the small intestines. About $2\frac{1}{2}$ feet of the small intestine, having a whitish color, appeared to be filled with food and had much of the characteristic feeling of a sausage. The rest of the small intestine had a dark-brown color, and the stomach and colon, distended with gas, were leaden-colored. The viscera had been exposed to the atmosphere for over an hour. Having nothing but cold Mississippi water to wash them with, Barnes preferred returning the intestines without any attempt at removing blood and dirt further than wiping with a cambric handkerchief and the stripping they would naturally be subjected to in being returned through the opening. In ten minutes they were returned ; they were carefully examined inch by inch for any wound, but none was found. Three silver sutures were passed through the skin, and a firm compress applied. The patient went to sleep shortly after his wound was dressed, and never had a single subsequent bad symptom ; he was discharged on May 24th, the wound being entirely healed, with the exception of a cartilage of a rib which had not reunited.

a 224, 1884, ii., 20.   b 847, 93.   c 847, 95.

Rogers[a] mentions the case of a carpenter of thirty-six who was struck by a missile thrown by a circular saw, making a wound two inches above the umbilicus and to the left. Through the opening a mass of intestines and a portion of the liver, attached by a pedicle, protruded. A portion of the liver was detached, and the liver, as well as the intestines, were replaced, and the man recovered.

Baillie,[b] Bhadoory,[c] Barker, Edmundson,[d] Johnson,[e] and others, record instances of abdominal wounds accompanied by extensive protrusion of the intestines, and recovery. Shah[f] mentions an abdominal wound with protrusion of three feet of small intestine. By treatment with ice, phenol, and opium, recovery was effected without peritonitis.

Among **nonfatal perforating gunshot wounds of the abdomen,** Loring[g] reports the case of a private in the First Artillery who recovered after a double gunshot perforation of the abdomen. One of the balls entered $5\frac{1}{2}$ inches to the left of the umbilicus, and two inches above the crest of the ilium, making its exit two inches above the crest of the ilium, on a line with and two inches from the 4th lumbar vertebra. The other ball entered four inches below and to the rear of the left nipple, making its exit four inches directly below the point of entrance. In their passages these balls did not wound any of the viscera, and with the exception of traumatic fever there was no disturbance of the health of the patient. Schell[h] records the case of a soldier who was wounded July 3, 1867, by a conoid ball from a Remington revolver of the Army pattern. The ball entered on the left side of the abdomen, its lower edge grazing the center of Poupart's ligament, and passing backward, inward, and slightly upward, emerged one inch to the left of the spinous process of the sacrum. On July 6th all the symptoms of peritonitis made their appearance. On July 11th there was free discharge of fecal matter from both anterior and posterior wounds. This discharge continued for three days and then ceased. By August 12th both wounds were entirely healed. Mineer[i] reports a case of a wound from a revolver-ball entering the abdomen, passing through the colon, and extracted just above the right ilium. Under simple treatment the patient recovered and was returned to duty about ten weeks afterward.

There are a number of cases on record in which a **bullet entering the abdominal cavity** is subsequently **voided** either **by the bladder or by the bowel.** Ducachet[j] mentions two cases at the Georgetown Seminary Hospital during the late war in which Minié balls entering the abdominal wall were voided by the anus in a much battered condition. Bartlett[k] reports the case of a young man who was accidentally shot in the abdomen with a Colt's revolver. Immediately after the accident he complained of constant and press-

a 269, 1875, 884. b 435, 1866, i., 9. c 435, 1872, vii., 135.
d 312, xxxvi., 209. e 536, 1867, iii., 225. f 435, ix., 297.
g 847, 55. h 847, 48. i Ibid. j 130, 1863, vii., 134. k 331, 1856.

ing desire to void his urine.   While urinating on the evening of the third day, the ball escaped from the urethra and fell with a click into the chamber. After the discharge of the ball the intolerable symptoms improved, and in two or three weeks there was complete recovery.   Hoag mentions a man who was wounded by a round musket-ball weighing 400 grains.   It had evidently passed through the lung and diaphragm and entered the alimentary canal ; it was voided by the rectum five days after the injury.   Lenox [a] mentions the fact of a bullet entering the abdominal wall and subsequently being passed from the rectum.   Day and Judkins report similar cases.   Rundle [b] speaks of the lodgment of a bullet, and its escape, after a period of seven and one-half years, into the alimentary canal, causing internal strangulation and death.

Wounds of the liver often end very happily, and there are many cases on record in which such injuries have been followed by recovery, even when associated with considerable loss of liver-substance.   In the older records, Glandorp [380] and Scultetus mention cures after large wounds of the liver. Fabricius Hildanus reports a case that ended happily, in which a piece of liver was found in the wound, having been separated by a sword-thrust.   There is a remarkable example [c] of recovery after multiple visceral wounds, self-inflicted by a lunatic.   This man had 18 wounds, 14 having penetrated the abdomen, the liver, colon, and the jejunum being injured ; by frequent bleeding, strict regimen, dressing, etc., he recovered his health and senses, but relapsing a year and a half later, he again attempted suicide, which gave the opportunity for a postmortem to learn the extent of the original injuries. Plater,[635] Schenck, Cabrolius,[245] the Ephemerides, and Nolleson [d] mention recovery after wounds of the liver.   Salmuth [706] and the Ephemerides report questionable instances in which portions of the liver were ejected in violent vomiting.   Macpherson [e] describes a wound of the liver occurring in a Hindoo of sixty who had been struck by a spear.   A portion of the liver was protruding, and a piece weighing $1\frac{1}{4}$ ounces was removed, complete recovery following.

Postempski [f] mentions a case of suture of the liver after a stab-wound.   Six sutures of chromicized cat-gut were carefully tightened and fastened with a single loop.   The patient left his bed on the sixth day and completely recovered.   Gann [g] reports a case of harpoon-wound of the liver.   While in a dory spearing fish in the Rio Nuevo, after a sudden lurch of the boat, a young man of twenty-eight fell on the sharp point of a harpoon, which penetrated his abdomen.   About one inch of the harpoon was seen protruding from below the tip of the ensiform cartilage ; the harpoon was seven inches long.   It was found that the instrument had penetrated the right lobe of the liver ; on passing the hand backward along the inferior surface of the liver, the point

a 250, 1872–73, 112.   b 548, 1866, i., 306.   c Mém. de l'Acad. Roy. des Sciences, 1705.
d 462, T. xxii., 258.   e 661, 1846.   f 684, June 9, 1888.   g 476, 1894, i., 1371.

could be felt projecting through its posterior border. On account of two sharp barbs on the spear-point, it was necessary to push the harpoon further in to disengage the barbs, after which it was easily removed. Recovery followed, and the patient was discharged in twenty-one days.

Romme[a] discusses the subject of punctured wounds of the liver, as a special text using the case of the late President Carnot. He says that in 543 cases of traumatism of the liver collected by Elder, 65 were caused by cutting or sharp-pointed instruments. Of this group, 23 recovered and 42 died. The chief causes of death were hemorrhage and peritonitis. The principal symptoms of wounds of the liver, such as traumatic shock, collapse, local and radiating pains, nausea, vomiting, and respiratory disturbances were all present in the case of President Carnot. From an experience gained in the case of the President, Romme strongly recommends exploratory celiotomy in all penetrating wounds of the liver. Zeidler[b] reports three cases of wound of the liver in which recovery ensued. The hemorrhage in one case was arrested by the tampon, and in the other by the Pacquelin cautery.

McMillan[c] describes a man of twenty who was kicked by a horse over the liver and rupturing that organ. A large quantity of offensive fluid was drawn off from the liver, and the man recovered. Frazer[d] reports a case of rupture of liver and kidney in a boy of thirteen who was squeezed between the tire and driving chain of a mill, but who recovered despite his serious symptoms. Allen[e] mentions recovery after an extensive incised wound of the abdomen, liver, and lung. Massie[f] cites an instance of gunshot wound of the right hypochondrium, with penetration and protrusion of the liver. The patient, a boy of seven, recovered after excision of a small part of the protruding liver. Lawson Tait has incised the liver to the extent of three inches, evacuated two gallons of hydatids, and obtained successful recovery in ten weeks.

There are several cases of wound of the liver followed by recovery reported by surgeons of the United States Army.[g] Whitehead mentions a man of twenty-two who on June 3, 1867, was shot in the liver by a slug from a pistol. At the time of the injury he bled freely from the wound of entrance, continuing to lose blood and bile until daylight the next morning, when the hemorrhage ceased, but the flow of bile kept on. By June 10th there was considerable improvement, but the wound discharged blood-clots, bile, and serum. When the patient left the hospital on July 15th the wound was healthy, discharging less than 1½ ounces during the twenty-four hours, of a mixture of free bile, and bile mixed with thick material. When last heard from—July 27, 1867—the patient was improving finely in flesh and strength. McKee mentions a commissary-sergeant stationed at Santa Fé,

a La Tribune Médicale, July 5, 1894.   b 300, Sept. 13, 1894.   c 476, 1860, ii., 431.
d 536, 1878, 200.   e 591, 1855.   f 593, ix., 146.   g 847, 49.

New Mexico, who recovered after a gunshot wound of the liver. Hassig reports the case of a private of twenty-six who was wounded in a fray near Paducah, Kentucky, by a conoid ball, which passed through the liver. The ball was cut out the same day. The patient recovered and was returned to duty in May, 1868. Patzki mentioned a private in the Sixth Cavalry, aged twenty-five, who recovered from a gunshot wound of the abdomen, penetrating the right lobe of the liver and the gall-bladder.

Resection of the Liver.—It is remarkable to what extent portions of the liver may be resected by the knife, cautery, or ligature, and the patient

Fig. 222.—Floating liver (Keen and White).

recover. Langenbuch records a case in which he successfully removed the greater portion of the left lobe of a woman of thirty. The lobe had been extensively deformed by tight lacing, and caused serious inconvenience. There was considerable hemorrhage, but the vessels were secured, and the woman made a good recovery. [845] McWhinnie, in The Lancet, records a case of dislodgment of an enlarged liver from tight lacing. Terrilon [a] mentions an instance in which a portion of the liver was removed by ligature after celiotomy. The ligature was removed in seven days, and the sphacelated portion of the liver came off with it. A cicatrix was completed at the end of six weeks, and the patient, a woman of fifty-three, made an excellent recovery. Bastianelli [b] discusses those cases in which portions of the liver, having been constricted from the general body of the organ and remaining attached by a pedicle, give rise to movable tumors of the abdomen. He records such a case in a woman of thirty-seven who had five children. A piece of liver weighing 500 grams was removed, and with it the gall-bladder, and the patient made an uninterrupted recovery. Tricomi reports a case in which it was found necessary to remove the left lobe of the liver. An attempt had been made to remove a liver-tumor the size of a fist by constricting the base with an elastic ligature. This attempt was a failure, and cure was also un-

a Quoted 536, 1890, ii., 263.

b 843, 236.

successfully attempted by wire ligature and the thermocautery. The growth was cut away, bleeding was arrested by the thermocautery and by iron-solution, the wound entirely healed, and the patient recovered. Valerian von Meister has proved that the liver has marvelous powers of regeneration, and that in rabbits, cats, and dogs, even three-fourths of the organ may be reproduced in from forty-five to sixty-five days. This regeneration is brought about chiefly by hypertrophy of the lobules.[a]

Floating liver is a rare malady in which the liver forms an abdominal prominence that may be moved about, and which changes its situation as the patient shifts the attitude. The condition usually arises from a lax abdominal wall following repeated pregnancies. The accompanying illustration (Fig. 222) exhibits a typical case verified by postmortem examination.[845]

Hypertrophy of the Liver.—The average weight of the normal liver is from 50 to 55 ounces, but as noted by Powell,[642] it may become so hypertrophic as to weigh as much as 40 pounds. Bonet describes a liver weighing 18 pounds ; and in his "Medical and Surgical Observations," Gooch speaks of a liver weighing 28 pounds. Vieussens, the celebrated anatomist,[b] reports an instance in which the liver weighed 20 pounds, and in his "Aphorisms," Vetter cites a similar instance. In 1811 Kraus of Germany describes a liver weighing 25 pounds ; modern instances of enlarged liver are too numerous to be quoted here.

Rupture of the gall-bladder, although generally followed by death, is not always fatal. In such cases bile is usually found in the abdominal cavity. Fergus [c] mentions a case in which, after this accident, the patient was considered convalescent and was walking about, when, on the seventh day, peritonitis suddenly developed and proved fatal in two days. Several cases of this accident have been reported as treated successfully by incision and drainage (Lane) or by inspiration (Bell). In these cases large quantities of bile escaped into the abdominal cavity. Peritonitis does not necessarily follow.[845]   **Cholecystotomy** for the relief of the distention of the gall-bladder from obstruction of the common or cystic duct and for the removal of gall-stones was first performed in 1867 by Bobbs of Indianapolis, but it is to Marion Sims, in 1878, that perfection of the operation is due. It has been gradually improved and developed, until to-day it is a most successful operation. Tait reports 54 cases with 52 perfect recoveries. **Cholyecystectomy,** or excision of the gall-bladder, was first practised in 1880 by Langenbuch of Berlin, and is used in cases in which gall-stones are repeatedly forming. Ashhurst's statistics show only four deaths in 28 cases.

At St. Bartholomew's Hospital, in London, is a preserved specimen of a gall-bladder which had formed the contents of a hernial sac, and which, near the fundus, shows a constriction caused by the femoral ring. It was

a 843, 237.   b "Traite des Mal. Internes," T. ii.   c 174, 400.

taken from a woman of forty-five who was admitted into the hospital with a strangulated femoral hernia. The sac was opened and its contents were returned. The woman died in a few days from peritonitis. The gall-bladder was found close to the femoral ring, and showed a marked constriction. The liver was misshapen from tight lacing, elongated and drawn downward toward the ring. There was no evidence that any portion of intestine or other structure besides the gall-bladder had passed through the ring.[619]

The fatality of **rupture of the spleen** is quite high. Out of 83 cases of injury to this organ collected by Elder, and quoted by MacCormac, only 11 recovered; but the mortality is less in **punctured or incised wounds** of this organ, the same authorities mentioning 29 recoveries out of 35 cases. In his "Surgery" Gooch says that at the battle of Dettingen one of Sir Robert Rich's Dragoons was left all night on the field, weltering in his blood, his spleen hanging out of his body in a gangrenous state. The next morning he was carried to the surgeons who ligated the large vessels, and extirpated the spleen; the man recovered and was soon able to do duty. In the Philosophical Transactions[a] there is a report of a man who was wounded in the spleen by a large hunting-knife. Fergusson found the spleen hanging from the wound and ligated it. It separated in ten days and the patient recovered.

Williams[b] reports a stab-wound of the spleen in a negro of twenty-one. The spleen protruded, and the protruding part was ligated by a silver wire, one-half of the organ sloughing off; the patient recovered. Sir Astley Cooper mentions a curious case, in which, after vomiting, during which the spleen was torn from its attachments, this organ produced a swelling in the groin which was supposed to be a hernia. The vomiting continued, and at the end of a week the woman died; it was then found that the spleen had been turned half round on its axis, and detached from the diaphragm; it had become enlarged; the twist interrupted the return of the blood. Portal[c] speaks of a rupture of the spleen simply from engorgement. There was no history of a fall, contusion, or other injury. Tait[d] describes a case of rupture of the spleen in a woman who, in attempting to avoid her husband's kick, fell on the edge of the table. There were no signs of external violence, but she died the third day afterward. The abdomen was found full of blood, and the spleen and peritoneal covering was ruptured for three inches.

Splenectomy, excision of the spleen, has been performed a number of times, with varying results, but is more successful when performed for injury than when for disease. Ashhurst[174] has tabulated a total of 109 operations, 27 having been for traumatic causes, and all but five having terminated successfully; of 82 operations for disease, only 32 recovered. Vulpius has collected 117 cases of splenectomy, with a death-rate of 50 per cent. If, how-

a 629, 1738.   b 230, xii., 86.   c 39, T. v., 345.   d 605, 1844, i., 104.

ever, from these cases we deduct those suffering with leukocythemia and lardaceous spleen, in which the operation should not be performed, the mortality in the remaining 85 cases is reduced to 33 per cent. Terrier speaks of splenectomy for torsion or twisting of the pedicle, and such is mentioned by Sir Astley Cooper, who has found records of only four such cases. Conklin[a] reports a successful case of splenectomy for malarial spleen, and in reviewing the subject he says that the records of the past decade in operations for simple hypertrophy, including malaria, show 20 recoveries and eight deaths. He also adds that extirpation in cases of floating or displaced spleen was attended with brilliant results. Zuccarelli[b] is accredited with reporting two cases of splenectomy for malarial spleen, both of which recovered early. He gives a table of splenectomies performed in Italy, in which there were nine cases of movable spleen, with two deaths; eight cases of simple hypertrophy, with three deaths; 12 cases of malarial spleen, with three deaths; four cases of leukemia and pseudoleukemia, with two deaths. In his experiments on rabbits it was proved by Tizzoni, and in his experiments on dogs, by Credé, that an individual could live without a spleen; but these observations were only confirmatory of what had long been known, for, in 1867, Péan successfully removed a spleen from a woman of twenty. Tricomi[c] reports eight cases in which he had extirpated the spleen for various morbid conditions, with a fortunate issue in all but one. In one case he ligated the splenic artery. In The Lancet[d] there is an account of three recent excisions of the spleen for injury at St. Thomas Hospital in London, and it is added that they are among the first of this kind in Great Britain.

Abnormalities of Size of the Spleen.—The spleen may be extremely small. Storck[e] mentions a spleen that barely weighed an ounce; Schenck speaks of one in the last century that weighed as much as 20 pounds. Frank[351] describes a spleen that weighed 16 pounds; there is another record of one weighing 15 pounds.[f] Elliot[g] mentions a spleen weighing 11 pounds; Burrows[h] one, 11 pounds; Blasius, four pounds; Osiander, nine pounds; Blanchard,[213] 3½ pounds; Richardson,[i] 3½ pounds; and Hare,[j] 93 ounces.

The thoracic duct, although so much protected by its anatomical position, under exceptional circumstances has been **ruptured or wounded.** Kirchner[k] has collected 17 cases of this nature, two of which were due to contusions of the chest, one each to a puncture, a cut, and a shot-wound, and three to erosion from suppuration. In the remaining cases the account fails to assign a definite cause. Chylothorax, or chylous ascites, is generally a result of this injury. Krabbel mentions a patient who was run over by an empty coal car, and who died on the fifth day from suffocation due to an effusion into the right pleural cavity. On postmortem examination it was found

a 538, July 28, 1894.   b 843, 252.   c Ibid.
d Quoted Amer. Med. Review, Dec., 1895   e 752, i., 114.   f 282, 1732, 260.
g 524, vii., 46.   h 528, vii.   i 548, 1852, ii., 399.   j 548, 1861, i., 289.   k 845, 454.

that the effusion was chyle, the thoracic duct being torn just opposite the 9th dorsal vertebra, which had been transversely fractured. In one of Kirchner's cases a girl of nine had been violently pushed against a window-sill, striking the front of her chest in front of the 3d rib. She suffered from pleural effusion, which, on aspiration, proved to be chyle. She ultimately recovered her health. In 1891 Eyer reported a case of rupture of the thoracic duct, causing death on the thirty-eighth day. The young man had been caught between a railroad car and an engine, and no bones were broken.

Manley[a] reports a case of rupture of the thoracic duct in a man of thirty-five, who was struck by the pole of a brewery wagon; he was knocked down on his back, the wheel passing squarely over his abdomen. There was subsequent bulging low down in the right iliac fossa, caused by the presence of a fluid, which chemic and microscopic examination proved was chyle. From five to eight ounces a day of this fluid were discharged, until the tenth day, when the bulging was opened and drained. On the fifteenth day the wound was healed and the man left the hospital quite restored to health.

Keen has reported four instances of accidental injury to the thoracic duct, near its termination at the base of the left side of the neck; the wounding was in the course of removals for deep-seated growths in this region. Three of the cases recovered, having sustained no detriment from the injury to the thoracic duct. One died; but the fatal influence was not specially connected with the wound of the duct.

Possibly the boldest operation in the history of surgery is that for **ligation of the abdominal aorta** for inguinal aneurysm. It was first practised by Sir Astley Cooper in 1817, and has since been performed several times with a uniformly fatal result, although Monteiro's patient survived until the tenth day, and there is a record in which ligature of the abdominal aorta did not cause death until the eleventh day.[b] Loreta of Bologna is accredited with operating on December 18, 1885, for the relief of a sailor who was suffering from an abdominal aneurysm caused by a blow. An incision was made from the ensiform cartilage to the umbilicus, the aneurysm exposed, and its cavity filled up with two meters of silver-plated wire. Twenty days after no evidence of pulsation remained in the sac, and three months later the sailor was well and able to resume his duties.

Ligation of the common iliac artery, which, in a case of gunshot injury, was first practised by Gibson of Philadelphia in 1812, is, happily, not always fatal. Of 82 cases collected by Ashhurst, 23 terminated successfully.

Foreign bodies loose in the abdominal cavity are sometimes voided at stool, or may suppurate externally. Fabricius Hildanus[334] gives us a history of a person wounded with a sword-thrust into the abdomen, the point break-

a 533, lxv.,1894, 491.   b 810, 1853.

ing off. The sword remained one year in the belly and was voided at stool. Erichsen [a] mentions an instance in which a cedar lead-pencil stayed for eight months in the abdominal cavity. Desgranges [b] gives a case of a fish-spine in the abdominal cavity, and ten years afterward it ulcerated through an abscess in the abdominal wall. Keetley [c] speaks of a man who was shot when a boy ; at the time of the accident the boy had a small spelling-book in his pocket. It was not until adult life that from an abscess of the groin was expelled what remained of the spelling-book that had been driven into the abdomen during boyhood. Kyle [d] speaks of the removal of a corn-straw 33 inches in length by an incision ten inches long, at a point about equidistant from the umbilicus to the anterior spinous process of the right ilium.

There are several instances on record of tolerance of **foreign bodies in the skin and muscles of the back** for an extended period. Gay [e] speaks of a curious case in which the point of a sheath-knife remained in the back of an individual for nine years. Bush reported to Sir Astley Cooper [f] the history of a man who, as he supposed, received a wound in the back by canister shot while serving on a Tartar privateer in 1779. There was no ship-surgeon on board, and in about a month the wound healed without surgical assistance. The man suffered little inconvenience and performed his duties as a seaman, and was impressed into the Royal Navy. In August, 1810, he complained of pain in the lumbar region. He was submitted to an examination, and a cicatrix of this region was noticed, and an extraneous body about $\frac{1}{2}$ inch under the integument was felt. An incision was made down it, and a rusty blade of a seaman's clasp-knife extracted from near the 3d lumbar vertebra. The man had carried this knife for thirty years. The wound healed in a few days and there was no more inconvenience.

Fracture of the lower part of the spine is not always fatal, and notwithstanding the lay-idea that a broken back means certain death, patients with well-authenticated cases of vertebral fracture have recovered. Warren [g] records the case of a woman of sixty who, while carrying a clothes-basket, made a misstep and fell 14 feet, the basket of wet clothes striking the right shoulder, chest, and neck. There was fracture of the 4th dorsal vertebra at the transverse processes. By seizing the spinous process it could be bent backward and forward, with the peculiar crepitus of fractured bone. The clavicle was fractured two inches from the acromial end, and the sternal end was driven high up into the muscles of the neck. The arm and hand were paralyzed, and the woman suffered great dyspnea. There was at first a grave emphysematous condition due to the laceration of several broken ribs. There was also suffusion and ecchymosis about the neck and shoulder. Although complicated with tertiary syphilis, the woman made a fair recovery,

a 550, 1855, 15.   b 463, iii., 343.   c 536, 1884, ii., 419.
d Western Lancet, Cincinnati, 1848.   e 218, 1850.   f 550, 1817.   g 520, 1882.

and eight weeks later she walked into a doctor's office.   Many similar and equally wonderful injuries to the spine are on record.

The results sometimes following the operation of **laminectomy** for fracture of the vertebræ are often marvelous.   One of the most successful on record is that reported by Dundore.[a]   The patient was a single man who lived in Mahanoy, Pa., and was admitted to the State Hospital for Injured Persons, Ashland, Pa., June 17, 1889, suffering from a partial dislocation of the 9th dorsal vertebra.   The report is as follows :—" He had been a laborer in the mines, and while working was injured March 18, 1889, by a fall of top rock, and from this date to that of his admission had been under the care of a local physician without any sign of improvement.   At the time of his admission he weighed but 98 pounds, his weight previous to the injury being 145.   He exhibited entire loss of motion in the lower extremities, with the exception of very slight movement in the toes of the left foot ; sensation was almost *nil* up to the hips, above which it was normal ; he had complete retention of urine, with a severe cystitis.   His tongue was heavily coated, the bowels constipated, and there was marked anorexia, with considerable anemia.   His temperature varied from 99° to 100° in the morning, and from 101° to 103° in the evening.   The time which had elapsed since the accident precluded any attempt at reduction, and his anemic condition would not warrant a more radical method.

" He was put on light, nourishing diet, iron and strychnin were given internally, and electricity was applied to the lower extremities every other day ; the cystitis was treated by irrigating the bladder each day with Thiersch's solution.   By August his appetite and general condition were much improved, and his weight had increased to 125 pounds, his temperature being 99° or less each morning, and seldom as high as 100° at night.   The cystitis had entirely disappeared, and he was able, with some effort, to pass his urine without the aid of a catheter.   Sensation in both extremities had slightly improved, and he was able to slightly move the toes of the right foot.   This being his condition, an operation was proposed as the only means of further and permanent improvement, and to this he eagerly consented, and, accordingly, on the 25th of August, the 9th dorsal vertebra was trephined.

" The cord was found to be compressed and greatly congested, but there was no evidence of laceration.   The laminæ and spinous processes of the 8th and 9th dorsal vertebræ were cut away, thus relieving all pressure on the cord ; the wound was drained and sutured, and a plaster-of-Paris jacket applied, a hole being cut out over the wound for the purpose of changing the dressing when necessary.   By September 1st union was perfect, and for the next month the patient remained in excellent condition, but without any sign of improvement as to sensation and motion.   Early in October he was able

a 533, Nov. 24, 1894.

to slightly move both legs, and had full control of urination; from this time on his paralysis rapidly improved; the battery was applied daily, with massage morning and evening; and in November the plaster-of-Paris jacket was removed, and he propelled himself about the ward in a rolling chair, and shortly after was able to get about slowly on crutches. He was discharged December 23d, and when I saw him six months later he walked very well and without effort; he carried a cane, but this seemed more from habit than from necessity. At present date he weighs 150 pounds, and drives a huckster wagon for a living, showing very little loss of motion in his lower extremities."

Although few cases show such wonderful improvement as this one, statistics prove that the results of this operation are sometimes most advantageous. Thorburn [a] collects statistics of 50 operations from 1814 to 1885, undertaken for relief of injuries of the spinal cord. Lloyd [b] has compiled what is possibly the most extensive collection of cases of spinal surgery, his cases including operations for both disease and injury. White has collected 37 cases of recent date; and Chipault [c] reports two cases, and collected 33 cases. Quite a tribute to the modern treatment by antisepsis is shown in the results of laminectomy. Of his non-antiseptic cases Lloyd reports a mortality of 65 per cent.; those surviving the operation are distributed as follows: Cured, one; partially cured, seven; unknown, two; no improvement, five. Of those cases operated upon under modern antiseptic principles, the mortality was 50 per cent.; those surviving were distributed as follows: Cured, four; partially cured, 15; no improvement, 11. The mortality in White's cases, which were all done under antiseptic precautions, was 38 per cent. Of those surviving, there were six complete recoveries, six with benefit, and 11 without marked benefit. Pyle [d] collects 52 cases of spinal disease and injury, in which laminectomy was performed. All the cases were operated upon since 1890. Of the 52 cases there were 15 deaths (a mortality of 29.4 per cent.), 26 recoveries with benefit, and five recoveries in which the ultimate result has not been observed. It must be mentioned that several of the fatal cases reported were those of cervical fracture, which is by far the most fatal variety.

Injury to the spinal cord does not necessarily cause immediate death. Mills and O'Hara, both of Philadelphia, have recorded instances of recovery after penetrating wound of the spinal marrow. [e] Eve [f] reports three cases of gunshot wound in which the balls lodged in the vertebral canal, two of the patients recovering. He adds some remarks on the division of the spinal cord without immediate death.

Ford [g] mentions a gunshot wound of the spinal cord, the patient living ten days; after death the ball was found in the ascending aorta. Henley [h] speaks of a mulatto of twenty-four who was stabbed in the back with a knife. The

a 224, No. 1747, 1894.   b 124, July, 1891.   c 162, 1890, ii., 673.   d 150, June, 1894.
e 547, 1879, ix., 265.   f 124, lvi., 103.   g 744, 1866, i., 286.   h 538, 1874, ix., 423.

blade entered the body of the 6th dorsal vertebra, and was so firmly embedded that the patient could be raised entirely clear of the bed by the knife alone. An ultimate recovery ensued.

Although the word **hernia** can be construed to mean the protrusion of any viscus from its natural cavity through normal or artificial openings in the surrounding structures, the usual meaning of the word is protrusion of the abdominal contents through the parietes—what is commonly spoken of as rupture. Hernia may be congenital or acquired, or may be single or multiple —as many as five having been seen in one individual.[a] More than two-thirds of cases of rupture suffer from inguinal hernia. In the oblique form of inguinal hernia the abdominal contents descend along the inguinal canal to the outer side of the epigastric artery, and enter the scrotum in the male, and the labium majus in the female. In this form of hernia the size of the sac is sometimes enormous, the accompanying illustration showing extreme cases of both scrotal and labial hernia [845] (Plate 7). Umbilical hernia may be classed under three heads: congenital, infantile, and adult. Congenital umbilical hernia occurs most frequently in children, and is brought about by the failure of the abdominal walls to close.

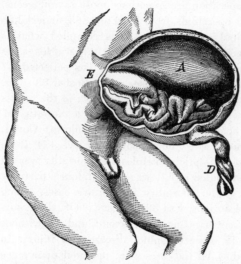

Fig. 223.—Congenital umbilical hernia. A, liver; C, intestine; D, cord; E, pedicle.

When of large size it may contain not only the intestines, but various other organs, such as the spleen, liver, etc. (Fig. 223). In some monsters all the abdominal contents are contained in the hernia. Infantile umbilical hernia is common, and appears after the separation of the umbilical cord; it is caused by the yielding of the cicatrix in this situation. It never reaches a large size, and shows a tendency to spontaneous cure. Adult umbilical hernia rarely commences in infancy. It is most commonly seen in persons with pendulous bellies, and is sometimes of enormous size, in addition to the ordinary abdominal contents, containing even the stomach and uterus. A few years since there was a man in Philadelphia past middle age, the victim of adult umbilical hernia so pendulous that while walking he had to support it with his arms and hands. It was said that this hernia did not enlarge until after his service as a soldier in the late war.

PLATE 7.

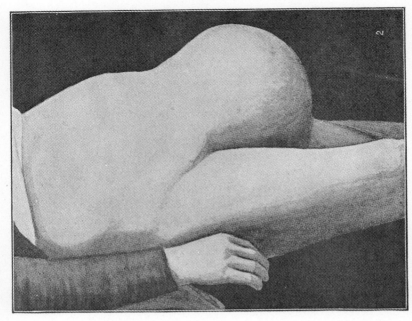

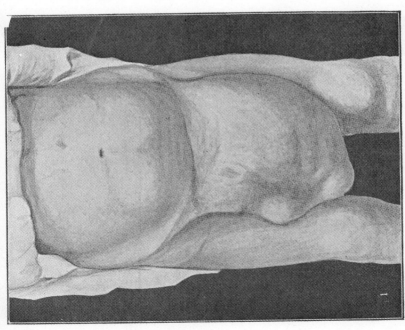

Fig. 1.—Large scrotal hernia.   Fig. 2.—Large labial hernia (Keen and White).

Abbott[a] recites the case of an Irish woman of thirty-five who applied to know if she was pregnant. No history of a hernia could be elicited. No pregnancy existed, but there was found a ventral hernia of the abdominal viscera through an opening which extended the entire length of the linea alba, and which was four inches wide in the middle of the abdomen.

Pim[b] saw a colored woman of twenty-four who, on December 29, 1858, was delivered normally of her first child, and who died in bed at 3 A. M. on February 12, 1859. The postmortem showed a tumor from the ensiform cartilage to the symphysis pubis, which contained the omentum, liver (left lobe), small intestines, and colon. It rested upon the abdominal muscles of the right side. The pelvic viscera were normally placed and there was no inguinal nor femoral hernia.

Hulke[c] reports a case remarkable for the immense size of the rupture which protruded from a spot weakened by a former abscess. There was a partial absence of the peritoneal sac, and the obstruction readily yielded to a clyster and laxative. The rupture had a transverse diameter of $14\frac{1}{2}$ inches, with a vertical diameter of $11\frac{1}{2}$ inches. The opening was in the abdominal walls outside of the internal inguinal ring. The writhings of the intestines were very conspicuous through the walls of the pouch.

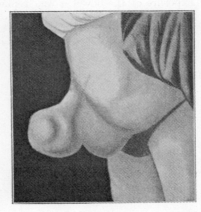

Dade[d] reports a case of prodigious umbilical hernia (Fig. 224). The patient was a widow of fifty-eight, a native of Ireland. Her family history was good, and she had never borne any

Fig. 224.—Prodigious umbilical hernia (Dade).

children. The present dimensions of the tumor, which for fifteen years had been accompanied with pain, and had progressively increased in size, are as follows: Circumference at the base, $19\frac{1}{2}$ inches; circumference at the extremity, $11\frac{1}{4}$ inches; distance of extremity from abdominal wall, $12\frac{3}{4}$ inches. Inspection showed a large lobulated tumor protruding from the abdominal wall at the umbilicus. The veins covering it were prominent and distended. The circulation of the skin was defective, giving it a blue appearance. Vermicular contractions of the small intestines could be seen at the distance of ten feet. The tumor was soft and velvety to the touch, and could only partially be reduced. Borborygmus could be easily heard. On percussion the note over the bulk was tympanitic, and dull at the base. The distal extremity contained a portion of the small intestine instead of the

a 218, lxv., 161.   b 703, xvii., 224.
c 476, 1878, 693.   d Louisville Med. Monthly, Feb., 1895.

colon, which Wood considered the most frequent occupant. The umbilicus was completely obliterated. Dade believed that this hernia was caused by the weakening of the abdominal walls from a blow, and considered that the protrusion came from an aperture near the umbilicus and not through it, in this manner differing from congenital umbilical hernia.

A peculiar form of hernia is **spontaneous rupture of the abdominal walls,** which, however, is very rare. There is an account of such a case[a] in a woman of seventy-two living in Pittsburg, who, after a spasmodic cough, had a spontaneous rupture of the parietes. The rent was four inches in length and extended along the linea alba, and through it protruded a mass of omentum about the size of a child's head. It was successfully treated and the woman recovered. Wallace[b] reports a case of spontaneous rupture of the abdominal wall, following a fit of coughing. The skin was torn and a large coil of ileum protruded, uncovered by peritoneum. After protracted exposure of the bowel it was replaced, the rent was closed, and the patient recovered.

a 545, 1862, vii., 53.   b 436, 1881, 340.

CHAPTER XIII.

SURGICAL ANOMALIES OF THE GENITO-URINARY SYSTEM.

Wounds of the kidney may be very severe without causing death, and even one entire kidney may be lost without interfering with the functions of life. Marvand,[a] the Surgeon-Major of an Algerian regiment, reports the case of a young Arab woman who had been severely injured in the right lumbar region by a weapon called a "yataghan," an instrument which has only one cutting edge. On withdrawing this instrument the right kidney was extruded, became strangulated between the lips of the wound, and caused considerable hemorrhage. A ligature was put around the base of the organ, and after some weeks the mass separated. The patient continued in good health the whole time, and her urinary secretion was normal. She was discharged in two months completely recovered. Price[b] mentions the case of a groom who was kicked over the kidney by a horse, and eighteen months later died of dropsy. Postmortem examination showed traces of a line of rupture through the substance of the gland; the preparation was deposited in St. George's Hospital Museum in London. The case is singular in that this man, with granular degeneration of the kidney, recovered from so extensive a lesion, and, moreover, that he remained in perfect health for over a year with his kidney in a state of destructive disease. Borthwick[c] mentions a dragoon of thirty who was stabbed by a sword-thrust on the left side under the short rib, the sword penetrating the pelvis and wounding the kidney. There was no hemorrhage from the external wound, nor pain in the spermatic cord or testicle. Under expectant treatment the man recovered. Castellanos[d] mentions a case of recovery from punctured wound of the kidney by a knife that penetrated the tubular and cortical substance, and entered the pelvis of the organ. The case was peculiar in the absence of two symptoms, viz., the escape of urine from the wound, and retraction of the corresponding testicle. Dusenbury[e] reports the case of a corporal in the army who was wounded on April 6, 1865, the bullet entering both the liver and kidney. Though there was injury to both these important organs, there was no impairment of the patient's health, and he recovered.

[a] Revue de Méd. de Militaire, Oct., 1875. [b] 779, Feb., 1860, 140.
[c] 149, 1799, 466. [d] 809, 1874, 281. [e] 124, Oct., 1865, 399.

Bryant[a] reports four cases of wound of the kidney, with recovery. All of these cases were probably extraperitoneal lacerations or ruptures. Cock[b] found a curious anomaly in a necropsy on the body of a boy of eighteen, who had died after a fall from some height. There was a compound, transverse rupture of the left kidney, which was twice as large as usual, the ureter also being of abnormal size. Further search showed that the right kidney was rudimentary, and had no vein or artery.

Ward[c] mentions a case of ruptured kidney, caused by a fall of seven feet, the man recovering after appropriate treatment. Vernon[d] reports a case of serious injury to the kidney, resulting in recovery in nine weeks. The patient fell 40 feet, landing on some rubbish and old iron, and received a wound measuring six inches over the right iliac crest, through which the lower end of the right kidney protruded; a piece of the kidney was lost. The case was remarkable because of the slight amount of hemorrhage.

Nephrorrhaphy is an operation in which a movable or floating kidney is fixed by suture through its capsule, including a portion of kidney-substance, and then through the adjacent lumbar fascia and muscles. The ultimate results of this operation have been most successful.

Nephrolithotomy is an operation for the removal of stone from the kidney. The operation may be a very difficult one, owing to the adhesions and thickening of all the perinephric tissues, or to the small size or remote location of the stone.

There was a recent exhibition in London,[619] in which were shown the **results of** a number of **recent operations on the kidney.** There was one-half of a kidney that had been removed on account of a rapidly-growing sarcoma from a young man of nineteen, who had known of the tumor for six months; there was a good recovery, and the man was quite well in eighteen months afterward. Another specimen was a right kidney removed at St. Bartholomew's Hospital. It was much dilated, and only a small amount of the kidney-substance remained. A calculus blocked the ureter at its commencement. The patient was a woman of thirty-one, and made a good recovery. From the Middlesex Hospital was a kidney containing a uric acid calculus which was successfully removed from a man of thirty-five. From the Cancer Hospital at Brompton there were two kidneys which had been removed from a man and a woman respectively, both of whom made a good recovery. From the King's College Hospital there was a kidney with its pelvis enlarged and occupied by a large calculus, and containing little secreting substance, which was removed from a man of forty-nine, who recovered. These are only a few of the examples of this most interesting collection. Large calculi of the kidney are mentioned in Chapter XV.

Rupture of the ureter is a very rare injury. Poland[e] has collected

a 392, vii., 1861, 41.   b 779, 1847, i., 293.   c 224, 1871, ii., 292.

d St. Bart. Hosp. Reports, London, 1866, ii., 124.   e 174, 400.

the histories of four cases, one of which ended in recovery after the evacuation by puncture, at intervals, of about two gallons of fluid resembling urine. The other cases terminated in death during the first, fourth, and tenth weeks respectively. Peritonitis was apparently not present in any of the cases, the urinary extravasation having occurred into the cellular tissue behind the peritoneum.

There are a few recorded cases of uncomplicated **wounds of the ureters.** The only well authenticated case in which the ureter alone was divided is the historic injury of the Archbishop of Paris,[a] who was wounded during the Revolution of 1848, by a ball entering the upper part of the lumbar region close to the spine. Unsuccessful attempts were made to extract the ball, and as there was no urine in the bladder, but a quantity escaping from the wound, a diagnosis of divided ureter was made. The Archbishop died in eighteen hours, and the autopsy showed that the ball had fractured the transverse process of the 3d lumbar vertebra, and divided the cauda equina just below its origin ; it had then changed direction and passed up toward the left kidney, dividing the ureter near the pelvis, and finally lodged in the psoas muscle.

It occasionally happens that the ureter is wounded in the removal of uterine, ovarian, or other abdominal tumors. In such event, if it is impossible to transplant to the bladder, the divided or torn end should be brought to the surface of the loin or vagina, and sutured there. In cases of malignant growth, the ureter has been purposely divided and transplanted into the bladder. Penrose,[b] assisted by Baldy, has performed this operation after excision of an inch of the left ureter for carcinomatous involvement. The distal end of the ureter was ligated, and the proximal end implanted in the bladder according to Van Hook's method, which consists in tying the lowered end of the ureter, then making a slit into it, and invaginating the upper end into the lower through this slit. A perfect cure followed. Similar cases have been reported by Kelly, Krug, and Bache Emmet.[c] Reed[d] reports a most interesting series in which he has successfully **transplanted ureters into the rectum.**

Ureterovaginal fistulæ following total extirpation of the uterus, opening of pelvic abscesses, or ulcerations from foreign bodies, are repaired by an operation termed by Bazy of Paris **ureterocystoneostomy,** and suggested by him as a substitute for nephrectomy in those cases in which the renal organs are unaffected. In the repair of such a case after a vaginal hysterectomy Mayo[e] reports a successful reimplantation of the ureter into the bladder.

Stricture of the ureter is also a very rare occurrence except as a result of compression of abdominal or pelvic new growths. Watson[f] has, however, reported two cases of stricture, in both of which a ureter was nearly or quite

a 363, 1848.   b Kansas City Medical Index, No. 5, 1894.   c 843, 446.
d 150, 1892.   e 538, Feb. 10, 1894.   f 845, 825.

obliterated by a dense mass of connective tissue. In one case there was a history of the passage of a renal calculus years previously. In both instances the condition was associated with pyonephrosis. Watson has collected the reports of four other cases from medical literature.

A remarkable procedure recently developed by gynecologists, particularly by Kelly of Baltimore, is catheterization and sounding of the ureters. McClellan [a] records a case of penetration of the ureter by the careless use of a catheter.

Injuries of the Bladder.—Rupture of the bladder may result from violence without any external wound (such as a fall or kick) applied to the abdomen. Jones [b] reports a fatal case of rupture of the bladder by a horse falling on its rider. In this case there was but little extravasation of urine, as the vesical aperture was closed by omentum and bowel. Assmuth reports two cases of rupture of the bladder from muscular action. Morris [c] cites the history of a case in which the bladder was twice ruptured : the first time by an injury, and the second time by the giving way of the cicatrix. The patient was a man of thirty-six who received a blow in the abdomen during a fight in a public house on June 6, 1879. At the hospital his condition was diagnosed and treated expectantly, but he recovered perfectly and left the hospital July 10, 1879. He was readmitted on August 4, 1886, over seven years later, with symptoms of rupture of the bladder, and died on the 6th. The postmortem showed a cicatrix of the bladder which had given way and caused the patient's death.

Rupture of the bladder is only likely to happen when the organ is distended, as when empty it sinks behind the pubic arch and is thus protected from external injury. The rupture usually occurs on the posterior wall, involving the peritoneal coat and allowing extravasation of urine into the peritoneal cavity, a condition that is almost inevitably fatal unless an operation is performed. Bartels collected the data of 98 such cases, only four recovering. When the rent is confined to the anterior wall of the bladder the urine escapes into the pelvic tissues, and the prognosis is much more favorable. Bartels collected 54 such cases, 12 terminating favorably. When celiotomy is performed for ruptured bladder, in a manner suggested by the elder Gross, the mortality is much less. Ashhurst collected the reports of 28 cases thus treated, ten of which recovered—a mortality of 64.2 per cent. Ashhurst remarks that he has seen an extraperitoneal rupture of the anterior wall of the bladder caused by improper use of instruments, in the case of retention of urine due to the presence of a tight urethral stricture.

There are a few cases on record in which the bladder has been ruptured by distention from the accumulation of urine, but the accident is a rare one, the urethra generally giving way first. Coats [d] reports two cases of uncomplicated rupture of the bladder. In neither case was a history of injury ob-

a 526, 1850, 692.   b 476, 1870, ii., 252.   c 476, 1887, i., 418.   d 224, July 21, 1894.

tainable. The first patient was a maniac; the second had been intoxicated previous to his admission to the hospital, with symptoms of acute peritonitis. The diagnosis was not made. The first patient died in five days and the second in two days after the onset of the illness. At the autopsies the rent was found to be in both instances in the posterior wall of the bladder a short distance from the fundus; the peritoneum was not inflamed, and there was absolutely no inflammatory reaction in the vesical wound. From the statistics of Ferraton and Rivington it seems that **rupture of the bladder is more common in intoxicated persons** than in others—a fact that is probably explained by a tendency to over-distention of the bladder which alcoholic liquors bring about. The liquor imbibed increases the amount of urine, and the state of blunted consciousness makes the call to empty the bladder less appreciated. The intoxicated person is also liable to falls, and is not so likely to protect himself in falling as a sober person.[a]

Gunshot Wounds of the Bladder.—Jackson[b] relates the remarkable recovery of a private in the 17th Tennessee Regiment who was shot in the pelvis at the battle of Mill Springs or Fishing Creek, Ky. He was left supposedly mortally wounded on the field, but was eventually picked up, and before receiving any treatment hauled 164 miles, over mountainous roads in the midst of winter and in a wagon without springs. His urine and excretions passed out through the wounds for several weeks and several pieces of bone came away. The two openings eventually healed, but for twenty-two months he passed pieces of bone by the natural channels.

Eve[c] records the case of a private in the Fifth Tennessee Cavalry who was shot in the right gluteal region, the bullet penetrating the bladder and making its exit through the pubis. He rode 30 miles, during which the urine passed through the wound. Urine was afterward voided through the left pubic opening, and spicules of bone were discharged for two years afterward; ultimate recovery ensued.

Barkesdale[d] relates the history of the case of a Confederate soldier who was shot at Fredericksburg in the median line of the body, $1\frac{1}{2}$ inches above the symphysis, the wound of exit being in the median line at the back, $\frac{1}{2}$ inch lower down. Urine escaped from both wounds and through the urethra. There were no bad symptoms, and the wounds healed in four weeks.

The bladder is not always injured by penetration of the abdominal wall, but may be wounded by **penetration through the anus or vagina,** or even by an instrument entering the **buttocks** and passing through the smaller sacrosciatic notch. Camper[e] records the case of a sailor who fell from a mast and struck upon some fragments of wood, one of which entered the anus and penetrated the bladder, the result being a rectovesical fistula. About a year later the man consulted Camper, who unsuccessfully attempted

a 843, 951. b 124, 1869, n. s. lxii., 281. c 579, 1867–68, 161.
d Virginia Clin. Rec., 1873–74, iii., 367. e 641, 296.

to extract the piece of wood; but by incising the fistula it was found that two calculi had formed about the wooden pieces, and when these were extracted the patient recovered. Perrin [a] gives the history of a man of forty who, while adjusting curtains, fell and struck an overturned chair; one of the chair-legs penetrated the anus. Its extraction was followed by a gush of urine, and for several days the man suffered from incontinence of urine and feces. By the tenth day he was passing urine from the urethra, and on the twenty-fifth day there was a complete cicatrix of the parts; fifteen days later he suffered from an attack of retention of urine lasting five days; this was completely relieved after the expulsion of a small piece of trouser-cloth which had been pushed into the bladder at the time of the accident. Post [b] reports the case of a young man who, in jumping over a broomstick, was impaled upon it, the stick entering the anus without causing any external wound, and penetrating the bladder, thus allowing the escape of urine through the anus. A peculiar sequela was that the man suffered from a calculus, the nucleus of which was a piece of the seat of his pantaloons which the stick had carried in.

Couper [c] reports a fatal case of stab-wound of the buttocks, in which the knife passed through the lesser sacrosciatic notch and entered the bladder close to the trigone. The patient was a man of twenty-three, a seaman, and in a quarrel had been stabbed in the buttocks with a long sailor's knife, with resultant symptoms of peritonitis which proved fatal. At the autopsy it was found that the knife had passed through the gluteal muscles and divided part of the great sacrosciatic ligament. It then passed through the small sacrosciatic notch, completely dividing the pudic artery and nerve, and one vein, each end being closed by a clot. The knife entered the bladder close to the trigone, making an opening large enough to admit the index finger. There were well-marked evidences of peritonitis and· cellulitis.

Old-time surgeons had considerable difficulty in extracting arrow-heads from persons who had received their injuries while on horseback. Conrad Gesner records an ingenious device of an old surgeon who succeeded in extracting an arrow which had resisted all previous attempts, by placing the subject in the very position in which he was at the time of reception of the wound. The following noteworthy case shows that the bladder may be penetrated by an arrow or bullet entering the buttocks of a person on horseback. Forwood [d] describes the removal of a vesical calculus, the nucleus of which was an iron arrow-head, as follows: "Sitimore, a wild Indian, Chief of the Kiowas, aged forty-two, applied to me at Fort Sill, Indian Territory, August, 1869, with symptoms of stone in the bladder. The following history was elicited: In the fall of 1862 he led a band of Kiowas against the Pawnee Indians, and was wounded in a fight near Fort Larned, Kansas. Being mounted and leaning over his horse, a Pawnee, on foot and within a

a 368, No. 49, 1872. b 538, 1872, vii., 518. c 548, 1879, i., 646. d 847, 260.

few paces, drove an arrow deep into his right buttock. The stick was withdrawn by his companions, but the iron point remained in his body. He passed bloody urine immediately after the injury, but the wound soon healed, and in a few weeks he was able to hunt the buffalo without inconvenience. For more than six years he continued at the head of his band, and traveled on horseback, from camp to camp, over hundreds of miles every summer. A long time after the injury he began to feel distress in micturating, which steadily increased until he was forced to reveal this sacred secret (as it is regarded by these Indians), and to apply for medical aid. His urine had often stopped for hours, at which times he had learned to obtain relief by elevating his hips, or lying in different positions. The urine was loaded with blood and mucus and with a few pus globules, and the introduction of a sound indicated a large, hard calculus in the bladder. The Indians advised me approximately of the depth to which the shaft had penetrated and the direction it took, and judging from the situation of the cicatrix and all the circumstances it was apparent that the arrow-head had passed through the glutei muscles and the obturator foramen and entered the cavity of the bladder, where it remained and formed the nucleus of a stone. Stone in the bladder is extremely rare among the wild Indians, owing, no doubt, to their almost exclusive meat diet and the very healthy condition of their digestive organs, and this fact, in connection with the age of the patient and the unobstructed condition of his urethra, went very far to sustain this conclusion. On August 23d I removed the stone without difficulty by the lateral operation through the perineum. The lobe of the prostate was enlarged, which seemed to favor the extent of the incision beyond what would otherwise have been safe. The perineum was deep and the tuberosities of the ischii unnaturally approximated. The calculus of the mixed ammoniaco-magnesian variety was egg-shaped, and weighed 19 drams. The arrow-point was completely covered and imbedded near the center of the stone. It was of iron, and had been originally about $2\frac{1}{2}$ inches long, by $\frac{7}{8}$ inch at its widest part, somewhat reduced at the point and edges by oxidation. The removal of the stone was facilitated by the use of two pairs of forceps,—one with broad blades, by which I succeeded in bringing the small end of the stone to the opening in the prostate, while the other, long and narrow, seized and held it until the former was withdrawn. In this way the forceps did not occupy a part of the opening while the large end of the stone was passing through it. The capacity of the bladder was reduced, and its inner walls were in a state of chronic inflammation. The patient quickly recovered from the effects of the chloroform and felt great relief, both in body and mind, after the operation, and up to the eighth day did not present a single unfavorable symptom. The urine began to pass by the natural channel by the third day, and continued more or less until, on the seventh day, it had nearly ceased to flow at the wound. But the restless spirit of the patient's friends could no longer be restrained. Open hostility with the whites was expected to begin at every moment, and they insisted on his removal. He needed purgative medicine on the eighth day, which they refused to allow him to take. They assumed entire charge of the case, and the following day started with him to their camps 60 miles away. Nineteen days after he is reported to have died ; but his immediate relatives have since assured me that his wound was well and that no trouble arose from it. They described his symptoms as those of bilious remittent fever, a severe epidemic of which was prevailing at the time, and from which several white men and many Indians died in that vicinity." The calculus was deposited in the Army Medical Museum at Washington, and is repre-

Fig. 225.—Calculus having an arrow-head for a nucleus (Sp. 5931, A. M. M., Wash., D. C.) (Forwood).

sented in the accompanying photograph (Fig. 225), showing a cross-section of the calculus with the arrow-head in situ.

As quoted by Chelius,[265] both Hennen and Cline relate cases in which men have been shot through the skirts of the jacket, the ball penetrating the abdomen above the tuberosity of the ischium, and entering the bladder, and the men have afterward urinated pieces of clothing, threads, etc., taken in by the ball. In similar cases the bullet itself may remain in the bladder and cause the formation of a calculus about itself as a nucleus, as in three cases mentioned by McGuire of Richmond, or the remnants of cloth or spicules of bone may give rise to similar formation.

McGuire[a] mentions the case of a man of twenty-three who was wounded at the Battle of McDowell, May 8, 1862. The ball struck him on the horizontal ramus of the left pubic bone, about an inch from the symphysis, passed through the bladder and rectum, and came out just below the right sacrosciatic notch, near the sacrum. The day after the battle the man was sent to the general hospital at Staunton, Va., where he remained under treatment for four months. During the first month urine passed freely through the wounds made by the entrance and exit of the ball, and was generally mixed with pus and blood. Fecal matter was frequently discharged through the posterior wound. Some time during the third week he passed several small pieces of bone by the rectum. At the end of the fifth week the wound of exit healed, and for the first time after his injury urine was discharged through the urethra. The wound of entrance gradually closed after five months, but opened again in a few weeks and continued, at varying intervals, alternately closed and open until September, 1865. At this time, on sounding the man, it was found that he had stone; this was removed by lateral operation, and was found to weigh $2\frac{1}{4}$ ounces, having for its nucleus a piece of bone about $\frac{1}{2}$ inch long. Dougherty[b] reports the operation of lithotomy, in which the calculus removed was formed by incrustations about an iron bullet.

In cases in which there is a **fistula of the bladder** the subject may live for some time, in some cases passing **excrement through the urethra,** in others, **urine by the anus.** These cases seem to have been of particular interest to the older writers, and we find the literature of the last century full of examples. Benivenius, Borellus, the Ephemerides, Tulpius, Zacutus Lusitanus, and others speak of excrement passing through the penis; and there are many cases of vaginal anus recorded. Langlet cites an instance in which the intestine terminated in the bladder. Arand[154] mentions recovery after atresia of the anus with passage of excrement from the vulva. Bartholinus, the Ephemerides, Fothergill,[c] de la Croix,[d] Riedlin,[683] Weber, and Zacutus Lusitanus mention instances in which gas was passed by the penis and urethra. Camper[e] records such a case from ulcer of the neighboring or connecting intestine; Frank, from cohesion and suppuration of the rectum; Marcellus Donatus,[f] from penetrating ulcer of the rectum; and Petit,[g] from communication of the rectum and bladder in which a cure was effected by the continued use of the catheter for the evacuation of urine.

Flatus through the vagina, vulva, and from the uterus is mentioned by Bartholinus, the Ephemerides, Meckel, Mauriceau, Paullini, Riedlin, Trnka, and many others in the older literature. Dickinson[h] mentions a Burmese male child, four years old, who had an imperforate anus and urethra, but who passed feces and urine successfully through an opening at the base

a 847, 248. b 847, 259. c 524, ii., 200. d 367, 1788, No. 48.
e 249, ii., 16. f 306, L. iv., c. xxix., 524. g 625, T. ii., 94. h 476, 1859, i., 534.

of the glans penis. Dickinson eventually performed a successful operation on this case. Modern literature has many similar instances.

In the older literature it was not uncommon to find accounts of persons **passing worms from the bladder,** no explanations being given to account for their presence in this organ. Some of these cases were doubtless instances of echinococcus, trichinæ, or the result of rectovesical fistula, but Riverius[a] mentions an instance in which, after drinking water containing worms, a person passed worms in the urine. In the old Journal de physique de Rozier is an account of a man of forty-five who enjoyed good health, but who periodically urinated small worms from the bladder. They were described as being about $1\frac{1}{2}$ lines long, and caused no inconvenience. There is also mentioned [b] the case of a woman who voided worms from the bladder. Tupper[c] describes a curious case of a woman of sixty-nine who complained of a severe, stinging pain that completely overcame her after micturition. An ulceration of the neck of the bladder was suspected, and the usual remedies were applied, but without effect. An examination of the urine was negative. On recommendation of her friends the patient, before going to bed, steeped and drank a decoction of knot-grass. During the night she urinated freely, and claimed that she had passed a worm about ten inches long and of the size of a knitting-needle. It exhibited motions like those of a snake, and was quite lively, living five or six days in water. The case seems quite unaccountable, but there is, of course, a possibility that the animal had already been in the chamber, or that it was passed by the bowel. A rectovaginal or vesical fistula could account for the presence of this worm had it been voided from the bowel ; nevertheless the woman adhered to her statement that she had urinated the worm, and, as confirmatory evidence, never complained of pain after passing the animal.

Foreign bodies in the bladder, other than calculi (which will be spoken of in Chapter XV.), generally gain entrance through one of the natural passages, as a rule being introduced, either in curiosity or for perverted satisfaction, through the urethra. Morand mentions an instance in which a long **wax taper** was introduced into the bladder through the urethra by a man. At the University Hospital, Philadelphia, White has extracted, by median cystotomy, a long wax taper which had been used in masturbation. The cystoscopic examination in this case was negative, and the man's statements were disbelieved, but the operation was performed, and the taper was found curled up and covered by mucus and folds of the bladder. It is not uncommon for **needles, hair-pins,** and the like to form nuclei for incrustations. Gross found three **caudal vertebræ of a squirrel** in the center of a vesical calculus taken from the bladder of a man of thirty-five. It was afterward elicited that the patient had practised urethral masturbation with the tail of this animal. Morand [563] relates the history of a man of sixty-two who introduced a sprig of wheat into his urethra for a supposed therapeutic purpose.

It slipped into the bladder and there formed the nucleus of a cluster calculus. Dayot[a] reports a similar formation from the introduction of the stem of a plant. Terrilon[b] describes the case of a man of fifty-four who introduced a **pencil** into his urethra. The body rested fifteen days in this canal, and then passed into the bladder. On the twenty-eighth day he had a chill, and during two days made successive attempts to break the pencil. Following each attempt he had a violent chill and intense evening fever. On the thirty-third day Terrilon removed the pencil by operation. Symptoms of perivesical abscess were present, and seventeen days after the operation, and fifty days after the introduction of the pencil, the patient died. Caudmont[c] mentions a man of twenty-six who introduced a pencil-case into his urethra, from whence it passed into his bladder. It rested about four years in this organ before violent symptoms developed. Perforation of the bladder took place, and the patient died. Poulet[d] mentions the case of a man of seventy-eight, in whose bladder a metallic sound was broken off. The fractured piece of sound, which measured 17 cm. in length, made its exit from the anus, and the patient recovered. Wheeler[e] reports the case of a man of twenty-one who passed a button-hook into his anus, from whence it escaped into his bladder. The hook, which was subsequently spontaneously passed, measured $2\frac{1}{2}$ inches in length and $\frac{1}{2}$ inch in diameter.

Among females, whose urethræ are short and dilatable, foreign bodies are often found in the bladder, and it is quite common for smaller articles of the toilet, such as hair-pins, to be introduced into the bladder, and there form calculi. Whiteside[f] describes a case in which a foreign body introduced into the bladder was mistaken for pregnancy, and giving rise to corresponding symptoms. The patient was a young girl of seventeen who had several times missed her menstruation, and who was considered pregnant. The abdomen was more developed than usual in a young woman. The breasts were voluminous, and the nipples surrounded by a somber areola. At certain periods after the cessation of menstruation, she had incontinence of urine, and had also repeatedly vomited. The urine was of high specific gravity, albuminous, alkaline, and exhaled a disagreeable odor. In spite of the signs of pregnancy already noted, palpitation and percussion did not show any augmentation in the size of the uterus, but the introduction of a catheter into the bladder showed the existence of a large calculus. Under chloroform the calculus and its nucleus were disengaged, and proved to be the **handle of a tooth-brush,** the exact size of which is represented in the accompanying illustration (Fig. 226). The handle was covered with calcareous deposits, and was tightly fixed in the bladder. At first the young woman would give no explanation for its presence, but afterward explained that she had several times used this instrument for relief in retention of urine, and one day it had fallen

a 641, 562. b 242, 1876, 651. c 242, 1850, 354.
d 641, 572. e 632, 1879, i., 262. f 476, Jan. 24, 1874, 127.

into the bladder. A short time after the operation menstruation returned for the first time in seven months, and was afterward normal. Bigelow [a] reports the case of a woman who habitually introduced hair-pins and common pins into her bladder. She acquired this mania after an attempt at dilatation of the urethra in the relief of an obstinate case of strangury. Rodé [368] reports the case of a woman who had introduced a hog's penis into her urethra. It was removed by an incision into this canal, but the patient died in five days of septicemia. There is a curious case quoted [b] of a young domestic of four-

teen who was first seen suffering with pain in the sides of the genital organs, retention of urine, and violent tenesmus. She was examined by a midwife who found nothing, but on the following day the patient felt it necessary to go to bed. Her general symptoms persisted, and meanwhile the bladder became much distended. The patient had made allusion to the loss of a hair-pin, a circumstance which corresponded with the beginning of her trouble. Examination showed the orifice of the urethra to be swollen and painful to the touch, and from its canal a hair-pin 6.5 cm. long was extracted. The patient was unable to urinate, and it was necessary to resort to catheterization. By evening the general symptoms had disappeared, and the next day the patient urinated as usual.

There are peculiar cases of **hair in the bladder,** in which all history as to the method of entrance is denied, and which leave as the only explanation the possibility that the bladder was in communication with some dermoid cyst. Hamelin [c] mentions a case of this nature. It is said [d] that all his life Sir William Elliot was annoyed by passing hairs in urination. They would lodge in the

Fig. 226.—Handle of a tooth-brush, removed from the bladder of a young girl.

urethra and cause constant irritation. At his death a stone was taken from the bladder, covered with scurf and hair. Hall [e] relates the case of a woman of sixty, from whose bladder, by dilatation of the urethra, was removed a bundle of hairs two inches long, which, Hall says, without a doubt had grown from the vesical walls.

Retention of Foreign Bodies in the Pelvis.—It is a peculiar fact that foreign bodies which once gain entrance to the pelvis may be tolerated in this location for many years. Baxter [f] describes a man who suffered an injury from a piece of white board which entered his pelvis, and remained in position for sixteen and a half years; at this time a piece of wood $7\frac{1}{2}$ inches

a 124, xxix., 57.   b 641, 637.   c 302, iv., 432.

d 629, 1700, iii., 164.   e 476, 1860, ii., 461.   f 218, 1883.

long was discharged at stool, and the patient recovered. Jones[a] speaks of a case in which splinters of wood were retained in the neighborhood of the rectum and vagina for sixteen years, and spontaneously discharged. Barwell[b] mentions a case in which a gum elastic catheter that had been passed into the vagina for the purpose of producing abortion became impacted in the pelvis for twenty months, and was then removed.

Rupture of the Male Urethra.—The male urethra is occasionally ruptured **in violent coitus.** Frank[351] and the Philosophical Transactions[c] are among the older authorities mentioning this accident. In Frank's case there was hemorrhage from the penis to the extent of five pounds. Colles[d] mentions a man of thirty-eight, prone to obesity, and who had been married two months, who said that in sexual congress he had hurt himself by pushing his penis against the pubic bone, and added that he had a pain that felt as though something had broken in his organ. The integuments of the penis became livid and swollen and were extremely painful. His urine had to be drawn by a catheter, and by the fifth day his condition was so bad that an incision was made into the tumor, and pus, blood, urine, and air issued. The patient suffered intense rigors, his abdomen became tympanitic, and he died. Postmortem examination revealed the presence of a ruptured urethra.

Watson[e] relates an instance of coitus performed *en postillon* by a man while drunk, with rupture of the urethra and fracture of the corpus spongiosum only. Loughlin mentions a rupture of the corpus spongiosum during coitus. Frank[351] cites a curious case of hemorrhage from a fall while the penis was erect. It is not unusual to find ruptured urethræ following traumatism, and various explanations are given for it in the standard works on surgery.

Fracture of the Penis.—A peculiar accident to the penis is fracture, which sometimes occurs in coitus. This accident consists in the laceration of the corpora cavernosa, followed by extensive extravasation of blood into the erectile tissue. It has also occurred from injury inflicted accidentally or maliciously, but always happening when the organ was erect. An annoying sequel following this accident is the tendency to curvature in erection, which is sometimes so marked as to interfere with coitus, and even render the patient permanently impotent.[845]

There is an account[f] of a laborer of twenty-seven who, in attempting to micturate with his penis erect, pressed it downward with considerable force and fractured the corpora cavernosa. Veazie[g] relates a case of fracture of the corpora cavernosa occurring in coitus. During the act the female suddenly withdrew, and the male, following, violently struck the pubes, with the resultant injury. Recovery ensued. M'Clellan[h] speaks of removing the

a 218, 1856.   b 650, 1874, viii., 280.   c 629, No. 4.   d 313, 1857, xxiii., 375.
e 218, 1885, cxiii., 463.   f Amer. Pract. & News, 1886, ii., 80.
g 593, 1884–85, xii., 321.   h Smith's Med. Jour., 1827, 256.

cavernous septum from a man of fifty-two, in whom this part had become infiltrated with lime-salts and resembled a long, narrow bone. When the penis was erect it was bent in the form of a semicircular bow.

The Transactions of the South Carolina Medical Association [a] contain an account of a negro of sixty who had **urethral stricture** from gonorrhea, and who had been treated for fifteen years by caustics. The penis was seven inches in circumference around the glans, and but little less near the scrotum. The glans was riddled with holes, and numerous fistulæ existed on the inferior surface of the urethra, the meatus being impermeable. So great was the weight and hypertrophy that amputation was necessary. John Hunter speaks of six strictures existing in one urethra at one time; Lallemand of seven; Bolot of eight; Ducamp of five; Boyer thought three could never exist together; Leroy D'Etoilles found 11, and Rokitansky met with four.

Sundry Injuries to the Penis.—Fabricius Hildanus [334] mentions a curious case of paraphimosis caused by violent coitus with a virgin who had an extremely narrow vagina. Joyce [b] relates a history of a stout man who awoke with a vigorous erection, and feeling much irritation, he scratched himself violently. He soon bled copiously, his shirt and underlying sheets and blankets being soaked through. On examination the penis was found swollen, and on drawing back the foreskin a small jet of blood spurted from a small rupture in the frenum. The authors have knowledge of a case in which hemorrhage from the frenum proved fatal. The patient, in a drunken wager, attempted to circumcise himself with a piece of tin, and bled to death before medical aid could be summoned. It sometimes happens that the virile member is amputated by an animal bite. Paullini [620] and Celliez [c] mention amputation of the penis by a dog-bite. Morgan [d] describes a boy of thirteen who was feeding a donkey which suddenly made a snap at him, unfortunately catching him by the trousers and including the penis in one of the folds. By the violence of the bite the boy was thrown to the ground, and his entire prepuce was stripped off to the root as if it had been done by a knife. There was little hemorrhage, and the prepuce was found in the trousers, looking exactly like the finger of a glove. Morgan stated that this was the third case of the kind of which he had knowledge. Bookey [e] records a case in which an artilleryman was seized by the penis by an infuriated horse, and the two crura were pulled out entire.

Amputation of the penis is not always followed by loss of the sexual power and instinct, but sometimes has the mental effect of temporarily increasing the desire. Haslam [f] reports the case of a man who slipped on the greasy deck of a whaler, and falling forward with great violence upon a large knife used to cut blubber, completely severed his penis, beside inflicting a wound in the abdomen through which the intestines protruded. After re-

a 1874-77, 90-92.   b 224, 1869, i., 209.   c 462, T. xx., 169.
d 536, 1869, vii., 31.   e Indian Med. Jour., 1886, v., 647.   f 476, 1828.

covery there was a distinct increase of sexual desire and frequent nocturnal emissions. In the same report there is recorded the history of a man who had entirely lost his penis, but had supplied himself with an ivory succedaneum. This fellow finally became so libidinous that it was necessary to exclude him from the workhouse, of which he was an inmate.

Norris[a] gives an account of a private who received a **gunshot wound of the penis** while it was partly erect. The wound was acquired at the second battle of Fredericksburg. The ball entered near the center of the glans penis, and taking a slightly oblique direction, it passed out of the right side of the penis $1\frac{1}{2}$ inches beyond the glans; it then entered the scrotum, and after striking the pelvis near the symphysis, glanced off around the innominate bone, and finally made its exit two inches above the anus. The after-effects of this injury were incontinence of urine, and inability to assume the erect position.

Bookey[b] cites the case of **six wounds from one bullet** with recovery. The bullet entered the sole and emerged from the dorsum of the foot. It then went through the right buttock and came out of the groin, only to penetrate the dorsum of the penis and emerge at the upper part of the glans. Rose[c] speaks of a case in which a man had his clothes caught in machinery, drawing in the external genital organs. The testicles were found to be uninjured, but the penis was doubled out of sight and embedded in the scrotum, from whence it was restored to its natural position and the man recovered.

Nélaton[d] describes a case of **luxation of the penis** in a lad of six who fell from a cart. Nélaton found the missing member in the scrotum, where it had been for nine days. He introduced Sir Astley Cooper's instrument for tying deeply-seated arteries through a cutaneous tube, and conducting the hook under the corporus cavernosum, seized this crosswise, and by a to-and-fro movement succeeded in replacing the organ.

Moldenhauer[e] describes the case of a farmer of fifty-seven who was injured in a runaway accident, a wheel passing over his body close to the abdomen. The glans penis could not be recognized, since the penis in toto had been torn from its sheath at the corona, and had slipped or been driven into the inguinal region. This author quotes Stromeyer's case,[f] which was that of a boy of four and a half years who was kicked by a horse in the external genital region. The sheath was found empty of the penis, which had been driven into the perineum.

Raven[g] mentions a case of **spontaneous retraction of the penis** in a man of twenty-seven. While in bed he felt a sensation of coldness in the penis, and on examination he found the organ (a normal-sized one) rapidly retracting or shrinking. He hastily summoned a physician, who found that

a 124, 1864.   b Indian Med. Jour., 1886, v., 647.   c 476, 1866, i., 67.
d 363, 1850, No. 86.   e 703, 1876, 232, n. s., xiii.
f "Handbook of Surgery," ii., 774.   g 476, 1886, ii., 250

the penis had, in fact, almost disappeared, the glans being just perceptible under the pubic arch, and the skin alone visible. The next day the normal condition was restored, but the patient was weak and nervous for several days after his fright. In a similar case, mentioned by Ivanhoff, the penis of a peasant of twenty-three, a married man, bodily disappeared, and was only captured by repeated effort. The patient was six days under treatment, and he finally became so distrustful of his virile member that, to be assured of its constancy, he tied a string about it above the glans.

Injuries of the penis and testicles self-inflicted are grouped together and discussed in Chapter XIV.

As a rule, **spontaneous gangrene of the penis** has its origin in some intense fever. Partridge[a] describes a man of forty who had been the victim of typhus fever, and whose penis mortified and dried up, becoming black and like the empty finger of a cast-off glove; in a few days it dropped off. Boyer[b] cites a case of edema of the prepuce, noticed on the fifteenth day of the fever, and which was followed by gangrene of the penis. Rostan[c] mentions gangrene of the penis from small-pox. Intermittent fever has been cited as a cause.[d] Koehler[e] reports a fatal instance of gangrene of the penis, caused by a prostatic abscess following gonorrhea. In this case there was thrombosis of the pelvic veins. Hutchinson[f] mentions a man who, thirty years before, after six days' exposure on a raft, had lost both legs by gangrene. At the age of sixty-six he was confined to bed by subacute bronchitis, and during this period his whole penis became gangrenous and sloughed off. This is quite unusual, as gangrene is usually associated with fever; it is more than likely that the gangrene of the leg was not connected with that of the penis, but that the latter was a distinct after-result. Possibly the prolonged exposure at the time he lost his legs produced permanent injury to the blood-vessels and nerves of the penis. There is a case on record in which, in a man of thirty-seven, gangrene of the penis followed delirium tremens, and was attributed to alcoholism.[g] Quoted by Jacobson,[443] Troisfontaines records a case of gangrene of the skin and body of the penis in a young man, and without any apparent cause. Schutz[h] speaks of **regeneration of the penis** after gangrenous destruction.

Gangrene of the penis does not necessarily hinder the performance of marital functions. Chance[i] mentions a man whose penis sloughed off, leaving only a nipple-like remnant. However, he married four years later, and always lived in harmony with his wife. At the time of his death he was the father of a child, subsequent to whose birth his wife had miscarried, and at the time of report she was daily expecting to be again confined.

Willett[j] relates the instance of a horseman of thirty-three who, after

a 779, xvi., 792.   b "Traité des Mal. Chirurg."   c 363, 1853.   d 260, Band., viii., 1874.
e 260, 1891.   f 160, ii., 364.   g Rev. Méd. de la Suisse Romande, 1888.
h 736, ii., 53.   i 313. xxxii.   j Med. and Surg. Month., 1866, i., 102.

using a combination of refuse oils to protect his horse from gnats, was prompted to urinate, and, in so doing, accidentally touched his penis with the mixture. Sloughing phagedena rapidly ensued, but under medical treatment he eventually recovered.

Priapism is sometimes seen as a curious symptom of lesion of the spinal cord. In such cases it is totally unconnected with any voluptuous sensation, and is only found accompanied by motor paralysis. It may occur spontaneously immediately after accident involving the cord, and is then probably due to undue excitement of the portion of the cord below the lesion, which is deprived of the regulating influence of the brain. Priapism may also develop spontaneously at a later period, and is then due to central irritation from extravasation into the substance of the cord, or to some reflex cause. It may also occur from simple concussion, as shown by a case reported by Le Gros Clark. Pressure on the cerebellum is supposed to account for cases of priapism observed in executions and suicides by hanging. There is an instance recorded of an Italian " castrata " who said he provoked sexual pleasure by partially hanging himself. He accidentally ended his life in pursuance of this peculiar habit. The facts were elicited by testimony at the inquest.

There are, however, in literature, records of **long continued priapism** in which either the cause is due to excessive stimulation of the sexual center, or in which the cause is obscure or unknown. There may or may not be accompanying voluptuous feelings. The older records contain instances of continued infantile priapism caused by the constant irritation of ascarides, and also records of prolonged priapism associated with intense agony and spasmodic cramps. Zacutus Lusitanus[831] speaks of a Viceroy of India who had a long attack of stubborn priapism without any voluptuous feeling. Gross refers to prolonged priapism, and remarks that the majority of cases seem to be due to excessive coitus.

Moore[a] reports a case in a man of forty who had been married fifteen years, and who suffered spasmodic contractions of the muscles of the penis after an incomplete coitus. This pseudopriapism continued for twenty-three days, during which time he had unsuccessfully resorted to the application of cold, bleeding, and other treatment; but on the twenty-sixth day, after the use of bladders filled with cold water, there was a discharge from the urethra of a glairy mucus, similar in nature to that in seminal debility. There was then complete relaxation of the organ. During all this time the man slept very little, only occasionally dozing. Donne[b] describes an athletic laborer of twenty-five who received a wound from a rifle-ball penetrating the cranial parietes immediately in the posterior superior angle of the parietal bone, and a few lines from the lambdoid suture. The ball did not make egress, but passed posteriorly downward. Reaction was established on the third day, but the inflammatory symptoms influenced the genitalia. Priapism began

a 129, 1823.   b 818, 1835, ii., 295.

on the fifth day, at which time the patient became affected with a salacious appetite, and was rational upon every subject except that pertaining to venery. He grew worse on the sixth day, and his medical adviser was obliged to prohibit a female attendant. Priapism continued, but the man went into a soporose condition, with occasional intervals of satyriasis. In this condition he survived nine days; there was not the slightest abatement of the priapism until a few moments before his death. Tripe [a] relates the history of a seaman of twenty-five, in perfect health, who, arriving from Calcutta on April 12, 1884, lodged with a female until the 26th. At this time he experienced an unusually fierce desire, with intense erection of the penis which, with pain, lasted throughout the night. Though coitus was frequently resorted to, these symptoms continued. He sought aid at the London Hospital, but the priapism was persistent, and when he left, on May 10th, the penis formed an acute angle with the pubes, and he again had free intercourse with the same female. At the time of leaving England the penis made an angle of about 45° with the pubes, and this condition, he affirmed, lasted three months. On his return to England his penis was flaccid, and his symptoms had disappeared.

Salzer [b] presents an interesting paper on priapism which was quoted in The Practitioner of London. Salzer describes one patient of forty-six who awoke one morning with a strong erection that could not be reduced by any means. Urine was voided by jerks and with difficulty, and only when the subject was placed in the knee and elbow position. Despite all treatment this condition continued for seven weeks. At this time the patient's spleen was noticed to be enormously enlarged. The man died about a year after the attack, but a necropsy was unfortunately refused. Salzer, in discussing the **theories of priapism,** mentions eight cases previously reported, and concludes, that such cases are attributable to leukemia. Kremine believes that continued priapism is produced by effusion of blood into the corpora cavernosa, which is impeded on its return. He thinks it corresponds to bleeding at the nose and rectum, which often occurs in perfectly healthy persons. Longuet regards the condition of the blood in leukemia as the cause of such priapism, and considers that the circulation of the blood is retarded in the smaller vessels, while, owing to the great increase in the number of white corpuscles, thrombi are formed. Neidhart and Matthias conclude that the origin of this condition might be sought for in the disturbance of the nerve-centers. After reviewing all these theories, Salzer states that in his case the patient was previously healthy and never had suffered the slightest hemorrhage in any part, and he therefore rejects the theory of extravasation. He is inclined to suppose that the priapism was due to the stimulation of the nervi erigentes, brought about either by anatomic change in the nerves themselves, or by pressure upon them by enlarged lumbar glands, an associate condition of leukemia.

a 476, 1845, ii., 8.   b 199, No. 11, 1879.

Burchard [a] reports a most interesting case of prolonged priapism in an English gentleman of fifty-three. When he was called to see the man on July 15th he found him suffering with intense pain in the penis, and in a state of extreme exhaustion after an erection which had lasted five hours uninterruptedly, during the whole of which time the organ was in a state of violent and continuous spasm. The paroxysm was controlled by $\frac{3}{4}$ grain morphin and $\frac{1}{50}$ grain atropin. Five hours later, after a troubled sleep, there was another erection, which was again relieved by hypodermic medication. During the day he had two other paroxysms, one lasting forty-five minutes, and another, three hours later, lasting eighteen minutes. Both these were controlled by morphin. There was no loss of semen, but after the paroxysms a small quantity of glairy mucus escaped from the meatus. The rigidity was remarkable, simulating the spasms of tetanus. No language could adequately describe the suffering of the patient. Burchard elicited the history that the man had suffered from nocturnal emissions and erotic dreams of the most lascivious nature, sometimes having three in one night. During the day he would have eight or ten erections, unaccompanied by any voluptuous emotions. In these there would rarely be any emission, but occasionally a small mucous discharge. This state of affairs had continued three years up to the time Burchard saw him, and, chagrined by pain and his malady, the patient had become despondent. After a course of careful treatment, in which diet, sponging, application of ice-bags, and ergot were features, this unfortunate man recovered.

Bruce [b] mentions the case of an Irishman of fifty-five who, without apparent cause, was affected with a painful priapism which lasted six weeks, and did not subside even under chloroform. Booth [c] mentions a case of priapism in a married seaman of fifty-five, due to local inflammation about the muscles, constricting the bulb of the penis. The affection lasted five weeks, and was extremely painful. There was a similar case of priapism which lasted for three weeks, and was associated with hydrocele in a man of forty-eight. [d]

Injuries of the testicle and scrotum may be productive of most serious issue. It is a well-known surgical fact that a major degree of shock accompanies a contusion of this portion of the body. In fact, Chevers [266] states that the sensitiveness of the testicles is so well known in India, that there are cases on record in which premeditated murder has been effected by Cossiah women, by violently squeezing the testicles of their husbands. He also mentions another case in which, in frustrating an attempt at rape, death was caused in a similar manner. Stalkartt [e] describes the case of a young man who, after drinking to excess with his paramour, was either unable, or indifferent in gratifying her sexual desire. The woman became so enraged that

a 597, 1887, xlv., 66.   b 476, 1873, i., 90.   c 476, 1887, i., 978.
d 476, 1863, ii., 162.   e 224, 1890, ii., 1411

she seized the scrotum and wrenched it from its attachments, exposing the testicles. The left testicle was completely denuded, and was hanging by the vas deferens and the spermatic vessels. There was little hemorrhage, and the wound was healed by granulation.

Avulsion of the male external genitalia is not always accompanied by serious consequences, and even in some cases the sexual power is preserved. Knoll [a] described a case in 1781, occurring in a peasant of thirty-six who fell from a horse under the wheels of a carriage. He was first caught in the revolving wheels by his apron, which drew him up until his breeches were entangled, and finally his genitals were torn off. Not feeling much pain at the time, he mounted his horse and went to his house. On examination it was found that the injury was accompanied with considerable hemorrhage. The wound extended from the superior part of the pubes almost to the anus; the canal of the urethra was torn away, and the penis up to the neck of the bladder. There was no vestige of either the right scrotum or testicle. The left testicle was hanging by its cord, enveloped in its tunica vaginalis. The cord was swollen and resembled a penis stripped of its integument. The prostate was considerably contused. After two months of suffering the patient recovered, being able to evacuate his urine through a fistulous opening that had formed. In ten weeks cicatrization was perfect. In his "Memoirs of the Campaign of 1811," Larrey describes a soldier who, while standing with his legs apart, was struck from behind by a bullet. The margin of the sphincter ani, the skin of the perineum, the bulbous portion of the urethra, some of the skin of the scrotum, and the right testicle were destroyed. The spermatic cord was divided close to the skin, and the skin of the penis and prepuce was torn. The soldier was left as dead on the field, but after four months' treatment he recovered.

Madden [b] mentions a man of fifty who fell under the feet of a pair of horses, and suffered avulsion of the testicles through the scrotum. The organs were mangled, the spermatic cord was torn and hung over the anus, and the penis was lacerated from the frenum down. The man lost his testicles, but otherwise completely recovered. Brugh [c] reports an instance of injury to the genitalia in a boy of eighteen who was caught in a threshing-machine. The skin of the penis and scrotum, and the tissue from the pubes and inguinal region were torn from the body. Cicatrization and recovery were complete. Brigham [d] cites an analogous case in a youth of seventeen who was similarly caught in threshing machinery. The skin of the penis and the scrotum was entirely torn away; both sphincters of the anus were lacerated, and the perineum was divested of its skin for a space $2\frac{1}{2}$ inches wide. Recovery ensued, leaving a penis which measured, when flaccid, three inches long and $1\frac{1}{2}$ inches in diameter.

a 682, vii., 594.   b 548, 1857, 260.

c 545, 1877, 207.   d West. Lancet, Cincin., 1875–76, iv., 517.

There is a case reported [a] of a man who had his testicles caught in machinery while ginning cotton. The skin of the penis was stripped off to its root, the scrotum torn off from its base, and the testicles were contused and lacerated, and yet good recovery ensued. A peculiarity of this case was the persistent erection of the penis when cold was not applied.

Gibbs [b] mentions a case in which the entire scrotum and the perineum, together with an entire testicle and its cord attached, and nearly all the integument of the penis were torn off, yet the patient recovered with preservation of sexual powers. The patient was a negro of twenty-two who, while adjusting a belt, had his coat (closely buttoned) caught in the shafting, and his clothes and external genitals torn off. On examination it was found that the whole scrotum was wrenched off, and also the skin and cellular tissue, from $2\frac{1}{2}$ inches above the spine of the pubes down to the edge of the sphincter ani, including all the breadth of the perineum, together with the left testicle with five inches of its cord attached, and all the integument and cellular covering of the penis except a rim nearly half an inch wide at the extremity and continuous with the mucous membrane of the prepuce. The right testicle was hanging by its denuded cord, and was apparently covered only by the tunica vaginalis as high up as the abdominal ring, where the elastic feeling of the intestines was distinctly perceptible. There was not more than half an ounce of blood lost. The raw surface was dressed, the gap in the perineum brought together, and the patient made complete recovery, with preservation of his sexual powers. Other cases of injuries to the external genital organs (self-inflicted) will be found in the next chapter.

The preservation of the sexual power after injuries of this kind is not uncommon. There is a case reported [c] of a man whose testicles were completely torn away, and the perineal urethra so much injured that micturition took place through the wound. After a tedious process the wound healed and the man was discharged, but he returned in ten days with gonorrhea, stating that he had neither lost sexual desire nor power of satisfaction. Robbins [d] mentions a man of thirty-eight who, in 1874, had his left testicle removed. In the following year his right testicle became affected and was also removed. The patient stated that since the removal of the second gland he had regular sexual desire and coitus, apparently not differing from that in which he indulged before castration. For a few months previous to the time of report the cord on the left side, which had not been completely extirpated, became extremely painful and was also removed.

Atrophy of the testicle may follow venereal excess, and according to Larrey, deep wounds of the neck may produce the same result, with the loss of the features of virility. Guthrie [e] mentions a case of spontaneous absorption of the testicle. According to Larrey, on the return of the French Army

a 760, 1886–87, iv., 300.   b 264, 1855, 154.   c 224, 1885, 375.
d Quoted 224, 1881, i., 171.   e 476, 1832, ii., 670.

from the Egyptian expedition the soldiers complained of atrophy and disappearance of the testicle, without any venereal affection. The testicle would lose its sensibility, become soft, and gradually diminish in size. One testicle at a time was attacked, and when both were involved the patient was deprived of the power of procreation, of which he was apprised by the lack of desire and laxity of the penis. In this peculiar condition the general health seemed to fail, and the subjects occasionally became mentally deranged. Atrophy of the testicles has been known to follow an attack of mumps.

In his description of the diseases of Barbadoes Hendy mentions several peculiar cases under his observation in which the scrotum sloughed, leaving the testicles denuded. Alix and Richter[a] mention a singular modification of rheumatic inflammation of the testicle, in which the affection flitted from one testicle to the other, and alternated with rheumatic pains elsewhere.

There is a case of **retraction of the testicle** reported[b] in a young soldier of twenty-one who, when first seen, complained of a swelling in the right groin. He stated that while riding bareback his horse suddenly plunged and threw him on the withers. He at once felt a sickening pain in the groin and became so ill that he had to dismount. On inspection an oval tumor was seen in the groin, tender to the touch and showing no impulse on coughing. The left testicle was in its usual position, but the right was absent. The patient stated positively that both testicles were in situ before the accident. An attempt at reduction was made, but the pain was so severe that manipulation could not be endured. A warm bath and laudanum were ordered, but unfortunately, as the patient at stool gave a sudden bend to the left, his testicle slipped up into the abdomen and was completely lost to palpation. Orchitis threatened, but the symptoms subsided; the patient was kept under observation for some weeks, and then as a tentative measure, discharged to duty. Shortly afterward he returned, saying that he was ill, and that while lifting a sack of corn his testicle came partly down, causing him great pain. At the time of report his left testicle was in position, but the right could not be felt. The scrotum on that side had retracted until it had almost disappeared; the right external ring was very patent, and the finger could be passed up in the inguinal canal; there was no impulse on coughing and no tendency to hernia.

A unique case of **ectopia of the testicle** in a man of twenty-four is given by Popoff.[c] The scrotum was normally developed, and the right testicle in situ. The left half of the scrotum was empty, and at the root of the penis there was a swelling the size of a walnut, covered with normal skin, and containing an oval body about four-fifths the size of the testicle, but softer in constituency. The patient claimed that this swelling had been present since childhood. His sexual power had been normal, but for the past six months he had been impotent. In childhood the patient had a small inguinal hernia, and Popoff thought this caused the displacement of the testicle.

a 535, lxi.   b 224, 1885, i., 536.   c 812, No. 4, 1888, 75.

A somewhat similar case occurred in the Hôtel-Dieu, Paris. Through the agency of compression one of the testes was forced along the corpus cavernosum under the skin as far as the glans penis. It was easily reduced, and at a subsequent autopsy it was found that it had not been separated from the cord. Guitéras [a] cites a parallel case of dislocation of the testicle into the penis. It was the result of traumatism—a fall upon the wheel of a cart. It was reduced under anesthesia, after two incisions had been made, the adhesions broken up, and the shrunken sac enlarged by stretching.

Rupture of the spermatic arteries and veins has caused sudden death. Schleiser [b] is accredited with describing an instance in which a healthy man was engaged in a fray in the dark, and, suddenly crying out, fell into convulsions and died in five minutes. On examination the only injury found was the rupture of both spermatic arteries at the internal ring, produced by a violent pull on the scrotum and testicles by one of his antagonists. Shock was evidently a strong factor in this case. Fabricius Hildanus [c] gives a case of impotency due to lesions of the spermatic vessels following a burn. There is an old record [d] of an aged man who, on marrying, found that he had erections but no ejaculations. He died of ague, and at the autopsy it was found that the verumontanum was hard and of the size of a walnut, and that the ejaculatory ducts contained calculi about the size and shape of peas.

Hydrocele is a condition in which there is an abnormal quantity of fluid in the tunica vaginalis. It is generally caused by traumatism, violent muscular efforts, or straining, and is much more frequent in tropic countries than elsewhere. It sometimes attains an enormous size. Leigh [483] mentions a hydrocele weighing 120 pounds, and there are records of hydroceles weighing 40 [e] and 60 pounds.[f] Larrey speaks of a sarcocele in the coverings of the testicle which weighed 100 pounds. Mursinna [577] describes a hydrocele which measured 27 inches in its longest and 17 in its transverse axis.

Tedford [g] gives a curious case of **separation of the ovary** in a woman of twenty-eight. After suffering from invagination of the bowel and inflammation of the ovarian tissue, an ovary was discharged through an opening in the sigmoid flexure, and thence expelled from the anus.

In discussing **injuries of the vagina,** the first to be mentioned will be a remarkable case reported by Curran.[h] The subject was an Irish girl of twenty. While carrying a bundle of clothes that prevented her from seeing objects in front of her, she started to pass over a stile, just opposite to which a goat was lying. The woman wore no underclothing, and in the ascent her body was partially exposed, and, while in this enforced attitude, the goat,

---

[a] 538, Jan. 4, 1896.   [b] Casper's Wochenschrift, Oct. 22, 1842.
[c] 334, cent. v., obs. xl.   [d] 215, Ann. 2.   [e] 106, 1725, 492.
[f] Mém. de la Acad. des Sciences de Paris, 1711, 30.   [g] 701, 1886.   [h] 536, 1837, i., 116.

frightened by her approach, suddenly started up, and in so doing thrust his horn forcibly into her anus and about two or three inches up her rectum. The horn then passed through the bowel and its coverings, just above the hymen, and was then withdrawn as she flinched and fell back. The resultant wound included the lower part of the vagina and rectum, the sphincter ani, the fourchet, and perineum. Hemorrhage was profuse, and the wound caused excruciating pain. The subject fainted on the spot from hemorrhage and shock. Her modesty forbade her summoning medical aid for three days, during which time the wound was undergoing most primitive treatment. After suturing, cicatrization followed without delay.

Trompert [a] mentions a case of rupture of the vagina by the horn of a bull. There is a case recorded in the Pennsylvania Hospital Reports [623] of a girl of nineteen who jumped out of a second-story window. On reaching the ground, her foot turned under her as she fell. The high heel of a French boot was driven through the perineum one inch from the median line, midway between the anus and the posterior commissure of the labia majora. The wound extended into the vagina above the external opening, in which the heel, now separated from the boot, projected, and whence it was removed without difficulty. This wound was the only injury sustained by the fall.

Beckett [b] records a case of impalement in a woman of forty-five who, while attempting to obtain water from a hogshead, fell with one limb inside the cistern, striking a projecting stave three inches wide and $\frac{1}{2}$ inch thick. The external labia were divided, the left crus of the clitoris separated, the nymphæ lacerated, and the vaginal wall penetrated to the extent of five inches ; the patient recovered by the fourth week.

Homans [c] reports recovery from extensive wounds acquired by a negress who fell from a roof, striking astride an upright barrel. There was a wound of the perineum, and penetration of the posterior wall of the vagina, with complete separation of the soft parts from the symphysis pubis, and extrusion of the bladder.

Howe [d] reports a case of impalement with recovery in a girl of fifteen who slid down a hay-stack, striking a hay-hook which penetrated her perineum and passed into her body, emerging two inches below the umbilicus and one inch to the right of the median line.

Injuries of the vagina may be so extensive as to allow **protrusion of the intestines,** and some horrible cases of this nature are recorded. In The Lancet for 1873 [e] there is reported a murder or suicide of this description. The woman was found with a wound in the vagina, through which the intestines, with clean-cut ends, protruded. Over $7\frac{1}{2}$ feet of the intestines had been cut off in three pieces. The cuts were all clean and carefully separated from the mesentery. The woman survived her injuries a whole week, finally

a 587, xix., 311.   b Med. Annals, Albany, 1881, ii., 136.
c 218, 1883, cviii., 344.   d 218, 1840, xxii., 71.   e 476, 1873, i., 673.

succumbing to loss of blood and peritonitis. Her husband was tried for murder, but was acquitted by a Glasgow jury. Taylor[756] mentions similar cases of two women murdered in Edinburgh some years since, the wounds having been produced by razor slashes in the vagina. Taylor remarks that this crime seems to be quite common in Scotland. Starkey[a] reports an instance in which the body of an old colored woman was found, with evidences of vomiting, and her clothing stained with blood that had evidently come from her vagina. A postmortem showed the abdominal cavity to be full of blood ; at Douglas' culdesac there was a tear large enough to admit a man's hand, through which protruded a portion of the omentum ; this was at first taken for the membranes of an abortion. There were distinct signs of acute peritonitis. After investigation it was proved that a drunken glass-blower had been seen leaving her house with his hand and arm stained with blood. In his drunken frenzy this man had thrust his hand into the vagina, and through the junction of its posterior wall with the uterus, up into the abdominal cavity, and grasped the uterus, trying to drag it out. Outside of obstetric practice the injury is quite a rare one.

There is a case of death from a **ruptured clitoris** reported by Gutteridge.[b] The woman was kicked while in a stooping position and succumbed to a profuse hemorrhage, estimated to be between three and four pounds, and proceeding from a rupture of the clitoris.

Discharge of Vaginal Parietes.—Longhi[c] describes the case of a woman of twenty-seven, an epileptic, with metritis and copious catamenia twice a month. She was immoderately addicted to drink and sexual indulgence, and in February, 1835, her menses ceased. On May 8th she was admitted to the hospital with a severe epileptic convulsion, and until the 18th remained in a febrile condition, with abdominal tenderness, etc. On the 21st, while straining as if to discharge the contents of the rectum, she felt a voluminous body pass through the vagina, and fancied it was the expected fetus. After washing this mass it was found to be a portion of the vaginal parietes and the fleshy body of the neck of the uterus. The woman believed she had miscarried, and still persisted in refusing medicine. Cicatrization was somewhat delayed ; immediately on leaving the hospital she returned to her old habits, but the pain and hemorrhage attending copulation was so great that she had finally to desist. The vagina, however, gradually yielding, ceased to interfere with the gratification of her desires. Toward the end of June the menses reappeared and flowed with the greatest regularity. The portions discharged are preserved in the Milan Hospital.

The **injuries** received **during coitus** have been classified by Spaeth as follows : Deep tears of the hymen with profuse hemorrhage ; tears of the clitoris and of the urethra (in cases of atresia hymenis) ; vesicovaginal fistula ; laceration of the vaginal fornices, posteriorly or laterally ; laceration

a 453, 1889–90.   b 476, 1846, ii., 478.   c 376, No. 22.

of the septum of a duplex vagina ; injuries following coitus after perineorrhaphy. In the last century Plazzoni reports a case of vaginal rupture occurring during coitus. Green of Boston ; Mann of Buffalo ; Sinclair and Munro of Boston, all mention lacerations occurring during coitus. There is an instance recorded [a] of extensive laceration of the vagina in a woman, the result of coitus with a large dog. Haddon and Ross [b] both mention cases of rupture of the vagina in coitus ; and Martin [c] reports a similar case resulting in a young girl's death. Spaeth [d] speaks of a woman of thirty-one who, a few days after marriage, felt violent pain in coitus, and four days later she noticed that fecal matter escaped from the vagina during stool. Examination showed that the columns of the posterior wall were torn from their attachment, and that there was a rectovaginal fistula admitting the little finger. Hofmokl [e] cites an instance in which a powerful young man, in coitus with a widow of fifty-eight, caused a tear of her fornix, followed by violent hemorrhage. In another case by the same author, coitus in a sitting posture produced a rupture of the posterior fornix, involving the peritoneum ; although the patient lost much blood, she finally recovered. In a third instance, a young girl, whose lover had violent connection with her while she was in an exaggerated lithotomy position, suffered a large tear of the right vaginal wall. Hofmokl also describes the case of a young girl with an undeveloped vagina, absence of the uterus and adnexa, who during a forcible and unsuccessful attempt at coitus, had her left labium majus torn from the vaginal wall. The tear extended into the mons veneris and down to the rectum, and the finger could be introduced into the vaginal wound to the depth of two inches. The patient recovered in four weeks, but was still anemic from the loss of blood.

Crandall [f] cites instances in which hemorrhage, immediately after coitus of the marriage-night, was so active as to almost cause death. One of his patients was married three weeks previously, and was rapidly becoming exhausted from a constant flowing which started immediately after her first coitus. Examination showed this to be a case of active intrauterine hemorrhage excited by coitus soon after the menstrual flow had ceased and while the uterus and ovaries were highly congested. In another case the patient commenced flooding while at the dinner table in the Metropolitan Hotel in New York, and from the same cause an almost fatal hemorrhage ensued. Hirst of Philadelphia has remarked that brides have been found on their marital beds completely covered with blood, and that the hemorrhage may have been so profuse as to soak through the bed and fall on the floor. Lacerations of the urethra from urethral coitus in instances of vaginal atresia or imperforate hymen may also excite serious hemorrhage.

Foreign Bodies in the Vagina.—The elasticity of the vagina allows the presence in this passage of the most voluminous foreign bodies. When we

a St. Louis Med. Review, April, 1893.   b 252, 1876.   c 435, 1873.

d 832, Band xix.   e International Klin., Ruudschau, 1890.   f 545, 1876.

consider the passage of a fetal head through the vagina the ordinary foreign bodies, none of which ever approximate this size, seem quite reasonable. Goblets, hair-pins, needles, bottles, beer glasses, compasses, bobbins, pessaries, and many other articles have been found in the vagina. It is quite possible for a phosphatic incrustation to be found about a foreign body tolerated in this location for some time. Hubbauer [a] speaks of a young girl of nineteen in whose vagina there was a glass fixed by incrustations which held it solidly in place. It had been there for six months and was only removed with great difficulty. Holmes [b] cites a peculiar case in which the neck of a bottle was found in the vagina of a woman. One point of the glass had penetrated the bladder and a calculus had formed on this as well as on the vaginal end.

When a foreign body remains in the vagina for a long time and if it is composed of material other than glass, it becomes influenced by the corrosive action of the vaginal secretion. For instance, Cloquet removed a foreign body which was incrusted in the vagina, and found the cork pessary which had formed its nucleus completely rotted. A similar instrument found by Gosselin [c] had remained in the vagina thirty-six years, and was incrustated with calcareous salts. Metal is always attacked by the vaginal secretions in the most marked manner. Cloquet mentions that at an autopsy of a woman who had a pewter goblet in her vagina, lead oxid was found in the gangrenous debris.

Fig. 227.—Pessary incrusted with phosphates after long sojourn in the vagina (after Poulet).

Long Retention of Pessaries, etc.—The length of time during which pessaries may remain in the vagina is sometimes astonishing. The accompanying illustration (Fig. 227) shows the phosphatic deposits and incrustations around a pessary after a long sojourn in the vagina. The specimen is in the Musée Dupuytren. Pinet mentions a pessary that remained in situ for twenty-five years. Gerould of Massilon, Ohio, reports a case in which a pessary had been worn by a German woman of eighty-four for more than fifty years. She had forgotten its existence until reminded of it by irritation some years before death. It was remarkable that when the pessary was removed it was found to have largely retained its original wax covering. Hurxthal [d] mentions the removal of a pessary which had been in the pelvis for forty-one years. Jackson[a] speaks of a glove-pessary remaining in the vagina thirty-five years. Mackey[b] reports the removal of a glass pessary after fifty-five years' incarceration.

There is an account[c] of a young girl addicted to onanism who died from the presence of a pewter cup in her vagina; it had been there fourteen months. Shame had led her to conceal her condition for all the period during which she suffered pain in the hypogastrium, and diarrhea. She had steadily refused examination. Bazzanella of Innsbruck removed a drinking glass from the vagina by means of a pair of small obstetric forceps. The glass had been placed there ten years previously by the woman's husband. Szigethy[d] reports the case of a woman of seventy-five who, some thirty years before, introduced into her vagina a ball of string previously dipped in wax. The ball was effectual in relieving a prolapsed uterus, and was worn with so little discomfort that she entirely forgot it until it was forced out of place by a violent effort. The ball was seven inches in circumference, and covered with mucus, but otherwise unchanged. Breisky[644] is accredited with the report of a case of a woman suffering with dysmenorrhea, in whose vagina was found a cotton reel which had been introduced seven years before. The woman made a good recovery. Pearse[e] mentions a woman of thirty-six who had suffered menorrhagia for ten days, and was in a state of great prostration and suffering from strong colicky pains. On examination he found a silk-bobbin about an inch from the entrance, which the patient had introduced fourteen years before. She had already had attacks of peritonitis and hemorrhage, and a urethro-vaginal fistula was found. The bobbin itself was black. This patient had been married twice, and had been cared for by physicians, but the existence of a body $\frac{3}{4}$ inch long had never been noticed. Poulet quotes two curious cases:[f] in one a pregnant woman was examined by a doctor who diagnosticated carcinomatous degeneration of the neck of the uterus. Capuron, who was consulted relative to the case, did not believe that the state of the woman's health warranted the diagnosis, and on further examination the growth was found to have been a sponge which had previously been introduced by the woman into the vagina. The other case, reported by Guyon, exemplified another error in diagnosis. The patient was a woman who suffered from continuous vaginal hemorrhage, and had been given extensive treatment without success. Finally, when the woman was in extreme exhaustion, an injection of vinegar-water was ordered, the use of which was followed by the expulsion from the vagina of a **live leech** of a species very abundant in the country. The hemorrhage immediately ceased and health returned.

There is a record[g] of a woman of twenty-eight who was suddenly surprised by some one entering her chamber at the moment she was introducing

a 437, 1882, iii., 83.   b 771, 1888.   c 789, March 4, 1848.

d 614, 1890.   e 224, June 28, 1873.   f 641, 621.   g 550, xxix., 15.

a cedar pencil into her vagina. With the purpose of covering up her act and dissembling the woman sat down, and the shank of the wood was pushed through the posterior wall of the vagina into the peritoneal cavity. The intestine was, without doubt, pierced in two of its curves, which was demonstrated later by an autopsy. A plastic exudation had evidently agglutinated the intestine at the points of penetration, and prevented an immediate fatal issue. Erichsen practised extraction eight months after the accident, and a pencil 5½ inches long, having a strong fecal odor, was brought out. The patient died the fourth day after the operation, from peritonitis, and an autopsy showed the perforation and agglutination of the two intestinal curvatures. Getchell [a] relates the description of a calculus in the vagina, formed about a hair-pin as a nucleus. It is reported that a country girl came to the Hôtel-Dieu to consult Dupuytren, and stated that several years before she had been violated by some soldiers, who had introduced an unknown foreign body into her vagina, which she never could extract. Dupuytren found this to be a small metallic pot, two inches in diameter, with its concavity toward the uterus. It contained a solid black substance of a most fetid odor.

Foreign bodies are generally introduced **in the uterus** either accidentally in vaginal applications, or for the purpose of producing abortion. Zuhmeister [720] describes a case of a woman who shortly after the first manifestations of pregnancy used a twig of a tree to penetrate the matrix. She thrust it so strongly into the uterus that the wall was perforated, and the twig became planted in the region of the kidneys. Although six inches long and of the volume of a goose feather, this branch remained five months in the pelvis without causing any particular inconvenience, and was finally discharged by the rectum. Brignatelli [b] mentions the case of a woman who, in culpable practices, introduced the stalk of a reed into her uterus. She suffered no inconvenience until the next menstrual epoch which was accompanied by violent pains. She presented the appearance of one in the pains of labor. The matrix had augmented in volume, and the orifice of the uterine cervix was closed, but there was hypertrophy as if in the second or third month of pregnancy. After examination a piece of reed three cm. long was extracted from the uterus, its external face being incrusted with hard calcareous material. Meschede of Schwetz, Germany, mentions death from a hair-pin in the uterine cavity.

Crouzit [c] was called to see a young girl who had attempted criminal abortion by a darning-needle. When he arrived a fetus of about three months had already been expelled, and had been wounded by the instrument. It was impossible to remove the needle, and the placenta was not expelled for two days. Eleven days afterward the girl commenced to have pains in the inguinal region, and by the thirty-fifth day an elevation was formed, and the pains increased in violence. On the seventy-ninth day a needle six inches

[a] 547, 1873, iii., 635.   [b] 641, 628.   [c] 162, 1823, T. iii.

long was expelled from the swelling in the groin, and the patient recovered. Lisfranc extracted from the uterus of a woman who supposed herself to be pregnant at the third month, a fragment of a large gum-elastic sound which during illicit maneuvers had broken off within five cm. of its extremity, and penetrated the organ. Lisfranc found there was not the slightest sign of pregnancy, despite the woman's belief that she was with child.

CHAPTER XIV.

MISCELLANEOUS SURGICAL ANOMALIES.

Marvelous Recoveries from Multiple Injuries.—There are injuries so numerous or so great in extent, and so marvelous in their recovery, that they are worthy of record in a section by themselves. They are found particularly in military surgery. In the Medical and Philosophical Commentaries for 1779 [a] is the report of the case of a lieutenant who was wounded through the lungs, liver, and stomach, and in whose armpit lodged a ball. It was said that when the wound in his back was injected, the fluid would immediately be coughed up from his lungs. Food would pass through the wound of the stomach. The man was greatly prostrated, but after eleven months of convalescence he recovered. In the brutal capture of Fort Griswold, Connecticut, in 1781, in which the brave occupants were massacred by the British, Lieutenant Avery had an eye shot out, his skull fractured, the brain-substance scattering on the ground, was stabbed in the side, and left for dead ; yet he recovered and lived to narrate the horrors of the day forty years after.

A French invalid-artillery soldier, from his injuries and a peculiar mask he used to hide them, was known as " *L'homme à la tête de cire.*" The Lancet gives his history briefly as follows : During the Franco-Prussian War, he was horribly wounded by the bursting of a Prussian shell. His whole face, including his two eyes, were literally blown away, some scanty remnants of the osseous and muscular systems, and the skull covered with hair being left. His wounds healed, giving him such a hideous and ghastly appearance that he was virtually ostracized from the sight of his fellows. For his relief a dentist by the name of Delalain constructed a mask which included a false palate and a set of false teeth. This apparatus was so perfect that the functions of respiration and mastication were almost completely restored to their former condition, and the man was able to speak distinctly, and even to play the flute. His sense of smell also returned. He wore two false eyes simply to fill up the cavities of the orbits, for the parts representing the eyes were closed. The mask was so well-adapted to what remained of the real face, that it was considered by all one of the finest specimens of the prothetic art that could be devised. This soldier, whose name was Moreau, was living and in perfect health at the time of the report, his bizarre face, without expression, and his sobriquet, as mentioned, making him an object of great curiosity. He wore the Cross of Honor, and nothing delighted him more than to talk about the war. To augment his meager pension he sold a pamphlet containing in detail an account of his injuries and a description of the skilfully devised apparatus by which his declining life was made endurable. A somewhat similar case is mentioned on page 585.

A most remarkable case of a soldier suffering numerous and almost incredible injuries and recovering and pursuing his vocation with undampened ardor is that of Jacques Roellinger, Company B, 47th New York Volunteers. [a] He appeared before a pension board in New York, June 29, 1865, with the following history: In 1862 he suffered a sabre-cut across the quadriceps extensor of the left thigh, and a sabre-thrust between the bones of the forearm at the middle third. Soon afterward at Williamsburg, Va., he was shot in the thigh, the ball passing through the middle third external to the femur. At Fort Wagner, 1863, he had a sword-cut, severing the spinal muscles and overlying tissue for a distance of six inches. Subsequently he was captured by guerillas in Missouri and tortured by burning splinters of wood, the cicatrices of which he exhibited; he escaped to Florida, where he was struck by a fragment of an exploding shell, which passed from without inward, behind the hamstring on the right leg, and remained embedded and could be plainly felt. When struck he fell and was fired on by the retiring enemy. A ball entered between the 6th and 7th ribs just beneath the apex of the heart, traversed the lungs and issued at the right 9th rib. He fired his revolver on reception of this shot, and was soon bayonetted by his own comrades by mistake, this wound also penetrating the body. He showed a depressed triangular cicatrix on the margin of the epigastrium. If the scars are at all indicative, the bayonet must have passed through the left lobe of the liver and border of the diaphragm. Finally he was struck by a pistol-ball at the lower angle of the left lower jaw, this bullet issuing on the other side of the neck. As exemplary of the easy manner in which he bore his many injuries during a somewhat protracted convalescence, it may be added that he amused his comrades by blowing jets of water through the apertures on both sides of his neck. Beside the foregoing injuries he received many minor ones, which he did not deem worthy of record or remembrance. The greatest disability he suffered at the time of applying for a pension resulted from an ankylosed knee. Not satisfied with his experience in our war, he stated to the pension examiners that he was on his way to join Garibaldi's army. This case is marvelous when we consider the proximity of several of the wounds to a vital part; the slightest deviation of position would surely have resulted in a fatal issue for this apparently charmed life. The following table shows the man's injuries in the order of their reception:—

(1) Sabre-cut across the quadriceps femoris of right leg, dividing the tendinous and muscular structures.

a 538, 1875, 685.

(2) Sabre-thrust between the bones in the middle third of the right forearm.

(3) Shot in the right thigh, the ball passing through the middle third.

(4) A sword-cut across the spinal muscles covering the lower dorsal vertebræ.

(5) Tortured by guerillas in Indian fashion by having burning splinters of wood applied to the surface of his right thorax.

(6) An exploded shell passed through the hamstring muscles of the right thigh and embedded itself in the ligamentous tissues of the internal condyle of the femur.

(7) Shot by a ball between the 6th and 7th ribs of the left side.

(8) Bayonetted through the body, the steel passing through the left lobe of the liver and penetrating the posterior border of the diaphragm.

(9) Pistol-ball shot through the sternocleido muscle of one side of the neck, emerging through the corresponding muscle of the other side of the neck.

(10) Sabre-thrust between the bones of the left forearm.

(11) Pistol-shot through the left pectoralis major and left deltoid muscles.

(12) Deep cut dividing the commissure between the left thumb and forefinger down to the carpal bones.

Somewhat analogous to the foregoing is a case reported in 1834 by McCosh from Calcutta. The patient was a native who had been dreadfully butchered in the Chooar campaign. One of his hands was cut off above the wrist. The remaining stump was nearly amputated by a second blow. A third blow penetrated the shoulder-joint. Beside these and several other slashes, he had a cut across the abdomen extending from the umbilicus to the spine. This cut divided the parietes and severed one of the coats of the colon. The intestines escaped and lay by his side. He was then left on the ground as dead. On arrival at the hospital his wounds were dressed and he speedily convalesced, but the injured colon ruptured and an artificial anus was formed and part of the feces were discharged through the wound. This man was subsequently seen at Midnapore healthy and lusty although his body was bent to one side in consequence of a large cicatrix; a small portion of the feces occasionally passed through the open wound.

There is an account [a] of a private soldier, aged twenty-seven, who suffered a gunshot wound of the skull, causing compound fracture of the cranium, and who also received compound fractures of both bones of the leg. He did not present himself for treatment until ten days later. At this time the head-injury caused him no inconvenience, but it was necessary to amputate the leg and remove the necrosed bones from the cranial wounds; the patient recovered.

Recovery After Injuries by Machinery, with Multiple Fractures, etc.—Persons accidentally caught in some portions of powerful machinery

[a] 597, 1866, 219.

usually suffer several major injuries, any one of which might have been fatal, yet there are marvelous instances of recovery after wounds of this nature. Phares [a] records the case of a boy of nine who, while playing in the saw-gate of a cotton-press, was struck by the lever in revolution, the blow fracturing both bones of the leg about the middle. At the second revolution his shoulder was crushed ; the third passed over him, and the fourth, with maximum momentum struck his head, carrying away a large part of the integument, including one eyebrow, portions of the skull, membranes, and brain-substance. A piece of cranial bone was found sticking in the lever, and there were stains of brain on all the 24 posts around the circumference of the hole. Possibly from $1\frac{1}{2}$ to two ounces of cerebral substance were lost. A physician was called, but thinking the case hopeless he declined to offer surgical interference. Undaunted, the father of the injured lad straightened the leg, adjusted the various fractures, and administered calomel and salts. The boy progressively recovered, and in a few weeks his shoulder and legs were well. About this time a loosened fragment of the skull was removed almost the size and shape of a dessertspoon, with the handle attached, leaving a circular opening directly over the eye as large as a Mexican dollar, through which cerebral pulsation was visible. A peculiar feature of this case was that the boy never lost consciousness, and while one of his playmates ran for assistance he got out of the hole himself, and moved to a spot ten feet distant before any help arrived, and even then he declined proffered aid from a man he disliked. This boy stated that he remembered each revolution of the lever and the individual injuries that each inflicted. Three years after his injury he was in every respect well. Fraser [b] mentions an instance of a boy of fifteen who was caught in the crank of a balance-wheel in a shingle-mill, and was taken up insensible. His skull was fractured at the parietal eminence and the pericranium stripped off, leaving a bloody tumor near the base of the fracture about two inches in diameter. The right humerus was fractured at the external condyle ; there was a fracture of the coronoid process of the ulna, and a backward dislocation at the elbow. The annular ligament was ruptured, and the radius was separated from the ulna. On the left side there was a fracture of the anatomic neck of the humerus, and a dislocation downward. The boy was trephined, and the comminuted fragments removed ; in about six weeks recovery was nearly complete. Gibson [c] reports the history of a girl of eight who was caught by her clothing in a perpendicular shaft in motion, and carried around at a rate of 150 or 200 times a minute until the machinery could be stopped. Although she was found in a state of shock, she was anesthetized, in order that immediate attention could be given to her injuries, which were found to be as follows :—

(1) An oblique fracture of the middle third of the right femur.

a Richmond Med. Jour., 1868.   b 124, 1869.   c 218, 1881, 61.

(2) A transverse fracture of the middle third of the left femur.

(3) A slightly comminuted transverse fracture of the middle third of the left tibia and fibula.

(4) A transverse fracture of the lower third of the right humerus.

(5) A fracture of the lower third of the right radius.

(6) A partial radiocarpal dislocation.

(7) Considerable injuries of the soft parts at the seats of fracture, and contusions and abrasions all over the body.

During convalescence the little patient suffered an attack of measles, but after careful treatment it was found by the seventy-eighth day that she had recovered without bony deformity, and that there was bony union in all the fractures. There was slight tilting upward in the left femur, in which the fracture had been transverse, but there was no perceptible shortening.

Hulke [a] describes a silver-polisher of thirty-six who, while standing near a machine, had his sleeve caught by a rapidly-turning wheel, which drew him in and whirled him round and round, his legs striking against the ceiling and floor of the room. It was thought the wheel had made 50 revolutions before the machinery was stopped. After his removal it was found that his left humerus was fractured at its lower third, and apparently comminuted. There was no pulse in the wrist in either the radial or ulnar arteries, but there was pulsation in the brachial as low as the ecchymosed swelling. Those parts of the hand and fingers supplied by the median and radial nerves were insensible. The right humerus was broken at the middle, the end of the upper fragment piercing the triceps, and almost protruding through the skin. One or more of the middle ribs on the right side were broken near the angle, and there was a large transverse rent in the quadriceps extensor. Despite this terrible accident the man made a perfect recovery, with the single exception of limitation of flexion in the left elbow-joint.

Dewey [b] details a description of a girl of six who was carried around the upright shaft of a flour mill in which her clothes became entangled. Some part of the body struck the bags or stones with each revolution. She sustained a fracture of the left humerus near the insertion of the deltoid, a fracture of the middle third of the left femur, a compound fracture of the left femur in the upper third, with protrusion of the upper fragment and considerable venous hemorrhage, and fracture of the right tibia and fibula at the upper third. When taken from the shafting the child was in a moribund state, with scarcely perceptible pulse, and all the accompanying symptoms of shock. Her injuries were dressed, the fractures reduced, and starch bandages applied; in about six weeks there was perfect union, the right leg being slightly shortened. Six months later she was playing about, with only a slight halt in her gait.

Miscellaneous Multiple Fractures.—Westmoreland [c] speaks of a man

[a] 767, 1878.   [b] 124, 1854.   [c] Atlanta Acad. of Med., 1874.

who was pressed between two cars, and sustained a fracture of both collar-bones and of the sternum ; in addition, six or eight ribs were fractured, driven into and lacerating the lung. The heart was displaced. In spite of these terrible injuries, the man was rational when picked up, and lived nearly half a day. In comment on this case Battey mentions an instance in which a mill-sawyer was run over by 20 or 30 logs, which produced innumerable fractures of his body, constituting him a surgical curiosity. He afterward completely recovered, and, as a consequence of his miraculous escape, became a soothsayer in his region. West[a] reports a remarkable recovery after a compound fracture of the femur, fracture of the jaw, and of the radius, and possibly injury to the base of the skull, and injury to the spine.

There is on record[b] an account of a woman of forty-three who, by muscular action in lifting a stone, fractured her pubes, external to the spine, on the left side. Not realizing her injury she continued hard work all that day, but fell exhausted on the next. She recovered in about a month, and was able to walk as well as ever.

Vinnedge[c] reports recovery after concussion of the brain and extreme shock, associated with fracture of the left femur, and comminuted fractures of the left tibia and fibula.

Tufnell[d] mentions recovery after compound comminuted fracture of the leg, with simple fracture of both collar-bones, and dislocation of the thumb. Nankivell[e] speaks of a remarkable recovery in an individual who suffered compound comminuted fracture of both legs, and fracture of the skull. It was found necessary to amputate the right thigh and left leg. Erichsen[f] effected recovery by rest alone, in an individual whose ribs and both clavicles were fractured by being squeezed.

Gilman[g] records recovery after injuries consisting of fracture of the frontal bone near the junction with the right parietal ; fracture of the right radius and ulna at the middle third and at the wrist ; and compound fracture of the left radius and ulna, $1\frac{1}{4}$ inches above the wrist. Boulting[h] reports a case of an individual who suffered compound fractures of the skull and humerus, together with extensive laceration of the thigh and chest, and yet recovered.

Barwell[i] mentions recovery after amputation of the shoulder-joint, in an individual who had suffered fracture of the base of the skull, fracture of the jaw, and compound fracture of the right humerus. There was high delirium followed by imbecility in this case. Bonnet[j] reports a case of fracture of both thighs, two right ribs, luxation of the clavicle, and accidental club-foot with tenotomy, with good recovery from all the complications. Beach[k] speaks

a 476, 1879.
b 672, Sept. 30, 1868.
c Toledo Med. and Surg. Jour., 1880.
d 312, xlvi., 337.
e 476, 1873, ii., 264.
f 476, 1861, ii., 229.
g 218, 1881, 275.
h 548, 1879, i., 702.
i 548, 1879, ii., 64.
j Bull. Soc. de Méd. de Poitiers, 1854, 305.
k 218, cii., 35.

of an individual who suffered fracture of both thighs, and compound comminuted fracture of the tibia, fibula, and tarsal bones into the ankle-joint, necessitating amputation of the leg. The patient not only survived the operation, but recovered with good union in both thighs. As illustrative of the numerous fractures a person may sustain at one time, the London Medical Gazette[a] mentions an injury to a girl of fourteen, which resulted in 31 fractures.

Remarkable Falls.—In this connection it is of interest to note from how great a height a person may fall without sustaining serious injury. A remarkable fall of a miner down 100 meters of shaft (about 333 feet) without being killed is recorded by M. Reumeaux in the Bulletin de l'Industrie Minérale. Working with his brother in a gallery which issued on the shaft, he forgot the direction in which he was pushing a truck; so it went over, and he after it, falling into some mud with about three inches of water. As stated in Nature, he seems neither to have struck any of the wood debris, nor the sides of the shaft, and he showed no contusions when he was helped out by his brother after about ten minutes. He could not, however, recall any of his impressions during the fall. The velocity on reaching the bottom would be about 140 feet, and time of fall 4.12 seconds; but it is thought he must have taken longer. It appears strange that he should have escaped simple suffocation and loss of consciousness during a time sufficient for the water to have drowned him.

While intoxicated Private Gough of the 42d Royal Highlanders[b] attempted to escape from the castle at Edinburgh. He fell almost perpendicularly 170 feet, fracturing the right frontal sinus, the left clavicle, tibia, and fibula. In five months he had so far recovered as to be put on duty again, and he served as an efficient soldier. There is an account[c] of recovery after a fall of 192 feet, from a cliff in County Antrim, Ireland. Manzini[d] mentions a man who fell from the dome of the Invalides in Paris, without sustaining any serious accident, and there is a record from Madrid[e] of a much higher fall than this without serious consequence. In 1792[f] a bricklayer fell from the fourth story of a high house in Paris, landing with his feet on the dirt and his body on stone. He bled from the nose, and lost consciousness for about forty-five minutes; he was carried to the Hôtel-Dieu where it was found that he had considerable difficulty in breathing; the regions about the external malleoli were contused and swollen, but by the eighth day the patient had recovered. In the recent reparation of the Hotel Raleigh in Washington, D. C., a man fell from the top of the building, which is above the average height, fracturing several ribs and rupturing his lung. He was taken to the Emergency Hospital where he was put to bed, and persistent treatment for shock was pursued; little hope of the man's recovery was

a Quoted 124, 1833. b 124, 1837. c 312, 1850.
d 363, 1841. e 354, 1846, ii. f 302, iv., 248.

entertained. His friends were told of his apparently hopeless condition. There were no external signs of the injury with the exception of the emphysema following rupture of the lung. Respiration was limited and thoracic movement diminished by adhesive straps and a binder; under careful treatment the man recovered.

Kartulus[a] mentions an English boy of eight who, on June 1, 1879, while playing on the terrace in the third story of a house in Alexandria, in attempting to fly a kite in company with an Arab servant, slipped and fell 71 feet to a granite pavement below. He was picked up conscious, but both legs were fractured about the middle. He had so far recovered by the 24th of July that he could hobble about on crutches. On the 15th of November of the same year he was seen by Kartulus racing across the playground with some other boys ; as he came in third in the race he had evidently lost little of his agility. Parrott[b] reports the history of a man of fifty, weighing 196 pounds, who fell 110 feet from the steeple of a church. In his descent he broke a scaffold pole in two, and fell through the wooden roof of an engine-house below, breaking several planks and two strong joists, and landing upon some sacks of cement inside the house. When picked up he was unconscious, but regained his senses in a short time, and it was found that his injuries were not serious. The left metacarpal bones were dislocated from the carpal bones, the left tibia was fractured, and there were contusions about the back and hips. Twelve days later he left for home with his leg in plaster. Farber and McCassy[c] report a case in which a man fell 50 feet perpendicularly through an elevator shaft, fracturing the skull. Pieces of bone at the superior angle of the occipital bone were removed, leaving the dura exposed for a space one by four inches. The man was unconscious for four days, but entirely recovered in eighteen days, with only a slightly subnormal hearing as an after-effect of his fall.

For many years there have been persons who have given exhibitions of **high jumps,** either landing in a net or in the water. Some of these hazardous individuals do not hesitate to **dive from enormous heights,** being satisfied to strike head first or to turn a somersault in their descent. Nearly all the noted bridges in this country have had their " divers." The death of Odlum in his attempt to jump from Brooklyn bridge is well known. Since then it has been claimed that the feat has been accomplished without any serious injury. It is reported that on June 20, 1896, a youth of nineteen made a headlong dive from the top of the Eads bridge at St. Louis, Mo., a distance of 125 feet. He is said to have swum 250 feet to a waiting tug, and was taken on board without having been hurt.

Probably the most interesting exhibition of this kind that was ever seen was at the Royal Aquarium, London, in the summer of 1895. A part of the regular nightly performance at this Hall, which is familiar on account of its immens-

a 476, 1880, i., 486.   b 224, 1886, ii., 451.   c Lancet-Clinic, Feb. 22, 1896.

ity, was the jump of an individual from the rafters of the large arched roof into a tank of water about 15 by 20 feet, and from eight to ten feet deep, sunken in the floor of the hall. Another performer, dressed in his ordinary street clothes, was tied up in a bag and jumped about two-thirds of this height into the same tank, breaking open the bag and undressing himself before coming to the surface. In the same performance a female acrobat made a backward dive from the topmost point of the building into a net stretched about ten feet above the floor. Nearly every large acrobatic entertainment has one of these individuals who seem to experience no difficulty in duplicating their feats night after night.

It is a common belief that people falling from great heights die in the act of descent. An interview with the sailor who fell from the top-gallant of an East Indiaman, a height of 120 feet, into the water, elicited the fact that during the descent in the air, sensation entirely disappeared, but returned in a slight degree when he reached the water, but he was still unable to strike out when rising to the surface. By personal observation this man stated that he believed that if he had struck a hard substance his death would have been painless, as he was sure that he was entirely insensible during the fall.[a]

A writer in the Pall Mall Gazette,[b] in speaking of the accidents which had happened in connection with the Forth Bridge, tells of a man who trusted himself to work at the height of 120 feet above the waters of the Firth, simply grasping a rope. His hands became numb with cold, his grasp relaxed, and he fell backward down into the water, but was brought out alive. In another instance a spanner fell a distance of 300 feet, knocked off a man's cap, and broke its way through a four-inch plank. Again, another spanner fell from a great height, actually tearing off a man's clothes, from his waistcoat to his ankle, but leaving him uninjured. On another occasion a staging with a number of workmen thereon gave way. Two of the men were killed outright by striking some portion of the work in their descent; two others fell clear of the girders, and were rescued from the Firth little worse for their great fall.

Resistance of Children to Injuries.—It is a remarkable fact that young children, whose bones, cartilages, and tissues are remarkably elastic, are sometimes able to sustain the passage over their bodies of vehicles of great weight without apparent injury. There is a record early in this century [c] of a child of five who was run over across the epigastrium by a heavy two-wheeled cart, but recovered without any bad symptoms. The treatment in this case is quite interesting, and was as follows: venesection to faintness, castor oil in infusion of senna until there was a free evacuation of the bowels, 12 leeches to the abdomen and spine, and a saline mixture every two hours! Such depleting therapeutics would in themselves seem almost sufficient to

[a] 476, 1889, ii., 466. [b] Sept., 1888. [c] 476, 1829, 652.

provoke a fatal issue, and were given in good faith as the means of effecting a recovery in such a case. In a similar instance[a] a wagon weighing 1200 pounds passed over a child of five, with no apparent injury other than a bruise near the ear made by the wheel.

Infant-vitality is sometimes quite remarkable, a newly-born child sometimes surviving extreme exposure and major injuries. There was a remarkable instance of this kind brought to light in the Mullings *vs.* Mullings divorce-case, recorded in The Lancet.[b] It appeared that Mrs. Mullings, a few hours after her confinement at Torquay, packed her newly-born infant boy in a portmanteau, and started for London. She had telegraphed Dr. J. S. Tulloch to meet her at Paddington, where he found his patient apparently in good condition, and not weak, as he expected in a woman shortly to be confined. On the way to her apartments, which had been provided by Dr. Tulloch, Mrs. Mullings remarked to the Doctor that she had already borne her child. Dr. Tulloch was greatly surprised, and immediately inquired what she had done with the baby. She replied that it was in a box on top of the cab. When the box was opened the child was found alive. The Lancet comments on the remarkable fact that, shortly after confinement, a woman can travel six or seven hours in a railroad train, and her newly-born babe conveyed the same distance in a portmanteau, without apparent injury, and without attracting attention.

Booth[c] reports a remarkable case of vitality of a newly-born child which came under his observation in October, 1894. An illegitimate child, abandoned by its mother, was left at the bottom of a cesspool vault; she claimed that ten hours before Booth's visit it had been accidentally dropped during an attempt to micturate. The infant lived despite the following facts : Its delivery from an ignorant, inexperienced, unattended negress ; its cord not tied ; its fall of 12 feet down the pit ; its ten hours' exposure in the cesspool ; its smothering by foul air, also by a heavy covering of rags, paper, and straw ; its pounding by three bricks which fell in directly from eight feet above (some loose bricks were accidentally dislodged from the sides of the vault, in the maneuvers to extricate the infant) ; its lowered temperature previous to the application of hot bottles, blankets, and the administration of cardiac stimulants. Booth adds that the morning after its discovery the child appeared perfectly well, and some two months afterward was brought into court as evidence in the case. A remarkable case of infant vitality is given on page 117.

Operations in the Young and Old.—It might be of interest to mention that such a major operation as ovariotomy has been successfully performed in an infant. In a paper on infant ovariotomy[d] several instances of this nature are mentioned. Roemer successfully performed ovariotomy on a child one year and eight months old ; Swartz, on a child of four ; Barker, on

a 218, 1847.   b 476, 1874, ii., 169.   c 792, Feb., 1895.   d 224, 1884, i., 234.

a child of four; Knowsley Thornton, on a child of seven, and Spencer Wells, Cupples, and Chenoweth, on children of eight. Rein performed ovariotomy on a girl of six, suffering from a multilocular cyst of the left ovary. He expresses his belief that childhood and infancy are favorable to laparotomy.

Kidd[a] removed a dermoid from a child of two years and eleven months; Hooks[b] performed the same operation on a child of thirty months. Chiene[c] extirpated an ovary from a child of three; Neville[d] duplicated this operation in a child one month younger; and Alcock[e] performed ovariotomy on a child of three.

Successful ovariotomies are infrequent in the extremely aged. Bennett[f] mentions an instance in a woman of seventy-five, and Davies[g] records a similar instance. Borsini[h] and Terrier[i] cite instances of successful ovariotomy in patients of seventy-seven. Carmichael[j] performed the operation at seventy-four. Owens[k] mentions it at eighty; and Homans[l] at eighty-two years and four months. Dewees[m] records a successful case of ovariotomy in a woman over sixty-seven; McNutt[n] reports a successful instance in a patient of sixty-seven years and six months; the tumor weighed 60 pounds, and there were extensive adhesions. Maury removed a monocystic ovarian tumor from a woman of seventy-four, his patient recovering. Pippingsköld mentions an ovariotomy at eighty. Terrier[o] describes double ovariotomy for fibromata in a woman of seventy-seven. Aron[p] speaks of an operation for pilous dermoid of the ovary in a woman of seventy-five. Shepherd[q] reports a case of recurrent proliferous cyst in a woman of sixty-three, on whom successful ovariotomy was performed twice within nine months. Wells[r] mentions an ovarian cyst in a woman of sixty-five, from which 72 pints of fluid were removed.

Hawkins[s] describes the case of a musician, M. Rochard, who at the age of one hundred and seven was successfully operated on for strangulated hernia of upward of thirty hours' duration. The wound healed by first intention, and the man was well in two weeks. Fowler[t] operated successfully for strangulated umbilical hernia on a patient of sixty-eight.

Repeated Operations.—Franzolini[u] speaks of a woman of fifty on whom he performed six celiotomies between June, 1879, and April, 1887. The first operation was for fibrocystic disease of the uterus. Since the last operation the woman had had remarkably good health, and there was every indication that well-merited recovery had been effected. The Ephemerides contains an account of a case in which cystotomy was repeated four times, and there is another record of this operation having been done five times on a man.[v] Instances of repeated Cesarean section are mentioned on page 130.

a 610, 1880, 241.   b 125, 1886, 1022.   c 318, 1883–84, 1132.
d Proc. Dublin Obst. Soc., 1879–80, 16.   e 476, 1871, ii., 850.   f 130, 1861.
g 223, 1887.   h 688, 1881.   i 653, 1888.   j 590, 1883.   k 223, 1889.   l 538, 1888.
m 548, 1864, i., 560.   n West. Lancet, San Francisco, 1879–80, viii., 485.
o 653, 1888, vii., 466.   p 363, xlvi., 1065.   q 476, 1886, i., 1162.   r 779, x., 189.
s 490, Dec. 9, 1842.   t 224, 1884, i., 555.   u 361, 1889.   v 708, 1718, 1985.

Before leaving this subject, we mention a **marvelous operation performed by Billroth** [a] on a married woman of twenty-nine, after her sixth pregnancy. This noted operator performed, synchronously, double ovariotomy and resections of portions of the bladder and ileum, for a large medullary carcinomatous growth of the ovary, with surrounding involvement. Menstruation returned three months after the operation, and in fifteen months the patient was in good health in every way, with no apparent danger of recurrence of the disease.

Self-performed Surgical Operations.—There have been instances in which surgeons and even laymen have performed considerable operations upon themselves. On the battlefield men have amputated one of their own limbs that had been shattered. In such cases there would be little pain, and premeditation would not be brought into play in the same degree as in the case of M. Clever de Maldigny, a surgeon in the Royal Guards of France, who successfully performed a lithotomy on himself before a mirror. He says that after the operation was completed the urine flowed in abundance; he dressed the wound with lint dipped in an emollient solution, and, being perfectly relieved from pain, fell into a sound sleep. On the following day, M. Maldigny says, he was as tranquil and cheerful as if he had never been a sufferer. A Dutch blacksmith and a German cooper each performed lithotomy on themselves for the intense pain caused by a stone in the bladder. Tulpius,[842] Walther,[815] and the Ephemerides each report an instance of self-performed cystotomy.

The following case is probably the only instance in which the patient, suffering from vesical calculus, tried to crush and break the stone himself. [b] J. B., a retired draper, born in 1828, while a youth of seventeen, sustained a fracture of the leg, rupture of the urethra, and laceration of the perineum, by a fall down a well, landing astride an iron bar. A permanent perineal fistula was established, but the patient was averse to any operative remedial measure. In the year 1852 he became aware of the presence of a calculus, but not until 1872 did he ask for medical assistance. He explained that he had introduced a chisel through his perineal fistula to the stone, and attempted to comminute it himself and thus remove it, and by so doing had removed about an ounce of the calculus. The physician started home for his forceps, but during the interval, while walking about in great pain, the man was relieved by the stone bursting through the perineum, falling to the floor, and breaking in two. Including the ounce already chiselled off, the stone weighed $14\frac{1}{2}$ ounces, and was $10\frac{5}{8}$ inches in its long circumference. B. recovered and lived to December, 1883, still believing that he had another piece of stone in his bladder.

In Holden's " Landmarks " we are told that the operation of dividing the Achilles tendon was first performed by an unfortunate upon himself, by means

a Wiener Med. Wochenschrift, Nos. ii. and iii., 1883.   b 381, 1889, i., 408.

of a razor. According to Patterson,[a] the late Mr. Symes told of a patient in North Scotland who, for incipient hip-disease, had the cautery applied at the Edinburgh Infirmary with resultant great relief. After returning home to the country he experienced considerable pain, and despite his vigorous efforts he was unable to induce any of the men to use the cautery upon him ; they termed it " barbarous treatment." In desperation and fully believing in the efficacy of this treatment as the best means of permanently alleviating his pain, the crippled Scotchman heated a poker and applied the cautery himself.

We have already mentioned the marvelous instances of Cesarean sections self-performed (page 131), and in the literature of obstetric operations many of the minor type have been done by the patient herself. In the foregoing cases it is to be understood that the operations have been performed solely from the inability to secure surgical assistance or from the incapacity to endure the pain any longer. These operations were not the self-mutilations of maniacs, but were performed by rational persons, driven to desperation by pain.

Possibly the most remarkable **instances of extensive loss of blood,** with recoveries, are to be found in the older records of venesection. The chronicles of excessive bleeding in the olden days are well known to everybody. Perhaps no similar practice was so universally indulged in. Both in sickness and in health, depletion was indicated, and it is no exaggeration to say that about the hospital rooms at times the floors were covered with blood. The reckless way in which venesection was resorted to, led to its disuse, until to-day it has so vanished from medical practice that even its benefits are overlooked, and depletion is brought about in some other manner. Turning to the older writers, we find Burton[b] describing a patient from whom he took 122 ounces of blood in four days. Dover speaks[307] of the removal of 111 and 190 ounces ; Galen, of six pounds ; and Haen,[395] of 114 ounces. Taylor[c] relates the history of a case of asphyxia in which he produced a successful issue by extracting one gallon of blood from his patient during twelve hours. Lucas[d] speaks of 50 venesections being practised during one pregnancy. Van der Wiel[e] performed venesection 49 times during a single pregnancy. Balmes[f] mentions a case in which 500 venesections were performed in twenty-five years. Laugier[g] mentions 300 venesections in twenty-six months. Osiander speaks of 8000 ounces of blood being taken away in thirty-five years. Pechlin[622] reports 155 venesections in one person in sixteen years, and there is a record of 1020 repeated venesections.[h]

The loss of blood through **spontaneous hemorrhage** is sometimes remarkable. Fabricius Hildanus[i] reports the loss of 27 pounds of blood in a few days ; and there is an older record of 40 pounds being lost in four days.[j] Horstius, Fabricius Hildanus, and Schenck, all record instances of death from

a 381, 1889, i., 408.   b American Med. Repository.   c 476, 1827, 718.
d Med. Obs. & Inquiries.   e Cent. i., obs. 65.   f 462, T. lxxi., 233.   g 462, T. xv.
h Samml. Med. Wahrnehm, Band 6, 408.   i 334, cent. vi., obs. 13.   j 470, 1683.

hemorrhage of the gums. Tulpius[842] speaks of hemoptysis lasting chronically for thirty years, and there is a similar record of forty years' duration in the Ephemerides. Chapman[a] gives several instances of extreme hemorrhage from epistaxis. He remarks that Bartholinus has recorded the loss of 48 pounds of blood from the nose ; and Rhodius, 18 pounds in thirty-six hours. The Ephemerides contains an account of epistaxis without cessation for six weeks. Another writer in an old journal[106] speaks of 75 pounds of blood from epistaxis in ten days. Chapman also mentions a case in which, by intestinal hemorrhage, eight gallons of blood were lost in a fortnight, the patient recovering. In another case a pint of blood was lost daily for fourteen days, with recovery. The loss of eight quarts in three days caused death in another case ; and Chapman, again, refers to the loss of three gallons of blood from the bowel in twenty-four hours. In the case of Michelotti, recorded in the Transactions of the Royal Society, a young man suffering from enlargement of the spleen vomited 12 pounds of blood in two hours, and recovered.

In hemorrhoidal hemorrhages, Lieutaud speaks of six quarts being lost in two days ; Hoffman, of 20 pounds in less than twenty-four hours, and Panaroli, of the loss of one pint daily for two years.

Arrow-Wounds.—According to Otis[b] the illustrious Baron Percy was wont to declare that military surgery had its origin in the treatment of wounds inflicted by darts and arrows ; he used to quote Book XI. of the Iliad in behalf of his belief, and to cite the cases of the patients of Chiron and Machaon, Menelaus and Philoctetes, and Eurypiles, treated by Patroclus ; he was even tempted to believe with Sextus[c] that the name ἰατρός, medicus, was derived from ἰός, which in the older times signified " sagitta," and that the earliest function of our professional ancestors was the extraction of arrows and darts. An instrument called beluleum was invented during the long Peloponnesian War, over four hundred years before the Christian era. It was a rude extracting-forceps, and was used by Hippocrates in the many campaigns in which he served. His immediate successor, Diocles, invented a complicated instrument for extracting foreign bodies, called graphiscos, which consisted of a canula with hooks. Otis states that it was not until the wars of Augustus that Heras of Cappadocia designed the famous duck-bill forceps which, with every conceivable modification, has continued in use until our time. Celsus[d] instructs that in extracting arrow-heads the entrance-wound should be dilated, the barb of the arrow-head crushed by strong pliers, or protected between the edges of a split reed, and thus withdrawn without laceration of the soft parts. According to the same authority, Paulus Aegineta also treated fully of wounds by arrow-heads, and described a method used in his time to remove firmly-impacted arrows. Albucasius[115] and others of the Arabian school did little or nothing toward aiding our knowledge of the means of

a " Eruptive Fevers."   b 847, 144.

c Advers. Math., L. I., cap. ii.   d 259, L. vii., cap. v.

extracting foreign bodies. After the fourteenth century the attention of surgeons was directed to wounds from projectiles impelled by gunpowder. In the sixteenth century arrows were still considerably used in warfare, and we find Paré[a] delineating the treatment of this class of injuries with the sovereign good sense that characterized his writings. As the use of firearms became prevalent the literature of wounds from arrows became meager, and the report of an instance in the present day is very rare.

Bill[b] has collected statistics and thoroughly discussed this subject, remarking upon the rapidity with which American Indians discharge their arrows, and states that it is exceptional to meet with only a single wound. It is commonly believed that the Indian tribes make use of **poisoned arrows,** but from the reports of Bill and others, this must be a very rare custom. Ashhurst states that he was informed by Dr. Schell, who was stationed for some time at Fort Laramie, that it is the universal custom to dip the arrows in blood, which is allowed to dry on them; it is not, therefore, improbable that septic material may thus be inoculated through a wound.

Many savage tribes still make use of the poisonous arrow. The Dyak uses a sumpitan, or blow-tube, which is about seven feet long, and having a bore of about half an inch. Through this he blows his long, thin dart, anointed on the head with some vegetable poison. Braidwood[c] speaks of the physiologic action of Dajaksch, an arrow-poison used in Borneo. Arnott[d] has made observations relative to a substance produced near Aden, which is said to be used by the Somalies to poison their arrows. Messer of the British Navy has made inquiries into the reputed poisonous nature of the arrows of the South Sea Islanders.

Otis[e] has collected reports of arrow-wounds from surgical cases occurring in the U. S. Army. Of the **multiple arrow-wounds,** six out of the seven cases were fatal. In five in which the cranial cavity was wounded, four patients perished. There were two remarkable instances of recovery after penetration of the pleural cavity by arrows. The great fatality of arrow-wounds of the abdomen is well known, and, according to Bill, the Indians always aim at the umbilicus; when fighting Indians, the Mexicans are accustomed to envelop the abdomen, as the most vulnerable part, in many folds of a blanket.

Of the arrow-wounds reported, nine were fatal, with one exception, in which the lesion implicated the soft parts only. The regions injured were the scalp, face, and neck, in three instances; the parietes of the chest in six; the long muscles of the back in two; the abdominal muscles in two; the hip or buttocks in three; the testis in one; the shoulder or arm in 13; forearm or hand in six; the thigh or leg in seven.

The force with which arrows are projected by Indians is so great that it

a 618, 445, et seq.   b 124, xliv., 365 and 439, ii.   c 318, 1864, x., 123.
d 777, 1855, ii., 314.   e 847, 144.

has been estimated that the initial velocity nearly equals that of a musket-ball. At a short distance an arrow will perforate the larger bones without comminuting them, causing a slight fissure only, and resembling the effect of a pistol-ball fired through a window-glass a few yards off.

Among extraordinary cases of **recovery from arrow-wounds,** several of the most striking will be recorded. Tremaine [a] mentions a sergeant of thirty-four who, in a fray with some hostile Indians, received seven arrow-wounds : two on the anterior surface of the right arm ; one in the right axilla ; one on the right side of the chest near the axillary border ; two on the posterior surface of the left arm near the elbow-joint, and one on the left temple. On June 1st he was admitted to the Post Hospital at Fort Dodge, Kan. The wound on the right arm near the deltoid discharged, and there was slight exfoliation of the humerus. The patient was treated with simple dressings, and was returned to duty in July, 1870.

Goddard [b] mentions an arrow-wound by which the body was transfixed. The patient was a sutler's helper at Fort Rice, Dakota Territory. He was accidentally wounded in February, 1868, by an arrow which entered the back three inches to the right of the 5th lumbar vertebra, and emerged about two inches to the right of the ensiform cartilage. During the following evening the patient lost about eight ounces of blood externally, with a small amount internally. He was confined to his bed some two weeks, suffering from circumscribed peritonitis with irritative fever. In four weeks he was walking about, and by July 1st was actively employed. The arrow was deposited in the Army Medical Museum.

Muller [c] gives a report of an arrow-wound of the lung which was productive of pleurisy but which was followed by recovery. Kugler [d] recites the description of the case of an arrow-wound of the thorax, complicated by frightful dyspnea and blood in the pleural cavity and in the bronchi, with recovery.

Smart [e] extracted a hoop-iron arrow-head, $1\frac{3}{4}$ inches long and $\frac{1}{2}$ inch in breadth, from the brain of a private, about a month after its entrance. About a dram of pus followed the exit of the arrow-head. After the operation the right side was observed to be paralyzed, and the man could not remember his name. He continued in a varying condition for a month, but died on May 13, 1866, fifty-two days after the injury. At the postmortem it was found that the brain-tissue, to the extent of $\frac{3}{4}$ inch around the track of the arrow as a center, was softened and disorganized. The track itself was filled with thick pus which extended into the ventricles.

Peabody reports a most remarkable case of recovery from multiple arrow-wounds.[f] In a skirmish with some Indians on June 3, 1863, the patient had been wounded by eight distinct arrows which entered different parts of the body. They were all extracted with the exception of one, which had entered at the outer and lower margin of the right scapula, and had passed inward

a 847, 156.   b 847, 153.   c 847, 151.   d Ibid.   e 847, 147.   f 847, 145.

and upward through the upper lobe of the right lung or trachea. The hemorrhage at this time was so great that all hope was abandoned. The patient, however, rallied, but continued to experience great pain on swallowing, and occasionally spat blood. In July, 1866, more than three years after the injury, he called on Dr. Peabody to undergo an examination with a view of applying for a pension, stating that his health was affected from the presence of an arrow-head. He was much emaciated, and expressed himself as tired of life. Upon probing through a small fistulous opening just above the superior end of the sternum, the point of the arrow was found resting against the bone, about $1\frac{1}{2}$ inches below, the head lying against the trachea and esophagus, with the carotid artery, jugular vein, and nerves overlying. After some little difficulty the point of the arrow was raised above the sternum, and it was extracted without the loss of an ounce of blood. The edge grazed against the sheath of the innominate artery during the operation. The missile measured an inch at the base, and was four inches long. The health of the patient underwent remarkable improvement immediately after the operation.

Serious Insect-stings.—Although in this country the stings of insects are seldom productive of serious consequences, in the tropic climates death not unfrequently results from them. Wounds inflicted by large spiders, centipedes, tarantulæ, and scorpions have proved fatal. Even in our country deaths, preceded by gangrene, have sometimes followed the bite of a mosquito or a bee, the location of the bite and the idiosyncrasy of the individual probably influencing the fatal issue. In some cases, possibly, some vegetable poison is introduced with the sting. Hulse, U. S. N.,[a] reports the case of a man who was bitten on the penis by a spider, and who subsequently exhibited violent symptoms simulating spinal meningitis, but ultimately recovered. Kunst[b] mentions a man of thirty-six who received several bee-stings while taking some honey from a tree, fell from the tree unconscious, and for some time afterward exhibited signs of cerebral congestion. Chaumeton[c] mentions a young man who did not perceive a wasp in a glass of sweet wine, and swallowed the insect. He was stung in the throat, followed by such intense inflammation that the man died asphyxiated in the presence of his friends, who could do nothing to relieve him. In connection with this case there is mentioned an English agriculturist who saved the life of one of his friends who had inadvertently swallowed a wasp with a glass of beer. Alarming symptoms manifested themselves at the moment of the sting. The farmer made a kind of paste from a solution of common salt in as little water as possible, which he gave to the young man, and, after several swallows of the potion, the symptoms disappeared as if by enchantment. There is a recent account from Bridgeport, Conn., of a woman who, while eating a pear, swallowed a hornet that had alighted on the fruit. In going down the throat the insect

a 124, 1839, 69.   b 545, 1878, 130.   c 302, i.

stung her on the tonsil. Great pain and inflammation followed, and in a short time there was complete deprivation of the power of speech.

Mease [a] relates the case of a corpulent farmer who, in July, 1835, was stung upon the temple by a common bee. He walked to a fence a short distance away, thence to his house, 20 yards distant, lay down, and expired in ten minutes. A second case, which occurred in June, 1811, is also mentioned by Mease.[b] A vigorous man was stung in the septum of the nose by a bee. Supported by a friend he walked to his house, a few steps distant, and lay down. He rose immediately to go to the well, stepped a few paces, fell, and expired. It was thirty minutes from the time of the accident to the man's death. A third case is reported by the same author from Kentucky. A man of thirty-five was stung on the right superior palpebrum, and died in twenty minutes. Mease reports a fourth case from Connecticut, in which a man of twenty-six was stung by a bee on the tip of the nose. He recovered after treatment with ten-grain doses of Dover's Powder, and persistent application of plantain leaves. A fifth case was that of a farmer in Pennsylvania who was stung in the left side of the throat by a wasp which he had swallowed in drinking cider. Notwithstanding medical treatment, death ensued twenty-seven hours afterward. A sixth case, which occurred in October, 1834, is given by the same author. A middle-aged man was stung by a yellow wasp on the middle finger of the right hand, and died in less than twenty minutes after having received his wound. A seventh case was that of a New York farmer who, while hoeing, was bitten on the foot by a spider. Notwithstanding medical treatment, principally bleeding, the man soon expired.

Desbrest [c] mentions the sting of a bee above the eyebrow followed by death. Zacutus saw a bee-sting which was followed by gangrene. Delaistre [d] mentions death from a hornet-sting in the palate. Nivison [e] relates the case of a farmer of fifty who was stung in the neck by a bee. The usual swelling and discoloration did not follow, but notwithstanding vigorous medical treatment the man died in six days. Thompson [f] relates three cases of bee-sting, in all of which death supervened within fifteen minutes,—one in a farmer of fifty-eight who was stung in the neck below the right ear ; a second in an inn-keeper of fifty who was stung in the neck, and a third of a woman of sixty-four who was stung on the left brow. "Chirurgus" [g] recalls the details of a case of a wasp-sting in the middle finger of the right hand of a man of forty, depriving him of all sense and of muscular power. Ten minutes after receiving it he was unconscious, his heart-beats were feeble, and his pulse only perceptible.

Syphilis from a Flea-bite.—Jonathan Hutchinson, in the October, 1895, number of his unique and valuable Archives of Surgery, reports a primary lesion of most unusual origin. An elderly member of the profession presented himself entirely covered with an evident syphilitic eruption, which

a 124, 1836–37, xix., 265.   b Ibid.   c 462, 1765.   d Gaz. de Santé, 1776.
e 594, 1857, 3 s., ii., 339.   f 224, 1869, i., 374.   g 535, 1819, xl., 479.

rapidly disappeared under the use of mercury. The only interest about the case was the question as to how the disease had been acquired. The doctor was evidently anxious to give all the information in his power, but was positive that he had never been exposed to any sexual risk, and as he had retired from practice, no possibility of infection in that manner existed. He willingly stripped, and a careful examination of his entire body surface revealed no trace of lesion whatever on the genitals, or at any point, except a dusky spot on one leg, which looked like the remains of a boil. This, the doctor stated, had been due to a small sore, the dates of the appearance and duration of which were found to fit exactly with those of a primary lesion. There had also been some enlargement of the femoral glands. He had never thought of the sore in this connection, but remembered most distinctly that it followed a flea-bite in an omnibus, and had been caused, as he supposed, by his scratching the place, though he could not understand why it lasted so long. Mr. Hutchinson concludes that all the evidence tends to show that the disease had probably been communicated from the blood of an infected person through the bite of the insect. It thus appears that even the proverbially trivial flea-bite may at times prove a serious injury.

Snake-bites.—A writer in an Indian paper asserts that the traditional **immunity of Indian snake-charmers** is due to the fact that having been accidentally bitten by poisonous serpents or insects more than once, and having survived the first attack, they are subsequently immune. His assertion is based on personal acquaintance with Madari Yogis and Fakirs, and an actual experiment made with a Mohammedan Fakir who was immune to the bites of scorpions provided by the writer. The animals were from five to seven inches long and had lobster-like claws. Each bite drew blood, but the Fakir was none the worse.

The venom of poisonous snakes may be considered the most typical of animal poisons, being unrivaled in the fatality and rapidity of its action. Fortunately in our country there are few snake-bites, but in the tropic countries, particularly India, the mortality from this cause is frightful. Not only are there numerous serpents in that country, but the natives are lightly dressed and unshod, thus being exposed to the bites of the reptiles. It is estimated by capable authorities that the deaths in India each year from snake-bites exceed 20,000. It is stated that there were 2893 human beings killed by tigers, leopards, hyenas, and panthers in India during the year 1894, and in the same year the same species of beasts, aided by snakes, killed 97,371 head of cattle. The number of human lives destroyed by snakes in India in 1894 was 21,538. The number of wild beasts killed in the same year was 13,447, and the number of snakes killed was 102,210.

Yarrow of Washington, who has been a close student of this subject, has found in this country no less than 27 species of poisonous snakes, belonging to four genera. The first genus is the Crotalus, or rattlesnake proper ; the second is the Caudisona, or ground-rattlesnake ; the third is the Ancistrodon, or moccasin, one of the species of which is a water-snake ; and the fourth is the Elaps, or harlequin snake.   There is some dispute over the exact degree of the toxic qualities of the venom of the Heloderma suspectum, or Gila monster.   In India the cobra is the most deadly snake.   It grows to the length of $5\frac{1}{2}$ feet, and is most active at night.   The Ophiophagus, or hooded cobra, is one of the largest of venomous snakes, sometimes attaining a length of 15 feet ; it is both powerful, active, and aggressive.   The common snakes of the deadly variety in the United States are the rattlesnake, the " copperhead," and the moccasin ; and it is from the bites of one of these varieties that the great majority of reported deaths are caused.   But in looking over medical literature one is struck with the scarcity of reports of fatal snake-bites.   This is most likely attributable to the fact that, except a few army-surgeons, physicians rarely see the cases.   The natural abode of the serpents is in the wild and uninhabited regions.

The venom is delivered to the victim through the medium of a long fang which is connected with a gland in which the poison is stored.   The supply may be readily exhausted ; for a time the bite would then be harmless.   Contrary to the general impression, snake-venom when swallowed is a deadly poison, as proved by the experiments of Fayrer, Mitchell, and Reichert. Death is most likely caused by paralysis of the vital centers through the circulation.   In this country the wounds invariably are on the extremities, while in India the cobra sometimes strikes on the shoulder or neck.

If called on to describe accurately the **symptoms of snake-venom poisoning,** few medical men could respond correctly.   In most cases the wound is painful, sometimes exaggerated by the mental condition, which is wrought up to a pitch rarely seen in other equally fatal injuries.   It is often difficult to discern the exact point of puncture, so minute is it.   There is swelling due to effusion of blood, active inflammation, and increasing pain.   If the poison has gained full entrance into the system, in a short time the swelling extends, vesicles soon form, and the disorganization of the tissues is so rapid that gangrene is liable to intervene before the fatal issue.   The patient becomes prostrated immediately after the infliction of the wound, and his condition strongly indicates the use of stimulants, even if the medical attendant were unfamiliar with the history of the snake-bite.   There may be a slight delirium ; the expression becomes anxious, the pulse rapid and feeble, the respiration labored, and the patient complains of a sense of suffocation.   Coma follows, and the respirations become slower and slower until death results.   If the patient lives long enough, the discoloration of the extremity and the swelling may spread to the neck, chest and back.   Loss of speech after snake-bite is discussed in Chapter XVII., under the head of Aphasia.

A peculiar complication is a distressing inflammation of the mouth of individuals that have sucked the wounds containing venom.   This custom is still quite common, and is preferred by the laity to the surer and much wiser method of immediate cauterization by fire. There is a curious case reported [a] of a young man who was bitten on the ankle by a viper; he had not sucked the wound, but he presented such an enormous swelling of the tongue as to be almost provocative of a fatal issue. In this case the lingual swelling was a local effect of the general constitutional disturbance.

Cases of Snake-bite.—The following case illustrative of the tenacity of virulence of snake-venom was reported by Mr. Temple, Chief Justice of Honduras, and quoted by a London authority.[b] While working at some wood-cutting a man was struck on a heavy boot by a snake, which he killed with an axe. He imagined that he had been efficiently protected by the boot, and he thought little of the incident. Shortly afterward he began to feel ill, sank into a stupor, and succumbed. His boots were sold after his death, as they were quite well made and a luxury in that country. In a few hours the purchaser of the boots was a corpse, and every one attributed his death to apoplexy or some similar cause. The boots were again sold, and the next unfortunate owner died in an equally short time. It was then thought wise to examine the boots, and in one of them was found, firmly embedded, the fang of the serpent. It was supposed that in pulling on the boots each of the subsequent owners had scratched himself and became fatally inoculated with the venom, which was unsuspected and not combated. The case is so strange as to appear hypothetic, but the authority seems reliable.

The following are three cases of snake-bite reported by surgeons of the United States Army, two followed by recovery, and the other by death: Middleton[c] mentions a private in the Fourth Cavalry, aged twenty-nine, who was bitten by a rattlesnake at Fort Concho, Texas, June 27, 1866. The bite opened the phalangeal joint of the left thumb, causing violent inflammation, and resulted in the destruction of the joint. Three years afterward the joint swelled and became extremely painful, and it was necessary to amputate the thumb. Campbell[d] reports the case of a private of the Thirteenth Infantry who was bitten in the throat by a large rattlesnake. The wound was immediately sucked by a comrade, and the man reported at the Post Hospital, at Camp Cooke, Montana, three hours after the accident. The only noticeable appearance was a slightly wild look about the eyes, although the man did not seem to be the least alarmed. The region of the wound was hard and somewhat painful, probably from having been bruised by the teeth of the man who sucked the wound; it remained so for about three hours. The throat was bound up in rancid olive oil (the only kind at hand) and no internal remedy was administered. There were no other bad consequences, and the patient soon returned to duty.

Le Carpentier[e] sends the report of a fatal case of rattlesnake-bite: A pri-

a Repert. di Medicina, Torino, 1828. b 548, 1856, ii., 597.
c 847, 164. d Ibid. e Ibid.

vate, aged thirty-seven, remarkable for the singularity of his conduct, was known in his Company as a snake-charmer, as he had many times, without injury, handled poisonous snakes. On the morning of July 13, 1869, he was detailed as guard with the herd at Fort Cummings, New Mexico, when, in the presence of the herders, he succeeded in catching a rattlesnake and proving his power as a sorcerer. The performance being over and the snake killed, he caught sight of another of the same class, and tried to duplicate his previous feat ; but his dexterity failed, and he was bitten in the middle finger of the right hand. He was immediately admitted to the Post Hospital, complaining only of a little pain, such as might follow the sting of a bee or wasp. A ligature was applied above the wound ; the two injuries made by the fangs were enlarged by a bistoury ; ammonia and the actual cautery were applied ; large doses of whiskey were repeated frequently, the constitution of the patient being broken and poor. Vomiting soon came on but was stopped without trouble, and there were doubts from the beginning as to his recovery. The swelling of the hand and arm gradually increased, showing the particular livid and yellowish tint following the bites of poisonous snakes. A blister was applied to the bitten finger, tincture of iodin used, and two ounces of whiskey given every two hours until inebriety was induced. The pulse, which was very much reduced at first, gained gradually under the influence of stimulants ; two grains of opium were given at night, the patient slept well, and on the next day complained only of numbness in the arm. The swelling had extended as far as the shoulder-joint, and the blood, which was very fluid, was incessantly running from the wound. Carbolic acid and cerate were applied to the arm, with stimulants internally. On the 15th his condition was good, the swelling had somewhat augmented, there was not so much lividity, but the yellowish hue had increased. On the 16th the man complained of pain in the neck, on the side of the affected limb, but his general condition was good. Examining his genitals, an iron ring $\frac{3}{4}$ inch in diameter was discovered, imbedded in the soft tissues of the penis, constricting it to such a degree as to have produced enormous enlargement of the parts. Upon inquiry it seemed that the ring had been kept on the parts very long, as a means of preservation of chastity ; but under the influence of the snake's venom the swelling had increased, and the patient having much trouble in passing water was obliged to complain. The ring was filed off with some difficulty. Gangrene destroyed the extremity of the bitten finger. From this date until the 30th the man's condition improved somewhat. The progress of the gangrene was stopped, and the injured finger was disarticulated at the metacarpal articulation. Anesthesia was readily obtained, but the appearance of the second stage was hardly perceptible. Le Carpentier was called early on the next morning, the patient having been observed to be sinking ; there was stertorous respiration, the pulse was weak and slow, and the man was only partly conscious. Electricity was applied to the spine, and brandy and potassium bromid were given, but death occurred about noon. A necropsy was made one hour after death. There was general softening of the tissues, particularly on the affected side. The blood was black and very fluid,—not coagulable. The ventricles of the brain were filled with a large amount of serum; the brain was somewhat congested. The lungs were healthy, with the exception of a few crude tubercles of recent formation on the left side. The right ventricle of the heart was empty, and the left filled with dark blood, which had coagulated. The liver and kidneys were healthy, and the gall-bladder very much distended with bile. The intestines presented a few livid patches on the outside.

Hydrophobia.—The bite of an enraged animal is always of great danger to man, and death has followed a wound inflicted by domestic animals or even fowls; a human bite has also caused a fatal issue. **Rabies** is frequently observed in herbivorous animals, such as the ox, cow, or sheep, but is most commonly found in the carnivora, such as the dog, wolf, fox, jackal, hyena, and cat and other members of the feline tribe. Fox [a] reports several cases of death from symptoms resembling those of hydrophobia in persons who were bitten by skunks. Swine, birds, and even domestic poultry have caused hydrophobia by their bites. Le Cat [b] speaks of the bite of an enraged duck causing death, and Thiermeyer mentions death shortly following the bite of a goose, as well as death in three days from a chicken-bite. Camerarius [c] describes a case of epilepsy which he attributed to a horse-bite. Among the older writers speaking of death following the bite of an enraged man, are van Meek'ren,[560] Wolff,[d] Zacutus Lusitanus,[831] and Glandorp.[380] The Ephemerides contains an account of hydrophobia caused by a human bite. Jones [e] reports a case of syphilitic inoculation from a human bite on the hand.

Hydrophobia may not necessarily be from a bite; a previously-existing wound may be inoculated by the saliva alone, conveyed by licking. Pliny, and some subsequent writers, attributed rabies to a worm under the animal's tongue which they called "lytta." There is said to be a superstition in India that, shortly after being bitten by a mad dog, the victim conceives pups in his belly; at about three months these move rapidly up and down the patient's intestines, and being mad like their progenitor, they bite and bark incessantly, until they finally kill the unfortunate victim. The natives of Nepaul firmly believe this theory.[f] All sorts of curious remedies have been suggested for the cure of hydrophobia. Crabs-claws, Spanish fly, and dragon roots, given three mornings before the new or full moon, was suggested as a specific by Sir Robert Gordon. Theodore De Vaux remarks that the person bitten should immediately pluck the feathers from the breech of an old cock and apply them bare to the bites. If the dog was mad the cock was supposed to swell and die. If the dog was not mad the cock would not swell;

a 481, 1872, vi., 119.   b 462, T. ii., 90.   c Diss. de Epilep., 15.
d Observ. de Med. Chirurg., ii., No. 5.   e 224, 1872, i., 313.   f 433, 1834, i., 202.

in either case the person so treated was immune.　Mad-stones, as well as snake-stones, are believed in by some persons at the present day.　According to Curran,[a] at one time in Ireland the fear of hydrophobia was so great that any person supposed to be suffering from it could be legally smothered.

According to French statistics, hydrophobia is an extremely fatal disease, although the proportion of people bitten and escaping without infection is overwhelmingly greater than those who acquire the disease.　The mortality of genuine hydrophobia is from 30 to 80 per cent., influenced by efficient and early cauterization and scientific treatment.　There is little doubt that many of the cases reported as hydrophobia are merely examples of general systemic infection from a local focus of sepsis, made possible by some primitive and uncleanly treatment of the original wound.　There is much superstition relative to hydrophobia ; the majority of wounds seen are filled with the hair of the dog, soot, ham-fat, and also with particles of decayed food and saliva from the mouth of some person who has practised sucking the wound.

Ordinarily, the **period of incubation of hydrophobia** in man is before the end of the second month, although rarely cases are seen as many as six months from the reception of the bite.　The first **symptoms** of the disease are melancholia, insomnia, loss of appetite, and occasionally shooting pains, radiating from the wound.　There may be severe pain at the back of the head and in the neck.　Difficulty in swallowing soon becomes a marked symptom.　The speech assumes a sobbing tone, and occasionally the expression of the face is wild and haggard.　As regards the crucial diagnostic test of a glass of water, the following account of a patient's attempt to drink is given by Curtis and quoted by Warren : [843] " A glass of water was offered the patient, which he refused to take, saying that he could not stand so much as that, but would take it from a teaspoon.　On taking the water from the spoon he evinced some discomfort and agitation, but continued to raise the spoon.　As it came within a foot of his lips, he gagged and began to gasp violently, his features worked, and his head shook.　He finally almost tossed the water into his mouth, losing the greater part of it, and staggered about the room gasping and groaning.　At this moment the respirations seemed wholly costal, and were performed with great effort, the elbows being jerked upward with every inspiration.　The paroxysm lasted about half a minute.　The act of swallowing did not appear to cause distress, for he could go through the motions of deglutition without any trouble.　The approach of liquid toward the mouth would, however, cause distress." It is to be remarked that the spasm affects the mechanism of the respiratory apparatus, the muscles of mastication and deglutition being only secondarily contracted.

Pasteur discovered that the virulence of the virus of rabies could be attenuated in passing it through different species of animals, and also that inoculation of this attenuated virus had a decided prophylactic effect on the disease ; hence, by cutting the spinal cord of inoculated animals into fragments a few centimeters long, and drying them, an emulsion could be made containing the virus. The patients are first inoculated with a cord fourteen days old, and the inoculation is repeated for nine days, each time with a cord one day fresher. The intensive method consists in omitting the weakest cords and giving the inoculations at shorter intervals. As a curious coincidence, Pliny and Pasteur, the ancient and modern, both discuss the particular virulence of saliva during fasting.

There is much discussion over the extent of injury a **shark-bite** can produce. In fact some persons deny the reliability of any of the so-called cases of shark-bites. Ensor[a] reports an interesting case occurring at Port Elizabeth, South Africa. While bathing, an expert swimmer felt a sharp pain in the thigh, and before he could cry out, felt a horrid crunch and was dragged below the surface of the water. He struggled for a minute, was twisted about, shaken, and then set free, and by a supreme effort, reached the landing stairs of the jetty, where, to his surprise, he found that a monstrous shark had bitten his leg off. The leg had been seized obliquely, and the teeth had gone across the joints, wounding the condyles of the femur. There were three marks on the left side showing where the fish had first caught him. The amputation was completed at once, and the man recovered. Macgrigor[b] reports the case of a man at a fishery, near Manaar, who was bitten by a shark. The upper jaw of the animal was fixed in the left side of the belly, forming a semicircular wound of which a point one inch to the left of the umbilicus was the upper boundary, and the lower part of the upper third of the thigh, the lower boundary. The abdominal and lumbar muscles were divided and turned up, exposing the colon in its passage across the belly. Several convolutions of the small intestines were also laid bare, as were also the three lowest ribs. The gluteal muscles were lacerated and torn, the tendons about the trochanter divided, laying the bone bare, and the vastus externus and part of the rectus of the thigh were cut across. The wound was 19 inches in length and four or five inches in breadth. When Dr. Kennedy first saw the patient he had been carried in a boat and then in a palanquin for over five miles, and at this time, three hours after the reception of the wound, Kennedy freed the abdominal cavity of salt water and blood, thoroughly cleansed the wound of the hair and the clots, and closed it with adhesive strips. By the sixteenth day the abdominal wound had perfectly closed, the lacerations granulated healthily, and the man did well. Boyle[c] reports recovery from extensive lacerated wounds from the bite of a shark. Both arms were amputated as a consequence of the injuries. Fayrer[d] mentions shark-bites in the Hooghley.

Leprosy from a Fish-bite.—Ashmead[e] records the curious case of a

[a] 476, 1883, i., 1160. [b] 550, ix. [c] 490, 1828–29, iii., 502.
[d] 548, 1871, i., 5. [e] 450, March 16, 1895.

man that had lived many years in a leprous country, and while dressing a fish had received a wound of the thumb from the fin of the fish. Swelling of the arm followed, and soon after bullæ upon the chest, head, and face. In a few months the blotches left from this eruption became leprous tubercles, and other well-marked signs of the malady followed. The author asked if in this case we have to do with a latent leprosy which was evoked by the wound, or if it were a case of inoculation from the fish?

Cutliffe[a] records recovery after amputation at the elbow-joint, as a consequence of an **alligator-bite** nine days before admission to the hospital. The patient exhibited a compound comminuted fracture of the right radius and ulna in their lower thirds, compound comminuted fractures of the bones of the carpus and metacarpus, with great laceration of the soft parts, laying bare the wrist-joint, besides several penetrating wounds of the arm and fore-arm. Mourray[b] gives some notes on a case of **crocodile-bite** with removal of a large portion of omentum. Sircar speaks of recovery from a crocodile-bite. Dudgeon[c] reports two cases of **animal-bites,** both fatal, one **by a bear,** and the other by a **camel.** There is mention[d] of a compound dislocation of the wrist-joint from a horse-bite. Fayrer[e] speaks of a **wolf-bite** of the fore-arm, followed by necrosis and hemorrhage, necessitating ligature of the brachial artery and subsequent excision of the elbow-joint.

Injuries from Lightning.—The subject of lightning-stroke, with its diverse range of injuries, is of considerable interest, and, though not uncommon, the matter is surrounded by a veil of superstition and mystery. It is well known that instantaneous or temporary unconsciousness may result from lightning-stroke. Sometimes superficial or deep burns may be the sole result, and again paralysis of the general nerves, such as those of sensation and motion, may be occasioned. For many years the therapeutic effect of a lightning-stroke has been believed to be a possibility, and numerous instances are on record. The object of this article will be to record a sufficient number of cases of lightning-stroke to enable the reader to judge of its various effects, and form his own opinion of the good or evil of the injury. It must be mentioned here that half a century ago Le Conte[f] wrote a most extensive article on this subject, which, to the present time, has hardly been improved upon.

The first cases to be recorded are those in which there has been complete and rapid **recovery from lightning-stroke.** Crawford[g] mentions a woman who, while sitting in front of her fireplace on the first floor of a two-story frame building, heard a crash about her, and realized that the house had been struck by lightning. The lightning had torn all the weather-boarding off the house, and had also followed a spouting which terminated in a wooden trough

a 435, 1870, v., 36.   b 435, 1877, xii., 245.
c Customs Gaz. Med. Rep., Shanghai, 1874, iv., 12.   d 548, xv., 351.
e 548, 1869, i., 5.   f 594, 1844, iii.   g 579, 1870, 12.

in a pig-sty, ten feet back of the house, and killed a pig. Another branch of the fluid passed through the inside of the building and, running along the upper floor to directly over where Mrs. F. was sitting, passed through the floor and descended upon the top of her left shoulder. Her left arm was lying across her abdomen at the time, the points of the fingers resting on the crests of the ilium. There was a rent in the dress at the top of the shoulder, and a red line half an inch wide running from thence along the inside of the arm and fore-arm. In some places there was complete vesication, and on its palmar surface the hand lying on the abdomen was completely denuded. The abdomen, for a space of four inches in length and eight inches in breadth, was also blistered. The fluid then passed from the fingers to the crest of the ilium, and down the outside of the leg, bursting open the shoes, and passing then through the floor. Again a red line half an inch wide could be traced from the ilium to the toes. The clothing was not scorched, but only slightly rent at the point of the shoulder and where the fingers rested. This woman was neither knocked off her chair nor stunned, and she felt no shock at the time. After ordinary treatment for her burns she made rapid and complete recovery.

Halton [a] reports the history of a case of a woman of sixty-five who, about thirty-five minutes before he saw her, had been struck by lightning. While she was sitting in an outbuilding a stroke of lightning struck and shattered a tree about a foot distant. Then, leaving the tree about seven feet from the ground, it penetrated the wall of the building, which was of unplastered frame, and struck Mrs. P. on the back of the head, at a point where her hair was done up in a knot and fastened by two ordinary hair-pins. The hair was much scorched, and under the knot the skin of the scalp was severely burned. The fluid crossed, burning her right ear, in which was a gold ear-ring, and then passed over her throat and down the left sternum, leaving a burn three inches wide, covered by a blister. There was another burn, 12 inches long and three inches wide, passing from just above the crest of the ilium forward and downward to the symphysis pubis. The next burn began at the patella of the right knee, extending to the bottom of the heel, upon reaching which it wound around the inner side of the leg. About four inches below the knee a sound strip of cuticle, about 1½ inches, was left intact. The lightning passed off the heel of the foot, bursting open the heel of a strongly sewed gaiter-boot. The woman was rendered unconscious but subsequently recovered.

A remarkable feature of a lightning-stroke is the fact that it very often strips the affected part of its raiment, as in the previous case in which the shoe was burst open. In a discussion before the Clinical Society of London, October 24, 1879,[b] there were several instances mentioned in which clothes had been stripped off by lightning. In one case mentioned by Sir James Paget, the clothes

[a] 124, 1869. [b] 476, 1879, ii., 656.

were wet and the man's skin was reeking with perspiration.   In its course the lightning traveled down the clothes, tearing them posteriorly, and completely stripping the patient.   The boots were split up behind and the laces torn out. This patient, however, made a good recovery.   Beatson [a] mentions an instance in which an explosion of a shell completely tore off the left leg of a sergeant instructor, midway between the knee and ankle.   It was found that the foot and lower third of the leg had been completely denuded of a boot and woolen stocking, without any apparent abrasion or injury to the skin.   The stocking was found in the battery and the boot struck a person some distance off. The stocking was much torn, and the boot had the heel missing, and in one part the sole was separated from the upper.   The laces in the upper holes were broken but were still present in the lower holes.   The explanation offered in this case is similar to that in analogous cases of lightning-stroke, that is, that the gas generated by the explosion found its way between the limb and the stocking and boot and stripped them off.

There is a curious collection of relics, consisting of the clothes of a man struck by lightning, artistically hung in a glass case in the Museum of the Royal College of Surgeons, London, and the history of the injury, of which these remnants are the result, is given by Professor Stewart, the curator, as follows : At half past four on June 8, 1878, James Orman and others were at work near Snave, in Romney Marsh, about eight miles from Ashford.   The men were engaged in lopping willows, when the violence of the rain compelled them to take refuge under a hedge.   Three of the men entered a shed near by, but Orman remained by the willow, close to the window of the shed. Scarcely were the three inside when a lightning-stroke entered the door, crossed the shed, and passed out the window, which it blew before it into the field.   The men noticed that the tree under which Orman stood was stripped of its bark.   Their companion's boots stood close to the foot of the tree, while the man himself lay almost perfectly naked a few yards further on, calling for help.   When they left him a few moments previously, he was completely clad in a cotton shirt, cotton jacket, flannel vest, and cotton trousers, secured at the waist with leather straps and buckles.   Orman also wore a pair of stout hobnail boots, and had a watch and chain.   After the lightning-stroke, however, all he had on him was the left arm of his flannel vest.   The field was strewn for some distance with fragments of the unfortunate man's clothing. Orman was thrown down, his eyebrows burned off, and his whiskers and beard much scorched.   His chest was covered with superficial burns, and he had sustained a fracture of the leg.   His strong boots were torn from his feet, and his watch had a hole burned right through it, as if a soldering iron had been used.   The watch-chain was almost completely destroyed, only a few links remaining.   Together with some fused coins, these were found close by, and are deposited in a closed box in the Museum.   According to Orman's account

a 224, 1890, i., 514.

of the affair, he first felt a violent blow on the chest and shoulders, and then he was involved in a blinding light and hurled into the air. He said he never lost consciousness ; but when at the hospital he seemed very deaf and stupid. He was discharged perfectly cured twenty weeks after the occurrence. The scientific explanation of this amazing escape from this most eccentric vagary of the electric fluid is given,—the fact that the wet condition of the man's clothing increased its power of conduction, and in this way saved his life. It is said that the electric current passed down the side of Orman's body, causing everywhere a sudden production of steam, which by its expansion tore the clothing off and hurled it away. It is a curious fact that where the flannel covered the man's skin the burns were merely superficial, whereas in those parts touched by the cotton trousers they were very much deeper. This case is also quoted and described by Dr. Wilks. [439]

There was a curious case of lightning-stroke reported at Cole Harbor, Halifax. A diver, while at work far under the surface of the water, was seriously injured by the transmission of a lightning-stroke, which first struck the communicating air pump to which the diver was attached. The man was brought to the surface insensible, but he afterward recovered.

Permanent Effect of Lightning on the Nervous System.—MacDonald [a] mentions a woman of seventy-eight who, some forty-two years previous, while ironing a cap with an Italian iron, was stunned by an extremely vivid flash of lightning and fell back unconscious into a chair. On regaining consciousness she found that the cap which she had left on the table, remote from the iron, was reduced to cinders. Her clothes were not burned nor were there any marks on the skin. After the stroke she felt a creeping sensation and numbness, particularly in the arm which was next to the table. She stated positively that in consequence of this feeling she could predict with the greatest certainty when the atmosphere was highly charged with electricity, as the numbness increased on these occasions. The woman averred that shortly before or during a thunder storm she always became nauseated. MacDonald offers as a physiologic explanation of this case that probably the impression produced forty-two years before implicated the right brachial plexus and the afferent branches of the pneumogastric, and to some degree the vomiting center in the medulla ; hence, when the atmosphere was highly charged with electricity the structures affected became more readily impressed. Camby [b] relates the case of a neuropathic woman of thirty-eight, two of whose children were killed by lightning in her presence. She herself was unconscious for four days, and when she recovered consciousness, she was found to be hemiplegic and hemianesthetic on the left side. She fully recovered in three weeks. Two years later, during a thunder storm, when there was no evidence of a lightning-stroke, she had a second attack, and three years later a third attack under similar circumstances.

[a] 655, 1886, 348.   [b] Soc. Méd. des Hôp., Paris, May 25, 1894.

There are some **ocular injuries from lightning** on record. In these cases the lesions have consisted of detachment of the retina, optic atrophy, cataract, hemorrhages into the retina, and rupture of the choroid, paralysis of the oculomotor muscles, and paralysis of the optic nerve. According to Buller of Montreal, such injuries may arise from the mechanic violence sustained by the patient rather than by the thermal or chemic action of the current. Buller describes a case of lightning-stroke in which the external ocular muscles, the crystalline lens, and the optic nerve were involved. Godfrey [a] reports the case of Daniel Brown, a seaman on H. M. S. Cambrian. While at sea on February 21, 1799, he was struck both dumb and blind by a lightning-stroke. There was evidently paralysis of the optic nerve and of the oculomotor muscles; and the muscles of the glottis were also in some manner deprived of motion.

That an **amputation** can be perfectly performed **by a lightning-stroke** is exemplified in the case of Sycyanko of Cracow, Poland.[b] The patient was a boy of twelve, whose right knee was ankylosed. While riding in a field in a violent storm, a loud peal of thunder caused the horse to run away, and the child fell stunned to the ground. On coming to his senses the boy found that his right leg was missing, the parts having been divided at the upper end of the tibia. The wound was perfectly round and the patella and femur were intact. There were other signs of burns about the body, but the boy recovered. Some days after the injury the missing leg was found near the place where he was first thrown from the horse.

The therapeutic effect of lightning-stroke is verified by a number of cases, a few of which will be given. Tilesius [367] mentions a peculiar case which was extensively quoted in London.[c] Two brothers, one of whom was deaf, were struck by lightning. It was found that the inner part of the right ear near the tragus and anti-helix of one of the individuals was scratched, and on the following day his hearing returned. Olmstead [d] quotes the history of a man in Carteret County, N. C., who was seized with a paralytic affection of the face and eyes, and was quite unable to close his lids. While in his bedroom, he was struck senseless by lightning, and did not recover until the next day, when it was found that the paralysis had disappeared, and during the fourteen years which he afterward lived his affection never returned. There is a record of a young collier [e] in the north of England who lost his sight by an explosion of gunpowder, utterly destroying the right eye and fracturing the frontal bone. The vision of the left eye was lost without any serious damage to the organ, and this was attributed to shock. On returning from Ettingshall in a severe thunder storm, he remarked to his brother that he had seen light through his spectacles, and had immediately afterward experienced a piercing sensation which

a 535, 1822, 369.   b 548, 1869, i., 363.   c 550, 1825.

d 594, 1844, 308.   e 476, 1888, ii., 178.

had passed through the eye to the back of the head. The pain was brief, and he was then able to see objects distinctly. From this occasion he steadily improved until he was able to walk about without a guide.

Le Conte mentions the case of a negress who was struck by lightning August 19, 1842, on a plantation in Georgia. For years before the reception of the shock her health had been very bad, and she seemed to be suffering from a progressive emaciation and feebleness akin to chlorosis. The difficulty had probably followed a protracted amenorrhea, subsequent to labor and a retained placenta. In the course of a week she had recovered from the effects of lightning and soon experienced complete restoration to health ; and for two years had been a remarkably healthy and vigorous laborer. Le Conte quotes five similar cases, and mentions one in which a lightning-shock to a woman of twenty-nine produced amenorrhea, whereas she had previously suffered from profuse menstruation, and also mentions another case of a woman of seventy who was struck unconscious ; the catamenial discharge which had ceased twenty years before, was now permanently reestablished, and the shrunken mammæ again resumed their full contour.

A peculiar feature or superstition as to lightning-stroke is its **photographic properties.** In this connection Stricker of Frankfort quotes the case of Raspail [a] of a man of twenty-two who, while climbing a tree to a bird's nest, was struck by lightning, and afterward showed upon his breast a picture of the tree, with the nest upon one of its branches. Although in the majority of cases the photographs resembled trees, there was one case in which it resembled a horse-shoe ; another, a cow ; a third, a piece of furniture ; a fourth, the whole surrounding landscape. This theory of lightning-photographs of neighboring objects on the skin has probably arisen from the resemblance of the burns due to the ramifications of the blood-vessels as conductors, or to peculiar electric movements which can be demonstrated by positive charges on lycopodium powder.

A lightning-stroke does not exhaust its force on a few individuals or objects, but sometimes produces serious **manifestations over a large area,** or on a great number of people. It is said [b] that a church in the village of Chateauneuf, in the Department of the Lower Alps, in France, was struck by three successive lightning strokes on July 11, 1819, during the installation of a new pastor. The company were all thrown down, nine were killed and 82 wounded. The priest, who was celebrating mass, was not affected, it is believed, on account of his silken robe acting as an insulator. Bryant [c] of Charlestown, Mass., has communicated the particulars of a stroke of lightning on June 20, 1829, which shocked several hundred persons. The effect of this discharge was felt over an area of 172,500 square feet with nearly the same degree of intensity. Happily, there was no permanent injury recorded. Le Conte reports that a person may be killed when some distance

[a] 161, xxii.   [b] 139, T. xii.   [c] 126, 1830.

—even as far as 20 miles away from the storm—by what Lord Mahon calls the " returning stroke."

Skin-grafting is a subject which has long been more or less familiar to medical men, but which has only recently been developed to a practically successful operation.   The older surgeons knew that it was possible to re-unite a resected nose or an amputated finger, and in Hunter's time tooth-replantation was quite well known.   Smellie [739] has recorded an instance in which, after avulsion of a nipple in suckling, restitution was effected.   It is not alone to the skin that **grafting** is applicable ; it is used **in the cornea, nerves, muscles, bones, tendons,** and **teeth.**   Wolfer has been success-ful in **transplanting the mucous membranes** of frogs, rabbits, and pigeons to a portion of mucous membrane previously occupied by cicatricial tissue, and was the first to show that on mucous surfaces, mucous membrane remains mucous membrane, but when transplanted to skin, it becomes skin. Attempts have been made to transplant a button of clear cornea of a dog, rabbit, or cat to the cornea of a human being, opaque as the result of oph-thalmia, and von Hippel has devised a special method of doing this.   Re-cently Fuchs [a] has reported his experience in cornea-grafting in sections, as a substitute for von Hippel's method, in parenchymatous keratitis and corneal staphyloma, and though not eminently successful himself, he considers the operation worthy of trial in cases that are without help, and doomed to blindness.

John Hunter was the first to perform the **implantation of teeth ;** and Younger the first to transplant the teeth of man in the jaws of man ; the initial operation should be called **replantation,** as it was merely the replace-ment of a tooth in a socket from which it had accidentally or intentionally been removed.   Hunter drilled a hole in a cock's comb and inserted a tooth, and held it by a ligature.   Younger drilled a hole in a man's jaw and im-planted a tooth, and proved that it was not necessary to use a fresh tooth. Ottolengni [b] mentions the case of a man who was struck by a ruffian and had his two central incisors knocked out.   He searched for them, washed them in warm water, carefully washed the teeth-sockets, and gently placed the teeth back in their position, where they remained firmly attached.   At the time of report, six years after the accident, they were still firmly in position. Pettyjohn [c] reports a successful case of tooth-replantation in his young daugh-ter of two, who fell on the cellar stairs, completely excising the central incis-ors.   The alveolar process ·of the right jaw was fractured, and the gum lacerated to the entire length of the root.   The teeth were placed in a tepid normal saline solution, and the child chloroformed, narcosis being in-duced in sleep ; the gums were cleaned antiseptically, and $3\frac{1}{2}$ hours afterward the child had the teeth firmly in place.   They had been out of the mouth fully an hour.   Four weeks afterward they were as firm as ever.   By their

[a] 838, Nov., 1894.   [b] 227, 1889, viii., 65.   [c] 632, Jan., 1896.

experiments Gluck and Magnus prove that there is a return of activity after **transplantation of muscle.** After excision of malignant tumors of muscles, Helferich of Munich, and Lange of New York, have filled the gap left by the excision of the muscle affected by the tumor with transplanted muscles from dogs. Gluck has induced reproduction of lost tendons by grafting them with cat-gut, and according to Ashhurst, Peyrot has filled the gaps in retracted tendons by **transplanting tendons,** taken in one case from a dog, and in another from a cat.

Nerve-grafting, as a supplementary operation to neurectomy, has been practised, and Gersung has transplanted the nerves of lower animals to the nerve stumps of man.

Bone-grafting is quite frequently practised, portions from a recently amputated limb, or portions removed from living animals, or bone-chips, may be used. Senn proposed decalcified bone-plates to be used to fill in the gaps. Shifting of the bone has been done, *e. g.*, by dividing a strip of the hard palate covered with its soft parts, parallel to the fissure in cleft palate, but leaving unsevered the bony attachments in front, and partially fracturing the pedicle, drawing the bony flaps together with sutures ; or, when forming a new nose, by turning down with the skin and periosteum the outer table of the frontal bone, split off with a chisel, after cutting around the part to be removed. [845] Trueheart reports a case of partial excision of the clavicle, successfully followed by the grafting of periosteal and osseous material taken from a dog. Robson and Hayes of Rochester, N. Y., have successfully supplemented excision of spina bifida by the transplantation of a strip of periosteum from a rabbit. Poncet hastened a cure in a case of necrosis with partial destruction of the periosteum by inserting grafts taken from the bones of a dead infant and from a kid. Ricketts speaks of bone-grafting and the use of ivory, and remarks that Poncet of Lyons restored a tibia in nine months by grafting to the superior articular surface. Recently amalgam fillings have been used in bone-cavities to supplant grafting.

In destructive injuries of the skin, various **materials** were **formerly used in grafting,** none of which, however, have produced the same good effect as the use of skin by the Thiersch Method, which will be described later.

Rodgers, U. S. N.,[a] reports the case of a white man of thirty-eight who suffered from gangrene of the skin of the buttocks caused by sitting in a pan of caustic potash. When seen the man was intoxicated, and there was a gangrenous patch four by six inches on his buttocks. Rodgers used grafts from the under wing of a young fowl, as suggested by Redard,[b] with good result. Vanmeter of Colorado[c] describes a boy of fourteen with a severe extensive burn ; a portion beneath the chin and lower jaw, and the right arm from the elbow to the fingers, formed a granulating surface which would not heal, and grafting was resorted to. The neck-grafts were supplied by the skin of the

[a] 269, 1888.   [b] 538, March 10, 1888.   [c] Annals of Surgery, St. Louis, 1890.

father and brother, but the arm-grafts were taken from two young puppies of the Mexican hairless breed, whose soft, white, hairless skin seemed to offer itself for the purpose with good prospect of a successful result.   The outcome was all that could be desired.   The puppy-grafts took faster and proved themselves to be superior to the skin-grafts.   There is a case reported [a] in which the skin of a greyhound seven days old, taken from the abdominal wall and even from the tail, was used with most satisfactory results in grafting an extensive ulcer following a burn on the left leg of a boy of ten.   Masterman has grafted with the inner membrane of a hen's egg, and a Mexican surgeon, Altramirano, used the gills of a cock.

Fowler of Brooklyn [b] has grafted with the skin from the back and abdomen of a large frog.   The patient was a colored boy of sixteen, who was extensively burned by a kerosene lamp.   The burns were on the legs, thighs, buttocks, and right ankle, and the estimated area of burnt surface was 247.95 square inches.   The frog skin was transferred to the left buttocks, and on the right buttocks eight long strips of white skin were transferred after the manner of Thiersch.   A strip of human skin was placed in one section over the frog skin, but became necrotic in four days, not being attached to the granulating surface.   The man was discharged cured in six months.   The frog skin was soft, pliable, and of a reddish hue, while the human white skin was firm and rapidly becoming pigmented.   Leale [c] cites the successful use of common warts in a case of grafting on a man of twenty who was burned on the foot by a stream of molten metal.   Leale remarks that as common warts of the skin are collections of vascular papillæ, admitting of separation without injury to their exceptionally thick layer of epidermis, they are probably better for the purposes of skin-grafting than ordinary skin of less vitality or vascularity.   Ricketts [d] has succeeded in grafting the skin of a frog to that of a tortoise, and also grafting frog skin to human skin.   Ricketts remarks that the prepuce of a boy is remarkably good material for grafting.   Sponge-grafts are often used to hasten cicatrization of integumental wounds.   There is recorded [e] an instance in which the breast of a crow and the back of a rat were grafted together and grew fast.   The crow dragged the rat along, and the two did not seem to care to part company.

Relative to skin-grafting proper, Bartens [f] succeeded in grafting the skin of a dead man of seventy on a boy of fourteen.   Symonds [g] reports cases of skin-grafting of large flaps from amputated limbs, and says this method is particularly available in large hospitals where they have amputations and grafts on the same day.   Martin has shown that, after many hours of exposure in the open air at a temperature of nearly 32° F., grafts could be successfully applied, but in such temperatures as 82° F., exposure of from six to seven hours destroyed their vitality, so that if kept cool, the limb of a healthy

a 476, March 6, 1890.   b Annals of Surgery, St. Louis, 1889.   c 538, 1879, xiv.
d 773, 1890.   e 548, 1860, i., 282.   f 199, 1888.   g 224, 1889, ii., 1331.

individual amputated for some accident, may be utilized for grafting purposes.

Reverdin originated the procedure of epidermic grafting. Small grafts the size of a pin-head doing quite as well as large ones. Unfortunately but little diminution of the cicatricial contraction is effected by Reverdin's method.

Thiersch contends that healing of a granulated surface results first from a conversion of the soft, vascular granulation-papillæ, by contraction of some of their elements into young connective-tissue cells, into "dry, cicatricial papillæ," actually approximating the surrounding tissues, thus diminishing the area to

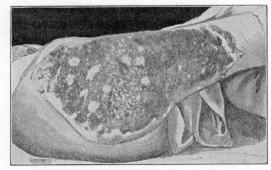

Fig. 228.—Extensive burn of the thigh, with skin-graft,—early stage (Harte).

be covered by epidermis ; and, secondly, by the covering of these papillæ by epidermic cells. Thiersch therefore recommends that for the prevention of cicatricial contraction, the grafting be performed with large strips of skin.

Harte[a] gives illustrations of a case of extensive skin-grafting on the thigh from six inches above the great trochanter well over the median line anteriorly and over the buttock. This extent is shown in Figure 228, taken five months after the accident, when the granulations had grown over the edge about an inch. Figure 229 shows the surface of the wound, six and one-half months after the accident and three months after the applications of numerous skin-grafts.

Fig. 229.—Extensive burn of the thigh, with skin-graft,—late stage.

Cases of **self-mutilation** may be divided into three classes :—those in which the injuries are inflicted in a moment of temporary insanity from hallucinations or melancholia ; with suicidal intent ; and in religious frenzy or emotion. Self-mutilation is seen **in the lower animals,** and Kennedy,[b] in mentioning the case of a hydrocephalic child who ate off its entire under lip, speaks also of a dog, of cats, and of a lioness who ate off their tails. Kennedy

a 792, Nov., 1892.   b 536, 1885, i., 211.

mentions the habit in young children of biting the finger-nails as an evidence of infantile trend toward self-mutilation. In the same discussion Collins states that he knew of an instance in India in which a horse lay down, deliberately exposing his anus, and allowing the crows to pick and eat his whole rectum. In temporary insanity, in fury, or in grief, the lower animals have been noticed by naturalists to mutilate themselves.

Self-mutilation in man is almost invariably the result of meditation over the generative function, and the great majority of cases of this nature are **avulsions or amputations of some parts of the genitalia.** The older records are full of such instances. Benivenius,[198] Blanchard,[213] Knackstedt, and Schenck cite cases. Smetius [a] mentions castration which was effected by using the finger-nails, and there is an old record in which a man avulsed his own genitals.[b] Scott [c] mentions an instance in which a man amputated his genitals and recovered without subsequent symptoms. Gockelius speaks of self-castration in a ruptured man, and Golding,[d] Guyon, Louis,[e] Laugier,[f] the Ephemerides, Alix, Marstral,[g] and others, record instances of self-castration. In his Essays Montaigne mentions an instance of complete castration performed by the individual himself.

Thiersch [h] mentions a case of a man who circumcised himself when eighteen. He married in 1870, and upon being told that he was a father he slit up the hypogastrium from the symphysis pubis to the umbilicus, so that the omentum protruded ; he said his object was to obtain a view of the interior. Although the knife was dirty and blunt, the wound healed after the removal of the extruding omentum. A year later he laid open one side of the scrotum. The prolapsed testicle was replaced, and the wound healed without serious effect. He again laid open his abdomen in 1880, the wound again healing notwithstanding the prolapse of the omentum. In May of the same year he removed the right testicle, and sewed the wound up himself. Four days later the left was treated the same way. The spermatic cord however escaped, and a hematoma, the size of a child's head, formed on account of which he had to go to the hospital. This man acted under an uncontrollable impulse to mutilate himself, and claimed that until he castrated himself he had no peace of mind.

There is a similar report in an Italian journal [360] which was quoted in London.[i] It described a student at law, of delicate complexion, who at the age of fourteen gave himself up to masturbation. He continually studied until the age of nineteen, when he fell into a state of dulness, and complained that his head felt as if compressed by a circle of fire. He said that a voice kept muttering to him that his generative organs were abnormally deformed or the seat of disease. After that, he imagined that he heard a cry of "amputation ! amputation !" Driven by this hallucination, he made his

[a] 730, 525.	[b] 458, T. xvii., 404.	[c] 524, ii., No. 7.	[d] 528, vii., No. 6.
[e] 462, T. ix.	[f] Ibid. [g] 462, T. viii.	[h] 491, 1881, 253.	[i] 548, 1854, ii., 94.

first attempt at self-mutilation ten days later. He was placed in an Asylum at Astino where, though closely watched, he took advantage of the first opportunity and cut off two-thirds of his penis, when the delirium subsided. Camp [a] describes a stout German of thirty-five who, while suffering from delirium tremens, fancied that his enemies were trying to steal his genitals, and seizing a sharp knife he amputated his penis close to the pubes. He threw the severed organ violently at his imaginary pursuers. The hemorrhage was profuse, but ceased spontaneously by the formation of coagulum over the mouth of the divided vessels. The wound was quite healed in six weeks, and he was discharged from the hospital, rational and apparently content with his surgical feat.

Richards [b] reports the case of a Brahman boy of sixteen who had contracted syphilis, and convinced, no doubt, that "nocit empta dolore voluptus," he had taken effective means of avoiding injury in the future by completely amputating his penis at the root. Some days after his admission to the hospital he asked to be castrated, stating that he intended to become an ascetic, and the loss of his testes as well as of his penis appeared to him to be an imperative condition to the attainment of that happy consummation. Chevers [266] mentions a somewhat similar case occurring in India.

Sands [c] speaks of a single man of thirty who amputated his penis. He gave an incomplete history of syphilis. After connection with a woman he became a confirmed syphilophobe and greatly depressed. While laboring under the hallucination that he was possessed of two bodies he tied a string around the penis and amputated the organ one inch below the glans. On loosening the string, three hours afterward, to enable him to urinate, he lost three pints of blood, but he eventually recovered. In the Pennsylvania Hospital Reports [623] there is an account of a married man who, after drinking several weeks, developed mania a potu, and was found in his room covered with blood. His penis was completely cut off near the pubes, and the skin of the scrotum was so freely incised that the testicles were entirely denuded, but not injured. A small silver cap was made to cover the sensitive urethra on a line with the abdominal wall.

There is a record [d] of a tall, powerfully-built Russian peasant of twenty-nine, of morose disposition, who on April 3d, while reading his favorite book, without uttering a cry, suddenly and with a single pull tore away his scrotum together with his testes. He then arose from the bank where he had been sitting, and quietly handed the avulsed parts to his mother who was sitting near by, saying to her : " Take that ; I do not want it any more." To all questions from his relatives he asked pardon and exemption from blame, but gave no reason for his act. This patient made a good recovery at the hospital. Alexeef,[e] another Russian, speaks of a similar injury occurring during an attack of delirium tremens.

a 593, 1852.   b 435, xii.   c 127, 1871.   d 697, 1887, 93, No. 5.   e 556, 1882, No. 22.

Black [a] details the history of a young man of nineteen who went to his bathroom and deliberately placing his scrotum on the edge of the tub he cut it crossways down to the wood. He besought Black to remove his testicle, and as the spermatic cord was cut and much injured, and hemorrhage could only be arrested by ligature, the testicle was removed. The reason assigned for this act of mutilation was that he had so frequent nocturnal emissions that he became greatly disgusted and depressed in spirit thereby. He had practiced self-abuse for two years and ascribed his emissions to this cause. Although his act was that of a maniac, the man was perfectly rational. Since the injury he had had normal and frequent emissions and erections.

Orwin [b] mentions the case of a laborer of forty who, in a fit of remorse after being several days with a prostitute, atoned for his unfaithfulness to his wife by opening his scrotum and cutting away his left testicle with a pocket knife. The missing organ was found about six yards away covered with dirt. At the time of infliction of this injury the man was calm and perfectly rational. Warrington [c] relates the strange case of Isaac Brooks, an unmarried farmer of twenty-nine, who was found December 5, 1879, with extensive mutilations of the scrotum ; he said that he had been attacked and injured by three men. He swore to the identity of two out of the three, and these were transported to ten years' penal servitude. On February 13, 1881, he was again found with mutilation of the external genitals, and again said he had been set upon by four men who had inflicted his injury, but as he wished it kept quiet he asked that there be no prosecution. Just before his death on December 31, 1881, he confessed that he had perjured himself, and that the mutilations were self-performed. He was not aware of any morbid ideas as to his sexual organs, and although he had an attack of gonorrhea ten years before he seemed to worry very little over it. There is an account [d] of a Scotch boy who wished to lead a " holy life," and on two occasions sought the late Mr. Liston's skilful aid in pursuance of this idea. He returned for a third time, having himself unsuccessfully performed castration.

A case of self-mutilation by a soldier who was confined in the guardhouse for drunkenness is related by Beck. [e] The man borrowed a knife from a comrade and cut off the whole external genital apparatus, remarking as he flung the parts into a corner : " Any —— fool can cut his throat, but it takes a soldier to cut his privates off ! " Under treatment he recovered, and then he regretted his action.

Sinclair [f] describes an Irishman of twenty-five who, maniacal from intemperance, first cut off one testicle with a wire nail, and then the second with a trouser-buckle. Not satisfied with the extent of his injuries he drove a nail into his temple, first through the skin by striking it with his hand, and then by butting it against the wall,—the latter maneuver causing his death.

a 536, 1889, ii, 32.   b 224, 1882, i., 105.   c 224, 1882, i., 72.
d 476, 1882, i., 118.   e 124, 1847, 265.   f 178, Jan., 1886.

There is on record [a] the history of an insane medical student in Dublin who **extirpated both eyes** and threw them on the grass. He was in a state of acute mania, and the explanation offered was that as a "grinder" before examination he had been diligently studying the surgery of the eye, and particularly that relating to enucleation. Another Dublin case quoted by the same authority was that of a young girl who, upon being arrested and committed to a police-cell in a state of furious drunkenness, tore out both her eyes. In such cases, as a rule, the finger-nails are the only instrument used. There is a French case also quoted of a woman of thirty-nine who had borne children in rapid succession. While suckling a child three months old she became much excited, and even fanatical, in reading the Bible. Coming to the passage, " If thy right eye offend thee, pluck it out, etc.," she was so impressed with the necessity of obeying the divine injunction that she enucleated her eye with a meat-hook. There is mentioned [b] the case of a young woman who cut off her right hand and cast it into the fire, and attempted to enucleate her eyes, and also to hold her remaining hand in the fire. Haslam [c] reports the history of a female who mutilated herself by grinding glass between her teeth.

Channing [d] gives an account of the case of Helen Miller, a German Jewess of thirty, who was admitted to the Asylum for Insane Criminals at Auburn, N. Y., in October, 1872, and readmitted in June, 1875, suffering from simulation of hematemesis. On September 25th she cut her left wrist and right hand ; in three weeks she became again "discouraged" because she was refused opium, and again cut her arms below the elbows, cleanly severing the skin and fascia, and completely hacking the muscles in every direction. Six weeks later she repeated the latter feat over the seat of the recently healed cicatrices. The right arm healed, but the left showed erysipelatous inflammation, culminating in edema, which affected the glottis to such an extent that tracheotomy was performed to save her life. Five weeks after convalescence, during which her conduct was exemplary, she again cut her arms in the same place. In the following April, for the merest trifle, she again repeated the mutilation, but this time leaving pieces of glass in the wounds. Six months later she inflicted a wound seven inches in length, in which she inserted 30 pieces of glass, seven long splinters, and five shoe-nails. In June, 1877, she cut herself for the last time. The following articles were taken from her arms and preserved : Ninety-four pieces of glass, 34 splinters, two tacks, five shoe-nails, one pin, and one needle, besides other things which were lost,—making altogether about 150 articles.

"**Needle-girls**," etc.—A peculiar type of self-mutilation is the habit sometimes seen in hysteric persons of piercing their flesh with numerous needles or pins. Herbolt of Copenhagen [e] tells of a young Jewess from whose

a 536, 1888, ii., 260.   b 476, 1851.   c Quoted 465, July, 1875.
d 123, xxxiv., 368.   e Journal des Debats, 1823.

body, in the course of eighteen months, were extracted 217 needles.   Sometime after 100 more came from a tumor on the shoulder.   As all the symptoms in this case were abdominal, it was supposed that during an epileptic seizure this girl had swallowed the needles ; but as she was of an hysteric nature it seems more likely they had entered the body through the skin.   There is an instance [a] in which 132 needles were extracted from a young lady's person. Caen [b] describes a woman of twenty-six, while in prison awaiting trial, succeeding in committing suicide by introducing about 30 pins and needles in the chest region, over the heart.   Her method was to gently introduce them, and then to press them deeper with a prayer-book.   An autopsy showed that some of the pins had reached the lungs, some were in the mediastinum, on the back part of the right auricle ; the descending vena cava was perforated, the anterior portion of the left ventricle was transfixed by a needle, and several of the articles were found in the liver.   Andrews [c] removed 300 needles from the body of an insane female.   The Lancet [d] records an account of a suicide by the penetration of a darning-needle in the epigastrium.   There were nine punctures in this region, and in the last the needle was left in situ and fixed by worsted.   In 1851 the same journal spoke of an instance in which 30 pins were removed from the limbs of a servant girl.   It was said that while hanging clothes, with her mouth full of pins, she was slapped on the shoulder, causing her to start and swallow the pins.   There is another report [e] of a woman who swallowed great numbers of pins.   On her death one pound and nine ounces of pins were found in her stomach and duodenum.   There are individuals known as "human pin-cushions," who publicly introduce pins and needles into their bodies for gain's sake.

The **wanderings of pins and needles in the body** are quite well known.   Schenck records the finding of a swallowed pin in the liver.   Haller mentions [f] one that made its way to the hand.   Silvy speaks of a case in which a quantity of swallowed pins escaped through the muscles, the bladder, and vagina ; there is another record in which the pins escaped many years afterward from the thigh.[g]   The Philosophical Transactions contain a record of the escape of a pin from the skin of the arm after it had entered by the mouth.   Gooch, Ruysch, Purmann, and Hoffman speak of needle-wanderings.   Stephenson [h] gives an account of a pin which was finally voided by the bladder after forty-two years' sojourn in a lady's body.   On November 15, 1802, the celebrated Dr. Lettsom spoke of an old lady who sat on a needle while riding in a hackney coach ; it passed from the injured leg to the other one, whence it was extracted.   Deckers tells of a gentleman who was wounded in the right hypochondrium, the ball being taken thirty years afterward from the knee.   Borellus [841] gives an account of a thorn entering the digit and passing out of the body by the anus.

a 440, 1853.   b 476, 1863, ii., 524.   c 123, July, 1872.   d 476, 1887, i., 230.
e 476, 1852.   f 398, i., 586.   g 398, i., 371.   h Detroit Med. Jour., 1887, i., 895.

Strange as it may seem, **a prick of a pin** not entering a vital center or organ has been **the indirect cause of death.** Augenius writes of a tailor who died in consequence of a prick of a needle between the nail and flesh of the end of the thumb. Amatus Lusitanus [119] mentions a similar instance in an old woman, although, from the symptoms given, the direct cause was probably tetanus. In modern times Cunninghame,[a] Boring,[b] and Hobart[c] mention instances in which death has followed the prick of a pin : in Boring's case the death occurred on the fifth day.

Manufacture of Crippled Beggars.—Knowing the sympathy of the world in general for a cripple, in some countries low in the moral scale, voluntary mutilation is sometimes practised by those who prefer begging to toiling. In the same manner **artificial monstrosities** have been manufactured solely for gain's sake. We quite often read of these instances in lay-journals, but it is seldom that a case comes under the immediate observation of a thoroughly scientific mind. There is, however, on record [d] a remarkable instance accredited to Jamieson of Shanghai who presented to the Royal College of Surgeons a pair of feet with the following history : Some months previously a Chinese beggar had excited much pity and made a good business by showing the mutilated stumps of his legs, and the feet that had belonged to them slung about his neck. While one day scrambling out of the way of a constable who had forbidden this gruesome spectacle, he was knocked down by a carriage in the streets of Shanghai, and was taken to the hospital, where he was questioned about the accident which deprived him of his feet. After selling the medical attendant his feet he admitted that he had purposely performed the amputations himself, starting about a year previously. He had fastened cords about his ankles, drawing them as tightly as he could bear them, and increasing the pressure every two or three days. For a fortnight his pain was extreme, but when the bones were bared his pains ceased. At the end of a month and a half he was able to entirely remove his feet by partly snapping and partly cutting the dry bone. Such cases appear to be quite common in China, and by investigation many parallels could elsewhere be found.

The Chinese custom of foot-binding is a curious instance of self-mutilation. In a paper quoted in the Philadelphia Medical Times, January 31, 1880, a most minute account of the modus operandi, the duration, and the suffering attendant on this process are given. Strapping of the foot by means of tight bandages requires a period of two or three years' continuance before the desired effect is produced. There is a varying degree of pain, which is most severe during the first year and gradually diminishes after the binding of all the joints is completed. During the binding the girl at night lies across the bed, putting her legs on the edge of the bedstead in such a manner as to make pressure under the knees, thus be-

a 381, 1829, ii., 21.   b 176, 1872, 218.   c 313, 1856, 473.   d 224, 1882, i.,397.

numbing the parts below and avoiding the major degree of pain.   In this
position, swinging their legs backward and forward, the poor Chinese girls
pass many a weary night.   During this period the feet are unbound once a
month only.   The operation is begun by placing the end of a long, narrow
bandage on the inside of the instep and carrying it over the four smaller toes,
securing them under the foot.   After several turns the bandage is reversed so
as to compress the foot longitudinally.   The young girl is then left for a month,
and when the bandage is removed the foot is often found gangrenous and
ulcerated, one or two toes not infrequently being lost.   If the foot is thus
bound for two years it becomes virtually dead and painless.   By this time
the calf disappears from lack of exercise, the bones are attenuated, and all
the parts are dry and shrivelled.   In after-life the leg frequently regains its
muscles and adipose tissue, but the foot always remains small.   The binding
process is said to exert a markedly depressing influence upon the emotional
character of the subject, which lasts through life, and is very characteristic.

To show how minute some of the feet of the Chinese women are, Figure
I. of the accompanying plate (Plate 8), taken from a paper by Kenthughes
on the " Feet of Chinese Ladies " [a] is from a photograph of a shoe that
measured only $3\frac{1}{4}$ inches anteroposteriorly.   The foot which it was intended
to fill must have been smaller still, for the bandage would take up a certain
amount of space.   Figure II. is a reproduction of a photograph of a foot
measuring $5\frac{1}{2}$ inches anteroposteriorly, the wrinkled appearance of the skin
being due to prolonged immersion in spirit.   This photograph shows well
the characteristics of the Chinese foot—the prominent and vertically placed
heel, which is raised generally about an inch from the level of the great toe ;
the sharp artificial cavus, produced by the altered position of the os calcis, and
the downward deflection of the foot in front of the mediotarsal joint ; the
straight and downward pointing great toe, and the infolding of the smaller
toes underneath the great toe.   In Figure III. we have a photograph of the
skeleton of a Chinese lady's foot about five inches in anteroposterior diameter.
The mesial axis of the os calcis is almost directly vertical, with a slight forward inclination, forming a right angle with the bones in front of the mediotarsal joint.   The upper three-quarters of the anterior articular surface
of the calcis is not in contact with the cuboid, the latter being depressed
obliquely forward and downward, the lower portion of the posterior facet
on the cuboid articulating with a new surface on the under portion of
the bone.   The general shape of the bone closely resembles that of a
normal one—a marked contrast to its wasted condition and tapering extremity in paralytic calcaneus.   Extension and flexion at the ankle are
only limited by the shortness of the ligaments ; there is no opposition from
the conformation of the bones.   The astragalus is almost of normal shape ;
the trochlea is slightly prolonged anteriorly, especially on the inner side, from

[a] Intercolonial Journal of Medicine and Surgery, Melbourne, 1894.

PLATE 8.

Fig. I.—Full Size.

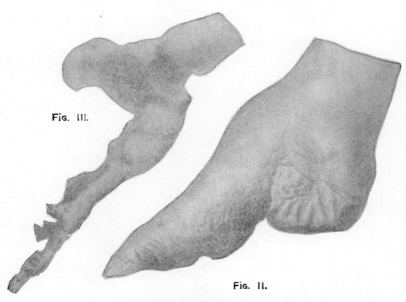

Fig. III.

Fig. II.

Chinese foot-binding (Kenthughes).

contact with the tibial articular surface. The cartilage on the exposed posterior portion of the trochlea seems healthy. The head of the astragalus is very prominent on the outer side, the scaphoid being depressed downward and inward away from it. The anterior articular surface is prolonged in the direction of the displaced scaphoid. The scaphoid, in addition to its displacement, is much compressed on the plantar surface, being little more than one-half the width of the dorsal surface. The cuboid is displaced obliquely downward and forward, so that the upper part of the posterior articular surface is not in contact with the calcis.

A professional leg-breaker is described in the Weekly Medical Review of St. Louis, April, 1890. This person's name was E. L. Landers, and he was accredited with earning his living by breaking or pretending to break his leg in order to collect damages for the supposed injury. Moreover, this individual had but one leg, and was compelled to use crutches. At the time of report he had succeeded in obtaining damages in Wichita, Kansas, for a supposed fracture. The Review quotes a newspaper account of this operation as follows :—

" According to the Wichita Dispatch he represented himself as a telegraph operator who was to have charge of the postal telegraph office in that city as soon as the line reached there. He remained about town for a month until he found an inviting piece of defective sidewalk, suitable for his purpose, when he stuck his crutch through the hole and fell screaming to the ground, declaring that he had broken his leg. He was carried to a hospital, and after a week's time, during which he negotiated a compromise with the city authorities and collected $1000 damages, a confederate, claiming to be his nephew, appeared and took the wounded man away on a stretcher, saying that he was going to St. Louis. Before the train was fairly out of Wichita, Landers was laughing and boasting over his successful scheme to beat the town. The Wichita story is in exact accord with the artistic methods of a one-legged sharper who about 1878 stuck his crutch through a coal-hole here, and, falling heels over head, claimed to have sustained injuries for which he succeeded in collecting something like $1500 from the city. He is described as a fine-looking fellow, well dressed, and wearing a silk hat. He lost one leg in a railroad accident, and having collected a good round sum in damages for it, adopted the profession of leg-breaking in order to earn a livelihood. He probably argued that as he had made more money in that line than in any other he was especially fitted by natural talents to achieve distinction in this direction. But as it would be rather awkward to lose his remaining leg altogether he modified the idea and contents himself with collecting the smaller amounts which ordinary fractures of the hip-joint entitle such an expert 'fine worker' to receive.

" He first appeared here in 1874 and succeeded, it is alleged, in beating the Life Association of America. After remaining for some time in the hospital he was removed on a stretcher to an Illinois village, from which point the negotiations for damages were conducted by correspondence, until finally a point of agreement was reached and an agent of the company was sent to pay him the money. This being accomplished the agent returned to the depot to take the train back to St. Louis when he was surprised to see the supposed sufferer stumping around on his crutches on the depot platform, laughing and jesting over the ease with which he had beaten the corporation.

" He afterward fell off a Wabash train at Edwardsville and claimed to have sustained serious injuries, but in this case the company's attorneys beat him and proved him to be an impostor. In 1879 he stumbled into the telegraph office at the Union Depot here, when Henry C. Mahoney, the superintendent, catching sight of him, put him out, with the curt remark that he didn't want him to stick that crutch into a cuspidor and fall down, as it was too expensive a performance for the company to stand. He beat the Missouri Pacific and several other railroads and municipalities at different times, it is claimed, and manages to get enough at each successful venture to carry him along for a year or eighteen months, by which time the memory of his trick fades out of the public mind, when he again bobs up serenely."

Anomalous Suicides.—The literature on suicide affords many instances of self-mutilations and ingenious modes of producing death. In the Dublin Medical Press for 1854 there is an extraordinary case of suicide, in which the patient thrust a red-hot poker into his abdomen and subsequently pulled it out, detaching portions of the omentum and 32 inches of the colon. Another suicide in Great Britain swallowed a red-hot poker.[a] In commenting on suicides, in 1835, Arntzenius speaks of an ambitious Frenchman who was desirous of leaving the world in a distinguished manner, and who attached himself to a rocket of enormous size which he had built for the purpose, and setting fire to it, ended his life. On September 28, 1895, according to the Gaulois and the New York Herald (Paris edition) of that date, there was admitted to the Hôpital St. Louis a clerk, aged twenty-five, whom family troubles had rendered desperate and who had determined to seek death as a relief from his misery. Reviewing the various methods of committing suicide he found none to his taste, and resolved on something new. Being familiar with the constituents of explosives, he resolved to convert his body into a bomb, load it with explosives, and thus blow himself to pieces. He procured some powdered sulphur and potassium chlorate, and placing each in a separate wafer he swallowed both with the aid of water. He then lay down on his bed, dressed in his best clothes, expecting that as soon as the two explosive materials came into contact he would burst like a bomb and his troubles would be over. Instead of the anticipated result the most violent collicky pains ensued, which finally became so great that he had to summon his neighbors, who took him to the hospital, where, after vigorous application with the stomach-pump, it

a 548, 1856, 103.

was hoped that his life would be saved. Sankey [a] mentions an epileptic who was found dead in his bed in the Oxford County Asylum ; the man had accomplished his end by placing a round pebble in each nostril, and thoroughly impacting in his throat a strip of flannel done up in a roll. In his " Institutes of Surgery " Sir Charles Bell remarks that his predecessor at the Middlesex Hospital entered into a conversation with his barber over an attempt at suicide in the neighborhood, during which the surgeon called the " would-be suicide " a fool, explaining to the barber how clumsy his attempts had been, at the same time giving him an extempore lecture on the anatomic construction of the neck, and showing him how a successful suicide in this region should be performed. At the close of the conversation the unfortunate barber retired into the back area of his shop, and following minutely the surgeon's directions, cut his throat in such a manner that there was no hope of saving him. It is supposed that one could commit suicide by completely gilding or varnishing the body, thus eliminating the excretory functions of the skin. There is an old story of an infant who was gilded to appear at a Papal ceremony who died shortly afterward from the suppression of the skin-function. The fact is one well established among animals, but after a full series of actual experiments, Tecontjeff of St. Petersburg concludes that in this respect man differs from animals. This authority states that in man no tangible risk is entailed by this process, at least for any length of time required for therapeutic purposes. " Tarred and feathered " persons rarely die of the coating of tar they receive. For other instances of peculiar forms of suicide reference may be made to numerous volumes on this subject, prominent among which is that by Brierre de Boismont,[226] which, though somewhat old, has always been found trustworthy, and also to the chapters on this subject written by various authors on medical jurisprudence.

Religious and Ceremonial Mutilations.—Turning now to the subject of self-mutilation and self-destruction from the peculiar customs or religious beliefs of people, we find pages of information at our disposal. It is not only among the savage or uncivilized tribes that such ideas have prevailed, but from the earliest times they have had their influence upon educated minds. In the East, particularly in India, the doctrines of Buddhism, that the soul should be without fear, that it could not be destroyed, and that the flesh was only its resting-place, the soul several times being reincarnated, brought about great indifference to bodily injuries and death. In the history of the Brahmans there was a sect of philosophers called the Gymnosophists, who had the extremest indifference to life. To them incarnation was a positive fact, and death was simply a change of residence. One of these philosophers, Calanus, was burned in the presence of Alexander ; and, according to Plutarch, three centuries later another Gymnosophist named Jarmenochegra, was similarly burned before Augustus. Since this time, according to Brierre

a 224, 1883, i., 88.

de Boismont,[226] the suicides from indifference to life in this mystic country are counted by the thousands. Penetrating Japan the same sentiment, according to report, made it common in the earlier history of that country to see ships on its coasts, filled with fanatics who, by voluntary dismantling, submerged the vessels little by little, the whole multitude sinking into the sea while chanting praises to their idols. The same doctrines produced the same result in China. According to Brucker[a] it is well known that among the 500 philosophers of the college of Confucius, there were many who disdained to survive the loss of their books (burned by order of the savage Emperor Chi-Koung-ti), and throwing themselves into the sea, they disappeared under the waves. According to Brierre de Boismont, voluntary mutilation or death was very rare among the Chaldeans, the Persians, or the Hebrews, their precepts being different from those mentioned. The Hebrews in particular had an aversion to self-murder, and during a period in their history of 4000 years there were only eight or ten suicides recorded. Josephus shows what a marked influence on suicides the invasion of the Romans among the Hebrews had.

In Africa, as in India, there were Gymnosophists. In Egypt Sesostris, the grandest king of the country, having lost his eyesight in his old age, calmly and deliberately killed himself. About the time of Mark Anthony and Cleopatra, particularly after the battle of Actium, suicide was in great favor in Egypt. In fact a great number of persons formed an academy called The Synapothanoumenes, who had for their object the idea of dying together. In Western Europe, as shown in the ceremonies of the Druids, we find among the Celts a propensity for suicide and an indifference to self-torture. The Gauls were similarly minded, believing in the dogma of immortality and eternal repose. They thought little of bodily cares and ills. In Greece and Rome there was always an apology for suicide and death in the books of the philosophers. *" Nil igitur mors est, ad nos neque pertinet hilum ; quando quidem natura animi mortalis habetur ! "* cries Lucretius. With the advent of Christianity, condemning as it did the barbarous customs of self-mutilation and self-murder, these practices seem to disappear gradually ; but stoicism and indifference to pain were exhibited in martyrdom. Toward the middle ages, when fanaticism was at its height and the mental malady of demoniacal possession was prevalent, there was something of a reversion to the old customs. In the East the Juggernaut procession was still in vogue, but this was suppressed by civilized authorities ; outside of a few minor customs still prevalent among our own people we must to-day look to the savage tribes for the perpetuation of such practices.

In an excellent article on the evolution of ceremonial institutions[b] Herbert Spencer mentions the Fuegians, Veddahs, Andamanese, Dyaks, Todas, Gonds, Santals, Bodos, and Dhimals, Mishmis, Kamchadales, and Snake

<hr>

a " Hist. Nat. Philos.," T. iv., 11 and 670.   b 638, April, 1878.

Indians, as among people who form societies to practise simple mutilations in slight forms. Mutilations in somewhat graver forms, but still in moderation, are practised by the Tasmanians, Tamaese, the people of New Guinea, Karens, Nagas, Ostiaks, Eskimos, Chinooks, Comanches, and Chippewas. What might be called mixed or compound mutilations are practised by the New Zealanders, East Africans, Kondes, Kukas, and Calmucks. Among those practising simple but severe mutilations are the New Caledonians, the Bushmen, and some indigenous Australians. Those tribes having for their customs the practice of compound major mutilations are the Fiji Islanders, Sandwich Islanders, Tahitians, Tongans, Samoans, Javanese, Sumatrans, natives of Malagasy, Hottentots, Damaras, Bechuanas, Kaffirs, the Congo people, the Coast Negroes, Inland Negroes, Dahomeans, Ashantees, Fulahs, Abyssinians, Arabs, and Dakotas. Spencer has evidently made a most extensive and comprehensive study of this subject, and his paper is a most valuable contribution to the subject. In the preparation of this section we have frequently quoted from it.

The practice of **self-bleeding** has its origin in other mutilations, although the Aztecs shed human blood in the worship of the sun. The Samoïedes have a custom of **drinking** the **blood** of warm animals. Those of the Fijians who were cannibals drank the warm blood of their victims. Among the Amaponda Kaffirs there are horrible accounts of kindred savage customs. Spencer quotes :—" It is usual for the ruling chief on his accession to be washed in the blood of a near relative, generally a brother, who is put to death for the occasion." During a Samoan marriage-ceremony the friends of the bride "took up stones and beat themselves until their heads were bruised and bleeding." In Australia a novitiate at the ceremony of manhood drank a mouthful of blood from the veins of the warrior who was to be his sponsor.

At the death of their kings the Lacedemonians met in large numbers and tore the flesh from their foreheads with pins and needles. It is said that when Odin was near his death he ordered himself to be marked with a spear ; and Niort, one of his successors, followed the example of his predecessor. Shakespeare speaks of " such as boast and show their scars." In the olden times it was not uncommon for a noble soldier to make public **exhibition of his scars** with the greatest pride ; in fact, on the battlefield they invited the reception of superficial disfiguring injuries, and to-day some students of the learned universities of Germany seem prouder of the possession of scars received in a duel of honor than in awards for scholastic attainments.

Lichtenstein tells of priests among the Bechuanas who made long cuts from the thigh to the knee of each warrior who slew an enemy in battle. Among some tribes of the Kaffirs a kindred custom was practised ; and among the Damaras, for every wild animal a young man destroyed his father made four incisions on the front of his son's body. Speaking of certain

Congo people, Tuckey says that they scar themselves principally with the idea of rendering themselves agreeable to the women of their tribe. Among the Itzaex Indians of Yucatan, a race with particularly handsome features, some are marked with scarred lines, inflicted as signs of courage.

Cosmetic Mutilations.—In modern times there have been individuals expert in removing facial deformities, and by operations of various kinds producing pleasing dimples or other artificial signs of beauty. We have seen an apparatus advertised to be worn on the nose during the night for the purpose of correcting a disagreeable contour of this organ. A medical description of the artificial **manufacture of dimples** is as follows :—[a] " The modus operandi was to make a puncture in the skin where the dimple was required, which would not be noticed when healed, and, with a very delicate instrument, remove a portion of the muscle. Inflammation was then excited in the skin over the subcutaneous pit, and in a few days the wound, if such it may be called, was healed, and a charming dimple was the result." It is quite possible that some of our modern operators have overstepped the bounds of necessity, and performed unjustifiable plastic operations to satisfy the vanity of their patients.

Dobrizhoffer says of the Abipones that boys of seven **pierce their little arms** in imitation of their parents. Among some of the indigenous Australians it is quite customary for ridged and linear scars to be self-inflicted. In Tanna the people produce elevated scars on the arms and chests. Bancroft recites that family-marks of this nature existed among the Cuebas of Central America, refusal being tantamount to rebellion. Schomburgk tells that among the Arawaks, after a Mariquawi dance, so great is their zeal for honorable scars, the blood will run down their swollen calves, and strips of skin and muscle hang from the mangled limbs. Similar practices rendered it necessary for the United States Government to stop some of the ceremonial dances of the Indians under their surveillance.

A peculiar custom among savages is the **amputation of a finger** as a sacrifice to a deity. In the tribe of the Dakotas the relatives of a dead chief pacified his spirit by amputating a finger. In a similar way, during his initiation, the young Mandan warrior, " holding up the little finger of his left hand to the Great Spirit," . . " expresses his willingness to give it as a sacrifice, and he lays it on the dried buffalo skull, when another chops it off near the hand with a blow of the hatchet." According to Mariner the natives of Tonga cut off a portion of the little finger as a sacrifice to the gods for the recovery of a superior sick relative. The Australians have a custom of cutting off the last joint of the little finger of females as a token of submission to powerful beings alive and dead. A Hottentot widow who marries a second time must have the distal joint of her little finger cut off; another joint is removed each time she remarries.

Among the mutilations submitted to on the death of a king or chief in the

[a] 224, 1880, ii., 609.

Sandwich Islands, Cook mentions in his " Voyages " the custom of **knocking out** from one to four **front teeth.**

Among the Australian tribes the age of virility and the transition into manhood is celebrated by ceremonial customs, in which the novices are subjected to minor mutilations. A sharp bone is used for lancing their gums, while the throw-stick is used for knocking out a tooth. Sometimes, in addition to this crude dentistry, the youth is required to submit to cruel gashes cut upon his back and shoulders, and should he flinch or utter any cry of pain he is always thereafter classed with women. Haygarth writes of a semi-domesticated Australian who said one day, with a look of importance, that he must go away for a few days, as he had grown to man's estate, and it was high time he had his teeth knocked out. It is an obligatory rite among various African tribes to lose two or more of their front teeth. A tradition among certain Peruvians was that the Conqueror Huayna Coapæ made a law that they and their descendants should have three front teeth pulled out in each jaw. Cieza speaks of another tradition requiring the extraction of the teeth of children by their fathers as a very acceptable service to their gods. The Damaras knock out a wedge-shaped gap between two of their front teeth ; and the natives of Sierra Leone file or chip their teeth after the same fashion.

Depilatory customs are very ancient, and although minor in extent are still to be considered under the heading of mutilations. The giving of hair to the dead as a custom, has been perpetuated through many tribes and nations. In Euripides we find Electra admonishing Helen for sparing her locks, and thereby defrauding the dead. Alexander the Great shaved his locks in mourning for his friend, Hephæstion, and it was supposed that his death was hastened by the sun's heat on his bare head after his hat blew off at Babylon. Both the Dakota Indians and the Caribs maintain the custom of sacrificing hair to the dead. In Peru the custom was varied by pulling out eyelashes and eyebrows and presenting them to the sun, the hills, etc. It is said this custom is still in continuance. When Clovis was visited by the Bishop of Toulouse he gave him a hair from his beard and was imitated by his followers. In the Arthurian legends we find " Then went Arthur to Caerleon ; and thither came messages from King Ryons who said, ' even kings have done me homage, and with their beards I have trimmed a mantle. Send me now thy beard, for there lacks yet one to the finishing of the mantle.' " The association between short hair and slavery arose from the custom of taking hair from the slain. It existed among the Greeks and Romans, and was well known among the indigenous tribes of this continent. Among the Shoshones he who took the most scalps gained the most glory.

In speaking of the prisoners of the Chicimecs Bancroft says they were often scalped while yet alive, and the bloody trophies placed on the heads of their tormentors. In this manner we readily see that long hair among the indigenous tribes and various Orientals, Ottomans, Greeks, Franks, Goths, etc., was considered a sign of respect and honor. The respect and preservation of the Chinese queue is well known in the present day. Wishing to divide their brother's kingdom, Clothair and Childebert consulted whether to cut off the hair of their nephews, the rightful successors, so as to reduce them to the rank of subjects, or to kill them. The gods of various people, especially the greater gods, were distinguished by their long beards and flowing locks. In all pictures Thor and Samson were both given long hair, and the belief in strength and honor from long hair is proverbial. Hercules is always pictured with curls. According to Goldzhier, long locks of hair and a long beard are mythologic attributes of the sun. The sun's rays are compared to long locks or hairs on the face of the sun. When the sun sets and leaves his place to the darkness, or when the powerful summer sun is succeeded by the weak rays of the winter sun, then Samson's long locks, through which alone his strength remains, are cut off by the treachery of his deceitful concubine Delilah (the languishing, according to the meaning of the name). The beaming Apollo was, moreover, called the "Unshaven;" and Minos cannot conquer the solar hero, Nisos, until the latter loses his golden hair. In Arabic "Shams-on" means the sun, and Samson had seven locks of hair, the number of the planetary bodies. In view of the foregoing facts it seems quite possible that the majority of depilatory processes on the scalp originated in sun-worship, and through various phases and changes in religions were perpetuated to the Middle Ages. Charles Martel sent Pepin, his son, to Luithprand, king of the Lombards, that he might cut his first locks, and by this ceremony hold for the future the place of his illustrious father. To make peace with Alaric, Clovis became his adopted son by offering his beard to be cut. Among the Caribs the hair constituted their chief pride, and it was considered unequivocal proof of the sincerity of their sorrow, when on the death of a relative they cut their hair short. Among the Hebrews shaving of the head was a funeral rite, and among the Greeks and Romans the hair was cut short in mourning, either for a relative or for a celebrated personage. According to Krehl the Arabs also had such customs. Spencer mentions that during an eruption in Hawaii, "King Kamahameha cut off part of his own hair" . . . "and threw it into the torrent (of lava)."

The Tonga regarded the pubic hairs as under the special care of the devil, and with great ceremony made haste to remove them. The female inhabitants of some portions of the coast of Guinea remove the pubic hairs as fast as they appear. A curious custom of Mohammedan ladies after marriage is to rid themselves of the hirsute appendages of the pubes. Depilatory ointments are employed, consisting of equal parts of slaked lime and arsenic made into a paste with rose-water. It is said that this important ceremony is not essential in virgins. One of the ceremonies of assuming the toga virilis among the indigenous Australians consists in submitting to having each particular hair plucked singly from the body, the candidate being required not to display evidences of pain during the operation. Formerly the Japanese women at marriage blackened their teeth and shaved or pulled out their eyebrows.

The custom of **boring the ear** is very old, mention of it being made in Exodus xxi., 5 and 6, in which we find that if a Hebrew servant served for six years, his freedom was optional, but if he plainly said that he loved his master, and his wife and children, and did not desire to leave their house, the master should bring him before the judges ; and according to the passage in Exodus, " he shall also bring him to the door or unto the doorpost, and his master shall bore his ear through with an awl ; and he shall serve him forever." All the Burmese, says Sangermano, without exception, have the custom of boring their ears. The days when the operations were performed

Fig. 230.—Perforation of the ears and lip practised by the Botocudos.

were kept as festivals. The ludicrous custom of piercing the ears for the wearing of ornaments, typical of savagery and found in all indigenous African tribes, is universally prevalent among our own people.

The extremists in this custom are the Botocudos, who represent the most cruel and ferocious of the Brazilian tribes, and who especially cherish a love for cannibalism. They have a fondness for disfiguring themselves by inserting in the lower parts of their ears and in their under lips variously shaped pieces of wood ornaments called *peleles*, causing enormous protrusion of the under lip and a repulsive wide mouth, as shown in Figure 230.

Tattooing is a peculiar custom originating in various ways. The materials used are vermilion, indigo, carbon, or gunpowder. At one time this custom was used in the East to indicate caste and citizenship. Both sexes of the Sandwich Islanders have a peculiar tattooed mark indicative of their tribe or district. Among the Uapes, one tribe, the Tucanoes, have three vertical blue lines. Among other people tattooed marks indicated servility, and Boyle says the Kyans, Pakatans, and Kermowits alone, among the Borneo people, practised tattooing, and adds that these races are the least esteemed for bravery. Of the Fijians the women alone are tattooed, possibly as a method of adornment.

The tattooing of the people of Otaheite, seen by Cook, was surmised by him to have a religious significance, as it presented in many instances " squares, circles, crescents, and ill-designed representations of men and dogs." Every one of these people was tattooed upon reaching majority. According to Carl Bock, among the Dyaks of Borneo all of the married women were tattooed on the hands and feet, and sometimes on the thighs. The decoration is one of the privileges of matrimony, and is not permitted to unmarried girls. Andrew Lang says of the Australian tribes that the Wingong or the Totem of each man is indicated by a tattooed representation of it on his flesh. The celebrated American traveler, Carpenter, remarks that on his visit to a great prison in Burmah, which contains more than 3000 men, he saw 6000 tattooed legs. The origin of the custom he was unable to find out, but in Burmah tattooing was a sign of manhood, and professional tattooers go about with books of designs, each design warding off some danger. Bourke quotes that among the Apaches-Yumas of Arizona the married women are distinguished by several blue lines running from the lower lip to the chin ; and he remarks that when a young woman of this tribe is anxious to become a mother she tattoos the figure of a child on her forehead. After they marry Mojave girls tattoo the chin with vertical blue lines ; and when an Eskimo wife has her face tattooed with lamp-black she is regarded as a matron in society. The Polynesians have carried this dermal art to an extent which is unequaled by any other people, and it is universally practised among them. Quoted by Burke, Sullivan states that the custom of tattooing continued in England and Ireland down to the seventh century. This was the tattooing with the woad. Fletcher remarks that at one time, about the famous shrine of Our Lady of Loretto, were seen professional tattooers, who for a small sum of money would produce a design commemorative of the pilgrim's visit to the shrine. A like profitable industry is pursued in Jerusalem.

Universal tattooing in some of the Eastern countries is used as a means of criminal punishment, the survival of the persecuted individual being immaterial to the torturers, as he would be branded for life and ostracized if he recovered. Illustrative of this O'Connell[a] tells of a case in Hebra's clinic. The patient, a man five feet nine inches in height, was completely tattooed from head to foot with all sorts of devices, such as elephants, birds, lions, etc., and across his forehead, dragons. Not a square of even a quarter inch had been exempt from the process. According to his tale this man had been

a 218, 1871, 323.

a leader of a band of Greek robbers, organized to invade Chinese Tartary, and, together with an American and a Spaniard, was ordered by the ruler of the invaded province to be branded in this manner as a criminal. It took three months' continuous work to carry out this sentence, during which his comrades succumbed to the terrible agonies. During the entire day for this extended period indigo was pricked in this unfortunate man's skin. Accounts such as this have been appropriated by exhibitionists, who have caused themselves to be tattooed merely for mercenary purposes. The accompanying illustration

(Fig. 231) represents the appearance of a "tattooed man" who exhibited himself. He claimed that his tattooing was done by electricity. The design showing on his back is a copy of a picture of the Virgin Mary surrounded by 31 angels.

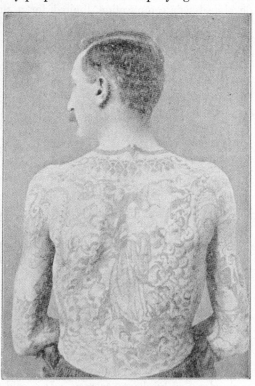

Fig. 231.—"Tattooed man."

The custom of tattooing the arms, chest, or back is quite prevalent, and particularly among sailors and soldiers. The sequences of this custom are sometimes quite serious. Syphilis has been frequently contracted in this manner, and Maury and Dulles have collected 15 cases of **syphilis acquired in tattooing.** Cheinisse [a] reports the case of a young blacksmith who had the emblems of his trade tattooed upon his right forearm. At the end of forty days small, red, scaly elevations appeared at five different points in the tattooed area. These broke down and formed ulcers. When examined these ulcers presented the peculiarities of chancres, and there was upon the body of the patient a well-marked syphilitic roseola. It was ascertained that during the tattooing the operator had moistened the ink with his own saliva.

Hutchinson exhibited [619] drawings and photographs showing the condition of the arms of two boys suffering from **tuberculosis of the skin,** who had been inoculated in the process of tattooing. The tattooing was done by the

[a] Arch. f. Dermatol. u. Syph., Band xxix., Heft 3.

brother of one of the lads who was in the last stages of phthisis, and who used his own saliva to mix the pigment.   The cases were under the care of Murray of Tottenham, by whom they had been previously reported.[a]   Williams[b] has reported the case of a militiaman of seventeen who, three days after an extensive tattooing of the left forearm, complained of pain, swelling, and tenderness of the left wrist.   A day later acute left-sided pneumonia developed, but rapidly subsided.   The left shoulder, knee, and ankle were successively involved in the inflammation, and a cardiac bruit developed.   Finally chorea developed as a complication, limited for a time to the left side, but shortly spreading to the right, where rheumatic inflammation was attacking the joints. The last, however, quickly subsided, leaving a general, though mild chorea and a permanently damaged heart.

Infibulation of the male and female external genital organs for the prevention of sexual congress is a very ancient custom.   The Romans infibulated their singers to prevent coitus, and consequent change in the voice, and pursued the same practice with their actors and dancers.   According to Celsus, Mercurialis, and others, the gladiators were infibulated to guard against the loss of vigor by sexual excesses.   In an old Italian work[c] there is a figure of an infibulated musician—a little bronze statue representing a lean individual tortured or deformed by carrying an enormous ring through the end of the penis.   In one of his pleasantries Martial[d] says of these infibulated singers that they sometimes break their rings and fail to place them back—" *et cujus refibulavit turgidum faber penem.*"   Heinsius considers Agamemnon cautious when he left Demodocus near Clytemnestra, as he remarks that Demodocus was infibulated.   For such purposes as the foregoing infibulation offered a more humane method than castration.

Infibulation by a ring in the prepuce was used to prevent premature copulation, and was in time to be removed, but in some cases its function was the preservation of perpetual chastity.   Among some of the religious mendicants in India there were some who were condemned to a life of chastity, and, in the hotter climates, where nudity was the custom, these persons traveled about exposing an enormous preputial ring, which was looked upon with adoration by devout women.   It is said these holy persons were in some places so venerated that people came on their knees, and bowing below the ring, asked forgiveness—possibly for sexual excesses.

Rhodius mentions the usage of infibulation in antiquity, and Fabricius d'Aquapendente remarks that infibulation was usually practised in females for the preservation of chastity.   No Roman maiden was able to preserve her virginity during participation in the celebrations in the Temples of Venus, the debauches of Venus and Mars, etc., wherein vice was authorized by divine injunction ; for this reason the lips of the vagina were

a 224, 1895, i., 1200.   b 224, No. 1800, 1440.
c Monumenti antichi inediti, Giov. Winkelman, Romæ, 1767.   d 509, epig., 81, L. vii.

closed by rings of iron, copper, or silver, so joined as to hinder coitus, but not prevent evacuation. Different sized rings were used for those of different ages. Although this device provided against the coitus, the maiden was not free from the assaults of the Lesbians. During the Middle Ages, in place of infibulation, **chastity-girdles** were used, and in the Italian girdles, such as the one exhibited in the Musée Cluny in Paris, both the anus and vulva were protected by a steel covering perforated for the evacuations. In the Orient, particularly in India and Persia, according to old travelers,[a] the labia were sewed together, allowing but a small opening for excretions. Buffon and Brown mention infibulation in Abyssinia, the parts being separated by a bistoury at the time of marriage. In Circassia the women were protected by a copper girdle or a corset of hide and skin which, according to custom, only the husband could undo. Peney [b] speaks of infibulation for the preservation of chastity, as observed by him in the Soudan. Among the Nubians this operation was performed at about the age of eight with great ceremony, and when the time for marriage approached the vulva had to be opened by incision. Sir Richard Buxton, a distinguished traveler, also speaks of infibulation, and, according to him, at the time of the marriage ceremony the male tries to prove his manhood by using only Nature's method and weapon to consummate the marriage, but if he failed he was allowed artificial aid to effect entrance. Sir Samuel Baker is accredited in The Lancet with giving an account in Latin text of the modus operandi of a practice among the Nubian women of removing the clitoris and nymphæ in the young girl, and abrading the adjacent walls of the external labia so that they would adhere and leave only a urethral aperture.

This ancient custom of **infibulation** is occasionally seen at the present day in civilized countries, and some cases of infibulation from jealousy are on record. There is mentioned, as from the Leicester Assizes,[c] the trial of George Baggerly for execution of a villainous design on his wife. In jealousy he " had sewed up her private parts." Recently, before the New York Academy of Medicine, Collier [d] reported a case of pregnancy in a woman presenting nympha-infibulation. The patient sought the physician's advice in the summer of 1894, while suffering from uterine disease, and being five weeks pregnant. She was a German woman of twenty-eight, had been married several years, and was the mother of several children. Collier examined her and observed two holes in the nymphæ. When he asked her concerning these, she reluctantly told him that she had been compelled by her husband to wear a lock in this region. Her mother, prior to their marriage, sent her over to the care of her future husband (he having left Germany some months before). On her arrival he perforated the labia minora, causing

[a] Schulz, Indes-Orientales, and others.
[b] Bull. de la Soc. de Geograph., Paris, Series iv., xvii., 339.
[c] 374, 1737, vii., 250.
[d] 132, Dec. 15, 1894.

her to be ill several weeks ; after she had sufficiently recovered he put on a padlock, and for many years he had practised the habit of locking her up after each intercourse. Strange to relate, no physician, except Collier, had ever inquired about the openings. In this connection the celebrated Harvey [a] mentions a mare with infibulated genitals, but these did not prevent successful labor.

Occasionally **infibulation** has been used **as a means of preventing masturbation.** De la Fontaine has mentioned this fact, and there is a case in this country in which acute dementia from masturbation was cured by infibulation.[b] In this instance the prepuce was perforated in two opposite places by a trocar, and two pewter sounds (No. 2) were introduced into the wounds and twisted like rings. On the eleventh day one of the rings was removed, and a fresh one introduced in a new place. A cure was effected in eight weeks. There is recent mention made [c] of a method of preventing masturbation by a cage fastened over the genitals by straps and locks. In cases of children the key was to be kept by the parents, but in adults to be put in some part of the house remote from the sleeping apartment, the theory being that the desire would leave before the key could be obtained.

Among some peoples the **urethra** was **slit up as a means of preventing conception,** making a meatus near the base of the penis. Herodotus remarks that the women of a certain portion of Egypt stood up while they urinated, while the men squatted. Investigation has shown that the women were obliged to stand up on account of elongated nymphæ and labia, while the men sought a sitting posture on account of the termination of the urethra being on the inferior side of the base of the penis, artificially formed there in order to prevent conception. In the Australian Medical Gazette, May, 1883, there is an account of some of the methods of the Central Australians of preventing conception. One was to make an opening into the male urethra just anterior to the scrotum, and another was to slit up the entire urethra so far as to make but a single canal from the scrotum to the glans penis. Bourke quotes Palmer in mentioning that it is a custom to split the urethra of the male of the Kalkadoon tribe, near Cloncurry, Queensland, Australia. Mayer of Vienna describes an operation of perforation of the penis among the Malays ; and Jagor and Micklucho-Maclay report similar customs among the Dyaks and other natives of Borneo, Java, and Phillipine Islands.

Circumcision is a rite of great antiquity. The Bible furnishes frequent records of this subject, and the bas-reliefs on some of the old Egyptian ruins represent circumcised children. Labat has found traces of circumcision and excision of nymphæ in mummies. Herodotus remarks that the Egyptians practised circumcision rather as a sanitary measure than as a rite. Voltaire stated that the Hebrews borrowed circumcision from the Egyptians ; but the Jews claimed that the Phœnicians borrowed this rite from the Israelites.

[a] 404, 346.   [b] 701, 1878, 266.   [c] 224, 1889, ii., 1315.

Spencer and others say that in the early history of the Christian religion, St. Paul and his Disciples did not believe in circumcision, while St. Peter and his followers practised it. Spencer mentions that the Abyssinians take a phallic trophy by circumcision from the enemy's dead body. In his " History of Circumcision," Remondino says that among the modern Berbers it is not unusual for a warrior to exhibit virile members of persons he has slain ; he also says that, according to Bergman, the Israelites practised preputial mutilations ; David brought 200 prepuces of the Philistines to Saul. Circumcision is practised in nearly every portion of the world, and by various races, sometimes being a civil as well as a religious custom. Its use in surgery is too well known to be discussed here. It might be mentioned, however, that Rake of Trinidad,[a] has performed circumcision 16 times, usually for phimosis due to leprous tuberculation of the prepuce. Circumcision, as practised on the clitoris in the female, is mentioned on page 308.

Ceremonial Ovariotomy.—In the writings of Strabonius and Alexander ab Alexandro, allusion is made to the liberties taken with the bodies of females by the ancient Egyptians and Lydians. Knott[b] says that ablation of the ovaries is a time-honored custom in India, and that he had the opportunity of physically examining some of the women who had been operated on in early life. At twenty-five he found them strong and muscular, their mammary glands wholly undeveloped, and the normal growth of pubic hairs absent. The pubic arch was narrow, and the vaginal orifice practically obliterated. The menses had never appeared, and there seemed to be no sexual desire. Micklucho-Maclay found that one of the most primitive of all existing races—the New Hollanders—practised ovariotomy for the utilitarian purpose of creating a supply of prostitutes, without the danger of burdening the population by unnecessary increase. MacGillibray found a native ovariotomized female at Cape York who had been subjected to the operation because, having been born dumb, she would be prevented from bearing dumb children,—a wise, though primitive, method of preventing social dependents.

Castration has long been practised, either **for the production of eunuchs, or castrata,** through vengeance or jealousy, for excessive cupidity, as a punishment for crime, in fanaticism, in ignorance, and as a surgical therapeutic measure (recently, for the relief of hypertrophied prostate). The custom is essentially Oriental in origin, and was particularly used in polygamous countries, where the mission of eunuchs was to guard the females of the harem. They were generally large, stout men, and were noted for their vigorous health. The history of eunuchism is lost in antiquity. The ancient Book of Job speaks of eunuchs, and they were in vogue before the time of Semiramis ; the King of Lydia, Andramytis, is said to have sanctioned castration of both male and female for social reasons. Negro eunuchs were common among the Romans. All the great emperors

a 703, April, 1893.   b 536, 1860, ii., 33.

and conquerors had their eunuchs. Alexander the Great had his celebrated eunuch, Bagoas, and Nero, his Sporus, etc. Chevers [266] says that the manufacture of eunuchs still takes place in the cities of Delhi, Lucknow, and Rajpootana. So skilful are the traveling eunuch-makers that their mortality is a small fraction of one per cent. Their method of operation is to encircle the external genital organs with a tight ligature, and then sweep them off at one stroke. He also remarks that those who retain their penises are of but little value or trusted. He divided the Indian eunuchs into three classes : those born so, those with a penis but no testicles, and those minus both testicles and penis. Curran [a] describes the traveling eunuch-makers in Central India, and remarks upon the absence of death after the operation, and invites the attention of gynecologists and operators to the successful, though crude, methods used. Curran says that, except those who are degraded by practices of sexual perversions, these individuals are vigorous bodily, shrewd, and sagacious, thus proving the ancient descriptions of them.

Jamieson [b] recites a description of the barbarous methods of making eunuchs in China. The operators follow a trade of eunuch-making, and keep it in their families from generation to generation ; they receive the monetary equivalent of about $8.64 for the operation. The patient is grasped in a semi-prone position by an assistant, while two others hold the legs. After excision the wounded parts are bathed three times with a hot decoction of pepper-pods, the wound is covered with paper soaked in cold water, and bandages applied. Supported by two men the patient is kept walking for two or three hours and then tied down. For three days he is allowed nothing to drink, and is not allowed to pass his urine, the urethra being filled with a pewter plug. It generally takes about one hundred days for the wound to heal, and two per cent. of the cases are fatal. There is nocturnal incontinence of urine for a long time after the operation.

Examples of **castration because of excessive cupidity, etc.,**—a most unwarranted operation,—are quite rare and are usually found among ecclesiastics. The author of "Faustin, or le Siécle Philosophique," remarked that there were more than 4000 castrated individuals among the ecclesiastics and others of Italy. The virtuous Pope Clement XIV. forbade this practice, and describes it as a terrible abuse ; but in spite of the declaration of the Pope the cities of Italy, for some time, still continued to contain great numbers of these victims. In France an article was inserted into the penal code providing severe punishment for such mutilations. Fortunately castration for the production of "castrata," or tenor singers, has almost fallen into disuse. Among the ancient Egyptians and Persians amputation of the virile member was inflicted for certain crimes of the nature of rape.

Castration as a religious rite has played a considerable rôle. With all their might the Emperors Constantine and Justinian opposed the delirious

a 655, April, 1886.   b 476, 1877. ii., 123.

religion of the priests of Cybele, and rendered their offence equivalent to homicide. At the annual festivals of the Phrygian Goddess Amma (Agdistis) it was the custom of young men to make eunuchs of themselves with sharp shells, and a similar rite was recorded among Phœnicians. Brinton names severe self-mutilators of this nature among the ancient Mexican priests. Some of the Hottentots and indigenous Australians enforced semicastration about the age of eight or nine.

The Skoptzies, religious castrators in Russia, are possibly the most famous of the people of this description. The Russian government has condemned members of this heresy to hard labor in Siberia, but has been unable to extinguish the sect. Pelikan, Privy Counsel of the government, has exhaustively considered this subject. Articles have appeared in Le Progrès Médical, December, 1876, and there is an account in the St. Louis Clinical Record, 1877–78. The name Skoptzy means "the castrated," and they call themselves the "White Doves." They arose about 1757 from the Khlish or flagellants. Paul I. caused Sseliwanow, the true founder, to return from Siberia, and after seeing him had him confined in an insane asylum. After an interview, Alexander I. transferred him to a hospital. Later

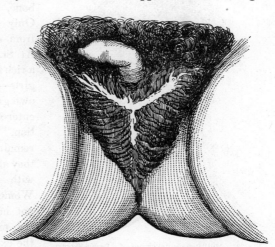

Fig. 232.—Mutilated genital organs of a male Skoptzy.

the Councillor of State, Jelansky, converted by Sseliwanow, set the man free, and soon the Skoptzies were all through Russia and even at the Court. The principal argument of these people is the nonconformity of orthodox believers, especially the priests, to the doctrines professed, and they contrast the lax morals of these persons with the chaste lives, the abstinence from liquor, and the continual fasts of the "White Doves." For the purpose of convincing novices of the Scriptural foundation of their rites and belief they are referred to Matthew xix., 12 : "and there be eunuchs which have made themselves for the kingdom of Heaven's sake," etc. ; and Mark ix., 43–47 ; Luke xxiii., 29 : "blessed are the barren," etc., and others of this nature. As to the operation itself, pain is represented as voluntary martyrdom, and persecution as the struggle of the spirit of darkness with that of light. They got persons to join the order by monetary offers. Another method was to take into service young boys, who soon became lost to society, and lied with effrontery and obstinacy. They had secret methods of communicating with one another, and exhibited a passion for riches, a fact that possibly accounts for their extended influence. The most perfect were those " worthy of mounting the white horse," the " bearers of the Imperial seal," who were deprived of the testicles, penis, and scrotum. The operation of castration among these people was performed at one stroke or at two different times, in the former case one cicatrix being left, and in the latter two. The greater number—those who had submitted to the " first purification," conferring upon them the " lesser seal "—had lost testicles and scrotum. These people are said to have lost the " keys of hell," but to retain the " key of the abyss" (female genitals). As instruments of excision the hot iron, pieces of glass, old wire, sharpened bone, and old razors are used. Only nine fatal cases resulting from the operation are known. At St. Petersburg Liprandi knew a rich Skoptzy who constantly kept girls—mostly Germans—for his own gratification, soon after having entered into the " first purification." Few of them were able to remain with him over a year, and they always returned to their homes with health irretrievably lost. Women members of the order do not have their ovaries removed, but mutilation is practised upon the external genitals, the mammæ, and nipples. The first ablation

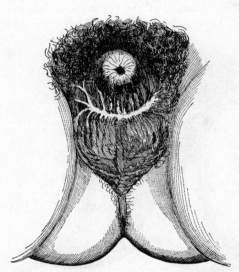

Fig. 233.—Mutilated genital organs of a female Skoptzy.

is obtained by applying fire or caustics to the nipples, the second by amputation of the breasts, one or both, the third by diverse gashes, chiefly across the breast, and the fourth by resection of the nymphæ or of the nymphæ and clitoris, and the superior major labia, the cicatrices of which would deform the vulva. Figure 232 represents the appearance of the external genital organs of a male Skoptzy after mutilation ; Figure 233 those of a female.[a]

Battey[b] speaks of Skoptzies in Roumania who numbered at the time of report 533 persons. They came from Russia and practised the same ceremonies as the heretics there.

a 653, Dec. 23, 1876.   b 176, Dec., 1873, xi., 483.

CHAPTER XV.

ANOMALOUS TYPES AND INSTANCES OF DISEASE.

Tumors.—In discussing tumors and similar growths no attempt will be made to describe in detail the various types. Only the anomalous instances or examples, curious for their size and extent of involvement, will be mentioned. It would be a difficult matter to decide which was the largest tumor ever reported. In reviewing literature so many enormous growths are recorded that but few can be given here. Some of the large cystic formations have already been mentioned; these are among the largest tumors. Scrotal tumors are recorded that weighed over 200 pounds; and a limb affected with elephantiasis may attain an astonishing size. Delamater is accredited with a report of a tumor that weighed 275 pounds, the patient only weighing 100 pounds at death.[a] Benign tumors will be considered first.

Pure **adenoma of the breast** is a rare growth. Gross was able to collect but 18 examples; but closely allied to this condition is what is known as **diffuse hypertrophy of the breast.** In some parts of the world, particularly in India and Africa, long, dependant breasts are signs of beauty. On the other hand we learn from Juvenal and Martial that, like ourselves, the Greeks detested pendant and bulky breasts, the signs of beauty being elevation, smallness, and regularity of contour. In the Grecian images of Venus the breasts are never pictured as engorged or enlarged. The celebrated traveler Chardin says that the Circassian and Georgian women have the most beautiful breasts in the world; in fact the Georgians are so jealous of the regular contour and wide interval of separation of their breasts that they refuse to nourish their children in the natural manner.

The amount of hypertrophy which is sometimes seen in the mammæ is extraordinary. Borellus [841] remarks that he knew of a woman of ordinary size, each of whose mammæ weighed about 30 pounds, and she supported them in bags hung about her neck. Durston[b] reports a case of sudden onset of hypertrophy of the breast causing death. At the postmortem it was found that the left breast weighed 64 pounds and the right 40 pounds. Boyer successfully removed two breasts at an interval of twenty-six days between the two operations. The mass excised was one-third of the total body-weight.

a 331, 1862, iv., 214.   b 629, 1669.

Schaeffer[a] speaks of hypertrophied mammæ in a girl of fourteen, the right breast weighing 3900 grams (136½ oz.) and the right 3500 grams (122½ oz.). Hamilton[b] reports a case of hypertrophied glands in a woman of thirty-two, which, within the short space of a year, reached the combined weight of 52 pounds. They were successfully excised. Velpeau, Billroth, and Labarracque have reported instances of the removal of enormously hypertrophied mammæ. In 1886 Speth of Munich described a hypertrophy of the right breast which increased after every pregnancy. At the age of twenty-six the woman had been five times pregnant in the space of a little over five years, and at this time the right breast hung down to the anterior superior spine of the ilium. It weighed 20 pounds, and its greatest circumference was 25

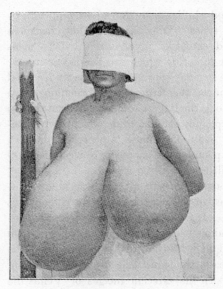

Fig. 234.—Diffuse hypertrophy of the breast (Warren).

inches. There was no milk in this breast, although the left was in perfect lactation. This case was one of pure hypertrophy and not an example of fibro-adenoma, as illustrated by Billroth. Warren figures a case of diffused hypertrophy of the breast which was operated on by Porter (Fig. 234). The right breast in its largest circumference measured 38 inches and from the chest-wall to the nipple was 17 inches long, the circumference at the base being 23 inches; the largest circumference of the left breast was 28 inches; its length from the chest-wall to the nipple was 14 inches, and its circumference at the base 23 inches. The skin was edematous and thickened. Throughout both breasts were to be felt hardened movable masses, the size of oranges. Microscopic examination showed the growth to be a diffused intracanalicular fibroma. A peculiar case was presented before the Faculty at Montpellier.[c] The patient was a young girl of fifteen and a half years. After a cold bath, just as the menses were appearing, it was found that the breasts were rapidly increasing in size; she was subsequently obliged to leave service on account of their increased size, and finally the deformity was so great as to compel her to keep from the public view. The circumference of the right breast was 94 cm. and of the left 105 cm.; the pedicle of the former measured 67 cm. and of the latter 69 cm.; only the slightest vestige of a nipple remained. Removal was advocated, as applications of iodin had failed; but she would not consent to operation. For eight years the hypertrophy remained constant, but, despite this fact, she found a husband. After marriage the breasts diminished, but she was unable to suckle either of her three children, the breasts becoming turgid but never lactescent. The hypertrophy diminished to such a degree that, at the age of thirty-two, when again pregnant, the circumference of the right breast was only 27 cm. and of the left 33 cm. Even thus reduced the breasts descended almost to the navel. When the woman was not pregnant they were still less voluminous and seemed to consist of an immense mass of wrinkled, flaccid skin, traversed by enormous dilated and varicose blood-vessels, the mammary glands themselves being almost entirely absent.

Diffuse hypertrophy of the breast is occasionally seen in the male subject. In one case reported from the Westminster Hospital in London, a man of sixty, after a violent fall on the chest, suffered enormous enlargement of the mammæ, and afterward atrophy of the testicle and loss of sexual desire.

Fig. 235.—Cystic goiter (Warren).

The names **goiter, struma,** and **bronchocele** are applied indiscriminately to all tumors of the thyroid gland ; there are, however, several distinct varieties among them that are true adenoma, which, therefore, deserves a place here. According to Warren,[a] Wölfler gives the following classification of thyroid tumors : 1. Hypertrophy of the thyroid gland, which is a comparatively rare disease ; 2. Fetal adenoma, which is a formation of gland tissue from the remains of fetal structures in the gland ; 3. Gelatinous or interacinous adenoma, which consists in an enlargement of the acini by an accumulation of colloid material, and an increase in the interacinous tissue by a growth of round cells. It is this latter form in which cysts are frequently found. The accompanying illustration (Fig. 235) pictures an extreme case of cystic goiter shown by Warren. A strange feature of tumors of the thyroid is that pressure-atrophy and flattening of the trachea do not take place in proportion to the size of the tumor. A small tumor of the middle lobe of the gland, not larger that a hen's egg, will do more damage to the trachea than will a large tumor, such as that shown by Senn,[b] after Bruns

[a] Surgical Pathology and Therapeutics, by J. C. Warren, Philadelphia, 1895.
[b] The Pathology and Surgical Treatment of Tumors, by N. Senn, Philadelphia, 1895.

(Fig. 236). When a tumor has attained this size, pressure-symptoms are often relieved by the weight of the tumor making traction away from the trachea. Goiter is endemic in some countries, particularly in Switzerland and Austria, and appears particularly at the age of childhood or of puberty. Some communities in this country using water containing an excess of calcium salt show distinct evidences of endemic goiter. **Extirpation of the thyroid** gland has in recent years been successfully practised. Warren has extirpated one lobe of the thyroid after preliminary ligation of the common carotid on the same side. Green practised rapid removal of the tumor and ligated the bleeding vessels later. Rose tied each

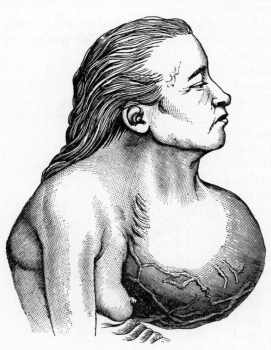

vessel before cutting, proceeding slowly. Senn remarks that in 1878 he witnessed one of Rose's operations which lasted for four hours. Although the operatic technic of removal of the thyroid gland for tumor has been greatly perfected by Billroth, Lücke, Julliard, Reverdin, Socin, Kocher, and others, the current opinion at the present day seems to be that complete extirpation of the thyroid gland, except for malignant disease, is unjustifiable. Partial extirpation of the thyroid gland is still practised ; and Wölfler has revived the operation of ligating the thyroid arteries in the treatment of tumors of the thyroid gland.

Fig. 236.—Enormous tumor of the thyroid gland (after Bruns).

Fibromata.—One of the commonest seats of fibroma is the skin. **Multiple fibromata of the skin** sometimes occur in enormous numbers and cover the whole surface of the body ; they are often accompanied by pendulous tumors of enormous size. Virchow called such tumors fibroma molluscum. Figure 237 represents a case of multiple fibromata of the skin shown by Octerlony. Pode[a] mentions a somewhat similar case in a man of fifty-six, under the care of Thom. The man was pale and emaciated, with anxious expression, complaining of a tumor which he described as a "wishing-mark." On examination he was found to be covered with a number of small tumors, ranging in

a 476, May 11, 1890.

Fig. 237.—Fibromata (after Octerlony).   Fig. 238.—Fibroma molluscum (Pode).

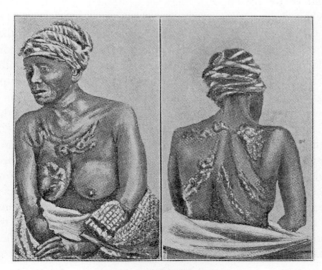

Fig. 239.—Multiple keloids (Collins).

size from that of a small orange to that of a pin's head ; from the thoracic wall over the lower true ribs of the right side was situated a large pendulous tumor, which hung down as far as the upper third of the thigh (Fig. 238). He said that it had always been as long as this, but had lately become thicker, and two months previously the skin over the lower part of the tumor had ulcerated. This large tumor was successfully removed ; it consisted of fibrous tissue, with large veins running in its substance. The excised mass weighed $5\frac{1}{2}$ pounds. The patient made an early recovery.

Keloids are fibromata of the true skin, which may develop spontaneously or in a scar. Although the distinction of true and false keloid has been made, it is generally discarded. According to Hebra a true typical keloid is found once in every 2000 cases of skin-disease. It is, however, particularly the false keloid, or keloid arising from cicatrices, with which we have mostly to deal. This tumor may arise from a scar in any portion of the body, and at any age. There seems to be a disposition in certain families and individuals to keloid-formations, and among negroes keloids are quite common, and often of remarkable size and conformation. The form of injury causing the cicatrix is no factor in the production of keloid, the sting of an insect, the prick of a needle, and even the wearing of ear-rings having been frequent causes of keloid-formations among the negro race. Collins[a] describes a negress of ninety (Fig. 239), born of African parents, who exhibited multiple keloids produced by diverse injuries. At fourteen she was burned over her breasts by running against a shovelful of hot coals, and several months later small tumors appeared, which never suppurated. When a young girl a tumor was removed from the front of her neck by operation, and cicatricial tumors then spread like a band encircling one-half her neck. There were keloids over her scapulæ, which followed the application of blisters. On her back, over, and following the direction of the ribs, were growths attributed to the wounds caused by a flogging. This case was quite remarkable for the predisposition shown to keloid at an early age, and the variety of factors in causation.

About 1867 Duhring had under his observation at the Philadelphia Hospital a negro whose neck was encircled by enormous keloids, which, although black, otherwise resembled tomatoes. A photograph of this remarkable case (Fig. 240) was published in Philadelphia in 1870.[b]

A **lipoma** is a tumor consisting of adipose tissue. When there is much fibrous tissue in the tumor it is much firmer, and is known as a fibro-lipoma. Brander[c] describes a young native of Manchuria, North China, from whom he removed a fibro-lipoma weighing 50 pounds. The growth had progressively enlarged for eleven years, and at the time of extirpation hung as an enormous mass from beneath the left scapula. In operating the tumor had to be swung on a beam (Fig. 241). The hemorrhage was slight and the patient was discharged in five days.

a 792, Oct., 1889.   b 631, 1870.   c 224, March 17, 1894.

Fig. 240.—Enormous keloids of the neck (Duhring).

Fig. 241.—Large fibro-lipoma (Brander).

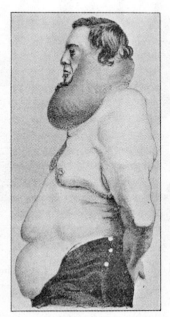

Fig. 242.—Diffuse lipoma of the neck and
abdomen (Warren).

Fig. 243.—Enormous lipoma of the
parietal region (Rotter).

The true lipoma must be distinguished from diffuse accumulations of fat in different parts of the body in the same way that fibroma is distinguished from elephantiasis. Circumscribed lipoma appears as a lobulated soft tumor, more or less movable, lying beneath the skin. It sometimes reaches enormous size and assumes the shape of a pendulous tumor.

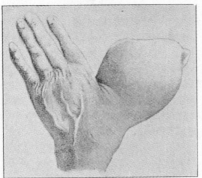

Fig. 244.—Enchondroma of the thumb (Warren).

Diffuse lipoma, occurring in the neck, often gives the patient a grotesque and peculiar appearance (Fig. 242). It is generally found in men addicted to the use of alcohol, and occurs between thirty-five and forty-five years of age ; in no case has general obesity been described. In one of Madelung's cases a large lobe extended downward over the clavicle. The growth has been found between the larynx and the pharynx. Black[a] reports a remarkable case of fatty tumor in a child one year and five months old which filled the whole abdominal cavity, weighing nine pounds and two ounces. Chipault[b] mentions a case of lipoma of the parietal region, observed by Rotter. This monstrous growth (Fig. 243) was three feet three inches long, descending to the knees. It had its origin in the left parietal region, and was covered by the skin of the whole left side of the face and forehead. The

Fig. 245.—Lad twenty years of age with multiple chondromata (after Steudel).

left ear was plainly visible in the upper third of the growth.

Chondroma, or enchondroma, is a cartilaginous tumor occurring princi-

a 298, 1878, i., 491.   b La Méd. Moderne, Dec. 11, 1895.

pally where cartilage is normally found, but sometimes in regions containing no cartilage. Enchondroma may be composed of osteoid tissue, such as is found in the ossifying callous between the bone and the periosteum, and, according to Virchow, then takes the name of osteochondroma. Virchow has divided chondromata into two forms— those which he calls ecchondromata, which grow from cartilage, and those that grow independently from cartilage, or the enchondromata, which latter are in the great majority. Enchondroma is often found on the long bones, and very frequently upon the bones of the hands or on the metatarsal bones.

Fig. 246.—Enormous fibroma growing from the parotid region.

Figure 244 represents an enchondroma of the thumb. Multiple enchondromata (Fig. 245) are most peculiar, and may attain enormous sizes. Whittaker [a] describes a farmer of forty who exhibited peculiar tumors of the fingers, which he calls multiple osteoecchondromata. His family history was negative. He stated that at an early age he received a stroke of lightning, which rendered him unconscious for some time. He knows of nothing else that could be in possible relation with his present condition. Nine months after this accident there was noticed an enlargement of the middle joint of the little finger, and about the same time an enlargement on the middle finger. Gradually all the joints of the right hand became involved. The enlargement increased so that at the age of twelve they were of the size of walnuts, and at this time the patient began to notice the same process developing in the left hand.

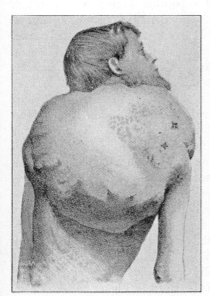

Fig. 247.—Hyaline enchondroma of the scapula (Warren).

a International Med. Magazine, Philadelphia, Feb., 1894.

The growths continued to develop, new nodules appearing, until the fingers presented the appearance of nodulated potatoes.

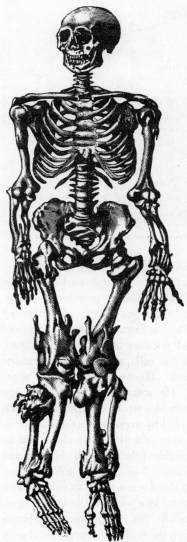

Fig. 248.—Exostoses of various dimensions (Pierret).

One of the most frequent of the fibro-cartilaginous tumors is the "mixed cartilaginous" tumor of Paget, which grows in the interstitial tissues of the parotid gland, and sometimes attains enormous size. Matas[a] presented the photograph of a negress having an enormous fibroma growing from the left parotid region (Fig. 246); and there is a photograph of a similar case in the Mütter Museum of the College of Physicians, Philadelphia.

The hyaline enchondroma is of slow growth, but may at times assume immense proportions, as is shown in the accompanying illustration (Fig. 247), given by Warren, of a patient in whom the growth was in the scapula.

In 1824 there is quoted[b] the description of a peculiar growth which, though not definitely described, may be spoken of here. It was an enormous encysted tumor, springing from the clavicle of a Veronese nobleman. Contrary to general expectations it was successfully removed by Portalupi, a surgeon of Venice. It weighed 57 pounds, being $20\frac{1}{2}$ inches long and 30 inches in circumference. It is said this tumor followed the reception of a wound.

Among the **benign bone tumors** are **exostoses**—homologous outgrowths differing from hypertrophies, as they only involve a limited part of the circumference. When developmental, originating in childhood, the outgrowths may be found on any part of the skeleton, and upon many and generally symmetric parts at the same time, as is shown in Figure 248.

Barwell[c] had a case of a girl with 38 exostoses. Erichsen[d] mentions a young man of twenty-one with 15 groups of symmetric exostoses in various portions of the body; they were spongy or cancellous in nature.

[a] 593, Feb., 1894.   [b] 476, 1824, 26.   [c] 476, 1861, ii., 446.   [d] 476, 1860.

Hartmann [a] shows two cases of multiple exostoses (Fig. 249), both in males, and universally distributed over the body.

Macland of the French navy [b] describes an affection of the bones of the

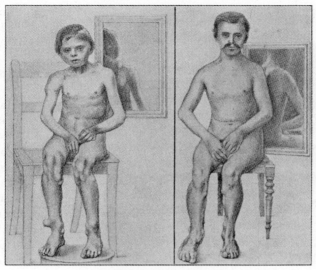

Fig. 249.—Multiple exostoses (Hartmann).

face known as **anakhrē** or **goundron** (gros-nez). It is so common that about one per cent. of the natives of certain villages on the Ivory Coast, West Africa, are subject to it. As a rule the earliest symptoms in child-

hood are: more or less persistent headache, particularly frontal, sanguine-ous and purulent discharge from the nostrils, and the formation of symmetric swellings the size of an almond in the region of the nasal processes of the superior maxilla. The cartilage does not seem to be involved, and, although it is not so stated, the nasal duct appears to remain in-

Fig. 250.—Gros-nez (Macland).

tact. The headache and discharge continue for a year, and the swelling con-tinually increases through life, although the symptoms gradually disappear, the

[a] Archiv für Klinische Chirurgie, Berlin, 1893.   [b] Quoted 224, 1895, i., 1217.

skin not becoming involved, and no pain being present. It has been noticed in young chimpanzees. The illustration (Fig. 250) represents a man of forty who suffered from the disease since puberty. Pressure on the eyeball had started and the native said he expected that in two years he would lose his sight. Figure 251 shows an analogous condition, called by Hutchinson symmetric osteomata of the nasal processes of the maxilla. His patient was a native of Great Britain.

Among neuromata, **multiple neurofibroma** is of considerable interest, chiefly for the extent of general involvement. According to Senn, Heusinger records the case of a sailor of twenty-three in whom all the nerves were affected by numerous nodular enlargements. Not a nerve in the entire body was found normal. The enlargement was caused by increase in the connective tissue, the axis-cylinders being normal. In this case there was neither pain nor tenderness. Prudden reports the case of a

Fig. 251.—Symmetric osteomata of the nasal processes of the superior maxilla (after Hutchinson).

girl of twenty-five who, during convalescence from variola, became paraplegic, and during this time multiple neuromata appeared. At the postmortem more than a thousand tumors were found affecting not only the peripheral branches and the sympathetic, but also the cranial nerves and the pneumogastric. Under the microscope these tumors showed an increase in the interfascicular as well as perivascular fibers, but the nerve-fibers were not increased in size

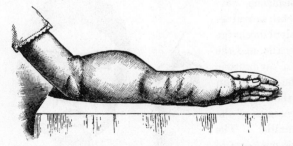

Fig. 252.—Arm in which the musculo-spiral nerve was neuromatous (after Campbell de Morgan).

or number. Virchow collected 30 cases of multiple neurofibromata. In one case he found 500, in another from 800 to 1000 tumors.

Plexiform neuroma is always congenital, and is found most frequently in the temporal region, the neck, and the sides of the face, but almost any part of the body may be affected. Christôt reports two cases in which the tumors were located upon the cheek and the neck. Czerny observed a case in which the tumor involved the lumbar plexus. Quoted by Senn, Campbell de Morgan met with a plexiform neuroma of the musculo-spiral nerve and its branches (Fig. 252). The patient was a young lady, and the tumor, which was not painful, had undergone myxomatous degeneration.

Neuroma of the vulva is a pathologic curiosity. Simpson reports a case

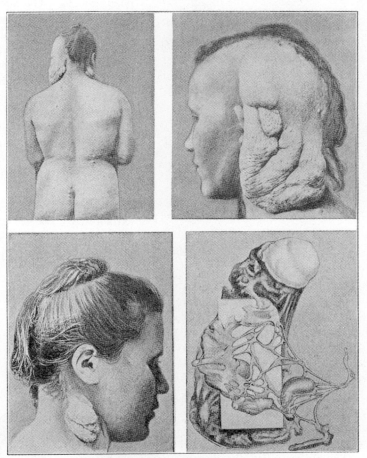

Fig. 253.—Plexiform neurofibroma (Tietze).

in which the tumor was a painful nodule situated near the urinary meatus. Kennedy mentions an instance in which the tumor appeared as extremely tender tubercles.

Tietze [a] describes a woman of twenty-seven who exhibited a marked type of plexiform neurofibroma (Fig. 253). The growth was simply excised and recovery was promptly effected.

[a] Archiv für klinische Chirurgie, Berlin, 1893.

Carcinomatous growths, if left to themselves, make formidable devastations of the parts which they affect.   Warren pictures a case of noli-me-tangere, a destructive type of epithelial carcinoma (Fig. 254).   The patient suffered no enlargement of the lymphatic glands.   The same absence of glandular involvement was observed in another individual, in whom there was extensive ulceration.   The disease had in this case originated in the scar of a gunshot wound received during the Civil War, and had destroyed the side of the nose, the eye, the ear, the cheek, including the corresponding half of the upper and lower lips.

Fig. 254.—Noli-me-tangere (Warren).

Harlan [a] reports a most extraordinary epithelioma of the orbit in a boy of about five years (Plate 9).   It followed enucleation, and attained the size depicted in a few months.

Sarcomata, if allowed full progress, may attain great size.   Plate 10 shows an enormous sarcoma of the buttocks in an adult negro.   Fascial sarcomata are often seen of immense size.   Senn shows a tumor of this variety which was situated between the scapulæ.

Schwimmer records a curious case of universal small sarcomata over the whole body of a teacher of the age of twenty-one, in the Hungarian lowlands.   The author called the disease sarcomata pigmentosum diffusum multiplex.

Fig. 255.—Deformity produced by a sarcoma of the nasal septum (after Moore).

The bones are a common seat of sarcomatous growths, the tumor in this instance being called **osteosarcoma.**   It may affect any bone, but rarely involves an articulation ; at times it skips the joint and goes to the neighboring bone.

[a] 765, May 18, 1894.

PLATE 9.

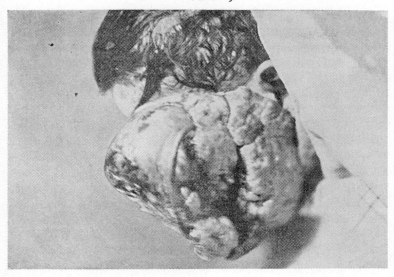

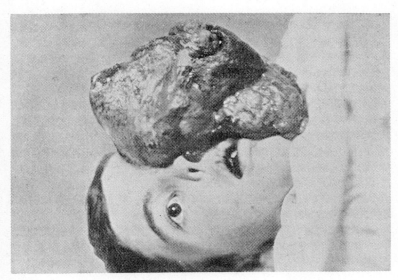

Epithelioma of the orbit (Harlan).

PLATE 10.

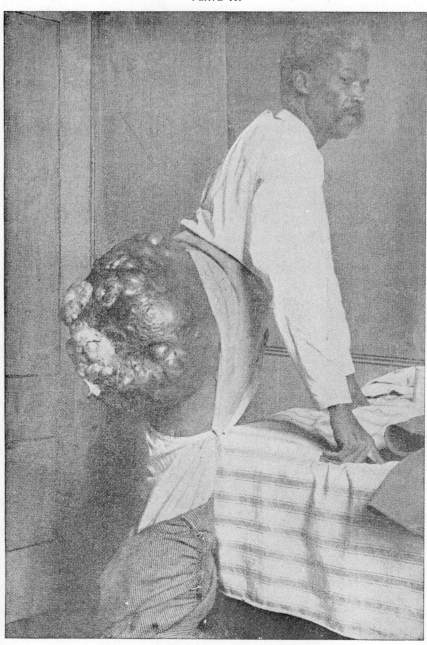

Enormous sarcoma of buttock (Keen and White).

A case of nasal sarcoma is shown by Moore (Fig. 255). The tumor was located in the nasal septum, and caused a frightful deformity. In this case pain was absent, the sense of smell was lost, and the sight of the right eye impaired. Moore attempted to remove the tumor, but in consequence of some interference of respiration the patient died on the table.

Tiffany [a] reports several interesting instances of sarcoma, one in a white female of nineteen following a contusion of tibia. The growth had all the clinical history of an osteosarcoma of the tibia, and was amputated and photographed after removal (Fig. 256). In another case, in a white male of

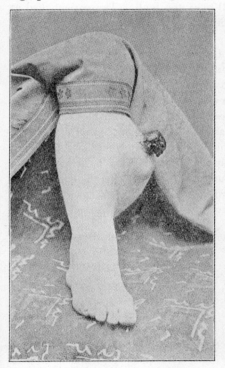

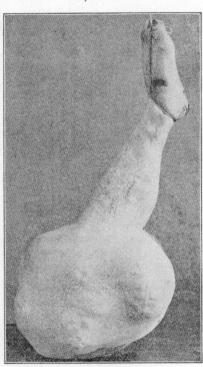

Fig. 256.—Osteosarcoma of the tibia (Tiffany).   Fig. 257.—Sarcoma of the thigh (Tiffany).

thirty, the same author successfully performed a hip-amputation for a large sarcoma of the left femur. The removed member was sent entire to the Army Medical Museum at Washington (Fig. 257).

The fatality and incurability of malignant growths has done much to stimulate daring and marvelous operations in surgery. The utter hopelessness of the case justifies almost any means of relief, and many of the visceral operations, resections of functional organs, and extraordinary amputations that were never dreamed of in the early history of medicine are to-day not only feasible and justifiable, but even peremptorily demanded.

[a] International Med. Magazine, Philadelphia, May, 1892.

Varicose veins sometimes become so enlarged and distorted as to simulate the appearance of one varicose tumor.   Adams[a] describes a curious case of congenital dilatation of the arteries and veins in the right lower limb,

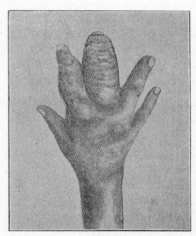

accompanied by an anastomosis with the interior of the os calcis.   The affected thigh exceeded the other in size by one-third, all the veins being immensely swelled and distorted.   The arteries were also distorted and could be felt pulsating all over the limb.   The patient died at thirty from rupture of the aneurysm.

Abbe[b] shows a peculiar **aneurysmal varix** of the finger in a boy of nine (Fig. 258).   When a babe the patient had, on the dorsum of the little finger, a small nevus, which was quiescent for many years.   He received a deep cut at the base of the thumb, and immediately after this accident the nevus began to enlarge

Fig. 258.—Aneurysmal varix of hand (Abbe).

rapidly.   But for the local aneurysmal thrill at the point of the scar the condition would have been diagnosed as angioma, but as a bruit could be heard over the entire mass it was called an aneurysmal varix, because it was believed there was a connection between a

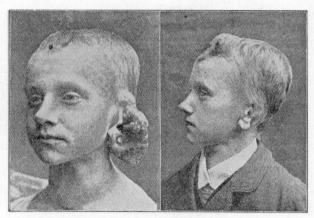

Fig. 259.—Cirsoid tumor of the ear before and after operation.

rather large artery and a vein close to the mass.   There is a curious case reported[c] of cirsoid tumor of the ear of a boy of thirteen.   Figure 259 shows the appearance before and after operation.

a 491, 1858, i., 189.   b 150, March, 1894.   c Rev. méd. de la Suisse Rom., Nov. 20, 1892.

Jessop[a] records a remarkable case of **multiple aneurysm.** This case was particularly interesting as it was accompanied by a postmortem examination. Pye-Smith[b] reports an extremely interesting case in which death occurred from traumatic aneurysm of an aberrant subclavian artery. The patient fell from a height of 28 feet, lost consciousness for a few minutes, but soon recovered it. There was no evidence of any fracture, but the man suffered greatly from dyspnea, pain between the shoulders, and collapse. The breath-sounds on auscultation and the difficulty in swallowing led to the belief that one of the bronchi was blocked by the pressure of a hematoma.

Dyspnea continued to increase, and eighteen days after admission the man was in great distress, very little air entering the chest. He had no pulse at the right wrist, and Pye-Smith was unable to feel either the temporal or carotid beats on the right side, although these vessels were felt pulsating on the left side. Laryngotomy was done with the hope of removing a foreign body, but the man died on the tenth day. A postmortem examination disclosed the existence of an aberrant right subclavian artery in the posterior mediastinum, and this was the seat of a traumatic aneurysm that had ruptured into the esophagus.

Relative to the **size of an aneurysm,** Warren[c] reported a case of the abdominal aorta which commenced at the origin of the celiac axis and passed on to the

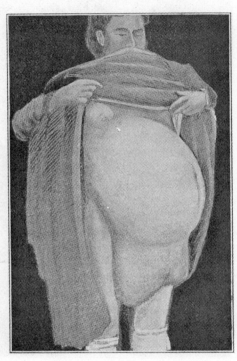

Fig. 260.—Enormous uterine tumor (McIntyre).

surfaces of the psoas and iliac muscles, descending to the middle of the thigh. The total length of the aneurysm was 19 inches, and it measured 18 inches in circumference.

A peculiar **sequence of an aortic aneurysm** is perforation of the sternum or rib. Webb[d] mentions an Irish woman who died of aneurysm of the aorta, which had perforated the sternum, the orifice being plugged by a large clot. He quotes 17 similar cases which he has collected as occurring from

a 476, November 17, 1894.   b Quarterly Medical Journal, April, 1895.
c New England Q. J. Med. and Sc., Boston, 1842–43, i., 256.   d 124, Oct., 1894.

1749 to 1874, and notes that one of the patients lived seven weeks after the rupture of the aneurysmal sac.

Large Uterine Tumors.—Before the meeting of the American Medical Association held in Washington, D. C., 1891, McIntyre [a] reported a case of great interest. The patient, a woman of thirty-eight, five feet 5½ inches in height, coarse, with masculine features, having hair on her upper lip and chin, and weighing 199½ pounds, was found in a poor-house in Trenton, Missouri, on November 26, 1890, suffering from a colossal growth of the abdomen.

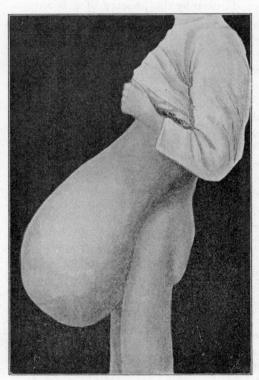

The accompanying illustration is from a photograph which was taken at the time of the first interview (Fig. 260). The measurements made at the time were as follows : circumference at the largest part, just below the umbilicus, 50 inches ; circumference just below the mammæ, 35 inches ; from the xiphoid cartilage to the symphysis pubis, 32 inches, not including the appendum, which is shown in the picture. Percussion suggested a fluid within a sac. The uterus was drawn up to the extent of from 12 to 14 inches. The woman walked with great difficulty and with a waddling gait, bending far backward the better to keep " the center of gravity within the base," and to enable her to sustain the enormous weight of the abdomen. She was compelled to pass her urine while standing. Attempts had been made six and two years before to tap this woman, but only a few drops of blood followed several thrusts of a large trocar. A diagnosis was made of multilocular ovarian cyst or edematous myoma of the uterus, and on the morning of December 7, 1890, an operation was performed. An incision 14 inches in length was first made in the linea alba, below the umbilicus, and afterward extended up to the xiphoid cartilage. The hemorrhage from the abdominal wall was very free, and the enormously distended vessels required the application of a

Fig. 261.—Uterine fibroma (Eastman).

a Western Medical Journal, Fort Scott, Kan., Jan., 1894.

large number of pressure-forceps. Adhesions were found almost everywhere, the most difficult to manage being those of the liver and diaphragm. The broad ligaments and Fallopian tubes were ligated on either side, the tumor turned out, the thick, heavy pedicle transfixed and ligated, and the enormous growth cut away. After operation the woman was immediately placed on platform scales, and it was found that she had lost $93\frac{1}{2}$ pounds. Unfortunately the patient developed symptoms of septicemia and died on the fifth day. In looking over the literature on this subject McIntyre found no mention of any solid tumor of this size having been removed. On April 18, 1881, Keith, late of Edinburgh, now of London, successfully removed an edematous myoma, together with the uterus, which was 42 pounds in weight. In a recent work Tait [a] remarks that the largest uterine myoma which he ever removed weighed 68 pounds, and adds that it grew after the menopause. McIntyre believes that his tumor, weighing $93\frac{1}{2}$ pounds, is the largest yet reported. Eastman [b] reports the removal of a fibroid tumor of the uterus weighing 60 pounds. The patient recovered from the operation (Fig. 261).

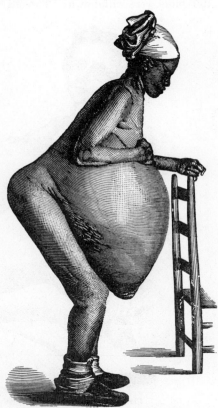

Fig. 262.—Fibrocyst of the uterus, weighing 135 pounds (Stockard).

It is quite possible for a **fibrocyst of the uterus** to attain an enormous size, equaling the ovarian cysts. Stockard [c] describes an instance of this nature in a negress of fifty, the mother of several children. About twelve years before a cyst in the right iliac region was tapped. The woman presented the following appearance (Fig. 262): The navel hung below her knees, and the skin near the umbilicus resembled that of an elephant. The abdomen in its largest circumference measured 68 inches, and 27 inches from the ensiform cartilage to the umbilicus. The umbilicus was five inches in diameter and three inches in length. Eight gallons and seven pints of fluid were removed by tapping, much remaining. The whole tumor weighed 135 pounds. Death from exhaustion followed on the sixth day after the tapping.

a "Diseases of Women and Abdominal Surgery," i., 187.

b No. Amer. Pract., Sept., 1893, 387.   c 538, Aug. 16, 1884.

Ovarian cysts, of which by far the greater number are of the glandular variety, form extremely large tumors ; ovarian dropsies of enormous dimensions are recorded repeatedly throughout medical literature.   Among the older writers Ford [a] mentions an instance of ovarian dropsy from which, by repeated operations, 2786 pints of water were drawn.   Martineau [b] describes a remarkable case of twenty-five years' duration, in which 80 paracenteses were performed and 6630 pints of fluid were withdrawn.   In one year alone 495 pints were withdrawn.   Tozzetti [c] mentions an ovarian tumor weighing

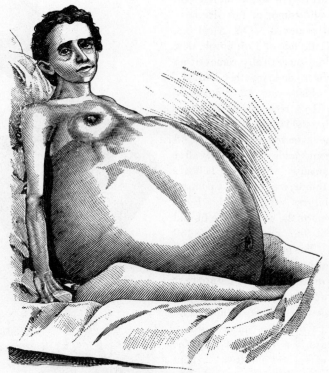

Fig. 263.—Large ovarian cyst, weighing 149 pounds (N. Y. Med. Journal).

150 pounds.   Morand [575] speaks of an ovarian cyst from which, in ten months, 427 pounds of fluid were withdrawn.   There are old records of tubal cysts weighing over 100 pounds.   Normand [d] speaks of an ovary degenerating into a scirrhous mass weighing 55 pounds.   Among recent operations Briddon [e] describes the removal of an ovarian cyst which weighed 152 pounds, death resulting.   Helmuth [f] mentions an ovarian cyst from which, in 12 tappings,

a 524, ii., No. 14.   b 629, 1748, 471.
c Raccolta, prima et cet., No. 1.   d 463, T. xviii., 360.
e 597, Feb. 8, 1890.   f Homœopath. Jour. of Obstet., N. Y., 1884–85.

559 pounds of fluid were withdrawn. Delivery was effected by instrumental aid. The tumor of 70 pounds was removed and death followed. McGilli- cuddy[a] mentions a case of ovarian cyst containing 132 pounds of fluid. The patient was a woman of twenty-eight whose abdomen at the umbilicus meas- ured 69 inches in circumference and 47 inches from the sternum to the pubes. Before the operation the great tumor hung down as far as the knees, the abdominal wall chafing the thighs. Figure 263 shows the appearance of a large ovarian cyst weighing 149 pounds. The emaciation of the subject is particularly noticeable. Reifsnyder[b] describes a native Chinese woman affected with an ovarian tumor seen at the Margaret Williamson Hospital at Shanghai. She was four feet eight inches in height, and twenty-five years of age. The tumor had been growing for six years until the circumference at the umbilicus measured five feet

7¾ inches; 88 quarts of fluid were drawn off and the woman recovered. In the College of Physicians, Philadelphia, there are photographs (Figs. 264 and 265) of this case, with an in- scription saying that the patient was a young Chinese woman who measured but four feet eight inches in height, while her girth was increased by an ova- rian cyst to five feet 9⅛ inches. The tumor was removed and weighed 182½ pounds; it con- tained 22 gallons of fluid. Fig- ure 265 shows the appearance of the woman two months after the

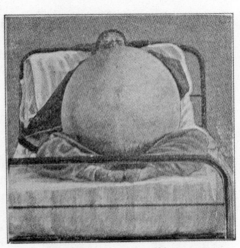

Fig. 264.—Large ovarian cyst in a Chinese woman (Reifsnyder).

operation, when the girth was reduced to normal. Stone[c] performed ovariot- omy on a girl of fifteen, removing a tumor weighing 81½ pounds. Ranney[d] speaks of the successful removal of a unilocular tumor weighing 95 pounds; and Wall[e] tells of a death after removal of an ovarian tumor of the same weight. Rodenstein[f] portrays (Fig. 266) the appearance of a patient of forty-five after death from an enormous glandular ovarian cystoma. The tumor was three feet high, covered the breasts, extended to the knees, and weighed 146 pounds. Kelly speaks of a cyst weighing 116 pounds; Keith[g] one of 89½ pounds; Gregory,[h] 80 pounds; Boerstler,[i] 65 pounds; Bixby,[j] 70 pounds; and Alston[k] a tumor of 70 pounds removed in the second opera- tion of ovariotomy.

a 121, April, 1825.	b 125, April, 1895.	c 606, 1883.	d 450, 1884.
e 230, 1878.	f 125, 1879, xii., 315.	g 318, 1885.	h 703, 1879.
i 609, 1885.	j 218, 1882.		k 667, 1871.

Dayot [a] reports the removal of an enormous ovarian cyst from a girl of seventeen. The tumor had been present three years, but the patient and her family refused an operation until the size of the tumor alarmed them. Its largest circumference was five feet 11 inches. The distance from the xiphoid to the symphysis pubis was three feet. The tumor was covered with veins the size of the little finger (Fig. 267). The apex of the heart was pushed to the 3d interspace and the umbilicus had disappeared. There were 65 quarts of a thick, brown fluid in the tumor. The patient recovered in twenty-five days.

Fig. 265.—Same woman two months after operation.

Cullingworth [b] of St. Thomas Hospital, London, successfully removed from a girl of sixteen an ovarian cyst weighing over 80 pounds. The patient was admitted to the hospital April 30, 1895. She gave a history of a single menstruation, which took place in March or April, 1893, and said that in the latter month she noticed that she was growing large. She was tapped at Christmas, 1893, when a large quantity of fluid was removed, and again in February, 1894, and a third time in May, 1894, but without useful results. For the previous six months she had been almost entirely bedridden because of the great size of the tumor. There were no symptoms referring to the bladder and rectum. At the time she entered the hospital she was much emaciated, the eyes were sunken, and her cheeks had a livid hue. The chest was thin and the lower ribs were everted; dulness began at the lower border of the 3d cartilage, and the apex-beat was best felt in the third space. Liver-dulness began at the 4th rib cartilage in the nipple line. The abdomen was enormously distended, and covered by large veins running from below upward to the thorax. About $3\frac{1}{2}$ inches above the umbilicus there was a sulcus with its convexity downward. There was dulness over the whole abdomen, except at the sides parallel with the lumbar spines, and a resonant band over the stomach. The greatest girth was $54\frac{1}{2}$ inches. By vaginal examination the cervix was found to be pulled up and obliterated; the anterior vaginal wall was bulged downward by the tumor. On May 3d

[a] 154, Sept., 1893; quoted 124, 1894, xxix, 710.   [b] 476, June 1, 1895.

abdominal section was performed. An incision eight inches long was made in the mid-line of the abdomen. A cystic tumor, formed of small cysts in its upper part and of somewhat larger ones in the lower part, was revealed. It was adherent to the abdominal wall, liver, spleen, and omentum. The adhesions were separated and the cyst tapped with a large trocar, and then the

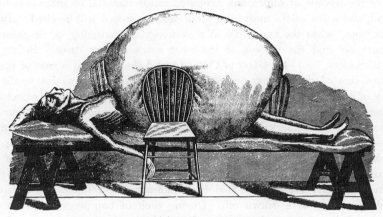

Fig. 266.—Enormous glandular ovarian cystoma (Rodenstein).

septa between the cysts were broken down with the fingers. The pedicle was rather small and was tied in the usual way, and the tumor was removed. Its seat of origin was the left ovary. The right ovary and the uterus were healthy, but poorly developed. The tumor weighed between 80 and 90 pounds,—the

Fig. 267.—Large ovarian cyst in a girl of seventeen (Dayot).

patient having weighed 170 pounds on the night before the operation, and 79½ pounds a week after the operation. Alarming symptoms of collapse were present during the night after the operation, but the patient responded to stimulation by hypodermic injections of $\frac{1}{20}$ grain of strychnin and of brandy, and after the first twenty-four hours the recovery was uninterrupted.   Cullingworth thinks that the most interesting points in the case are : the age of the patient, the enormous size of the tumor, and the advice given by the surgeon who first attended the patient (insisting that no operation should be performed).   This case shows anew the uselessness of tapping ovarian cysts.

In the records of **enormous dropsies** much material of interest is to be found, and a few of the most interesting cases on record will be cited.   In the older times, when the knowledge of the etiology and pathology of dropsies was obscure, we find the records of the most extraordinary cases.   Before the Royal Society, in 1746, Glass of Oxford [a] read the report of a case of preternatural size of the abdomen, and stated that the dropsy was due to the absence of one kidney.   The circumference of the abdomen was six feet four inches, and the distance from the xiphoid to the os pubis measured four feet $\frac{1}{2}$ inch.   In this remarkable case 30 gallons of fluid were drawn off from the abdomen after death.   Bartholinus [b] mentions a dropsy of 120 pounds ; and Gockelius one of 180 pounds ; there is recorded [c] an instance of a dropsy of 149 pounds.   There is an old record [d] of a woman of fifty who had suffered from ascites for thirty years.   She had been punctured 154 times, and each time about 20 pints were drawn off.   During each of two pregnancies she was punctured three or four times ; one of her children was still living.   It has been said [462] that there was a case in Paris of a person who was punctured 300 times for ascites.   Scott [e] reports a case of ascites in which 928 pints of water were drawn off in 24 successive tappings, from February, 1777, to May, 1778.   Quoted by Hufeland, Van Wy mentions 1256 pounds of fluid being drawn from the abdomen of a woman in five years.   Kaltschmid [f] describes a case of ascites in which, in 12 paracenteses, 500 pounds of fluid were removed.   In 1721 Morand reported two cases of ascites in one of which, by the means of 57 paracenteses, 970 pounds of fluid were drawn off in twenty-two months.   In the other case 1708 pounds of fluid issued in ten months.   There is a record of 484 pounds of "pus" being discharged during a dropsy.[g]

The Philosophical Transactions contain the account of a case of **hydronephrosis** in which there were 240 pounds of water in the sac.   There are several cases on record in which ovarian dropsies have weighed over 100 pounds ; and Blanchard mentions a uterine dropsy of 80 pounds.

The Ephemerides contains an account of a case of **hydrocephalus** in which there were 24 pounds of fluid, and similar cases have been noted.

Elliotson [h] reports what he calls the largest quantity of pus from the liver on record.   His patient was a man of thirty-eight, a victim of **hydatid disease of the liver,** from whom he withdrew one gallon of offensive material.

a 629, 1743–50, 1030.   b 110, i., obs., viii.   c 282, 1731, 227.
d Bull. des Sciences Méd. Depart. de l'Eure.   e 534, 1779, 440.
f 282, 1738, 361.   g 452, Band iv., 601.   h 476, 1831–32, i., 756.

Lieutaud cites a case, reported by Blanchard,[213] in which, in a case of hydatid disease, the stomach contained 90 pounds of fluid.

Ankylosis of the articulations, a rare and curious anomaly, has been seen in the human fetus by Richaud, Joulin, Bird, and Becourt. Ankylosis of all the joints, with muscular atrophy, gives rise to a condition that has been popularly termed **"ossified man."** A case of this nature is described,[a] the patient being a raftsman, aged seventeen, who suffered with inflammatory symptoms of the right great toe, which were followed in the next ten years by progressive involvement of all the joints of the extremities, and of the vertebræ and temporomaxillary articulations, with accompanying signs of acute articular rheumatism. At the age of thirty-one the pains had subsided, leaving him completely disabled. All the joints except the fingers and toes had become ankylosed, and from nonusage the muscles had atrophied (Fig. 268). There were no dislocations, anesthesia, or bedsores, and the viscera were normal; there were apparently no gouty deposits, as an examination of the urine was negative.

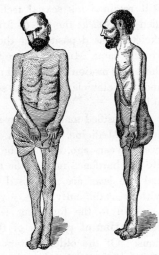

Fig. 268.—Ossified man (front and side views).

J. R. Bass, the well-known " ossified man " of the dime museums, has been examined by many physicians, and was quite intelligent and cheerful in spite of his complete ankylosis. Figure 269 represents his appearance in 1887.

Percy[b] speaks of a man named Simoore, born in 1752, who at the age of

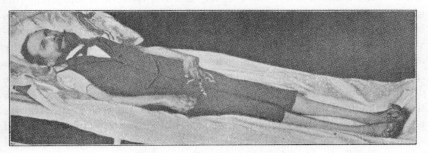

Fig. 269.—J. R. Bass, the "ossified man."

fifteen was afflicted with ankylosis of all the joints, and at different angles. He was unable to move even his jaw, and his teeth had to be extracted in order to supply him with nourishment. Even his ribs were ankylosed; his chest

a International Jour. of Surg., Feb., 1889.   b 302, iv., 245.

puffed up, and the breathing was entirely abdominal.   In spite of his infirmities, after his pains had ceased he lived a comparatively comfortable life.   His digestion was good, and his excretory functions were sufficient.   The urine always showed phosphates, and never the slightest sign of free phosphoric acid.   He still retained his sexual feeling, and occasionally had erections.   This man died in 1802 at the age of fifty, asphyxia being the precursor of death.   His skeleton was deposited in the Museum of the École de Médecine de Paris. In the same Museum there was another similar skeleton, but in this subject there was motion of the head upon the first vertebra, the lower jaw was intact, and the clavicle, arms, and some of the digits of the right hand were movable.

An ossified man has been recently found and exhibited to the Paris Academy of Medicine.   He is a Roumanian Jew of thirty who began to ossify twelve years ago, first up the right side of his back, then down the left side. He has hardened now to the nape of the neck, his head is turned to the left, and the jaws are ankylosed.   He can still move his arms and legs a little with great difficulty.

Akin to the foregoing condition is what is known as **petrifaction or ossification** of portions of the living human body other than the articulations.   Of the older writers Hellwigius,[414] Horstius,[423] and Schurig[a] speak of petrifaction of the arm.   In the Philosophical Transactions there was a case recorded in which the muscles and ligaments were so extensively converted into bone that all the joints were fixed, even including the vertebræ, head, and lower jaw.   In a short time this man was, as it were, one single bone from his head to his knees, the only joints movable being the right wrist and knee.   For over a century there has been in the Trinity College at Dublin the skeleton of a man who died about 20 miles from the city of Cork.   The muscles about the scapula, and the dorsum of the ilium (the glutei) were converted into great masses of bone, equal to the original muscles in thickness and bulk.   Half of the muscles of the hips and thighs were converted into bone, and for a long time this specimen was the leading curiosity of the Dublin Museum.[b]   In the Isle of Man, some years ago, there was a case of ossification which continued progressively for many years.   Before death this man was reduced to almost a solid mass of bony substance.   With the exception of one or two toes his entire frame was solidified.   He was buried in Kirk Andreas Churchyard, and his grave was strictly guarded against medical men by his friends, but the body was finally secured and taken to Dublin by Dr. McCartney.[c]

Calculi.—In reviewing the statistics of **vesical calculi,** the strangest anomalies in their size and weight have been noticed.   Among the older writers the largest weights have been found.   Le Cat speaks of a calculus weighing over three pounds, and Morand is accredited with having seen a

---

[a] " Lithologia," p. 69.   [b] 548, 1861, ii., 470.   [c] 548, 1861, ii., 392.

calculus which weighed six pounds. In his statistics in 1883 Cross collected reports on 704 stones, and remarked that only nine of these weighed above four ounces, and only two above six, and that with the last two the patient succumbed. Of those removed successfully Harmer of Norwich reports one of 15 ounces; Kline, one of 13 ounces 30 grains; Mayo of Winchester, 14 ounces two drams; Cheselden, 12 ounces; and Paré in 1570 removed a calculus weighing nine ounces. Sir Astley Cooper remarks that the largest stone he ever saw weighed four ounces, and that the patient died within four hours after its removal. Before the Royal Society of London in 1684 Birch reported an account of a calculus weighing five ounces. Fabricius Hildanus mentions calculi weighing 20 and 21 ounces; Camper, 13 ounces; Foschini, 19 ounces six drams; Garmannus, 25 ounces; Greenfield, 19 ounces; Heberden,[a] 32 ounces; Wrisberg, 20 ounces; Launai,[b] 51 ounces; Lemery, [418] 27 ounces; Paget, in Kuhn's Journal, 27 ounces (from a woman); Pauli, 19 ounces; Rudolphi, 28 ounces; Tozzetti, 39 ounces; Threpland, 35 ounces; and there is a record of a calculus weighing over six pounds.[c] There is preserved in Trinity College, Cambridge, a stone weighing 34 ounces taken from the bladder of the wife of Thomas Raisin, by Gutteridge, a surgeon of Norwich. This stone was afterward sent to King Charles II. for inspection. In his "Journey to Paris" Dr. Lister said that he saw a stone which weighed 51 ounces; it had been taken from one of the religious brothers in June, 1690, and placed in the Hôpital de la Charité. It was said that the monk died after the operation. There is a record of[d] a calculus taken from the bladder of an individual living in Aberdeen. This stone weighed two pounds, three ounces, and six drams. In the Hunterian Museum in London there is a stone weighing 44 ounces, and measuring 16 inches in circumference. By suprapubic operation Duguise removed a stone weighing 31 ounces from a patient who survived six days. A Belgian surgeon by the name of Uytterhoeven,[174] by the suprapubic method extracted a concretion weighing two pounds and measuring 6½ inches long and four wide. Frére Côme performed a high operation on a patient who died the next day after the removal of a 24-ounce calculus. Verduc mentions a calculus weighing three pounds three ounces. It was said that a vesical calculus was seen in a dead boy at St. Edmund's which was as large as the head of a new-born child. It has been remarked that Thomas Adams, Lord Mayor of London, who died at the age of eighty-two, had in his bladder at the time of his death a stone which filled the whole cavity, and which was grooved from the ureters to the urethral opening, thus allowing the passage of urine. Recent records of large calculi are offered: by Holmes, 25 ounces; Hunter,[e] 25 ounces; Cayley,[f] 29 ounces; Humphrys,[g] 33 ounces; Eve, 44 ounces; and Janeway,[h] 51 ounces. Kirby[i] has collected reports of a number of large vesical calculi.

a 629, li. b 398, i., 548. c 232, 1739.

d 629, 1700, 150. e 476, 1886, i., 132. f 476, 1885, i., 559.

g 476, 1885, ii., 146. h 597, 1877, xxvi., 210. i 792, April, 1896.

Barton [a] speaks of **stone** in the bladder **in very young children.** There is a record of a stone at one month,[b] and another at three years.[c] Todd [d] describes a stone in the bladder of a child of sixteen months. May [e] removed an enormous stone from a young girl, which had its nucleus in a brass penholder over three inches long.

Multiple Vesical Calculi.—Usually the bladder contains a single calculus, but in a few instances a large number of stones have been found to coexist. According to Ashhurst, the most remarkable case on record is that of the aged Chief Justice Marshal, from whose bladder Dr. Physick of Philadelphia is said to have successfully removed by lateral lithotomy more than 1000 calculi. Macgregor mentions a case in which 520 small calculi coexisted with a large one weighing 51 ounces.[174] There is an old record of 32 stones having been removed from a man of eighty-one, a native of Dantzic, 16 of which were as large as a pigeon's egg. Kelly [f] speaks of 228 calculi in the bladder of a man of seventy-three, 12 being removed before death. The largest weighed 111 grains. Goodrich [g] took 96 small stones from the bladder of a lad. Among the older records of numerous calculi Burnett mentions 70; Desault, over 200; the Ephemerides, 120; Weickman, over 100; Fabricius Hildanus, 2000 in two years; and there is a remarkable case of 10,000 in all issuing from a young girl.[h] Greenhow [i] mentions 60 stones removed from the bladder. An older issue of The Lancet contains an account of lithotrity performed on the same patient 48 times.

Occasionally the **calculi** are **discharged spontaneously.** Trioen [784] mentions the issue of a calculus through a perineal aperture, and there are many similar cases on record. There is an old record of a stone weighing five ounces being passed by the penis. [j] Schenck mentions a calculus perforating the bladder and lodging in the groin. Simmons [k] reports a case in which a calculus passed through a fistulous sore in the loins without any concomitant passage of urine through the same passage. Vosberg [l] mentions a calculus in a patent urachus; and calculi have occasionally been known to pass from the umbilicus. Gourges [m] mentions the spontaneous excretion of a five-ounce calculus; and Thompson [n] speaks of the discharge of two calculi of enormous size.

Of the **extravesical calculi** some are true calculi, while others are simply the result of calcareous or osseous degeneration. **Renal and biliary calculi** are too common to need mention here. There are some extraordinary calculi taken from a patient at St. Bartholomew's Hospital and deposited in the museum of that institution. The patient was a man of thirty-eight. In the

a 476, 1890, i., 978.   b 491, 1882, 287.   c 536, 1889, i., 369.

d 491, 1889, 486.   e 124, 1852, xxiii., 411.   f 218, 1852.   g 629, 1700, 149.

h Jour. der Pract. Heilkunde, Hufeland, c. 18, Band i., p. 115.   i 490, 1837, xx., 551–53.

j Samml. med. Wahrnehm, Band viii., p. 258.   k 629, 1774, 108.

l 538, 1877, xii., 606.   m 462, T. viii., 351.   n 779, 1857–58, 295.

right kidney were found a calculus weighing 36½ ounces, about 1000 small calculi, and a quantity of calcareous dust. In the left kidney there was a calculus weighing 9¾ ounces, besides a quantity of calcareous dust. The calculi in this case consisted chiefly of phosphate of magnesium and ammonium.[a] Cordier of Kansas City, Mo., successfully removed a renal calculus weighing over three ounces from a woman of forty-two. The accompanying illustration (Fig. 270) shows the actual size of the calculus.

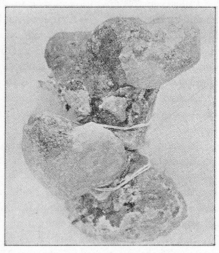

Fig. 270.—Renal calculus (full size) (Cordier).

At the University College Hospital, London, there are exhibited 485 gall-stones that were found postmortem in a gall-bladder. Vanzetti reports [b] the removal of a **preputial calculus** weighing 224 grams. Phillipe [c] mentions the removal of a calculus weighing 50 grams from the prepuce of an Arab boy of seven. Croft [d] gives an account of some preputial calculi removed from two natives of the Solomon Islands by an emigrant medical officer in Fiji. In one case 22 small stones were removed, and in the other a single calculus weighing one ounce 110 grains. Congenital phimosis is said to be very common among the natives of Solomon Islands.

In September, 1695, Bernard [e] removed two stones from the meatus urinarius of a man, after a lodgment of twenty years. Block [f] mentions a similar case, in which the lodgment had lasted twenty-eight years. Walton [g] speaks of a **urethral calculus** gradually increasing in size for fifty years. Ashburn [h] shows (Fig. 271) what he considers the largest calculus ever removed from the urethra. It was 2⅛ inches long, and 1¼

Fig. 271.—Urethral calculus (full size) (Ashburn).

inches in diameter ; it was white on the outside, very hard, and was shaped and looked much like a potato. Its dry weight was 660 grains. At one end was a polished surface that corresponded with a similar surface on a smaller stone that lay against it ; the latter calculus was shaped like a lima bean, and

a See 550, vol. lvii., 77.   b 242, 1844.   c 662, 1843, 226.   d 767, xviii., 8.
e 629, 1700, 153.   f 104, 1748, viii., 441.   g 476, 1862, i., 384.   h 553, Nov. 23, 1895.

weighed 60 grains.   Hunt[a] speaks of eight calculi removed from the urethra of a boy of five.   Herman and the Ephemerides mention cases of calculi in the seminal vesicles.

Calcareous degeneration is seen in the ovary, and Peterman[b] speaks of a **stone in the ovary.   Uterine calculi** are described by Cuevas[c] and Harlow;[d] the latter mentions that the calculus he saw was egg-shaped.   There is an old chronicle of a stone taken from the womb of a woman near Trent, Somersetshire, at Easter, 1666, that weighed four ounces.   The Ephemerides speaks of a calculus coming away with the menstrual fluid.

Stones in the heart are mentioned by medical writers, and it is said[e] that two stones as large as almonds were found in the heart of the Earl of Balcarres.

Morand[f] speaks of a calculus ejected from the mouth by a woman.

An old record says[g] that stones in the brain sometimes are the cause of convulsions.   D'Héricourt reports the case of a girl who died after six months' suffering, whose pineal gland was found petrified, and the incredible size of a chicken's egg.   Blasius, Diemerbroeck, and the Ephemerides, speak of stones in the location of the pineal gland.

Salivary calculi are well known; they may lodge in any of the buccal ducts.   There is a record of the case[h] of a man of thirty-seven who suffered great pain and profuse salivation.   It was found that he had a stone as large as a pigeon's egg under his tongue.

Umbilical calculi are sometimes seen, and Dean[i] reports such a case. There is a French record[j] of a case of exstrophy of the umbilicus, attended with abnormal concretions.

Aetius, Marcellus Donatus, Scaliger, and Schenck mention calculi of the eyelids.

There are some extraordinary cases of **retention and suppression of urine** on record.   Actual retention of urine, that is, urinary secretion passed into the bladder, but retention in the latter viscus by inanition, stricture, or other obstruction, naturally cannot continue any great length of time without mechanically rupturing the vesical walls; but suppression of urine or absolute anuria may last an astonishingly extended period.   Of the cases of retention of urine, Féréol[k] mentions that of a man of forty-nine who suffered absolute retention of urine for eight days, caused by the obstruction of a uric acid calculus.   Cunyghame[l] reports a case of mechanic obstruction of the flow of urine for eleven days.   Trapenard speaks of retention of urine for seven days.   Among the older writers Bartholinus[189] mentions ischuria lasting fourteen days; Cornarius, fourteen days; Rhodius, fifteen days; the Ephemerides, ten, eleven, and twelve days.   Croom[m] notes a case of retention of

a 130, 1861, ii., 129.   b Obs. Med. dec., ii.   c 323, 1875, ii., 35.   d 218, 1870, 70.
e 629, 1700, 158.   f Paris, 1754.   g 462, iv.   h 462, vol. v.   i 176, 1859.
j 363, 443.   k 653, 1890, 152.   l 318, 1874–75, xx., 317.   m 318, 1885, xxxi., 734.

urine from laceration of the vagina during first coitus. Foucard [a] reports a case of retention of urine in a young girl of nineteen, due to accumulation of the menstrual fluid behind an imperforate hymen.

The accumulation of urine in cases of ischuria is sometimes quite excessive. De Vilde [b] speaks of 16 pints being drawn off. Mazoni cites a case in which 15 pounds of urine were retained ; and Wilson [c] mentions 16 pounds of urine being drawn off. Frank [d] reports instances in which both 12 and 30 pounds of urine were evacuated. There is a record at the beginning of this century [e] in which it is stated that 31 pounds of urine were evacuated in a case of ischuria.

Following some toxic or thermic disturbance, or in diseased kidneys, suppression of urine is quite frequently noticed. The older writers report some remarkable instances : Haller [397] mentions a case lasting twenty-two weeks ; Domonceau,[f] six months ; and Marcellus Donatus,[306] six months.

Whitelaw [g] describes a boy of eight who, after an attack of scarlet fever, did not pass a single drop of urine from December 7th to December 20th, when two ounces issued, after vesication over the kidneys. On January 2d two ounces more were evacuated, and no more was passed until the bowel acted regularly. On January 5th a whole pint of urine passed ; after that the kidneys acted normally and the boy recovered. It would be no exaggeration to state that this case lasted from December 5th to January 5th, for the evacuations during this period were so slight as to be hardly worthy of mention.

Lemery [h] reports observation of a monk who during eight years vomited periodically instead of urinating in a natural way. Five hours before vomiting he experienced a strong pain in the kidneys. The vomitus was of dark-red color, and had the odor of urine. He ate little, but drank wine copiously, and stated that the vomiting was salutary to him, as he suffered more when he missed it.

Bryce [i] records a case of anuria of seventeen days' standing. Butler [j] speaks of an individual with a single kidney who suffered suppression of urine for thirteen days, caused by occlusion of the ureter by an inspissated thrombus. Dubuc [k] observed a case of anuria which continued for seventeen days before the fatal issue. Fontaine [l] reports a case of suppression of urine for twenty-five days. Nunneley [m] showed the kidneys of a woman who did not secrete any urine for a period of twelve days, and during this time she had not exhibited any of the usual symptoms of uremia. Peebles [n] mentions a case of suspension of the functions of the kidneys more than once for five weeks, the patient exhibiting neither coma, stupor, nor vomiting. Oke [o]

[a] 100, xxx., 103.   [b] 462, T. xlvii., 134.   [c] 524, ii.   [d] 351, L. vi., 282.
[e] 565, 1810.   [f] 462, T. xi., 117.   [g] 476, 1877, ii., 460.   [h] 302, iv., 225.
[i] South. Clinic, Richmond, 1881, iv., 545.   [j] 476, 1890, i., 79.   [k] 789, 1879, 715.
[l] 809, 1874, i., 407.   [m] 779, xi., 145.   [n] 318, 1836, xlvi., 158.   [o] 656, 1849, x., 259.

speaks of total suppression of urine during seven days, with complete recovery ; and Paxon mentions a case in a child that recovered after five days' suppression.   Russell [a] reports a case of complete obstructive suppression for twenty days followed by complete recovery.   Scott and Shroff mention recovery after nine days' suppression.

The most **persistent constipation** may exist for weeks, or even months, with fair health.   The fact seemed to be a subject of much interest to the older writers.   De Cabalis [b] mentions constipation lasting thirty-seven days ; Caldani, sixty-five days ; Lecheverel,[c] thirty-four days ; and Pomma [d] eight months ; Sylvaticus, thirty months ; Baillie,[e] fifteen weeks ; Blanchard,[213] six weeks ; Smetius,[730] five months ; Trioen,[784] three months ; Devilliers,[f] two years ; and Gignony,[g] seven years.   Riverius [687] mentions death following constipation of one month, and says that the intestines were completely filled. Moosman [h] mentions death from the same cause in sixty days.   Frank speaks of constipation from intestinal obstructions lasting for three weeks, and Manget mentions a similar case lasting three months.

Early in the century Révolat reported in Marseilles an observation of an eminently nervous subject addicted to frequent abuse as regards diet, who had not had the slightest evacuation from the bowel for six months.   A cure was effected in this case by tonics, temperance, regulation of the diet, etc. In Tome xv. of the Commentaries of Leipzig there is an account of a man who always had his stercoral evacuations on Wednesdays, and who suffered no evil consequences from this abnormality.   This state of affairs had existed from childhood, and, as the evacuations were abundant and connected, no morbific change or malformation seemed present.   The other excretions were slightly in excess of the ordinary amount.   There are many cases of constipation on record lasting longer than this, but none with the same periodicity and without change in the excrement.   Tommassini [i] records the history of a man of thirty, living an ordinary life, who became each year more constipated.   Between the ages of twenty and twenty-four the evacuations were gradually reduced to one in eight or ten days, and at the age of twenty-six, to one every twenty-two days.   His leanness increased in proportion to his constipation, and at thirty his appetite was so good that he ate as much as two men.   His thirst was intense, but he secreted urine natural in quantity and quality.   Nothing seemed to benefit him, and purgatives only augmented his trouble.   His feces came in small, hard balls.   His tongue was always in good condition, the abdomen not enlarged, the pulse and temperature normal.

Emily Plumley was born on June 11, 1850, with an imperforate anus, and lived one hundred and two days without an evacuation.   During the whole

---

[a] 548, 1879, i., 474.   [b] Phenom. Medica.   [c] 463, July, 1810, p. 74.   [d] Ibid.
[e] Trans. Soc. for Improvement of Surg. and Med. Knowl., ii., No. 14.[*]   [f] 462, T. iv., 256.
[g] 462, T. x., 410.   [h] 524, 1797.   [i] Journal de Méd. de Parme., 1808.

period there was little nausea and occasional regurgitation of the mother's milk, due to over-feeding.[a] Cripps [b] mentions a man of forty-two with stricture of the rectum, who suffered complete intestinal obstruction for two months, during which time he vomited only once or twice. His appetite was good, but he avoided solid food. He recovered after the performance of proctotomy.

Fleck [c] reports the case of a Dutchman who, during the last two years, by some peculiar innervation of the intestine, had only five or six bowel movements a year. In the intervals the patient passed small quantities of hard feces once in eight or ten days, but the amount was so small that they constituted no more than the feces of one meal. Two or three days before the principal evacuation began the patient became ill and felt uncomfortable in the back ; after sharp attacks of colic he would pass hard and large quantities of offensive feces. He would then feel better for two or three hours, when there would be a repetition of the symptoms, and so on until he had four or five motions that day. The following day he would have a slight diarrhea and then the bowels would return to the former condition. The principal fecal accumulations were in the ascending and transverse colon and not only could be felt but seen through the abdominal wall. The patient was well nourished and had tried every remedy without success. Finally he went to Marienbad where he drank freely of the waters and took the baths until the bowel movements occurred once in two or three days.

There is a record [d] of a man who stated that for two years he had not passed his stool by the anus, but that at six o'clock each evening he voided feces by the mouth. His statement was corroborated by observation. At times the evacuation took place without effort, but was occasionally attended with slight pain in the esophagus and slight convulsions. Several hours before the evacuation the abdomen was hard and distended, which appearance vanished in the evening. In this case there was a history of an injury in the upper iliac region.

The first accurate ideas in reference to **elephantiasis arabum** are given by Rhazes, Haly-Abas, and Avicenna, and it is possibly on this account that the disease received the name elephantiasis arabum. The disease was afterward noticed by Forestus, Mercurialis, Kaempfer, Ludoff, and others. In 1719 Prosper Alpinus wrote of it in Egypt, and the medical officers of the French army that invaded Egypt became familiar with it ; since then the disease has been well known.

Alard relates as a case of elephantiasis that of a lady of Berlin, mentioned in the Ephemerides of 1694, who had an abdominal tumor the lower part of which reached to the knees. In this case the tumor was situated in the skin and no vestige of disease was found in the abdominal cavity and no sensible alteration had taken place in the veins. Delpech quotes a similar case of ele-

a 656, 1851, 123.   b 476, 1886, ii., 444.   c 821, quoted 224, 1879, i., 594.   d 822, 1891.

phantiasis in the walls of the abdomen in a young woman of twenty-four, born at Toulouse.

Lymphedema, or elephantiasis arabum, is a condition in which, in the substance of a limb or a part, there is diffused dilatation of the lymphatics, with lymphostasis. Such a condition results when there is obstruction of so large a number of the ducts converging to the root of the extremity or part that but little relief through collateral trunks is possible. The affected part becomes swollen and hardened, and sometimes attains an enormous size. It is neither reducible by position nor pressure. There is a corresponding dilatation and multiplication of the blood-vessels with the connective-tissue hypertrophy. The muscles waste, the skin becomes coarse and hypertrophied. The swollen

Fig. 272.—Lymphedema of the left leg five years after its onset (Keen and White).

Fig. 273.—Lymphedema in its later stage (Keen and White).

limb presents immense lobulated masses, heaped up at different parts, separated from one another by deep sulci, which are especially marked at the flexures of the joints. Although elephantiasis is met with in all climates, it is more common in the tropics, and its occurrence has been repeatedly demonstrated in these localities to be dependent on the presence in the lymphatics of the filaria sanguinis hominis. The accompanying illustration (Fig. 272)[845] shows the condition of the limb of a girl of twenty-one, the subject of lymphedema, five years after the inception of the disease. The changes in the limb were as yet moderate. The photograph from which the cut was made was taken in 1875. At the present time (seventeen years later) the case presents the typical condition of the worst form of elephantiasis. Repeated attacks of lymphangitis have occurred during this period, each producing an aggravation of the previous condition. The leg below the knee has become enormously deformed by the production of the elephantoid masses ; the outer side of the thigh remains healthy, but the skin of the inner side has developed so as to form a very large and pendant lobulated mass. A similar condition has begun to develop in the other leg, which is now about in the condition of the first, as shown in the figure. Figure 273 represents this disease in its most aggravated form, a condition rarely observed in this country.

Fig. 274 —Elephantiasis of enormous development (" Barbadoes leg") (after Smith).

As an example of the change in the weight of a person after the inception of this disease, we cite a case reported by Griffiths.[a] The patient was a woman of fifty-two who, five years previous, weighed 148 pounds. The elephantoid change was below the waist, yet at the time of report the woman weighed 387 pounds. There was little thickening of the skin. The circumference of the calf was 28 inches ; of the thigh, 38 inches ; and of the abdomen, 80 inches ; while that of the arm was only 15 inches.

The condition commonly known as " Barbadoes leg " (Fig. 274) is a form of elephantiasis deriving its name from its relative frequency in Barbadoes.

Fig. 275.—Elephantoid change of both feet.

[a] Kansas City Med. Index, Dec., 1894.

Figure 275 represents a well-known exhibitionist who, from all appearances, is suffering from an elephantoid hypertrophy of the lower extremities, due to a lymphedema.   Quite a number of similar exhibitionists have been shown in recent years, the most celebrated of whom was Fanny Mills, one of whose feet alone was extensively involved, and was perhaps the largest foot ever seen.

Elephantiasis seldom attacks the **upper extremities.**   Of the older cases Rayer reports four collected by Alard.   In one case the hard and permanent swelling of the arm occurred after the application of a blister ; in another the arm increased so that it weighed more than 200 Genoese pounds, 40 of which consisted of serum.   The swellings of the arm and forearm resembled a distended bladder.   The arteries, veins, and nerves had not undergone any alteration, but the lymphatics were very much dilated and loaded with lymph.

Fig. 276. —Elephantoid change of the hand.

The third case was from Fabricius Hildanus, and the fourth from Hendy. Figure 276 represents a remarkable elephantoid change in the hand of an elderly German woman. Unfortunately there is no medical description of the case on record, but the photograph is deemed worthy of reproduction.

Terry [a] describes a French mulatto girl of eleven whose left hand was enormously increased in weight and consistency, the chief enlargement being in the middle finger, which was $6\frac{1}{2}$ inches long, and $5\frac{1}{2}$ inches about the nail, and $8\frac{1}{2}$ around the base of the finger.   The index finger was two inches thick and four inches long, twisted and drawn, while the other fingers were dwarfed.   The elephantiasis in this case slowly and gradually increased in size until the hand weighed $3\frac{1}{2}$ pounds. The skin of the affected finger, contrary to the general appearance of a part affected with elephantiasis, was of normal color, smooth, shiny, showed no sensibility, and the muscles had undergone fatty degeneration.   It was successfully amputated in August, 1894.   The accompanying illustration (Fig. 277) shows a dorsal view of the affected hand.

Magalhaes of Rio Janeiro [b] reports a very interesting case of **elephantiasis of the scalp,** representing dermatolysis, in which the fold of hypertrophied skin fell over the face like the hide of an elephant (Fig. 278), somewhat similar in appearance to the " elephant-man."   Figure 279 represents a some-

a 593, July, 1895.   b 124, 1893.

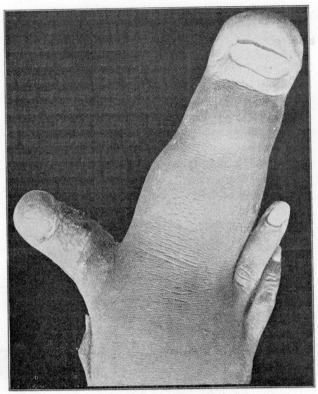

Fig. 277.—Elephantiasis of the middle finger (Terry).

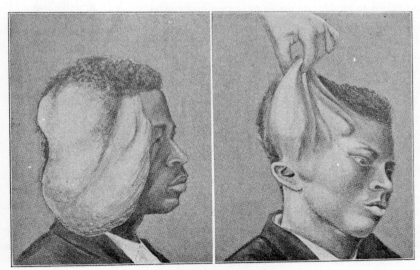

Fig. 278.—Elephantiasis of the scalp (Magalhaes).

what similar hypertrophic condition of the scalp and face reported in the Photographic Review of Medicine and Surgery, 1870.

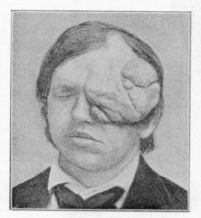

Fig. 279.—Hypertrophic tumor of the scalp and face.

Elephantiasis of the face sometimes only attacks it on one side. Such a case was reported by Alard, in which the elephantiasis seems to have been complicated with eczema of the ear. Willier, also quoted by Alard, describes a remarkable case of elephantiasis of the face. After a debauch this patient experienced violent pain in the left cheek below the zygomatic arch ; this soon extended under the chin, and the submaxillary glands enlarged and became painful ; the face swelled and became erythematous, and the patient experienced nausea and slight chills. At the end of six months there was another attack, after which the patient perceived that the face continued puffed. This attack was followed by several others, the face growing larger and larger. In similar cases tumefaction assumes enormous proportions, and Schenck [a] speaks of a man whose head exceeded that of an ox in size, the lower part of the face being entirely covered with the nose, which had to be raised to enable its unhappy owner to breathe.

Rayer cites two instances in which **elephantiasis of the breast** enlarged these organs to such a degree that they hung to the knees. Salmuth [b] speaks of a woman whose breasts increased to such a size that they hung down to her knees. At the same time she had in both axillæ glandular tumors as large as the head of a fetus. Borellus [841] also quotes the case of a woman whose breasts became so large that it was necessary to support them by straps, which passed over the shoulders and neck.

Elephantiasis is occasionally seen in the genital regions of the female (Fig. 280), but more often in the **scrotum** of the male, in which location it

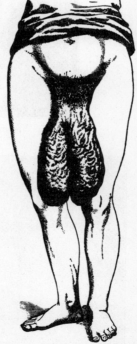

Fig. 280.—Elephantiasis of the labia (Scanzoni).

produces enormous tumors, which sometimes reach to the ground and become so heavy as to prevent locomotion. This condition is curious in the fact that

[a] 718, L. i., 12.   [b] 706, cent. ii., obs. ix.

these immense tumors have been successfully removed, the testicles and penis, which had long since ceased to be distinguished, saved, and their function restored. Alibert mentions a patient who was operated upon by Clot-Bey, whose scrotum when removed weighed 110 pounds ; the man had two children after the disease had continued for thirteen years, but before it had obtained its monstrous development—a proof that the functions of the testicles had not been affected by the disease.

There are several old accounts of scrotal tumors which have evidently been elephantoid in conformation. In the Ephemerides in 1692 there was mentioned a tumor of the scrotum weighing 200 pounds. In the West Indies it was reported that rats have been known to feed on these enormous tumors, while the deserted subjects lay in a most helpless condition. Larrey mentioned a case of elephantiasis of the scrotum in which the tumor weighed over 200 pounds. Sir Astley Cooper removed a tumor of 56 pounds weight from a Chinese laborer. It extended from beneath the umbilicus to the anterior border of the anus ; it had begun in the prepuce ten years previously.[a] Clot-Bey [b] removed an elephantoid tumor of the scrotum weighing 80 pounds, performing castration at the same time. Alleyne [c] reports a case of elephantiasis, in which he successfully removed a tumor of the integuments of the scrotum and penis weighing 134 pounds.

Bicet [d] mentions a curious instance of elephantiasis of the penis and scrotum which had existed for five years. The subject was in great mental misery and alarm at his unsightly condition. The parts of generation were completely buried in the huge mass. An operation was performed in which all of the diseased structures that had totally unmanned him were removed, the true organs of generation escaping inviolate. Thebaud [e] mentions a tumor of the scrotum, the result of elephantiasis, which weighed $63\frac{1}{2}$ pounds. The weight was ascertained by placing the tumor on the scales, and directing the patient to squat over them without resting any weight of the body on the scales. This man could readily feel his penis, although his surgeons could not do so. The bladder was under perfect control, the urine flowing over a channel on the exterior of the scrotum, extending 18 inches from the meatus. Despite his infirmity this patient had perfect sexual desire, and occasional erections and emissions. A very interesting operation was performed with a good recovery.

Partridge [f] reports an enormous scrotal tumor which was removed from a Hindoo of fifty-five, with subsequent recovery of the subject. The tumor weighed $111\frac{1}{2}$ pounds. The ingenious technic of this operation is well worth perusal by those interested. Goodman [g] successfully removed an elephantiasis of the scrotum from a native Fiji of forty-five. The tumor weighed 42 pounds, without taking into consideration the weight of the fluid

a 476, 1831, ii., 86.   b 363, 1834.   c 523, 1852.   d 434, 1837, ii., 251.
e 597, May, 1867.   f 548, 1880, i., 660.   g 476, 1876, ii., 889.

which escaped in abundance during the operation and also after the operation, but before it was weighed.   Van Buren and Keyes mention a tumor of the scrotum of this nature weighing 165 pounds.   Quoted by Russell, Hendy describes the case of a negro who had successive attacks of glandular swelling of the scrotum, until finally the scrotum was two feet long and six feet in circumference.   It is mentioned that mortification of the part caused this patient's ultimate death.

Figure 281 is taken from a photograph loaned to the authors by Dr. James Thorington.   The patient was a native of Fiji, and was successfully operated on, with preservation of the testes.   The tumor, on removal, weighed 120 pounds.

W. R. Browne, Surgeon-General, reports from the Madras General Hospital an operation on a patient of thirty-five with elephantoid scrotum of six years' duration.   The proportions of the scrotum were as follows : Horizontally the circumference was six feet $6\frac{1}{2}$ inches, and vertically the circumference was six feet ten inches. The penis was wholly hidden, and the urine passed from an opening two feet $5\frac{1}{2}$ inches from the pubis. The man had complete control of his bladder, but was unable to walk. The operation for removal occupied one hour and twenty minutes, and the tumor removed weighed $124\frac{3}{4}$ pounds.   Little blood was lost on account of an elastic cord tied about the neck of the tumor, and secured by straps to a leather waist-belt.   Recovery was prompt.   Cody [a] speaks of the successful removal of a scrotal tumor weighing 56 pounds.

Fig. 281.—Elephantiasis of the scrotum in a native of Fiji.

Fenger [b] describes a case of the foregoing nature in a German of twenty-three, a resident of Chicago.   The growth had commenced eight years previously, and had progressively increased.   There was no pain or active inflammation, and although the patient had to have especially constructed trousers he never ceased his occupation as a driver.   The scrotum was represented by a hairless tumor weighing 22 pounds, and hanging one inch below the knees.   No testicles or penis could be made out.   Fenger removed the tumor, and the man was greatly improved in health.   There was still swelling of the inguinal glands on both sides, but otherwise the operation

[a] 476, 1882.   [b] 124, Oct., 1891.

was very successful. The man's mental condition also greatly improved. Fenger also calls especial attention to the importance of preserving the penis and testes in the operation, as although these parts may apparently be obliterated their functions are undisturbed.

The statistics of this major operation show a surprisingly small mortality. Fayrer operated on 28 patients with 22 recoveries and six deaths, one from shock and five from pyemia. The same surgeon collected 193 cases, and found the general mortality to be 18 per cent. According to Ashhurst, Turner, who practised as a medical missionary in the Samoan Islands, claims to have operated 136 times with only two deaths. McLeod, Fayrer's successor in India, reported 129 cases with 23 deaths.

Early in this century Rayer described a case of elephantiasis in a boy of seventeen who, after several attacks of erysipelas, showed marked diminution of the elephantoid change ; the fact shows the antagonism of the streptococcus erysipelatis to hypertrophic and malignant processes.

Acromegaly is a term introduced by Marie, and signifies large extremities. It is characterized by an abnormally large development of the extremities and of the features of the face,—the bony as well as the soft parts. In a well-marked case the hands and feet are greatly enlarged, but not otherwise deformed, and the normal functions are not disturbed. The hypertrophy involves all the tissues, giving a curious spade-like appearance to the hands. The feet are similarly enlarged, although the big toe may be relatively much larger. The nails also become broad and large. The face increases in volume and becomes elongated, in consequence of the hypertrophy of the superior and inferior maxillary bones. The latter often projects beyond the upper teeth. The teeth become separated, and the soft parts increase in size. The nose is large and broad, and the skin of the eyelids and ears is enormously hypertrophied. The tongue is greatly hypertrophied. The disease is of long duration, and late in the history the bones of the spine and thorax may acquire great deformity. As we know little of the influences and sources governing nutrition, the pathology and etiology of acromegaly are obscure. Marie regards the disease as a systemic dystrophy analogous to myxedema, due to a morbid condition of the pituitary body, just as myxedema is due to disease of the thyroid. In several of the cases reported the squint and optic atrophy and the amblyopia have pointed to the pituitary body as the seat of a new growth of hypertrophy. Pershing[a] shows a case of this nature (Fig. 282). The enlargement of the face and extremities was characteristic, and the cerebral and ocular symptoms pointed to the pituitary body as the seat of the lesion. Unverricht, Thomas, and Ransom [843] report cases in which the ocular lesions, indicative of pituitary trouble, were quite prominent. Of 22 cases collected by Tamburini[b] 19 showed some change in the pituitary body, and in the remaining three cases either the diagnosis was uncertain or the disease was

[a] Inter. Med. Mag., June, 1894.   [b] Centralbl. f. Nerv. u. Pscych., Dec., 1894.

of very short duration.   Linsmayer [a] reported a case in which there was a softened adenoma in the pituitary body, and the thymus was absent.

Hersman [b] reports an interesting case of progressive enlargement of the

Fig. 282.

Mrs. A. B., aged twenty years, showing normal appearance of the patient.

Same patient, aged forty-two years, affected with acromegaly.

(Pershing.)

hands in a clergyman of fifty.   Since youth he had suffered with pains in the joints.   About three years before the time of report he noticed enlargement

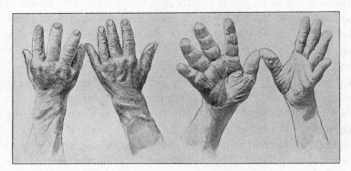

Fig. 283.—Progressive enlargements of the hands, anterior and posterior views (Hersman).

of the phalangeal joint of the third finger of the right hand.   A short time later the whole hand became gradually involved and the skin assumed a darker

a 838, 1894, No. 14.   b Inter. Med. Mag., Oct., 1894.

hue. Sensation and temperature remained normal in both hands ; acromegaly was excluded on account of the absence of similar changes elsewhere. Hersman remarks that the change was probably due to increase in growth of the fibrous elements of the subcutaneous lesions about the tendons, caused by rheumatic poison. Figure 283 shows the palmar and dorsal surfaces of both hands.

Chiromegaly is a term that has been applied by Charcot and Brissaud to the pseudoacromegaly that sometimes occurs in syringomyelia. Most of the cases that have been reported as a combination of these two diseases are now thought to be only a syringomyelia. A recent case is reported by Marie.[789] In this connection it is interesting to notice a case of what might be called acute symptomatic transitory pseudoacromegaly, reported by Potovski : [a] In an insane woman, and without ascertainable cause, there appeared an enlargement of the ankles, wrists, and shoulders, and later of the muscles, with superficial trophic disturbances that gradually disappeared. The author excludes syphilis, tuberculosis, rheumatism, gout, hemophilia, etc., and considers it to have been a trophic affection of cerebral origin. Cases of pneumonic osteoarthropathy simulating acromegaly have been reported by Korn [b] and Murray.[c]

Megalocephaly, or as it was called by Virchow, **leontiasis ossea**, is due to a hypertrophic process in the bones of the cranium. The cases studied by Virchow were diffuse hyperostoses of the cranium. Starr [d] describes what he supposes to be a case of this disease, and proposes the title megalocephaly as preferable to Virchow's term, because the soft parts are also included in the hypertrophic process. A woman of fifty-two, married but having no children, and of negative family history, six years before the time of report showed the first symptoms of the affection, which began with formication in the finger-tips. This gradually extended to the shoulders, and was attended with some uncertainty of tactile sense and clumsiness of movement, but actual anesthesia had never been demonstrated. This numbness had not invaded the trunk or lower extremities, although there was slight uncertainty in the gait. There had been a slowly progressing enlargement of the head, face, and neck, affecting the bone, skin, and subcutaneous tissues, the first to the greatest degree. The circumference of the neck was 16 inches ; the horizontal circumference of the head was 24 inches ; from ear to ear, over the vertex, 15 inches ; and from the root of the nose to the occipital protuberance, 16 inches. The cervical vertebræ were involved, and the woman had lost five inches in height. It may be mentioned here that Brissaud and Meige noticed the same loss in height, only more pronounced, in a case of gigantism, the loss being more than 15 inches. In Starr's case the tongue was normal and there was no swelling of the thyroid.

Cretinism is an endemic disease among mountainous people who drink largely of lime water, and is characterized by a condition of physical, physiologic, and mental degeneracy and nondevelopment, and possibly goiter. The subjects of this disease seldom reach five feet in height, and usually not more than four. The word cretin is derived from the Latin *creatura*. They are found all over the world. In Switzerland it is estimated that in some cantons there is one cretin to every 25 inhabitants. In Styria, the Tyrol, and along the Rhine cretins are quite common, and not long since cases existed in Derbyshire. These creatures have been allowed to marry and generate, and thus extend their species. In "Le Médicin de Campagne," Balzac has given a vivid picture of the awe and respect in which they were held and the way in which they were allowed to propagate. Speaking of the endemic cretins, Beaupré says: "I see a head of unusual form and size, a squat and bloated figure, a stupid look, bleared, hollow, and heavy eyes, thick, projecting eyelids, and a flat nose. His face is of a leaden hue, his skin dirty, flabby, covered with tetters, and his thick tongue hangs down over his moist, livid lips ; his mouth, always open and full of saliva, shows teeth going to decay. His chest is narrow, his back curved, his breath asthmatic, his limbs short, misshapen, without power. The knees are thick and inclined inward, the feet flat. The large head droops listlessly on the breast ; the abdomen is like a bag." The cretin is generally deaf and dumb, or only able to give a hoarse cry. He is indifferent to heat and cold, and even to the most revolting odors. The general opinion has always been that the sexual desire and genital organs are fully developed.

A quotation under our observation credits Colonel Sykes with the following statistics of cretinism, which show how in some locations it may be a decided factor of population. In December, 1845, in a population of 2,558,349 souls (the locality not mentioned), there were 18,462 people with simple goiter. Of the cretins without goiter there were 2089. Of cretins with goiter there were 3909 ; and cretins in which goiter was not stated 962, making a total of 6960. Of these 2185 had mere animal instincts ; 3531 possessed very small intellectual faculties ; 196 were almost without any ; 1048 not classified. Of this number 2483 were born of healthy and sane fathers ; 2285 from healthy mothers ; 961 from goitrous fathers ; 1267 from goitrous mothers ; 49 from cretin fathers ; 41 from cretin mothers ; 106 from cretin fathers with goiter ; 66 from cretin mothers with goiter ; 438 fathers and 405 mothers were not specified.

Sporadic cretinism, or congenital myxedema, is characterized by a congenital absence of the thyroid, diminutiveness of size, thickness of neck, shortness of arms and legs, prominence of the abdomen, large size of the face, thickness of the lips, large and protruding tongue, and imbecility or idiocy (Fig. 284). It is popularly believed that coitus during intoxication is the cause of this condition. Osler[a] was able to collect 11 or 12 cases in this country. The diagnosis is all-important, as the treatment by the thyroid extract produces the most noteworthy results. There are several remarkable

a 124, Nov., 1893.

recoveries on record, but possibly the most wonderful is the case of J. P. West of Bellaire, Ohio,[a] the portraits of which are reproduced in Plate 11. At seventeen months the child presented the typical appearance of a sporadic cretin. The astonishing results of six months' treatment with thyroid extract are shown in the second figure. After a year's treatment the child presents the appearance of a healthy and well-nourished little girl.

Myxedema proper is a constitutional condition due to the loss of the function of the thyroid gland. The disease was first described by Sir William Gull as a cretinoid change, and later by William Ord of London, who suggested the name. It is characterized clinically by a mxyedematous condition of the subcutaneous tissues and mental failure, and anatomically by atrophy of the thyroid gland. The symptoms of myxedema, as given by Ord, are marked increase in the general bulk of the body, a firm, inelastic swelling of the skin, which does not pit on pressure; dryness and roughness which tend, with swelling, to obliterate the lines of expression in the face; imperfect nutrition of the hair; local tumefaction of the skin and subcutaneous tissues, particularly in the supraclavicular region. The physiognomy is remarkably altered; the features are coarse and broad, the lips thick, the nostrils broad and thick, and the mouth enlarged. There is a striking slowness of thought and of movement; the memory fails, and conditions leading to incipient dementia intervene. The functions of the thoracic and abdominal organs seem to be normal,

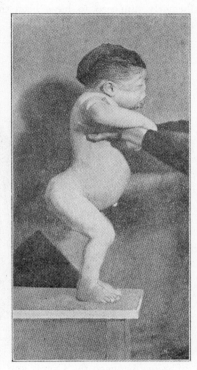

Fig. 284.—Sporadic cretinism.

and death is generally due to some intercurrent disease, possibly tuberculosis.

A condition akin to myxedema occurs after operative removal of the thyroid gland.

In a most interesting lecture Brissaud [b] shows the intimate relation between myxedema, endemic cretinism, sporadic cretinism, or myxedematous idiocy, and infantilism. He considers that they are all dependent upon an inherited or acquired deficiency or disease of the thyroid gland, and he presents cases illustrating each affection. Figure 285 shows a case of myxedema, one of myxedema in a case of arrested development—a transition case between myxedema of the adult and sporadic cretinism—and a typical case of sporadic cretinism.

Cagots are an outcast race or clan of dwarfs in the region of the Pyrenees, and formerly in Brittany, whose existence has been a scientific problem since the sixteenth century, at which period they were known as Cagots, Gahets, Gafets, Agotacs, in France; Agotes or Gafos, in Spain; and Cacous, in Lower Brittany. Cagot meant the dog of a Goth; they were of supposed Gothic origin by some, and of Tartar origin by others. These people were formerly supposed to have been the descendants of lepers, or to have been the victims of leprosy themselves. From the descriptions there is a decided

Fig. 285.—Cases of myxedema and sporadic cretinism (Brissaud).

difference between the Cagots and the cretins. In a recent issue of Cosmos a writer describes Cagots as follows :—

"They inhabit the valley of the Ribas in the northwestern part of the Spanish province now called Gerona. They never exceed $51\frac{1}{2}$ inches in height, and have short, ill-formed legs, great bellies, small eyes, flat noses, and pale, unwholesome complexions. They are usually stupid, often to the verge of idiocy, and much subject to goiter and scrofulous affections. The chief town of the Ribas Valley is Ribas, a place of 1500 inhabitants, about 800 feet above sea-level. The mountains rise about the town to a height of from 6000 to 8000 feet, and command an amazingly beautiful panorama of mountain, plain, and river, with Spanish cities visible upon the one side and French upon the other. The region is rich, both agri-

PLATE II.

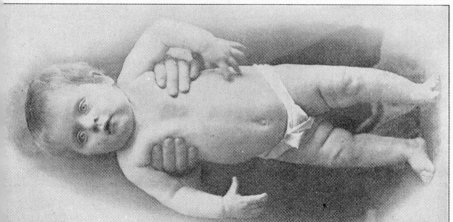

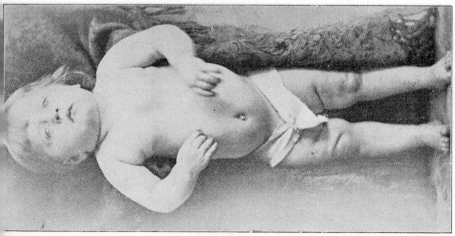

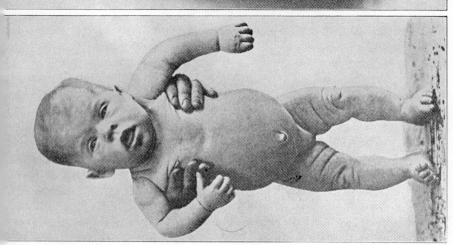

Case of infantile myxœdema (West) : the picture in the center represents the case after six months' thyroid treatment ; the picture on the right, after one year's treatment.

culturally and minerally, and is famous for its medicinal springs. In this paradise dwell the dwarfs, perhaps as degraded a race of men and women as may be found in any civilized community. They are almost without education, and inhabit wretched huts when they have any shelter. The most intelligent are employed as shepherds, and in summer they live for months at an elevation of more than 6000 feet without shelter. Here they see no human creature save some of their own kind, often idiots, who are sent up every fifteen or twenty days with a supply of food.

"It is said that formal marriage is almost unknown among them. The women in some instances are employed in the village of Ribas as nurses for children, and as such are found tender and faithful. Before communication throughout the region was as easy as it is now, it was thought lucky to have one of these dwarfs in a family, and the dwarfs were hired out and even sold to be used in beggary in neighboring cities. There are somewhat similar dwarfs in other valleys of the Pyrenees, but the number is decreasing, and those of the Ribas Valley are reduced to a few individuals."

Hiccough is a symptom due to intermittent, sudden contraction of the diaphragm. Obstinate cases are most peculiar, and sometimes exhaust the physician's skill. Symes divides these cases into four groups :—

(1) Inflammatory, seen particularly in inflammatory diseases of the viscera or abdominal membranes, and in severe cases of typhoid fever.

(2) Irritative, as in direct stimulus of the diaphragm in swallowing some very hot substance; local disease of the esophagus near the diaphragm, and in many conditions of gastric and intestinal disorder, more particularly those associated with flatus.

(3) Specific or idiopathic, in which there are no evident causes present; it is sometimes seen in cases of nephritis and diabetes.

(4) Neurotic, in which the primary cause is in the nervous system,—hysteria, epilepsy, shock, or cerebral tumors.

The obstinacy of continued hiccough has long been discussed. Osler calls to mind that in Plato's "Symposium" the physician, Eryximachus, recommended to Aristophanes, who had hiccough from eating too much, either to hold his breath or to gargle with a little water; but if it still continued, "tickle your nose with something and sneeze, and if you sneeze once or twice even the most violent hiccough is sure to go." The attack must have been a severe one, as it is stated subsequently that the hiccough did not disappear until Aristophanes had excited the sneezing.

Among the older medical writers Weber speaks of singultus lasting for five days; Tulpius,[842] for twelve days; Eller and Schenck,[a] for three months; Taranget,[b] for eight months; and Bartholinus,[190] for four years.

At the present day it is not uncommon to read in the newspapers accounts of prolonged hiccoughing. These cases are not mythical, and are paral-

a 718, L. iii., obs. 49. b 462, lxxxvi., 363.

leled by a number of instances in reliable medical literature.   The cause is not always discernible, and cases sometimes resist all treatment.

Holston [a] reports a case of chronic singultus of seven years' standing.   It had followed an attack of whooping-cough, and was finally cured apparently by the administration of strychnin.   Cowan [b] speaks of a shoemaker of twenty-two who experienced an attack of constant singultus for a week, and then intermittent attacks for six years.   Cowan also mentions instances of prolonged hiccough related by Heberden, Good, Hoffman, and Wartmouth. Barrett [c] is accredited with reporting a case of persistent hiccough in a man of thirty-five.   Rowland [d] speaks of a man of thirty-five who hiccoughed for twelve years.   The paroxysms were almost constant, and occurred once or twice a minute during the hours when the man was not sleeping.   There was no noise with the cough.   There is another case related in the same journal of a man who died on the fourth day of an attack of singultus, probably due to abscess of the diaphragm, which no remedy would relieve.   Moore [e] records a case of a child, injured when young, who hiccoughed until about twenty years of age (the age at the time of report).   Foot [f] mentions a lad of fifteen who, except when asleep, hiccoughed incessantly for twenty-two weeks, and who suffered two similar, but less severe, attacks in the summer of 1879, and again in 1880.   The disease was supposed to be due to the habit of pressing the chest against the desk when at school.   Dexter [g] reports a case of long-continued singultus in an Irish girl of eighteen, ascribed to habitual masturbation.   There was no intermission in the paroxysm, which increased in force until general convulsions ensued. The patient said that the paroxysm could be stopped by firm pressure on the upper part of the external genital organs.   Dexter applied firm pressure on her clitoris, and the convulsions subsided, and the patient fell asleep.   They could be excited by firm pressure on the lower vertebræ.   Corson [h] speaks of a man of fifty-seven who, after exposure to cold, suffered exhausting hiccough for nine days ; and also records the case of an Irish servant who suffered hiccough for four months ; the cause was ascribed to fright.   Stevenson [i] cites a fatal instance of hiccough in a stone-mason of forty-four who suffered continuously from May 14th to May 28th.   The only remedy that seemed to have any effect in this case was castor-oil in strong purgative doses.

Willard [j] speaks of a man of thirty-four who began to hiccough after an attack of pneumonia, and continued for eighty-six hours.   The treatment consisted of the application of belladonna and cantharides plasters, bismuth, and lime-water, camphor, and salts of white hellebore inhaled through the nose in finest powder.   Two other cases are mentioned by the same author.   Gapper [k] describes the case of a young man who was seized with loud and dis-

a West. Lancet, Cincin., 1849.   b 476, 1841–42, ii., 398.   c 703, xlvii., 377.
d Ibid.   e Ibid.   f 310, 1881.   g 218, xxxii., 195.   h 594, 1857, ii., 264.
i 476, 1883, i., 1043.   j 616, 1871–72, v., 507.   k 535, 1801, vi., 17.

tressing hiccough that never ceased for a minute during eighty hours. Two ounces of laudanum were administered in the three days without any decided effect, producing only slight languor.

Ranney [a] reports the case of an unmarried woman of forty-four who suffered from paroxysms of hiccough that persisted for four years. A peculiarity of this attack was that it invariably followed movements of the upper extremities. Tenderness and hyperesthesia over the spinous processes of the 4th, 5th, and 6th cervical vertebræ led to the application of the thermo-cautery, which, in conjunction with the administration of ergot and bromids, was attended with marked benefit, though not by complete cure. Barlow [b] mentions a man with a rheumatic affection of the shoulder who hiccoughed when he moved his joints. Barlow also recites a case of hiccough which was caused by pressure on the cicatrix of a wound in the left hand.

Beilby [c] reports a peculiar case in a girl of seventeen who suffered an anomalous affection of the respiratory muscle, producing a sound like a cough, but shriller, almost resembling a howl. It was repeated every five or six seconds during the whole of the waking moments, and subsided during sleep. Under rest and free purgation the patient recovered, but the paroxysms continued during prolonged intervals, and in the last six years they only lasted from twenty-four to forty-eight hours.

Parker [d] reports four rebellious cases of singultus successfully treated by dry cups applied to the abdomen. In each case it was necessary to repeat the operation after two hours, but recovery was then rapid. Tatevosoff reports a brilliant cure in a patient with chronic chest trouble, by the use of common snuff, enough being given several times to induce lively sneezing. Griswold [e] records a successful treatment of one case in a man of fifty, occurring after a debauch, by the administration of glonoin, $\frac{1}{150}$ of a grain every three hours. Heidenhain [f] records a very severe and prolonged case caused, as shown later at the operation and postmortem examination, by carcinoma of the pancreas. The spasms were greatly relieved by cocain administered by the mouth, as much as 15 grains being given in twelve hours. Laborde and Lépine [g] report the case of a young girl who was relieved of an obstinate case of hiccough lasting four days by traction on her tongue. After the tongue had been held out of the mouth for a few minutes the hiccoughs ceased. Laborde referred to two cases of a similar character reported by Viand.

Anomalous Sneezing.—In the olden times sneezing was considered a good omen, and was regarded as a sacred sign by nearly all of the ancient peoples. This feeling of reverence was already ancient in the days of Homer. Aristotle inquired into the nature and origin of the superstition, somewhat profanely wondering why sneezing had been deified rather than coughing. The Greeks traced the origin of the sacred regard for sneezing to the

a 533, 1884, xliv., 695. b 476, 1840–41, i., 295. c 318, 1835. d 632, Oct., 1894.
e 450, Oct. 27, 1894. f 199, June 11, 1884. g Quoted 533, March 28, 1896, 354.

days of Prometheus, who blessed his man of clay when he sneezed. According to Seguin the rabbinical account says that only through Jacob's struggle with the angel did sneezing cease to be an act fatal to man. Not only in Greece and Rome was sneezing revered, but also by races in Asia and Africa, and even by the Mexicans of remote times. Xenophon speaks of the reverence as to sneezing, in the court of the King of Persia. In Mesopotamia and some of the African towns the populace rejoiced when the monarch sneezed. In the present day we frequently hear " God bless you " addressed to persons who have just sneezed, a perpetuation of a custom quite universal in the time of Gregory the Great, in whose time, at a certain season, the air was filled with an unwholesome vapor or malaria which so affected the people that those who sneezed were at once stricken with death-agonies. In this strait the pontiff is said to have devised a form of prayer to be uttered when the paroxysm was seen to be coming on, and which, it was hoped, would avert the stroke of the death-angel.

There are some curious cases of anomalous sneezing on record, some of which are possibly due to affections akin to our present " hay fever," while others are due to causes beyond our comprehension. The Ephemerides records a paroxysm of continual sneezing lasting thirty days. Bonet,[216] Lancisi,[475] Fabricius Hildanus,[334] and other older observers speak of sneezing to death. Morgagni [576] mentions death from congestion of the vasa cerebri caused by sneezing. The Ephemerides records an instance of prolonged sneezing which was distinctly hereditary.

Ellison [a] makes an inquiry for treatment of a case of sneezing in a white child of ten. The sneezing started without apparent cause and would continue 20 or 30 times, or until the child was exhausted, and then stop for a half or one minute, only to relapse again. Beilby [b] speaks of a boy of thirteen who suffered constant sneezing (from one to six times a minute) for one month. Only during sleep was there any relief. The patient recovered under treatment consisting of active leeching, purgation, and blisters applied behind the ear, together with the application of olive oil to the nostrils.

Lee [c] reports a remarkable case of **yawning followed by sneezing** in a girl of fifteen who, just before, had a tooth removed without difficulty. Half an hour afterward yawning began and continued for five weeks continuously. There was no pain, no illness, and she seemed amused at her condition. There was no derangement of the sexual or other organs and no account of an hysteric spasm. Potassium bromid and belladonna were administered for a few days with negative results, when the attacks of yawning suddenly turned to sneezing. One paroxysm followed another with scarcely an interval for speech. She was chloroformed once and the sneezing ceased, but was more violent on recovery therefrom. Ammonium bromid in half-drachm doses, with rest in bed for psychologic reasons, checked the sneezing. Woakes [d] presented a

a Memphis Jour. Med. Sc., 1889, i., 100. b 318, 1835.
c 536, 1888, i., 28. d 476, 1880, i., 253.

paper on what he designated "**ear-sneezing,**" due to the caking of cerumen in one ear. Irritation of the auricular branch of the vagus was produced, whence an impression was propagated to the lungs through the pulmonary branches of the vagus. Yawning was caused through implication of the third division of the 5th nerve, sneezing following from reflex implication of the spinal nerves of respiration, the lungs being full of air at the time of yawning. Woakes also speaks of "ear-giddiness" and offers a new associate symptom—superficial congestion of the hands and forearm.

A case of anomalous sneezing immediately prior to sexual intercourse is mentioned on page 511.

Hemophilia is an hereditary, constitutional fault, characterized by a tendency to uncontrollable bleeding, either spontaneous or from slight wounds. It is sometimes associated with a form of arthritis (Osler). This hemorrhagic diathesis has been known for many years; and the fact that there were some persons who showed a peculiar tendency to bleed after wounds of a trifling nature is recorded in some of the earliest medical literature. Only recently, however, through the writings of Buel, Otto, Hay, Coates, and others, has the hereditary nature of the malady and its curious mode of transmission through the female line been known. As a rule the mother of a hemophile is not a "bleeder" herself, but is the daughter of one. The daughters of a hemophile, though healthy and free from any tendency themselves, are almost certain to transmit the disposition to the male offspring. The condition generally appears after some slight injury in the first two years of life; but must be distinguished from the hemorrhagic affections of the new-born, which will be discussed later. The social condition of the family does not alter the predisposition; the old Duke of Albany was a "bleeder";[a] and bleeder families are numerous, healthy looking, and have fine, soft skins.

The duration of this tendency, and its perpetuation in a family, is remarkable. The Appleton-Swain family of Reading, Mass., has shown examples for two centuries. Osler has been advised of instances already occurring in the seventh generation. Kolster[b] has investigated hemophilia in women, and reports a case of bleeding in the daughter of a hemophilic woman. He also analyzes 50 genealogic trees of hemophilic families, and remarks that Nasse's law of transmission does not hold true. In 14 cases the transmission was direct from the father to the child, and in 11 cases it was direct from the mother to the infant.

The hemorrhagic symptoms of bleeders may be divided into external bleedings, either spontaneous or traumatic; interstitial bleedings, petechiæ, and ecchymoses; and the joint-affections. The external bleedings are seldom spontaneous, and generally follow cuts, bruises, scratches, and often result seriously. A minor operation on a hemophile may end in death; so slight an operation as drawing a tooth has been followed by the most disastrous consequences.

a 476, 1852, i., 360.   b Finska Läkar. Handlingar, March, 1895.

Armstrong,[a] Blagden,[b] and Roberts,[c] have seen fatal hemorrhage after the extraction of teeth. MacCormac observed five bleeders at St. Thomas Hospital, London, and remarks that one of these persons bled twelve days after a tooth-extraction. Buchanan and Clay cite similar instances. Cousins [d] mentions an individual of hemorrhagic diathesis who succumbed to extensive extravasation of blood at the base of the brain, following a slight fall during an epileptic convulsion. Dunlap [e] reports a case of hemorrhagic diathesis, following suppression of the catamenia, attended by vicarious hemorrhage from the gums, which terminated fatally. Erichsen [f] cites an instance of extravasation of blood into the calf of the leg of an individual of hemophilic tendencies. A cavity was opened, which extended from above the knee to the heel; the clots were removed, and cautery applied to check the bleeding. There was extension of the blood-cavity to the thigh, with edema and incipient gangrene, necessitating amputation of the thigh, with a fatal termination.

Mackenzie [g] reports an instance of **hemophilic purpura of the retina,** followed by death. Harkin gives an account of vicarious bleeding from the under lip in a woman of thirty-eight. The hemorrhage occurred at every meal and lasted ten minutes. There is no evidence that the woman was of hemophilic descent.

Of 334 cases of bleeding in hemophilia collected by Grandidier, 169 were from the nose, 43 from the mouth, 15 from the stomach, 36 from the bowels, 16 from the urethra, 17 from the lungs, and a few from the skin of the head, eyelids, scrotum, navel, tongue, finger-tips, vulva, and external ear. Osler remarks that Professor Agnew knew of a case of a bleeder who had always bled from cuts and bruises above the neck, never from those below. The joint-affections closely resemble acute rheumatism. Bleeders do not necessarily die of their early bleedings, some living to old age. Oliver Appleton, the first reported American bleeder, died at an advanced age, owing to hemorrhage from a bed-sore and from the urethra. Fortunately the functions of menstruation and parturition are not seriously interfered with in hemophilia. Menstruation is never so excessive as to be fatal. Grandidier states that of 152 boy subjects 81 died before the termination of the seventh year. Hemophilia is rarely fatal in the first year.

Of the **hemorrhagic diseases of the new-born** three are worthy of note. In **syphilis hæmorrhagica neonatorum** the child may be born healthy, or just after birth there may appear extensive cutaneous extravasations with bleeding from the mucous surfaces and from the navel; the child may become deeply jaundiced. Postmortem examination shows extensive extravasations into the internal viscera, and also organic syphilitic lesions.

Winckel's disease, or epidemic hemoglobinuria, is a very fatal affection,

---

a Trans. Belfast Clin. and Path. Soc., 1854.   b 550, 1820.

c 476, 1841–42, i., 752.   d 548, 1869, ii., 277.   e 594, 1850, iv., 314.

f 476, 1856, i., 511.   g 548, 1877, i., 258.

sometimes epidemic in lying-in institutions ; it develops about the fourth day after birth. The principal symptom is hematogenous icterus with cyanosis,— the urine contains blood and blood-coloring matter. Some cases have shown in a marked degree acute fatty degeneration of the internal organs —Buhl's disease.

Apart from the common visceral hemorrhages, the results of injuries at birth, bleeding from one or more of the surfaces is a not uncommon event in the new-born, particularly in hospital-practice. According to Osler Townsend reports 45 cases in 6700 deliveries, the hemorrhage being both general and from the navel alone. Bleeding also occurs from the bowels, stomach, and mouth, generally beginning in the first week, but in rare instances it is delayed to the second or third. Out of 50 cases collected by Townsend 31 died and 19 recovered. The nature of the disease is unknown, and postmortem examination reveals no pathologic changes, although the general and not local nature of the affection, its self-limited character, the presence of fever, and the greater prevalence of the disease in hospitals, suggest an infectious origin (Townsend). Kent[a] speaks of a new-born infant dying of spontaneous hemorrhage from about the hips.

Infantile scurvy, or Barlow's disease, has lately attracted marked attention, and is interesting for the numerous extravasations and spontaneous hemorrhages which are associated with it. A most interesting collection of specimens taken from the victims of Barlow's disease were shown in London in 1895.[619]

In an article on the successful **preventive treatment of tetanus neonatorum,** or the "scourge of St. Kilda," of the new-born, Turner[b] says the first mention of trismus nascentium or tetanus neonatorum was made by Rev. Kenneth Macaulay in 1764, after a visit to the island of St. Kilda in 1758. This gentleman states that the infants of this island give up nursing on the fourth or fifth day after birth ; on the seventh day their gums are so clinched together that it is impossible to get anything down their throats ; soon after this they are seized with convulsive fits and die on the eighth day. So general was this trouble on the island of St. Kilda that the mothers never thought of making any preparation for the coming baby, and it was wrapped in a dirty piece of blanket till the ninth or tenth day, when, if the child survived, the affection of the mother asserted itself. This lax method of caring for the infant, the neglect to dress the cord, and the unsanitary condition of the dwellings, make it extremely probable that the infection was through the umbilical cord. All cases in which treatment was properly carried out by competent nurses have survived. This treatment consisted in dressing the cord with iodoform powder and antiseptic wool, the breast-feeding of the baby from the first, and the administration of one-grain doses of potassium bromid at short intervals. The infant death-rate on the island of St. Kilda has, consequently, been much reduced. The author suggests the use of a new iodin-preparation called loretin for dressing the cord. The powder is free from odor and is nonpoisonous.

Human Parasites.—Worms in the human body are of interest on account of the immense length some species attain, the anomalous symptoms which they cause, or because of their anomalous location and issue. According to modern writers the famous Viennese collection of helminths contains chains of **tænia saginata** 24 feet long. The older reports, according to which the tænia solium (*i. e.*, generally the tænia saginata) grew to such lengths as 40, 50, 60, and even as much as 800 yards, are generally regarded as erroneous. The observers have apparently taken the total of all the fragments of the worm or worms evacuated at any time and added them, thus obtaining results so colossal that it would be impossible for such an immense mass to be contained in any human intestine.

The name solium has no relation to the Latin *solus*, or *solium*. It is quite possible for a number of **tapeworms** to exist simultaneously in the human body. Palm[a] mentions the fact of four tapeworms existing in one person; and Mongeal[b] has made observations of a number of cases in which several teniæ existed simultaneously in the stomach. David[c] speaks of the expulsion of five teniæ by the ingestion of a quantity of sweet wine. Cobbold[d] reports the case of four simultaneous tapeworms; and Aguiel[e] describes the case of a man of twenty-four who expelled a mass weighing a kilogram, 34.5 meters long, consisting of several different worms. Garfinkel[812] mentions a case which has been extensively quoted,[f] of a peasant who voided 238 feet of tapeworms, 12 heads being found. Laveran[g] reports a case in which 23 teniæ were expelled in the same day. Greenhow[h] mentions the occurrence of two tæniæ mediocanellata.

The size of a tapeworm in a small child is sometimes quite surprising. Even the new-born have exhibited signs of teniæ, and Haussmann[i] has discussed this subject. Armor[j] speaks of a fully-matured tapeworm being expelled from a child five days old. Kennedy[k] reports cases in which tapeworms have been expelled from infants five, and five and one-half months old. Heisberg[l] gives an account of a tapeworm eight feet in length which came from a child of two. Twiggs[m] describes a case in which a tapeworm 36 feet long was expelled from a child of four; and Fabre[n] mentions the expulsion of eight teniæ from a child. Occasionally the tapeworm is expelled from the mouth. Such cases are mentioned by Hitch[o] and Martel.[p] White[q] speaks of a tapeworm which was discharged from the stomach

a 476, 1885, ii., 991.   b 162, 1840, 310.   c 368, 1843, xi., 41.
d 476, 1885, ii., 566.   e 728, 1883.   f 476, 1885, ii., 1221.
g Arch. de méd. et pharm. mil., Paris, 1885, v., 173.   h 476, 1863, ii., 699.
i 224, 1872, ii., 466.   j 597, 1871, xiv., 518.
k " Proceedings of the Pathological Society of Dublin," 1885–87.
l 538, Nov. 24, 1878.   m 744, 1847, iii., 413.   n 368, 1887, v., 447.
o 224, 1882, ii., 789.   p 363, 1886, 101.   q 149, 1798, ii., 292.

after the use of an emetic.   Lile [a] mentions the removal of a tapeworm which had been in the bowel twenty-four years.

The peculiar effects of a tapeworm are exaggerated appetite and thirst, nausea, headaches, vertigo, ocular symptoms, cardiac palpitation, and Mursinna [b] has even observed a case of trismus, or lockjaw, due to tænia solium. Féréol [c] speaks of a case of vertigo, accompanied with epileptic convulsions, which was caused by teniæ.   On the administration of kousso three heads were expelled simultaneously.   There is a record of an instance of cardiac pulsation rising to 240 per minute, which ceased upon the expulsion of a large tapeworm.[d]   It is quite possible for the presence of a tapeworm to indirectly produce death.   Garroway [e] describes a case in which death was apparently imminent from the presence of a tapeworm.   Kisel [f] has recorded a fatal case of anemia, in a child of six, dependent on teniæ.

The number of **ascarides** or **round-worms** in one subject is sometimes enormous.   Victor [g] speaks of 129 round-worms being discharged from a child in the short space of five days.   Pole [h] mentions the expulsion of 441 lumbricoid worms in thirty-four days, and Fauconneau-Dufresne [i] has reported a most remarkable case in which 5000 ascarides were discharged in less than three years, mostly by vomiting.   The patient made an ultimate recovery.

There are many instances in which the lumbricoid worms have pierced the intestinal tract and made their way to other viscera, sometimes leading to an anomalous exit.   There are several cases on record in which the lumbricoid worms have been found in the bladder.   Paré speaks of a case of this kind during a long illness ; and there is mention[j] of a man who voided a worm half a yard long from his bladder after suppression of urine.   The Ephemerides contains a curious case in which a stone was formed in the bladder, having for its nucleus a worm.   Fontanelle presented to the Royal Academy of Medicine of Paris several yards of tapeworm passed from the urethra of a man of fifty-three.   The following is a quotation from the British Medical Journal : [k]   " I have at present a patient passing in his urine a worm-like body, not unlike a tapeworm as far as the segments and general appearance are concerned, the length of each segment being about ¼ inch, the breadth rather less ; sometimes 1½ segments are joined together.   The worm is serrated on the one side, each segment having 1½ cusps.   The urine pale, faintly acid at first, within the last week became almost neutral.   There was considerable vesical irritation for the first week, with abundant mucus in the urine ; specific gravity was 1010 ; there were no albumin nor tube-casts nor uric acid

a 545, 1890, 42. b Lond. Med. Rev. and Mag., 1799–1800, ii., 290.
c 237, 1876, 172. d 224, June, 1867. e 224, 1868, ii., 221.
f Trudi. obsch. dietsk vrach, St. Petersburg, 1869, ii., 67. g 435, 1885, 319.
h Med. Chron., Balt., 1882–83, i., 184. i 789, 1880, 186.
j 629, 1700, 135. k 224, 1895, ii., 512.

in the urinary sediments. Later there were pus-cells and abundant pus.
Tenderness existed behind the prostate and along the course of left ureter.
Temperature of patient oscillated from 97.5° to 103.2° F. There was no
history at any time of recto-vesical fistula. Can anyone suggest the name,
etc., of this helminth ?"

Other cases of worms in the bladder are mentioned in Chapter XIII.

Mitra [a] speaks of the passage of round-worms through the umbilicus of
an adult ; and there is a case mentioned [b] in which round-worms about seven
inches long were voided from the navel of a young child. Borgeois [c] speaks of
a lumbricoid worm found in the biliary passages, and another in the air passages.

Turnbull [d] has recorded two cases of perforation of the tympanic membrane from lumbricoides. Dagan [e] speaks of the issue of a lumbricoid from
the external auditory meatus. Laughton [f] reports an instance of lumbricoid in
the nose. Rake [g] speaks of asphyxia from a round-worm. Morland [h] mentions the ejection of numerous lumbricoid worms from the mouth.

Worms have been found **in the heart ;** and it is quite possible that in
cases of **trichinosis,** specimens of the trichinæ may be discovered anywhere
in the line of cardiac or lymphatic circulation. Quoted by Fournier, [302] La-
peyronnie has seen worms in the pericardial sac, and also in the ventricle.
There is an old record of a person dying of intestinal worms, one of which
was found in the left ventricle. [i] À Castro and Vidal speak of worms in the
aorta. Rake [j] reports a case of sudden death from round-worm ; and
Brown [k] has noted a similar instance.

The **echinococcus** is a tiny cestode which is the factor in the production
of the well-known hydatid cysts which may be found in any part of the body.
Delafield and Prudden report the only instance of multilocular echinococcus
seen in this country. Their patient was a German who had been in this country five years. There are only about 100 of these cases on record, most of
them being in Bavaria and Switzerland.

The **filaria sanguinis hominis** is a small worm of the nematode species,
the adult form of which lives in the lymphatics, and either the adult or the
prematurely discharged ova (Manson) block the lymph-channels, producing the
conditions of hematochyluria, elephantiasis, and lymph-scrotum. The Dra-
cunculus medinensis or Guinea-worm is a widely-spread parasite in parts of
Africa and the West Indies. According to Osler several cases have occurred
in the United States. Jarvis reports a case in a post-chaplain who had lived
at Fortress Monroe, Va., for thirty years. Van Harlingen's patient, a man
of forty-seven, had never lived out of Philadelphia, so that the worm must be
included among the parasites infesting this country.

a 436, 1891, ii., 381.   b Lond. Med. Jour., 1786, vii., 372.   c 789, 1856, x., 279.
d 545, 1881, 32.   e Jour. de méd. et chir. prat., Paris, 1883, 258.
f 547, 1870–71, i., 181.   g 224, 1887, i., 1274.   h 218, 1867, 409.
i 469, 1772.   j 703, 1890, 26.   k 776, 1824, i., 663.

In February, 1896, Henry of Philadelphia showed microscopic slides containing blood which was infested with numbers of living and active filaria embryos. The blood was taken from a colored woman at the Woman's Hospital, who developed hematochyluria after labor. Henry believed that the woman had contracted the disease during her residence in the Southern States.

Curran [a] gives quite an exhaustive article on the disease called in olden times **"eaten of worms,"**—a most loathsome malady. Herod the Great, the Emperor Galerius, and Philip II. of Spain perished from it. In speaking of the Emperor Galerius, Dean Milman, in his "History of Latin Christianity," [b] says, "a deep and fetid ulcer preyed on the lower parts of his body and ate them away into a mass of living corruption." Gibbon, in his "Decline and Fall," [c] also says that "his (Galerius's) death was caused by a very painful and lingering disorder. His body, swelled by an intemperate course of life to an unwieldy corpulence, was covered with ulcers and devoured by immense swarms of those insects who have given their names to this most loathsome disease." It is also said that the African Vandal King, the Arian Huneric, died of the disease. Antiochus, surnamed the "Madman," [d] was also afflicted with it; and Josephus makes mention of it as afflicting the body of Herod the Great. The so-called "King Pym" died of this "morbus pedicularis," but as prejudice and passion militated against him during his life and after his death, this fact is probably more rumor than verity. A case is spoken of by Curran, which was seen by an army-surgeon in a very aged woman in the remote parts of Ireland, and another in a female in a dissecting-room in Dublin. The tissues were permeated with lice which emerged through rents and fissures in the body.

Instances of the larvæ of the estrus or the **bot-fly** in the skin are not uncommon. In this country Allen [e] removed such larvæ from the skin of the neck, head, and arm of a boy of twelve. Bethune, Delavigne, Howship, Jacobs, Jannuzzi, and others, report similar cases. These flesh-flies are called creophilæ, and the condition they produce is called myiosis. According to Osler, in parts of Central America, the eggs of a bot-fly, called the dermatobia, are not infrequently deposited in the skin, and produce a swelling very like the ordinary boil. Matas has described a case in which the estrus larvæ were found in the gluteal region. Finlayson of Glasgow has recently reported an interesting case in a physician who, after protracted constipation and pain in the back and sides, passed large numbers of the larvæ of the flower-fly, anthomyia canicularis, and there are other instances of myiosis interna from swallowing the larvæ of the common house-fly.

There are forms of nasal disorder caused by larvæ, which some native surgeons in India regard as a chronic and malignant ulceration of the mucous

[a] 536, 1886, ii., 142.   [b] Vol. i., 227.   [c] Vol. ii., 122.
[d] Maccabes, ch. ix., verses 1, 5, 9, and 10.   [e] 218, lxxxvii., 306.

membranes of the nose and adjacent sinuses in the debilitated and the scrofulous.   Worms lodging in the cribriform plate of the ethmoid feed on the soft tissues of that region.   Eventually their ravages destroy the olfactory nerves, with subsequent loss of the sense of smell, and they finally eat away the bridge of the nose.   The head of the victim droops, and he complains of crawling of worms in the interior of the nose.   The eyelids swell so that the patient cannot see, and a deformity arises which exceeds that produced by syphilis.   Lyons[a] says that it is one of the most loathsome diseases that comes under the observation of medical men.   He describes the disease as " essentially a scrofulous inflammation of the Schneiderian membrane, . . . which finally attacks the bones."   Flies deposit their ova in the nasal discharges, and from their infection maggots eventually arise.   In Sanskrit *peenash* signifies disease of the nose, and is the Indian term for the disease caused by the deposition of larvæ in the nose.   It is supposed to be more common in South America than in India.

[a] Indian Annals of Medicine, Oct., 1885.

CHAPTER XVI.

ANOMALOUS SKIN-DISEASES.

Ichthyosis is a disease of the skin characterized by a morbid development of the papillæ and thickening of the epidermic lamellæ ; according as the skin is affected over a larger or smaller area, or only the epithelial lining of the follicles, it is known as ichthyosis diffusa, or ichthyosis follicularis. The hardened masses of epithelium develop in excess, the epidermal layer loses in integrity, and the surface becomes scaled like that of a fish. Ichthyosis may be congenital, and over sixty years ago Steinhausen [a] described a fetal monster in the anatomic collection in Berlin, the whole surface of whose body was covered with a thick layer of epidermis, the skin being so thick as to form a covering like a coat-of-mail. According to Rayer the celebrated **" porcupine-man "** who exhibited himself in England in 1710 was an example of a rare form of ichthyosis. This man's body, except the face, the palms of the hands, and the soles of the feet, was covered with small excrescences in the form of prickles. These appendages were of a reddish-brown color, and so hard and elastic that they rustled and made a noise when the hand was passed over their surfaces. They appeared two months after birth and fell off every winter, to reappear each summer. In other respects the man was in very good health. He had six children, all of whom were covered with excrescences like himself. The hands of one of these children has been represented by Edwards in his " Gleanings of Natural History." A picture of the hand of the father is shown in the fifty-ninth volume of the Philosophical Transactions.

Pettigrew [b] mentions a man with warty elongations encasing his whole body. At the parts where friction occurred the points of the elongations were worn off. This man was called **" the biped armadillo."** His great grandfather was found by a whaler in a wild state in Davis's Straits, and for four generations the male members of the family had been so encased. The females had normal skins. All the members of the well-known family of Lambert had the body covered with spines. Two members, brothers, aged twenty-two and fourteen, were examined by Geoffroy-Saint-Hilaire. This thickening of the epidermis and hair was the effect of some morbid predisposition which was transmitted from father to son, the daughters not being affected. Five generations could be reckoned which had been affected in the manner described.

[a] 368, 1831, T. ii., 10.   [b] 476, 1832, ii., 146.

The "porcupine-man" seen by Baker contracted small-pox, and his skin was temporarily freed from the squamæ, but these reappeared shortly afterward. There are several older records of prickly men or porcupine-men. Ascanius[a] mentions a porcupine-man, as do Buffon and Schreber. Autenreith speaks of a porcupine-man who was covered with innumerable verrucæ. Martin[b] described a remarkable variety of ichthyosis in which the

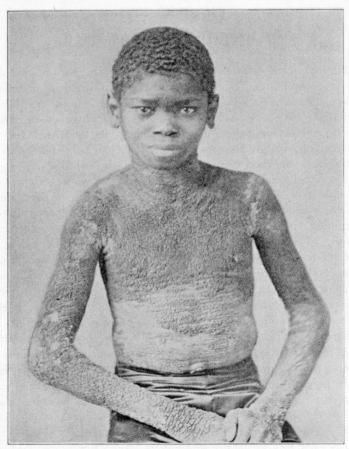

Fig. 286.—An alligator-boy.

skin was covered with strong hairs like the bristles of a boar. When numerous and thick the scales sometimes assumed a greenish-black hue. An example of this condition was the individual who exhibited under the name of the "**alligator-boy.**" Figure 286 represents an "alligator-boy" exhibited by C. T. Taylor. The skin affected in this case resembled in color and consistency that of a young alligator. It was remarked that his olfactory sense was intact.

[a] 462, T. iv., 216.   [b] 550, ix., part i., 53.

The harlequin fetus, of which there are specimens in Guy's Hospital, London Hospital, and the Royal College of Surgeons Museum, is the result of ichthyosis congenita. According to Crocker either after the removal of the vernix caseosa, which may be thick, or as the skin dries it is noticeably red, smooth, shiny, and in the more severe cases covered with actual plates. In the harlequin fetus the whole surface of the body is thickly covered with fatty epidermic plates, about $\frac{1}{16}$ inch in thickness, which are broken up by horizontal and vertical fissures, and arranged transversely to the surface of the body like a loosely-built stone wall. After birth these fissures may extend down into the corium, and on movement produce much pain. The skin is so stiff and contracted that the eyes cannot be completely opened or shut, the lips are too stiff to permit of sucking, and are often inverted ; the nose and ears are atrophied, the toes are contracted and cramped, and, if not born dead, the child soon dies from starvation and loss of heat. When the disease is less severe the child may survive some time. Crocker had a patient, a male child one month old, who survived three months. Hallopeau and Elliot also report similar cases.

Contagious follicular keratosis is an extremely rare affection in which there are peculiar, spine-like outgrowths, consisting in exudations of the mouths of the sebaceous glands. Leloir and Vidal shorten the name to **acné cornée.**

Erasmus Wilson speaks of it as ichthyosis sebacea cornea. H. G. Brooke describes a case in a girl of six. The first sign had been an eruption of little black spots on the nape of the neck. These spots gradually developed into papules, and the whole skin took on a dirty yellow color. Soon afterward the same appearances occurred on both shoulders, and, in the same order, spread gradually down the outer sides of the arms—first black specks, then papules, and lastly pigmentation. The black specks soon began to project, and comedo-like plugs and small, spine-like growths were produced. Both the spines and plugs were very hard and firmly-rooted. They resisted firm pressure with the forceps, and when placed on sheets of paper rattled like scraps of metal. A direct history of contagion was traced from this case to others.

Mibelli[a] describes an uncommon form of **keratodermia** (porokeratosis). The patient was a man of twenty-one, and exhibited the following changes in his skin : On the left side of the neck, beyond a few centimeters below the lobe of the ear, there were about ten small warty patches, irregularly scattered, yellowish-brown in color, irregular in outline, and varying in size from a lentil to a half-franc piece, or rather more. Similar patches were seen on other portions of the face. Patches of varying size and form, sharply limited by a kind of small, peripheral "dike," sinuous but uninterrupted, of a color varying from red to whitish-red, dirty white, and to a hue but little different

a "International Atlas of Rare Skin-Diseases."

from that of the healthy skin. Similar patches were seen on the right hand, and again on the back of the right hand was a wide space, prolonged upward in the form of a broad band on the posterior surface of the forearm to just below the olecranon, where the skin was a little smoother and thinner than the surrounding skin, and altogether bare of hairs. The disease was noticed at the age of two, and gradually progressed. The patient always enjoyed the most perfect health, but had contracted syphilis three years before. A brother of the patient, aged twenty-four, for sixteen years has had the same skin-affection as this patient, on the back of the hand, and the sister and father had noticed similar lesions.

Diffuse symmetric scleroderma, or **hide-bound disease,** is quite rare, and presents itself in two phases : that of infiltration (more properly called hypertrophy) and atrophy, caused by shrinkage. The whole body may be involved, and each joint may be fixed as the skin over it becomes rigid. The muscles may be implicated independently of the skin, or simultaneously, and they give the resemblance of rigor mortis. The whole skin is so hard as to suggest the idea of a frozen corpse, without the coldness, the temperature being only slightly subnormal. The skin can neither be pitted nor pinched. As Crocker has well put it, when the face is affected it is gorgonized, so to speak, both to the eye and to the touch. The mouth cannot be opened ; the lids usually escape, but if involved they are half closed, and in either case immovable. The effect of the disease on the chest-walls is to seriously inter-fere with the respiration and to flatten and almost obliterate the breasts ; as to the limbs, from the shortening of the distended skin the joints are fixed in a more or less rigid position. The mucous membranes may be affected, and the secretion of both sweat and sebum is diminished in proportion to the degree of the affection, and may be quite absent. The atrophic type of scleroderma is preceded by an edema, and from pressure-atrophy of the fat and muscles the skin of the face is strained over the bones ; the lips are shortened, the gums shrink from the teeth and lead to caries, and the nostrils are compressed. The strained skin and the emotionless features (relieved only by telangiectatic striæ) give the countenance a ghastly, corpse-like aspect. The etiology and pathology of this disease are quite obscure. Happily the prognosis is good, as there is a tendency to spontaneous recovery, although the convalescence may be extended.

Although regarded by many as a disease distinct from scleroderma, **morphea** is best described as a circumscribed scleroderma, and presents itself in two clinical aspects : patches and bands, the patches being the more common.

Scleroderma neonatorum is an induration of the skin, congenital and occurring soon after birth, and is invariably fatal. A disease somewhat analogous is edema neonatorum, which is a subcutaneous edema with indura-tion affecting the new-born. If complete it is invariably fatal, but in a few cases in which the process has been incomplete recovery has occurred.

Gerard [a] reports recovery from a case of sclerema neonatorum in an infant five weeks old, which seemed in perfect health but for this skin-affection. The back presented a remarkable induration which involved the entire dorsal aspect, including the deltoid regions, the upper arms, the buttocks, and the thighs, down to and involving the popliteal spaces. The edges of the indurated skin were sharply defined, irregular, and map-like. The affected skin was stretched, but not shiny, and exhibited a pink mottling; it could not be pinched between the fingers; pressure produced no pitting, but rendered the surface pale for a time. The induration upon the buttocks had been noticed immediately after birth, and the region was at first of a deep pink color. During the first nine days the trouble had extended to the thighs, but only shortly before the examination had it attacked the arms. Inunctions of cod-liver oil were at first used, but with little improvement. Blue ointment was substituted, and improvement commenced. As the induration cleared up, outlying patches of the affected skin were left surrounded by normal integument. No pitting could be produced even after the tension of the skin had decreased during recovery. The lowest rectal temperature was 98° F. In a little more than four months the skin became normal. The treatment with mercurial ointment was stopped some time before recovery.

Possibly the most interesting of the examples of skin-anomaly was the "**elephant-man**" of London (Figs. 287 and 288). His real name was Merrick. He was born at Leicester, and gave an elaborate account of shock experienced by his mother shortly before his birth, when she was knocked down by an elephant at a circus; to this circumstance he attributed his unfortunate condition. He derived his name from a proboscis-like projection of his nose and lips, together with a peculiar deformity of the forehead. He was victimized by showmen during his early life, and for a time was shown in Whitechapel Road, where his exhibition was stopped by the police. He was afterward shown in Belgium, and was there plundered of all his savings. The gruesome spectacle he presented ostracized him from the pleasures of friendship and society, and sometimes interfered with his travels. On one occasion a steamboat captain refused to take him as a passenger. Treves exhibited him twice before the Pathological Society of London.[b] His affection was not elephantiasis, but a complication of congenital hypertrophy of certain bones and pachydermatocele and papilloma of the skin. From his youth he suffered from a disease of the left hip-joint. The papillary masses developed on the skin of the back, buttock, and occiput. In the right pectoral and posterior aspect of the right axillary region, and over the buttocks, the affected skin hung in heavy pendulous flaps. His left arm was free from disease. His head grew so heavy that at length he had great difficulty in holding it up. He slept in a sitting or crouching position, with his hands clasped over his legs, and his head on his knees. If he lay down flat, the

[a] 476, May 4, 1895.   [b] 224, 1890, i., 916.

heavy head showed a tendency to fall back and produce a sense of suffocation. For a long time he was an inmate of the London Hospital, where special quarters were provided for him, and it was there that he was found dead,

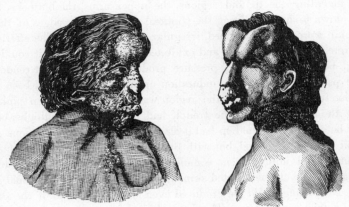

Fig. 287.—Head of the " Elephant-man."

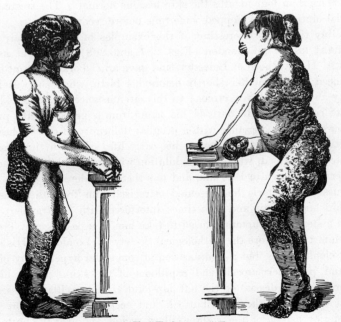

Fig. 288.—The " Elephant-man" (Treves).

April 11, 1890; while in bed his ponderous head had fallen backward and dislocated his neck.

Ainhum may be defined as a pathologic process, the ultimate result of which is a spontaneous amputation of the little toe. It is confined almost exclusively to negroes, chiefly males, and of African descent. In Brazil it is called "ainham" or "quigila." "Ainham" literally means to saw, and is doubtless a colloquial name derived from a supposed slow, sawing process. The Hindoo name for it is "sukha pakla," meaning dry suppuration.

In 1866 da Silva Lima of Bahia, at the Misericordia Hospital, gave the first reports of this curious disease, and for quite a period it was supposed to be confined to Brazilian territory. Since then, however, it has been reported from nearly every quarter of the globe. Relative to its geographic distribution, Pyle[a] states that da Silva Lima and Seixas of Bahia have reported numerous cases in Brazil, as have Figueredo, Pereira, Pirovano, Alpin, and Guimares. Toppin reports it in Pernambuco. Mr. Milton reports a case from Cairo, and Dr. Creswell at Suez, both in slaves. E. A. G. Doyle reports several cases at the Fernando Hospital, Trinidad. Digby reports its prevalence on the west coast of Africa, particularly among a race of negroes called Krumens. Messum reports it in the South African Republic, and speaks of its prevalence among the Kaffirs. Eyles reports it on the Gold Coast. It has also been seen in Algiers and Madagascar. Through the able efforts of Her Majesty's surgeons in India the presence of ainhum has been shown in India, and considerable investigation made as to its etiology, pathologic histology, etc. Wise at Dacca, Smyth and Crombie at Calcutta, Henderson at Bombay, and Warden, Sen, Crawford, and Cooper in other portions of Southern India have all rendered assistance in the investigation of ainhum. In China a case has been seen, and British surgeons speak of it as occurring in Ceylon. Von Winckler presents an admirable report of 20 cases at Georgetown, British Guiana. Dr. Potoppidan sends a report of a case in a negress on St. Thomas Island. The disease has several times been observed in Polynesia.

Dr. Hornaday reports a case in a negress from North Carolina, and, curious to relate, Horwitz of Philadelphia and Shepherd of Canada found cases in negroes both of North Carolina antecedents. Dr. James Evans reports a case in a negro seventy-four years of age, at Darlington, S. C. Dr. R. H. Days of Baton Rouge, La., had a case in a negress, and Dr. J. L. Deslates, also of Louisiana, reports four cases in St. James Parish. Pyle has seen a case in a negress aged fifty years, at the Emergency Hospital in Washington.

So prevalent is the disease in India that Crawford found a case in every 2500 surgical cases at the Indian hospitals. The absence of pain or inconvenience in many instances doubtless keeps the number of cases reported few, and again we must take into consideration the fact that the class of persons afflicted with ainhum are seldom brought in contact with medical men.

The disease usually affects the 5th phalanx at the interphalangeal joint. Cases of the 4th and other phalanges have been reported. Cooper speaks of

[a] 533, Jan. 26, 1895.

a young Brahman who lost his left great toe by this process. Crombie speaks of a simultaneous amputation of both fourth toes. Potoppidan reports a similar case in a negress on St. Thomas Island. Sen reports a case in a supernumerary digit in a child, whose father, a Hindoo, lost a toe by ainhum. Eyles reports a case in a negro in whom the second finger was affected. Mirault, at Angiers, speaks of a case in which two fingers were lost in fifteen days, a fact which makes his diagnosis dubious. Béranger-Ferraud has seen all the toes amputated, and there is a wax model by Baretta, Paris, in the Army Medical Museum at Washington, in which all the toes of the right foot have been amputated, and the process is fast making progress at the middle third of the leg.

Ainhum is much more common in males than in females ; it is, in fact, distinctly rare in the latter. Of von Winckler's 20 cases all were males.

Fig. 289.

Ainhum (dorsal surface). Plantar surface (Ohmann-Dumesnil).

It may occur at any age, but is most common between thirty and thirty-five. It has been reported in utero by Guyot, and was seen to extend up to the thigh, a statement that is most likely fallacious. However, there are well-authenticated cases in infants, and again in persons over seventy years of age.

In some few cases the metatarso-phalangeal joint is affected ; but no case has been seen at the base of the ungual phalanx. The duration of the disease is between two and four years, but Dr. Evans's case had been in progress fifty years. It rarely runs its full course before a year.

Ainhum begins as a small furrow or crack, such as soldiers often experience, at the digito-plantar fold, seen first on the inner side. This process of furrowing never advances in soldiers, and has been given a name more expressive than elegant. In ainhum the toe will swell in a few days, and a pain, burning or shooting in nature, may be experienced in the foot and leg affected. Pain, however, is not constant. There may be an erythematous eruption accompanying the swelling. The furrow increases laterally and in depth, and meets on the dorsal aspect of the toe, giving the toe the appearance of being constricted by a piece of fine cord. As the furrow deepens the distal end of the toe becomes ovoid, and soon an appearance as of a marble attached to the toe by a fibrous pedicle presents itself. By this time the swelling, if any, has subsided. The distal end of the toe bends under the foot, and becomes twisted when walking, and causes inconvenience, and, unfortunately, says Eyles, it is in this last stage only that the Fanti presents himself. There is in the majority of cases a small ulcer in or near the digito-plantar fold, which causes most of the pain, particularly when pressed upon. This ulcer does not occur early, and is not constant. The case under Pyle's observation showed no ulceration, and was absolutely painless, the negress applying for diagnosis rather than treatment. The furrow deepens until spontaneous amputation takes place, which rarely occurs, the patient generally hastening the process by his own operation, or by seeking surgical treatment. A dry scab forms at the furrow, and when picked and repicked constantly re-forms, being composed of horny desquamation or necrosis.

The *histology* of ainhum shows it to be a direct ingrowth of epithelium, with a corresponding depression of surface due to a rapid hyperplasia that pushes down and strangles the papillæ, thus cutting off the blood supply from the epithelial cells, causing them to undergo a horny change.

The disease is not usually symmetric, as formerly stated, nor is it simultaneous in different toes. There are no associated constitutional symptoms, no tendency to similar morbid changes in other parts, and no infiltration elsewhere. There is little or no edema with ainhum. In ainhum there is, first, simple hypertrophy, then active hyperplasia. The papillæ degenerate when deprived of blood supply, and become horny. Meanwhile the pressure thus exerted on the nervi vasorum sets up vascular changes which bring about epithelial changes in more distant areas, the process advancing anteriorly, that is, in the direction of the arteries. This makes the cause, according to Eyles, an inflammatory and trophic phenomenon due mainly to changes following pressure on the vasomotor nerves.

Etiology.—The theories of the causation of ainhum are quite numerous. The first cause is the admirable location for a furrow in the digito-plantar fold, and the excellent situation of the furrow for the entrance of sand or other particles to make the irritation constant, thus causing chronic inflammatory changes, which are followed subsequently by the changes peculiar to ainhum. The cause has been ascribed to the practice of wearing rings on the toes ; but von Winckler says that in his locality (British Guinea) this practice is confined to the coolie women, and in not one of his 20 cases had a ring been previously worn on the toe ; in fact all of the patients were males. Digby says, however, that the Krumens, among whom the disease is common, have long worn brass or copper rings on the fifth toe. Again the natives of India, who are among those most frequently afflicted, have no such custom.

Injury, such as stone-bruise, has been attributed as the initial cause, and well-authenticated cases have been reported in which traumatism is distinctly remembered ; but Smyth, Weber, and several other observers deny that habits, accidents, or work, are a feature in causation.

Von Düring reports a curious case which he calls **sclerodactylia annularis ainhumoides.** The patient was a boy about twelve years old, born in Erzeroum, brought for treatment for scabies, and not for the affection about to be described. A very defective history led to the belief that a similar affection had not been observed in the family. When he was six years old it began on the terminal phalanges of the middle fingers. A myxomatous swelling attacked the phalanges and effected a complete absorption of the terminal phalanx. It did not advance as far as gangrene or exfoliation of bone. At the time of report the whole ten fingers were involved ; the bones seemed to be thickened, the soft parts being indurated or sclerosed. In the right index finger a completely sclerosed ring passed around the middle phalanx. The nails on the absorbed phalanges had become small and considerably thickened plates. No analogous changes were found elsewhere, and sensation was perfectly normal in the affected parts. There were no signs whatever of a multiple neuritis nor of a leprous condition.

There is a rare and curious condition known as **" deciduous skin "** or **keratolysis,** in which the owners possess a skin, which, like that of a serpent, is periodically cast off, that of the limbs coming off like the finger of a glove. Preston[a] of Canterbury, New Zealand, mentions the case of a woman who had thus shed her skin every few weeks from the age of seven or even earlier. The woman was sixty-seven years of age ; the skin in every part of the body came away in casts and cuticles which separated entire and sometimes in one unbroken piece like a glove or stocking. Before each paroxysm she had an associate symptom of malaise. Even the skin of the nose and ears came off complete. None of the patient's large family showed this idiosyncrasy, and she said that she had been told by a medical man that it had been due to catching cold after an attack of small-pox. Frank[b] mentions a case in which there was periodic and complete shedding of the cuticle and nails of the hands and feet, which was repeated for thirty-three consecutive years on July 24th of each year, and between the hours of 3 P. M. and 9 P. M. The patient remembered shedding for the first time while a child at play. The paroxysms always commenced abruptly, constitutional febrile symptoms were first experienced, and the skin became dry and hot. The acute symptoms subsided in three or four hours and were entirely gone in twelve hours, with the exception of the redness of the skin, which did not disappear for thirty-six hours more. The patient had been delirious during this period. The cuticle began to shed some time between the third and twelfth day, in large sheets, as pictured in the accompanying illustrations (Figs. 290 and 291). The nails were shed in about four weeks after the acute stage. Crocker had an instance of this nature in a man with tylosis palmæ, in which the skin was cast off every autumn, but the process lasted two months. Lang observed a case in which the fingers alone were affected.

There is a case of **general and habitual desquamation** of the skin in the Ephemerides of 1686 ; and Newell [a] records a case which recovered under the use of Cheltenham water for several seasons. Latham [b] describes a man of fifty who was first seized about ten years previously with a singular kind of fever, and this returned many times afterward, even twice in the course of the same year, attended with the same symptoms and circumstances, and appearing to be brought on by obstructed perspiration, in consequence of catching cold. Besides the common febrile symptoms, upon the invasion of the disease his skin universally itched, more especially at the joints, and the itching was followed by many little red spots, with a small degree of swelling. Soon after this his fingers became stiff, hard, and painful at the ends, and at the roots of the nails. In about twenty-four hours the cuticle began to separate from the cutis, and in ten or twelve days this separation was general from head to foot, during which time he completely turned the cuticle off from the wrists to the fingers' ends like a glove, and in like manner on the legs to the toes, after which his nails shot gradually from their roots, at first with exquisite pain, which abated as the separation of the cuticle advanced, and the old nails were generally thrown off by new ones in about six months. The cuticle rose in the palms and soles like blisters, having, however, no fluid beneath, and when it came off it left the underlying cutis exposed for a few days. Sometimes, upon catching cold, before quite free from feverish symptoms, a second separation of the cuticle from the cutis occurred, but it appeared so thin as to be like scurf, demonstrating the quick renewal of the parts.

There is a similar case in the Philosophical Transactions [c] in a miller of thirty-five who was exposed to great heat and clouds of dust. On the first cold a fever attacked him, and once or twice a year, chiefly in the autumn, this again occurred, attended with a loosening and detachment of the cuticle. The disorder began with violent fever, attended with pains in the head, back, limbs, retching, vomiting, dry skin, furred tongue, urgent thirst, constipation, and high-colored urine. Usually the whole surface of the body then became yellow. It afterward became florid like a rash, and then great uneasiness was felt for several days, with general numbness and tingling; the urine then began to deposit a thick sediment. About the third week from the first attack the cuticle appeared elevated in many places, and in eight or ten days afterward became so loose as to admit of its easy removal in large flakes. The cuticle of the hands, from the wrists to the fingers' ends, came off

[a] 490, iii., 576. [b] 629, lx., 451. [c] 629, lix., 281.

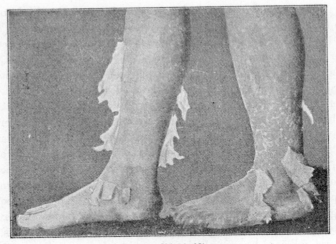

Fig. 290.—Skin-shedding.

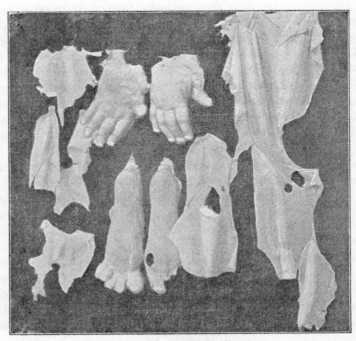

Fig. 291.—Casts of a case of skin-shedding (Frank).

like a glove. The patient was never disposed to sweat, and when it was attempted to force perspiration he grew worse ; nor was he much at ease until his urine deposited a sediment, after which he felt little inconvenience but from the rigidity of the skin. The nails were not detached as in the previous case.

It is quite natural that such cases as this should attract the attention of the laity, and often find report in newspapers. The following is a lay-report of a " **snake-boy** " in Shepardstown, Va. :—

" Jim Twyman, a colored boy living with his foster-parents ten miles from this place, is a wonder. He is popularly known as the " snake-boy." Mentally he is as bright as any child of his age, and he is popular with his playmates, but his physical peculiarities are probably unparalleled. His entire skin, except the face and hands, is covered with the scales and markings of a snake. These exceptions are kept so by the constant use of Castile soap, but on the balance of his body the scales grow abundantly. The child sheds his skin every year. It causes him no pain or illness. From the limbs it can be pulled in perfect shape, but off the body it comes in pieces. His feet and hands are always cold and clammy. He is an inordinate eater, sometimes spending an hour at a meal, eating voraciously all the time, if permitted to do so. After these gorgings he sometimes sleeps two days. There is a strange suggestion of a snake in his face, and he can manipulate his tongue, accompanied by hideous hisses, as viciously as a serpent."

Under the name of **dermatitis exfoliativa neonatorum**, Ritter has described an eruption which he observed in the foundling asylum at Prague, where nearly 300 cases occurred in ten years. According to Crocker it begins in the second or third week of life, and occasionally as late as the fifth week, with diffuse and universal scaling, which may be branny or in laminæ like pityriasis rubra, and either dry or with suffusion beneath the epidermis. Sometimes it presents flaccid bullæ like pemphigus foliaceus, and then there are crusts as well as scales, with rhagades on the mouth, anus, etc. ; there is a total absence of fever or other general symptoms. About 50 per cent. die of marasmus and loss of heat, with or without diarrhea. In those who recover the surface gradually becomes pale and the desquamation ceases. Opinions differ regarding it, some considering it of septic origin, while others believe it to be nothing but pemphigus foliaceus. Kaposi regards it as an aggravation of the physiologic exfoliation of the new-born. Elliott of New York [a] reports two cases with a review of the subject, but none have been reported in England. Cases on the Continent have been described by Billard, von Baer, Caspary, those already mentioned, and others.

The name **epidemic exfoliative dermatitis** has been given to an epidemic skin-disease which made its appearance in 1891 in England ; 425 cases were collected in six institutions, besides sporadic cases in private houses.

[a] 124, Jan., 1888.

In 1895, in London,[619] some photographs and sketches were exhibited that were taken from several of the 163 cases which occurred in the Paddington Infirmary and Workhouse, under the care of Dr. Savill, from whose negatives they were prepared. They were arranged in order to illustrate the successive stages of the disorder. The eruption starts usually with discrete papules, often in stellate groups, and generally arranged symmetrically when on the limbs. These become fused into crimson, slightly raised maculæ, which in severe cases become further fused into red thickened patches, in which the papules can still be felt and sometimes seen. Vesicles form, and exudation occurs in only about one-third of the cases. Desquamation of the epidermis is the invariable feature of all cases, and it usually commences between the fourth and eighth days. In severe cases successive layers of the epidermis are shed, in larger or smaller scales, throughout the whole course of the malady. One-half of the epidermis shed from the hand of a patient is exhibited in this collection.

Of **sphaceloderma,** or **gangrene of the skin,** probably the most interesting is **Raynaud's disease** of symmetric gangrene, a vascular disorder, which is seen in three grades of intensity : there is local syncope, producing the condition known as dead-fingers or dead-toes, and analogous to that produced by intense cold ; and local asphyxia, which usually follows local syncope, or may develop independently. Chilblains are the mildest manifestation of this condition. The fingers, toes, and ears, are the parts usually affected. In the most extreme degree the parts are swollen, stiff, and livid, and the capillary circulation is almost stagnant ; this is local or symmetric gangrene, the mildest form of which follows asphyxia. Small areas of necrosis appear on the pads of the fingers and of the toes ; also at the edges of the ears and tip of the nose. Occasional symmetric patches appear on the limbs and trunk, and in extensive cases terminate in gangrene. Raynaud suggested that the local syncope was produced by contraction of the vessels ; the asphyxia is probably caused by a dilatation of the capillaries and venules, with persistence of the spasm of the arterioles. According to Osler two forms of congestion occur, which may be seen in adjacent fingers, one of which may be swollen, intensely red, and extremely hot ; the other swollen, cyanotic, and intensely cold. Sometimes all four extremities are involved, as in Southey's case,[a] in a girl of two and a half in whom the process began on the calves, after a slight feverish attack, and then numerous patches rapidly becoming gangrenous appeared on the backs of the legs, thighs, buttocks, and upper arms, worse where there was pressure ; the child died thirty-two hours after the onset. The whole phenomenon may be unilateral, as in Smith's case, quoted by Crocker,— in a girl of three years in whom the left hand was cold and livid, while on the right there was lividity, progressing to gangrene of the fingers and of the thumb up to the first knuckles, where complete separation occurred.

a 779, xxxiv., 286.

A considerable number of cases of apparently **spontaneous gangrene of the skin** have been recorded in medical literature as occurring generally in hysteric young women. Crocker remarks that they are generally classified as erythema gangrænosum, and are always to be regarded with grave suspicion of being self-induced. Ehrl[a] records an interesting case of this nature with an accompanying illustration. The patient was a girl of eighteen whose face, left breast, anus, legs, and feet became affected every autumn since her sixth year, after an attack of measles. At first the skin became red, then water-blisters formed, the size of a grain of corn, and in three days reaching the size of a hazel-nut; these burst and healed, leaving no scars. The menses appeared at the fifteenth year, lasted eight days, with great loss of blood, but there was no subsequent menstruation, and no vicarious hemorrhage. Afterward the right half of the face became red for three or four weeks, with a disturbance of the sensibility of this part, including the right half of the mucosa of the mouth and the conjunctiva of the right eye. At the seventeenth year the patient began to have a left-sided headache and increased sweating of the right half of the body. In 1892 the periodically-appearing skin-affection became worse. Instead of healing, the broken vessels became blackish and healed slowly, leaving ulcers, granulations, and scars, and the gangrenous tendency of the skin increased. Disturbance of the sight shortly intervened, associated with aphonia. The sensibility of the whole body, with the exception of the face, was greatly impaired, and there was true gangrene of the corium. A younger sister of the patient was similarly affected with symptoms of hysteria, hemianesthesia, etc.

Neuroses of the skin consist in augmentation of sensibility or **hyperesthesia** and diminution of sensibility or **anesthesia**. There are some curious old cases of loss of sensation. Ferdinandus[b] mentions a case of a young man of twenty-four who, after having been seized with insensibility of the whole body with the exception of the head, was cured by purgatives and other remedies. Bartholinus cites the case of a young man who lost the senses of taste and feeling; and also the case of a young girl who could permit the skin of her forehead to be pricked and the skin of her neck to be burned without experiencing any pain. In his "Surgery" Lamothe mentions a case of insensibility of the hands and feet in consequence of a horse-kick in the head without the infliction of any external wound. In the "Mémoires de l'Académie des Sciences" for the year 1743, we read an account of a soldier who, after having accidentally lost all sensation in his left arm, continued to go through the whole of the manual exercise with the same facility as ever. It was also known that La Condamine was able to use his hands for many years after they had lost their sensation. Rayer gives a case of paralysis of the skin of the left side of the trunk without any affection of the muscles, in a man of forty-three of apoplectic constitution. The paralysis extended from the left mammary region to the haunch, and from the vertebræ to the linea alba. Throughout this whole extent the skin was insensible and could be pinched or even punctured without the patient being aware that he was even touched. The parts did not present any perceptible alteration in texture or in color. The patient was free from fever and made no complaint except a slight headache. Rayer quotes another case in a man of sixty who had been bitten three years previously by a dog that was not

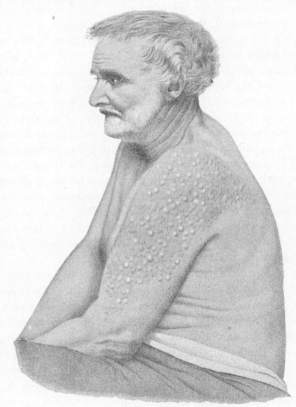

Fig. 292.—Neuroma cutis dolorosum (Duhring).

mad. He was greatly frightened by the accident and every time he saw a dog he trembled violently, and on one occasion he suffered a convulsive attack for one and a half hours. The convulsions increased in number and frequency, he lost his memory, and exhibited other signs of incipient dementia. He was admitted to the hospital with two small wounds upon the head, one above the left eyebrow and the other on the scalp, occasioned by a fall on his entrance into the hospital. For several days a great degree of insensibility of the skin of the whole body was observed without any implication of the power of voluntary motion. He was entirely cured in eighteen days.

Duhring[a] reports a very rare form of disease of the skin, which may be designated **neuroma cutis dolorosum,** or painful neuroma of the skin (Fig. 292). The patient was a boiler-maker of seventy who had no family history bearing on the disease. Ten years previously a few cutaneous tubercles the size and shape of a split-pea were noticed on the left shoulder, attended with decided itching but not with pain. The latter symptom did not come on until three years later. In the course of a year or two the lesions increased in number, so that in four years the shoulder and arm were thickly studded with them. During the next five years no particular changes occurred either in lesions or in the degree of pain. The region affected simply looked like a solid sheet of variously-sized, closely-packed, confluent tubercles, hard and dense. The tubercles were at all times painful to the touch, and even the contact of air was sufficient to cause great suffering. During the paroxysms, which occurred usually at several short intervals every day, the skin changed color frequently and rapidly, passing through various reddish and violet tints, at times becoming purplish.

As a paroxysm came on the man was in the habit of gently pressing and holding the arm closely to his body. At one time he endured the attack in a standing posture, walking the floor, but usually he seated himself very near a hot stove, in a doubled-up, cramped position, utterly unmindful of all surroundings, until the worst pain had ceased. Frequently he was unable to control himself, calling out piteously and vehemently and beseeching that his life be terminated by any means. In desperation he often lay and writhed on the floor in agony. The intense suffering lasted, as a rule, for about a half hour, but he was never without pain of the neuralgic type. He was freer of pain in summer than in winter. Exsection of the brachial plexus was performed, but gave only temporary relief. The man died in his eighty-fourth year of senile debility.

According to Osler the tubercula dolorosa or true fascicular neuroma is not always made up of nerve-fibers, but, as shown by Hoggan, may be an adenomatous growth of the sweat-glands.

Yaws may be defined as an endemic, specific, and contagious disease, characterized by raspberry-like nodules with or without constitutional disturbance. Its synonym, **frambesia,** is from the French, *framboise,* a raspberry. Yaws is derived from a Carib word, the meaning of which is doubtful. It is a disease confined chiefly to tropical climates, and is found on the west coast of Africa for about ten degrees on each side of the equator, and also on the east coast in the central regions, but rarely in the north. It is also found in Madagascar, Mozambique, Ceylon, Hindoostan, and nearly all the tropical islands of the world. Crocker believes it probable that the

[a] 124, Oct., 1881.

button-scurvy of Ireland, now extinct, but described by various writers of 1823 to 1857 as a contagious disease which was prevalent in the south and in the interior of the island, was closely allied to yaws, if not identical with it. The first mention of the yaws disease is by Oviedo, in 1535, who met with it in San Domingo. Although Sauvages at the end of the last century was the first to give an accurate description of this disease, many physicians had observed it before.

Frambesia or yaws was observed in Brazil as early as 1643,[a] and in America later by Lebat in 1722. In the last century Winterbottom and Hume describe yaws in Africa, Hume calling it the African distemper. In 1769 in an essay on the "Natural History of Guiana," Bancroft mentions yaws; and Thomson[b] speaks of it in Jamaica. Hillary in 1759 describes yaws in Barbadoes; and Bajou in Domingo and Cayenne in 1777, Dazille having already observed it in San Domingo in 1742.[c]

Crocker takes his account of yaws from Numa Rat of the Leeward Islands, who divides the case into four stages: incubation, primary, secondary, and tertiary. The incubation stage is taken from the date of infection to the first appearance of the local lesion at the sight of inoculation. It varies from three to ten weeks. The symptoms are vague, possibly palpitation, vertigo, edema of the limbs and eyelids. The primary stage begins with the initial lesion, which consists of a papule which may be found most anywhere on the body. This papule ulcerates. The secondary stage commences about a fortnight after the papule has healed. There is intermittent fever, headache, backache, and shooting pains in the limbs and intercostal spaces, like those of dengue, with nocturnal exacerbations. An eruption of minute red spots appears first on the face, and gradually extends so that the whole body is covered at the end of three days. By the seventh day the apex of the papule is of a pale yellow color, and the black skin has the appearance of being dotted over with yellow wax. The papule then develops into nodules of cylindric shape, with a dome-shaped, thick, yellow crust. It is only with the crust off that there is any resemblance to a raspberry. During the month following the raspberry appearance the skin is covered with scabs which, falling off, leave a pale macula; in dark races the macula becomes darker than normal, but in pale races it becomes paler than the natural skin, and in neither case is it scarcely ever obliterated. Intense itching is almost always present, and anemia is also a constant symptom. The disease is essentially contagious and occurs at all ages and among all sexes, to a lesser degree in whites and hybrids, and is never congenital. It seems to have a tendency to undergo spontaneous recovery.

Furunculus orientalis, or its synonyms, Oriental boil, Aleppo boil, Delhi boil, Biskra button, etc., is a local disease occurring chiefly on the face

---

a De medicina Bræsilium, 1643.   b 318, xv., 321.

c Obs. sur les maladies des negres, Paris, 1742.

and other uncovered spots, endemic in limited districts in hot climates, characterized by the formation of a papule, a nodule, and a scab, and beneath the last a sharply punched-out ulcer. Its different names indicate the districts in which it is common, nearly always in tropical or subtropical climates. It differs from yaws in the absence of febrile symptoms, in its unity, its occurrence often on the feet and the backs of the hands, its duration, and the deep scar which it leaves. A fatal issue is rare, but disfiguring and disabling cicatrices may be left unless great care is employed.

Pigmentary Processes.—Friction, pressure, or scratching, if long continued, may produce extensive and permanent pigmentation. This is seen in its highest degree in itching diseases like prurigo and pityriasis. Greenhow [a] has published instances of this kind under the name of "**vagabond's disease**," a disease simulating morbus addisonii, and particularly found in tramps and vagrants. In aged people this condition is the pityriasis nigra of Willan. According to Crocker in two cases reported by Thibierge, the oral mucous membrane was also stained. Carrington and Crocker both record cases of permanent pigmentation following exposure to great cold.[b] Gautier is accredited with recording in 1890 the case of a boy of six in whom pigmented patches from sepia to almost black began to form at the age of two, and were distributed all over the body. Precocious maturity of the genital organs preceded and accompanied the pigmentation, but the hair was illy developed.

Chloasma uterinum presents some interesting anomalies. Swayne records a singular variety in a woman in whom, during the last three months of three successive pregnancies, the face, arms, hands, and legs were spotted like a leopard, and remained so until after her confinement. Crocker speaks of a lady of thirty whose skin during each pregnancy became at first bronze, as if it had been exposed to a tropical sun, and then in spots almost black. Kaposi knew a woman with a pigmented mole two inches square on the side of the neck, which became quite black at each pregnancy, and which was the first recognizable sign of her condition. It is quite possible that the black disease of the Garo Hills in Assam [c] is due to extreme and acute development of a pernicious form of malaria. In chronic malaria the skin may be yellowish, from a chestnut-brown to a black color, after long exposure to the influence of the fever. Various fungi, such as tinea versicolor and the Mexican "Caraati," may produce discoloration on the skin.

Acanthosis Nigricans may be defined as a general pigmentation with papillary mole-like growths. In the "International Atlas of Rare Skin Diseases" there are two cases pictured, one by Politzer in a woman of sixty-two, and the other by Janovsky in a man of forty-two. The regions affected were mostly of a dirty-brown color, but in patches of a bluish-gray. The disease began suddenly in the woman, but gradually in the man. Crocker has

a 767, ix.   b 767, xiv.   c 224, Nov. 29, 1884.

reported a case somewhat similar to these two, under the head of general bronzing without constitutional symptoms, in a Swedish sailor of twenty-two, with rapid onset of pigmentation.[a]

Xeroderma pigmentosum, first described by Kaposi in 1870, is a very rare disease, but owing to its striking peculiarities is easily recognized. Crocker saw the first three cases in England, and describes one as a type. The patient was a girl of twelve, whose general health and nutrition were good. The disease began when she was between twelve and eighteen months old, without any premonitory symptom. The disease occupied the parts habitually uncovered in childhood. The whole of these areas was more or less densely speckled with pigmented, freckle-like spots, varying in tint from a light, raw umber to a deep sepia, and in size from a pin's head to a bean, and of a roundish and irregular shape. Interspersed among the pigment-spots, but not so numerous, were white atrophic spots, which in some parts coalesced, forming white, shining, cicatrix-like areas. The skin upon this was finely wrinkled, and either smooth or shiny, or covered with thin, white scales. On these white areas bright red spots were conspicuous, due to telangiectasis, and there were also some stellate vascular spots and striæ interspersed among the pigment. Small warts were seen springing up from some of the pigment-spots. These warts ulcerated and gave rise to numerous superficial ulcerations, covered with yellow crusts, irregularly scattered over the face, mostly on the right side. The pus coming from these ulcers was apparently inocuous. The patient complained neither of itching nor of pain. Archambault[b] has collected 60 cases, and gives a good resume to date. Amiscis reports two cases of brothers, in one of whom the disease began at eight months, and in the other at a year, and concludes that it is not a lesion due to external stimuli or known parasitic elements, but must be regarded as a specific, congenital dystrophy of the skin, of unknown pathogenesis. However, observations have shown that it may occur at forty-three years (Riehl), and sixty-four years (Kaposi). Crocker believes that the disease is an atrophic degeneration of the skin, dependent on a primary neurosis, to which there is a congenital predisposition.

Nigrities is a name given by the older writers to certain black blotches occurring on the skin of a white person—in other words, it is a synonym of melasma. According to Rayer it is not uncommon to see the scrotum and the skin of the penis of adults almost black, so as to form a marked contrast with the pubes and the upper part of the thighs. Haller[c] met with a woman in whom the skin of the pubic region was as black as that of a negress. During nursing the nipples assume a deep black color which disappears after weaning. Le Cat speaks of a woman of thirty years, whose forehead assumed a dusky hue of the color of iron rust when she was pregnant about the seventh month. By degrees the whole face became black except the eyes and the edges of the

a 767, xiv., 152.   b "Thèse de Bordeaux," 1890.   c 400, v., 18.

lips, which retained their natural color. On some days this hue was deeper than on others ; the woman being naturally of a very fair complexion had the appearance of an alabaster figure with a black marble head. Her hair, which was naturally exceedingly dark, appeared coarser and blacker. She did not suffer from headache, and her appetite was good. After becoming black, the face was very tender to the touch. The black color disappeared two days after her accouchement, and following a profuse perspiration by which the sheets were stained black. Her child was of a natural color. In the following pregnancy, and even in the third, the same phenomenon reappeared in the course of the seventh month ; in the eighth month it disappeared, but in the ninth month this woman became the subject of convulsions, of which she had one each day. The existence of accidental nigrities rests on well-established facts which are distinctly different from the pigmentation of purpura, icterus, or that produced by metallic salts. Chomel [a] quotes the case of a very apathic old soldier, whose skin, without any appreciable cause, became as brown as that of a negro in some parts, and a yellowish-brown in others. Rustin [b] has published the case of a woman of seventy who became as black as a negress in a single night. Goodwin [302] relates the case of an old maiden lady whose complexion up to the age of twenty-one was of ordinary whiteness, but then became as black as that of an African. Wells and Rayer have also published accounts of cases of accidental nigrities. One of the latter cases was a sailor of sixty-three who suffered from general nigrities, and the other was in a woman of thirty, appearing after weaning and amenorrhea.

Mitchell Bruce has described an **anomalous discoloration of the skin and mucous membranes** resembling that produced by silver or cyanosis. The patient, a harness-maker of forty-seven, was affected generally over the body, but particularly in the face, hands, and feet. The conjunctival, nasal, and aural mucosa were all involved. The skin felt warm, and pressure did not influence the discoloration. The pains complained of were of an intermittent, burning, shooting character, chiefly in the epigastric and left lumbar regions. The general health was good, and motion and sensation were normal. Nothing abnormal was discovered in connection with the abdominal and thoracic examinations. The pains and discoloration had commenced two years before his admission, since which time the skin had been deepening in tint. He remained under observation for three months without obvious change in his symptoms. There was nothing in the patient's occupation to account for the discoloration. A year and a half previously he had taken medicine for his pains, but its nature could not be discovered. He had had syphilis.

Galtier mentions congenital and bronze spots of the skin. A man born in Switzerland the latter part of the last century, calling himself Joseph Galart, attracted the attention of the curious by exhibiting himself under the

[a] Bull. de la Fac. de Méd. de Paris, 1814, No. 6.   [b] Ibid., 1817, Nos. 9 and 10.

name of the "**Living Angel.**" He presented the following appearance : The skin of the whole posterior part of the trunk, from the nape of the neck to the loins, was of a bronze color. This color extended over the shoulders and the sides of the neck, and this part was covered with hairs of great fineness and growing very thick ; the skin of the rest of the body was of the usual whiteness. Those parts were the darkest which were the most covered with hair ; on the back there was a space of an inch in diameter, which had preserved its whiteness, and where the hairs were fewer in number, darker at their bases, and surrounded by a very small black circle ; the hair was thinner at the sides of the neck ; there were a great many individual hairs surrounded by circles of coloring matter ; but there were also many which presented nothing of this colored areola. In some places the general dark color of the skin blended with the areola surrounding the roots of the hair, so that one uniform black surface resulted. In many places the dark color changed into black. The irides were brown. The man was of very unstable character, extremely undecided in all his undertakings, and had a lively but silly expression of countenance. A distinct smell, as of mice, with a mixture of a garlicky odor, was emitted from those parts where the excessive secretion of the coloring matter took place. In those places the heat was also greater than natural. Rayer recites the case of a young man whom he saw, whose eyelids and adjacent parts of the cheeks were of a bluish tint, similar to that which is produced on the skin by the explosion of gunpowder.

Billard[a] has published an extraordinary case of **blue discoloration of the skin** in a young laundress of sixteen. Her neck, face, and upper part of the chest showed a beautiful blue tint, principally spreading over the forehead, the alæ, and the mouth. When these parts were rubbed with a white towel the blue parts of the skin were detached on the towel, coloring it, and leaving the skin white. The girl's lips were red, the pulse was regular and natural, and her strength and appetite like that of a person in health. The only morbid symptom was a dry cough, but without mucous rattle or any deficiency of the sound of the chest or alteration of the natural beat of the heart. The catamenia had never failed. She had been engaged as a laundress for the past two years. From the time she began this occupation she perceived a blueness around her eyes, which disappeared however on going into the air. The phenomenon reappeared more particularly when irons were heated by a bright charcoal fire, or when she worked in a hot and confined place. The blueness spread, and her breast and abdomen became shaded with an azure blue, which appeared deeper or paler as the circulation was accelerated or retarded. When the patient's face should have blushed, the face became blue instead of red. The changes exhibited were like the sudden transition of shades presented by the chameleon. The posterior part of the trunk, the axillæ, the sclerotic coats of the eyes, the nails, and the skin of the head remained in

a 162, T. xxvi., 453.

their natural state and preserved their natural color. The linen of the patient was stained blue. Chemical analysis seemed to throw no light on this case, and the patient improved on alkaline treatment. She vomited blood, which contained sufficient of the blue matter to stain the sides of the vessel. She also stated that in hemorrhage from the nose she had seen blue drops among the drops of blood. One cannot but suspect indigo as a factor in the causation of this anomalous coloration.

Artificial discolorations of the skin are generally produced by tattooing, by silver nitrate, mercury, bismuth, or some other metallic salt.

Melasma has been designated as an accidental and temporary blackish discoloration of the skin. There are several varieties : that called Addison's disease, that due to uterine disease, etc. In this affection the skin assumes a dark and even black hue.

Leukoderma is a pathologic process, the result of which is a deficiency in the normal pigmentation of the skin, and possibly its appendages. Its synonyms are leukopathia, vitiligo, achroma, leukasmus, and chloasma album. In India the disease is called sufaid-korh, meaning white leprosy. It has numerous colloquial appellations, such as chumba or phoolyree (Hindoo), buras (Urdu), cabbore (Singalese), kuttam (Taneil), dhabul (Bengal). It differs from albinism in being an acquired deficiency of pigment, not universal and not affecting the eye. Albinism is congenital, and the hair and eyes are affected as well as the skin.

The disease is of universal distribution, but is naturally more noticeable in the dark-skinned races. It is much more common in this country among the negroes than is generally supposed.

The " leopard-boy of Africa," so extensively advertised by dime museums over the country, was a well-defined case of leukoderma in a young mulatto, a fitting parallel for the case of ichthyosis styled the " alligator-boy."

Figure 293 represents a family of three children, all the subjects of leukoderma. Leukoderma is more common among females. It is rarely seen in children, being particularly a disease of middle age. Bissell reports a case in an Indian ninety years of age, subsequent to an attack of rheumatism thirty years previous. It is of varying duration, nearly every case giving a different length of time. It may be associated with most any disease, and is directly attributable to none. In a number of cases collected rheumatism has been a marked feature. It has been noticed following typhoid fever and pregnancy.

In white persons there are spots or blotches of pale, lustreless appearance, either irregular or symmetric, scattered over the body. In the negro and other dark-skinned races a mottled appearance is seen. If the process goes to completion, the whole surface changes to white. The hair, though rarely affected, may present a mottled appearance. There seems to be no constitutional disturbances, no radical change in the skin, no pain—in fact, no disturbance worthy of note. The eye is not affected; but in a negro the sclerotic generally appears muddy.

It appears first in small spots, either on the lips, nose, eyelids, soles, palms, or forehead, and increases peripherally—the several spots fusing together. The skin is peculiarly thin and easily irritated. Exposure to the sun readily blisters it, and after the slightest abrasion it bleeds freely. Several cases have been reported in which the specific gravity of the urine was extremely high, due to an excess of urea. Wood calls attention to the wave-

Fig. 293.—"The leopard family."

like course of leukoderma, receding on one side, increasing on the other. The fading is gradual, and the margins may be abrupt or diffuse. The mucous membranes are rosy. The functions of the sweat-glands are unimpaired.

The theory of the absence of pigment causing a loss of the olfactory sense, spoken of by Wallace, is not borne out by several observations of Wood and others. Wilson says: "Leukasma is a neurosis, the result of weakened innervation of the skin, the cause being commonly referable to the organs of assimilation or reproduction." It is not a dermatitis, as a dermatitis usually causes deposition of pigment. The rays of the sun bronze the skin ; mustard, cantharides, and many like irritants cause a dermatitis, which is accompanied by a deposition of pigment. Leukoderma is as common in housemaids as in field-laborers, and is in no way attributable to exposure of sun or wind. True leukodermic patches show no vascular changes, no infiltration, but a partial obliteration of the rete mucosum. It has been ascribed to syphilis ; but syphilitic leukoderma is generally the result of cicatrices following syphilitic ulceration.

Many observers have noticed that negroes become several degrees lighter after syphilization ; but no definite relation between syphilis and leukoderma has yet been demonstrated in this race. Postmortem examinations of leukodermic persons show no change in the suprarenal capsule, a supposed organ of pigmentation.

Climate has no influence. It is seen in the Indians of the Isthmus of Darien, the Hottentots, and the Icelanders. Why the cells of the rete mucosum should have the function in some races of manufacturing or attracting pigment in excess of those of other races, is in itself a mystery. By his experiments on the pigment-cells of a frog Lister has established the relation existing between these elements and innervation, which formerly had been supposititious.

Doubtless a solution of the central control of pigmentation would confirm the best theory of the cause of leukoderma—i. e., faulty innervation of the skin. At present, whether the fault is in the cell proper, the conducting media, or the central center, we are unable to say. It is certainly not due to any vascular disturbances, as the skin shows no vascular changes.

White spots on the nails are quite common, especially on young people. The mechanic cause is the presence of air between the lamellæ of the affected parts, but their origin is unknown. According to Crocker in some cases they can be shown to be a part of trophic changes. Bielschowsky [a] records the case of a man with peripheral neuritis, in whom white spots appeared at the lower part of the finger-nails, grew rapidly, and in three weeks coalesced into a band across each nail a millimeter wide. The toes were not affected. Shoemaker mentions a patient who suffered from relapsing fever and bore an additional band for each relapse. Crocker quotes a case reported by Morison of Baltimore, in which transverse bars of white, alternating with the normal color, appeared without ascertainable cause on the finger-nails of a young lady and remained unchanged.

Giovannini describes a case of **canities unguium** in a patient of twenty-nine, following an attack of typhoid fever. On examining the hands of this patient the nails showed in their entire extent a white, opaque, almost ivory color. An abnormal quantity of air found in the interior of the nails explains in this particular case their impaired appearance. It is certain that the nails,

[a] 224, Jan. 17, 1891.

in order to have admitted such a large quantity of air into their interior must have altered in their intimate structure ; and Giovannini suggests that they were subject to an abnormal process of keratinization. Unna describes a similar case, which, however, he calls leukonychia.

Plica polonica, or, as it was known in Cracow—*weichselzopf,* is a disease peculiar to Poland, or to those of Polish antecedents, characterized by the agglutination, tangling, and anomalous development of the hair, or by an alteration of the nails, which become spongy and blackish. In older days the disease was well known and occupied a prominent place in books on skin-diseases. Hercules de Saxonia and Thomas Minadous, in 1610, speak of plica as a disease already long known. The greater number of writers fix the date of its appearance in Poland at about the year 1285, under the reign of Lezekle-Noir. Lafontaine[a] stated that in the provinces of Cracow and Sandomir plica formerly attacked the peasantry, beggars, and Jews in the proportion of $1\frac{1}{2}$ in 20 ; and the nobility and burghers in the proportion of two in 30 or 40. In Warsaw and surrounding districts the disease attacked the first classes in the proportion of one to ten, and in the second classes one to 30. In Lithuania the same proportions were observed as in Warsaw ; but the disease has gradually grown rarer and rarer to the present day, although occasional cases are seen even in the United States.

Plica has always been more frequent on the banks of the Vistula and Borysthenes, in damp and marshy situations, than in other parts of Poland. The custom formerly prevailing in Poland of shaving the heads of children, neglect of cleanliness, the heat of the head-dress, and the exposure of the skin to cold seem to favor the production of this disease.

Plica began after an attack of acute fever, with pains like those of acute rheumatism in the head and extremities, and possibly vertigo, tinnitus aurium, ophthalmia, or coryza. Sometimes a kind of redness was observed on the thighs, and there was an alteration of the nails, which became black and rough ; and again, there was clammy sweat. When the scalp was affected the head was sore to the touch and excessively itchy. A clammy and agglutinating sweat then occurred over the cranium, the hair became unctuous, stuck together, and appeared distended with an adhesive matter of reddish-brown color, believed by many observers to be sanguineous. The hair was so acutely sensitive that the slightest touch occasioned severe pain at the roots. A viscid matter of a very offensive smell, like that of spoiled vinegar, or according to Rayer like that of mice or garlic, exuded from the whole surface of each affected hair. This matter glued the hairs together, at first from their exit at the skin, and then along the entire length ; it appeared to be secreted from the whole surface of the scalp and afterward dried into an incrustation. If there was no exudation the disease was called plica sicca. The hair was matted and stuck together in a variety of ways, so as to resemble ropes (plica mul-

a Traité de la Plique Polonaise, etc., Paris, 1808.

tiformis). Sometimes these masses united together and formed one single thick club like the tail of a horse (plica caudiformis). Again, and particularly in females, the hair would become matted and glued together into one uniform intricate mass of various magnitudes. The hair of the whole body was likely to be attacked with this disease. Kalschmidt of Jena possessed the pubes of a woman dead of plica, the hair of which was of such length that it must have easily gone around the body. There was formerly a superstition that it was dangerous to cut the hair until the discharge diminished. Lafontaine, Schlegel, and Hartman all assure us that the section of the affected masses before this time has been known to be followed by amaurosis, convulsions, apoplexy, epilepsy, and even death. Alarmed or taught by such occurrences, the common people often went about all their lives with the plica gradually dropping off. Formerly there was much theorizing and discussion regarding the etiology and pathology of plica, but since this mysterious affection has been proved to be nothing more than the product of neglect, and the matting due to the inflammatory exudation, excited by innumerable pediculi, agglutinating the hair together, the term is now scarcely mentioned in dermatologic works. Crocker speaks of a rare form which he entitles neuropathic plica, and cites two cases, one reported by Le Page [a] whose specimen is in the Royal College of Surgeons Museum ; and the other was in a Hindoo described by Pestonji.[b] Both occurred in young women, and in both it came on after washing the hair in warm water, one in a few minutes, and the other in a few hours. The hair was drawn up into a hard tangled lump, impossible to unravel, limited to the right side in Le Page's patient, who had very long hair, and in Pestonji's case to the back of the head, where on each side was an elongated mass, very hard and firm, like a rope and about the size of the fist. There was no reason to believe that it was ascribable to imposture ; the Hindoo woman cut the lumps off herself and threw them away. Le Page found the most contracted hairs flattened. Stellwagon [c] reports a case of plica in a woman. It occupied a dollar-sized area above the nape of the neck, and in twelve years reached the length of 12 feet. There was no history of its manner of onset.

Tinea nodosa is a name given by Morris and Cheadle to a case of nodular growth on the beard and whiskers of a young man. In a case noticed by Crocker this disease affected the left side of the mustache of a medical man, who complained that the hair, if twisted up, stuck together. When disintegrated the secretion in this case seemed to be composed of fungous spores. Epithelium fragments, probably portions of the internal root-sheath, sometimes adhere to the shaft of the hair as it grows up, and look like concretions. Crocker states that he is informed by White of Boston that this disease is common in America in association with alopecia furfuracea, and is erroneously thought to be the cause of the loss of hair, hence the popular name, " **hair-eaters.**"

[a] 224, Jan. 26, 1884.   [b] 476, Sept. 3, 1885.   [c] 124, Dec., 1892.

Thomson describes a case of **mycosis fungoides** [a] in a young girl of the age of fourteen, whom he saw in Brussels toward the end of October, 1893. She was the third of a family of 13 children of whom only five survived. Of the children born subsequently to the patient, the first were either premature or died a few days after their births. The seventh was under treatment for interstitial keratitis and tuberculous ulceration of the lips and throat. The disease in the patient made its appearance about seven months previously, as a small raised spot in the middle of the back just above the buttocks. Many of the patches coalesced. At the time of report the lumbar region was the seat of the disease, the affection here presenting a most peculiar appearance, looking as if an enormous butterfly had alighted on the patient's back, with its dark blue wings covered with silvery scales, widely expanded. The patient was not anemic and appeared to be in the best of

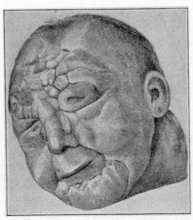

Fig. 294.—Mycosis fungoides (Jamieson, Edin. Med. Jour., March, 1893).

health. None of the glands were affected. According to Thomson there is little doubt that this disease is caused by non-pyogenic bacteria gaining access to the sweat-glands. The irritation produced by their presence gives rise to proliferation of the connective-tissue corpuscles.

Jamieson reports a case of mycosis in a native of Aberdeenshire aged thirty-eight. There was no history of any previous illness. The disease began three years previous to his application for treatment, as a red, itching, small spot on the cheek. Two years later lumps presented themselves, at first upon his shoulders. The first thing to strike an observer was the offensive odor about the patient. In the hospital wards it made all the occupants sick. The various stages of the disease were marked upon the different parts of the body. On the chest and abdomen it resembled an eczema ; on the shoulders there were brown, pinkish-red areas. On the scalp the hair was scanty, the eye-brows denuded, and the eyelashes absent. The forehead was leonine in aspect. From between the various nodosities a continual discharge exuded, the nodosities being markedly irregular over the limbs. The backs of the hands, the dorsums of the feet, the wrists and ankles, had closely approximating growths upon them, while under the thick epidermis of the palms of the hands were blisters. Itching was intense. The patient became emaciated and died thirteen days after his admission into the hospital. A histologic examination showed the sarcomatous nature of the various growths. The disease differed

a "Internat. Atlas Rare Skin Diseases."

PLATE 12.

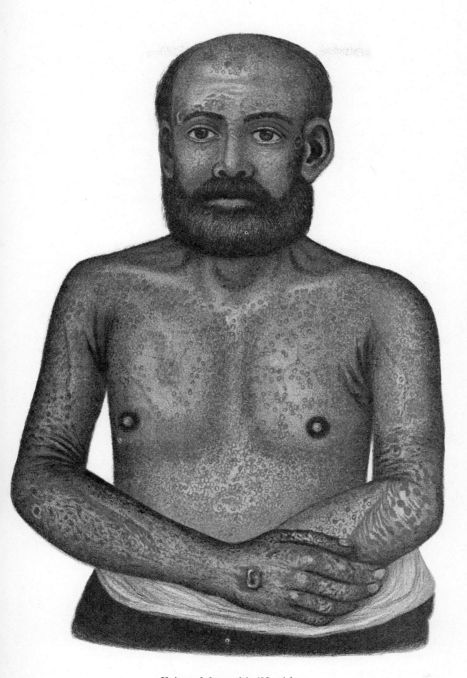

Universal dermatitis (Morris).

from "button-scurvy." Mycosis fungoides approximates, clinically and histologically, granulomata and sarcomata.

Morris [a] described an interesting case of **universal dermatitis**, probably a rare variety of mycosis fungoides (Plate 12). The patient had for many years a disease which had first appeared on the arms and legs, and which was usually regarded by the physicians who saw the case as eczema. At times the disease would entirely disappear, but it relapsed, especially during visits to India. At the time the patient came under the care of Morris, his general health seemed unaffected. The skin of the whole body, except the face, the scalp, and the front of the chest, was of a mahogany color. The skin of the lips was so thickened that it could not be pinched into folds, and was of a mottled appearance, due to hemorrhagic spots. All over the thickened and reddened surface were scattered crops of vesicles and boils. The nails were deformed, and the toes beyond the nails were tense with a serous accumulation. The glands in the right axilla and the groin were much enlarged. The hair on the pubes had disappeared. The abdomen was in a condition similar to that upon the limbs, but less in degree. The front of the chest below the nipples was covered with dark papules the size of a pin's head. The back, the buttocks, the face, and the scalp presented similar lesions. The most striking lesions were three ulcers—one on the back of the right hand, one on the right temple, and the other on the left cheek. The largest was the size of a florin, and had elevated borders, somewhat infiltrated ; they were covered with a brown, dry scab. The patient suffered from itching at night so that he could not sleep. He was kept under observation, and in spite of treatment the malady advanced in a periodic manner, each exacerbation being preceded by a feeling of tension in the parts, after which a crop of vesicles would appear. Sometimes, especially on the feet, bullæ formed. The patient finally left the hospital and died of an intercurrent attack of pneumonia. A microscopic examination revealed a condition which might be found with a number of the chronic affections of the skin, but, in addition, there were certain cell-inclusions which were thought to represent psorosperms. Morris thought this case corresponded more to mycosis fungoides than any other malady.

[a] 224, June 2, 1894.

CHAPTER XVII.

ANOMALOUS NERVOUS AND MENTAL DISEASES.

Epilepsy has been professionally recognized as a distinct type of disease since the time of Hippocrates, but in earlier times, and popularly throughout later times, it was illy defined. The knowledge of the clinical symptoms has become definite only since the era of cerebral local anatomy and localization. Examination of the older records of epilepsy shows curious forms recorded. The Ephemerides speaks of epilepsy manifested only on the birthday. Testa[758] mentions epilepsy recurring at the festival of St. John, and Bartholinus[190] reports a case in which the convulsions corresponded with the moon's phases. Paullini[620] describes epilepsy which occurred during the blowing of wind from the south, and also speaks of epilepsy during the paroxysms of which the individual barked. Fabricius[332] and the Ephemerides record dancing epilepsy. Bartholinus and Hagendorn mention cases during which various splendors appeared before the eyes during the paroxysm. Godart[a] Portius, and Salmuth[706] speak of visions occurring before and after epileptic paroxysms. The Ephemerides contains records of epilepsy in which blindness preceded the paroxysm, in which there was singing during it, and a case in which the paroxysm was attended with singultus. Various older writers mention cases of epilepsy in which curious spots appeared on the face; and the kinds of aura mentioned are too numerous to transcribe.

Baly[b] mentions a case of epilepsy occasioned by irritation in the socket of a tooth. Webber[c] reports a case of epilepsy due to phimosis and to irritation from a tooth. Beardsley[d] speaks of an attempt at strangulation that produced epilepsy. Brown-Séquard[e] records an instance produced by injury to the sciatic nerve. Doyle[f] gives an account of the production of epilepsy from protracted bathing in a pond. Duncan[g] cites an instance of epilepsy connected with vesical calculus that was cured by lithotomy. Muscroft mentions an analogous case. Greenhow[h] speaks of epilepsy arising from an injury to the thumb. Garmannus, early in the eighteenth century, describes epilepsy arising from fright and terror. Bristowe in 1880, and Farre[i] speak of similar instances. In Farre's case the disease was temporarily cured by

---

[a] 462, xiii., 393. [b] 490, xlviii., 534. [c] 218, c., 513. [d] 476, 1856, i., 454.
[e] 538, 1872, 472. [f] West. Med. and Phar. Jour., Cincin., 1828–29, ii., 454.
[g] 318, 1868–69, xiv., 140. [h] 548, 1863, i., 538. [i] 476, 1861, i., 628.

an attack of acute rheumatism. Thorington of Philadelphia has seen a paroxysm of epilepsy induced by the instillation of atropia in the eye of a child nearly cured of the malady. It was supposed that the child was terrified on awakening and finding its vision suddenly diminished, and that the convulsions were directly due to the emotional disturbance. Orwin describes epilepsy from prolonged lactation, and instances of ovarian and uterine epilepsy are quite common.

There is a peculiar case of running epilepsy recorded.[a] The patient was a workman who would be suddenly seized with a paroxysm, and unconsciously run some distance at full speed. On one occasion he ran from Peterborough to Whittlesey, where he was stopped and brought back. Once he ran into a pit containing six feet of water, from which he was rescued. Yeo[b] says that sexual intercourse occasionally induces epilepsy, and relates a case in which a severe epileptic fit terminated fatally three days after the seizure, which occurred on the nuptial night.

Drake[c] reports the case of a man who was wounded in the War of 1812, near Baltimore, the ball passing along the left ear and temple so close as to graze the skin. Eighteen years after the accident he suffered with pain in the left ear and temple, accompanied by epileptic fits and partial amnesia, together with an entire loss of power of remembering proper names and applying them to the objects to which they belonged. He would, for instance, invariably write Kentucky for Louisville. Beirne[d] records the case of a dangerous lunatic, an epileptic, who was attacked by a fellow-inmate and sustained an extensive fracture of the right parietal bone, with great hemorrhage, followed by coma. Strange to say, after the accident he recovered his intellect, and was cured of his epileptic attacks, but for six years he was a paralytic from the hips down.

The Dancing Mania.—Chorea has appeared in various epidemic forms under the names of St. Vitus's dance, St. Guy's dance, St. Anthony's dance, choromania, tanzplage, orchestromania, dance of St. Modesti or St. John, the dancing mania, etc.; although these various functional phenomena of the nervous system have been called chorea, they bear very little resemblance to what, at the present day, is called by this name. The epidemic form appeared about 1374, although Hecker[408] claims that, at that time, it was no new thing. Assemblages of men and women were seen at Aix-la-Chapelle who, impelled by a common delusion, would form circles, hand in hand, and dance in wild delirium until they fell to the ground exhausted, somewhat after the manner of the Ghost-Dance or Messiah-Dance of our North American Indians. In their Bacchantic leaps they were apparently haunted by visions and hallucinations, the fancy conjuring up spirits whose names they shrieked out. Some of them afterward stated that they appeared to be immersed in a stream of blood which obliged them to leap so high. Others saw the

a 224, 1879, ii., 78.   b 476, 1878, i., 89.   c 816, 1835.   d 312, 1843, x., 146.

heavens open and disclose the Saviour enthroned with the Virgin Mary. The participants seemed to suffer greatly from tympanites which was generally relieved by compression or thumping on the abdomen. A few months after this dancing malady had made its appearance at Aix-la-Chapelle it broke out at Cologne, and about the same time at Metz, the streets of which were said to have been filled with 1100 dancers. This rich city became the scene of the most ruinous disorder. Peasants left their plows, mechanics their ,shops, servants their masters, children their homes ; and beggars and idle vagabonds, who understood how to imitate the convulsions, roved from place to place, inducing all sorts of crime and vice among the afflicted. Strasburg was visited by the dancing plague in 1418, and it was here that the plague assumed the name of St. Vitus's dance. St. Vitus was a Sicilian youth who, just at the time he was about to undergo martyrdom by order of Diocletian, in the year 303, is said to have prayed to God that He might protect all those who would solemnize the day of his commemoration and fast upon its eve. The people were taught that a voice from heaven was then heard saying, " Vitus, thy prayer is accepted."

Paracelsus called this malady (Chorus sancti viti) the lascivious dance, and says that persons stricken with it were helpless until relieved by either recovery or death. The malady spread rapidly through France and Holland, and before the close of the century was introduced into England. In his " Anatomy of Melancholy " Burton refers to it, and speaks of the idiosyncrasies of the individuals afflicted. It is said they could not abide one in red clothes, and that they loved music above all things, and also that the magistrates in Germany hired musicians to give them music, and provided them with sturdy companions to dance with. Their endurance was marvelous. Plater speaks of a woman in Basle whom he saw, that danced for a month. In Strasburg many of them ate nothing for days and nights until their mania subsided. Paracelsus, in the beginning of the sixteenth century, was the first to make a study of this disease. He outlined the severest treatment for it, and boasted that he cured many of the victims. Hecker conjectures that probably the wild revels of St. John's day, 1374, gave rise to this mental plague, which thenceforth visited so many thousands with incurable aberrations of mind and disgusting distortions of the body. Almost simultaneous with the dance of " St. With," there appeared in Italy and Arabia a mania very similar in character which was called **" tarantism,"** which was supposed to originate in the bite of the tarantula. The only effective remedy was music in some form. In the Tigrè country, Abyssinia, this disease appeared under the name of " Tigretier." The disease, fortunately, rapidly declined, and very little of it seems to have been known in the sixteenth century, but in the early part of the eighteenth century a peculiar sect called the " Convulsionnaires " arose in France ; and throughout England among the Methodist sect, insane convulsions of this nature were witnessed ; and even to the present day in some of the primitive religious meetings of our people, something not unlike this mania of the Middle Ages is perpetuated.

Paracelsus divided the sufferers of St. Vitus's dance into three classes :—

(1) Those in which the affliction arose from imagination (chorea imaginativa).

(2) Those which had their origin in sexual desires depending on the will.

(3) Those arising from corporeal causes (chorea naturalis). This last case, according to a strange notion of his own he explained by maintaining that in certain vessels which are susceptible of an internal pruriency, and thence produced laughter, the blood is set into commotion in consequence of an alteration in the vital spirits, whereby are occasioned involuntary fits of intoxicating joy, and a propensity to dance. The great physician Sydenham gave the first accurate description of what is to-day called chorea, and hence the disease has been named "Sydenham's chorea." So true to life was his portrayal of the disease that it has never been surpassed by modern observers.

The disease variously named **palmus, the jumpers, the twitchers, lata, miryachit,** or, as it is sometimes called, the **emeryaki** of Siberia, and the tic-convulsif of La Tourette, has been very well described by Gray [a] who says that the French authors had their attention directed to the subject by the descriptions of two American authors—those of Beard upon " The Jumpers of Maine," published in 1880, and that of Hammond upon " Miryachit," a similar disease of the far Orient. Beard found that the jumpers of Maine did unhesitatingly whatever they were told to do. Thus, one who was sitting in a chair was told to throw a knife that he had in his hand, and he obeyed so quickly that the weapon stuck in a house opposite ; at the same time he repeated the command given him, with a cry of alarm not unlike that of hysteria or epilepsy. When he was suddenly clapped upon the shoulder he threw away his pipe, which he had been filling with tobacco. The first parts of Virgil's Æneid and Homer's Iliad were recited to one of these illiterate jumpers, and he repeated the words as they came to him in a sharp voice, at the same time jumping or throwing whatever he had in his hand, or raising his shoulder, or making some other violent motion. It is related by O'Brien, an Irishman serving on an English naval vessel, that an elderly and respectable Malay woman, with whom he was conversing in an entirely unsuspecting manner, suddenly began to undress herself, and showed a most ominous and determined intention of stripping herself completely, and all because a by-standing friend had suddenly taken off his coat ; at the same time she manifested the most violent anger at what she deemed this outrage to her sex, calling the astonished friend an abandoned hog, and begging O'Brien to kill him. O'Brien, furthermore, tells of a cook who was carrying his child in his arms over the bridge of a river, while at the same time a sailor carried a log of wood in like manner; the sailor threw his log

[a] 124, May, 1894, 195.

of wood on an awning, amusing himself by causing it to roll over the cloth, and finally letting it fall to the bridge ; the cook repeated every motion with his little boy, and killed him on the spot.   This miryachit was observed in Malaysia, Bengal, among the Sikhs and the Nubians, and in Siberia, whilst Beard has observed it in Michigan as well as in Maine.   Crichton [a] speaks of a leaping ague in Angusshire, Scotland.

Gray has seen only one case of acute palmus, and records it as follows : " It was in a boy of six, whose heredity, so far as I could ascertain from the statements of his mother, was not neurotic.   He had had trouble some six months before coming to me.   He had been labeled with a number of interesting diagnoses, such as chorea, epilepsy, myotonia, hysteria, and neurasthenia.   His palmodic movements were very curious.   When standing near a table looking at something, the chin would suddenly come down with a thump that would leave a black-and-blue mark, or his head would be thrown violently to one side, perhaps coming in contact with some adjacent hard object with equal force, or, while standing quietly, his legs would give a sudden twitch, and he would be thrown violently to the ground, and this even happened several times when he was seated on the edge of a stool.   The child was under my care for two weeks, and, probably because of an intercurrent attack of diarrhea, grew steadily worse during that time, in spite of the full doses of arsenic which were administered to him.   He was literally covered with bruises from the sudden and violent contacts with articles of furniture, the floor, and the walls.   At last, in despair at his condition, I ordered him to be undressed and put to bed, and steadily pushed the Fowler's solution of arsenic until he was taking ten drops three times a day, when, to my great surprise, he began to improve rapidly, and at the end of six weeks was perfectly well.   Keeping him under observation for two weeks longer I finally sent him to his home in the West, and am informed that he has since remained perfectly well.   It has seemed to me that many of the cases recorded as paramyoclonus multiplex have been really acute palmus."

Gray mentions two cases of general palmus with pseudomelancholia, and describes them in the following words :—

" The muscular movements are of the usual sudden, shock-like type, and of the same extent as in what I have ventured to çall the general form.   With them, however, there is associated a curious pseudomelancholia, consisting of certain fixed melancholy suspicious delusions, without, however, any of the suicidal tendencies and abnormal sensations up and down the back of the head, neck, or spine, or the sleeplessness, which are characteristic of most cases of true melancholia.   In both of my cases the palmus had existed for a long period, the exact limits of which, however, I could not determine, because the patient scouted the idea that he had had any trouble of the kind, but which the testimony of friends and relatives seemed to vouch for.   They were

[a] 318, 1829, 299.

both men, one thirty-six and one thirty-eight years of age. The pseudo-melancholia, however, had only existed in one case for about a year, and in the other for six months. One case passed away from my observation, and I know nothing of its further course. The other case recovered in nine months' treatment, and during the three years that have since elapsed he has been an active business man, although I have not seen him myself during that period, as he took a great dislike to me because I was forced to take strong measures to keep him under treatment, so persistent were his suspicions."

Athetosis was first described by Hammond in 1871, who gave it the name because it was mainly characterized by an inability to retain the fingers and toes in any position in which they might be placed, as well as by their continuous motion. According to Drewry [a] "athetosis is a cerebral affection, presenting a combination of symptoms characterized chiefly by a more or less constant mobility of the extremities and an inability to retain them in any fixed position. These morbid, grotesque, involuntary movements are slow and wavy, somewhat regular and rigid, are not jerky, spasmodic, nor tremulous. The movements of the digits are quite different from those attending any other disease, impossible to imitate even by the most skilful malingerer, and, if once seen, are not likely to be forgotten. In an athetoid hand, says Starr, the interossei and lumbricales, which flex the metacarpo-phalangeal and extend the phalangeal joints, are affected; rarely are the long extensors and the long flexors affected. Therefore the hand is usually in the so-called interosseal position, with flexion of the proximal and extension of the middle and distal phalanges. The athetoid movements of the toes correspond to those of the fingers in point of action. In a great majority of cases the disease is confined to one side (hemiathetosis), and is a sequel of hemiplegia. The differential diagnosis of athetosis is generally easily made. The only nervous affections with which it could possibly be confounded are chorea and paralysis agitans. Attention to the twitching, spasmodic, fibrillary movements, having a quick beginning and a quick ending, which is characteristic in Sydenham's chorea, would at once exclude that disease. These jerky movements peculiar to St. Vitus's dance may be easily detected in a few or many muscles, if moderate care and patience be exercised on the part of the examiner. This form of chorea is almost always a disease of childhood. So-called post-hemiplegic chorea is, in the opinion of both Hammond and Gray, simply athetosis. The silly, dancing, posturing, wiry movements, and the facial distortion observed in Huntington's chorea would hardly be mistaken by a careful observer for athetosis. The two diseases, however, are somewhat alike. Paralysis agitans (shaking palsy), with its coarse tremor, peculiar facies, immobility, shuffling gait, the 'bread-crumbling' attitude of the fingers, and deliberate speech, would be readily eliminated even by a novice. It is, too, a disease of advanced

a 809, May, 1895.

life, usually.   Charcot, Gray, Ringer, Bernhardt, Shaw, Eulenberg, Grasset, Kinnicutt, Sinkler, and others have written on this affection."

The following is the report of a case by Drewry, of double (or, more strictly speaking, quadruple) athetosis, associated with epilepsy and insanity : "The patient was a negro woman, twenty-six years old when she was admitted into this, the Central State (Va.) Hospital, in April, 1886.   She had had epilepsy of the *grand mal* type for a number of years, was the mother of one child, and earned her living as a domestic.   A careful physical examination revealed nothing of importance as an etiologic factor.   Following in the footsteps of many of those unfortunates afflicted with epilepsy, she degenerated into a state of almost absolute imbecility.

"Some degree of mental deficiency seems usually to accompany athetosis, even when uncomplicated by any other degenerating neurosis.   Athetoid symptoms of an aggravated character, involving both upper and both lower extremities, had developed previous to her admission into this hospital, but it was impossible to find out when and how they began.   She had never had, to the knowledge of her friends, an attack of 'apoplexy,' nor of paralysis. The head was symmetric, and without scars thereon.   The pedal extremities involuntarily assumed various distorted positions and were constantly in motion. The toes were usually in a state of tonic spasm,—contracted, and drawn downward or extended, pointing upward, and slightly separated.   Irregular alternate extension and flexion of the toes were marked.   The feet were moved upon the ankles in a stiff and awkward manner.   During these 'complex involuntary movements,' the muscles of the calf became hard and rigid.   The act of walking was accomplished with considerable difficulty, on account of contractures, and because the feet were not exactly under the control of the will.   The unnatural movements of the hands corresponded to those of the lower extremities, though they were more constant and active.   The fingers, including the thumbs, were usually widely separated and extended, though they were sometimes slightly flexed.   The hands were continually in slow, methodic, quasi-rhythmic motion, never remaining long in the same attitude.   In grasping an object the palm of the hand was used, it being difficult to approximate the digits.   The wrist-joints were also implicated, there being alternate flexion and extension.   In fact these odd contortions affected the entire limb from the shoulder to the digital extremities.   When standing or walking the arms were held out horizontally, as if to maintain the equilibrium of the body.   The patient's general physical health was fairly good. She frequently complained of headache, and when she was exceedingly irritable and violent all the athetoid movements would be intensified.   Speech was jerky and disordered, which gave it a distinctive character.   The special senses seemed to be unimpaired, and the pupils were normal, except when an epileptic attack came on.   Death occurred in January, 1895, after an obstinate attack of status epilepticus."

Paramyoclonus multiplex is a condition of chronic muscular spasm affecting the trunk, occasionally the muscles of the face, abdomen, or diaphragm. The muscles affected are usually in the trunk and in the limbs, and not in the toes and hand; occasionally the movements are tonic as well as clonic; the degree of spasm varies greatly, and according to Gray may sometimes be so violent as to throw the patient down or out of the chair.

Saltatoric spasm is an extremely rare condition, first observed by Bamberger in 1859. The calf, hip, knee, and back-muscles are affected by clonic spasm, causing springing or jumping movements when the patient attempts to stand. The disease is transient, and there are no mental symptoms.

Progressive muscular atrophy has been observed as far back as Hippocrates, but it is only in recent times that we have had any definite knowledge

Fig. 295.—Facial hemiatrophy (Dana).

of the subject. It is divided into four types, the hand type (causing the griffin- or claw-hand, or the ape-hand); the juvenile type (generally in the muscles of the shoulder and arm); the facial type; and the peroneal type. Generalized progressive atrophy leads to a condition that simulates the appearance of a " living skeleton."

Facial hemiatrophy is an incurable disease, as yet of unknown pathology. It consists of wasting of the bones, subcutaneous tissues, and muscles of one-half of the face or head, the muscles suffering but slightly. The accompanying illustration (Fig. 295) shows a case in which there was osseous depression of the cranium and a localized alopecia. The disease is very rare, only about 100 cases having been reported. Of five cases seen by Dana, three were in females and two in males; in all the cases that could be found the origin was between the tenth and twentieth years. It is a chronic affection, usually beginning in early life, increasing slowly for years, and then becoming stationary. It is distinguished from one-sided muscular atrophy by the electric reaction, which is not lost in the facial muscles in facial hemiatrophy, and there is no atrophy of other muscles of the body.

Burr [a] contributes an exhaustive paper on **hemiatrophy of the tongue** with report of a case as follows: " L. B., female, mulatto, thirty-one years old, married, came to the Medico-Chirurgical Hospital, Philadelphia, September 23, 1895, complaining that her 'tongue was crooked.' Save that she had had syphilis, her personal history is negative. In February, 1895, she began to suffer from headache, usually behind the left ear, and often preventing sleep. At times there is quite severe vertigo. Several weeks after the onset, headache persisting, she awoke in the night and found the left side of the tongue swollen, black, and painless. For some hours she could neither speak nor chew, but breathing was not interfered with. After a few days all symptoms passed away except headache, and she thought no more of the matter until recently, as stated above, she noticed by accident that her tongue was deformed. She is a spare, poorly-fed, muddy-skinned mulatto girl. The left half of the tongue is only about one-half as large as the right. The upper surface is irregularly depressed and elevated. There are no scars. When protruded it turns sharply to the left. Fibrillary twitching is not present. The mucous membrane is normal. Common sensation and taste are preserved. The pharyngeal reflex is present. The palate moves well. There is no palsy or wasting of the face. The pupils are of normal size and react well to light and with accommodation. Station and gait are normal. There is no incoordination of movement in the arms or legs. The knee-jerks are much increased. There is an attempt at, but no true, clonus ; that is, passive flexion of the foot causes two or three jerky movements. There is no glandular swelling or tumor about the jaw or in the neck. Touch and pain-sense are normal in the face and hands, but she complains of numbness in the hands as if she had on tight gloves. There is no trouble in speaking, chewing, or swallowing. There is no pain or rigidity in the neck muscles. Examination of the pharynx reveals no disease of the bones. Under specific treatment the patient improved."

Astasia-abasia was named by Blocq, who collected 11 cases. According to Knapp, four cases have been reported in America. The disease consists in an inability to stand erect or walk normally, although there is no impairment of sensation, of muscular strength, or of the coordination of other muscles in walking than the lower extremities. In attempting to walk the legs become spasmodic ; there are rapid flexions and extensions of the legs on the thighs, and of the thighs on the pelvis. The steps are short, and the feet drag ; the body may make great oscillations if the patient stands, walks, or sits, and the head and arms make rhythmical movements ; walking

a 466, July, 1896.

may become impossible, the patient appearing to leap up on one foot and then up on the other, the body and head oscillating as he advances ; he may be able to walk cross-legged, or by raising the legs high ; or to walk on his hands and feet ; he may be able to walk at certain times and not at others ; or to hop with both feet together ; he may succeed with great strides and with the arms extended ; or finally he may be able to use his legs perfectly if suspended (Gray). There are various types which have been called the paralytic, the choreic, and the saltatory. A tendency to go backward or **retropulsion** has been observed, according to Gray, as has also a tendency to go forward or **propulsion**. A curious phenomenon in this disease is that the patient can use the legs perfectly well lying in bed. The prognosis seems to be favorable.

Ménière's disease is a disease probably of the semicircular canals, characterized by nausea, vomiting, vertigo, deafness, tinnitus aurium, and various other phenomena. It is also called aural or auditory vertigo. The salient symptom is vertigo, and this varies somewhat in degree according to the portions of the ear affected. If the disease is in the labyrinth, the patient is supposed to stagger to one side, and the vertigo is paroxysmal, varying to such a degree as to cause simple reeling, or falling as if shot. Gray [a] reports the history of a patient with this sensational record : He had been a peasant in Ireland, and one day crossing one of the wide moors in a dog-cart, he was suddenly, as he thought, struck a violent blow from behind, so that he believed that he lost consciousness for some time. At all events, when he was able to get up he found his horse and cart some distance off, and, of course, not a soul in sight. Under the belief that he had been struck by some enemy he went quietly home and said nothing about it. Some time afterward, however, in crossing another lonely place he had a similar experience, and as he came to the conclusion that nobody could have been near him, he made up his mind that it was some malevolent stroke of the devil, and he consulted a priest who agreed with him in his belief, and gave him an amulet to wear. A series of similar attacks occurred and puzzled as to whether there was some diabolical agency at work, or whether he was the victim of some conspiracy, he emigrated to America ; for several months he had no attacks. A new paroxysm occurring he consulted Gray, who found indubitable evidence of labyrinthine disease. The paroxysms of this disease are usually accompanied by nausea and vomiting, and on account of the paleness of the face, and the cold, clammy perspiration, attacks have frequently been mistaken for apoplexy. In disease of the middle ear the attacks are continuous rather than paroxysmal. If the disease is in the middle or internal ears, loud noises are generally heard, but if the disease is in the external ear, the noises are generally absent, and the vertigo of less degree but continuous. The prognosis varies with the location of the disease, but is always serious.

[a] "Treatise on Mental and Nervous Diseases," Phila., 1893, 522.

Human rumination has been known for many years. Bartholinus, Paullinus, Blanchard, Bonet, the Ephemerides, Fabricius Hildanus, Horstius, Morgagni, Peyer, Rhodius, Vogel, Salmuth, Percy, Laurent, and others describe it. Fabricius d'Aquapendente personally knew a victim of rumination, or, as it is generally called, **merycism.** The dissection by Bartholinus of a merycol showed nothing extraordinary in the cadaver. Winthier [a] knew a Swede of thirty-five, in Germany, apparently healthy, but who was obliged when leaving the table to retire to some remote place where he might eject his food into his mouth again, saying that it gave him the sensation of sweetest honey. The patient related that from his infancy he had been the subject of acid eructations, and at the age of thirty he commenced rumination as a means of relief. To those who are interested in the older records of these cases Percy and Laurent [b] offer the descriptions of a number of cases.

In a recent discussion before the American Neurological Association Hammond defined merycism as the functions of remastication and rumination in the human subject. He referred to several cases, among them that of the distinguished physiologist, Brown-Séquard, who acquired the habit as a result of experiments performed upon himself. Hammond reported a case of a young man who was the subject of merycism, and whose mental condition was also impaired. No special treatment was undertaken, but the patient was trephined, with the purpose of improving his mental condition. There were no unusual features connected with the operation, but it was noticed that there were no ruminations with the meals he took until the fifth day, when a slight rumination occurred. Eight days later a similar button was removed from the corresponding side of the left skull, and from that time (about six months) to the time of report, there had been no regurgitation. Whether the cure of the merycism in this case was directly due to the operations on the cranium, or the result of the mental improvement, is a question for discussion. Hammond added that, when acquired, merycism was almost invariably the result of over-eating and loading the esophagus, or the result of fast eating.

In remarks upon Hammond's paper Knapp said that two cases had come to his knowledge, both in physicians, but one of them he knew of only by hearsay. The other man, now over thirty, had regurgitated his food from early childhood, and he did not know that he had anything very unusual the matter with him until he began some investigations upon the functions and diseases of the stomach. This man was not nervous, and was certainly not an idiot. He had done active work as a physician, and called himself in perfect health. He was something of an epicure, and never suffered from indigestion. After a hearty meal the regurgitation was more marked. Food had been regurgitated, tasting as good as when first eaten, several hours after the eating. If he attempted to check the regurgitation he sometimes had a slight feeling of fulness in the stomach. Lloyd said that these cases were forms of neuroses, and were types of hysteric vomiting. There was no gustatory satisfaction connected with any form of hysteric vomiting that he had seen. In some of these cases of hysteric vomiting the food does not appear to enter the stomach, but is rejected by a sort of spasm of the esophagus. This has been called " esophagismus," and is apparently closely allied to this neurosis, which some have called " merycism." The President of the Association said that this would seem to be an affection common among physicians. A student friend of his who had been affected in this way, had written an elaborate monograph on the subject. He was disgusted with the habit, and finally overcame it by the exercise of his will-power.

Runge[a] discusses three cases of hereditary rumination. These patients belonged to three generations in the male line. The author subjected the contents of the stomach of one patient to quite an extensive analysis, without finding any abnormality of secretion.

Wakefulness.—Generally speaking, the length of time a person can go without sleep is the same as that during which he can survive without food. Persons, particularly those of an hysteric nature, are prone to make statements that they have not slept for many days, or that they never sleep at all, but a careful examination and watch during the night over these patients show that they have at least been in a drowsy, somnolent condition, which is in a measure physiologically equivalent to sleep. Accounts of long periods of wakefulness arise from time to time, but a careful examination would doubtless disprove them. As typical of these accounts, we quote one from Anderson, Indiana, December 11, 1895 :—

" David Jones of this city, who attracted the attention of the entire medical profession two years ago by a sleepless spell of ninety-three days, and last year by another spell which extended over one hundred and thirty-one days, is beginning on another which he fears will be more serious than the preceding ones. He was put on the circuit jury three weeks ago, and counting to-day has not slept for twenty days and nights. He eats and talks as well as usual, and is full of business and activity. He does not experience any bad effects whatever from the spell, nor did he during his one hundred and thirty-one days. During that spell he attended to all of his farm business. He says now that he feels as though he never will sleep again. He does not seem to bother himself about the prospects of a long and tedious wake. He cannot attribute it to any one thing, but thinks that it was probably superinduced by his use of tobacco while young."

Somnambulism, or, as it has been called, noctambulation, is a curious phase of nocturnal cerebration analogous to the hypnotic state, or double consciousness occasionally observed in epileptics. Both Hippocrates and Aristotle discuss somnambulism, and it is said that the physician Galen was a vic-

a 218, May 23, 1895.

tim of this habit.   Horstius, ab Heers, and many others of the older writers recorded interesting examples of this phenomenon.   Schenck remarks on the particular way in which somnambulists seem to escape injury.   Haller, Hoffmann, Gassendi, Caelius Rhodiginus, Pinel, Hechler, Bohn, Richter,—in fact nearly all the ancient physiologists and anatomists have written on this subject.   The marvelous manifestations of somnambulism are still among the more surprising phenomena with which science has to deal.   That a person deeply immersed in thought should walk and talk while apparently unconscious, excites no surprise, but that anyone should when fast asleep perform a series of complicated actions which undoubtedly demand the assistance of the senses is marvelous indeed.   Often he will rise in the night, walk from room to room, go out on porticoes, and in some cases on steep roofs, where he would not dare to venture while awake.   Frequently he will wander for hours through streets and fields, returning home and to bed without knowledge of anything having transpired.

The state of the eyes during somnambulism varies considerably.   They are sometimes closed, sometimes half-closed, and frequently quite open ; the pupil is sometimes widely dilated, sometimes contracted, sometimes natural, and for the most part insensible to light.

Somnambulism seems to be hereditary.   Willis cites an example in which the father and the children were somnambulists, and in other cases several individuals in the same family have been afflicted.   Horstius gives a history of three young brothers who became somnambulistic at the same epoch.   A remarkable instance of somnambulism [a] was the case of a lad of sixteen and a half years who, in an attack of somnambulism, went to the stable, saddled his horse, asked for his whip, and disputed with the toll-keeper about his fare, and when he awoke had no recollection whatever of his acts, having been altogether an hour in his trance.

Marville [b] quotes the case of an Italian of thirty, melancholic, and a deep thinker, who was observed one evening in his bed.   It was seen that he slept with his eyes open but fixed and immovable.   His hands were cold, and his pulse extremely slow.   At midnight he brusquely tore the curtains of his bed aside, dressed himself, went to his stable, and mounted a horse.   Finding the gate of the court-yard closed he opened it with the aid of a large stone.   Soon he dismounted, went to a billiard room, and simulated all the movements of one playing.   In another room he struck with his empty hands a harpsichord, and finally returned to his bed.   He appeared to be irritated when anybody made a noise, but a light placed under his nose was apparently unnoticed.   He awoke if his feet were tickled, or if a horn was blown in his ear.   Tissot transmits to us the example of a medical student who arose in the night, pursued his studies, and returned to bed without awaking ; and there is another record of an ecclesiastic who finished his sermon in his sleep.

a 476, 1823, 40.   b Mél. d'hist. et de litt., T. i., 242.

The Archbishop of Bordeaux attests the case of a young ecclesiastic who was in the habit of getting up during the night in a state of somnambulism, taking pen, ink, and paper, and composing and writing sermons. When he had finished a page he would read aloud what he had written and correct it. In order to ascertain whether the somnambulist made any use of his eyes the Archbishop held a piece of cardboard under his chin to prevent his seeing the paper upon which he was writing. He continued to write without being in the slightest degree incommoded. In this state he also copied out pieces of music, and when it happened that the words were written in too large characters and did not stand over the corresponding notes he perceived his error, blotted them out, and wrote them over again with great exactness.

Negretti, a sleep-walker, sometimes carried a candle about with him as if to furnish him light in his employment, but when a bottle was substituted he carried it, fancying that he had the candle. Another somnambulist, Castelli, was found by Dr. Sloane translating Italian and French and looking out words in his dictionary. His candle was purposely extinguished, whereupon he immediately began groping about, as if in the dark, and, although other lighted candles were in the room, he did not resume his occupation until he had relighted his candle at the fire. He was insensible to the light of every candle excepting the one upon which his attention was fixed.

Tuke tells of a school-boy who being unable to master a school-problem in geometry retired to bed still thinking of the subject; he was found late at night by his instructor on his knees pointing from spot to spot as though he were at the blackboard. He was so absorbed that he paid no attention to the light of the candle, nor to the speech addressed to him. The next morning the teacher asked him if he had finished his problem, and he replied that he had, having dreamt it and remembered the dream. There are many such stories on record. Quoted by Gray, Mesnet speaks of a suicidal attempt made in his presence by a somnambulistic woman. She made a noose of her apron, fastened one end to a chair and the other to the top of a window. She then kneeled down in prayer, made the sign of the cross, mounted a stool, and tried to hang herself. Mesnet, scientific to the utmost, allowed her to hang as long as he dared, and then stopped the performance. At another time she attempted to kill herself by violently throwing herself on the floor after having failed to fling herself out of the window. At still another time she tried poison, filling a glass with water, putting several coins into it, and hiding it after bidding farewell to her family in writing; the next night, when she was again somnambulistic, she changed her mind once more, writing to her family explaining her change of purpose. Mesnet relates some interesting experiments made upon a French sergeant in a condition of somnambulism, demonstrating the excitation of ideas in the mind through the sense of touch in the extremities. This soldier touched a table, passed his hands over it, and finding nothing on it, opened the drawer, took out a pen, found paper

and an inkstand, and taking a chair he sat down and wrote to his commanding officer speaking of his bravery, and asking for a medal. A thick metallic
plate was then placed before his eyes so as to completely intercept vision.
After a few minutes, during which he wrote a few words with a jumbled
stroke, he stopped, but without any petulance. The plate was removed and he
went on writing. Somnambulism may assume such a serious phase as to result in the commission of murder. There is a case [a] of a man of twenty-
seven, of steady habits, who killed his child when in a state of somnambulism.
He was put on trial for murder, and some of the most remarkable facts of
his somnambulistic feats were elicited in the evidence. It is said that once
when a boy he arose at night while asleep, dressed himself, took a pitcher
and went for milk to a neighboring farm, as was his custom. At another
time he worked in a lumber-yard in a rain-storm while asleep. Again, when
about twenty-one, he was seen in a mill-pond wading about attempting to save
his sister who he imagined was drowning. The worst phase of his somnambulism was the impending fears and terrible visions to which he was subjected. Sometimes he would imagine that the house was on fire and the
walls about to fall upon him, or that a wild beast was attacking his wife and
child ; and he would fight, screaming inarticulately all the while. He would
chase the imaginary beast about the room, and in fact had grasped one of his
companions, apparently believing he was in a struggle with a wild beast. He
had often injured himself in these struggles, and had often attacked his
father, his wife, sister, fellow-lodgers, and while confined in jail he attacked
one of his fellow-prisoners. His eyes would always be wide open and star-
ing ; he was always able to avoid pieces of furniture which were in his
way, and he occasionally threw them at his visionary enemies. At the time
of the murder of his child, in a somnambulistic attack, he imagined that he
saw a wild beast rise up from the floor and fly at his child, a babe of eighteen
months. He sprang at the beast and dashed it to the ground, and when
awakened, to his horror and overwhelming grief he found that he had killed
his beloved baby. A similar record has been reported of a student who attempted during the night to stab his teacher ; the man was disarmed and
locked up in another portion of the building ; but he had not the slightest
remembrance of the events of the night.

Yellowlees [b] speaks of homicide by a somnambulist. According to a
prominent New York paper, one of the most singular and at the same time
sad cases of somnambulism occurred a few years ago near Bakersville, N. C.
A young man there named Garland had been in the habit of walking in his
sleep since childhood. Like most other sleep-walkers when unmolested, his
ramblings had been without harm to himself or others. Consequently his wife
paid little attention to them. But finally he began to stay away from the
house longer than usual and always returned soaking wet. His wife followed

a Glasgow Med. Jour., 1878, p. 371.   b 465, 1878, 451.

him one night. Leaving his home he followed the highway until he came to a rough, narrow pig-trail leading to the Tow River. His wife followed with difficulty, as he picked his way through the tangled forest, over stones and fallen trees and along the sides of precipitous cliffs. For more than a mile the sleeper trudged on until he came to a large poplar tree, which had fallen with its topmost branches far out in the river. Walking on the log until he came to a large limb extending over the water, he got down on his hands and knees and began crawling out on it. The frightened wife screamed, calling to him to wake up and come back. He was awakened by the cries, fell into the river, and was drowned. Each night for weeks he had been taking that perilous trip, crawling out on the limb, leaping from it into the river, swimming to the shore, and returning home unconscious of anything having happened.

Dreams, nightmare, and night terrors form too extensive a subject and one too well known to be discussed at length here, but it might be well to mention that sometimes dreams are said to be **pathognomonic or prodromal of approaching disease.** Cerebral hemorrhage has often been preceded by dreams of frightful calamities, and intermittent fever is often announced by persistent and terrifying dreams. Hammond has collected a large number of these prodromic dreams, seeming to indicate that before the recognizable symptoms of disease present themselves a variety of morbid dreams may occur. According to Dana, Albers says: " Frightful dreams are signs of cerebral congestion. Dreams about fire are, in women, signs of impending hemorrhage. Dreams about blood and red objects are signs of inflammatory conditions. Dreams of distorted forms are frequently a sign of abdominal obstruction and diseases of the liver."

Catalepsy, trance, and lethargy, lasting for days or weeks, are really examples of spontaneously developed mesmeric sleep in hysteric patients or subjects of incipient insanity. If the phenomenon in these cases takes the form of catalepsy there is a waxy-like rigidity of the muscles which will allow the limbs to be placed in various positions, and maintain them so for minutes or even hours. In lethargy or trance-states the patient may be plunged into a deep and prolonged unconsciousness lasting from a few hours to several years. It is in this condition that the lay journals find argument for their stories of premature burial, and from the same source the fabulous " sleeping girls " of the newspapers arise. Dana says that some persons are in the habit of going into a mesmeric sleep spontaneously. In these states there may be a lowering of bodily temperature, a retarding of the respiration and heart-action, and excessive sluggishness of the action of the bowels. The patients can hear and may respond to suggestions, though apparently insensible to painful impressions, and do not appear to smell, taste, or see ; the eyes are closed, turned upward, and the pupils contracted as in normal sleep.

This subject has been investigated by such authorities as Weir Mitchell and Hammond, and medical literature is full of interesting cases, many differing in the physiologic phenomena exhibited ; some of the most striking of these will be quoted. Van Kasthoven of Leyden reports a strange case of a peasant of Wolkwig who, it is alleged, fell asleep on June 29, 1706, awakening on January 11, 1707, only to fall asleep again until March 15th of the same year. Tuke has resurrected the remarkable case reported by Arnold of Leicester, early in this century. The patient's name was John Engelbrecht. This man passed into a condition of catalepsy in which he heard everything about him distinctly, but in his imagination he seemed to have passed away to another world, this condition coming on with a suddenness which he describes as with " far more swiftness than any arrow can fly when discharged from a cross-bow." He also lost his sensation from the head downward, and recovered it in the opposite direction. At Bologna there was observed the case of a young female who after a profound grief had for forty-two successive days a state of catalepsy lasting from midday to midnight. [a] Muller of Lowenburg [468] records a case of lethargy in a young female, following a sudden fright in her fourteenth year, and abrupt suppression of menstruation. This girl was really in a sleep for four years. In the first year she was awake from one minute to six hours during the day. In the second and third years she averaged four hours wakefulness in ninety-six hours. She took very little nourishment and sometimes had no bowel-movement for sixteen days. Scull [b] reports the history of a man of twenty-seven suffering with incipient phthisis, who remained bedridden and in a state of unconsciousness for fifteen months. One day while being fed he spoke out and asked for a glass of water in his usual manner, and so frightened his sister that she ran from the room. The man had remembered nothing that had occurred during the fifteen months, and asked who was president and seemed eager for news. One curious fact was that he remembered a field of oats which was just sprouting about the time he fell in the trance. The same field was now standing in corn knee-high. After his recovery from the trance he rapidly became worse and died in eighteen months. There is a record [c] of a man near Rochester, N. Y., who slept for five years, never waking for more than sixteen hours at a time, and then only at intervals of six weeks or over. When seized with his trance he weighed 160, but he dwindled down to 90 pounds. He passed urine once or twice a day, and had a stool once in from six to twenty days. Even such severe treatment as counter-irritation proved of no avail. Gunson [d] mentions a man of forty-four, a healthy farmer, who, after being very wet and not changing his clothes, contracted a severe cold and entered into a long and deep sleep lasting for twelve hours at a time, during which it was impossible to waken him. This attack lasted eight or nine months, but in 1848 there was a recurrence accompanied by a slight trismus which lasted over eighteen months, and again

a 476, 1832–33, i., 663.   b 131, 1874.   c 596, 1853.   d 224, June 13, 1863.

in 1860 he was subjected to periods of sleep lasting over twenty-four hours at a time. Blaudet [a] describes a young woman of eighteen who slept forty days, and again after her marriage in her twentieth year she slept for fifty days ; it was necessary to draw a tooth to feed her. Four years later, on Easter day, 1862, she became insensible for twelve months, with the exception of the eighth day, when she awoke and ate at the table, but fell asleep in the chair. Her sleep was so deep that nothing seemed to disturb her ; her pulse was slow, the respirations scarcely perceptible, and there were apparently no evacuations.

Weir Mitchell [b] collected 18 cases of protracted sleep, the longest continuing uninterruptedly for six months. Chilton's case lasted seventeen weeks. Six of the 18 cases passed a large part of each day in sleep, one case twenty-one hours, and another twenty-three hours. The patients were below middle life ; ten were females, seven males, and one was a child whose sex was not given. Eight of the 18 recovered easily and completely, two recovered with loss of intellect, one fell a victim to apoplexy four months after awakening, one recovered with insomnia as a sequel, and four died in sleep. One recovered suddenly after six months' sleep and began to talk, resuming the train of thought where it had been interrupted by slumber. Mitchell reports a case in an unmarried woman of forty-five. She was a seamstress of dark complexion and never had any previous symptoms. On July 20, 1865, she became seasick in a gale of wind on the Hudson, and this was followed by an occasional loss of sight and by giddiness. Finally, in November she slept from Wednesday night to Monday at noon, and died a few days later. Jones of New Orleans [c] relates the case of a girl of twenty-seven who had been asleep for the last eighteen years, only waking at certain intervals, and then remaining awake from seven to ten minutes. The sleep commenced at the age of nine, after repeated large doses of quinin and morphin. Periods of consciousness were regular, waking at 6 A. M. and every hour thereafter until noon, then at 3 P. M., again at sunset, and at 9 P. M., and once or twice before morning. The sleep was deep, and nothing seemed to arouse her. Gairdner [d] mentions the case of a woman who, for one hundred and sixty days, remained in a lethargic stupor, being only a mindless automaton. Her life was maintained by means of the stomach tube. The Revue d'Hypnotisme contains the report of a young woman of twenty-five, who was completing the fourth year of an uninterrupted trance. She began May 30, 1883, after a fright, and on the same day, after several convulsive attacks, she fell into a profound sleep, during which she was kept alive by small quantities of liquid food, which she swallowed automatically. The excretions were greatly diminished, and menstruation was suppressed. There is a case reported [e] of a Spanish soldier of twenty-two, confined in the Mili-

a 548, 1864, ii., 518.   b 768, iii.   c 538, May 1, 1869.

d 476, 1884, i., 5.   e Quoted 476, 1885, ii., 354.

tary Hospital of San Ambrosio, Cuba, who had been in a cataleptic state for fourteen months. His body would remain in any position in which it was placed; defecation and micturition were normal; he occasionally sneezed or coughed, and is reported to have uttered some words at night. The strange feature of this case was that the man was regularly nourished and increased in weight ten pounds. It was noted that, some months before, this patient was injured and had suffered extreme depression, which was attributed to nostalgia, after which he began to have intermittent and temporary attacks, which culminated as related. Camuset and Planés in January, 1896, [144] mention a man who began to have grand hallucinations in 1883. In March, 1884, he exhibited the first signs of sleep, and on March 10th it was necessary to put him to bed, where he remained, more or less continuously for three months, awakening gradually, and regaining his normal condition by the middle of June. He was fed by hand three times daily, was placed on a night-chair, and with one exception never evacuated in bed. Five months afterward he showed no signs of relapse. The latest report of a "sleeping girl" is that of the young Dutch maiden, Maria Cvetskens, of Stevenswerth, who on December 5, 1895, had been asleep for two hundred and twenty days. She had been visited by a number of men of good professional standing who, although differing as to the cause of her prolonged sleep, universally agreed that there was no deception in the case. Her parents were of excellent repute, and it had never occurred to them to make any financial profit out of the unnatural state of their daughter.

Hypnotism.—The phenomenon of hypnotism was doubtless known to the Oriental nations, and even to the Greeks, Romans, and Egyptians, as well as to other nations since the downfall of the Roman Empire. "The fakirs of India, the musicians of Persia, the oracles of Greece, the seers of Rome, the priests and priestesses of Egypt, the monastic recluses of the Middle Ages, the ecstatics of the seventeenth and early part of the eighteenth century exhibited many symptoms that were, and are still, attributed by religious enthusiasts to supernatural agencies, but which are explainable by what we know of hypnotism. The Hesychasts of Mount Athos who remained motionless for days with their gaze directed steadily to the navel; the Taskodrugites who remained statuesque for a long period with the finger applied to the nose; the Jogins who could hibernate at will; the Dandins of India who became cataleptoid by 12,000 repetitions of the sacred word 'Om;' St. Simeon Stylites who, perched on a lofty pillar, preserved an attitude of saint-like withdrawal from earthly things for days; and even Socrates, of whom it was said that he would stand for hours motionless and wordless—all these are probable instances of autohypnotism." (Gray.)

Hypnotism is spoken of as a morbid mental state artificially produced, and characterized by perversion or suspension of consciousness, and abeyance of volition; a condition of suggestibility leads the patient to yield readily to commands of external sense-impressions, and there is intense concentration of the mental faculties upon some idea or feeling. There are several methods of inducing hypnosis, one of which is to give particular direction to the subject's imagination by concentrating the attention upon an arbitrary point, or by raising an image of the hypnotic state in the patient's mind. The latter is most readily induced by speech. Faria formerly strained the attention of the subject as much as possible, and suddenly called out, "Sleep!" This method has been used by others. Physical methods consist of certain stimuli of sight, hearing, and touch. Taste and smell have generally given negative results. Fixation of the gaze has been the most successful, but the ticking of a watch has been used. According to Moll, among uncivilized races particular instruments are used to produce similar states, for example, the magic drum's sound among the Lapps, or among other races the monotony of rhythm in song, etc. Instead of these continuous, monotonous, weak stimulations of the senses, we find also that sudden and violent ones are made use of—for example in the Salpêtrière, the field of Charcot's work, the loud noise of a gong, or a sudden ray of light; however, it is more than doubtful whether these sudden, strong, physical stimuli, without any mental stimuli, can induce hypnosis. Perhaps we have to do here with states not far removed from paralysis from fright. The sense of touch is also brought into play in hypnosis; Richet set great value on the so-called mesmeric strokes or passes. It is often stated that touches on the forehead induce a sleepy state in many persons. Hypnotism is practised by stimulation of the muscular sense, such as cradle-rocking, used to send little children to sleep. Similar states are said to be produced among uncivilized people by violent whirling or dancing movements; the movements are, however, accompanied by music and other mental excitations.

Hypnosis is spoken of by Huc and Hellwald of the Buddhist convents in Thibet; and Sperling, who has had a particularly wide experience in the field of hypnotism, and whose opinion is of particular value, says that he has seen dervishes in Constantinople who, from the expression of their eyes and their whole appearance, as well as from peculiar postures they maintain for a long time, impressed him as being in a hypnotic state. The state may have been induced by singing and uniform whirling motions. Hildebrandt, Jacolliot, Fischer, Hellwald, and other trustworthy witnesses and authors tell us strange things about the fakirs of India, which set any attempt at explanation on the basis of our present scientific knowledge at defiance—that is, if we decline to accept them as mere juggler's tricks. Hypnotism seems to be the only explanation. It is a well known fact that both wild and domestic beasts can be hypnotized and the success of some of the animal-tamers is due to this fact. In hypnotism we see a probable explanation for the faith-cures which have extended over many centuries, and have their analogy in the supposed therapeutic powers of the Saints.

The medicolegal aspect of hypnotism may be called in to answer whether crime may be committed at suggestion. Such examples have already been before the public in the recent trial of the Parisian strangler, Eyraud. It was claimed that his accomplice in the crime, Gabrielle Bompard, had been hypnotized. Bernheim narrates a case of outrage effected in the hypnotic condition, which was brought to light by a trial in the South of France.

As to the therapeutic value of hypnotism, with the exception of some minor benefits in hysteric cases and in insomnia, the authors must confess that its use in Medicine seems very limited.

African sleep-sickness is a peculiar disorder, apparently infectious in character, which occurs among the negroes of the western coast of Africa. It has been transported to other regions but is endemic in Africa. According to Dana it begins gradually with malaise and headache. Soon there is drowsiness after meals which increases until the patient is nearly all the time in a stupor. When awake he is dull and apathetic. There is no fever; the temperature may be subnormal. The pulse, too, is not rapid, the skin is dry, the tongue moist but coated, the bowels regular. The eyes become congested and prominent. The cervical glands enlarge. The disease ends in coma and death. Recovery rarely occurs. Sometimes the disease is more violent, and toward the end there are epileptic convulsions and muscular tremors. Autopsies have revealed no pathologic changes.

Recently Forbes [a] contributes an interesting paper on the sleeping sickness of Africa. The disease may occur in either sex and at any age, though it is most frequent from the twelfth to the twentieth years, and in the male sex. It begins with enlargement of the cervical glands, and drowsiness and sleep at unusual hours. At first the patient may be aroused, but later sinks into a heavy stupor or coma. Death occurs in from three to twelve months, and is due to starvation. Forbes reports 11 fatal cases, and two that passed from observation. At the autopsy are found hyperemia of the arachnoid, and slight chronic leptomeningitis and pachymeningitis. There is also anemia of the brain-substance. In one of his cases the spleen was enlarged. He was inclined to regard the disease as a neurosis.

Aphasia is a disease of the faculty of language, that is, a disturbance of the processes by which we see, hear, and at the same time appreciate the meaning of symbols. It includes also the faculty of expressing our ideas to others by means of the voice, gesture, writing, etc. The trouble may be central or in the conducting mediâ. The varieties of aphasia are :—

(1) Amnesia of speech.

(2) Amnesia of speech and written language.

(3) Amnesia of speech, written language, and gesture.

In most cases there is no paralysis of the tongue or speech-forming organs. As a rule the intellect is unaffected, the patient has the ideas, but lacks the

a 476, May 19, 1894.

power to give them proper expression through words, written language, or gesture. If the patient is unable to write, the condition is known as agraphia. Word-blindness, word-deafness, etc., are terms of different forms of aphasia.

What was probably a case of incomplete aphasia is mentioned by Pliny, that of Messala Corvinus who was unable to tell his own name; and many instances of persons forgetting their names are really nothing but cases of temporary or incomplete aphasia. In some cases of incomplete and in nearly all cases of complete aphasia, involuntary sentences are ejaculated. According to Seguin [a] a reverend old gentleman affected with amnesia of words was forced to utter after the sentence, " Our Father who art in heaven," the words " let Him stay there." A lady seen by Trousseau would rise on the coming of a visitor to receive him with a pleased and amiable expression of countenance, and show him to a chair, at the same time addressing to him the words, " *cochon, animal, fichue bête,*" French words hardly allowable in drawing-room usage. She was totally aphasic but not paralyzed. Women often use semi-religious expressions like " Oh dear," or " Oh Lord." Men of the lower classes retain their favorite oaths remarkably. Sometimes the phrases ejaculated are meaningless, as in Broca's celebrated case.

Aphasia may be the result of sudden strong emotions, in such cases being usually temporary ; it may be traumatic ; it may be the result of either primary or secondary malnutrition or degeneration.

There are some cases on record in which the sudden loss and the sudden return of the voice are quite marvelous.

Habershon [b] reports the case of a woman who on seeing one of her children scalded fell unconscious and motionless, and remained without food for three days. It was then found that she suffered from complete aphasia. Five weeks after the incident she could articulate only in a very limited vocabulary.

In the Philosophical Transactions Archdeacon Squire tells of the case of Henry Axford, who lost the power of articulation for four years ; after a horrible dream following a debauch he immediately regained his voice, and thereafter he was able to articulate without difficulty.

Ball [c] records a curious case of what he calls hysteric aphonia. The patient was a young lady who for several months could neither sing nor speak, but on hearing her sister sing a favorite song, she began to sing herself ; but, although she could sing, speech did not return for several weeks. Ball remarks that during sleep such patients may cry out loudly in the natural voice.

Wadham [d] reports the case of a boy of eighteen who was admitted to his ward suffering with hemiplegia of the left side. Aphasia developed several days after admission and continued complete for three months. The boy

a Quart. Jour. Psych. Med., N. Y., 1868, ii., 74.   b 476, 1870, ii., 402.
c 476, 1889, i., 373.   d 700, 1869, iv., 245.

gradually but imperfectly recovered his speech.   Over six months after the original admission he was readmitted with necrosis of the jaw, for which he underwent operation, and was discharged a month later.   From this time on he became progressively emaciated until his death, twelve months after Wadham first saw him.   A postmortem examination showed nearly total destruction of the Island of Reil, popularly called the speech-center.   Jackson [a] mentions a hemiplegic patient with aphasia who could only utter the words " come on to me," " come on," and " yes " and " no."   Bristowe [b] cites the history of a sailor of thirty-six, a patient of St. Thomas Hospital, London, who suffered from aphasia for nine months.   His case was carefully explained to him and he nodded assent to all the explanations of the process of speech as though he understood all thoroughly.   He was gradually educated to speak again by practising the various sounds.   It may be worth while to state that after restoration of speech he spoke with his original American accent.

Ogle [c] quotes six cases of **loss of speech after bites of venomous snakes.**   Two of the patients recovered.   According to Russ [d] this strange symptom is sometimes instantaneous and in other instances it only appears after an interval of several hours.   In those who survive the effects of the venom it lasts for an indefinite period.   One man seen by Russ had not only lost his speech in consequence of the bite of a fer-de-lance snake, but had become, and still remained, hemiplegic.   In the rest of Russ's cases speech alone was abolished.   Russ remarks that the intelligence was altogether intact, and sensibility and power of motion were unaffected.   One woman who had been thus condemned to silence, suddenly under the influence of a strong excitement recovered her speech, but when the emotion passed away speech again left her.   Ogle accounts for this peculiar manifestation of aphasia by supposing that the poison produces spasm of the middle cerebral arteries, and when the symptom remains a permanent defect the continuance of the aphasia is probably due to thrombosis of arteries above the temporary constriction.

Anosmia, or loss of smell, is the most common disorder of olfaction ; it may be caused by cortical lesions, olfactory nerve-changes, congenital absence, or over-stimulation of the nerves, or it may be a symptom of hysteria.

Ogle,[e] after mentioning several cases of traumatic anosmia, suggests that a blow on the occiput is generally the cause.   Legg [f] reports a confirmatory case, but of six cases mentioned by Notta [g] two were caused by a blow on the crown of the head, and two on the right ear.   The prognosis in traumatic anosmia is generally bad, although there is a record [h] of a man who fell while working on a wharf, striking his head and producing anosmia with partial loss of hearing and sight, and who for several weeks neither smelt nor tasted, but gradually recovered.

a 476, March 17, 1868.   b 767, 1870, iii., 92.   c 700, 1868, iii., 167.
d 243, 1861, 220.   e 550, vol. liii., 1870, 264.   f 476, 1873, ii., 689.
g 162, April, 1870, 385.   h 218, 1878.

Mitchell [a] reports a case of a woman of forty who, after an injury to her nose from a fall, suffered persistent headache and loss of smell. Two years later, at bedtime, or on going to sleep, she had a sense of horrible odors, which were fecal or animal, and most intense in nature. The case terminated in melancholia, with delirium of persecution, during which the disturbance of smell passed away.

Anosmia has been noticed in leukoderma and allied disturbances of pigmentation. Ogle [b] mentions a negro boy in Kentucky whose sense of smell decreased as the leukoderma extended. Influenza, causing adhesions of the posterior pillars of the fauces, has given rise to anosmia.

Occasionally overstimulation of the olfactory system may lead to anosmia. Graves [c] mentions a captain of the yeomanry corps who while investigating the report that 500 pikes were concealed at the bottom of a cesspool in one of the city markets superintended the emptying of the cesspool, at the bottom of which the arms were found. He suffered greatly from the abominable effluvia, and for thirty-six years afterward he remained completely deprived of the sense of smell.

In a discussion upon anosmia before the Medico-Chirurgical Association of London, January 25, 1870, there was an anosmic patient mentioned who was very fond of the bouquet of moselle, and Carter mentioned that he knew a man who had lost both the senses of taste and smell, but who claimed that he enjoyed putrescent meat. Leared spoke of a case in an epileptic affected with loss of taste and smell, and whose paroxysms were always preceded by an odor of peach-blossoms.

Hyperosmia is an increase in the perception of smell, which rarely occurs in persons other than the hysteric and insane. It may be cultivated as a compensatory process, as in the blind, or those engaged in particular pursuits, such as tea-tasting. **Parosmia** is a rare condition, most often a symptom of hysteria or neurasthenia, in which everything smells of a similar, peculiar, offensive odor. Hallucinations of odor are sometimes noticed in the insane. They form most obstinate cases, when the hallucination gives rise to imaginary disagreeable, personal odors.

Perversion of the tactile sense, or wrong reference to the sensation of pain, has occasionally been noticed. The Ephemerides records a case in which there was the sense of two objects from a single touch on the hypochondrium. Weir Mitchell [d] remarks that soldiers often misplace the location of pain after injuries in battle. He also mentions several cases of wrong reference of the sensation of pain. These instances cannot be called reflex disturbances, and are most interesting. In one case the patient felt the pain from a urethral injection in gonorrhea, on the top of the head. In another an individual let an omnibus-window fall on his finger, causing but brief pain in the finger, but violent pains in the face and neck of that side. Mitchell

a 124, 1890.   b 550, 1870, 263.   c 309, 1884, vi., 69.   d 533, March 16, 1895.

also mentions a naturalist of distinction who had a small mole on one leg which, if roughly rubbed or pinched, invariably seemed to cause a sharp pain in the chin.

Nostalgia is the name generally given to that variety of melancholia in which there is an intense longing for home or country. This subject has apparently been overlooked in recent years, but in the olden times it was extensively discussed. Swinger, Harderus, Tackius, Guerbois, Hueber, Therrin, Castellanau, Pauquet, and others have written extensively upon this theme. It is said that the inhabitants of cold countries, such as the Laplanders and the Danes, are the most susceptible to this malady. For a long time many writers spoke of the frequency and intensity of nostalgia among the Swiss. Numerous cases of suicide from this affliction have been noticed among these hardy mountaineers, particularly on hearing the mountain-song of their homes, " Ranz des vaches." This statement, which is an established fact, is possibly due to the social constitution of the Swiss mountaineers, who are brought up to a solitary home life, and who universally exhibit great attachment to and dependence upon their parents and immediate family. In the European armies nostalgia has always been a factor in mortality. In the Army of the Moselle, and in Napoleon's Alpine Army, the terrible ravages of suicide among the young Bretons affected with nostalgia have been recorded ; it is among the French people that most of the investigation on this subject has been done. Moreau speaks of a young soldier in a foreign country and army who fell into a most profound melancholy when, by accident, he heard his native tongue. According to Swinger and Sauvages women are less subject to nostalgia than men. Nostalgia has been frequently recorded in hospital wards. Percy and Laurent [a] have discussed this subject very thoroughly, and cite several interesting cases among emigrants, soldiers, marines, etc. Hamilton [b] speaks of a recruit who became prostrated by longing for his home in Wales. He continually raved, but recovered from his delirium when assured by the hospital authorities of his forthcoming furlough. Taylor [c] records two cases of fatal nostalgia. One of the victims was a Union refugee who went to Kentucky from his home in Tennessee. He died talking about and pining for his home. The second patient was a member of a regiment of colored infantry ; he died after repeatedly pining for his old home.

Animals are sometimes subject to nostalgia, and instances are on record in which purchasers have been compelled to return them to the old home on account of their literal home-sickness. Oswald tells of a bear who, in the presence of food, committed suicide by starvation.

Hypochondria consists of a mild form of insanity in which there is a tendency to exaggerate the various sensations of the body and their importance, their exaggeration being at times so great as to amount to actual

[a] 302, xxxvi.   [b] 524, 1787, 343.   [c] Amer. Med. Bi-Weekly, 1879, 121.

delusion. All sorts of symptoms are dwelt upon, and the doctor is pestered to the extreme by the morbid fears of the patient.

Morbid fears or impulses, called by the Germans *Zwangsvorstellungen,* or *Zwangshandlungen,* and by the French, *peurs maladies,* have only been quite recently studied, and form most interesting cases of minor insanity. Gélineau [370] has made extensive investigations in this subject, and free reference has been made to his work in the preparation of the following material.

Aichmophobia is a name given by the French to the fear of the sight of any sharp-pointed instrument, such as a pin, needle, fish-spine, or naked sword. An illustrious sufferer of this 'phobia was James I. of England, who could never tolerate the appearance of a drawn sword. Gélineau reports an interesting case of a female who contracted this malady after the fatigue of lactation of two children. She could not tolerate knives, forks, or any pointed instruments on the table, and was apparently rendered helpless in needle-work on account of her inability to look at the pointed needle.

Agoraphobia is dread of an open space, and is sometimes called **Kenophobia.** The celebrated philosopher Pascal was supposed to have been affected with this fear. In agoraphobia the patient dreads to go across a street or into a field, is seized with an intense feeling of fright, and has to run to a wall or fall down, being quite unable to proceed. There is violent palpitation, and a feeling of constriction is experienced. According to Suckling, pallor and profuse perspiration are usually present, but there is no vertigo, confusion of mind, or loss of consciousness. The patient is quite conscious of the foolishness of the fears, but is unable to overcome them. The will is in abeyance and is quite subservient to the violent emotional disturbances. Gray mentions a patient who could not go over the Brooklyn Bridge or indeed over any bridge without terror. Roussel speaks of a married woman who had never had any children, and who was apparently healthy, but who for the past six months had not been able to put her head out of the window or go upon a balcony. When she descended into the street she was unable to traverse the open spaces. Chazarin mentions a case in a woman of fifty, without any other apparent symptom of diathesis. Gélineau [370] quotes a case of agoraphobia, secondary to rheumatism, in a woman of thirty-nine. There is a corresponding fear of high places often noticed, called **acrophobia ;** so that many people dare not trust themselves on high buildings or other eminences.

Thalassophobia is the fear of the view of immense spaces or uninterrupted expanses. The Emperor Heraclius, at the age of fifty-nine, had an insurmountable fear of the view of the sea ; and it is said that when he crossed the Bosphorus a bridge of boats was formed, garnished on both sides with plants and trees, obscuring all view of the water over which the Emperor peacefully traversed on horseback. The moralist Nicole, was equally a thalassophobe, and always had to close his eyes at the sight of a large sheet of water, when he was seized with trembling in all his limbs.   Occasionally some accident in youth has led to an aversion to traversing large sheets of water, and there have been instances in which persons who have fallen into the water in childhood have all their lives had a terror of crossing bridges.

Claustrophobia is the antithesis of agoraphobia.   Raggi[a] describes a case of such a mental condition in a patient who could not endure being within an enclosure or small space.   Suckling[b] mentions a patient of fifty-six who suffered from palpitation when shut in a railway carriage or in a small room.   She could only travel by rail or go into a small room so long as the doors were not locked, and on the railroad she had to bribe the guard to leave the doors unlocked.   The attacks were purely mental, for the woman could be deceived into believing that the door to a railroad carriage was unlocked, and then the attack would immediately subside.   Suckling also mentions a young woman brought to him at Queen's Hospital who had a great fear of death on getting into a tram car, and was seized with palpitation and trembling on merely seeing the car.   This patient had been in an asylum. The case was possibly due more to fear of an accident than to true claustrophobia.   Gorodoichze[c] mentions a case of claustrophobia in a woman of thirty-eight, in whose family there was a history of hereditary insanity.   Ball[d] speaks of a case in a woman who was overcome with terror half way in the ascension of the Tour Saint-Jacques, when she believed the door below was closed.   Gélineau quotes the case of a brave young soldier who was believed to be afraid of nothing, but who was unable to sleep in a room of which the door was closed.

Astrophobia or **astropaphobia** is a morbid fear of being struck by lightning.   It was first recognized by Bruck of Westphalia, who knew a priest who was always in terror when on a country road with an unobstructed view of the sky, but who was reassured when he was under the shelter of trees. He was advised by an old physician always to use an umbrella to obstruct his view of the heavens, and in this way his journeys were made tranquil.   Beard knew an old woman who had suffered all her life from astrophobia.   Her grandmother had presented the same susceptibility and the same fears.   Sometimes she could tell the approach of a storm by her nervous symptoms.   Caligula, Augustus, Henry III., and other celebrated personages, were overcome with fear during a storm.

Mysophobia is a mild form of insanity characterized by a dread of the contact of dirt.   It was named by Hammond, whose patient washed her hands innumerable times a day, so great was the fear of contamination.   These patients make the closest inspection of their toilet, their eating and drinking utensils, and all their lives are intensely worried by fear of dirt.

Hematophobia is a horror of blood, which seems to be an instinctive sentiment in civilized man, but which is unknown among savages.   When

a 363, 1878.   b 124, 1890.   c Jour. de l'Hypnotisme, Sept., 1893.   d 144, 1879.

the horror is aggravated to such an extent as to cause distressing symptoms or unconsciousness, it takes the name of hematophobia. There are many cases on record and nearly every physician has seen one or more, possibly among his colleagues.

Necrophobia and **thanatophobia** are allied maladies, one being the fear of dead bodies and the other the fear of death itself.

Anthropophobia is a symptom of mental disease consisting in fear of society. Beard, Mitchell, Baillarger, and others have made observations on this disease. The antithesis of this disease is called **monophobia.** Patients are not able to remain by themselves for even the shortest length of time. This morbid dread of being alone is sometimes so great that even the presence of an infant is an alleviation. Gélineau cites an instance in a man of forty-five which was complicated with agoraphobia.

Bacillophobia is the result of abnormal pondering over bacteriology. Huchard's case was in a woman of thirty-eight who, out of curiosity, had secretly read the works of Pasteur, and who seemed to take particular pleasure in conning over the causes of death in the health-reports. Goyard mentions an instance in a Swiss veterinary surgeon.

Kleptophobia, examples of which have been cited by Cullère,[a] is the fear of stealing objects in view, and is often the prelude of **kleptomania.** The latter disease has gained notoriety in this country, and nearly every large store has agents to watch the apparently growing number of kleptomaniacs. These unfortunate persons, not seldom from the highest classes of society, are unable to combat an intense desire to purloin articles. Legal proceedings have been instituted against many, and specialists have been called into court to speak on this question. Relatives and friends have been known to notify the large stores of the thieving propensities of such patients.

Le Grande du Saulle has given to the disease in which there is a morbid doubt about everything done, the name **folie de doute.** Gray mentions a case in a patient who would go out of a door, close it, and then come back, uncertain as to whether he had closed it, close it again, go off a little way, again feel uncertain as to whether he had closed it properly, go back again, and so on for many times. Hammond relates the history of a case in an intelligent man who in undressing for bed would spend an hour or two determining whether he should first take off his coat or his shoes. In the morning he would sit for an hour with his stockings in his hands, unable to determine which he should put on first.

Syphilophobia is morbid fear of syphilis. **Lyssophobia** is a fear of hydrophobia which sometimes assumes all the symptoms of the major disease, and even produces death. Gélineau, Colin, Berillon, and others have studied cases. In Berillon's case the patient was an artist, a woman of brunet complexion, who for six years had been tormented with the fear of becoming mad, and in whom the symptoms became so intense as to constitute

[a] " Les frontières de la folie," p. 82.

pseudohydrophobia. At their subsidence she was the victim of numerous hallucinations which almost drove her to the point of suicide.

Spermatophobia has been noticed among the ignorant, caused or increased by inspection of sensational literature, treatises on the subject of spermatorrhea, etc. Ferré mentions a woman of thirty-six, of intense religious scruples, who was married at eighteen, and lost her husband six years afterward. She had a proposition of marriage which she refused, and was prostrated by the humid touch of the proposer who had kissed her hand, imagining that the humidity was due to semen. She was several times overcome by contact with men in public conveyances, her fear of contamination being so great. **Zoophobia,** or dread of certain animals, has been mentioned under another chapter under the head of idiosyncrasies. **Pantophobia** is a general state of fear of everything and everybody. **Phobophobia,** the fear of being afraid, is another coinage of the wordmakers. The minor 'phobias, such as **pyrophobia,** or fear of fire; **stasophobia,** or inability to arise and walk, the victims spending all their time in bed; **toxicophobia** or fear of poison, etc., will be left to the reader's inspection in special works on this subject.

Demonomania is a form of madness in which a person imagines himself possessed of the devil. Ancient records of this disease are frequent, and in this century Lapointe [a] reports the history of demonomania in father, mother, three sons, and two daughters, the whole family, with the exception of one son, who was a soldier, being attacked. They imagined themselves poisoned by a sorceress, saw devils, and had all sorts of hallucinations, which necessitated the confinement of the whole family in an asylum for over a month. They continued free from the hallucinations for two years, when first the mother, and then gradually all the other members of the family, again became afflicted with demonomania and were again sent to the asylum, when, after a residence therein of five months, they were all sufficiently cured to return home.

Particular aversions may be temporary only, that is, due to an existing condition of the organism, which, though morbid, is of a transitory character. Such, for instance, are those due to dentition, the commencement or cessation of the menstrual function, pregnancy, etc. These cases are frequently of a serious character, and may lead to derangement of the mind. Millington relates the history of a lady who, at the beginning of her first pregnancy, acquired an overpowering aversion to a half-breed Indian woman who was employed in the house as a servant. Whenever this woman came near her she was at once seized with violent trembling; this ended in a few minutes with vomiting and great mental and physical prostration lasting several hours. Her husband would have sent the woman away, but Mrs. X insisted on her remaining, as she was a good servant, in order that she might overcome what she regarded as an unreasonable prejudice. The effort was, however, too

[a] 144, Nov., 1846.

great, for upon one occasion when the woman entered Mrs. X's apartment rather unexpectedly, the latter became greatly excited, and, jumping from an open window in her fright, broke her arm, and otherwise injured herself so severely that she was confined to her bed for several weeks. During this period, and for some time afterward, she was almost constantly subject to hallucinations, in which the Indian woman played a prominent part. Even after her recovery the mere thought of the woman would sometimes bring on a paroxysm of trembling, and it was not till after her confinement that the antipathy disappeared.

Circular or periodic insanity is a rare psychosis. According to Drewry reports of very few cases have appeared in the medical journals. "Some systematic writers," says Drewry, " regard it as a mere subdivision of periodic insanity (Spitzka). A distinguished alienist and author of Scotland however has given us an admirable lecture on the subject. He says : ' I have had under my care altogether about 40 cases of typical *folie circulaire.*' In the asylum at Morningside there were, says Dr. Clouston, in 800 patients 16 cases of this peculiar form of mental disease. Dr. Spitzka, who was the first American to describe it, found in 2300 cases of pauper insane four per cent. to be periodic, and its sub-group, circular, insanity. Dr. Stearns states that less than one-fourth of one per cent. of cases in the Hartford (Conn.) Retreat classed as mania and melancholia have proved to be *folie circulaire.* Upon examination of the annual reports of the superintendents of hospitals for the insane in this country, in only a few are references made to this as a distinct form of insanity. In the New York State hospitals there is a regular uniform classification of mental diseases in which ' circular (alternating) insanity' occupies a place. In the report of the Buffalo Hospital for 1892, in statistical table No. 4, ' showing forms of insanity in those admitted, etc., since 1888,' out of 1428 cases, only one was ' alternating (circular) insanity.' In the St. Lawrence Hospital only one case in 992 was credited to this special class. In the institution in Philadelphia, of which Dr. Chapin is the superintendent, 10,379 patients have been treated, only three of whom were diagnosed cases of *manie circulaire.* Of the 900 cases of insanity in the State Hospital at Danville, Pa., less than four per cent. were put in this special class. There are in the Central (Va.) State Hospital (which is exclusively for the colored insane) 775 patients, three of whom are genuine cases of circular insanity, but they are included in ' periodic insanity.' This same custom evidently prevails in many of the other hospitals for the insane."

Drewry[a] reports three cases of circular insanity, one of which was as follows :—

" William F., a negro, thirty-six years old, of fair education, steady, sober habits, was seized with gloomy depression a few weeks prior to his

[a] 466, April, 1895.

admission to this hospital, in September, 1886.   This condition came on after a period of fever.   He was a stranger in the vicinity and scarcely any information could be obtained regarding his antecedents.   When admitted he was in a state of melancholic hypochondriasis ; he was the very picture of abject misery.   Many imaginary ills troubled his peace of mind.   He spoke of committing suicide, but evidently for the purpose of attracting attention and sympathy. On one occasion he said he intended to kill himself, but when the means to do so were placed at his command, he said he would do the deed at another time.   The most trivial physical disturbances were exaggerated into very serious diseases.   From this state of morbid depression he slowly emerged, grew brighter, more energetic, neater in personal appearance, etc.   During this period of slow transition or partial sanity he was taken out on the farm where he proved to be a careful and industrious laborer.   He escaped, and when brought back to the hospital a few weeks subsequently he was in a condition of great excitement and hilarity.   His expression was animated, and he was, as it were, overflowing with superabundance of spirit, very loquacious, and incessantly moving.   He bore an air of great importance and self-satisfaction ; said he felt perfectly well and happy, but abused the officers for keeping him ' confined unjustly in a lunatic asylum.'   It was his habit almost daily, if not interfered with, to deliver a long harangue to his fellow-patients, during which he would become very excited and noisy.   He showed evidences of having a remarkable memory, particularly regarding names and dates.   (Unusual memory is frequently observed in this type of insanity, says Stearns.)   He was sometimes disposed to be somewhat destructive to furniture, etc., was neat in person, but would frequently dress rather 'gorgeously,' wearing feathers and the like in his hat, etc.   He was not often noisy and sleepless at night, and then only for a short time.   His physical health was good.   This 'mental intoxication,' as it were, lasted nearly a year.   After this long exacerbation of excitement there was a short remission and then depression again set in, which lasted about fifteen months.   At this time this patient is in the depressed stage or period of the third circle.   So, thus the cycles have continuously repeated their weary rounds, and in all probability they will keep this up ' until the final capitation in the battle of life has taken place.' "

Katatonia, according to Gray, is a cerebral disease of cyclic symptoms, ranging in succession from primary melancholia to mania, confusion, and dementia, one or more of these stages being occasionally absent, while convulsive and epileptoid symptoms accompany the mental changes.

It is manifestly impossible to enter into the manifold forms and instances of insanity in this volume, but there is one case, seldom quoted, which may be of interest.   It appeared under the title, " A Modern Pygmalion." [a]   It recorded a history of a man named Justin, who died in the Bicêtre Insane

[a] 476, 1879, ii., 436.

Asylum. He had been an exhibitor of wax works at Montrouge, and became deeply impressed with the beautiful proportions of the statue of a girl in his collection, and ultimately became intensely enamored with her. He would spend hours in contemplation of the inanimate object of his affections, and finally had the illusion that the figure, by movements of features, actually responded to his devotions. Nemesis as usual at last arrived, and the wife of Justin, irritated by his long neglect, in a fit of jealousy destroyed the wax figure, and this resulted in a murderous attack on his wife by Justin who resented the demolition of his love. He was finally secured and lodged in Bicêtre, where he lived for five years under the influence of his lost love.

An interesting condition, which has been studied more in France than elsewhere, is **double consciousness,** dual personality, or, as it is called by the Germans, *Doppelwahrnehmungen*. In these peculiar cases an individual at different times seems to lead absolutely different existences. The idea from a moralist's view is inculcated in Stevenson's "Dr. Jekyl and Mr. Hyde." In an article on this subject [a] Weir Mitchell illustrated his paper by examples, two of which will be quoted. The first was the case of Mary Reynolds who, when eighteen years of age, became subject to hysteric attacks, and on one occasion she continued blind and deaf for a period of five or six weeks. Her hearing returned suddenly, and her sight gradually. About three months afterward she was discovered in a profound sleep. Her memory had fled, and she was apparently a new-born individual. When she awoke it became apparent that she had totally forgotten her previous existence, her parents, her country, and the house where she lived. She might be compared to an immature child. It was necessary to recommence her education. She was taught to write, and wrote from right to left, as in the Semitic languages. She had only five or six words at her command—mere reflexes of articulation which were to her devoid of meaning. The labor of re-education, conducted methodically, lasted from seven to eight weeks. Her character had experienced as great a change as her memory ; timid to excess in the first state, she became gay, unreserved, boisterous, daring, even to rashness. She strolled through the woods and the mountains, attracted by the dangers of the wild country in which she lived. Then she had a fresh attack of sleep, and returned to her first condition ; she recalled all the memories and again assumed a melancholy character, which seemed to be aggravated. No conscious memory of the second state existed. A new attack brought back the second state, with the phenomenon of consciousness which accompanied it the first time. The patient passed successively a great many times from one of these states to the other. These repeated changes stretched over a period of sixteen years. At the end of that time the variations ceased. The patient was then thirty-six years of age ; she lived in a mixed state, but more closely resembling the second than the first ; her character was neither sad nor boisterous, but more reasonable. She died at the age of sixty-five years.

The second case was that of an itinerant Methodist minister named Bourne, living in Rhode Island, who one day left his home and found himself, or rather his second self, in Norristown, Pennsylvania. Having a little money, he bought a small stock in trade, and instead of being a minister of the gospel under the Methodist persuasion, he kept a candy shop under the name of A. J. Brown, paid his rent regularly, and acted like other people. At last, in the middle of the night, he awoke to his former consciousness, and finding himself in a strange place, supposed he had made a mistake and might be taken for a burglar. He was found in a state of great alarm by his neighbors, to whom he stated that he was a minister, and that his home was in Rhode Island. His friends were sent for and recognized him, and he returned to his home after an absence of two years of absolutely foreign existence. A most careful investigation of the case was made on behalf of the London Society for Psychical Research.

An exhaustive paper on this subject, written by Richard Hodgson in the proceedings of the Society for Psychical Research, states that Mr. Bourne had in early life shown a tendency to abnormal psychic conditions; but he had never before engaged in trade, and nothing could be remembered which would explain why he had assumed the name A. J. Brown, under which he did business. He had, however, been hypnotized when young and made to assume various characters on the stage, and it is possible that the name A. J. Brown was then suggested to him, the name resting in his memory, to be revived and resumed when he again went into a hypnotic trance.

Alfred Binet describes a case somewhat similar to that of Mary Reynolds: "Felida, a seamstress, from 1858 up to the present time (she is still living) has been under the care of a physician named Azam in Bordeaux. Her normal, or at least her usual, disposition when he first met her was one of melancholy and disinclination to talk, conjoined with eagerness for work. Nevertheless her actions and her answers to all questions were found to be perfectly rational. Almost every day she passed into a second state. Suddenly and without the slightest premonition save a violent pain in the temples she would fall into a profound slumber-like languor, from which she would awake in a few moments a totally different being. She was now as gay and cheery as she had formerly been morose. Her imagination was over-excited. Instead of being indifferent to everything, she had become alive to excess. In this state she remembered everything that had happened in the other similar states that had preceded it, and also during her normal life. But when at the end of an hour or two the languor reappeared, and she returned to her normal melancholy state, she could not recall anything that had happened in her second, or joyous, stage. One day, just after passing into the second stage, she attended the funeral of an acquaintance. Returning in a cab she felt the period coming on which she calls her crisis (normal state). She dozed several seconds, without attracting the attention of the ladies who were in the cab, and awoke in the other state, absolutely at a loss to know why she was in a mourning carriage with people who, according to custom, were praising the qualities of a deceased person whose name she did not even know. Accustomed to such positions, she waited; by adroit questions she managed to understand the situation, and no one suspected what had happened. Once when in her abnormal condition she discovered that her husband had a mistress, and was so overcome that she sought to commit suicide. Yet in her normal mind she meets the woman with perfect equilibrium and forgetfulness of any cause for quarrel. It is only in her abnormal state that the jealousy recurs. As the years went on the second state became her usual condition. That which was at first accidental and abnormal now constitutes the regular center of her psychic life. It is rather satisfactory to chronicle that as between the two *egos* which alternately possess her, the more cheerful has finally reached the ascendant."

Jackson [a] reports the history of the case of a young dry-goods clerk who was seized with convulsions of a violent nature during which he became unconscious. In the course of twenty-four hours his convulsions abated, and about the third day he imagined himself in New York paying court to a lady, and having a rival for her favors; an imaginary quarrel and duel ensued. For a half-hour on each of three days he would start exactly where he had left off on the previous day. His eyes were open and to all appearances he was awake during this peculiar delirium. When asked what he had been doing he would assert that he had been asleep. His language assumed a refinement above his ordinary discourse. In proportion as his nervous system became composed, and his strength improved, this unnatural manifestation of consciousness disappeared, and he ultimately regained his health.

A further example of this psychologic phenomenon was furnished quite recently at a meeting of the Clinical Society of London, where a well known physician exhibited a girl of twelve, belonging to a family of good standing, who displayed in the most complete and indubitable form this condition of dual existence. A description of the case is as follows :—

" Last year, after a severe illness which was diagnosed to be meningitis, she became subject to temporary attacks of unconsciousness, on awakening from which she appeared in an entirely different character. In her normal condition she could read and write and speak fluently, and with comparative correctness. In the altered mental condition following the attack she loses all memory for ordinary events, though she can recall things that have taken place during previous attacks. So complete is this alteration of memory, that at first she was unable to remember her own name or to identify herself or her parents. By patient training in the abnormal condition she has

[a] 124, 1869.

been enabled to give things their names, though she still preserves a baby-fashion of pronouncing. She sometimes remains in the abnormal condition for days together and the change to her real self takes place suddenly, without exciting surprise or dismay, and she forthwith resumes possession of her memory for events of her ordinary life. During the last month or two she appears to have entered on a new phase, for after a mental blank of a fortnight's duration she awakened completely oblivious of all that had happened since June, 1895, and she alludes to events that took place just anterior to that date as though they were of recent occurrence; in fact she is living mentally in July, 1895. These cases, though rare, are of course not infrequently met with, and they have been carefully studied, especially in France, where women appear more prone to neurotic manifestations. The hypothesis that finds most favor is that the two halves of the brain do not work in unison; in other words, that there has been some interference with the connections which in the ordinary normal being make of a wonderful composite organ like the brain one organic whole."

Proust [a] tells a story of a Parisian barrister of thirty-three. His father was a heavy drinker, his mother subject to nervous attacks, his younger brother mentally deficient, and the patient himself was very impressionable. It was said that a judge in a court, by fixing his gaze on him, could send him into an abnormal state. On one occasion, while looking into a mirror in a café, he suddenly fell into a sleep, and was taken to the Charité where he was awakened. He suffered occasional loss of memory for considerable lengths of time, and underwent a change of personality during these times. Though wide awake in such conditions he could remember nothing of his past life, and when returned to his original state he could remember nothing that occurred during his secondary state, having virtually two distinct memories. On September 23, 1888, he quarreled with his stepfather in Paris and became his second self for three weeks. He found himself in a village 100 miles from Paris, remembering nothing about his journey thereto; but on inquiry he found that he had paid a visit to the priest of the village who thought his conduct odd, and he had previously stayed with an uncle, a bishop, in whose house he had broken furniture, torn up letters, and had even had sentence passed upon him by a police court for misdemeanor. During these three weeks he had spent the equivalent of $100, but he could not recall a single item of expenditure. Davies [b] cites a remarkable case of sudden loss of memory in a man who, while on his way to Australia, was found by the police in an exhausted condition and who was confined in the Kent County Insane Asylum. He suffered absolute loss of all memory with the exception of the names of two men not close acquaintances, both of whom failed to recognize him in his changed condition in confinement. Four months later his memory returned and his identity was established.

a Quoted 224, 1890, i., 1143.   b 123, 1886.

In the Revue Philosophique for 1885 there are the details of a case of a young man who seemed able to assume six states of what might be fairly called different personalities. The memories attached to each of these states were very different, though only one was completely exclusive of the others. The handwriting varied from complete competence to complete incompetence. His character varied between childish timidity, courteous reserve, and reckless arrogance ; and to four of his conditions there was a form of hysteric paralysis attached. Mere suggestion would not only induce any one of these varied forms of paralysis, but also the memories, capacities, and characters habitually accompanying it.

A young man named Spencer, an inmate of the Philadelphia Hospital, was exhibited before the American Neurological Society in June, 1896, as an example of dual personality. At the time of writing he is and has been in apparently perfect health, with no evidence of having been in any other condition. His faculties seem perfect, his education manifests itself in his intelligent performance of the cleric duties assigned to him at the hospital, yet the thread of continuous recollection which connects the present moment with its predecessors—consciousness and memory—has evidently been snapped at some point of time prior to March 3d and after January 19th, the last date at which he wrote to his parents, and as if in a dream, he is now living another life. The hospital staff generally believe that the man is not "shamming," as many circumstances seem to preclude that theory. His memory is perfect as to everything back to March 3d. The theory of hypnotism was advanced in explanation of this case.

The morbid sympathy of twin brothers, illustrated in Dumas's "Corsican Brothers," has been discussed by Sedgwick, Elliotson, Trousseau, Laycock, Cagentre, and others. Marshall Hall relates what would seem to verify the Corsican myth, the history of twin brothers nine months of age, who always became simultaneously affected with restlessness, whooping and crowing in breathing three weeks previous to simultaneous convulsions, etc. Rush [a] describes a case of twin brothers dwelling in entirely different places, who had the same impulse at the same time, and who eventually committed suicide synchronously. Baunir [b] describes a similar development of suicidal tendency in twin brothers. A peculiar case of this kind was that of the twin brothers Laustand who were nurses in a hospital at Bordeaux ; they invariably became ill at the same time, and suffered cataract of the lens together.[c]

Automatism has been noticed as a sequel to cranial injuries, and Huxley quotes a remarkable case reported by Mesnet.[d] The patient was a young man whose parietal bone was partially destroyed by a ball. He exhibited signs of hemiplegia on the right side, but these soon disappeared and he became subject to periodic attacks lasting from twenty-four to forty-eight

a 368, 1837, 559.   b 144, 1863, No. 2.   c 221, July, 1844, 169.   d 362, July 17, 1874.

hours, during which he was a mere automaton. In these attacks he walked continually, incessantly moving his jaw, but not uttering a word. He was insensible to pain, electric shock, or pin-prick. If a pen was placed in his hand he would write a good letter, speaking sensibly about current topics. When a cigarette-paper was placed in his hand he sought his tobacco box, and adroitly rolled a cigarette and lighted it. If the light went out he procured another, but would not allow another to substitute a match. He allowed his mustache to be burned without resistance, but would not allow a light to be presented to him. If chopped charpie was put in his pocket instead of tobacco he knew no difference. While in his periods of automatism he was in the habit of stealing everything within his grasp. He had been a concert singer, and a peculiar fact was that if given white gloves he would carefully put them on and commence a pantomime of the actions of a singer, looking over his music, bowing, assuming his position, and then singing.

It is particularly in hypnotic subjects that manifestations of automatism are most marked. At the suggestion of battle an imaginary struggle at once begins, or if some person present is suggested as an enemy the fight is continued, the hypnotic taking care not to strike the person in question. Moll conceded that this looked like simulation, but repetition of such experiments forced him to conclude that these were real, typical hypnoses, in which, in spite of the sense-delusions, there was a dim, dreamy consciousness existing, which influenced the actions of the subject, and which prevented him from striking at a human being, although hitting at an imaginary object. Many may regard this behavior of hypnotics as pure automatism ; and Moll adds that, as when walking in the street while reading we automatically avoid knocking passers-by, so the hypnotic avoids hitting another person, although he is dimly or not at all aware of his existence.

Gibbs [a] reports a curious case of lack of integrity of the will in a man of fifty-five. When he had once started on a certain labor he seemed to have no power to stop the muscular exercise that the task called forth. If he went to the barn to throw down a forkful of hay, he would never stop until the hay was exhausted or someone came to his rescue. If sent to the wood-pile for a handful of wood, he would continue to bring in wood until the pile was exhausted or the room was full. On all occasions his automatic movements could only be stopped by force.

At a meeting in Breslau Meschede [b] rendered an account of a man who suffered from simple misdirection of movement without any mental derangement. If from his own desire, or by direction of others, he wanted to attempt any muscular movement, his muscles performed the exact opposite to his inclinations. If he desired to look to the right, his eyes involuntarily moved to the left. In this case the movement was not involuntary, as the

[a] Penins. and Ind. Med. Jour., Detroit, 1859–60, ii., 14.   [b] 465, Oct., 1876, 474.

muscles were quiet except when called to action by the will, and then they moved to the opposite.

Presentiment, or divination of approaching death, appearing to be a hypothetic allegation, has been established as a strong factor in the production of a fatal issue in many cases in which there was every hope for a recovery. In fact several physicians have mentioned with dread the peculiar obstinacy of such presentiment. Hippocrates, Romanus, Moller, Richter, Jordani, and other older writers speak of it. Montgomery[a] reports a remarkable case of a woman suffering from carcinoma of the uterus. He saw her on October 6, 1847, when she told him she had a strong presentiment of death on October 28th. She stated that she had been born on that day, her first husband had died on October 28th, and she had married her second husband on that day. On October 27th her pulse began to fail, she fell into a state of extreme prostration, and at noon on the 28th she died. In substantiation of the possibility of the influence of presentiment Montgomery cites another case in which he was called at an early hour to visit a lady, the mother of several children. He found her apparently much agitated and distressed, and in great nervous excitement over a dream she had had, in which she saw a handsome monument erected by some children to their mother. She had awakened and became dreadfully apprehensive, she could not tell as to what. The uneasiness and depression continued, her pulse continued to grow weak, and she died at twelve that night without a struggle. Andrews[b] has made several observations on this subject, and concludes that presentiment of death is a dangerous symptom, and one which should never be overlooked. One of his cases was in a man with a fractured leg in the Mercy Hospital at Pittsburg. The patient was in good health, but one day he became possessed of a cool, quiet, and perfectly clear impression that he was about to die. Struck with his conviction, Andrews examined his pulse and general condition minutely, and assured the patient there was not the slightest ground for apprehension. But he persisted, and was attacked by pneumonia three days later which brought him to the verge of the grave, although he ultimately recovered. In another instance a young man of ruddy complexion and apparent good health, after an operation for varicocele, had a very clear impression that he would die. Careful examination showed no reason for apprehension. After five or six days of encouragement and assurance, he appeared to be convinced that his reasoning was foolish, and he gave up the idea of death. About the ninth day the wound presented a healthy, rosy appearance, and as the patient was cheerful he was allowed to leave his bed. After a few hours the nurse heard the noise of labored breathing, and on investigation found the patient apparently in a dying condition. He was given stimulants and regained consciousness, but again relapsed, and died in a few moments. At the necropsy the heart was found healthy, but there were two or three spots of

[a] 308, 1857, n. s., vol. iv., 18.   [b] 526, 1872.

extravasated blood in the brain, and evidences of cerebral congestion. Vos [a] remarks that he remembers a case he had when dressing for Mr. Holden at St. Bartholomew's Hospital : " A man who had been intemperate was rolling a sod of grass, and got some grit into his left palm. It inflamed ; he put on hot cow-dung poultices by the advice of some country friends. He was admitted with a dreadfully swollen hand. It was opened, but the phlegmonous process spread up to the shoulder, and it was opened in many places, and at last, under chloroform, the limb was amputated below the joint. The stump sloughed, and pus pointing at the back of the neck, an opening was again made. He became in such a weak state that chloroform could not be administered, and one morning he had such a dread of more incisions that, saying to us all standing round his bed, ' I can bear it no more, I must now die,' he actually did die in a few minutes in our presence. His was the last arm that Mr. Holden ever amputated at St. Bartholomew's."

a 224, 1895, ii., 460.

CHAPTER XVIII.

HISTORIC EPIDEMICS.

A short history of the principal epidemics, including as it does the description of anomalous diseases, many of which are now extinct, and the valuable knowledge which finally led to their extinction, the extraordinary mortalities which these epidemics caused, and many other associate points of interest would seem fitting to close the observations gathered in this volume. As the illustrious Hecker says, in the history of every epidemic, from the earliest times, the spirit of inquiry was always aroused to learn the machinery of such stupendous engines of destruction ; and even in the earliest times there was neither deficiency in courage nor in zeal for investigation. " When the glandular plague first made its appearance as a universal epidemic, whilst the more pusillanimous, haunted by visionary fears, shut themselves up in their closets, some physicians at Constantinople, astonished at the phenomena, opened the boils of the deceased. The like has occurred both in ancient and modern times, not without favorable results for Science ; nay, more mature views excited an eager desire to become acquainted with similar or still greater visitations among the ancients, but, as later ages have always been fond of referring to Grecian antiquity, the learned of those times, from a partial and meagre predilection, were contented with the descriptions of Thucydides, even where nature had revealed, in infinite diversity, the workings of her powers."

There cannot but be a natural interest in every medical mind to-day in the few descriptions given of the awful ravages of the epidemics which, fortunately, in our enlightened sanitary era, have entirely disappeared. In the history of such epidemics the name of Hecker stands out so prominently that any remarks on this subject must necessarily, in some measure, find their origin in his writings, which include exhaustive histories of the black death, the dancing mania, and the sweating sickness. Few historians have considered worthy of more than a passing note an event of such magnitude as the black death, which destroyed millions of the human race in the fourteenth century and was particularly dreadful in England. Hume has given but a single paragraph to it and others have been equally brief. Defoe has given us a journal of the plague, but it is not written in a true scientific spirit ; and Caius, in 1552, gave us a primitive treatise on the sweating sickness. It

is due to the translation of Hecker's " Epidemics of the Middle Ages " by Babbington, made possible through the good offices of the Sydenham Society, that
a major part of the knowledge on this subject of the English-reading populace has been derived.

The Black Death, or, as it has been known, the Oriental plague, the
bubonic plague, or in England, simply the plague, and in Italy, " **la Mor-
talega** " (the great mortality) derived its name from the Orient; its inflammatory boils, tumors of the glands, and black spots, indicative of putrid decomposition, were such as have been seen in no other febrile disease. All the symptoms were not found in every case, and in many cases one symptom alone preceded death. Although afflicted with all the manifestations of the plague, some
patients recovered. According to Hecker the symptoms of cephalic affliction
were seen; many patients were stupefied and fell into a deep sleep, or became
speechless from palsy of the tongue, while others remained sleepless and without rest. The fauces and tongue were black and as if suffused with blood; no
beverage could assuage the burning thirst, so that suffering continued without
alleviation until death, which many in their despair accelerated with their own
hands. Contagion was evident, for attendants caught the disease from their
parents and friends, and many houses were emptied of their inhabitants. In
the fourteenth century this affection caused still deeper sufferings, such as had
not been hitherto experienced. The organs of respiration became the seats of
a putrid inflammation, blood was expectorated, and the breath possessed a pes-
tiferous odor. In the West an ardent fever, accompanied by an evacuation of
blood, proved fatal in the first three days. It appears that buboes and inflammatory boils did not at first appear, but the disease in the form of carbun-
cular affection of the lungs (anthrax artigen) caused the fatal issue before the
other symptoms developed. Later on in the history of the plague the inflammatory boils and buboes in the groins and axillæ were recognized at once as
prognosticating a fatal issue.

The history of this plague extends almost to prehistoric times. There
was a pest in Athens in the fifth century before Christ. There was another
in the second century, A. D., under the reign of Marcus Aurelius, and again
in the third century, under the reign of the Gauls; following this was the
terrible epidemic of the sixth century, which, after having ravaged the territory of the Gauls, extended westward. In 542 a Greek historian, Procopius, born about the year 500, gives a good description of this plague in a
work, " Pestilentia Gravissima," so called in the Latin translation. Dupouy
in " Le Moyen Age Médical," [314] says that it commenced in the village of
Peleuse, in Egypt, and followed a double course, one branch going to Alexandria and the other to Palestine. It reached Constantinople in the Spring
of 543, and produced the greatest devastation wherever it appeared. In the
course of the succeeding half century this epidemic became pandemic and
spread over all the inhabited earth. The epidemic lasted four months in

Constantinople, from 5000 to 10,000 people dying each day. In his "History of France," from 417 to 591, Gregorius speaks of a malady under the name *inguinale* which depopulated the Province of Arles. In another passage this illustrious historian of Tours says that the town of Narbonne was devastated by a *maladie des aines*. We have records of epidemics in France from 567 to 590, in which bubonic symptoms were a prominent feature. About the middle of the fourteenth century the bubonic plague made another incursion from the East. In 1333, fifteen years before the plague appeared in Europe, there were terrible droughts in China followed by enormous floods in which thousands of people perished. There are traditions of a plague in Tche in 1334, following a drought, which is said to have carried off about 5,000,000 people. During the fifteen years before the appearance of the plague in Europe there were peculiar atmospheric phenomena all over the world, besides numerous earthquakes. From the description of the stinking atmosphere of Europe itself at this time it is quite possible that part of the disease came, not from China, but originated in Southern Europe itself. From China the route of caravans ran to the north of the Caspian Sea, through Asia, to Tauris. Here ships were ready to take the produce of the East to Constantinople, the capital of commerce, and the medium of communication between Europe, Asia, and Africa. Other caravans went from Europe to Asia Minor and touched at the cities south of the Caspian Sea, and lastly there were others from Bagdad through Arabia to Egypt; the maritime communication on the Red Sea to Arabia and Egypt was also not inconsiderable. In all these directions contagion found its way, though doubtless Constantinople and the harbors of Asia Minor were the chief foci of infection, whence it radiated to the most distant seaports and islands. As early as 1347 the Mediterranean shores were visited by the plague, and in January, 1348, it appeared in the south of France, the north of Italy, and also in Spain. Place after place was attacked throughout the year, and after ravishing the whole of France and Germany, the plague appeared in England, a period of three months elapsing before it reached London. The northern kingdoms were attacked in 1349, but in Russia it did not make its appearance before 1351.

As to the **mortality** of this fearful epidemic Dupouy considers that in the space of four years more than 75,000,000 fell victims, that is, about half of the population of the countries visited. Hecker estimates that from 1347 to 1351, 25,000,000 people died, or one-quarter of the total population of Europe. It was reported to Pope Clement that throughout the East, probably with the exception of China, nearly 24,000,000 people had fallen victims to the plague. Thirteen millions are said to have died in China alone. Constantinople lost two-thirds of its population. When the plague was at its greatest violence Cairo lost daily from 10,000 to 15,000, as many as modern plagues have carried off during their whole course. India was depopulated. Tartary, Mesopotamia,

Syria, Armenia, and Arabia were covered with dead bodies. In this latter country Arabian historians mention that Maara el nooman, Schisur, and Harem in some unaccountable manner remained free. The shores of the Mediterranean were ravaged and ships were seen on the high seas without sailors. In "The Decameron" Boccaccio gives a most graphic description of the plague and states that in Florence, in four months, 100,000 perished; before the calamity it was hardly supposed to contain so many inhabitants. According to Hecker, Venice lost 100,000; London, 100,000; Paris, 50,000; Siena, 70,000; Avignon, 60,000; Strasburg, 16,000; Norwich, 51,100. Dupouy says that in one month there were 56,000 victims in Marseilles, and at Montpellier three-quarters of the population and all the physicians were stricken with the epidemic.

Johanna of Burgundy, wife of King Philip VI. of Valois; Johanna II., Queen of Navarre, granddaughter of Philippe le Bel; Alphonse XI. of Castile, and other notable persons perished. All the cities of England suffered incredible losses. Germany seems to have been particularly spared; according to a probable calculation, only about 1,250,000 dying. Italy was most severely visited, and was said to have lost most of its inhabitants. In the north of Europe two of the brothers of Magnus, King of Sweden, died; and in Westgothland alone 466 priests died. The plague showed no decrease in the northern climates of Iceland and Greenland, and caused great havoc in those countries.

The moral effect of such a great pandemic plague can be readily surmised. The mental shock sustained by all nations during the prevalence of the black plague is beyond parallel and description. An awful sense of contrition and repentance seized Christians of every community. They resolved to forsake their vices, and to make restitution for past offenses; hence extreme religious fanaticism held full sway throughout Europe. The zeal of the penitents stopped at nothing. The so-called Brotherhood of the Cross, otherwise known as the Order of Flagellants, which had arisen in the thirteenth century, but was suppressed by the mandates and strenuous efforts of the Church, was revived during the plague, and numbers of these advocates of self-chastisement roamed through the various countries on their great pilgrimages. Their power increased to such an extent that the Church was in considerable danger, for these religious enthusiasts gained more credit among the people, and operated more strongly on their minds than the priests from whom they so entirely withdrew that they even absolved each other. Their strength grew with such rapidity, and their numbers increased to such an extent daily, that the State and the Church were forced to combine for their suppression. Degeneracy, however, soon crept in, crimes were committed, and they went beyond their strength in attempting the performance of miracles. One of the most fearful consequences of this frenzy was the persecution of the Jews. This alien race was given up to the merciless fury and cruelty of the populace.

The persecution of the Jews commenced in September and October, 1348, at Chillon on Lake Geneva, where criminal proceedings were instituted against them on the mythic charge of poisoning the public wells. These persecuted people were summoned before sanguinary tribunals, beheaded and burned in the most fearful manner. At Strasburg 2000 Jews were burned alive in their own burial-ground, where a large scaffold had been erected, their wealth being divided among the people. In Mayence 12,000 Jews were said to have been put to a cruel death. At Eslingen the whole Jewish community burned themselves in their synagogue, and mothers were often seen throwing their children on the pile, to prevent them from being baptized, and then precipitating themselves into the flames. The cruel and avaricious desires of the monarchs against these thrifty and industrious people added fuel to the flames of the popular passion, and even a fanatic zeal arose among the Jews to perish as martyrs to their ancient religion. When we sum up the actual effects as well as the after effects of the black death, we are appalled at the magnitude of such a calamity, the like of which the world had never seen before.

In the fifteenth and sixteenth centuries the plague was generally diffused throughout Europe, and in the latter half of the seventeenth century a final Occidental incursion of the plague took place. From 1603 to 1604 over 30,000 people perished in London from the plague, and in 1625 the mortality in that city amounted to 35,417 persons. But **the great plague of London** did not begin until 1664. In this plague the patient at first became sensible of great weariness and fatigue, had slight chills, nausea, vomiting, vertigo, and pains in the loins. The mental disturbance rapidly increased, and stupor and delirium ensued. The face was alternately flushed and pallid, and a sense of constriction was experienced in the region of the heart. Darting pains were felt all over the body, soon followed by the enlargement of the lymphatic glands, or by the formation of carbuncles in various parts of the body. About the third day the tongue became dry and brown, and the gums, tongue, and teeth were covered with a dark fur, and the excretions became offensive; paralysis intervened; ecchymosed patches or stripes due to extravasation appeared on the skin; finally the pulse sank, the body grew cold and clammy, delirium or coma seized the victim, and in five or six days, sometimes in two or three, the painful struggle was at an end.

It was supposed that the disease originated in the Orient and was brought to London from Holland. In his " Journal of the Plague in London " Defoe describes its horrors, and tells of the dead-cart which went through the streets gathering the victims. A few extracts from Pepys's " Diary," the evidence of an eye-witness and a contemporary, show the ghastly aspects of this terrible visitation. On August 31st he writes: " In the City, this week, died 7496, and of them 6102 died of the plague. But it is found that the true number of the dead this week is nearer 10,000; partly from the poor who cannot be taken care of through the greatness of the number, and partly from the Quakers and others that will not have any bell rung for them." According to Adams, John Evelyn noted in his "Kalendarium" :—"Sept. 7th.— Near 10,000 now died weekly ; however, I went all along the City and suburbs from Kent street to St. James's, a dismal passage, and dangerous to see so many coffins exposed in the streets ; the streets thin of people, the shops shut up, and all in silence, no one knowing whose turn might be next."

As the cold weather came on the plague diminished in intensity and the people regained their confidence and returned to the city. According to Adams, [a] in the first week of March, 1666, deaths by the plague had decreased to 42 ; and by the end of the month it was nearly extinct after carrying off about 100,000 victims. In our days we can hardly comprehend the filthy hygienic conditions under which the people in the cities lived, and it was probably to this fact that the growth and perpetuation of this plague was due.

As to the bubonic plague recently raging in Camptown, China, Mary Niles [b] says that it was the same disease as the great London plague, and was characterized mainly by glandular enlargement. It had not appeared in the Canton district for forty years or more, though it was endemic in Yunnan. In some places it began in the winter ; and as early as January she herself found the first case in Canton in an infected house. In no case was direct contagiousness found to exist. The glands enlarged twelve hours after the fever began, and sometimes suppurated in nonfatal cases in a short time. Kitasato has recently announced the discovery of the specific cause of the bubonic plague.

Sweating Sickness.—According to Hecker, very shortly after Henry's triumphant march from Bosworth Field, and his entry into the capital on August 8, 1485, the sweating sickness began its ravages among the people of the densely populated city. According to Lord Bacon the disease began about September 21st, and lasted to the end of October, 1485. The physicians could do little or nothing for the people, and seemed to take no account of the clinical history of the disease,—in this respect not unlike the Greek physicians who for four hundred years paid no attention to small-pox because they could find no description of it in the immortal works of Galen. The causes seemed to be uncleanliness, gluttony, immoderate drinking, and also severe inundations leaving decaying vegetation. Richmond's army has been considered a factor in the germination of the seeds of pestilent disorder which broke out soon after in the camps of Litchfield, and on the banks of the Severn.

Sweating sickness was an inflammatory rheumatic fever, with great disorder of the nervous system, and was characterized by a profuse and injurious perspiration. In the English epidemic the brain, meninges, and the nerves were affected in a peculiar manner. The functions of the pneumo-

[a] "The Healing Art," London, 1887.   [b] 597, Oct. 13, 1894.

gastric nerves were violently disordered in this disease, as was shown by the oppressed respiration and extreme anxiety, with nausea and vomiting,—symptoms to which modern physicians attach much importance. The stupor and profound lethargy show that there was an injury to the brain, to which, in all probability, was added a stagnation of black blood in the torpid veins. Probably decomposing blood gave rise to the offensive odor of the person. The function of the lungs was considerably impaired. The petechial fever in Italy in 1505 was a form of the sweating sickness. There were visitations in 1506 and in 1515 in England. In 1517 the disease lasted full six months and reached its greatest height about six weeks after its appearance, but was apparently limited to England. Meningeal symptoms were characteristic of the third visitation of the disease. In 1528 and 1529 there was a fourth visitation which resulted in the destruction of the French Army before Naples. It is said that in 1524 a petechial fever carried off 50,000 people in Milan, and possibly this was the same disease. In 1529 the disease had spread all over Europe, attended with great mortality.

Germany, France, and Italy were visited equally. The famine in Germany, at this time, is described by authorities in a tone of deep sympathy. Swabia, Lorraine, Alsace, and provinces on the border of the lower Rhine, were frightfully affected, so that the disease reached the same heights there as in France. In England Henry VIII. endeavored to avoid the epidemic by continual traveling, until at last he grew tired of so unsettled a life and determined to await his destiny at Tytynhangar. It was not the inhabitants of the land alone who were affected, but even fish and the fowls of the air sickened. According to Schiller, in the neighborhood of Freiburg in Breisgau, dead birds were found scattered under the trees with boils as large as peas under their wings,—indicating among them a disease, and this extended far beyond the southern districts of the Rhine. The disease was undoubtedly of a miasmatic infectious nature, as was proved by its rapid spread and the occasional absence of a history of contagion. It was particularly favored in its development by high temperature and humidity.

The moral effect of the sweating sickness, similar to that of the black plague, was again to increase religious fanaticism and recreate the zeal of persecution.

On the 15th of April, 1551, there was an outbreak of the fifth and last epidemic of sweating fever in Shrewsbury, on the Severn. With stinking mists it gradually spread all over England, and on the 9th of July it reached London. The mortality was very considerable. The English residents were particularly susceptible, foreigners being comparatively exempt. The epidemic terminated about the 30th of September. Since that time the sweating sickness has never reappeared in England ; but in the beginning of the eighteenth century a disease very similar in symptoms and course broke out in Picardy, in Northern France. Toward the end of the century it spread to the South of France, and since that time has appeared epidemically, 195 distinct outbreaks having been observed in the course of one hundred and sixty-nine years, from 1618 to 1787. The disease has frequently appeared in Italy since 1755, and in various parts of Germany since 1801. In Belgium it has been observed in a few places within the present century (Rohé).

Chronologic Table of the Principal Plagues.—In December, 1880, H. P. Potter, F. R. C. S., published a chronologic table of some of the principal plagues on record.[a] In comments on his table, Potter says that he has doubtless included mention of many plagues which, although described under that name, are probably a dissimilar disease, writers having applied the terms pestilential and pestilent in a generic sense to diseases specifically different. It must also be remembered that, in some cases, death must have been due to famine, want, and privation, which are so frequently coexistent with pestilence. Following the idea of Hecker, the dancing manias have been included in this table.

TABLE OF PLAGUES.

DATE.	LOCALITY.	MORTALITY.	REMARKS.
B.C. 1495, . . .	Egypt, ...	. . .	During the reign of Pharaoh, King of Egypt, A.M. 2509. — Exodus xii.
1471, . . .	Desert of Paran, ...	14,000	. . .
1490, . . .	In the wilderness, ...	. . .	Numbers xi.
1310, . . .	Æguia (island of), ...	. . .	Ovid's Metam., lib. vii.
1141, . . {	Ashdod, a place between Guza and Joppa, . .	. . .	Among the Philistines, 1 Sam. v. and vi.
1190, . . .	Troy (siege of), ...	. . .	In the Grecian camp, Homer's Iliad, lib. i.
1017, . . .	Canaan, ...	70,000 in three days,	In the time of David, 2 Sam. xxiv.
790, . . .	Rome, ...	. . .	. . .
738, . . .	Rome, ...	. . .	Plutarch's Life of Romulus.
710, . . .	Rome, ...	185,000	Assyrian armies at the siege of Jerusalem.
694, . . { 671, . . {	. . .	. . .	Described by Livy.
545, ...	Velitrae, ...	Depopulated, .	Small town near Rome.
594, ...	Jerusalem, ...	One-third of inhabitants,	. . .
480, ...	Army of Xerxes, ...	150,000	. . .
476, ...	Spain, ...	. . .	. . .
463, ...	Rome, ...	. . .	Livy, iii., 6.
452, ...	Rome, ...	Half the inhabitants,	Livy, iii., 32.
430, ...	Athens, ...	. . .	Continued without interruption for five years. — Thucydides, ii., 48.
427, ...	Spain (from Egypt), . . .	. . .	. . .
404, ...	Carthage, ...	Depopulated, .	Justin, xix., 2; Diod. Sic., xiii.
393 and 383, {	Gaul and Rome (armies of), ...	. . .	. . .
366, ...	Rome, ...	10,000 daily, .	Livy, vii., 1; Short, On Air.
362.	Murviedro (Sicily), . . .	. . .	. .

[a] Jour. Statis. Soc. Lond., Dec., 1880.

TABLE OF PLAGUES.—*Continued.*

DATE.	LOCALITY.	MORTALITY.	REMARKS.
B.C.			
346, . . . ⎫			
332, . . . ⎪	Rome, ...	. . .	Livy.
296, . . . ⎬			
291, . . . ⎭			
237, ...	Cadiz, ...	. . .	. . .
218, ...	Carthaginian **armies,** . . .	. . .	⎰ On their route to besiege Tagun-⎱ tum.
216, . . .	Carthage, ...	. . .	. . .
213, . . . ⎱	Carthaginian and Roman ⎱ armies, ... ⎰	. . .	Before Syracuse, Livy, xxv.
206, ...	Capua, ...	. . .	. . .
182–177, . .	Rome and all Italy, . . .	. . .	Livy, xli., 21.
144, ...	Rome, ...	. . .	. . .
140, ...	Rome, ...	. . .	. . .
134 and ⎰ 130, ⎱	Italy, ...	. . .	. . .
126, ...	Numidia, ...	800,000 ⎱	Orosius, lib. v.
. . .	Seacoast of Carthage, . .	200,000 ⎰	
89, ...	Roman armies, ...	10,000	. . .
88, ...	Rome (people in), ...	30.000	. . .
60, ...	Spain, ...	. . .	? Leprosy.
A.D.			
68, ...	Rome, ...	. . .	⎰ Tacitus Annals, xv. ⎱ Orosius, lib. vii.
114, ...	Wales, ...	45,000	. . .
187, ...	Rome and Italy, ...	. . .	. . .
158, ...	Arabia, ...	. . .	. . .
175 and ⎰ 178, ⎱	Rome, ...	. . .	. . .
252, ...	Alexandria, ...	. . .	. . .
262, ...	Rome, ...	5,000 daily,	Zonaras, lib. xii.
310, ...	England, ...	40,000	. . .
325, ...	Britain, ...	. . .	. . .
365–394, . .	Italy and Syria, ...	. . .	. . .
400, ...	Asia, Africa, and Europe, .	71,719	Nicephorus, xiii.
450–67 and ⎱ 473, ⎰	Rome, ...	. . .	. . .
562, ...	Scotland, ...	. . .	. . .
517, ...	Palestine, ...	. . .	. . .
544, ...	France, ...	. . .	? Dysentery.
565–610, . ⎰ ⎱	Especially France, Ger-⎱ many, and Italy, . . ⎰	. . .	⎰ A plague raging, with intermis-⎪ sions, in most parts of the ⎱ world.—Niceph., xvii.
590, ...	Rome, ...	. . .	. . .
654, ...	Constantinople, ...	. . .	. . .
664, ...	South Britain, ...	. . .	. . .
665–683, . .	England, ...	. . .	With intermissions.
696, ...	Constantinople, ...	. . .	. . .
703 and ⎱ 713, ⎰	Scotland, ...	. . .	. . .
717, 724, ⎱ and 729, ⎰	Constantinople, ...	30,000	. . .
732, . . . ⎰ ⎱	Norwich in England, and ⎱ Syria, ... ⎰	. . .	. . .
740, . . . ⎰ ⎱	Various parts of Europe ⎱ and the East, . . . ⎰	. . .	Raged for 260 years.
762, ...	Wales. In Chichester, . .	34,000	. . .
853, ...	Scotland, ...	. . .	. . .
896, ...	Gaul, Germany, and Italy,	. . .	. . .
937, ...	England, ...	. . .	. . .
940, ...	North of Europe, ...	. . .	Affecting chiefly the cattle.

TABLE OF PLAGUES.—*Continued.*

DATE.	LOCALITY.	MORTALITY.	REMARKS.
A.D. 964, ...	. . .	. . .	Emperor Otho's army.
1005, . . .	. . .	Half the human race,	Raged for three years.
1012–25, . .	England and other parts of Europe, ...	. . .	With intermissions.
1027, . . .	. . .	. . .	Convulsive disease; dance of St. Vitus.
1029–31 and 1033,	England and Gaul, . . .	. . . .	. . .
1064, . . .	Saracen army, ...	Many thousands, . .	Marching to invade Rome; raged for two years.
1068, . . .	York and Durham, . . .	. . .	. . .
1075, . . .	Constantinople, ...	. . .	. . .
1096–1111, .	Europe (various parts), . .	. . .	. . .
1120, . . .	Various parts of the globe,	. . .	Lasted 272 years.
1126–28, 1133–46,	England, ...	. .	. . .
1172, . . .	England, ...	. .	? Dysentery.
1183, . . .	England and Rome, . . .	. .	. . .
1193–96, 1200–1201,	England, ...	. .	. . .
1217, . . .	Damietta, ...	Only 3 persons out of 70,000 survived, .	. . .
1235, . . .	London, ...	20,000	. . .
1237, . . .	Egypt, ...	. . .	Dancing disease among the children.
1278, . . .	Utrecht, ...	. . .	Dancing mania.
1283, . . .	Spain, ...	4,000	King Philip of France invaded Spain with 20,000 infantry and 8,600 cavalry.
1335, . . .	England, ...	Great mortality,	. . .
1345, . .	Spain, and spread over the whole world, . .	Leaving scarcely a quarter of the human race,	. . .
1346, . . .	Florence, ...	60,000	. . .
1347, . . .	London, ...	50,000	. . .
. . .	Venice, ...	100,000	. . .
. . .	Lubeck, ...	90,000	. . .
. . .	Spain, ...	200,000	. . .
1348, . .	Syria, Greece, Italy, Cyprus,	. . .	. . .
1350–51, . .	Ireland, ...	. . .	. . .
1352, . . .	China, ...	900,000	. . .
. . .	London, ...	50,000	Interred in one graveyard.
1355, . . .	Florence, ...	100,000	. . .
. . .	Norwich, ...	37,104	. . .
. . .	Yarmouth, ...	7,502	. . .
1363, . . .	Spain, ...	. . .	. . .
1365, . . .	Cologne, ...	20,000	. . .
1368–70, . .	England and Ireland, . .	. . .	. . .
1371, . . .	Barcelona, ...	. . .	. . .
1372, . .	Germany, Egypt, Greece, and all the East, . . .	Lubeck, 90,000	. . .
1374, . .	Holland, France, and Rhenish provinces, . .	. . .	Dancing disease of St. Vitus or St. John.
1379, . . .	England, ...	. . .	. . .
1383, . . .	Seville, ...	. . .	. . .
1384, . . .	Mallorca, ...	. . .	. . .
1387, . . .	Portugal, ...	. . .	. . .
1391, . .	England, York, and Norfolk especially, . . .	. . .	. . .

TABLE OF PLAGUES.—*Continued.*

DATE.	LOCALITY.	MORTALITY.	REMARKS.
A.D.			
1394, . . .	Spain, ...	. . .	. . .
1401, . . .	London, ...	30,000	. . .
1410, . . .	Seville, ...	. . .	. . .
1418, . . .	Strasburg, ...	. . .	Dancing disease.
1429, . . .	Barcelona, ...	. . .	. . .
1439, . . {	Huescar in the kingdom of Aragon, ... }	. . .	. . .
1450, . . {	Italy, Gaul, Germany, and Spain, ... }	. . .	. . .
1465, . . .	Italy, ...	. . .	. . .
1468, . . .	Parma, ...	. . .	. . .
1482, . . .	France, ...	. . .	. . .
1485, . . .	Seville, ...	. . . {	"Sweating sickness" in England.
1488, . . .	Andalusia, ...	. . .	. . .
1489, . . .	Barcelona, ...	. . .	. . .
1493, . . .	Mallorca, ...	. . .	. . .
1495, . . .	Saragossa, ...	. . .	. . .
1499, . . .	Britain, ...	London, 30,000,	Spread to Brabant, Flanders, etc.
1529, . . .	England, ...	. . .	. . .
1530, . . .	Germany, ...	. . .	Sweating sickness.
1535, . . .	Cork and Dresden, ...	. . .	. . .
1537–39, . .	England, ...	. . .	. . .
1541, . . .	Constantinople, ...	. . .	. . .
1543, . . .	Metz, ...	. . .	. . .
1547, . . {	England, Holland, and Germany, ... }	. . .	. . .
1556, . . .	Spain, ...	. . .	Spotted fever.
1558, . . .	Murcia, ...	. . .	. . .
1562, . . {	London and most of the principal cities of Europe, ... }	. . .	. . .
1564, . . .	Barcelona, ...	Saragossa, 10,000	
1565, . . .	Lyons, ...	. .	. . .
1566, . . .	"Morbus Hungaricus," .	. . .	. . .
1570, . . .	Spain, ...	. . .	. . .
1572, . . .	Dresden, ...	. . .	. . .
1574, . . .	Spain and Italy, ...	. . .	. . .
1579, . . .	Rome, ...	4,000	. . .
. . .	Lubeck, ...	8,000	. . .
	Hamburg, ...	3,000	. . .
1580–81, . .	Cairo and the East, . . .	500,000	. . .
1582, . . .	Spain, especially Cadiz, .	. . .	. . .
1585–86, . {	Narva and Revel, in Livonia, ... }	Revel, 6,000	. . .
1589, . . .	Seville, ...	. . .	. . .
1590, . . .	Dresden, ...	. . .	. . .
1593, . . .	Malta, ... {	70,000 in Lisbon and Spain, }	. . .
1600–1602, .	Muscovy, ...	500,000	. . .
. . .	Livonia, ...	30,000	. . .
1603, . . .	London, ...	36,000	. . .
. . .	Paris, ...	2,000 weekly,	. . .
1606, . . .	Throughout Europe, . . .	. . .	. . .
1609, . . .	Seville, ...	. . .	. . .
1610, . . .	Granada, ...	. . .	. . .
. . .	Constantinople, ...	200,000	. . .
1613, . . {	France and Constantinople, ... }	. . .	. . .
1616, . . {	Germany, Denmark, Egypt, and Levant, . . }	. . .	. . .

TABLE OF PLAGUES.—*Continued.*

DATE.	LOCALITY.	MORTALITY.	REMARKS.
A.D.		1st year, 8,000	
1622, . . .	London, ...	2d " 11,000 3d " 12,000 4th " 35,417	Lasted four years.
1625, . . .	Throughout England, . .	London, 30,000	. . .
1626, . . .	Lyons, ...	60,000	. . .
1634, . . .	Dresden, ...	. . .	. . .
1635, . . .	Leyden and Nineguen, . .	Leyden, 20,000	. . .
		London, 10,000	
1644, . . .	Madrid, ...	. . .	. . .
1649, . . .	Spain, ...	200,000	. . .
1653, . . .	Moscow, ...	200,000	. . .
. . .	Riga, ...	9,000	. . .
. . .	Amsterdam, ...	13,200	. . .
. . .	Leyden, ...	13,000	. . .
1656, . . .	Naples, ...	240,000	Three-quarters of the inhabitants.
. . .	Benevento, ...	9,000	. . .
. . .	Genoa, ...	10,000	. . .
. . .	Rome, ...	10,000	. . .
. . .	Neapolitan territories, . .	400,000	. . .
1662, . . .	Venice, ...	60,000	. . .
1663, . . .	England, ...	. . .	. . .
1664, . . .	Amsterdam, ...	24,000	. . .
1665, . . .	London, ...	68,596	. . .
1673, . . .	Spain, ...	. . .	. . .
1675, . . .	Malta, ...	11,300	. . .
1677, . . .	Murcia and Carthagena, .	. . .	. . .
1679, . . .	Germany, ...	. . .	. . .
1691, . . .	Germany, ...	. . .	. . .
1698, . . .	Spain, ...	. . .	. . .
1705, . . .	Ceuta, ...	. . .	. . .
1710, . . .	Copenhagen, ...	25,000	In six months, the "sweating sickness."
. . .	Stockholm, ...	30,000	
1720, . . .	Marseilles, ...	. . .	. . .
1722, . . {	Vienna, Hungary, and in the East, ...	. . .	. . .
1727, . . .	Spain, ...		Epidemic mania.
1732, . . .	London, ...	1,500 in one week,	. . .
1735, . . .	Egypt, ...	Many thousands, . .	. . .
1736, . . .	Cairo, ...	100,000	7,000 buried daily for some days.
1740, . . .	Ireland, ...	. . .	. . .
1743, . . .	Aleppo, ...	. . .	. . .
1751, . . .	Cordova, ...	40,000 in Cairo and Constantinople, . . .	. . .
1751–60, . .	Ireland and France, . .	30,000 in Cyprus, . . .	. . .
1761, . . .	Carthagena, ...		. . .
1762, . . {	Aleppo, Jerusalem, and Damascus, ...	. . .	. . .
1763, . . .	Naples, ...	20,000	. o .
1769, . . .	Bengal, ...	"3 millions and upward,"	. . .
1770, . . .	Poland and Russia, . . .	20,000	. . .
. . .	Bohemia, ...	168,000	. . .
. . .	Constantinople, ...	1,000 buried daily for some weeks,	

TABLE OF PLAGUES. — *Continued.*

DATE.	LOCALITY.	MORTALITY.	REMARKS.
A.D.			
1771, . . .	Moscow, ... {	133,299 in 18 } months, . }	. . .
. . .	Bassora, ...	80,000	. . .
1783–85, . {	Egypt, Dalmatia, Con-} stantinople, etc., . . }	. . .	. . .
1792, . . .	Egypt, ...	800,000	
1799, . . .	Barbary, ...	3,000 daily,	In the French army in Egypt.
. . .	Fez, ...	247,000	. . .
1809, . . .	Portugal, ...	. . .	Among British troops.
1810, . . .	Gibraltar, ... {	Out of 14,000 } only 28 es-} caped, . . }	. . .
1812, . . .	Constantinople, ...	160,000	. . .
1813, . . .	Malta, ...	4,483	. . .
1815, . . .	Corfu, ...	. . .	. . .
1817, . . {	Throughout the habitable } globe, ... }	. . .	. . .
1841, . . {	Syria, especially about } Erzeroum, ... }	. . .	Dancing mania.
1843, . . .	Asiatic Turkey, ...	. . .	. . .
1844, . . .	Egypt, ...	. . .	. . .
1873–76, . .	Mesopotamia, ...	20,000 in 1876,	. . .
1877, . . .	Resht, near the Caspian, .	. . .	. . .

Small-pox.—From certain Chinese records it appears that small-pox, or a disease with similar symptoms, was known in China before the Christian era, and it was supposed to have been known at a very early period in India. Most likely it was introduced into Europe in the second century by a Roman army returning from Asia. Before the sixth century, the terrible century of the great plague, there seem to be no records of small-pox or other eruptive fevers. Neither Hippocrates, Galen, nor the Greek physicians who practised at Rome, mention small-pox, although it is now believed that the Emperor Marcus Aurelius died of this disease. According to Dupouy, the first document mentioning variola was in 570 A. D., by Marius, a scholar of Avenches, in Switzerland. (*"Anno 570, morbus validus cum profluvio ventris, et variola, Italiam Galliamque valde affecit."*) Ten years later Gregory of Tours describes an epidemic with all the symptoms of small-pox in the fifth reign of King Childebert (580); it started in the region of Auvergne, which was inundated by a great flood ; he also describes a similar epidemic in Touraine in 582. Rhazes, or as the Arabs call him, Abu Beer Mohammed Ibn Zacaríyá Ar-Razi, in the latter part of the ninth century wrote a most celebrated work on small-pox and measles, which is the earliest accurate description of these diseases, although Rhazes himself mentions several writers who had previously described them, and who had formulated rules for their cure. He explained these diseases by the theory of fermentation, and recommended the cooling treatment. Adams remarks that although it is probable that small-pox existed for ages in Hindoostan and China, being completely isolated in those countries from the European world, it was not introduced into the West until the close of the seventh century. Imported into Egypt by the Arabians, it followed in the tracks of their conquests, and was in this way propagated over Europe. The foregoing statement disagrees with Dupouy and others. It is well known that small-pox was prevalent in Europe before Rhazes's description of it, and after the Crusades it spread over Central and Western Europe, but did not extend to the northern countries until some years later. In 1507 the Spaniards introduced it into San Domingo, and in 1510 into Mexico, where it proved a more fatal scourge than the swords of Cortez and his followers, for according to Robertson it swept away in Mexico three millions and a half of people. In 1707 it appeared in Iceland, and carried off more than one-fourth of its inhabitants; in 1733, according to Collinson, it almost depopulated Greenland. The Samoyeds, Ostiaks, and other natives of Eastern Siberia, have frequently suffered from devastating epidemics. In Kamchatka the disease was introduced in 1767, and many villages were completely depopulated. According to Moore, at the beginning of the eighteenth century nearly one-fourteenth of the population died from small-pox in England, and at the end of the century the number of the victims had increased to one-tenth. In the last century the statement was made in England that one person in every three was badly pock-marked. The mortality of the disease at the latter half of the eighteenth century was about three to every thousand inhabitants annually. India has always been a fertile ground for the development of small-pox, and according to Rohé [a] the mortality from small-pox has been exceedingly great for the past twenty years. From 1866 to 1869, 140,000 persons died in the Presidencies of Bombay and Calcutta, and several years later, from 1873 to 1876, 700,000 died from this disease. China, Japan, and the neighboring countries are frequently visited with small-pox, and nearly all the inhabitants of Corea are said to bear evidences of the disease. In the Marquesas Islands one-fourth of the inhabitants had fallen victims to the disease since 1863. It was first introduced into the Sandwich Islands in 1853, and it then carried off eight per cent. of the natives. Australia, Tasmania, New Zealand, and the Fiji Archipelago have to the present day remained exempt from small-pox; although it has been carried to Australia in vessels, rigorous quarantine methods have promptly checked it. On the American continent it was believed that small-pox was unknown until the conquest of Mexico. It has been spread through various channels to nearly all the Indian tribes of both North and South America, and among these primitive people, unprotected by inoculation or vaccination, its ravages have been frightful.

That small-pox—a disease so general and so fatal at one time—has, through the ingenuity of man, in civilized communities at least, become almost extinct, is one of the greatest triumphs of medicine.

[a] " Text-Book of Hygiene," Phila., 1890.

Inoculation was known in Europe about 1700, and in 1717 the famous letter of Lady Montagu from Adrianople was issued, containing in part the following statements :—

" The small-pox, so fatal and so general amongst us, is here entirely harmless, by the invention of ingrafting, which is the term they give it. There is a set of old women who make it their business to perform the operation every autumn in the month of September, when the great heat is abated. People send to one another to know if any of their family has a mind to have the small-pox ; they make parties for this purpose, and when they are met, the old woman comes with a nut-shell full of the matter of the best sort of small-pox, and asks what vein you please to have opened. She immediately rips open that you offer her with a large needle, and puts into the vein as much matter as can lie upon the head of her needle, and after that binds up the little wound with a hollow shell, and in this manner opens four or five veins."

Soon after this letter Lady Montagu had her son inoculated in Turkey, and four years later her daughter was to be the first subject inoculated in England. She made rapid progress notwithstanding the opposition of the medical profession, and the ignorance and credulity of the public. The clergy vituperated her for the impiety of seeking to control the designs of Providence. Preaching in 1722, the Rev. Edward Massey, for example, affirmed that Job's distemper was confluent small-pox, and that he had been inoculated by the Devil. Lady Montagu, however, gained many supporters among the higher classes. In 1721 Mead was requested by the Prince of Wales to superintend the inoculation of some condemned criminals, the Prince intending afterward to continue the practice in his own family ; the experiment was entirely successful, and the individuals on whom it was made afterward received their liberty (Adams).

According to Rohé, inoculation was introduced into this country in 1721 by Dr. Zabdiel Boylston of Boston, who had his attention directed to the practice by Cotton Mather, the eminent divine. During 1721 and 1722 286 persons were inoculated by Boylston and others in Massachusetts, and six died. These fatal results rendered the practice unpopular, and at one time the inoculation hospital in Boston was closed by order of the Legislature. Toward the end of the century an inoculating hospital was again opened in that city.

Early in the eighteenth century inoculation was extensively practised by Dr. Adam Thomson of Maryland, who was instrumental in spreading a knowledge of the practice throughout the Middle States.

Despite inoculation, as we have already seen, during the eighteenth century the mortality from small-pox increased. The disadvantage of inoculation was that the person inoculated was affected with a mild form of small-pox, which, however, was contagious, and led to a virulent form in uninoculated persons.

As universal inoculation was manifestly impracticable, any half-way measure was decidedly disadvantageous, and it was not until vaccination from cow-pox was instituted that the first decided check on the ravages of small-pox was made.

Vaccination was almost solely due to the persistent efforts of **Dr. Edward Jenner,** a pupil of the celebrated John Hunter, born May 17, 1749.

In his comments on the life of Edward Jenner, Adams, in "The Healing Art," has graphically described his first efforts to institute vaccination, as follows : " To the ravages of small-pox, and the possibility of finding some preventive Jenner had long given his attention. It is likely enough that his thoughts were inclined in this direction by the remembrance of the sufferings inflicted upon himself by the process of inoculation. Through six weeks that process lingered. He was bled, purged, and put on a low diet, until ' this barbarism of human veterinary practice' had reduced him to a skeleton. He was then exposed to the contagion of the small-pox. Happily, he had but a mild attack ; yet the disease itself and the inoculating operations, were probably the causes of the excessive sensitiveness which afflicted him through life.

" When Jenner was acting as a surgeon's articled pupil at Sudbury, a young countrywoman applied to him for advice. In her presence some chance allusion was made to the universal disease, on which she remarked : ' I shall never take it, for I have had the cow-pox.' The remark induced him to make inquiries ; and he found that a pustular eruption, derived from infection, appeared on the hands of milkers, communicated from the teats of cows similarly disordered ; this eruption was regarded as a safeguard against small-pox. The subject occupied his mind so much that he frequently mentioned it to John Hunter and the great surgeon occasionally alluded to it in his lectures, but never seems to have adopted Jenner's idea that it might suggest some efficacious substitute for inoculation. Jenner, however, continued his inquiries, and in 1780 he confided to his friend, Edward Gardner, his hope and prayer that it might be his work in life to extirpate small-pox by the mode of treatment now so familiar under the name of vaccination.

" At the meetings of the Alveston and Radborough Medical Clubs, of both of which Jenner was a member, he so frequently enlarged upon his favorite theme, and so repeatedly insisted upon the value of cow-pox as a prophylactic, that he was denounced as a nuisance, and in a jest it was even proposed that if the orator further sinned, he should then and there be expelled. Nowhere could the prophet find a disciple and enforce the lesson upon the ignorant ; like most benefactors of mankind he had to do his work unaided. Patiently and perseveringly he pushed forward his investigations. The aim he had in view was too great for ridicule to daunt, or indifference to discourage him. When he surveyed the mental and physical agony inflicted by the disease, and the thought occurred to him that he was on the point of finding a sure and certain remedy, his benevolent heart overflowed with unselfish gladness. No feeling of personal ambition, no hope or desire of fame, sullied the purity of his noble philanthropy. 'While the vaccine discovery was progressive,' he writes, ' the joy at the prospect before me of being the instrument destined to take away from the world one of its greatest calamities, blended with the fond hope of enjoying independence, and domestic peace and happiness, were often so excessive, that, in pursuing my favorite subject among the meadows, I have sometimes found myself in a kind of reverie. It is pleasant to recollect that those reflections always ended in devout acknowledgments to that Being from whom this and all other blessings flow.' At last an opportunity occurred of putting his theory to the test. On the 14th day of May, 1796,—the day marks an epoch in the Healing Art, and is not less worthy of being kept as a national thanksgiving than the day of Waterloo—the cow-pox matter or pus was taken from the hand of one Sarah Holmes, who had been infected from her master's cows, and was inserted by two superficial incisions into the arms of James Phipps, a healthy boy of about eight years of age. The cow-pox ran its ordinary course without any injurious effect, and the boy was afterward inoculated for the small-pox,—happily in vain. The protection was complete; and Jenner thenceforward pursued his experiments with redoubled ardor. His first summary of them, after having been examined and approved by several friends, appeared under the title of 'An Inquiry into the Causes and Effects of the Variolæ Vaccinæ,' in June, 1798. In this important work he announced the security against the small-pox afforded by the true cow-pox, and proceeded to trace the origin of that disease in the cow to a similar affection of the horse's heel."

This publication produced a great sensation in the medical world, and vaccination spread so rapidly that in the following summer Jenner had the indorsement of the majority of the leading surgeons of London. Vaccination was soon introduced into France, where Napoleon gave another proof of his far-reaching sagacity by his immediate recognition of the importance of vaccination. It was then spread all over the continent; and in 1800 Dr. Benjamin Waterhouse of Boston introduced it into America; in 1801, with his sons-in-law, President Jefferson vaccinated in their own families and those of their friends nearly 200 persons. Quinan [a] has shown that vaccination was introduced into Maryland at least simultaneously with its introduction into Massachusetts. De Curco introduced vaccination into Vienna, where its beneficial results were displayed on a striking scale ; previously the average annual mortality had been about 835 ; the number now fell to 164 in 1801, 61 in 1802, and 27 in 1803. After the introduction of vaccination in England the mortality was reduced from nearly 3000 per million inhabitants annually to 310 per million annually. During the small-pox epidemic in

[a] 510, June 23 and 30, 1883.

London in 1863, Seaton and Buchanan examined over 50,000 school children, and among every thousand without evidences of vaccination they found 360 with the scars of small-pox, while of every thousand presenting some evidence of vaccination, only 1.78 had any such traces of small-pox to exhibit. Where vaccination has been rendered compulsory, the results are surprising. In 1874 a law was established in Prussia that every child that had not already had small-pox must be vaccinated in the first year of its life, and every pupil in a private or public institution must be revaccinated during the year in which his or her twelfth birthday occurs. This law virtually stamped small-pox out of existence ; and according to Frölich [a] not a single death from small-pox occurred in the German army between 1874 and 1882. Notwithstanding the arguments advanced in this latter day against vaccination, the remembrance of a few important statistic facts is all that is necessary to fully appreciate the blessing which Jenner conferred upon humanity. In the last century, besides the enormous mortality of small-pox (it was computed that, in the middle of the last century, 2,000,000 victims perished in Russia from small-pox), the marks of affliction, blindness, deafness, etc., were plain in at least one member of every family.

Asiatic cholera probably originated centuries ago in India, where it is now endemic and rages to such an extent as to destroy 750,000 inhabitants in the space of five years. There is questionable evidence of the existence of cholera to be found in the writings of some of the classic Grecian and Indian authors, almost as far back as the beginning of the Christian era. In the sixteenth and seventeenth centuries travelers in the East gave accounts of this disease. Sonnerat, a French traveler, describes a pestilence having all the characteristics of Asiatic cholera which prevailed in the neighborhood of Pondicherry and the Coromandel coast from 1768 to 1769, and which, within a year, carried off 60,000 of those attacked. According to Rohé, Jasper Correa, an officer in Vasco da Gama's expedition to Calicut, states that Zamorin, the chief of Calicut, lost 20,000 troops by the disease. Although cholera has frequently extended to Europe and America, its ravages have never been nearly as extensive as in the Oriental outbreaks. An excellent short historic sketch of the epidemics of the cholera observed beyond the borders of India has been given by Rohé.[b] In 1817 cholera crossed the boundaries of India, advancing southeasterly to Ceylon, and westerly to Mauritius, reaching the African coast in 1820. In the following two years it devastated the Chinese Empire and invaded Japan, appearing at the port of Nagasaki in 1822. It advanced into Asiatic Russia, and appeared as far east as St. Petersburg in 1830, from whence it spread north to Finland. In 1831 it passed through Germany, invading France and the western borders of Europe, entering the British Isles in 1832, and crossing the Atlantic Ocean for the first time, appeared in Canada, having been carried thence by some Irish emigrants.

[a] " Militär-Medicin," p. 461.　　　　　　　　　　　[b] Loc. cit., p. 315.

From Canada it directly made its way to the United States by way of Detroit. In the same year (1832) it appeared in New York and rapidly spread along the Atlantic coast.

" During the winter of 1832 it appeared at New Orleans, and passed thence up the Mississippi Valley. Extending into the Indian country, causing sad havoc among the aborigines, it advanced westward until its further progress was stayed by the shores of the Pacific Ocean. In 1834 it reappeared on the east coast of the United States, but did not gain much headway, and in the following year New Orleans was again invaded by way of Cuba. It was again imported into Mexico in 1833. In 1835 it appeared for the first time in South America, being restricted, however, to a mild epidemic on the Guiana coast.

" In 1846 the disease again advanced beyond its natural confines, reaching Europe by way of Turkey, in 1848. In the autumn of this year it also appeared in Great Britain, Belgium, the Netherlands, Sweden, and the United States, entering by way of New York and New Orleans. In the succeeding two years the entire extent of country east of the Rocky Mountains was invaded. During 1851 and 1852 the disease was frequently imported by emigrants, who were annually arriving in great numbers from the various infected countries of Europe. In 1853 and 1854 cholera again prevailed extensively in this country, being, however, traceable to renewed importation of infected material from abroad. In the following two years it also broke out in numerous South American States, where it prevailed at intervals until 1863. Hardly had this third great pandemic come to an end before the disease again advanced from the Ganges, spreading throughout India, and extending to China, Japan, and the East Indian Archipelago, during the years 1863 to 1865. In the latter year it reached Europe by way of Malta and Marseilles. It rapidly spread over the Continent, and in 1866 was imported into this country by way of Halifax, New York, and New Orleans. This epidemic prevailed extensively in the Western States, but produced only slight ravages on the Atlantic Coast, being kept in check by appropriate sanitary measures. In the same year (1866) the disease was also carried to South America, and invaded for the first time the states bordering on the Rio de la Plata and the Pacific coast of the Continent.

" Cholera never entirely disappeared in Russia during the latter half of the sixth decade, and in 1870 it again broke out with violence, carrying off a quarter of a million of the inhabitants before dying out in 1873. It spread from Russia into Germany and France and was imported, in 1873, into this country, entering by way of New Orleans and extending up the Mississippi Valley. None of the Atlantic coast cities suffered from this epidemic in 1873, and since that year the United States has been entirely free from the disease, with the exception of a few imported cases in New York harbor in 1887 " (and in 1893).

In 1883 an epidemic of cholera raged in Egypt and spread to many of the Mediterranean ports, and reappeared in 1885 with renewed violence. In Spain alone during this latter epidemic the total number of cases was over one-third of a million, with nearly 120,000 deaths. In 1886 cholera caused at least 100,000 deaths in Japan. In the latter part of 1886 cholera was carried from Genoa to Buenos Ayres, and crossing the Andean range invaded the Pacific coast for a second time. In Chili alone there were over 10,000 deaths from cholera in the first six months of 1887. Since then the entire Western hemisphere has been virtually free from the disease.

In 1889 there was an epidemic of cholera in the Orient ; and in 1892 and 1893 it broke out along the shores of the Mediterranean, invading all the lines of commerce of Europe, Hamburg in the North and Marseilles in the South being especially affected. In the summer of 1893 a few cases appeared in New York Bay and several in New York city, but rigorous quarantine methods prevented any further spread.

Typhus fever is now a rare disease, and epidemics **are** quite infrequent. It has long been known under the names of hospital-fever, spotted-fever, jail-fever, camp-fever, and ship-fever, and has been the regular associate of such social disturbances as overcrowding, excesses, famine, and war. For the past eight centuries epidemics of typhus have from time to time been noticed, but invariably can be traced to some social derangement.

Yellow Fever is a disease prevailing endemically in the West Indies and certain sections of what was formerly known as the Spanish Main. Guitéras recognizes three areas of infection :—

(1) The focal zone from which the disease is never absent, including Havana, Vera Cruz, Rio, and the other various Spanish-American points.

(2) The perifocal zone, or regions of periodic epidemics, including the ports of the tropical Atlantic and Africa.

(3) The zone of accidental epidemics, between the parallels of 45° north and 35° south latitude.

In the seventeenth century Guadaloupe, Dominica, Martinique, and Barbadoes suffered from epidemics of yellow fever. After the first half of the seventeenth century the disease was prevalent all through the West Indies. It first appeared in the United States at the principal ports of Boston, Philadelphia, and Charleston, in 1693, and in 1699 it reappeared in Philadelphia and Charleston, and since that time many invasions have occurred, chiefly in the Southern States.

The epidemic of 1793 in Philadelphia, so graphically described by Matthew Carey, was, according to Osler, the most serious that has ever prevailed in any city of the Middle States. Although the population of the city was only 40,000, during the months of August, September, October, and November the mortality, as given by Carey, was 4041, of whom 3435 died in the months of September and October. During the following ten years epidemics of a lesser degree occurred along the coast of the United States, and in 1853 the disease raged throughout the Southern States, there being a mortality in New Orleans alone of nearly 8000. In the epidemic of 1878 in the Southern States the mortality was nearly 16,000. South America was invaded for the first time in 1740, and since 1849 the disease has been endemic in Brazil. Peru and the Argentine Republic have also received severe visitations of yellow fever since 1854. In Cuba the disease is epidemic during June, July, and August, and it appears with such certainty that the Revolutionists at the present time count more on the agency of yellow fever in the destruction of the unacclimated Spanish soldiers than on their own efforts.

Leprosy is distinctly a malady of Oriental origin, and existed in prehistoric times in Egypt and Judea. It was supposed to have been brought into Europe by a Roman army commanded by Pompey, after an expedition into Palestine. Leprosy was mentioned by several authors in the Christian era. France was invaded about the second century, and from that time on to the Crusades the disease gradually increased. At this epoch, the number of lepers or ladres becoming so large, they were obliged to confine themselves to certain portions of the country, and they took for their patron St. Lazare, and small hospitals were built and dedicated to this saint. Under Louis VIII. 2000 of these hospitals were counted, and later, according to Dupouy, there were 19,000 in the French kingdom. Various laws and regulations were made to prevent the spread of the contagion. In 1540 it was said that there were as many as 660 lepers in one hospital in Paris.

No mention is made in the Hippocratic writings of elephantiasis græcorum, which was really a type of leprosy, and is now considered synonymous with it. According to Rayer, some writers insist that the affection then existed under the name of the Phœnician disease. Before the time of Celsus, the poet Lucretius first speaks of elephantiasis græcorum, and assigns Egypt as the country where it occurs. Celsus gives the principal characteristics, and adds that the disease is scarcely known in Italy, but is very common in certain other countries. Galen supplies us with several particular but imperfect cases—histories of elephantiasis græcorum, with a view to demonstrate the value of the flesh of the viper, and in another review he adds that the disease is common in Alexandria. Aretæus has left a very accurate picture of the symptoms of elephantiasis græcorum ; and Pliny recapitulates the principal features and tells us that the disease is indigenous in Egypt. The opinion of the contagiousness of elephantiasis græcorum which we find announced in Herodotus and Galen is more strongly insisted upon by Cælius Aurelianus who recommends isolation of those affected. Paulus Ægenita discusses the disease. The Arabian writers have described elephantiasis græcorum under the name of juzam, which their translators have rendered by the word lepra. Later, Hensler, Fernel, Paré, Vesalius, Horstius, Forestus, and others have discussed it.

The statistics of leprosy in Europe pale before the numbers affected in the East. The extent of its former ravages is unknown, but it is estimated that at the present day there are over 250,000 lepers in India, and the number in China is possibly beyond computation. According to Morrow, in 1889 in the Sandwich Islands there were 1100 lepers in the settlement at Molokai. Berger states that there were 100 cases at Key West; and Blanc found 40 cases at New Orleans. Cases of leprosy are not infrequently found among the Chinese on the Pacific coast, and an occasional case is seen in the large cities of this country. At the present day in Europe, where leprosy was once so well known, it is never found except in Norway and the far East.

Possibly few diseases have caused so much misery and suffering as leprosy. The banishment from all friends and relatives, the confiscation of property and seclusion from the world, coupled with poverty and brutality of treatment,—all emphasize its physical horror a thousandfold. As to the leper himself, no more graphic description can be given than that printed in *The Nineteenth Century*, August, 1884 : " But leprosy ! Were I to describe it no one would follow me. More cruel than the clumsy torturing weapons of old, it distorts, and scars, and hacks, and maims, and destroys its victim inch by inch, feature by feature, member by member, joint by joint, sense by sense, leaving him to cumber the earth and tell the horrid tale of a living death, till there is nothing left of him. Eyes, voice, nose, toes, fingers, feet, hands, one after the other are slowly deformed and rot away, until at the end of ten, fifteen, twenty years, it may be, the wretched leper, afflicted in every sense himself, and hateful to the sight, smell, hearing, and touch of others, dies, despised and the most abject of men."

Syphilis.—Heretofore the best evidence has seemed to prove that syphilis had its origin in 1494, during the siege of Naples by Charles VIII. of France ; but in later days many investigators, prominent among them Buret, have stated that there is distinct evidence of the existence of syphilis in prehistoric times. Buret finds evidence of traces of syphilis among the Chinese five thousand years ago, among the Egyptians at the time of the Pharaohs, among the Hebrews and Hindoos in biblic times, and among the Greeks and Romans after Christ. Some American writers claim to have found evidences of syphilitic disease in the skulls and other bones of the prehistoric Indian mounds, thus giving further evidence to the advocates of the American origin of syphilis. The Spaniards claimed that, returning from America in 1493, Columbus brought with him syphilis. Friend says : " One thing is remarkable ; the Spaniards, upon their first expedition to America, brought home from thence this contagious disorder, and soon after carried another affection thither, the small-pox, of which the Indian Prince Montezuma died." The first descriptions of syphilis are given under the name of *morbus gallicus*, while the French in return called it *morbus neapolitanus* or *mal d' Italie*. The name of syphilis was said to have been first given to it by a physician of Verona, in a poem describing the disease. Inspired by heroic epics Fracastor places before us the divinities of paganism, and supposes that a shepherd, whom he called Syphilus, had addressed words offensive to Apollo, and had deserted his altars. To punish him the God sent him a disease of the genitals, which the inhabitants of the country called the disease of Syphilus.

" *Syphilidemque ab eo labem dixêre coloni.*" [a]

Buret traces the origin of the word syphilis from σύν, with, and φιλία, love, the companion of love ; which means in plain language that the pox is a disease transmitted more especially by venereal relations. The first great epidemic of syphilis occurred between 1493 and 1496, and attacked all ranks, neither the Church nor the Crown being spared. The ravages of this disease were increased by the treatment with mercury which soon afterward was found in proper doses to be a specific in this disease. It is possible that the terrible manifestations of syphilis of which we read in the older writers were in a great measure due to the enormous doses of mercury. At the present day syphilis is universally prevalent. In his excellent monograph Sturgis estimated in New York, in 1873, that one out of 18 suffered from it ; and White of Philadelphia pronounces the opinion that " not less than 50,000 people in that city are affected with syphilis." According to Rohé, on this basis Gihon estimates the number of syphilitics in the United States at one time as 2,000,000.

To-day no disease, except possibly tuberculosis, is a greater agency in augmenting the general mortality and furthering sickness than syphilis. Its hereditary features, the numerous ways in which it may be communicated outside of the performance of the sexual act, and the careful way in which it is kept from the sanitary authorities render it a scourge which, at the present day, we seem to have no method of successfully repressing.

Modern Mortality from Infectious Diseases.—As to the direct influence on the mortality of the most common infectious diseases of the present day, **tuberculosis,** universally prevalent, is invariably in the lead. No race or geographic situation is exempt from it. Osler mentions that in the Blood Indian Reserve of the Canadian Northwest Territories, during six years, among a population of about 2000 there were 127 deaths from pulmonary consumption. This enormous death-rate, it is to be remembered, occurred in a tribe occupying one of the finest climates of the world, among the foothills of the Rocky Mountains, a region in which consumption is extremely rare among the white population, and in which cases of tuberculosis from the Eastern provinces do remarkably well. Mayo-Smith [b] quotes a table illustrating the annual deaths (based on the returns from 1887 to 1891) from certain infectious diseases per 10,000 European inhabitants. The figures for each disease give a rough measure of its prevalence in different countries. The large figures as to small-pox show the absence in Italy and

[a] "Hieronymi Fracastorii," Veronæ, 1530.   [b] Statistics and Sociology, New York, 1885.

Austria of vaccination; diphtheria seems to be very fatal in Germany and Austria; Italy has a large rate for typhoid fever, and the same is true of the other fevers; France, Germany, and Austria show a very large rate for tuberculosis, while Italy has a small rate.

DEATHS FROM CERTAIN DISEASES PER 10,000 INHABITANTS.

COUNTRY.	SMALL-POX.	MEASLES.	SCARLET FEVER.	DIPHTHE-RIA.	TYPHOID FEVER.	TUBERCU-LOSIS.
Italy, ...	3.86	6.17	2.99	6.08	7.49	13.61
France (cities), ...	2.3	5.18	3.1	6.66	5.32	33.
England, ...	0.11	4.68	2.31	1.74	1.9	16.09
Ireland, ...	0.01	2.01	1.22	0.76	2.33	21.15
Germany (cities), ...	0.04	2.8	2.15	10.21	2.11	31.29
Prussia, ...	0.03	3.2	2.46	14.17	2.26	28.06
Austria, ...	4.43	5.36	5.57	13.2	5.42	37.2
Switzerland, ...	0.06	1.53	1.22	3.53	1.47	21.07
Belgium, ...	1.52	6.2	1.62	5.77	3.83	19.87
Holland, ...	0.02	3.93	0.38	1.45	2.5	19.21
Sweden, ...	0.01	2.3	3.69	3.89	2.22	. .

Based upon the Tenth Census Reports, we figure that of every 10,000 inhabitants of the United States the number of deaths for the census year from similar diseases was as follows :—

	Rural.	Cities.
Measles, ...	1.62	1.54
Scarlet Fever, ...	2.84	5.54
Diphtheria, ...	7.53	8.
Croup, ...	3.51	4.08
Typhoid Fever, ...	4.75	3.46
Tuberculosis, ...	16.29	28.55

The general average of deaths from small-pox was about 0.14.

BIBLIOGRAPHIC INDEX.

BEING A PARTIAL BIBLIOGRAPHY NUMERICALLY ARRANGED FOR PURPOSE
OF REFERENCE.*

A.

100. Abeille (L') médicale. Paris.
101. Abhandlungen der königl. Schwedischen Akademie, etc. Vol. for 1763. Leipzig, 1768.
102. Abhandlungen der k. k. medizinisch-chirurgischen Josephs - Akademie zu Wien. 1801.
103. Abhandlungen der physikalisch-medizinischen Societät zu Erlangen. 1810-.
104. Acad. nat. curios. ephemerides. Francofurti et Lipsæ, 1712; Noribergæ, 1715–17. (The Ephemerides.)
105. Acta Acad. Cæsareæ-naturæ curiosorum. Norimbergæ, 1727-.
106. Acta Eruditorum. Leipzig.
107. Acta Helvetica physico-mathematico-botanico-medica. Basilæ, 1751–77.
108. Acta medicorum Berolinensium, etc. Berolini, 1717-.
109. Acta regiæ Societatis medicæ Haviensis. Havniæ.
110. Acta medica Hafniensia, Prodromus, etc. Hafniæ et Lipsæ, 1775-.
111. Aerztliches Intelligenz-Blatt. München.
112. Albertus (Michaelis). Dissertatio de Longevitati, etc. 1728.
113. Albertus (Michaelis). Systema jurisprudentiæ medicæ. 6 vols., 4°. Halæ, 1736–47.
114. Albinus (Bernhardus). Dissertatio de sterilitatis.
115. Albucasis. De chirurgia. Arabice et Latine. Oxford, 1778.

116. Aldrovandus (Ulysses). Opera. 13 vols. Bonon., 1646–48.
117. Allgemeine Literatur-Zeitung. Jena.
118. Allgemeine Wiener medizinische Zeitung.
119. Amatus Lusitanus (J. R.). Curationum medicinalium medici physici, etc. 8°. Venetiis, 1557.
120. Amman (Paulus). Medicina critica. Erffurti, 1670.
121. American Gynæcological and Obstetrical Journal. New York.
122. American Homœopathist. Chicago.
123. American Journal of Insanity. Utica, N. Y.
124. American Journal of Medical Science. Philadelphia.
125. American Journal of Obstetrics. New York.
126. American Journal of Science and Arts. New Haven, Conn.
127. American Journal of Syphilography and Dermatology. New York.
128. American Medical Monthly. New York.
129. American Medical Recorder. Philadelphia.
130. American Medical Times. New York.
131. American Medical Weekly. Louisville, Ky.
132. American Medico-Surgical Bulletin. New York.
133. American Practitioner. Louisville, Ky.
134. American Therapist. New York.
135. Annalen der Entbindungs-Lehranstalt auf der Universität zu Göttingen. Von Osiander.

* The numbers in this index have been used in all the reference foot-notes and in the text to indicate the corresponding authorities.

915

136. Annalen der Staatsarzneikunde. Tübingen, 1836-.
137. Annalen der Staatsarzneykunde. Züllichau, 1790-.
138. Annalen für die gesammte Heilkunde. Karlsruhe, 1824-.
139. Annales de chimie et de physique. Paris.
140. Annales de gynécologie. Paris.
141. Annales d'hygiène, etc. Paris.
142. Annales des maladies des organes génito-urinaires. Paris.
143. Annales de médecine belge et étrangère. Bruxelles.
144. Annales médico - psychologiques. Paris.
145. Annales d'oculistique. Bruxelles.
146. Annales de la Société de médecine de Saint-Étienne et de la Loire.
147. Annales de la Société de médecine-pratique de Montpellier.
148. Annals of the Anatomical and Surgical Society. Brooklyn.
149. Annals of Medicine. Edinburgh.
150. Annals of Surgery. New York.
151. Annali di medicina. Milano, 1802.
152. Annali di ostetricia, etc. Milano.
153. Annali universali di medicina. Milano. (Omodei.)
154. Arand (Franciscus). Observationes medico - chirurgicæ. 8°. Goettingæ, 1770.
155. Archiv der Heilkunde. Leipzig.
156. Archiv der Pharmacie. Halle.
157. Archiv für Anthropologie. Braunschweig.
158. Archiv für praktische Medizin und Klinik. Berlin, 1807-.
159. Archiv für medizinische Erfahrung. 1801-. (Horn.)
160. Archiv für die Geburtshülfe, etc. J. C. Stark, Jena. (1798–1800 as N. Archiv, etc.)
161. Archiv für pathologische Anatomie und Physiologie, etc. Berlin. (Virchow's Archives.)
162. Archives générales de médecine. Paris.
163. Archives de médecine navale. Paris.
164. Archives provinciales chirurgie. Paris.
165. Archives of Pediatrics.
166. Archives of Surgery. London. (Hutchinson.)
167. Archives of Surgery. New York.

168. Archives de tocologie. Paris.
169. Aristoteles. Opera omnia. 5 vols. Parisiis, 1862–74.
170. Aristoteles. Historia de Animalibus. Tolos, 1619.
171. Art (L') médical. Bruxelles.
172. Arzneykundige Annalen von Tode. Kopenhagen, 1787-.
173. Asclepiad. London.
174. Ashhurst (John, Jr.). Principles and Practice of Surgery. Philadelphia, 1889.
175. Association Medical Journal. London.
176. Atlanta Medical and Surgical Journal. Atlanta, Ga.
177. Aurran (J. F.). E linguis feminæ loquela. Argentinæ, 1766.
178. Australasian Medical Gazette. Sydney.
179. Australian Medical Gazette. Melbourne.
180. Australian Medical Journal. Melbourne.
181. Autenrieth (J. F. H.). Handbuch der Physiologie. 3 vols. 8°. Tübingen, 1801.

B.

182. Bacchetoni (H. L.). Anatomia medicinæ, etc. Oeniponti, 1740.
183. Bailey (J. B.). Modern Methusalehs. 8°. London, 1888.
184. Baily (T.). Records of Longevity. 8°. London, 1857.
185. Ballonius (Guilielmus). Opera medica omnia. 4 vols. Genevæ, 1762.
186. Baltimore Medical Journal.
187. Baltimore Medical and Surgical Journal and Review.
188. Bartholinus (Thomas). Acta medica et philosophica. Hafniensia, 1671–79.
189. Bartholinus (Thomas). Epistolarum medicinalium. Hafniæ, 1663.
190. Bartholinus (Thomas). Historiarum anatomicarum rariorum. Cent. i–vi. Hafniæ, 1654–61.
191. Bateman (—). The Doome. 1581. (In the British Museum.)
192. Becker (J. C.). De submersorum Morte, etc. Giessæ, 1704
193. Becker (Dan.). Cultrivori Prussiaci Curatio singulis. Lugd. Bat., 1640.

194. Bell (Charles). Institutes of Surgery, etc. 8°. Philadelphia, 1840.

195. Bellini (Laurentius). Opera omnia. 4°. Venetiis, 1732.

196. Benedictus (Crispus). Commentarium medicinale.

197. Benivenius (A.). Mem. observat. exempla rara colon., 1581.

198. Benivenius (A.). De abditis nonnulis ac mirandis Morborum et Sanationum Causis, 1521.

199. Berliner klinische Wochenschrift.

200. Berlinische Sammlungen zur Beförderung der Arzneywissenschaft, etc. Berlin, 1768–79.

201. Bernstein (J. G.). Wien, 1805.

202. Berthold (A. A.). Ueber das Gesetz der Schwangerschaftsdauer. 4°. Göttingen, 1844.

203. Beyträge zum Archiv der medizinischen Polizei, etc. Leipzig, 1789–99.

204. Bianchi (Giovanni). De monstris, etc. Venetiis, 1749.

205. Bianchi (Giovanni). Storia del monstros di due Corp., etc. Turin, 1748.

206. Bibliothek für die Chirurgie. Göttingen. Von Langenbeck.

207. Bibliothek for Laeger. Kjøbenhavn.

208. Bibliothek der praktischen Heilkunde. Berlin, 1799–1843.

209. Bichat (M.-F.-X.). Anatomie générale appliquée à la physiologie et à la médecine.

210. Bierling (C. T.). Adversariorum curiosorum, etc. Jenæ, 1679.

211. Bierling (C. G.). Thesaurus Theoretico-practicus, etc. Jenæ, 1694.

212. Blanc (L.). Les anomalies chez l'homme et des mammifères. Paris, 1893.

213. Blanchard (S.) (editor). Collectanæ medico-physica, etc. Amsterdam, 1680.

214. Blasius (Gerardus). Observationes medicæ rariores. Accedit monstri triplicis historia. 1677.

215. de Blegny (Nicolas). Zodiacus medico-gallicus, etc. Geneva.

216. Bonet (Théophilius). Sepulchretum, etc. Genevæ, 1679.

217. Bontius (Jacob). De medicina Indorum. Lugd. Bat., 1642.

218. Boston Medical and Surgical Journal.

219. Bouchut (E.). Les signes de la mort, etc. Paris, 1883.

220. Braithwaite's Retrospect of Medicine.

221. British and Foreign Medical Review. London.

222. British and Foreign Medico-Chirurgical Review. London.

223. British Gynæcological Journal. London.

224. British Medical Journal. London.

225. British Record of Obstetric Medicine and Surgery. Manchester, 1848–.

226. Brierre de Boismont (A.). Du suicide et de la folie suicide. Paris, 1865.

227. Brooklyn Medical Journal.

228. Bruyerinus (Joannes). De re cibaria libri xxii, etc. Lugduni, 1560.

229. Büttner (C. G.). Sechs seltene Anatomisch - chirurgische Wahrnehmungen. Königsberg, 1774.

230. Buffalo Medical and Surgical Journal.

231. Buffalo Medical Journal.

232. Buffon (G.-L.-L.). Œuvres complètes. 6 vols. Bruxelles, 1828–.

233. Bulletin de l'Académie de médecine. Paris.

234. Bulletin de l'Academie royale de médecine de Belgique. Bruxelles.

235. Bulletin gén. de thérapeutique méd. et chir. Paris.

236. Bulletin médical du nord. Lille.

237. Bulletins et mémoires de la Société médicale des hôpitaux de Paris.

238. Bulletin et Mém. Société de Obst. et Gynecol. de Paris.

239. Bulletin de la Société médicale de la Suisse Romande. Lausanne.

240. Bulletin des Sciences médicales. Paris, 1824–.

241. Bulletin des Sciences Naturelles et de Géologie. Paris. (Brouginart.)

242. Bulletin de la Société anatomique de Paris.

243. Bulletin de la Société d'anthropologie de Paris.

244. Büttner (Chr. Gottl.). Sechs seltene Anatomisch - chirurgische Wahrnehmungen. 4°. Königsberg, 1774. (Same as 229.)

C.

245. Cabrolius (Bartholomæus). Observationes.

246. California Medical Gazette. San Francisco.

247. Camerarius (J. R.). Sylloges memo-
     rabilium medicinæ, etc. Tubingæ,
     1683.
248. Campbell (C.-J.). De l'accouchement
     des femmes qui meurent à une
     epoque avancée de la grossesse.
     Paris, 1849. (Thesis.)
249. Camper (Petrus). Demonstrationum
     anatomico - pathologicarum. Am-
     stelodami, 1760-.
250. Canada Lancet. Toronto.
251. Canada Medical Journal. Montreal.
252. Canada Medical and Surgical Jour-
     nal. Montreal.
253. Canadian Journal of Medical Science.
     Toronto.
254. Capuron (Joseph). La médecine
     légale relative à l'art des accouche-
     ments. Paris, 1821.
255. Cardanus (Jerome). Opera omnia.
     10 vols. Lugduni, 1663.
256. Carolina Journal of Medicine, Science,
     and Agriculture. Charleston, 1825.
257. à Castro (Rodericus). De universa
     muliebrium morborum medicina.
     Hamburgi, 1617.
258. Cattieri (Isaac). Observationes medi-
     cinales raræ.
259. Celsus (A. C.). De medicina, libri
     octo.
260. Centralblatt für Chirurgie. Leipzig.
261. Centralblatt für Gynäkologie. Leip-
     zig.
262. Centralblatt für praktische Augen-
     heilkunde. Leipzig.
263. Charité-Annalen. Berlin.
264. Charleston Medical Journal and Re-
     view. Charleston, S. C.
265. von Chelius (M. J.). Surgery, trans-
     lated by J. F. South. Philadel-
     phia, 1847.
266. Chevers (N.). A Manual of Medical
     Jurisprudence for India.
267. Chicago Medical Examiner.
268. Chicago Medical Journal.
269. Chicago Medical Journal and Exam-
     iner.
270. Chirurgicheskaja Laitopsis. Moskva,
     1891-.
271. Cincinnati Journal of Medicine. Cin-
     cinnati and Indianapolis.
272. Cincinnati Lancet and Clinic.
273. Cincinnati Medical Repertory.
274. Clinic (The). Cincinnati, 1871-78.
275. Clinical Sketches. London.

276. Clinique (La) des hôpitaux et de la
     ville. Paris.
277. Cohausen (J. H.). Lumen novum
     Phosphoris. Amstelodami, 1717.
278. Coimbra medica. Coimbra.
279. Coindet (E.-N.-P.). Des déchirures
     traumatiques spontanées du pou-
     mon. Paris, 1860.
280. Collection academique, etc. Dijon et
     Paris, 1755-79.
281. Comitis Mythyologie libri decem, etc.
     Genevæ, 1656.
282. Commercium literarium, etc. Norim-
     bergæ, 1731.
283. Comptes rendus hebdomadaires des
     séances de l'Académie des Sciences.
     Paris.
284. Crantz (H. J. N.). Comm. de rupt.
     in partu dolor a fet. uterus, etc.
     Translation by Clay.
285. Cruikshank (William). The Anatomy
     of the Absorbing Vessels. 4°. Lon-
     don, 1786.

D.

286. Daniel's Texas Medical Journal.
     Austin.
287. Dantes (Alfred). Dictionnaire bio-
     graphique et bibliographique.
     Paris, 1875.
288. Darwin (Chas. R.). On the Origin
     of Species, etc.
289. Darwin (Chas. R.). The Descent of
     Man, etc.
290. Debes (Lucas). Natürliche und poli-
     tische Historie der Inseln Färöe.
     Kopenhagen, 1757.
291. Debierre (Ch.). L'hermaphrodisme.
     Paris, 1891.
292. Dechambre (director) Dict. encyclo-
     ped. des Sciences médicales. 102
     vols. Paris.
293. Delestre (J. B.). De la physiogno-
     monie. Paris, 1846.
294. Deneux (L.-C.). Essai sur la rupture
     de la matrice, etc. Paris, 1804.
     (Thesis.)
295. Denkschriften der vaterländischen
     Gesellschaft der Aerzte und Natur-
     forscher Schwabens. Tübingen,
     1805-.
296. Dental Cosmos. Philadelphia.
297. Desault (P.-J.). Journal de chirur-
     gie. Paris, 1791-.

298. Detroit Lancet.

299. Detroit Review of Medicine and Pharmacy.

300. D e u t s c h e medizinische Wochenschrift. Berlin.

301. Dewees (W. P.). Medical Miscellanies. Philadelphia, 1805.

302. Dictionnaire des sciences médicales. 60 vols. Paris, 1812-.

303. de Diemerbroeck (Isbrand). Anatome corporis humani. 1672.

304. de Diemerbroeck (Isbrand). Opera omnia. 4°. Ultraj., 1685.

305. Dilthey (P. M.). Diss. sistens observationem rariorum de valvulis in ureteribus repertis. 1723.

306. Donatus (Marcellus). De medica historia mirabili libri sex. 4°. Mantuæ, 1586.

307. Dover (Thomas). The Ancient Physician's Legacy, etc. 8°. London, 1762.

308. Dublin Hospital Gazette.

309. Dublin Journal of Medical and Chemical Science.

310. Dublin Journal of Medical Science.

311. Dublin Hospital Reports. 1818-.

312. Dublin Medical Press.

313. Dublin Quarterly Journal of Medical Sciences.

314. Dupouy (E.). Le moyen age médicale. Paris, 1895.

E.

315. Eclectic Medical Journal. Cincinnati.

316. Eclectic Repertory, etc. Philadelphia.

317. Edinburgh Journal of Medical Science.

318. Edinburgh Medical and Surgical Journal (after July, 1855-, Edinburgh Medical Journal).

319. Edinburgh Monthly Journal of Medical Science.

320. Ehrlich (J. A.). Chirurgische Beobachtungen.

321. Eira. Göteburg.

322. Elliotson (John). Human Physiology. London, 1841.

323. Emulacion (La). Mérida.

324. Encyclopedia Britannica.

325. Engelmann (G. J.). La pratique des accouchements chez les peuples primitifs ; edition français par Rodet. Paris, 1886.

326. Escuela médica. Carácas.

327. Eudes de Mézeray (François). Histoire de France. Vol. iii.

328. European Magazine and London Review.

329. Ethnological Journal, London.

330. Experience (L'), journal de médecine et de chirurgie. Paris.

331. Extracts from the Records of the Boston Society for Medical Improvement.

F.

332. Fabricius (P. C.). Diss. sistens ægrum epilepsia, etc. 4°. Giessæ, 1738.

333. Fabricius (P. C.). Idea anatomicæ practicæ. Wetzlariæ, 1741.

334. Fabricius Hildanus (Guilielmus). Opera omnia. Francof. a. M., 1646.

335. Fantoni (Joh.). Opuscula medica et physiologica. Genevæ, 1738.

336. Facultad (La). Madrid.

337. Fanzago (F. L.). Storia del monstro di due corpi, etc. Padova, 1803.

338. Farmer (J.). Select Cases in Surgery. 4°. London, 1758.

339. Fatio (Joh.). Helvetisch-vernünftige Wehe-Mutter, etc. Basle, 1752.

340. Fernelius (Jo.). Universa medicina. 1645.

341. Ficker (Wilhelm Anton). Comment, etc. Göttingen, 1791.

342. Fickius (J. J.). Diss. de abortu epidemicus. Jenæ, 1697.

343. Figuer (L.). L'homme primitif. Paris, 1870.

344. Flajani (Giuseppe). Medizinischchirurgische Beobachtungen. Translated from the Italian.

345. Flourens (P). De la longévité humaine. Paris, 1856.

346. Foissac (P.). Hygiène philosophique de l'ame. Paris, 1860.

347. Fontanus (Nicolaus). Responsionum et curationum medicinalium. Amstelodami, 1639.

348. Forestus (Petrus). Observationem et curationem medicinalium ac chirurgicarum. 1653.

349. France (La) médicale. Paris.

350. Francus de Frankenau (Georgius). Satyræ medicæ. Lipsiæ, 1722.

351. Frank (J. P.). De curandis hominum morbis, etc. Viennæ, 1810.

407. Hebra (Ferdinand). On Diseases of the Skin. Translated from the German. London, 1866–.
408. Hecker (J. F. C.). The Epidemics of the Middle Ages. Translated by Babbington. London, 1859.
409. ab Heers (Henricus). Observatiorum medicarum. Lugd. Bat., 1645.
410. Heister (Laurenz). Compendium anatomicum, etc. Altorfi et Norimb., 1727.
411. Heister (Laurenz). Diss. Altorfi, 1720.
412. Heister (Laurenz). Medicinische, chirurgische und anatomische Wahrnehmungen. Rostock, 1753.
413. van Helmont (J. B.). Opuscula medica inaudita. Venetiis, 1651.
414. Hellwigius (J.). Observationes physico-medicæ, etc. Augustæ Vindelicorum, 1680.
415. Herodotus. Historiarum. Libri ix. Francofurti, 1608.
416. Hippocrates. Opera omnia, or the edition translated by Adams. In two vols. 8°. London, 1849.
417. Hirst and Piersol. Human Monstrosities. Philadelphia.
418. Histoire de l'Académie des sciences. Paris.
419. Hodge (H. L.). Principles and Practice of Obstetrics. Philadelphia, 1864.
420. Hoffmann (Frid.). A System of Practical Medicine. Translated by Lewis. London, 1783.
421. Hollerius (Jacobus). Omnia opera practica, ad Calcem, etc. Genevæ, 1623.
422. Holmes (Timothy). A System of Surgery, etc. Philadelphia, 1881.
423. Horstius (Gregorius). Opera medica. 1660.
424. Hospital Gazette and Archives of Clinical Surgery. New York.
425. Hospitals-Tidende. Kjøbehavn, 1858–.
426. Hufeland (C. W.). Die Kunst, das menschliche Leben zu verlängern.
427. Hufeland (C. W.). Art of Prolonging Life. Edited by Erasmus Wilson. Philadelphia, 1870.
428. Huxham (John). Opera physicomedica. Lipsiæ, 1773.

I.

429. Illustration (L'). Paris.
430. Illustrated Medical News. London.
431. Index Catalogue of the Library of the Surgeon-General's Office. Washington, 1879–.
432. Index Medicus.
433. Indian Annals of Medical Science. Calcutta.
434. India Journal of Medical and Physical Science. Calcutta.
435. Indian Medical Gazette. Calcutta.
436. Indian Medical Record. Calcutta.
437. Independent Practitioner. Baltimore, and continued elsewhere.
438. International Clinics. Philadelphia, 1891–.
439. International Encyclopedia of Surgery. Edited by John Ashhurst, Jr. 1881–84.
440. Iowa Medical Journal. Keokuk.
441. Insfeldt (J. C.). De lusibus naturæ. 4°. Lugd. Bat., 1772.
442. Isenflamm et Rosenmüller. Beyträge für die Zerg.

J.

443. Jacobson (W. H. A.). Diseases of the Male Organs of Generation. 8°. London, 1893.
444. Jahrbuch der Staatsarzneikunde. Frankfurt a. M. (Kopp.)
445. Jeaffreson (William). A Practical Treatise on Diseases of the Eye. 8°. London, 1844.
446. Johns Hopkins Bulletin. Baltimore.
447. Jonston (Joh.). Thaumatographia naturalis. 1665.
448. Josephus (Flavius). Historia, etc. Paris, 1528.
449. Joubert (Laurentius). Traité du ris, etc. Paris, 1579.
450. Journal of the American Medical Association.
451. Journal of Anatomy and Physiology. London.
452. Journal der praktischen Arzneykunde und Wundarzneykunde. Herausgegeben von C. W. Hufeland.
453. Journal of the National Association of Railway Surgeons. Fort Wayne, Indiana.

454. Journal complémentaire du dictionnaire des sciences médicales. Paris,
1818-.

455. Journal of Cutaneous and Venereal
Diseases. New York.

456. Journal für die Chirurgie, etc. Von
Loder. Jena, 1797.

457. Journal für Geburtshülfe, etc. Frankfurt a. M., 1813-.

458. Journal général de médecine, de chirurgie, et de pharmacie. Paris.

459. Journal of the Gynæcological Society
of Boston.

460. Journal de méd., chir., pharm., etc.
Paris, 1754–93.

461. Journal de méd., chir., pharm., etc.
Paris, 1801–17.

462. Journal de médecine. Paris. (See
460.)

463. Journal de médecine. Paris (continued). (See 461.)

464. Journal de médecine militaire. Paris,
1782-.

465. Journal of Mental Science. London.

466. Journal of Nervous and Mental Diseases. New York.

467. Journal Politique de Manheim.

468. Journal der praktischen Heilkunde.
Berlin, 1801–41.

469. Journal des Savans. Paris.

470. Journal de Sçavans. etc. Paris.

471. Journal de la section de médecine de
la Société académique, etc., Loire-
Inférieure. Nantes.

472. Journal da Sociedade das sciencias
medicas de Lisboa.

K.

473. Kerckringius (Theodorus). Spicilegium anatomicum. Amstelodami,
1670.

L.

474. de La Motte (G. M.). Traité complet des accouchements, etc. 4°.
Paris, 1722.

475. Lancisi (J.-M.). De subitaneis mor-
tibus. Romæ, 1707.

476. Lancet, London.

477. Lanzoni (Josephus). Opera omnia.
Lausanne, 1738.

478. Larrey (D.-J.). Memoires de chirurgie militaire et campagnes. 4
vols. 8°. Paris, 1812–17.

479. Laurent (E.). Les bisexués, gynéco-
mastes, et hermaphrodites. Paris,
1894.

480. Laurentius (Andreas). Historia anatomica humani corporis, etc.
Francofurti, 1636.

481. Leavenworth Medical Herald.

482. Lebert (Herman). Ueber Keratose.
8°. Breslau, 1864.

483. Leigh (Charles). Exercitationes
quinque. Oxonii, 1697. 8°.

484. Lentilius (Rosinus). Misc. medico-
practica, etc. Ulmæ, 1698.

485. Lhéritier (S. - D.). Traité complet
des maladies de la femme. 8°.
Paris, 1838.

486. Licetus (Fortunius). De monstris.
4°. Amstelodami, 1665.

487. Loaring (H. J.). Epitaphs, etc.
London.

488. Lobstein (J.-G.-C. F.-M.). Traité
d'anatomie pathologique. Paris,
1829.

489. Loeseke (J. L. L.). Observationes
anatomico-chirurgico-medicæ, etc.
Berolini, 1754.

490. London Medical Gazette.

491. London Medical Record.

492. London Medical and Surgical Journal.

493. Lonsdale (E. F.). A Practical Treatise on Fractures. 8°. London,
1838.

494. Louisville Medical News. Louisville,
Ky.

495. Lucina. Leipzig, 1802–11. Editor
A. E. von Siebold.

496. Lycosthenes (Wolffhart) (C.). Prodigiorum ac ostentorum chronicon.
Basileæ, 1557.

497. Lyon médical.

498. Lyser (Michael). Observationes medicæ. Hafniæ, 1665.

M.

499. Mackenzie (Sir M.). A Manual of
Diseases of the Throat and Nose,
etc. London, 1884.

500. Madras Quarterly Journal of Medical
Science.

501. Magazin vor Aerzte. Von Baldinger.
(Also N. Mag., etc.)

502. Magazin der ausländischen Literatur
der gesammten Heilkunde, etc.
Hamburg. (Julius und Gerson.)

503. Magazin für die neuesten Entdeckungen in der gesammten Naturkunde. Berlin, 1807-.
504. Magazin für die gesammte Heilkunde, etc. Berlin. (Herausgegeben von Rust.)
505. Mandelslo (J. A.). Schreiben von Olearium. Schlesswig, 1658.
506. Martin de Pedro (Ecequiel). Estudios de teratologia, etc. 8°. Madrid, 1879.
507. Marold (J. O.). De abortu per vomitum rejecto. Altdorff, 1669.
508. de Marque (Jacques). Traité des Bandages, etc. Paris, 1662.
509. Martialis (Marcus Valerius). Epigrammata lib. xiiii.
510. Maryland Medical Journal. Baltimore.
511. Maryland Medical and Surgical Journal, etc. Baltimore.
512. Massachusetts Medical Journal. Boston.
513. Mauriceau (François). Traité des maladies des femmes grosses, etc. 4°. Paris, 1683.
514. Mazinus (J. B.). Opera omnia. Brixiæ, 1743.
515. Mead (Richard). De imperio solis ac lunæ in corpora humana et morbis unde oriundis. 16°. Londoni, 1704.
516. Meckel's Archive für Anatomie und Physiologie. Leipzig, 1789-.
517. de Meara (Edmundo). Historiæ medicæ rariores. Amstelodami, 1667.
518. Medical Age. Detroit.
519. Medical Archives. St. Louis.
520. Medical Bulletin. Philadelphia.
521. Medical Chronicle. Manchester.
522. Medical Chronicle. Montreal.
523. Medical Circular. London.
524. Medical Commentaries. Edinburgh.
525. Medical Counselor. Columbus, Ohio.
526. Medical Examiner. Philadelphia.
527. Medical Essays and Observations. Revised and published by a society in Edinburgh. 1733-.
528. Medical Facts and Observations. London, 1791-.
529. Medical Fortnightly. St. Louis.
530. Medical Herald. Louisville, Ky.
531. Medical Independent, etc. Detroit.
532. Medical Mirror. London.
533. Medical News. Philadelphia.

534. Medical and Philosophical Commentaries. London, 1774-.
535. Medical and Physical Journal. London.
536. Medical Press and Circular. London.
537. Medical Quarterly Review. London.
538. Medical Record. New York.
539. Medical Records and Researches of a Private Medical Association. London, 1798.
540. Medical Reporter. Calcutta.
541. Medical Repository. New York.
542. Medical Standard. Chicago.
543. Medical Summary. Philadelphia.
544. Medical and Surgical History of the War of the Rebellion.
545. Medical and Surgical Reporter. Philadelphia.
546. Medical Times. London.
547. Medical Times. Philadelphia.
548. Medical Times and Gazette. London.
549. Medico-Chirurgical Review. London.
550. Medico-Chirurgical Transactions. London.
551. Medicorum Silesiacorum Satyræ. Wratislaviæ et Lipsiæ, 1736.
552. Medicinische und chirurgische Berlinische wöchentliche Nachrichten. Von Schaarschmidt. Berlin, 1738-.
553. Medizinische Jahrbücher. Wien.
554. Medicinische Zeitung. Berlin.
555. Medicinisches Journal von Baldinger. Göttingen.
556. Meditsinskiy Vestnik. St. Petersburg.
557. Meditsinskoye Obozrainie. Moskva.
558. Medicinisch-chirurgische Bibliothek von Tode. Copenhagen, 1775.
559. Medicinisch-Chirurgische Zeitung. Salsburg, 1790-.
560. van Meek'ren (Job). Observationes medico-chirurgicæ. Amstelodami, 1682.
561. Meibomius (H.). Dissertationes, etc. Helmæstadi, 1668.
562. Mélanges biologiques, etc., de l'Académie impériale des sciences de St. Petersbourg.
563. Mémoires de l'Académie royale de chirurgie. Paris.
564. Memoirs of the Medical Society of London.
565. Mémoires de la Société médicale d'émulation de Paris. 1796-.

617. Panaroli (Dominico). Iatrologismorum seu. med. observ. pentecostæ, etc. Romæ, 1652.
618. Paré (Ambroise). Œuvres. Fifth Edition. Paris, 1598.
619. Pathological Museum of the British Medical Association at the Meeting in London, 1895. (Catalogue.)
620. Paullini (C. F.). Observationes medico-physicæ raræ, selectæ et curiosæ, etc. 12°. Lipsiæ, 1706.
621. Pechlin (J. N.). De aëris et alimenti defectu, etc. Kiloni, 1676.
622. Pechlin (J. N.). Observationum physico - medicarum, etc. Hamburgi, 1691.
623. Pennsylvania Hospital Reports. Philadelphia.
624. Petermann and Albrecht. Scrutinium icteri ex calculi vesisculæ, etc. Lipsiæ, 1696.
625. Petit (J.-L.). Traité des maladies chirurgicales, etc. 8°. Paris, 1790.
626. Pétrequin (J.-P-É.). Traité d'anatomie médico-chirurgical, etc. 8°. Paris, 1844.
627. Peyer (J. C.). Myrecologia. Basileæ, 1685.
628. Pfaff's Mittheilungen aus dem Gebiete der Medizin, Chirurgie, und Pharmacologie. Kiel, 1832-.
629. Philosophical Transactions of the Royal Society of London.
630. Phlegon Trallianus. de Mirab. in Opuscula. 4°. 1620.
631. Photographic Review of Medicine and Surgery. Philadelphia.
632. Physician and Surgeon. Ann Arbor, Mich.
633. Piccinelli (G. A.). Opuscoli scelti sulle Scienze, etc. 1778.
634. Pittsburgh Medical Review.
635. Plater (Felix). Observationum, etc. Basileæ, 1680.
636. Plinius (Cajus Secundus). Historiæ naturalis.
637. Plot (Robert). The Natural History of Staffordshire. Oxford, 1686.
638. Popular Science Monthly. New York.
639. Portal (Antoine). Cours d'anatomie médicale. 5 vols. 4°. Paris, 1804.
640. Porvenir (El). México.
641. Poulet (A.). Traité des corps étrangers en chirurgie. Paris, 1879.

642. Powell (Richard). Observations on Bile, etc. 8°. London, 1800.
643. Practitioner. London.
644. Prager medizinische Wochenschrift.
645. Presse (La) médicale belge. Bruxelles.
646. Presse (La) médicale. Paris.
647. Proceedings of the Connecticut Medical Society.
648. Proceedings of the Kings County Medical Society. Brooklyn, N. Y.
649. Proceedings of the Louisiana State Medical Association.
650. Proceedings of the Royal Medical and Chirurgical Society of London.
651. Proceedings of the Royal Society of London. 1854-.
652. Prochaska (Georgius). Adnotationum academicarum. Pragæ, 1780.
653. Progrès (Le) médical. Paris.
654. Provincial Medical Journal. Halifax.
655. Provincial Medical Journal. Leicester, 1885.
656. Provincial Medical and Surgical Journal. London.
657. Przeglad lekarski, etc. Kraków.

Q.

658. Quercetanus (Josephus). Diæteticon polyhistoricum. 4°. Francofurti, 1607.

R.

659. Raccoglitore medico di Fano.
660. Ramazzini (Bernardino). Epist., an. 1692.
661. Ranking's Half-Yearly Abstract. London, 1845–64.
662.' Recueil de mémoires de médecine, de chirurgie et de pharmacie militaires. Paris.
663. Recueil periodique d'observations de médecine de chirurgie et de pharmacie. Paris, 1754-.
664. Recueil periodique de la Société de médecine de Paris, 1797-.
665. Recueil periodique de la Société de santé de Paris.
666. Reference Handbook of the Medical Sciences. Wm. Wood & Co., New York.
667. Revista médico-quirúrgica. Buenos Aires.
668. Revista médica de Chile. Santiago de Chile.

669. Revue des cours scientifiques, etc. Paris.

670. Revue général de clinique et de thérapeutique. Paris, 1887–.

671. Revue de l'hypnotism, etc. Paris, 1886–.

672. Revue de médecine. Paris.

673. Revue médicale de Limoges.

674. Revue mensuelle des maladies de l'enfance. Paris.

675. Revue militaire de médecine et de chirurgie. Paris, 1881–.

676. Revue philosophique, etc. Paris, 1887–.

677. Revue photographique des hôpitaux de Paris.

678. Revue de therapeutique médico-chirurgicale. Paris.

679. Rhodiginus (L. C.). Lectionum antiquarium libri xxx. Basileæ, 1524.

680. Rhodius (Joannes). Mantissa anatomica. 8°. 1654.

681. Richmond and Louisville Medical Journal. Louisville, Ky.

682. Richter (A. G.). Chirurgische Bibliothek. Göttingen, 1771–.

683. Riedlin (Vitus). Lineæ medicæ singulos. 1695–.

684. Riforma (La) medica. Napoli.

685. Riolan (Jean) fils. Anthropographia. Parisiis, 1618.

686. Riolan (Jean) fils. Encheiridium anatomicum, etc. 16°. Paris, 1648.

687. Riverius (Lazarus). Observationes medicæ et curationes insignes. Londini, 1646.

688. Rivista italiana di terapia ed igiene. Piacenza.

689. Roger of Wendover. Flowers of History. Bohn's edition, 1849, vol. i.

690. von Rokitansky (Carl). Lehrbuch der pathologischen Anatomie. 3 vols. 8°. Wien, 1855–.

691. Rosenbladt (A. C.). Dissertationes. 1781.

692. Rossius (P. M.). Observationes med. chirurg. et practicæ, etc. 12°. Francofurti, 1608.

693. Royal London Ophthalmic Hospital Reports. London.

694. Rudtoffer (F. X.). Abhandlungen, etc. 2 vols. 8°. Wien, 1805–.

695. Rudolph (J. P. J.). De partu sicco. Erlangæ, 1790.

696. Rush (Benj.). Medical Inquiries and Observations. Philadelphia, 1805.

697. Russkaya Meditsina. St. Petersburg, 1883–.

698. Ruysch (Fredericus). Adversariorum anatomico-medico-chirurgicorum. Decas tertia, 1723.

699. Ruysch (Fredericus). Opera omnia. 4 vols. 8°. Amstelodami, 1737.

S.

700. Saint George's Hospital Reports. London.

701. St. Louis Clinical Record. St. Louis, Mo.

702. St. Louis Courier of Medicine, etc.

703. St. Louis Medical and Surgical Journal. St. Louis, Mo.

704. St. Petersburger medicinische Wochenschrift.

705. St. Thomas' Hospital Reports. London.

706. Salmuth (P.). Observationem medicarum centuriæ tres posthumæ. 4°. Brunsvigæ, 1648.

707. Salute (La). Genova.

708. Sammlung von Natur- und Medizin-Gesch., etc. Breslau. (Buchner.)

709. Sandifort (Eduard). Museum anatomicum, etc. Lugd. Bat., 1793.

710. Sandifort (Gerard). Tabulæ anatomicæ. 4 fasc. 1804.

711. Sangalli (Giacomo). La scienza e la practica della anatomia patologica. Milano, 1873–.

712. Savannah Journal of Medicine. Savannah, Ga.

713. Saviard (Barth.). Observationes chirurgicales. Paris, 1784.

714. Savonarola (G. M.). Practica, in sex tractus. Venetiis impressum, 1497.

715. Scarpa (Antonius). De structura fenestræ rotundæ, etc., 1772.

716. Schacher (P. G.). De polypis. Lipsiæ, 1721.

717. Schacher (P. G.). De superfœtatione. Lipsiæ, 1721.

718. Schenck (J.). Observationum medicarum. etc. 2 vols. 8°. Francofurti, 1600.

719. Schlichting (J. D.). Traumatologia. Amsterdam, 1748.

720. Schmidt's Jahrbücher. Leipzig.

721. Schmucker (J. L.). Vermischte chirurgische Schriften. Berlin, 1772–.

722. Schrader (H. H. C.). Observ. rariorum, etc. Guelpherbyti, 1760.

723. Scribner's Magazine. New York.

724. Schurig (Martin). Parthenologia historico-medica, etc. 4°. Dresden et Lipsiæ, 1729.

725. Schurig (Martin). Gynæcologia, etc. Dresden et Lipsiæ, 1730.

726. Schurig (Martin). Embryologia, etc. Dresden, 1732.

727. Science. Cambridge and New York.

728. Semaine (La) médicale. Paris.

729. Semi-monthly Medical News. Louisville, Ky.

730. Smetius (Heinrich). Miscellanea medica, etc. Francof. a. M., 1611.

731. de Senac (J. B.). Traité de la structure da cœur. Paris, 1749.

732. Sennert (Daniel). Paraphimosis. Wittebergæ, 1642.

733. Sermon (William). English Midwifery. 8°. London, 1671.

734. Severinus (M. A.). De efficaci medicina. Francofurti, 1671.

735. von Siebold (J. B.). . . . . chirurgischen Clinicums. Würzburg, 1814.

736. von Siebold (J. B.). Sammlung, etc. 3 vols. 12°. Rudolstadt, 1805–12.

737. Sinibaldus (J. B.). Geneanthropeiæ, etc. Romæ, 1642.

738. Skene (A. J. C.). Diseases of Women. New York, 1892.

739. Smellie (G.). Thesaurus medicus, etc. Edinburgi, 1778–.

740. Societatis medicæ Havniensis collectanea. Havniæ.

741. Solingen (Cornelius). . . . . Bysondere aanmerkingen. Amsterdam, 1698.

742. Solingen (Cornelius). . . . . Sonderbare Anmerckungen. Wittenberger, 1712. (Same as 741.)

743. de Sorbait (Paulus). Praxios medicæ, etc. Viennæ, 1680.

744. Southern Medical and Surgical Journal. Augusta, Ga.

745. Sozinskey (T. S.). Medical Symbolism. Philadelphia, 1891.

746. Spallanzani (Lo). Modena.

747. Sperimentale (Lo). Firenze.

748. Spindler (Paulus). Observationum medicinalium centuria, etc. Francof. ad M., 1691.

749. Spitalul. Bucuresci, 1881–.

750. Stalpart van der Wiel (Cornelius). Observ. rariorum. Lugd. Bat., 1687.

751. Stoll (Maximilian). Rationis medendi. Paris, 1787.

752. Storck (Antonius). Annus medicus.

753. Sue (Pierre). Essais historique, etc. Paris, 1779.

754. Suetonius. De xii Cæsaribus.

755. van Swieten (G. L. B.). Commentaria in Hermanni Boerhaave aphorismos, etc. 1742–76.

T.

756. Tardieu (A.). Étude médico-légale sur les attentats aux Moeurs. Paris, 1862.

757. Taylor (A. F.). A Manual of Medical Jurisprudence.

758. Testa (A. G.). Bemerkungen über die per. Veränderungen, etc. Leipzig, 1790.

759. Teratologia. London and Edinburgh. Edited by Ballantyne.

760. Texas Courier-Record of Medicine. Dallas, Tex.

761. Todd (R. B.). Cyclopedia of Anatomy and Physiology. London, 1835–.

762. Tolberg (J. G.). Diss. de ovar. hymen. Halæ, 1791.

763. Transactions of the Albany Institute. Albany, N. Y.

764. Transactions of the American Gynecological Society. Boston.

765. Transactions of the American Ophthalmological Society. New York.

766. Transactions of the Associated Apothecaries, etc. London.

767. Transactions of the Clinical Society of London.

768. Transactions of the College of Physicians of Philadelphia.

769. Transactions of the Edinburgh Obstetrical Society.

770. Transactions of the Medical Association of the State of Alabama.

771. Transactions of the South Carolina Medical Association.

772. Transactions of the Medical Society of the State of Georgia.

773. Transactions of the Medical Society of the State of New York.
774. Transactions of the Medical Society of Tennessee.
775. Transactions of the Medical and Chirurgical Faculty of Maryland.
776. Transactions of the Medico-Chirurgical Society of Edinburgh.
777. Transactions of the Medical and Physical Society of Bombay.
778. Transactions of the Obstetrical Society of London.
779. Transactions of the Pathological Society of London.
780. Transactions of the Philadelphia Obstetrical Society.
781. Transactions of the Provincial Medical and Surgical Association. London.
782. Transactions of the Ninth International Medical Congress. Washington, 1887.
783. Transylvania Medical Journal. Lexington, Ky.
784. Trioen (Cornelius). Observ. medicochirurgicarum. Lugd. Bat., 1743.
785. Trnka de Krzowitz (W.). Historia Tympanitidis. 1788.
786. Trousseau (Armand). Clinique medicale, etc. 3 vols. Paris, 1865.
787. Tweedie (Alex.). Cyclopedia of Practical Medicine. Philadelphia, 1845.

U.

788. Union (L') médicale du Canada. Montreal.
789. Union (L') médicale. Paris.
790. United States Medical Investigator. Chicago.
791. Universal Medical Journal. Philadelphia.
792. University Medical Magazine. Philadelphia.

V.

793. Valentini (M. B.). Novellæ medicolegales, etc. Francof. ad M., 1711.
794. Valentini (M. B.). Polychresta exotica. Francof. ad M., 1700.
795. Vallée (Leon). Bibliographie des bibliographies. Paris, 1883.
796. Vallisneri (Antonio). Opere fisicomediche. Venezia, 1733.

797. Van Oven (Barnard). On Decline of Life, Longevity, etc. London, 1853.
798. Velschius (G. H.). Curationum exotericarum. Ulmæ, 1676.
799. Verduc (J. B.). Pathologie de Chirurgie. 12°. Paris, 1723.
800. Verhandlungen der Genootsch. t. Bevord. d. Heelk. te Amsterdam.
801. Verhandlungen der physikalisch-medicinischen Gesellschaft in Würzburg.
802. Vermischte chirurgische Schriften. Berlin und Stettin, 1776-.
803. Vesalius (Andreas). Anatomia, etc. fol. Amstelodami, 1617.
804. Vesalius (Andreas). Suorum de humani corporis fabrica lib. epitome, 1543.
805. Veslingius (Joannes). Syntagma anatomicum. Patav., 1647.
806. Veterinary Journal and Annals of Comparative Pathology. London.
807. Vierteljahrsschrift für gerichtliche Medicin, etc. Berlin.
808. Vierteljahrsschrift für die praktische Heilkunde. Prag.
809. Virginia Medical Monthly. Richmond, Va.
810. Virginia Medical and Surgical Journal. Richmond, Va.
811. Vrachebniya Vaidomosti. St. Petersburg.
812. Vrach. St. Petersburg.

W.

813. Walford (Cornelius). The Insurance Cyclopædia. London, 1871–80.
814. Walther (A. F.). De obstetricum erroribus, etc. 4°. Leipzig, 1729.
815. Walther (C. L.). Thesaurus medicochirurg. observationum curiosarum, etc. Leipzig, 1715.
816. Western Journal of Medical and Physical Sciences. Cincinnati.
817. Western Journal of Medicine and Surgery. Louisville, Ky.
818. Western Medical Gazette. Cincinnati.
819. Western Medical and Physical Journal. Cincinnati.
820. Wiener Klinik.
821. Wiener medizinische Blätter. Wien.
822. Wiener medizinische Presse.
823. Wienerische Beyträge zur praktischen Arzneykunde, etc. Wien, 1781.

824. Willoughby (P.). Observations in Midwifery. Re-edited in Warwick, 1863.

825. Wilmer (Bradford). Cases and Remarks in Surgery. 8°. London, 1779.

826. Wilson (Sir W. J. Erasmus). On Diseases of the Skin. 8°. London, 1867.

827. Wochenschrift für die gesammte Heilkunde. Berlin.

828. Wolff (Casp. F.). Theoria generationis. Halæ, 1759.

829. Wood (H. C.). Therapeutics, etc. Philadelphia, 1890.

Z.

830. Zacchias (Paulus) Quaestiones medico-legales. Lugd., 1701.

831. Zacutus Lusitanus (Abraham). Praxis medica admiranda, etc. Lugdupi, 1637. 8°.

832. Zeitschrift für Geburtshülfe und Gynäkologie. Stuttgart.

833. Zeitschrift der k. k. Gesellschaft der Aerzte zu Wien.

834. Zeitschrift für die Staatsarzneikunde. Erlangen, 1821. (Henke.)

835. Zittman (J. F.). Medicina Forensis. Francof. a. M., 1706.

836. Zoologist. London.

ADDENDA.

837. Transactions of the American Surgical Association. Philadelphia,1888.

838. Wiener klinische Wochenschrift.

839. Archiv für Gynäkologie.

840. Devergie (Alph.). Médecine Légale. Paris, 1840.

841. Borellus (Peter). Historiam et observat. medico-physicarum, 1676.

842. Tulpius (Nicolas). Observat. medicæ. Fifth edition, 1716.

843. The American Year-Book of Medicine and Surgery. Gould. Philadelphia, 1896.

844. American Text-Book of Obstetrics. Norris. Philadelphia, 1896.

845. An American Text-Book of Surgery. Keen and White. Philadelphia, 1895.

846. Warren (J. C.). Surgical Pathology and Therapeutics. Philadelphia, 1895.

847. Circular No. 3. War Department, Surgeon-General's Office, Washington, August 17, 1871.

INDEX.

A.

B.

E.

Ear, anomalies of, 261 ; foreign bodies in, 539, 540 ; injuries to, 537 ; insects in, 539 ; menstruation from, 24 ; nitric acid in, 540 ; piercing, 749 ; power to move, 263

" Ear-sneezing," 815

Eastman on fibroma of the uterus, 781

Easton on teeth swallowed, 639

" Eaten of worms," 821

Ebersbach on ectopic fetus, 53

Ebstein on obesity, 353

Echinococcus cyst, 820 ; in the eye, 534 ; removal of, during pregnancy, 105

Ecker on bearded women, 229

Eckley on supernumerary lung, 285

Ectopic children, ultimate fate of, 62 ; gestation of, 50 ; multiple, 57

Eddowes on large infant, 349

Edentulousness, 243 ; association with alopecia, 227

Eder on opium-eating, 507

Edge on chorea in pregnancy, 103

Edwards on impregnation with the hymen intact, 41

Eggs, idiosyncrasy to, 490

Ehrl on spontaneous gangrene of the skin, 837

Eight children at a birth, 153

Eikam on short pregnancy, 67

Eisenmenger on prolificity, 157

" Elastic-skin man," 217

Elder and MacCormac on rupture of the spleen, 656

Eldredge on a ferrule in the bronchus, 614

Eldridge on separation of the symphysis pubis, 140

Electric anomalies, 429

"Electric Lady," 430

Electric light, injuries of the eyes by, 537

Elephantiasis arabum, 795 ; of the face, 800 ; of the lower extremities, 798 ; of the scalp, 798 ; of the scrotum, 800 ; of the upper extremities, 798

"Elephant-man," 81, 827

Eleven children at a birth, 153

Elliotson on hydatid disease of the liver, 786 ; on obesity, 352 ; on unilateral sweating, 388

Elliott on dermatitis exfoliativa neonatorum, 835

Ellis on ischiopagus, 183 ; on ligature of the carotids, 575 ; on oxalic acid, 499

Ellison on anomalous sneezing, 814

" Elixir of Life," 368

Elvert on protracted pregnancy, 70

Ely on chalk-eating, 412

Emeryaki, 855

Emmet on protracted menstruation, 33

Emond on pregnancy with unruptured hymen, 42

Emotions causing death, 524

Empedocles on prolificity, 146

Enchondromata, 766

Engelmann on fistula-operation in pregnancy, 105

Engleman on obstetric customs, 113

Englisch on double penis, 198

Enguin on protracted pregnancy, 69

Enos on absence of the epiglottis, 256

Ensor on shark-bite, 721

Enterostomy, 645

Enucleation of the eye, self-performed, 735

Epidemics, 891; of abortion, 109 ; chronologic table of the principal, 898

Epidermis, congenital defect of, 217

Epigastrium, blows upon the, 526

Epiglottis, anomalies of, 256 ; double, with double voice, 357

Epignathus, 193

Epilepsy, 852 ; birth in, 113 ; peculiar forms of, 852

Epispadias, 318

Epistaxis, extensive, 710 ; through the eyes, 534

Epithelioma, 772

Epley on painless labor, 116

Epsom salts, idiosyncrasy to, 496, 503

Equestrians, 460

Equilibrists, 449

Erba, Luigi, experiments of, 158

Erection of the penis, long continued, 683

Ergot, idiosyncrasy to, 502

Ergotism, 502

Erich on expulsion of ectopic fetus, 53

Erichsen on exostoses, 768 ; on hemophilia, 816 ; on foreign body in the abdomen, 659 ; on multiple fractures, 702

Esophagismus, 863

Esophagotomy for foreign bodies, 574

Esophagus, anomalies of, 284 ; foreign bodies in, 570 ; perforation of, 573 ; rupture of, 628 ; wounds of, 575

Esquimaux, menstruation among, 29

Estrus, larvæ of the, 821

Eunuch-making, 755

Eustaches and Tzetzes on jumping, 462

Evans on birth in membranes, 123 ; on foreign body in the esophagus, 571

Evans, William, 329

Eve, birth of, 200

Eve on injury to the spinal cord, 661 ; on a nail in the bronchus, 614 ; on rupture of the bladder, 671 ; on thoracic wounds, 610

Eventration, 650 ; congenital, 292

Evisceration, 650

Evrard, Gustav, 269

Ewald on obesity, 356

Exophthalmos, 527

Exostoses, 768

Exostosis on the sacrum, 138

Exstrophy of the bladder, 295

Extrauterine pregnancy, 50 ; combined with uterine, 54 ; discharge of the fetus in, 52 ; long retention of the fetus in, 62 ; successful delivery in, 57 ; termination of, 51

Extremities, absence of, 263 ; menstruation from, 25 ; supernumerary, 269

Eyelid, supernumerary, 259

Eyer on rupture of the thoracic duct, 659

Eyes, congenital absence of, 257 ; congenital defects of the muscles of, 260 ; enucleation of, 527 ; self-performed, 735 ; epistaxis through, 534 ; foreign bodies in, 532 ; injuries to, 527 ; by birds, 533 ;

G.

formed, 131, 708, 732 ; on the young and
old, 706
Opium, tolerance of, and untoward action
of, 505
Opium-eating, 506
Opport on fetomancy, 214
Orbit, epithelioma of, 772 ; foreign bodies
in, 531 ; gunshot injuries of, 529 ; inju-
ries of, 528
Ord on anomaly of the Müllerian ducts,
295 ; on myxedema, 807
Orissa Sisters, 171
Orloff, 603
Orman, James, 724
Ormançey on anomalous growth of nails,
588
Ormerod on hyperthermy, 422
Orton on telegony, 89
Orwin on self-mutilation, 734
Osiander on antepartum crying, 128 ; on
birth during sleep, 114 ; on protracted
pregnancy, 69 ; on venesection, 709
Osler on anorexia nervosa, 414 ; on dilata-
tion of the colon, 287 ; on filaria sangui-
nis hominis, 820 ; on hemophilia, 815 ;
on hypertrophy of the heart, 626 ; on spo-
radic cretinism, 806 ; on tuberculosis,
913 ; on yellow fever, 910
Ossicles, anomalous, 263
"Ossified man," 787
Osteitis deformans, 603
Osteoarthropathy, pneumonic, 805
Osteomalacia, 600
Osteosarcoma, 772
Ostmann on postmortem birth, 127
Oswald on wolf-children, 445
Otis on arrow-wounds, 710 ; on rupture of
the lung, 609
Otte on ovarian hernia, 310
Otto on enlarged clitoris, 308
Ottolengni on teeth-replantation, 728
Oudet on edentula, 244
Ovariotomy in aged women, 707 ; cere-
monial, 755 ; in children, 79, 706 ; dur-
ing pregnancy, 104 ; menstruation after,
26
Ovary, absence of the, 309 ; cysts of the,
782 ; hernia of the, 310 ; separation of
the, 689 ; supernumerary, 310
Overton on idiosyncrasy to wheat flour,
492 ; on spontaneous human combustion,
427
Owen on longevity, 366 ; on maternal im-
pression, 84
Owens on ovariotomy in old age, 707
Oxalic acid, tolerance of, 499

P.

Packard on centipede in the nostril, 564 ;
on combined fetation, 57 ; on foreign
body in the appendix, 642
Paddock on quintuplets, 150
Paget on colored saliva, 383 ; on lightning-
stroke, 723 ; on osteitis deformans, 603 ;
on teeth in the larynx, 582 ; on vicarious
menstruation, 24

Pain, births without, 113 ; endurance of,
475 ; morbid desire for, 480 ; sexual
enjoyment from, 480 ; relation of shock
to, 480 ; supersensitiveness to, 480
Palate, anomalies of the, 256 ; artificial, 256
Palfrey on birth during sleep, 114
Palmer on pregnancy with unruptured
hymen, 42
Palmus, 855
Pamo, Gomez, on prolonged lactation, 394
Pancoast on horns, 226 ; on Millie-Christine,
179
Pancreas, anomalies of the, 291
Pantophobia, 880
Paracelsus on the dancing mania, 854, 855
Paramyoclonus multiplex, 859
Paraplegia, delivery during, 116
Parasites, human, 818
Parasitic terata, 189
Paré on an armless man, 265 ; on cardiac
injury, 617 ; on cranial fractures, 559 ;
on a dog-boy, 162 ; on double hermaph-
rodities, 165 ; on false tongue, 566 ; on
hermaphroditism, 206 ; on ischiopagi,
181 ; on knife-swallowing, 635 ; on a
legless boy, 266 ; on maternal impressions, 82 ; on a monster, 164 ; on multiple birth, 154 ; on parasitic terata, 190 ;
on perverted appetites in pregnancy, 80 ;
on prolificity, 146 ; on quintuplets, 150 ;
on supernumerary limbs, 270 ; on teratology, 164 ; on a three-headed sheep, 166 ;
on vicarious menstruation, 20 ; on worms
in a fetus, 112
Pareira on arsenic, 500
Park on hypertrophy of the digits, 276 ; on
rupture of the sciatic nerve, 592
Parker on foreign body in the nose, 564 ; on
hiccough, 813 ; on nose-making, 562
Parosmia, 875
Parr, Thomas, 373
Parravini on Cesarean section, 130
Parrot on vicarious menstruation, 18, 19 ;
on high falls, 704
Parry on protracted menstruation, 32 ; on a
viable ectopic fetus, 57
Parsley, idiosyncrasy to, 491
Parsons on pregnancy after ovariotomy, 46 ;
on superfetation, 48
Parsons, Walter, 329
Partridge on cryptorchids, 321 ; on elephan-
tiasis of the scrotum, 801 ; on gangrene
of the penis, 682 ; on rupture of the tri-
ceps tendon, 593
Parturition, difficulties of, 113 ; painless,
113 ; rapid, 116
Parvin on maternal impressions, 84 ; on a
"turtle man," 267 ; on viable ectopic
fetus, 57 ; on vicarious menstruation, 27
Paschal on protracted pregnancy, 70
Pastorello on defect of the skin, 217
Pastrana, Julia, 229
Paternal impressions, 85
Paternity, possibilities of, 157
Paterson on hernia of the stomach, 287
Patterson on anomalies of the gall-bladder,
290 ; on self-performed operations, 709
Patzki on wound of the liver, 654
Paull on amazia, 297

W.